ANNUAL REVIEW OF
PHYSIOLOGY

ANNUAL REVIEW OF PHYSIOLOGY

VOLUME 60, 1998

JOSEPH F. HOFFMAN, *Editor*
Yale University School of Medicine

PAUL De WEER, *Associate Editor*
University of Pennsylvania School of Medicine

KLINCK MEMORIAL LIBRARY
Concordia University
River Forest, IL 60305-1499

http://annualreviews.org   science@annurev.org   650-493-4400

ANNUAL REVIEWS   4139 EL CAMINO WAY,   P.O. BOX 10139   PALO ALTO, CALIFORNIA 94303-0139

ANNUAL REVIEWS
Palo Alto, California, USA

International Standard Serial Number: 0066-4278
International Standard Book Number: 0-8243-0360-1
Library of Congress Catalog Card Number: 39-15404

TYPESETTING BY TECHBOOKS, FAIRFAX, VIRGINIA
PRINTED AND BOUND IN THE UNITED STATES OF AMERICA

PREFACE

CALL FOR OPINIONS AND SUGGESTIONS.   Often in the past, I have used this space for commentaries on issues and trends thought to be of interest to our readership. This year, however, I thought it would be instructive to elicit the views of our readers with regard to the future of the physiological sciences. There is no question that this is a field in transition and that, together with refinements in traditional areas, there is an emergence of a new physiology that has in its many forms been evident for some years (e.g. this space in 1993 and 1996).

The editors of the *Annual Review of Physiology* are eager to adjust our sights and to direct our coverage to include developments in these areas. Thus we request comments and suggestions with regard to the way our series is organized and whether the subject divisions are realistic and representative of physiology for the next decade. Are we fulfilling our responsibilities for coverage of the major developments in the field? Have (are) the boundaries of the section(s) changed? We sincerely hope that responses will be forthcoming, either to me (e-mail: joseph.hoffman@yale.edu) or to any of the Section editors.

JOSEPH F. HOFFMAN
EDITOR

Annual Review of Physiology
Volume 60 (1998)

CONTENTS

OTHER REVIEWS OF INTEREST TO PHYSIOLOGISTS

(*Continued*)   ix

From the *Annual Review of Neuroscience*, Volume 21, 1998:

From Biophysics to Models of Network Function, E. Marder

Local Circuits in Primary Visual Cortex of the Macaque Monkey, E. M. Callaway

Rab3 and Synaptotagmin: The Yin and Yang of Synaptic Membrane Fusion,
M. Geppert, T. C. Sudhoff

CREB and Memory, A. J. Silva, J. H. Kogan, P. W. Frankland, S. Kida

Sense and the Single Neuron: Probing the Physiology of Perception, A. J. Parker,
W. T. Newsome

Signal Transduction in the Caenorhabditis elegans *Nervous System*, C. I. Bargman,
J. M. Kaplan

Inducible Gene Expression in the Nervous System of Transgenic Mice, J. R. Gingrich,
J. Roder

Gene Discovery in Drosophila: *New Insights for Learning and Memory*, J. Dubnau,
T. Tully

From the *Annual Review of Nutrition*, Volume 17, 1997:

Energy Sources and Requirements of the Exercising Horse, P. Harris

Intracellular Lipid-Binding Proteins and Their Genes, D. A. Bernlohr,
M. A. Simpson, A. Vogel Hertzel, L. J. Banaszak

*Mechanisms by Which Carbohydrates Regulate Expression of Genes for Glycolytic
and Lipogenic Enzymes*, J. Girard, P. Ferre, F. Foufelle

Hormonal Regulation of Human Muscle Protein Metabolism, O. E. Rooyackers,
K. Sreekumaran Nair

Role of Blood Flow in the Regulation of Muscle Glucose Uptake, A. D. Baron,
M. G. Clark

From the *Annual Review of Pharmacology & Toxicology*, Volume 38, 1998:

Insights from In Vivo Modification of Adrenergic Gene Expression, D. K. Rohrer,
B. K. Kobilka

*The Role of Receptor Kinases and Arrestins in G Protein-Coupled Receptor
Regulation*, J. G. Krupnick, J. L. Benovic

Role of Organic Cation Transporters in Drug Absorption and Elimination, L. Zhang,
C. M. Brett, K. M. Giacomini

Cyclooxygenases 1 and 2, J. R. Vane, Y. S. Bakhle, R. M. Botting

*From GAGA$_A$ Receptor Diversity Emerges a Unified Vision of GAGAergic
Inhibition*, E. Costa

For the convenience of readers, a detachable order form/envelope is bound into the back of this volume.

NOTICE TO READERS

It has been brought to the attention of Annual Reviews that the review "Cholecystokinin cells" by Dr. Rodger A. Liddle, published in the *Annual Review of Physiology*, 59:221–42, includes without attribution several consecutive sentences (paragraph, p. 237) and graphical material (Figure 5, p. 237) that appeared in "Electrophysiology of intestinal cholecystokinin secretion," a paper published in 1995 by Dr. Allen W. Mangel in *Regulatory Peptides*, 56:121–29.

Annual Reviews wishes to bring this correction to the attention of the reader. We have contacted the author, Dr. Liddle, and he acknowledges this error of omission and states to us that it was inadvertent. He apologizes to the readers.

BOARD OF DIRECTORS
ANNUAL REVIEWS

Annu. Rev. Physiol. 1998. 60:1–18

BY CHOICE OR BY CHANCE:
Factors that Influenced My Life
and Career

R. M. Berne
Department of Molecular Physiology and Biological Physics, University of Virginia
Health Sciences Center, P.O. BOX 10011, Charlottesville, Virginia 22906-0011;
e-mail: rmb9a@virginia.edu

It is an honor to be invited to write the prefatory chapter for the *Annual Review of Physiology*, but it is also a gentle reminder that in case you may have forgotten, you are now in the twilight of your life—or less gently, you are over the hill.

Once you accept this honor, you have to decide what type of article you will write. But you feel no pressure to decide because you have over a year to come up with a manuscript. In fact, you might get off the hook because you're not even sure that you will be around by the time of the deadline. However, as with every task one accepts, there is a day of reckoning. The question was should I write a state-of-the-art essay in my chosen field, or should I write a biographical sketch. After a moment's thought, I decided to do the latter for two simple reasons: First, the research in my area has moved much more rapidly than I have, and I consequently feel incapable of preparing a satisfactory up-to-date perspective about it. The second reason I chose an abbreviated biography is that although I enjoyed the science in previous prefatory chapters, I especially relished reading about the personal events in the lives of the authors. I would also add that now that I have more time to read, I find biographies high on my priority list. I am fully aware that my life may not be particularly interesting to others, but it has been interesting to me. Therefore, with apologies, I describe some of the happenings that I remember and indicate how some of the choices I made and the chances that occurred have shaped my life.

The Formative Years

I was born in Yonkers, New York, in 1918, and the most important thing about my birth was that it kept my father out of World War I. However, my mother,

1

father, and I contracted the flu during the terrible 1918 epidemic but survived intact. In the first few years of my life, we lived in the country, in Ardsley, Dobbs Ferry, and the Bronx (sort of country at that time). Several years later, the family, now including a sister, moved to Brooklyn where I started the first grade in public school. What stands out most about that year was the awful fear I had of a huge red-headed teacher who made us sit erect, with hands clasped on our desks and absolutely quiet for what seemed like interminable periods of time. Fortunately, my mother got a job as a physical education teacher at the Brooklyn Ethical Culture School and part of the deal was that the school would accept my sister and me as students. It was a fine education with many interesting projects in which the students became deeply involved. For instance, I remember that when studying Greek history, I learned that the Greek athletes were anointed with olive oil that was then scraped off, thereby cleansing them. Whether this was indeed true, I really don't know, but I insisted that I be so treated, in lieu of a bath. My mother agreed, but it was only done once. Perhaps it was no delight to be near me when the oil started to turn rancid.

Things went reasonably well for several years, but with time I seemed to get into more and more mischief, and each time I got out of line, my mother would get a verbal report from one of my teachers. Finally, she decided that being in the same small school was not good for either of us and transferred me to public school. In retrospect, this was a good move, and I did well there and even skipped a term, but at the time I was very resentful, especially because my sister continued on in private school.

Growing up during my years in grammar school was very different than it is today. For one thing, the city was a safe place and as pre-teenagers and early teenagers we had a lot of independence. From the age of seven or eight on I could go anywhere in New York on the subway, by myself, or with friends. Of course, we had a family life and with it some rules about such things as mealtime, cleaning your plate, bedtime, and a few chores around the house, but between the time school let out and supper, I was on my own. There were no organized activities like Little League, soccer, and basketball, or lessons in tennis, horseback riding, or acrobatics. No coaching dads or soccer moms. We played on the street, stickball, roller skate hockey, touch football, stoop ball, and several running variations on the game of hide and seek. I also spent time just hanging out and getting into mischief, especially on occasions like Halloween, when it was only trick, no treat. Not infrequently I got into fights over trivial things and would come home with a black eye or a bloody nose. You had to fight to keep your position in the pecking order on the block. On weekends, I would spend all day on the street, a true street urchin, and often forget to go home for lunch. In fact I would lose track of time and would also be late for supper. On one such occasion, we were all to go to the circus and my punishment was to stay home alone while my parents and sister went to the circus. When they returned, I was asleep, but every light in the apartment was on. My parents rarely knew where I was at any time, nor did they know any of my street friends. It was like the old questions and answers between parents and child—"Where have you been?" "Out." "What were you doing?" "Nothing." In other words, between 3:00 and 7:00 PM I played with my friends in our own little world. When my own children were growing up, there were organized games and other extracurricular activities, but nothing like the schedules our grandchildren endure. When several of them spend an occasional weekend with us, my wife and I hardly see each other. We wave and toot the horn as we pass driving one or another grandchild to his or her next activity.

In summer I entered a different world. My parents rented a very simple cottage from June through August (my father came up on weekends) on a working farm about 20 miles from Albany, New York. It had no electricity or running water. It had an outhouse about 30 yards away and barrels under the downspouts from the gutters to collect rainwater for bathing and cleaning up. The stove and lights ran on kerosene, and we hauled drinking water from a well at the farmer's house, about a quarter of a mile away. We were close to a nice lake for swimming and a mile or two from an adult camp where they had horseback riding. The stable was my hangout. The owner of the riding academy, who had no immediate family, became close friends of my parents and sort of adopted me. I spent almost all my days at the stable, cleaning horses, mucking out stalls, saddle-soaping leather, feeding and watering horses, bringing them in from pasture, taking them to the blacksmith, and teaching riding to guests at the camp. I adored my adopted uncle and life at the stable. My greatest joy was when my parents let me sleep on a pile of hay in one of the empty stalls. My uncle gave me a pinto pony that I trained to follow me and do some tricks, like walk a short distance on his hind legs or climb a few stairs. He also gave me a goat and cart that I would ride in when the goat was agreeable, which was seldom.

When it came time to go to high school, I chose Boys High, which had an excellent reputation and where my father and uncles had gone years before. Travel to and from high school took about an hour each way on a trolley and subway, but it was worth it. The students were very competitive, and competition was encouraged by the school with the posting of the highest 50 or so averages after each term. Even though I worked hard and had lots of homework, I still went out to play whatever sport was in season as soon as I got home in the afternoon. One trouble I had was with my size. I was very skinny and small and was one of the few kids in my class who still wore knickers.

Despite my mother's efforts to put weight on me by giving me thick milk shakes and putting lots of butter and heavy cream on my cereal, I failed to gain weight and grow at the expected rate. Things came to a head in my third year of high school. That winter I developed a persistent cough, and the doctor suspected I had tuberculosis. Sputum examination and chest X-rays were negative, but I had a positive tuberculin test, and the doctor decided to treat me as a tubercular patient. I was taken out of school and put on complete bed rest for a period of about six months, the first three months in Brooklyn and the summer months in a home my parents rented in Westport, Connecticut. My mother, being a strict disciplinarian, followed the doctor's orders to the letter and I vegetated while I consumed high caloric meals. It was probably the most difficult time of my life. I was devastated. Suddenly cut off from my friends and changing from a very active to a totally inactive life was depressing. Time seemed endless, and I well remember watching the slow budding and unfolding of the leaves on a tree I could see through the window near my bed. It was a major turning point in my life. For a while I had no interest in anything. Then gradually I started to read and play card games with my mother. But mostly I did a lot of thinking about what lay ahead of me, especially about my health and how I would make a living.

This eternal summer finally came to an end and with all the high-caloric food and total inactivity, I gained about 20 pounds of pure blubber. I was shocked at my appearance when I finally got out of bed and had my first look in a full-length mirror. After gradual mobilization, I went back to high school on a half-day schedule, and by the second term I was back to a normal schedule and had received enough credits to catch up with my class. Over the next year I grew taller and thinner as I used the stored fat for growth.

The Higher-Education Years

The next choice was college. I desperately wanted to go to a college away from home, but I did not know if my parents could afford it. Fortunately, I was accepted at the University of North Carolina at Chapel Hill, which is an excellent school and one that was within my parents' budget. College was a liberating experience and scholastically much less demanding than high school. There was time for lots of extracurricular activities, and one of these, for someone like me who had a delayed adolescence, was to discover girls. I also tried alcohol, but the first exposure proved to be more than I could handle. I got drunk, broke a window in a movie kiosk and was arrested. I spent the night in jail in a $7 \times 7 \times 3$ ft cage with two bedbunks, the other one occupied by another drunk. We both became sick and cold sober during the night and had to wait in bitter cold until 9:00 AM to be released. I had to pay a fine and was sure I would be expelled from school. Fortunately, there were no repercussions, but I was very careful about what and how much I imbibed from then on. I majored in chemistry and enjoyed every minute of it, particularly organic chemistry where we were given unknown compounds and required to identify them by whatever means we could employ. I had my heart set on going to graduate school to become a chemist but was told by several advisers that there would be no future for me in chemistry. It was then that I decided to go to medical school. The summers were spent either as a children's camp counselor or teaching horseback riding and caring for the horses.

I applied to a number of medical schools and was elated when I was accepted at Harvard. However, the elation was short lived. The first semester was dreadful. It consisted of gross anatomy, histology, and neuroanatomy. We had excellent lecturers in anatomy and histology but the material was boring beyond description. It was nothing but pure memorization and the details seemed so trivial and would certainly not be retained beyond the final examination. But toward the end of the semester, it got even worse when we started neuroanatomy. The professor of neuroanatomy had left Harvard, and the school recruited young faculty from other basic science departments to teach a subject that was unfamiliar as well as uninteresting to them. Neuroanatomy was all taught two dimensionally. There was little attempt to get across a three-dimensional concept of the central nervous system, and to this day I have a poor understanding of the anatomy of the brain. I was very discouraged with the first semester of medical school and seriously considered dropping out. The only bright spots during that first year were two voluntary courses. One was a clinical physiology session conducted on Wednesday afternoons at the Beth Israel Hospital by Herman Blumgart, who beautifully illustrated the relevancy of basic science to medicine with real live patients. The other was a very colorful Saturday morning with Elliot Cutler, the head of surgery at the Peter Bent Brigham hospital, who held a surgical clinic for us in a whole-class exercise and let us observe him in the operating room in small groups. Cutler was not the most modest man, and on more than one occasion he told us that there was plenty of room at the top in his field of surgery. One day during a clinical pathological conference where the first year students sat at the back of the auditorium and the clinical professors sat in the first row, Cutler walked in during a discussion of a patient's X rays and the lights were out. Not being dark adapted, he could not see that all the front row seats were taken, and as he stumbled from one occupied seat to another a clear, loud voice rang out from the back of the auditorium, "Dr. Cutler, there is still plenty of room here at the top," whereupon the place exploded in laughter.

Physiology and biochemistry in the second semester were encouraging but not terribly stimulating. Biochemistry was still in its infancy and dealt mainly with the ions, compounds, and gases in blood and urine. In the laboratory, we spent hours doing Van Slykes, Haldanes, and analyses for such things as total plasma proteins, blood urea nitrogens, etc. Physiology was more exciting, and we had the privilege of having Walter B Cannon lecture to us on several occasions. However, the dark side of Dr. Cannon's lectures was his habit of calling students by name to answer questions he would pose. We all lived in dread of the time we might be called upon. The other impressive lecturer we had in physiology was Arturo Rosenblueth, whose energy and enthusiasm were partly offset by his strong Spanish accent. At times he was difficult to understand. Overall physiology was a good course but not one that inspired me to consider it as a profession.

Most of the second year was devoted to microbiology, pathology, and pharmacology. I remember little about microbiology except that one of my classmates contracted typhoid fever from mishandling cultures of typhoid bacilli and that Professor John Enders, later to receive the Nobel Prize and share it with two of his postdoctoral fellows, was an inspiring teacher and one of the finest people I was exposed to in medical school. In pathology, our professor was S Burt Wolbach, a jaunty, erect and diminutive person who was always impeccably dressed in a dark suit with a red carnation in his buttonhole and who strutted back and forth as he lectured to us. One day a group of students with red carnations in their buttonholes filled the first row of seats before Dr. Wolbach entered the auditorium. When he walked in he took one look at the first row students and practically convulsed in laughter, shortly accompanied by the entire class. Pharmacology was not a very exciting subject, and if it had not been for the superb teaching of Otto Krayer, it would have been a total bore. Dr. Krayer put on the most elaborate and interesting demonstrations for us, but he lacked a sense of humor. One of his simple demonstrations was the injection of a previously fed dog with apomorphine. He just told the class to observe the dog but said nothing further. Suddenly the dog vomited, and the class, having no idea what to expect, burst into laughter. That was the end of that session. Dr. Krayer walked out of the auditorium with an angry scowl on his face. By the next class all was forgotten. During an extremely boring pharmacology lecture by another professor on the treatment of syphilis with bismuth and its possible use as a prophylatic agent, Ernest Craige, a classmate with artistic talent drew a cartoon. It depicted a partly clad, sexy woman in a provocative pose holding a syringe and about to inject herself in the hip. Looking on was one of Ernie's wimp-like characters sitting nearby and drooling. The caption read "Bismuth before pleasure." Episodes like this made it a little easier to combat the boredom.

The third and fourth years, the clinical years, were very busy ones, particularly doing medicine at the Brigham during my fourth year when most of the medical interns at the Brigham were hospitalized for viral pneumonia and we served as substitute interns. It was at this time that I also got involved in research and selected a project for the wrong reason. I did not seek out a faculty member for research supervision because I was motivated by the excitement of research but because several of my classmates had become engaged in research projects and I thought I was missing out on something. Dr. Weinman had given a lecture on toxoplasmosis, for which there was no cure at that time, and I prevailed on him to let me explore the possibility that one or more of the sulfa drugs might be effective in treating the disease in mice. To my great surprise, I got a kick out of the experiments and even obtained positive results that ultimately were published in the *Journal of the American Medical Association.* The major problem while serving as substitute medical intern and doing research was time. I worked on the wards from early morning until about midnight and then crossed the street to do my experiments until two or three in the morning. Although I suffered from chronic fatigue, I was so intoxicated with all the fascinating things I was doing that I never really minded the lack of sleep. In fact that brief research experience sparked an interest in research that resurfaced several years later.

Between my second and third years at medical school, I had a free month in the summer and got a job as a chauffeur for a doctor in New York. His wife and two daughters stayed in a summer house on a lake about 50 miles from the city, and I would drive the doctor between the two places, as well as on house calls, and spend Wednesdays and weekends at the lake. It was a cushy job—tennis, swimming, canoeing, superb meals, and driving, which I loved. To get paid for this seemed outrageous. But, little did I know at that time that four years later I would marry that doctor's little 14-year-old daughter who kept pestering me to teach her how to drive, and who could have killed us both when she nearly drove the car through the back of the garage onto a tennis court 30 feet below.

Intern, Army, and Resident Years

A classmate of mine, Stan Lee, and I started our rotating internship at Mount Sinai Hospital in New York on April 1, 1943, right after we left medical school without a graduation exercise. This proved to be another intensive learning period with very busy days and alternate nights, for which we received room, board, and laundry. Most of the clinical instruction came from the residents but occasional pearls were dropped by visiting physicians. Half of us were eligible for a second nine-month stint as assistant residents for which we all drew lots. I drew one of the lucky numbers, and spent a second nine months seeing a variety of medical problems and doing a modest number of surgical procedures, such as appendectomies and hernia repairs. In March of 1944, I became engaged and a large wedding was planned for May 30. But that was not to be. I picked up hepatitis from a house officer I was taking care of and the wedding was postponed until June. I was accused of being yellow, which indeed I was. In retrospect, it is surprising that more hospital patients and personnel did not get hepatitis because, unaware of the danger of transmission of the virus, we were careless in handling blood and urine samples, and used the same syringe but with different needles for drawing blood from patients on the wards. In June, I tried another means of escape from marriage by getting a strep throat. This delayed the ceremony again, and we finally married in a very small affair at my in-laws' home. For years we had the most elegant scrap paper in the form of unused wedding invitations.

On October 4, 1944, I went on active service in the Army and spent my six weeks of basic training at Carlisle, Pennsylvania. From there, I was assigned to Fort Jackson, South Carolina, where I was put in charge of the wards for dependents of officers and enlisted men. It was real medicine, but unfortunately it only lasted three months and was the last medicine I did until I was discharged from the Army. After waiting a month on the west coast, I sailed by troop ship to the Philippines, a trip lasting about a month because of the course the ship took plus brief stops in Hawaii and Hollandia. A short stay at a replacement depot was followed by a permanent assignment as battalion surgeon to an infantry division that had just moved to a beach on Luzon to train for the invasion of Japan. There was little to do at first. Just shots and first aid and inspections of kitchens and latrines, and for recreation a swim or shower in warm water, or a drink of warm beer. Everything was the same temperature. Soon, transport ships carrying landing craft appeared offshore and training for a beach landing began in earnest. Twice a day we would practice going over the side into landing crafts to "storm" the beach. The only good part was that we sometimes got a cold drink or ice cream if we happened to be on the mother ship at the right time. As the training intensified, the tension of the soldiers increased, especially among the new, young recruits. One 18-year old became so upset, that he "accidentally" put a bullet through his foot and was sent to the nearest field hospital. It was not until the atom bombs were dropped in August that the evident emotional strain vanished. Many years later, at some stage of their early education, each of our four children was asked by his or her teacher to write an essay on whether the United States should have dropped the atom bomb on Japan. They all concluded that the bomb should not have been dropped. I then informed them that had the bomb not been dropped, an invasion of Japan would have been necessary, and there was little chance that they would be here today. My battalion aid station was scheduled for the third wave, and postwar information revealed that the Japanese knew the details of the US invasion plan and had their guns hidden in caves and zeroed in on the beaches.

A few days after the peace agreement was signed, we sailed to Japan and arrived at Wakayama on an afternoon in late September. Our unit was initially stationed in Otsu, not far from Kyoto and Nara, both of which were undamaged by the war and quite beautiful. After a few months, I was bored to tears with the routine of sick call and kitchen and latrine inspections, and yearned to get some exposure to medical problems. With permission of my commanding officer, whose division was about to be sent home, I requested transfer to a hospital in Kyoto where they were in need of doctors. I received no reply and was transferred to another infantry division and spent the balance of my time in Japan in several other cities on Honshu. One of those was Tsuruga, a city on the west coast that had been completely destroyed by fire bombs. Our battalion was quartered in an old Japanese army barracks and being the only medical officer in the area, I was designated the health officer of the city. This meant inspecting not only the American facilities but also the Japanese facilities, of which there was little to see. Several days after our arrival, the local chief of police asked me to accompany him on a tour of the city in my Jeep. As we drove through the rubble-strewn streets, he directed the driver toward a distant and apparently new building that stood alone in this expanse of total destruction. When we reached the building, the police chief proudly pointed to a large sign over the entrance that read Brothel House; inside were several rooms, an older woman—the madam—and a group of young girls, who had been sold into prostitution by their parents. Obviously, the brothel had been built solely for the use of American soldiers. My first thought was to thank the police chief for his efforts and declare it off-limits to American soldiers. Then, I remembered the very high incidence of venereal disease among our men whom I had to treat or hospitalize soon after we arrived in Japan. The idea struck me that since sex was inevitable, hardly a new discovery, why not set up a prophylactic station in the brothel. We took over a room next to the entrance (also the exit), staffed it with aid station personnel whose duty was to see that no customer could leave the premises without prophylactic treatment. It worked like a charm, and for a few months we had essentially no incidents of venereal disease. Then, an order came down from Army headquarters to close all houses of prostitution in response to some soldiers' complaints that the Army was fostering prostitution. Of course, we had to comply. The girls vanished into the city, and the incidence of venereal disease soared. So much for my career in the sex industry!

After a year in Japan, and seeing the extent of communicable diseases and the inadequacy of public health measures, I was frustrated and itching to go home where at least I could do something medically constructive. My aid station was open to Japanese civilians as well as American soldiers, and I was shocked by the number of gastrointestinal diseases, as well as venereal diseases, in the general population, and particularly the large number of new cases of tuberculosis among young, unprotected nurses who cared for patients with rampant disease. The changes in disease control between 1945 and 1979, when I next visited Japan to participate in a scientific meeting, was striking. It finally came my turn to go home in October, 1946, and one week before I was due to leave for the States, I received a reply to my request for transfer to a hospital setting from Sixth Army Headquarters—request denied!

Upon my discharge from the Army, I returned to Mount Sinai hospital to complete my clinical training, hungry to do medicine. I elected to go into internal medicine and was interviewed for a residency by Dr. I Snapper, the new head of one of the two medical services. Snapper was a most impressive person. For one thing, he was physically big and for another he had been everywhere and done everything in the broad field of medicine. He was Dutch, and in his early thirties he was appointed head of medicine at the University of Amsterdam; before escaping to the United States from China during World War II, he was chief of medicine at the Peiping Union Medical School. His book *Chinese Lessons to Western Medicine*, based on his experiences in China, is a classic. Snapper offered me the chief residency on his medical service, but it could not start until April 1947. To fill in the gap until I could start on the wards, I worked with Snapper on his research project on the treatment of multiple myeloma with stilbamidine, a drug effective in the treatment of leishmaniasis. The rationale for the use of stilbamidine in multiple myeloma was questionable. Nevertheless, word of this treatment spread rapidly, and myeloma cases were sent to Mount Sinai from all over the globe. Unfortunately, the treatment proved to be ineffective, but during the study the patients would usually tell Snapper how much they had improved, whereas only an hour before Snapper's ward rounds, they complained to the house staff that they were no better. It pointed out very clearly to me how wanting a certain result in an experiment can be a very dangerous thing.

A short while after I started the residency, I was working around the clock and learning at a rate I have never achieved since. Snapper was a tough chief and demanded that the chief resident be prepared to present any one of the 80 patients on his wards at any time. He also insisted that interns and assistant residents personally do blood smears and urine analyses on their patients. In addition to being a superb clinician, often picking up things such as enlarged spleens that the house staff had missed, Snapper had an encyclopedic knowledge of medicine. His diagnostic ability was exceptional, and he could always recall similar cases and cite specific literature references from memory.

During my chief residency, my mother developed metastatic lung cancer from an obvious lesion that was missed in a routine chest X-ray done while I was overseas. No one told her the diagnosis, and although I saw her two or three times a week to do thoracenteses, I could never get myself to tell her the true diagnosis. It was a time when you told the family the bad news, but never told the patient, quite different from now when the diagnosis and prognosis are usually discussed in detail with the patient. The traditional secrecy was very traumatic for me, and I still have guilt feelings about my failure to break the barrier and talk about the diagnosis that we both knew but could not articulate.

The Productive Years

Before long, my residency was almost over, and I had to decide what I would do next. I liked cardiology and decided to become a cardiologist. To be a good cardiologist, I felt the need of a solid foundation in cardiovascular physiology, and after several inquiries, I applied to Carl Wiggers who was regarded by many as the outstanding leader in the field. To my surprise, he accepted me on the condition that I obtain my own support. This I did and with a $2200 fellowship from Mount Sinai hospital, I arrived at the Department of Physiology at Western Reserve University on July 1, 1948.

In addition to Wiggers, the Department of Physiology at Western Reserve (now Case Western Reserve) consisted of four faculty members, one secretary, no technicians, and two postdoctoral fellows—Matthew Levy and me. My introduction to Matt Levy was the start of a long collaboration and a permanent friendship that is as strong today as it was 49 years ago. Wiggers suggested that we work on the mechanisms involved in congestive heart failure, which we obediently proceeded to do. Because there was no such thing as technical assistance, Matt and I served as each other's technician.

This arrangement worked out very well, and we accomplished a lot during the year as postdoctoral fellows. We tried to produce chronic heart failure in the dog by gradual constriction of the pulmonary artery with a modified Goldblatt clamp. After a very low success rate, primarily caused by erosion of the aorta by the adjacent metal clamp, we changed to acute heart failure in the anesthetized dog. Later, we discovered that while we were struggling unsuccessfully to produce chronic congestive failure, Jim Davis, then at the National Institutes of Health, had succeeded in inducing right heart failure by pulmonary artery constriction. The secret of his success was the use of a nylon tennis racket string insulated from the pulmonary artery and the aorta by dacron gauze.

Once we had studied the cardiodynamics of acute pulmonic stenosis, we became interested in how the reduction in cardiac output affected the renal circulation and renal function. Each of these experiments took a week to complete, Mondays we did the acute experiment, euthanized the dog, and cleaned up. That night, we measured blood oxygen levels by the Scholander technique. By daybreak on Tuesday, we would go home to get some sleep, return that afternoon to set up for creatinine and PAH measurements for renal clearance, which we did on Wednesday. Thursday we did flame photometry for sodium and potassium, and Fridays we washed glassware and setup for the next Monday. Saturday and Sunday we played tennis and/or squash. The place where we did the blood oxygens was adjacent to the outside wall of Dr. Wiggers' second office, referred to as his inner sanctum by the staff, because when he retreated to this office no one was to disturb him. The light we used at night to do the Scholanders was very weak, and we persuaded Wiggers to let us have a fluorescent light before we went blind. One day the electrician came to install the light fixture, and while he was pounding away on the wall and I was sitting quietly at my antique rolltop desk, Wiggers stormed in, ordered the workman to get out and yelled at me, "Who ordered this?" Without waiting for an answer, which I was undoubtedly too scared to give anyway, he said, "This is ridiculous, we used to use a kerosene lamp," and left me stunned. Ever since that incident, we all referred to our lonely two-foot fluorescent light as our kerosene lamp. From these experiments we began to explore renal function, particularly the effects of the renal nerves and catecholamines on renal blood flow and sodium excretion.

By this time, I was well into my second year at Western Reserve, and had been appointed to the faculty as an instructor, having skipped the lowest faculty rank of demonstrator. I still planned to go back to New York and, after suitable training, become a cardiologist, but I enjoyed the research and the teaching (student laboratory and two or three lectures) so much that I decided to stay another year. And so it went for the next few years, as I became a senior instructor and an assistant professor and drifted slowly away from the pursuit of a clinical career toward one in physiology. Matt Levy's and my research interests also drifted apart. He became interested in rheology, and I became curious about the hemodynamics and coronary blood flow in hypothermia, which was being used to reduce myocardial oxygen needs in the early days of cardiac surgery. However, we still taught together, and one term Matt and I were given full responsibility for the entire Dental Physiology course. That turned out to be one of the most rewarding teaching experiences in my life. In prior years, the dental course received short shrift. Nobody wanted to teach it, and those who did could not disguise their resentment, which was sensed and returned by the dental students. In fact, the dental students had received reports from upperclassmen and were already on their guard when we started teaching. Our enthusiasm and excitement masked our abysmal ignorance and completely disarmed the students. Each time they expressed appreciation for our teaching, it reinforced our efforts, and the term flew by in a wonderful feeling of pleasure and gratitude on all sides.

In research, Wiggers gave everyone a free rein and let his staff pursue whatever interested them, even though initially all the support of departmental research came from money granted to Wiggers by various agencies. Nevertheless, Wiggers kept a close eye on the research activities of his department. In fact, he would occasionally visit you during one of your experiments. Because electronic recording of pressure and flow was not yet available, we used a bulky and elaborate plumbing system with many tubes and stopcocks. Whenever, Wiggers stepped into your laboratory while an experiment was in progress you began to tremble. Not for fear of Wiggers, but because you knew that while inquiring about your experiment he could not resist reaching for and turning one of the key stopcocks. Usually the result was catastrophic. Blood and saline would spew all over the place, and Wiggers would mumble some words of apology as he beat a hasty retreat and you would frantically try to restore things to normal before irreparable damage occurred. When you completed a study and submitted the manuscript to Wiggers for his critique, he would take great pains to go over every detail and often rewrite sections into more readable English. Despite the fact that he often suggested the research project, guided you throughout its progress, and reworked the manuscript, he never put his name on any of the papers from his department. Toward the end of his chairmanship at Western Reserve, most of the faculty took jobs elsewhere, and when Wiggers retired he moved to the Cleveland Clinic where he started *Circulation Research*. George Sayers became the new chairman of Physiology and brought a whole retinue of endocrinologists. Bob Alexander and I were the only leftovers from the Wiggers era, and within a short time, Bob left for the University of Georgia and later went on to become chairman of Physiology at Albany under the deanship of Carl Wiggers' son Harold.

The 1950s were exciting times at Western Reserve. In addition to many well-funded research programs and a relatively new basic science chairman, there was the new integrated curriculum, which served as a model for several medical curricular changes elsewhere. The integrated curriculum catalyzed interaction among the basic science departments and also between the clinicians and basic scientists. I believe that as much of the enhancement of the teaching program was accomplished by virtue of the interest and enthusiasm generated by the new approach as was by the rearrangement of the teaching schedules of the participating departments. With time, however, the original faculty became a bit jaded, the new faculty lacked some of the enthusiasm for the new curriculum, and the popularity waned. Nevertheless, it represents a clear advance over the traditional teaching program.

The new curriculum also required that there be a cadre of physicians who were well enough versed in basic sciences that they could teach the medical students mechanisms of diseases. Because there was a paucity of faculty with the appropriate background to do this type of clinical teaching, several of us were recruited from the basic sciences and given second appointments in medicine. It proved to be a lot of fun, and we made ward rounds three days a week for three-month periods, which greatly bolstered my faltering confidence in my skills in clinical medicine. However, after a couple of years, the combined physiology and medicine teaching plus my research program, now with graduate students and postdoctoral fellows, had become a stressful burden. Something had to give and the opportunity for a choice came when the new clinical research building was completed and I had to decide if I wanted my research laboratory in medicine or physiology. I decided to keep my laboratory in physiology and curtailed my teaching in medicine. However, over the years I have often thought how my career might have differed if I had taken the other fork in the road.

A broader interest in the coronary circulation and cardiac metabolism grew out of my studies on the effects of hypothermia on the heart. Along with graduate students and postdoctoral fellows, I explored the multiple factors that affect coronary blood flow. From these studies emerged the idea that a labile substance was released from the heart (presumably from the myocardial cells) when the oxygen supply became inadequate for the oxygen needs of the heart, and the labile substance dilated the coronary-resistance vessels, thereby increasing coronary blood flow and restoring the balance between oxygen need and supply. From the old literature and a screening study we did on nucleotides and nucleosides, only the adenine nucleotides and adenosine proved to be potent vasodilators. We postulated that the phosphorylated compounds were less likely to cross the sarcolemma of the myocardial cells and considered the possibility that adenosine served as the mediator of the vasodilation observed with a decrease in the oxygen supply:oxygen demand ratio. The work leading to this adenosine hypothesis was completed by the time I went on sabbatical in Amsterdam in 1959, but I was so reluctant to stick my neck out that I did not publish the study until 1963. The adenosine hypothesis has had some rough treatment, which is, of course, part of the search for scientific truth. But the worst blow was when I was skiing with Larry Rowell and Eric Feigl and some of their postdocs on one of my many visits to Seattle. As I lost control on a steep slope and proceeded to crash, a voice rang out from one of the postdocs on the ski-lift as he viewed the carnage, "There goes the adenosine hypothesis." Over the years studies on adenosine were expanded to investigate its role in the regulation of blood flow in vascular beds other than the coronary circulation. Also, the dromotropic, chronotropic, and cardioprotective actions of adenosine were examined, as well as the treatment of supraventricular tachycardia in humans. A number of colleagues, as graduate students, postdoctoral fellows, or junior faculty from other departments, participated in the adenosine research and, along with many other investigators around the world, have delved deeply into the subject. Four receptors have been identified and cloned and found to be involved in several physiological and pathophysiological processes, and most recently, adenosine has been proposed as a sleep-inducing factor in cats.

My sabbatical in 1959–60 was with EC Slater in the Department of Biochemistry at the University of Amsterdam. One of the projects I worked on was the relaxing factor in skeletal muscle. I learned a number of useful biochemical techniques, but I also learned from Seturo Ebashi (who visited Slater's department on return to Japan from his work in the United States) that he had just submitted a paper for publication showing essentially what I had found on the relaxing factor. It was comforting to be in agreement, but it was disappointing to have been scooped.

Our family life in Amstelveen, a suburb of Amsterdam, was a memorable experience. We made many friends and enjoyed weekend trips all through Holland, as well as the daily delivery of all foods and flowers. We sent our school-age daughters to the local Dutch school where they quickly learned to speak Dutch fluently. In fact, our six-year-old daughter forgot English and would claim, in Dutch, that she was speaking English when my wife would ask her to please speak in English. In October of 1996 my wife and I visited Amsterdam for a few days, her first and my second visit since 1960. There were, of course, some striking changes (e.g. the laboratory building where I worked was torn down and a new building was under construction at that site) but we experienced a warm feeling of remembrance about the city, despite the nasty weather.

Upon my return to Cleveland, the adenosine work was continued, and with the help of Rafael Rubio, who had joined me to get a doctorate in Physiology and later became a member of the faculty at Virginia, we expanded our studies to encompass many aspects of adenosine research and watched the field grow exponentially.

The Administrative Years

In the early 1960s I received a few feelers about chairmanships in physiology. I really was not interested in moving because my research was well funded and progressing nicely. Sometime in 1964 I was approached by the University of Virginia, and because I was quite happy at Western Reserve, I decided to indicate my lack of interest in making a move. However, I knew that Merton Utter, a friend of mine in the Department of Biochemistry at Western Reserve, had looked at the chairmanship in biochemistry at Virginia and thought it best to check with him before closing the door. He assured me that the opportunities for building a first-class basic science department at Virginia were excellent and that I would be a fool not to at least visit Charlottesville and see for myself. The only reason Utter did not accept the biochemistry chairmanship at Virginia was that Harland Wood agreed to step down as chairman at Western Reserve so that Utter could take the chairmanship and not have to move.

My first visit lasted a couple of days and was a resounding success. The plans for basic science across the board as outlined by the Dean, Ken Crispell, were remarkable—all new basic science department chairmen, an opportunity to build the departments essentially from scratch, a new basic science building with input from the new chairmen, and enough money to recruit excellent faculties, to completely renovate existing space, and to launch graduate programs in each of the basic science departments. But perhaps the most impressive thing was the Dean himself, a sincere, caring, straight-shooting person who bubbled with enthusiasm and who backed up every promise with fact and deed. After two more visits, accompanied by my wife, and a meeting with Tom Thompson, the candidate for the biochemistry chairmanship, whom I liked right away, and who became one of my closest friends, I accepted the job. However, I was in line for a second sabbatical and decided that between jobs would be a good time to take it. I was once again fortunate to get a Commonwealth Fellowship, this time to work with Gustav Born in the Pharmacology Department at the Royal College of Surgeons in London. We shared a mutual interest in adenosine and the microcirculation, his being the anti-aggregation effect of adenosine in ADP-induced platelet aggregation. Therefore, we agreed to study the primary action of vasoactive substances on arterioles unmasked from any upstream or downstream effects of the substance under study. This was accomplished by microiontophoresis on discrete sections of arterioles, and although no new concepts were revealed, the experiments put the reported vascular effects of epinephrine and acetylcholine on a firmer basis.

The sabbatical year ended with my second bout of hepatitis, which I apparently picked up from eating inadequately cooked clam chowder when visiting Gibraltar in April. Our plans for travel in England had to be scratched, as did my expectation to play tennis on grass with Andrew Szent Gyorgyi, a friend from Woods Hole, who was spending some time at Cambridge. I stayed in bed at home and received a lot of attention from several doctors, colleagues, and from Henry and Biddy Barcroft who lived nearby and with whom we had become quite friendly. The only people who really suffered were my family who all had to get gamma globulin shots. By the end of June I was mobilized, and we returned to the United States where I convalesced in our house in Woods Hole.

In September, 1966 we arrived in Charlottesville. For me it was a busy and exciting time; for my children it was new schools, lost friends, and all the horrors of a move to a strange, new place. Only three faculty remained in the Physiology Department, which left seven slots to be filled. Also, the microbiology and the pharmacology chairs were still open, but were filled within two years. Thus all the basic science chairs were appointed within four years. A Health Science Advancement Award was made to the Medical School from the National Institutes of Health, and plans for the new basic sciences building went forward. During the first year, I hired faculty, started a graduate program, and succeeded in getting a training grant to support it. Once the new chairmen were all on board, they met regularly and worked together to build strong basic science departments. The Dean made our task easy and would drop in on us unexpectedly and ask, "How is it going?" "What do you need?" I haven't heard that second question in a long time. In addition, I collaborated with Matt Levy on the first edition of our cardiovascular monograph.

In my second year at Virginia, Brian Duling joined me as a postdoctoral fellow and elected to continue the microcirculation project that I had started in London. After completion of his postdoctoral fellowship, Brian joined the faculty, and expanded his research on the microcirculation and is currently one of the top investigators in the field and heads the Cardiovascular Research Center at Virginia.

Duling is one of a number of people who came through my laboratory during my years at Virginia, and I get a great vicarious thrill when I read about their successes in science. Also very satisfying to me has been my association with the American Physiological Society and serving as its president, which enabled me to make the election of officers more democratic by the use of mail ballots and to explore ways of recruiting more women into the discipline of physiology.

The Reflective Years

It has been fun for me to reminisce, but I hope it has not been an utter bore for the reader. I don't think I would have changed anything in my life, which probably sounds very smug. But it really is an indication that I've had a wonderful time. One of the many things I learned from Carl Wiggers is when to quit, to step down before one becomes an embarrassment to one's colleagues and to oneself. Packing it in provides me with the time to do many of the things I was too busy to do such as reading solely for pleasure, fishing, and traveling to places of interest without spending all of the time at meetings inside hotels. Knowing when to hang up my spurs also applies to this biographical sketch, and so I end it.

Visit the *Annual Reviews home page* at
http://www.AnnualReviews.org.

Literature Cited

1. Berne RM. 1963. Cardiac nucleotides in hypoxia: possible role in regulation of coronary blood flow. *Am. J. Physiol.* 204: 317–22
2. Rubio R, Berne RM. 1969. Release of adenosine by the normal myocardium in dogs and its relationship to the regulation of coronary resistance. *Circ. Res.* 25:407–15
3. Berne RM, Rubio R, Curnish RR. 1974. Release of adenosine from ischemic brain, its effect on cerebral vascular resistance and its incorporation into cerebral adenine nucleotides. *Circ. Res.* 35:262–71
4. Schrader J, Rubio R, Berne RM. 1975. Inhibition of slow action potentials of guinea pig atrial muscle by adenosine: a possible effect on Ca^{2+} influx. *J. Mol. Cell. Cardiol.* 7:427–33
5. Watkinson WP, Foley DH, Rubio R, Berne RM. 1979. Myocardial adenosine formation with increased cardiac performance in

the dog. *Am. J. Physiol.* 236:H13–21

6. Foley DH, Miller WL, Rubio R, Berne RM. 1979. Transmural distribution of myocardial adenosine content during coronary constriction. *Am. J. Physiol.* 236:H833–38

7. Winn HR, Welsh JE, Rubio R, Berne RM. 1980. Changes in brain adenosine during bicuculline-induced seizure in rats: effects of hypoxia and altered systemic blood pressure. *Circ. Res.* 47:568–77

8. Berne RM. 1980. The role of adenosine in the regulation of coronary blood flow. *Circ. Res.* 47:807–13

9. Belardinelli L, Mattos E, Berne RM. 1981. Evidence for adenosine mediation of atrioventricular block in the ischemic canine myocardium. *J. Clin. Invest.* 68:195–205

10. Bacchus AN, Ely SW, Knabb RM, Rubio R, Berne RM. 1982. Adenosine and coronary blood flow in conscious dogs during normal physiological stimuli. *Am. J. Physiol.* 243:H628–33

11. Belardinelli L, Fenton RA, West A, Linden J, Althaus JS, Berne RM. 1982. Extracellular action of adenosine and the antagonism by aminophylline on the atrioventricular conduction of isolated perfused guinea pig and rat hearts. *Circ. Res.* 51:569–79

12. Knabb RM, Ely SW, Bacchus AN, Rubio R, Berne RM. 1983. Consistent parallel relationships among myocardial oxygen consumption, coronary blood flow, and pericardial infusate adenosine concentration with various interventions and β-blockade in the dog. *Circ. Res.* 53:33–41

13. Ely SW, Knabb RM, Bacchus AN, Rubio R, Berne RM. 1983. Measurements of coronary plasma and pericardial infusate

adenosine concentrations during exercise in conscious dog: relationship to myocardial oxygen consumption and coronary blood flow. *J. Mol. Cell. Cardiol.* 15:673–83

14. Belardinelli L, Shryock J, West GA, Clemo HF, DiMarco JP, Berne RM. 1984. Effects of adenosine and adenine nucleotides on the atrioventricular node of isolated guinea pig hearts. *Circulation* 70:1083–91

15. Van Wylen DGL, Park TS, Rubio J, Berne RM. 1989. The effect of local infusion of adenosine and adenosine analogues on local cerebral blood flow. *J. Cereb. Blood Flow Metaab.* 9:556–62

16. Headrick JP, Matherne GP, Berr SS, Han DC, Berne RM. 1991. Metabolic correlates of adenosine formation in stimulated guinea pig heart. *Am. J. Physiol.* 260:H165–72

17. Headrick JP, Matherne GP, Berr SS, Berne RM. 1991. Effects of graded perfusion and isovolumic work on epicardial and venous adenosine and cytosolic metabolism. *J. Mol. Cell. Cardiol.* 23:309–24

18. Ely SW, Berne RM. 1992. Protective effects of adenosine in myocardial ischemia. *Circulation* 85:893–904

19. Ely SW, Matherne GP, Coleman SD, Berne RM. 1992. Inhibition of adenosine metabolism increases myocardial interstitial adenosine concentrations and coronary flow. *J. Mol. Cell. Cardiol.* 24:1321–32

20. Headrick JP, Ely SW, Matherne GP, Berne RM. 1993. Myocardial adenosine, flow and metabolism during adenosine antagonism and adrenergic stimulation. *Am. J. Physiol.* 264:H61–70

Annu. Rev. Physiol. 1998. 60:19–32

THE PHYSIOLOGICAL BASIS OF DIVING TO DEPTH: Birds and Mammals

G. L. Kooyman and P. J. Ponganis

Scripps Institution of Oceanography, University of California, San Diego, La Jolla, California 92093-0204; e-mail: gkooyman@ucsd.edu

KEY WORDS: Aptenodytes, Leptonychotes, Mirounga, oxygen stores, pressure

ABSTRACT

There is wide diversity in the animals that dive to depth and in the distribution of their body oxygen stores. A hallmark of animals diving to depth is a substantial elevation of muscle myoglobin concentration. In deep divers, more than 80% of the oxygen store is in the blood and muscles. How these oxygen stores are managed, particularly within muscle, is unclear. The aerobic endurance of four species has now been measured. These measurements provide a standard for other species in which the limits cannot be measured. Diving to depth requires several adaptations to the effects of pressure. In mammals, one adaptation is lung collapse at shallow depths, which limits absorption of nitrogen. Blood N_2 levels remain below the threshold for decompression sickness. No such adaptive model is known for birds. There appear to be two diving strategies used by animals that dive to depth. Seals, for example, seldom rely on anaerobic metabolism. Birds, on the other hand, frequently rely on anaerobic metabolism to exploit prey-rich depths otherwise unavailable to them.

INTRODUCTION

In the past 10 years, there has been an explosion of information about the diving traits of some aquatic animals, especially penguins, seals, and sea lions. We now know that some seals will dive to depths of nearly 1600 m (1) and that emperor penguins, *Aptenodytes forsteri*, occasionally reach depths of nearly 550 m (2). The deepest dives are not necessarily the longest, and the record 22 min submersion for the emperor penguin (G Robertson, unpublished observations) and

19

120 min for the elephant seal, *Mirounga leonina* (3), were both well below their record depths. These rare observations represent the results of tens of thousands of recorded dives. The reasons and physiology of such diving extremes are not understood.

Equally important as the extremes are what these animals routinely do. The best examples for comparative purposes are elephant seals, Weddell seals (*Leptonychotes weddellii*), and emperor penguins. Weddell seals, although capable of a maximum dive of at least 82 min (4), usually dive for 10 to 20 min when hunting at depths of 50 to 600 m (5). Elephant seal diving durations last about 20 to 30 min while feeding at depths between 200 and 800 m (3). Emperor penguins hunt for about 2 to 10 min between depths of 50 and 500 m (2).

In this paper, we address the magnitude and distribution of oxygen stores of different divers, the utilization of those stores, and the effects of pressure. Recently, Butler & Jones (6) gave an excellent, extensive review of the physiological responses to breath-holding. However, little was mentioned about the responses of diving to depth and the possible physiological and anatomical adaptations to pressure. Yet, pressure is perhaps as powerful a variable affecting the dive as the submersion and the prerequisite breath-hold. Little is known about pressure because it is such a difficult variable to incorporate into experiments.

Oxygen Stores

An increased total body O_2 store has long been considered an essential factor in the breath-hold capacity of diving birds and mammals. The distribution of O_2 among the respiratory, blood, and muscle compartments is dependent on diving lung volume, blood volume, hemoglobin concentration, myoglobin concentration, and muscle mass. These parameters and calculated O_2 stores are reviewed for both shallow- and deep-diving penguins, pinnipeds, and cetaceans in Tables 1 and 2. Few diving lung volumes and end-of-dive O_2 contents have been measured in species that dive to depth (7–9). It is also debated whether cetaceans, especially large whales, dive at full or partial lung capacity (10). Nonetheless, available data reveal that the respiratory O_2 compartment decreases in magnitude in deep divers. Presumably, this decreases the amount of nitrogen as well as oxygen absorption at depth, and minimizes the associated risks of decompression sickness and nitrogen narcosis. Eighty to 90% of O_2 stores are concentrated in the blood and muscle of these deep divers (Table 2). This is a result of significant increases in blood volume, cell volume, and hemoglobin concentration, as well as myoglobin content. In the emperor penguin, it is primarily a result of an increased myoglobin concentration in the swimming muscles. In fact, the swimming muscles alone contain 19% more O_2 than the entire blood volume of the emperor penguin.

Table 1 Deep versus shallow divers oxygen store determinants

Species	DLV (ml kg^{-1})	BV (ml kg^{-1})	Hb (G 100 ml^{-1})	Muscle mass (% BM)	Mb (g 100 g^{-1})
Adelie penguin	165[a,8]	87[70]	16[70]	40[b]	3.0[c,71]
Emperor penguin	69[a,d]	100[15]	18[15]	38[15]	6.4[c,15]
California sea lion	35[62]	96[31]	18[31]	37[31]	2.7[31]
Weddell seal	27[7]	210[25]	26[25]	35[72]	5.4[25]
Atlantic bottlenose dolphin	81[64]	71[73]	14[73]	30[b]	3.3[74]
Sperm whale	54[e,58]	200[75]	22[10]	34[76]	5.4[63]

[a]No correction for air in feathers.
[b]Assumed.
[c]Pectoral muscle concentration.
[d]PJ Ponganis, unpublished observations.
[e]Lung volume estimates for sperm whales, *Physeter catodon*, are based on measurements from fin whales, *Balaenoptera physalus*. Abbreviations: DLV, diving lung volume; BV, blood volume; Hb, hemoglobin; BM, body mass; mb, myoglobin. Superscript numbers refer to references.

The O_2 storage capacity of the high myoglobin concentrations in seals was demonstrated by Scholander and co-workers in 1942 (11). Since that time, the myoglobin concentration in the muscles of numerous types of divers has been measured. It is now clear that one of the most consistent hallmarks of oxygen storage in all birds and mammals that dive to depth is an elevated myoglobin concentration (6, 12). This trait is more characteristic of deep divers than any changes in blood volume, hemoglobin concentration, or respiratory volumes. Muscle myoglobin concentrations increase proportionately with diving capacities and are highest in penguins, pinnipeds, and cetaceans. Intermediate concentrations are found in shallow-diving, short-duration divers such as manatees,

Table 2 Magnitude and distribution of oxygen stores in penguins, seals, and cetaceans

Species	Body mass (kg)	Total body oxygen (ml O_2 kg^{-1})	Respiratory system %	Blood %	Muscle %
Adelie penguin	5	55	45	29	26
Emperor penguin	25	53	19	34	47
California sea lion	35	39	21	45	34
Weddell seal	400	87	5	66	29
Atlantic bottlenose dolphin	200	36	34	27	39
Sperm whale	10000	77	10	58	34

Based on data in Table 1 and oxygen saturation and extraction assumptions as in Reference 25. Assumed uniform myoglobin concentration except in emperor penguin [swim muscles: 25% body mass, myoglobin 6.4 g 100 g^{-1}; other muscle: 13% body mass, myoglobin 2.1 g 100 g^{-1} (15)]. Body masses for sea lion and sperm whale were those of the animals in blood volume studies (31, 75).

muskrats, beavers, and dabbling ducks. It is notable that myoglobin concentrations are usually higher in primary locomotory muscles (13–15).

Management of Oxygen Stores

Oxygen store calculations are based on assumptions that require further evaluation. The magnitude of the blood O_2 store is dependent on the arterial/venous blood volume distribution and on the degree of hemoglobin desaturation during diving. The distribution of blood between the large spleens (16–18) and equally capacious hepatic sinuses and abdominal vasculature (19–21) of phocid seals potentially affects both of these parameters. Although the spleen of Weddell seals expands rapidly after isolated dives (17), it does not change fast enough to significantly affect hematocrit during repetitive, foraging dives when surface intervals are 2–4 min (17, 22, 23). In addition, the O_2 saturation status of the splenic effluent is not known. Even if the spleen concentrates fully saturated red cells during each surface period, under current assumptions regarding arterial extraction and venous O_2 depletion during diving, there is not a significant increase in the calculated blood O_2 store (18).

There have also been few studies of the degree of blood O_2 store depletion during diving. A single arterial P_{O_2} sample prior to the end of a 27-min dive of a Weddell seal corresponded to a 28% hemoglobin saturation (23, 24). End-tidal P_{O_2} values during the first post-dive breaths of a free-diving Weddell seal were 3.06 kPa (23 torr) to 1.7 kPa (13 torr) after dives of 21 to 32 min (25). These correspond to a hemoglobin saturation of no less than 45 to 20%, respectively, assuming a normal pH. Actual arterial P_{O_2} is probably lower because of the usual difference in arterial-alveolar oxygen tensions. For seals, these data justify the use of the 20% end-arterial saturation used in O_2 store calculations. A similar assumption for sea lions, cetaceans, and birds is less certain.

The diving durations during which O_2 stores allow metabolism to be primarily aerobic have been assessed by the measurement of post-dive blood lactate concentrations (Figure 1). This is based on Scholander et al's findings (11) that significant muscle lactate accumulation does not occur until the muscle O_2 store is depleted. The aerobic dive limit (ADL), defined as the diving duration beyond which blood lactate concentration increases above resting levels (26), was first measured in adult and juvenile Weddell seals (27, 28). It is the diving duration beyond which there is a net increase in lactate production. ADLs have now also been measured in Weddell seal pups; Baikal seals, *Phoca sibirica*; California sea lions, *Zalophus californianus*; and emperor penguins (29–32). We consider this post-dive lactate accumulation secondary to localized O_2 store depletion and glycolysis in some tissue in the body, most likely in the propulsive muscles. It is important to emphasize that the ADL does not imply exhaustion of all O_2 stores for that dive duration. The rates and magnitude of O_2 store

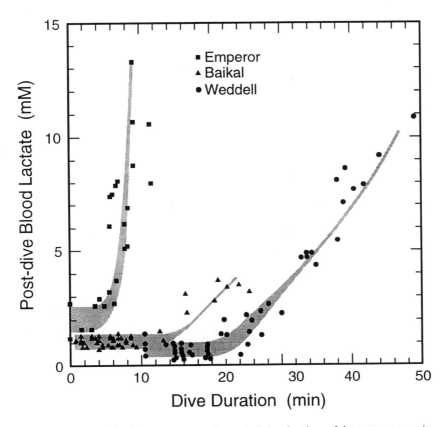

Figure 1 Post-dive blood lactate concentrations and diving durations of the emperor penguin, Baikal seal, and Weddell seal. Lactate concentrations are from whole blood of Weddell seals and emperor penguins (27, 32) and from plasma of Baikal seals (30).

depletion and lactate production at known tissue site(s) require further research in free-diving animals.

In adult Weddell seals and in Baikal seals, the measured ADL (Figure 1) can be predicted by dividing the body O_2 stores by the average diving metabolic rate (25, 27, 32). This metabolic rate is the so-called event metabolic rate, i.e. total O_2 consumed during the surface interval (surface interval duration + dive duration) (4). A calculated ADL has been applied to many species in the analysis of diving durations at sea (6, 29, 33). Although this is useful to the ecologist or behaviorist in the evaluation of foraging theory, there are inaccuracies because only estimates of diving metabolic rate and O_2 stores are available in many species. We also question whether doubly-labeled water-determined metabolic rates of entire foraging trips to sea represent accurate estimations of diving metabolic rate. Such estimations have led to a recent calculation of a 10-min ADL in southern elephant seals (33). We consider this value highly improbable, as did the authors who were testing a null hypothesis that calculated ADLs can result in close approximations of the measured value. Although they rejected the hypothesis, it may have been for unwarranted reasons. The oxygen consumption rate used was four times resting, which is almost equivalent, on a relative basis, to that of a Tour de France cyclist (34). It is near the upper limit of sustained metabolic scope (34). It is also at least twice the measured diving oxygen consumption of a Weddell seal (4, 25). Underwater observations of seals, sea lions, and penguins suggest to us that diving animals do not work at high oxygen consumption rates. It is also necessary to emphasize that although this ADL calculation may predict the onset of increased post-dive lactate concentration, it does not imply that all O_2 stores are depleted at that time, nor that the event metabolic rate is the actual O_2 store depletion rate during the diving period. Moreover, event metabolic rates vary within a species. Those measured in Weddell seals correlate inversely with dive duration, are often highest during very short, possibly recovery dives after long dives, and are higher in foraging dives than in exploratory dives (4, 25).

Two especially important factors controlling the duration of a dive are the oxygen store depletion rates and the lowest tolerable level of the blood oxygen store. Only a few arterial O_2 depletion rates are available from isolated dives of Weddell seals (24). Venous O_2 store depletion and myoglobin desaturation in the primary locomotory muscles have not been examined. The kidneys, splanchnic organs, and heart account for about 40% of resting oxygen consumption. Metabolic rate of the heart is directly related to heart rate, and renal and hepatic O_2 consumption are perfusion dependent. Therefore, primary determinants of the rate of blood O_2 store depletion should be changes in heart rate and accompanying changes in renal and splanchnic blood flow. Recent advances in technology have allowed examination of some of these factors. The bradycardia during dives to depth is variable, may be as extreme as bradycardia during forced submersions, and is probably dependent on the nature of the dive (31, 35–42). During repetitive foraging dives of Weddell seals, hepatic and renal clearances are maintained (36), whereas in prolonged or stress dives, they are reduced (36, 43).

The degree of muscle perfusion during diving also strongly affects both the blood and muscle O_2 stores. The desaturation rate of myoglobin is dependent on the level of muscle perfusion during diving and on the energy demands of muscle, which vary between locomotory and nonlocomotory muscle. These factors make both the measurement and interpretation of such data complex (44). Metabolic rate in the primary locomotory muscles is indirectly dependent on swim speed and directly dependent on flipper or fluke stroke effort: stroke frequency and amplitude. Even though swim velocity remains constant, stroke effort may decrease significantly during descent in deep dives secondary to changes in buoyancy with depth. Measurement of blood flow in exercising muscles during shallow submersions of tufted ducks showed an elevation in perfusion over resting levels (45). However, similar measurements in animals diving to depth have been an elusive goal not yet attained.

Several significant observations on muscle energy metabolism have been made in a magnetic resonance study of Pekin ducks, *Anas platyrhynchos* (46). These findings included (*a*) no reduction in resting muscle ATP turnover rate during forced submersion, (*b*) partial maintenance of muscle ATP turnover rate by a reduction in creatine phosphate concentration, and (*c*) an increase in lactate concentration sufficient to maintain ATP turnover rates. Although ion channel arrest and a reduction in glycolytic rate (reversed Pasteur effect) have been postulated as mechanisms of tissue hypometabolism in diving animals (43, 47), and occur to some degree in anoxic turtle brain and liver preparations (48, 49), these processes are not apparent in muscle of the Pekin duck.

The contribution of creatine phosphate to muscle energy metabolism is relevant to the original arguments for tissue hypometabolism made by Scholander et al (11). In their examination of muscle oxygen consumption and lactate production during forced submersions of harbor seals, *Phoca vitulina*, hypometabolism appeared to occur during the second 5-min interval of the submersion. In this 5-min period when the oxygen store was depleted and significant lactate production began, there was almost a 50% decrease in metabolic rate (based on measured oxygen depletion and lactate accumulation). In terms of ATP turnover, it was 1.3 mmol ATP kg^{-1} muscle min^{-1} or about 6.5 mmol kg^{-1} muscle over 5 min. However, if creatine phosphate breakdown contributes to ATP synthesis during that interval, there need be no shortfall in ATP turnover rate. Because creatine phosphate concentration is 15–20 mmol kg^{-1} in mammals, the concentration of creatine phosphate need only decrease by one third in order to maintain a constant metabolic rate. Thus there appears to be no biochemical evidence for muscle hypometabolism during forced submersions of either birds or mammals. It should be noted that those authors were aware of creatine phosphate's potential contribution; however, they did not consider it in their calculations because of a lack of available data at that time (50).

Body temperature may also affect oxygen store utilization. Metabolic rate reduction may be either a result or a cause of changes in temperature. Decreased body temperatures during forced submersions of harbor seals were originally attributed to about a 50% reduction in resting metabolic rate (50). However, in their calculation, it was assumed that 200-ml O_2 min^{-1} = 10 kcal min^{-1}, but 200-ml O_2 min^{-1} = 0.96 kcal min^{-1} (51), not 10 kcal min^{-1}. Correction of this factor results in a required 400-ml O_2 min^{-1} metabolic rate reduction in a seal with a 200-ml O_2 min^{-1} resting/presubmersion metabolic rate. Although severe bradycardia and organ hypoperfusion may decrease metabolic rate during the forced submersion, such a large change is unlikely, if not impossible. Therefore, hypometabolism alone cannot account for such large and rapid temperature declines. Other mechanisms must be sought. Body temperatures are a complex result of heat production, heat conduction, and peripheral heat loss. Vascular adaptations may play a significant role in thermoregulation (52). The recording of body temperature changes during diving is just now beginning. The role of metabolic rate, cold prey ingestion, insulation, alterations in peripheral heat loss mechanisms, and high convective losses during swimming will require thorough investigation before the mechanisms and effects of such temperature changes are understood.

Effects of Pressure

Much has been learned about the behavioral traits of divers in the past 10 years. However, little new information has been reported about the effects of pressure on diving birds and mammals during this same period of time. The physiological state of animals at depth will remain a mystery until new kinds of instrumentation become available to the field physiologist.

There are several possible adverse effects of diving to depth. Four of the most notable are (a) mechanical distortion or compression of tissues, especially gas-filled spaces; (b) higher gas tensions in the lung that result in increased gas absorption into tissues; (c) dissolved gas tensions that may be higher than ambient pressure during ascent, which results in the potential for gas bubble formation in blood and tissues; and (d) at depth the diver is a long way from its most precious resource, oxygen.

Distortion of the chest requires flexibility in the bones and tissue of the chest to prevent pressure differentials with the resulting rupturing of membranes. Concomitantly with the compression of the air space, the lung gas tensions rise and are more readily absorbed into the blood and into the blood-perfused tissues. The inability to compensate for these effects may result in nitrogen narcosis if the blood and tissue nitrogen tensions become too high. The mechanical compression of nervous tissue can cause a condition called high-pressure nervous syndrome that is manifested in humans and other non-aquatic animals at depth equivalents of about 150 m (53–55) if the rate of descent is about 100 m min^{-1}, the equivalent rate of a marine diver. This is not of much concern for many species of divers that do not descend to such great depths. However, for those species that commonly dive into this region, we might surmise that the structure of the nervous system has modifications adapted for a life exposed to such high pressure.

Lungs are a liability for deep divers because, in contrast to the muscle and blood discussed above, they are a better nitrogen store than oxygen store. Perhaps this is one of the reasons the lungs of marine mammals are the most structurally modified of any mammalian group (56, 57). Volume pressure curves of the chest wall and lung of the ribbon seal, *Phoca fasciata*, show that both are nearly limitless in the degree of compression collapse they can tolerate (58). This must be so for other diving mammals as well, but there are few observations to verify this. Compressibility of the chest and lungs has been qualitatively or quantitatively shown also for dolphins (58–60) and for other seals and sea lions (9, 61, 62).

The toothed whales, especially small dolphins, show the most extreme modifications within the lung among marine mammals, or any other mammal. The most notable examples are the reinforcement of peripheral airways, the loss of respiratory bronchioles, and the presence of a series of bronchial sphincters (56). Sea lions also have robust cartilaginous airway reinforcement extending to the alveolar sac, but there are no bronchial sphincters. In seals, the terminal airway is fortified by connective tissue and smooth muscle but not cartilage (56).

It has been proposed that the pinniped and cetacean airways enable a graded collapse of the lung to occur during a dive to depth. The result is that most of the lung air is forced into the upper airways where gas exchange with the blood is blunted (7, 63). Radiographic evidence in Weddell seals during forced submersion and compression to 300 m supports this hypothesis (9). Other functions are also possible. The exceptional shortening and thickness of peripheral airways in sea lions and dolphins may meet the more pedestrian need of moving air out of the lung at high rates so that the animal may catch a breath within the short interval when it passes through the air/water interface at high speed (59, 64).

In the Weddell seal and the California sea lion, the measured total lung capacity is about twice the diving lung volume (62, 65). From Table 1 it is inferred that some, if not all, pinnipeds dive with a lung volume well below capacity. Nevertheless, because of the depth and duration of dives, blood and tissue PN_2 could rise substantially if no airway structural adaptations existed. How low PN_2 actually remains during a deep dive was shown in several experiments.

The most extreme case was the forcible submersion in a compression chamber of elephant seals and a Weddell seal (7). Because N_2 tension in blood and tissue is dependent upon the distribution of circulating blood, in addition to depth and duration of the dive, the restricted blood flow during forced submersion would concentrate the N_2 absorbed in the lungs and raise the PaN_2 to the highest possible level. Under these conditions, the PaN_2 of elephant seals peaked at 300 kPa and equilibrated to 200 kPa, where it was approximately the same as venous PN_2 (7). This was independent of the ambient pressure from 37 to 138 m (1480 kPa). Similar values were obtained for Weddell seals diving voluntarily to depths as great as 230 m (2400 kPa) (61). The PaN_2 never exceeded 323 kPa. These modest increases in PaN_2 indicate that lung collapse in both species occurred between 20 and 50 m. The early occurrence of lung collapse in seals makes the lung almost useless as an O_2 store, whereas it limits N_2 absorption during the dive. Furthermore, the muscle tissue PN_2 measurements in bottlenose dolphins, *Tursiops truncatus*, diving to depths of 100 m never rose above 213 kPa. It was concluded that lung collapse probably occurred at about 70 m (66). All these reported N_2 values are below the minimum PN_2 of 330 kPa found to be necessary for bubble formation in cats (67).

Adelie penguins, *Pygoscelis adeliae*, and gentoo penguins, *P. papua*, dive with a large gas store that in relation to body mass is five to six times that of a diving seal (8). During simulated dives to 68 m (8), blood N_2 tensions in Adelie penguins were slightly higher than those measured in elephant seals. These levels are not dangerously high, and natural diving durations are shorter than were those experimental dives. Therefore, the shortness and shallowness of dives in these species would seem to prevent high blood PN_2 (8).

However, during routine deep dives of emperor and king penguins, ambient pressures may reach 3000 to 5000 kPa. During such a deep dive to 450 m by an emperor penguin, for example, the total time below 100 m is about 8.5 min. This weakens the premise, at least for king and emperor penguins, that the main protection of diving birds is short, shallow dives (8). Furthermore, the ascent rates from deep dives may exceed 100 m/min. This is probably too fast to allow for adequate N_2 elimination if much had been absorbed earlier in the dive.

If tissue nitrogen uptake is simply the result of the differential between ambient and tissue partial pressures, it is possible to show by traditional decompression theory that tissue nitrogen pressures could become a serious liability during serial dives to depth (68). Although the long recoveries after extended deep dives of emperor penguins are more likely driven by a metabolic acidosis resulting from a substantial O_2 debt, an additional value is that the bird remains at or near the surface. During that time absorbed nitrogen might wash out through the lungs without injuring the bird. Also, any shallow dives within the interval before the next deep dive might act as decompression stops and reduce the decompression risk as long as the tissue N_2 remains in solution (68, 69). Like the mysteries of high flying birds, those of deep divers need further study in order to develop suitable gas exchange models.

Concluding Remarks

Efficacy of a marine diver is based on the dual adaptations to pressure and hypoxia. This is different from freshwater divers, most of which are basically surface breath-holders. The adaptations manifested for diving to depth range from anatomical modifications of the respiratory system to elevation in muscle oxygen stores. Only recently have models been developed that might explain some of the peculiar anatomical and physiological properties of these animals. No doubt many more are to follow.

We speculate that there are at least two types of deep divers: Those that rely on aerobic metabolism the great majority of the time, and those that often push this limit and make frequent use of anaerobic glycolysis. Weddell and elephant seals fall into the former category. By virtue of their large oxygen stores and size-related low metabolic rate, they are able to conduct most of their daily diving routines while relying very little on anaerobic glycolysis. On occasional dives, however, intense bradycardia and peripheral vasoconstriction will conserve the large blood oxygen store for metabolism by the central nervous system. Anaerobic conditions will eventually prevail in muscle and other peripheral tissues, resulting in lactate accumulation. Sea lions and dolphins, which rely more on speed in their underwater forays, will have higher muscle metabolic demands and therefore shorter time until muscle exhaustion. Consequently, blood oxygen stores have not been enhanced to the level of seals. Furthermore, the oxygen requirements of the large brain of dolphins are an additional handicap that limit the breath-hold tolerance of this group. Finally, penguins with their small brains and massive propulsive muscles have opted for large oxygen stores in the muscle to help maintain rapid swimming while they often push the limits of those stores. By virtue of their mass-related high metabolic rate, they must frequently rely on anaerobic metabolism in the muscle as the oxygen store depletes when they exploit depths that would otherwise be unavailable to them. Emperor and king penguins are the best examples of this strategy.

There are currently few data to support the hypotheses in the previous paragraph, but as we move into the next century, one of the goals of diving physiology should be to determine if there are distinctive oxygen store management strategies among deep divers. Those strategies might be (a) large brain/large circulating stores/large muscle stores for infrequently exceeding their ADL (seals); (b) very large brain/normal circulating stores/moderate muscle stores for seldom exceeding their ADL (dolphins); (c) large brain/normal circulating stores/moderately elevated muscle stores for seldom exceeding their ADL (sea lions, fur seals); and (d) small brain/normal circulating stores/large muscle stores for frequently exceeding their ADL (penguins).

ACKNOWLEDGMENTS

Preparation of this review was supported by the National Science Foundation, Office of Polar Programs grant 9219872. We thank R Howard for reviewing the manuscript and his many helpful suggestions.

> Visit the *Annual Reviews home page* at
> **http://www.AnnualReviews.org.**

Literature Cited

1. Stewart BS, DeLong RL. 1993. Postbreeding foraging migrations of northern elephant seals. In *Elephant Seals: Population, Ecology, Behavior and Physiology*, ed. BJ Le Boeuf, RM Laws, pp. 290–309. Berkeley: Univ. Calif. Press

2. Kooyman GL, Kooyman TG. 1995. Diving behavior of emperor penguins nurturing chicks at Coulman Island, Antarctica. *Condor* 97:536–49

3. Hindell MA, Slip DJ, Burton HR, Bryden MM. 1991. Physiological implications of continuous, prolonged, and deep dives of southern elephant seals. *Can. J. Zool.* 70:370–79

4. Castellini MA, Kooyman GL, Ponganis PJ. 1992. Metabolic rates of freely diving Weddell seals: correlations with oxygen stores, swim velocity, and diving duration. *J. Exp. Biol.* 165:181–94

5. Castellini MA, Davis RW, Kooyman GL. 1992. *Diving Behavior of the Weddell Seal: Annual Cycles,* Vol. 28. Berkeley: Univ. Calif. Press. 54 pp.

6. Butler PW, Jones DR. 1997. The physiology of diving of birds and mammals. *Physiol. Rev.* 77:837–99

7. Kooyman GL, Schroeder JP, Denison DM, Hammond DD, Wright JJ, Bergman WD. 1972. Blood N_2 tensions of seals during simulated deep dives. *Am. J. Physiol.* 223:1016–20

8. Kooyman GL, Schroeder JP, Greene DG, Smith VA. 1973. Gas exchange in penguins during simulated dives to 30 and 68 m. *Am. J. Physiol.* 225:1467–71

9. Kooyman GL, Hammond DD, Schroeder JP. 1970. Bronchograms and tracheograms of seals under pressure. *Science* 169:82–84

10. Ridgway SH. 1986. Diving by cetaceans. In *Diving in Animals and Man*, ed. AO Brubakk, JW Kanwisher, G Sundnes, pp. 33–62. Trondheim: Royal Nor. Soc. Sci. Lett.

11. Scholander PF, Irving L, Grinnell SW. 1942. Aerobic and anaerobic changes in seal muscle during diving. *J. Biol. Chem.* 142:431–40

12. Kooyman GL, Ponganis PJ, Howard RS. 1997. *Diving Animals.* New York: Dekker. In press

13. MacArthur RA. 1990. Seasonal changes in the oxygen storage capacity and aerobic dive limits of the muskrat (*Ondatra zibethicus*). *J. Comp. Physiol. B* 160:593–99

14. Petrov EA, Shoshenko KA. 1987. Total store of oxygen and duration of diving of the Nerpa. In *Morphology and Ecology of Fish*, ed. GI Galazii, pp. 110–28. Novbosibirsk: Acad. Sci. Russia, Siberian Div.

15. Ponganis PJ, Costello ML, Starke LN, Mathieu-Costello O, Kooyman GL. 1997. Structural and biochemical characteristics of locomotory muscles of emperor penguins, *Aptenodytes forsteri. Respir. Physiol.* In press

16. Bryden MM, Lim GHK. 1969. Blood parameters of the southern elephant seal (*Mirounga leonina*) in relation to diving. *Comp. Biochem. Physiol.* 28:139–48

17. Hurford WE, Hochachka PW, Schneider RC, Guyton GP, Stanek KS, et al. 1996. Splenic contraction, catecholamine release, and blood volume redistribution during diving in the Weddell seal. *J. Appl. Physiol.* 80:298–306

18. Ponganis PJ, Kooyman GL, Sartoris D, Jobsis PF. 1992. Pinniped splenic volumes. *Am. J. Physiol.* 262:R322–25

19. Elsner RW, Scholander P F, Craig AB, Dimond EG, Irving L, et al. 1964. A venous blood oxygen reservoir in the diving elephant seal. *Physiologist* 7:124

20. Harrison RJ, Tomlinson JDW. 1956. Observations on the venous system in certain Pinnipedia and Cetacea. *Proc. Zool. Soc. London* 126:205–33

21. Ronald K, McCarter R, Selley LJ. 1977. Venous circulation of the Harp seal (*Pagophilus groenlandicus*). In *Functional Anatomy of Marine Mammals*, ed. RJ

Harrison, pp. 235–70. New York: Academic

22. Castellini MA, Davis RW, Kooyman GL. 1988. Blood chemistry regulation during repetitive diving in Weddell seals. *Physiol. Zool.* 61:379–86

23. Qvist J, Hill RD, Schneider RC, Falke KJ, Liggins GC, et al. 1986. Hemoglobin concentrations and blood gas tensions of free-diving Weddell seals. *J. Appl. Physiol.* 61:1560–69

24. Qvist J, Weber RE, Zapol WM. 1981. Oxygen equilibrium properties of blood and hemoglobin of fetal and adult Weddell seals. *J. Appl. Physiol.* 50:999–1005

25. Ponganis PJ, Kooyman GL, Castellini MA. 1993. Determinants of the aerobic dive limit of Weddell seals: analysis of diving metabolic rates, post-dive end tidal PO_2S, and blood and muscle oxygen stores. *Physiol. Zool.* 66:732–49

26. Kooyman GL. 1985. Physiology without restraint in diving mammals. *Mar. Mamm. Sci.* 1:166–78

27. Kooyman GL, Wahrenbrock EA, Castellini MA, Davis RW, Sinnett EE. 1980. Aerobic and anaerobic metabolism during diving in Weddell seals: evidence of preferred pathways from blood chemistry and behavior. *J. Comp. Physiol.* 138:335–46

28. Kooyman GL, Castellini MA, Davis RW, Maue RA. 1983. Aerobic dive limits in immature Weddell seals. *J. Comp. Physiol.* 151:171–74

29. Burns JM, Castellini MA. 1996. Physiological and behavioral determinants of the aerobic dive limit in Weddell seal (*Letonychotes weddellii*) pups. *J. Comp. Physiol. B* 166:473–83

30. Ponganis PJ, Kooyman GL, Baronov EA, Thorson PH, Stewart BS. 1997. The aerobic submersion limit of Baikal seals, *Phoca sibirica. Can. J. Zool.* In press

31. Ponganis, PJ, Kooyman GL, Winter LM, Starke LN. 1997. Heart rate and plasma lactate responses during submerged swimming and diving in California seal lions (*Zalophus californianus*). *J. Comp. Physiol. B* 167:9–16

32. Ponganis PJ, Kooyman GL, Starke LN, Kooyman CA, Kooyman TG. 1997. Post-dive blood lactate concentrations in emperor penguins, *Aptenodytes forsteri. J. Exp. Biol.* 200:1623–26

33. Boyd IL, Croxall JP. 1996. Dive durations in pinnipeds and seabirds. *Can. J. Zool.* 74:1696–705

34. Peterson CC, Nagy KA, Diamond J. 1990. Sustained metabolic scope. *Proc. Natl. Acad. Sci. USA* 87:2324–28

35. Bevan RM, Boyd IL, Reid K, Woakes AJ, Croxall JP. 1997. Heart rates and abdominal temperatures of free-ranging south Georgian shags, *Phalacrocorax georgianus. J. Exp. Biol.* 200:661–75

36. Davis RW, Castellini MA, Kooyman GL, Maue R. 1983. Renal GFR and hepatic blood flow during voluntary diving in Weddell seals. *Am. J. Physiol.* 245:743–48

37. Hill RD, Schneider RC, Liggins GC, Schuette AH, Elliott RL, et al. 1987. Heart rate and body temperature during free diving of Weddell seals. *Am. J. Physiol.* 253:R344–51

38. Fedak MA, Pullen MR, Kanwisher J. 1988. Circulatory responses of seals to periodic breathing: heart rate and breathing during exercise and diving in the laboratory and open sea. *Can. J. Zool.* 66:53–60

39. Fedak MA, Thompson D. 1993. Behavioural and physiological options in diving seals. *Symp. Zool. Soc. London* 66:333–48

40. Kooyman GL, Ponganis PJ, Castellini MA, Ponganis EP, Ponganis KV, et al. 1992. Heart rates and swim speeds of emperor penguins diving under sea ice. *J. Exp. Biol.* 165:161–80

41. Butler PJ. 1994. To what extent can heart rate be used as an indicator of metabolic rate in free-living marine mammals? In *Marine Mammals: Advances in Behavioural and Population Biology*, ed. IL Boyd, 66:317–32. London: Zool. Soc. London

42. Elsner R, Wartzok D, Sonafrank NB, Kelly BP. 1989. Behavioral and physiogical reactions of arctic seals during under-ice pilotage. *Can. J. Zool.* 67:2506–13

43. Guppy M, Hill RD, Liggins GC, Zapol WM, Hochachka PW. 1986. Microcomputer assisted metabolic studies of voluntary diving of Weddell seals. *Am. J. Physiol.* 250:175–87

44. Guyton, GP, Stanek KS, Schneider RC, Hochachka PW, Hurford WE, et al. 1995. Myoglobin-saturation in free-diving Weddell seals. *J. Appl. Physiol.* 79:1148–55

45. Bevan RM, Butler PJ. 1992. Cardiac output and blood flow distribution during swimming and voluntary diving of the tufted duck (*Aythya fuligula*). *J. Exp. Biol.* 1668:199–217

46. Stephenson R, Jones DR. 1992. Metabolic responses to forced dives in Pekin duck measured by indirect calorimetry and ^{31}P-MRS. *Am. J. Physiol.* 262:R1309–17

47. Hochachka PW, Guppy M. 1987. *Metabolic Arrest and the Control of*

Biological Time. Cambridge, MA: Harvard Univ. Press

48. Land SC, Sanger RH, Smith PJS. 1997. O_2 availability modulates transmembrane Ca^{2+} flux via second-messenger pathways in anoxia-tolerant hepatocytes. *J. Appl. Physiol.* 82:776–83

49. Lutz PL, Nilsson GE. 1997. Contrasting strategies for anoxic brain survival—glycolysis up or down. *J. Exp. Biol.* 200: 411–19

50. Scholander PF, Irving L, Grinnell SW. 1942. On the temperature and metabolism of the seal during diving. *J. Cell. Comp. Physiol.* 19:67–78

51. Schmidt-Nielsen K. 1983. *Animal Physiology: Adaptation and Environment.* Cambridge: Cambridge Univ. Press. 619 pp. 3rd ed.

52. Rommell SA, Pabst DA, McLellan WA, Williams TM, Friedl WA. 1994. Temperature regulation of the testes of the bottlenose dolphin (*Tursiops truncatus*): evidence from colonic temperatures. *J. Comp. Physiol. B* 164:130–34

53. Bennett PB. 1975. The high pressure nervous syndrome: man. In *The Physiology and Medicine of Diving and Compressed Air Work*, ed. PB Bennett, DH Elliott, pp. 248–63. Baltimore: Williams & Wilkins

54. Brauer RW. 1975. The high pressure nervous syndrome: animals. In *The Physiology and Medicine of Diving and Compressed Air Work*, ed. PB Bennett, DH Elliott, pp. 231–47. Baltimore: Williams & Wilkins

55. Kooyman GL. 1989. *Diverse Divers: Physiology and Behavior. Zoophysiology Series*, ed. K Johansen, DS Farner, Vol. 23. New York: Springer-Verlag. 216 pp.

56. Belanger LF. 1940. A study of the histological structure of the respiratory portion of the lungs of aquatic mammals. *Am. J. Anat.* 67:437–61

57. Denison DM, Kooyman GL. 1973. The structure and the function of the small airways in pinniped and sea otter lungs. *Respir. Physiol.* 17:1–10

58. Leith D. 1976. Comparative mammalian respiratory mechanics. *Physiologist* 19: 485–510

59. Kooyman GL, Sinnett EE. 1979. Mechanical properties of the harbor porpoise lung. *Respir. Physiol.* 36:287–300

60. Ridgway SH, Scronce BL, Kanwisher J. 1969. Respiration and deep diving in the bottlenose porpoise. *Science* 166:1651–54

61. Falke KJ, Hill RD, Qvist J, Schneider RC, Guppy M, et al. 1985. Seal lungs collapse during free diving: evidence from arterial nitrogen tensions. *Science* 229:556–58

62. Kooyman GL, Sinnett EE. 1982. Pulmonary shunts in harbor seals and sea lions during simulated dives to depth. *Physiol. Zool.* 55:105–11

63. Scholander PF. 1940. Experimental investigations on the respiratory function in diving mammals and birds. *Hvalradets Skrif.* 22:1–131

64. Kooyman GL, Cornell LH. 1981. Flow properties of expiration and inspiration in a trained bottlenose porpoise. *Physiol. Zool.* 54:55–61

65. Kooyman GL, Kerem DH, Campbell W, Wright JJ. 1971. Pulmonary function in free-diving Weddell seals. *Respir. Physiol.* 12:271–83

66. Ridgway SH, Howard R. 1979. Dolphin lung collapse and intramuscular circulation during free diving: evidence from nitrogen washout. *Science* 206:1182–83

67. Harvey EN, McElroy WD, Whitely AH, Warren GH, Pease DC. 1944. Bubble formation in animals. III. An analysis of gas tension and hydrostatic pressure in cats. *J. Cell. Comp. Physiol.* 24:117–32

68. Hills BA. 1968. Relevant phase conditions for predicting occurrence of decompression sickness. *J. Appl. Physiol.* 25:310–15

69. Griffiths HB. 1971. On the role of separated gas in decompression sickness. *Proc. R. Soc. London Ser. B* 178:389–406

70. Lenfant C, Kooyman GL, Elsner R, Drabek CM. 1969. Respiratory function of the blood of the Adelie penguin (*Pygoscelis adeliae*). *Am. J. Physiol.* 216:1598–600

71. Weber RE, Hemmingsen EA, Johansen K. 1974. Functional and biochemical studies of penguin myoglobins. *Comp. Biochem. Physiol.* 49:197–214

72. Fujise Y, Hidaka H, Tatsukawa R, Miyazaki N. 1985. External measurements and organ weights of five Weddell seals (*Leptonychotes weddellii*) caught near Syowa Station. *Antarc. Rec. (Tokyo)* 85:96–101

73. Ridgway SH, Johnston DG. 1966. Blood oxygen and ecology of porpoises of three genera. *Science* 151:456–58

74. Blessing MH. 1972. Studies on the concentration of myoglobin in the sea-cow and porpoise. *Comp. Physiol. Biochem.* 41A:475–80

75. Sleet RB, Sumich JL, Weber LJ. 1981. Estimates of total blood volume and total body weight of sperm whale (*Physeter catodon*). *Can. J. Zool.* 59:567–70

76. Lockyer C. 1976. Body weights of some species of large whales. *J. Const. Int. Explor. Mer.* 36:259–73

Annu. Rev. Physiol. 1998. 60:33–53

ANIMAL ADAPTATIONS FOR TOLERANCE AND EXPLOITATION OF POISONOUS SULFIDE

Manfred K. Grieshaber and *Susanne Völkel*[#]
*Institut für Zoophysiologie, Heinrich-Heine-Universität, D-40225 Düsseldorf,
Germany; e-mail: griesha@uni-duesseldorf.de; [#]Lehrstuhl für Tierphysiologie,
Humboldt-Universität zu Berlin, D-10115 Berlin, Germany;
e-mail: susanne=voelkel@biologie.hu-berlin.de

KEY WORDS: sulfide metabolism, blood-based oxidation, mitochondrial oxidation mechanisms,
             thiosulfate production, oxygen consumption, sulfide-dependent anaerobiosis,
             ATP synthesis

ABSTRACT

Many aquatic animal species can survive sulfide exposure to some extent through oxidation of the sulfide, which results mainly in thiosulfate. In several species, sulfide oxidation is localized in the mitochondria and is accompanied by ATP synthesis. In addition, blood-based and intracellular compounds can augment sulfide oxidation. The formation of thiosulfate requires oxygen, which results in an increase in oxygen consumption of some species. If not all sulfide is detoxified, cytochrome c oxidase is inhibited. Under these conditions, a sulfide-dependent anaerobic energy metabolism commences.

INTRODUCTION AND HISTORY

The existence of sulfide-rich environments, resulting either from anthropogenic waste production or natural occurrences, has received attention for many years because hydrogen sulfide developing in sewage systems or industrial waste water has often affected humans. Furthermore, animal mass mortalities in sulfidic marine and limnetic habitats (1) support the view of hydrogen sulfide as a dangerous, lethal toxin (2) in the presence of which no animal life would be possible. However, early investigations (1931) on animals from the Black Sea (3) and on some invertebrates from the Baltic Sea (4) that were experimentally exposed

33

to high sulfide concentrations demonstrated that not every species succumbed to these detrimental abiotic conditions; some could survive for days or even weeks. Similar results (1972) were published, again on sulfide-resistant invertebrates from the Baltic Sea (5), but even 25 years ago, the authors remarked: "Unbeantwortet muss die sehr interessante Frage bleiben, welche Besonderheiten im Stoffwechsel der resistenten Arten solch lange Überlebenszeiten bei Anwesenheit des normalerweise extrem giftigen H_2S ermöglichen."[1]

Renewed and rapidly growing interest in physiological and metabolic adaptations of animals living in sulfidic aquatic environments was stimulated by the discovery of complex animal communities around hydrothermal vents on the ocean floor (6, 7), because it became apparent that animals from vents were exposed to appreciable concentrations of sulfide (8, 9). Soon it was shown that sulfide was not only tolerated, but exploited via endosymbiotic sulfur-oxidizing chemoautotrophic bacteria living within the tissues of most of the sessile species of the vent community (10–12). This discovery sparked a deluge of publications on the hydrothermal vent fauna, and there are already several reviews on different aspects of their biology (13–18). In addition, studies were initiated on the macro- and meiofauna in other sulfidic environments such as the sediments or sea grass beds of the intertidal zone, sublittoral sediments, marine sewage outfalls, or the hypolimnion of eutrophic seas, ponds, and gravel pits. This work contributed some unique and interesting findings concerning adaptations for sulfide in animal life occurring in these environments. Some of the results have already been summarized (19–22). This review focuses on recent research dealing with the physiology and metabolism of some sulfide-tolerant and sulfide-exploiting invertebrates living in various habitats other than hydrothermal vents.

ECOLOGICAL ROLE OF SULFIDE

General Aspects of Sulfide and Sulfidic Habitats

The partial pressure of oxygen (PO_2) and the concentration of sulfide[2] in the aquatic layer or in the sediment of different environments are usually inversely related. The low diffusion coefficient of oxygen in water, the increase in the diffusion distance in interstitial water, and the biological oxygen demand within the sediment contribute to maintaining a low PO_2 (24). Under these conditions, putrefication of organic, thiol-containing material is a major source of hydrogen sulfide in limnetic environments (25). In marine sediments, anaerobic

---

[1]For the time being, it cannot be answered which special metabolic design enables sulfide tolerant species to survive the normally extremely toxic hydrogen sulfide.

[2]The term sulfide refers to all three forms of hydrogen sulfide, namely hydrogen sulfide gas, H_2S; the bisulfide anion, HS^- (pK_1 7.02); and the sulfide anion S^{2-} (p$K_2 > 12$) (23).

sulfate-reducing bacteria, e.g. *Desulfovibrio* or *Desulfomaculatum*, use organic compounds such as lactate, pyruvate, and short-chain fatty acids as carbon and energy sources to reduce sulfate to sulfide (25, 26). Dissimilatory sulfate reduction may result in a buildup of sulfide in marine sediments and the overlying water column. Muddy sediments become stratified and are anoxic a few millimeters below the surface; sulfide levels increase with further depth (27, 28). The level of sulfide within the sediment varies with the time of the year and is higher in summer than during the winter season. The distribution of sulfide is also patchy because it is dependent on the amount of organic material present (29). Thus species that live in the substratum encounter not only transient moderate or severe hypoxic conditions (30), but also elevated sulfide levels during burrowing activity. Animals living in permanent burrows can be exposed to sulfide during low tide when this compound diffuses from the pore water along the chemical gradient into the burrows. Sulfide concentrations up to 66 μM have been measured in the burrow water of the echiuran worm *Urechis caupo* after 4 h of tidal exposure (31). In an environment inhabited in high numbers by lugworms (*Arenicola marina*, Polychaeta), sulfide concentrations in the pore water of the sediment range from 3.2 to 336 μM during summer and from 1.7 to 138 μM during the fall and spring, respectively (32). Concentrations of up to 36 μM could be found in some burrows (33). The sediment of eulittoral environments in the Western Baltic contained 665 μM sulfide (34). The elaborate burrows of mud shrimps (Thalassinidea) constructed in sediments of eulittoral and sublittoral marine environments were usually hypoxic, hypercapnic, and contained sulfide concentrations from 0 to 206 μM (35). These levels were even higher than those at the hydrothermal vents found near the Galapagos Islands, where sulfide concentrations between 0 and 110 μM were measured (9). During 4 h of tidal exposure in summer time, a high percentage of *Arenicola marina* were found to contain $\approx$150 μM sulfide within their body fluids, which decreased to 15 μM in October (33). In the coelomic fluid of freshly caught specimens of the priapulid worm *Halicryptus spinulosus*, which lives in severely hypoxic sediments in the eulittoral of the Western Baltic, sulfide concentrations of 86–445 μM were measured (34).

The influx of sulfide into the body and its distribution in different body compartments of various animals have been studied in detail in laboratory experiments. The diffusion coefficient of H_2S in tissues of meiofauna species was assumed to be $5 \cdot 10^{-6}$ cm^2 s^{-1} (36). The diffusion coefficient for hydrogen sulfide has been estimated to be $4 \cdot 10^{-5}$ cm^2 s^{-1} in the peanut worm (*Sipunculus nudus*, Sipunculidae) (32) and $8 \cdot 10^{-7}$ cm^2 s^{-1} in the ostracod *Cyprideis torosa* (Crustacea, Ostracoda) (37). Permeation coefficients of 0.17 and 0.063 cm h^{-1} for H_2S and HS$^-$, respectively, were reported for the body wall tissue of *Urechis caupo* (38). The sulfide concentration in body compartments of *Arenicola marina* were dependent at a given pH on the ambient sulfide concentration and on the ambient P_{O_2}. The highest concentrations were recorded in the body wall tissue; the concentrations in the blood and coelomic fluid were considerably lower (39). The concentration in the body wall always remained somewhat below that in the incubation medium due to a more acidic pH in the coelomic fluid than in the medium (39, 40). A detailed study on the shrimp *Crangon crangon* demonstrated the expected dependence of the internal hydrogen sulfide concentration on pH_e and pH_i, i.e. lowest at high pH values (41). One can assume, therefore, that sulfide can permeate the body wall of most invertebrates, and at least some of the species encountering sulfide within their habitat can be affected by this compound.

Toxicity of Sulfide

Hydrogen sulfide is generally considered a highly toxic substance for aerobic organisms, mainly impairing pulmonary function as well as oxygen transport in mammals and potently inhibiting cytochrome c oxidase by reversibly binding at the heme site to cytochrome aa_3 (2, 42). The toxic effects inhibit aerobic energy supply. In addition, sulfide reacts as a strong nucleophile, reducing disulfide bridges and binding to heme rings (2, 43, 44). The latter reaction may explain the reduction in the rate of hemoglobin deoxygenation of the cytoplasmic hemoglobin in the bivalve *Solemya reidi* (45). Hemoglobin may also react with sulfide to form hematin, which may catalyze the oxidation of sulfide (46, 47). These reactions significantly reduce oxygen transport, and at high sulfide concentrations, the respiratory pigment may become dysfunctional. The effect of sulfide on hemocyanin is unclear, although in contrast to hemoglobin it may not be poisoned by this compound (48, 49).

The extreme toxicity of hydrogen sulfide present in different aquatic environments may result in a fauna with low species diversity, although the abundance of individual species may be quite high. A dominant species of some intertidal sediments, the lugworm *A. marina*, was shown to be tolerant of not only hypoxia (50) but also of hydrogen sulfide. The first mechanistic explanations for animal adaptations to sulfide were given for *A. marina* (40, 46) and for meiofauna that comprise sulfide-tolerant and non-tolerant species living in reducing and well-oxygenated environments, respectively (51, 52).

MECHANISMS OF SULFIDE PROTECTION IN INVERTEBRATES

Some proposed adaptive mechanisms for sulfide tolerance and protection include exclusion of sulfide at the body wall owing to its impermeability or the presence of a thick cover of sulfide-oxidizing bacteria; insensitive cytochrome c

oxidase; reversible sulfide binding to blood components; mitochondrial sulfide oxidation to less toxic sulfur compounds with a concomitant ATP synthesis; reliance on anaerobiosis at toxic sulfide levels; and oxidation of sulfide by symbiotic bacteria with utilization of bacteria-borne metabolites by the invertebrate host (13–22). In the context of this review, we discuss mitochondrial sulfide oxidation and the transition to an anaerobic energy metabolism during sulfide exposure, mainly in invertebrates.

Chemical versus Biological Sulfide Oxidation

In the presence of oxygen, sulfide reacts spontaneously and may form various oxidation products such as elemental sulfur, sulfite, thiosulfate, and sulfate (53). The autoxidation of sulfide is pH dependent and is catalyzed by metal ions such as Ni^{2+}, Mn^{2+}, Cu^{2+}, and Fe^{2+} (54–57). Despite this reactivity, sulfide can coexist with oxygen in aqueous solutions and its half-life in oxygen-saturated seawater is in the order of a few hours (58).

Sulfide oxidation is also a widespread phenomenon within the animal kingdom. It has been demonstrated in many animal groups, including bivalves, polychaetes, and crustaceans (19, 21, 22). In most cases, the oxidation of sulfide can be regarded as a detoxification mechanism because sulfide is removed from the tissue by its oxidation to non-toxic or less toxic sulfur compounds.

Sulfide oxidation occurs within the body in different tissues. For example, it can take place in body wall tissue, which serves as a first defense and thus may prevent sulfide from reaching the internal organs. Sulfide oxidation within body wall tissue has been demonstrated in the priapulid worm *Halicryptus spinulosus* (34), in the lugworm *A. marina* (59), and in the echiuran worm *Urechis caupo* (60). In the crustacean *Bythograea thermydron* (49) and in the isopod *Saduria entomon* (61), sulfide was oxidized in the hepatopancreas. Another sulfide oxidizing mechanism resides in the blood found in the clams *Solemya reidi, Calyptogena magnifica*, and *Lucinoma annulata* (62), in the polychaete worm *Hediste* (as *Nereis*) *diversicolor* (47) and in *U. caupo* (31, 62, 63).

In a number of species, sulfide oxidation does not take place within an animal tissue proper. These animals harbor chemoautotrophic, sulfide-oxidizing bacteria in modified, highly specialized tissues (13–18). This kind of symbiosis has been most extensively studied in the clam *S. reidi* (64–68) and in the vestimentiferan tube worm *Riftia pachyptila* (11, 12, 69–74), but it also occurs in several other species, including some solemyid, lucinid, vesicomyid, and mytilid bivalves (75–79).

In some species, sulfide oxidation is not restricted to one site or to one organ. Sulfide oxidation takes place in body wall tissue and in the blood of *U. caupo* (60) and of *Halicryptus spinulosus* (34). In *S. reidi* the initial step of sulfide oxidation is located in the animal's tissues, whereas the oxidized sulfur compounds are transported to and further oxidized by the bacterial symbionts (64, 73, 80, 81).

Rate of Biological Sulfide Oxidation

The rates of sulfide oxidation reported from different animal tissues range between nmol to several μmol $\cdot$ min^{-1} g fresh weight^{-1} (47, 49, 61, 82). The measured values depend largely on the method used for estimating sulfide oxidation. The significance of the reported activities measured, using the artificial electron acceptor benzyl viologen (47, 61, 62, 82), has been questioned because of the non-physiological assay conditions used (19). A tenfold lower oxidizing activity was found in extracts of the hepatopancreas of *Saduria entomon* when the reaction product thiosulfate was measured instead of the reduction of benzyl viologen (61). Therefore, most present studies estimate sulfide oxidation by monitoring oxidized thiols using the bimane method (83–86).

Products of Sulfide Oxidation

In most of the macrofaunal species studied so far, thiosulfate ($S_2O_3^{2-}$) was the main product of sulfide oxidation. During sulfide exposure, thiosulfate accumulated in the tissues and/or body fluids of some crustaceans (35, 49, 61, 87) and various worms (32, 34, 59, 60). In the endosymbiont-containing clams *S. reidi* and *Lucinoma aequizonata*, thiosulfate was also the main product of the initial sulfide oxidation step, which is located in the animal's tissue, and only small amounts of sulfite (SO_3^{2-}) or sulfate (SO_4^{2-}) were found (81, 88).

The reason that thiosulfate is the most common sulfide oxidation product may be the favorable ratio of sulfide to oxygen (52). If sulfide is directly oxidized by oxygen, the production of 1 mol of thiosulfate consumes 2 mol of sulfide, but only 1.5 mol of oxygen. In contrast, with sulfate as the end product of sulfide oxidation, only 1 mol of sulfide is detoxified, at the cost of 2 mol of oxygen. Under oxygen-limiting conditions, it is important to spend as little oxygen as possible on sulfide detoxification. Accordingly, sulfite and sulfate were the primary end products of sulfide detoxification in some meiofauna species living in the upper, oygen-containing layer of the sediment, whereas thiosulfate and elemental sulfur were accumulated in other species living under oxygen-limiting conditions (52).

Various sulfur compounds can be the end products of sulfide oxidation in endosymbiotic bacteria. In the bacterial symbiont from *Riftia pachyptila*, sulfide was oxidized mostly to elemental sulfur, although sulfate and polysulfides were also produced (74). The bacteria of *S. reidi* and other clams oxidize thiosulfate and sulfide to sulfate. In the presence of excess sulfide or thiosulfate, both compounds could be converted to temporary elemental sulfur deposits (64, 89).

Oxygen-Dependent Sulfide Oxidation and Sulfide-Dependent Anaerobiosis

Sulfide oxidation is generally oxygen dependent and can therefore increase the respiration of an animal beyond the rate of oxygen consumption characteristic for the standard metabolic rate at normoxic conditions. During hypoxia, the presence of sulfide will compete with the electron transport chain for oxygen and thus force an animal to commence anaerobiosis at higher P_{O_2} values than under low levels of oxygen alone. Sulfide can also inhibit cytochrome c oxidase, thereby depressing oxygen-dependent ATP production, but a partial oxygen consumption can continue if sulfide oxidation still uses oxygen for further thiosulfate production by other than mitochondrial pathways. Even if no sulfide is present, symbiont-containing species can consume oxygen at rates above their normal respiration rates because oxygen is required for the oxidation of elemental sulfur accumulated previously from microbial sulfide exploitation (64, 90). Thus oxygen consumption in sulfide-exposed animals is difficult to correlate with any specific metabolic pathway and, in particular, one cannot deduce from measurements of oxygen consumption ($\dot{M}_{O_2}$) alone whether energy is provided aerobically or anaerobically.

In invertebrates lacking chemoautotrophic bacteria, an elevated $\dot{M}_{O_2}$ during sulfide exposure could be the result of sulfide oxidation. When kept under normoxic conditions and at sulfide concentrations comparable to those found in the field, a slight but insignificant increase in $\dot{M}_{O_2}$ could be measured in *U. caupo*. $\dot{M}_{O_2}$ of the isolated coelomic fluid, however, increased significantly probably because of hematin-mediated oxidation of sulfide (91). In the lugworm *A. marina*, the presence of 25 μM sulfide had no significant effect on the oxygen consumption over the whole range of ambient P_{O_2} (39). In contrast, at sulfide levels between 25 and 200 μM, a drastic decrease in $\dot{M}_{O_2}$ was found for both species (39, 91). At low sulfide levels and normoxic conditions, only 1.4% of the oxygen consumed by lugworms was used for sulfide detoxification to thiosulfate, and the oxygen percentage increased to 3.4% at a P_{O_2} of 4.9 kPa. In the presence of 200 μM sulfide, the oxygen consumption of lugworms was already significantly reduced when compared with controls without sulfide and, of this, 50% was used for thiosulfate production (39, 92). Accordingly, the amount of oxygen available to maintain aerobiosis was markedly reduced.

Oxygen consumption has also been estimated in several sulfide-exposed crustaceans. It was reduced by approximately 50% and was maintained at this reduced level during exposure to sulfide levels as high as 250 μM in the mud shrimp *Neotrypaea* (*Callianassa*) *californiensis* (R Kochevar & J Childress, unpublished reference within Reference 91). Different results were obtained for the mud-shrimp (*Calocaris macandreae*) (35). This species was able to maintain or even increase, albeit insignificantly, its oxygen consumption when exposed to sulfide concentrations in excess of 150 μM under normoxia and in excess of 100 μM under hypoxia. The significance of an increase in $\dot{M}O_2$ during sulfide exposure may be masked by individual variation in respiration and sulfide-oxidizing capacity. A highly significant threefold increase of oxygen consumption was measured with excised gills of the estuarine ribbed mussel *Geukensia demissa* (formerly *Modiolus demissus*) kept at sulfide concentrations between 200 and 500 μM. $\dot{M}O_2$ remained stimulated even at a sulfide concentration of 1 mM (93). This pronounced increase in $\dot{M}O_2$ was only found in specimens freshly collected from *Spartina* grass tide marshes, where pore water can contain millimolar concentrations of sulfide. Maintenance of this bivalve in sulfide-free conditions resulted in small increases of gill oxygen consumption at less than 500 μM sulfide and inhibition between 500 and 1000 μM sulfide. Obviously, sulfide-stimulated oxygen consumption was correlated with ambient exposure to sulfide, leading to an induction of sulfide-oxidizing systems (93).

In species that harbor symbiotic sulfur-oxidizing chemoautotrophic bacteria, oxygen consumption rates increased significantly as shown in *S. reidi* when ambient sulfide levels were raised to 100 μM sulfide. At sulfide concentrations higher than 100 μM, $\dot{M}O_2$ declined and was similar to control levels at 500 μM sulfide (64). During 3 h of incubation, the addition of 0.5 mM sulfide stimulated average oxygen uptake of whole *Soleyma velum* from 65.2 to 115.4 μl O_2 g^{-1} h^{-1} (94). These data can be interpreted as indicating that part of the oxygen consumed was used for direct sulfide oxidation, either by the animal's tissue or by the sulfur bacteria. It remains to be seen whether sulfide oxidation was sufficient to prevent inhibition of cytochrome c oxidase, thus maintaining an aerobic energy metabolism, or whether the mitochondria were poisoned, thus resulting in a sulfide-induced anaerobiosis. It should be kept in mind, however, that sulfide oxidation could use such a sufficiently large amount of oxygen that it becomes limiting as an acceptor for NADH-borne hydrogen.

To answer these questions, several invertebrates were exposed to various oxygen and sulfide concentrations, and the onset of anaerobiosis was deduced from the accumulation of anaerobic glycolytic end products. These products were lactate in crustacea and opines, occurring mainly in molluscs and annelids, as well as acetate and propionate, which resulted from the anaerobic mitochondrial pathway (30). In the latter pathway, succinate is an intermediate that lends itself well as an indicator of sulfide-dependent anaerobiosis. As soon as cytochrome c oxidase can no longer transfer electrons to oxygen, either because of limiting ambient oxygen tensions or sulfide inhibition, the mitochondria of many marine or limnetic invertebrates reduce fumarate to succinate. Succinate immediately increases to higher steady state levels than under aerobiosis and remains at these elevated levels during sustained anaerobiosis (95–97).

The first direct evidence for a maintained aerobic energy metabolism during sulfide exposure was provided for *S. reidi*, which did not show any increase of succinate above aerobic levels in the presence of 100 μM sulfide and air saturation. Specimens that were incubated at 250 and 500 μM sulfide and air saturation, however, developed succinate levels characteristic of anaerobic animals (65). Similar results were obtained for *A. marina*, in which succinate contents in the body wall tissue increased to anaerobic levels only when the lugworms were exposed to sulfide levels above 300 μM (59).

In the field, high sulfide concentrations often occur in combination with low oxygen levels. Under these conditions, the sulfide-dependent oxygen consumption could force an animal into anaerobiosis at a much higher P_{O_2} than in the absence of sulfide. This was indeed the case in the marine oligochaete *Tubificoides benedii*, which under normoxic conditions could maintain a completely aerobic metabolism at sulfide concentrations up to 175 μM. At 300 μM sulfide, anaerobic pathways were utilized to only a small extent, and even at sulfide concentrations as high as 450 to 600 μM, a partially aerobic metabolism was sustained. However, if ambient oxygen concentrations were decreased to 1.5 kPa, 40 μM sulfide was sufficient to give rise to an anaerobic metabolism (98). Not all invertebrates that are adapted to sulfide can remain aerobic at low P_{O_2}, but switch gradually to anaerobiosis depending on ambient sulfide levels (39, 92). It is obvious that sulfide limits oxygen availability for aerobic ATP provision, in particular under ambient oxygen deficiency, but the use of an anaerobic energy metabolism compensates for a transient sulfide inhibition of cytochrome *c* oxidase.

Further Fate of Sulfide Oxidation Products

Little is known about the final fate of sulfide oxidation products. Most are probably metabolized and/or excreted within a short time to enable continued sulfide oxidation. Even thiosulfate, which is almost non-toxic (99, 100) and highly soluble, cannot be accumulated to infinite concentrations within the body of an animal. The passive diffusion of thiosulfate through biological membranes is slow (101, 102). An active thiosulfate-transporting mechanism has not yet been found in animals, although it seems present in some bacteria (103, 104). Another possible pathway would be the excretion of thiosulfate via nephridial organs and, finally, thiosulfate could be metabolized and eliminated as another sulfur compound. In a number of endosymbiont-containing species, thiosulfate produced within the host tissue is further oxidized by the bacteria and is thought to be eliminated as sulfate. The clearance of thiosulfate from the blood of these species, appears to be slow. In the blood of *S. reidi*, thiosulfate concentrations slowly decreased from 280 to 20 μM within 12 h of recovery in sulfide-free, aerated seawater (68).

Only a few studies have dealt with the elimination of thiosulfate in animals without symbionts. In the coelomic fluid of *A. marina*, the thiosulfate concentration decreased from 2.9 to 0.9 mM during 12 h of recovery in sulfide-free, aerated seawater and was 0.6 mM after 24 h (K Hauschild & MK Grieshaber, manuscript in preparation). Thiosulfate was not further metabolized in *A. marina*. Of the recorded decrease in thiosulfate, 39% came from passive paracellular diffusion through the body wall and an additional 43% was excreted via the metanephridia (K Hauschild & MK Grieshaber, manuscript in preparation). Also, in the crab *Bythograea thermydron*, thiosulfate was not rapidly cleared from the blood (49). Gorodezky & Childress (87) reported a slow, concentration-dependent elimination of thiosulfate. They suggested that diffusion across the gills was the major route of thiosulfate elimination in *B. thermydron*. Diffusion may be supplemented by an active process that is capable of moving thiosulfate against a concentration gradient. The authors showed that, as in *A. marina*, thiosulfate and not sulfate was the primary excretion product of these crabs (87). Arp et al (60) investigated the thiosulfate permeability of different epithelia of *U. caupo*. They found that the hindgut tissue was 150 times more permeable to thiosulfate than the body wall tissue and estimated that half of the thiosulfate in the coelomic fluid could be eliminated within 2 h by diffusion. However, the anal sacs (the excretory organs) of *U. caupo* may also participate in the elimination of sulfide oxidation products (60, 105). Together, these findings suggest that in animals without endosymbionts, thiosulfate is generally not further metabolized and that outward diffusion plays a significant role in its elimination.

MECHANISMS OF SULFIDE OXIDATION

It is well known that numerous species of animals oxidize sulfide when they are exposed to it (see above). The mechanisms of sulfide oxidation, however, are only partly understood. In free-living bacteria, the oxidation mechanisms vary greatly between the genera and among different species within the same genus. In some sulfur bacteria, for example, sulfide oxidation is coupled to the respiratory chain at the level of cytochrome *c*; whereas in others, it can couple at cytochrome *b* or even higher in the respiratory chain (106–108). Sulfide oxidation with the aid of symbiotic bacteria is a widespread strategy (see above). Little is known about the sulfide-oxidizing mechanisms in symbiotic sulfur bacteria (109). For example, it was demonstrated that cytochrome c_{552} is involved in sulfide oxidation of the *S. reidi* symbiont (110). A thorough discussion of the endosymbiotic systems, however, is beyond the scope of this paper, and the reader is referred to relevant reviews (10, 13–18, 109, 111–113).

In animal tissue, two main strategies appear to be involved in sulfide oxidation: mitochondrial sulfide oxidation and sulfide oxidation by blood components. These two oxidation mechanisms are discussed in the following sections.

Mitochondrial Sulfide Oxidation

Mitochondrial sulfide oxidation in animals was first demonstrated by Powell & Somero (80). They found that oxygen consumption of isolated mitochondria from the gill and foot tissue of *S. reidi* was stimulated by the addition of 20 μM sulfide. Sulfide-based oxygen consumption was unaffected by the respiratory chain inhibitors rotenone (complex I) and antimycin (complex III), whereas full inhibition was achieved by cyanide and high levels of sulfide (complex IV) (80). The authors concluded that sulfide oxidation was linked to the respiratory electron transport chain and that electrons from sulfide oxidation entered the respiratory chain at the level of cytochrome *c* (Figure 1). These findings were supported by O'Brien & Vetter (81) who were able to show that sulfide was exclusively oxidized to thiosulfate in the mitochondria of *S. reidi*. Using ^{35}S, they found that the oxidation of sulfide to thiosulfate involved at

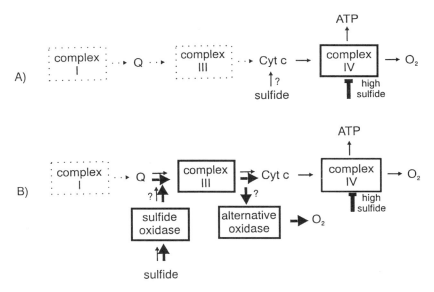

Figure 1   Model of electron transport and ATP production during sulfide oxidation in (*A*) *S. reidi* (from Reference 80) and in (*B*) *A. marina* (modified from References 116, 118). *Thin solid arrows* indicate electron flow and ATP production at low sulfide concentrations; *thick arrows* and *T bars* represent electron flow and inhibition of complex IV at high sulfide concentrations; *dotted arrows* from *dotted boxes* indicate pathways that are not involved in sulfide oxidation. Q, ubiquinone; Cyt c, cytochrome *c*. See text for further explanations.

least two steps, with sulfite formed as an intermediate at the beginning of the reaction. It has also been demonstrated that sulfide was oxidized to thiosulfate in liver mitochondria of the fishes *Fundulus parvipinnis* and *Citharichthys stigmaeus* (114). Mitochondrial sulfide oxidation in these species was stimulated by low sulfide concentrations, but inhibited by high sulfide concentrations and low levels of cyanide. The authors (114) concluded that the mechanism of sulfide oxidation in *F. parvipinnis* and *C. stigmaeus* was the same as in *S. reidi.* More recently, mitochondrial sulfide oxidation, which is sensitive to high concentrations of sulfide and cyanide, has also been demonstrated in a number of species including the priapulid *Halicryptus spinulosus* (34) and the polychaete *Heteromastus filiformis* (115).

A different mechanism of sulfide oxidation has been found in the mitochondria of the lugworm *A. marina* (59, 116). In this species, mitochondrial sulfide oxidation is also linked to the respiratory electron transport chain. In contrast to other sulfide-oxidizing species mentioned above, sulfide oxidation in *A. marina* is not inhibited by high concentrations of sulfide or by low levels of cyanide (59, 117), although the animal's cytochrome *c* oxidase is sulfide sensitive (118). Inhibitor studies reveal that electrons from sulfide enter the respiratory chain at the level of ubiquinone or at complex III (116; Figure 1). Besides the complex III pathway, there may be two electron pathways: (*a*) At low sulfide concentrations, the electrons are transferred to oxygen by cytochrome *c* and cytochrome *c* oxidase. (*b*) However, at high sulfide concentrations, the cytochrome *c* oxidase is blocked. Under these conditions the flow of electrons from sulfide oxidation deviates from the main respiratory chain and is channeled to oxygen via a proposed alternative terminal oxidase (116; Figure 1). This alternative oxidase appears to be sulfide insensitive and enables the lugworm to oxidize sulfide even at high tissue levels of this toxin (59, 116). Recently, it was suggested that an alternative terminal oxidase may also participate in mitochondrial sulfide oxidation in the polychaete *Hediste* (as *Nereis*) *diversicolor* and in the clam *Mya arenaria* (119).

Maximal sulfide oxidation rates in the mitochondria of different species were between 4 and 18 nmol sulfide $\cdot$ min^{-1} $\cdot$ mg protein^{-1} in the absence of ADP or any other substrate (34, 59, 80, 114, 115, 118). The lowest rate was measured in *Heteromastus filiformis* (115) and the highest in *A. marina* (59, 118). In most of these species, sulfide oxidation was stimulated by the addition of ADP, thus indicating that mitochondrial sulfide oxidation is coupled with oxidative phosphorylation.

Energy Exploitation During Sulfide Oxidation

Sulfide is a potent reductant with electrode potentials between -0.402 and -0.116 V, depending on the oxidation-reduction couple involved (106). The complete oxidation of sulfide to sulfate yields 797 KJ · mol^{-1} (109). A number of free-living and symbiotic bacteria are able to obtain the energy they need for growth from the oxidation of inorganic sulfur compounds (120). However, the thermodynamic efficiency of sulfur-oxidizing bacteria, calculated as the ratio between the energy conserved from CO_2 fixation and the energy liberated in sulfur compound oxidation, is a matter of some debate. Efficiencies as high as 26–73% have been reported in the literature (64, 70, 121). More recently, efficiency values between 3.2 and 15.4% were calculated, based on a different assumption about the source of electrons used for CO_2 reduction (109).

Apart from bacterial sulfide-oxidizing systems, some animal species are able to use sulfide directly as an inorganic energy source during mitochondrial sulfide oxidation. Sulfide oxidation is coupled to oxidative phosphorylation in *S. reidi* (80), *Fundulus parvipinnis*, *Citharichthys stigmaeus* (114), *Heteromastus filiformis* (115), and *A. marina* (118). In all these species, the cytochrome *c* oxidase appears to be the only coupling site of sulfide-stimulated ATP production. The ratio of ATP exploited per sulfide consumed ranges from 0.5 to 1.25 (80, 114, 118). As discussed in detail by O'Brien & Vetter (81), the potential for ATP production from mitochondrial sulfide oxidation is 2.0–4.3 mol ATP per mol sulfide if sulfide oxidation takes place outside the mitochondrial inner membrane. The measured values, however, were lower than the estimated values, which in part may be due to an uncoupling effect of the H_2S molecule. The low efficiency of ATP coupling during sulfide oxidation may be profitable considering the necessity of sulfide detoxification. Loosely coupled mitochondria will allow a more rapid sulfide oxidation when independent from cellular ATP utilization (81).

It is still unclear whether ATP provision from sulfide oxidation can contribute significantly to an animal's energy supply in vivo. Under conditions of limited food but sufficient oxygen, ATP production from sulfide oxidation may serve as a supplementary energy source. However, sulfide competes with normal carbon substrates for O_2 as the terminal electron acceptor. ATP production rate and ADP/O ratio (ADP phosphorylated to oxygen consumed) with sulfide as the substrate are generally lower when compared with other substrates such as succinate or malate (80, 114, 118). Under limiting oxygen conditions, therefore, mitochondrial sulfide oxidation constitutes a costly oxygen drain on the animal. In addition, ATP production can be stimulated only by low concentrations of sulfide. With increasing sulfide concentrations, ATP formation gradually decreases until complete inhibition occurs at sulfide concentrations of approximately 50 μM (80, 114, 115, 118).

Not much is known about a possible sulfide-supported ATP production in intact cells and tissues or about energy exploitation in vivo. Sulfide-supported cellular work in whole living tissues has been investigated in *Geukensia demissa*, which inhabits high sulfide sediments, and in *Mytilus edulis* as well as *M. galloprovincialis*, which live in sulfide-free environments (93, 122). The oxygen consumption rate of excised gills from *G. demissa* was stimulated at sulfide concentrations up to 1 mM. In support of the increased energy demand, oxygen consumption was stimulated even further by the addition of serotonin, a neurohormonal stimulant of ciliary beating (93). In contrast to oxygen consumption rate, ciliary beat frequency of *G. demissa* gills decreased in the presence of sulfide (BK Gaschen, DW Kraus & JE Doeller, manuscript in preparation). When gills were treated with antimycin A, an inhibitor of complex III in the respiratory chain that blocks the flow of electrons from reducing equivalents produced during catabolism on endogenous organic substrates to cytochrome *c* oxidase, both MO_2 and ciliary beat frequency were depressed. However, both processes were stimulated when sulfide was added to the medium. These results suggest that when electrons from oxidation of endogenous substrates are prevented from reaching cytochrome *c* oxidase, sulfide serves as an alternate substrate for oxidative phosphorylation (BK Gaschen, DW Kraus & JE Doeller, manuscript in preparation).

In vivo, oxygen consumption rates of some symbiont-free animals are enhanced during exposure to low sulfide concentrations (35, 91), likely indicating the animal's capacity to use energy from sulfide oxidation. However, in vivo measurements of MO_2 may not be suitable for the assessment of sulfide-supported energy exploitation, as discussed above.

Some evidence for sulfide exploitation in vivo has been found in two marine polychaete worms. The survival rate of *Heteromastus filiformis* was three times higher in the presence of sulfide and normoxic PO_2 as compared with normoxia without sulfide (123). In *Marenzellaria viridis*, the metabolic heat production, as measured by microcalorimetry, increased in the presence of sulfide (124). It is possible that the enhanced metabolic rate was due to detoxification processes that are coupled with an energy-gaining system used by the animal itself or are associated with bacteria (124).

Sulfide Oxidation by Blood Compounds

It has been long known that mammalian blood can oxidize sulfide (125). However, Sörbo (126) demonstrated that sulfide oxidation in a fresh hemolysate of rat blood was insignificant. Only heated blood, crystalline hemoglobin, or free hemin (the ferric heme that is not associated with protein), rapidly oxidized the sulfide (126). Hemin catalyzed the oxidation of sulfide to free sulfur (127, 128) and to thiosulfate (126). The question whether free hemin occurs in the blood of animals in vivo is still a matter of some debate (129). Patel & Spencer (46) reported that the blood of *A. marina* contains an active catalyst of sulfide oxidation. The sulfide-oxidizing activity has been ascribed to a so-called brown pigment, which is the oxidation product of hemoglobin. It has been suggested that the formation of brown pigment involves a modification of the protein-prosthetic group linkage so that it behaves like free hemin (46, 130). Evidence for a hematin-catalyzed sulfide oxidation has been found in the blood of *Hediste* (as *Nereis*) *diversicolor* and *Nereis virens* (47); in *U. caupo*; and in the clams *S. reidi, Calyptogena magnifica,* and *Lucinoma annulata* (62); and in blood, spleen, kidney, liver, and gills of thirteen shallow-water marine fishes (82). In these studies, however, sulfide-oxidizing activity was estimated with the benzyl viologen assay. Using radiolabeled sulfide under near-physiological conditions, it was found that in contrast to earlier results obtained with benzyl viologen, killifish blood does not catalyze sulfide oxidation to any appreciable extent (82, 131). Although the ferric hemoglobin of *Fundulus parvipinnis* and *Gillichthys mirabilis* does catalyze the oxidation of sulfide to thiosulfate in vitro, this phenomenon probably has no in vivo significance (131). Nevertheless, several studies indicate that sulfide detoxification in *U. caupo* involves heme compounds present in the coelomic fluid (31, 63, 91). Whole coelomic fluid, isolated hemoglobin, and hematin of *U. caupo* catalyzed the oxidation of sulfide to thiosulfate with the ferric iron atom of the hematin as the catalyst in these reactions (60, 132).

Other Sulfide Oxidation Mechanisms

Mechanisms other than mitochondrial or blood-based sulfide oxidation may be present, for example, in the hepatopancreas of the crabs *Bythograea thermydron* (49) and *Saduria entomon* (61). Several possibilities of enzymatic and non-enzymatic sulfide oxidation have been discussed (19, 21, 22, 113). Sulfide-oxidizing activity may also be present in some unusual organelles termed sulfide-oxidizing bodies (SOBs), which have been described originally in *S. reidi* (67). SOBs have also been found in the hindgut and body wall tissue of *U. caupo* (132–134). In the hindgut tissue of *U. caupo*, the density of SOBs varies significantly with sulfide exposure, and their sulfur content was significantly higher in sulfide-exposed worms than in those maintained in sulfide-free seawater (60). It has been suggested that the SOBs in *U. caupo* may be secondary lysosomes, containing phagocytosed, sulfide-damaged, and degenerating mitochondria. The heme iron from these mitochondria may then be used to catalyze sulfide oxidation (60).

CONCLUDING REMARKS

The capability of animals to live in the presence of sulfide has been proven in many aquatic species. They can oxidize sulfide to several sulfur compounds, with thiosulfate being the most important end product of sulfide oxidation. In several species, the process of thiosulfate formation is coupled to ATP synthesis. Thus, some of the mechanisms of sulfide oxidation and detoxification, unknown to authors 25 years ago (5), have been unraveled mainly through renewed intense investigations sparked by the discovery of the fauna that live at hydrothermal vents.

ACKNOWLEDGMENTS

We thank Dr. Alan Taylor for critically reading and giving insightful comments on our manuscript. The studies from our laboratories cited in this review were supported by Bundesminister für Forschung und Technologie under the project DYSMON II (03F0123B) and Fonds der Chemischen Industrie.

Visit the *Annual Reviews home page* at
http://www.AnnualReviews.org.

Literature Cited

1. Brongersma-Sanders M. 1948. Mass mortality in the sea. In *Treatise on Marine Ecology and Palaeoecology,* ed. JW Hedgpeth, 1:941–1010. Baltimore: Waverly
2. National Research Council. 1979. *Hydrogen Sulfide.* Baltimore: University Park Press. 183 pp.
3. Jacubowa L, Malm E. 1931. Die Beziehungen einiger Benthosformen des Schwarzen Meeres zum Medium. *Biol. Zbl.* 51:105–16
4. Theede H, Ponat A, Hiroki K, Schlieper C. 1969. Studies on the resistance of marine bottom invertebrates to oxygen-deficiency and hydrogen sulphide. *Mar. Biol.* 2:325–37
5. von Oertzen JA, Schlungbaum G. 1972. Experimentell-ökologische Untersuchungen über O$_2$-Mangel und H$_2$S-Resistenz an marinen Everterbraten der westlichen Ostsee. *Beitr. Meeresk.* 29: 79–91
6. Corliss JB, Ballard RD. 1977. Oases of life in the cold abyss. *Nat. Geogr.* 152:441–53
7. Lonsdale PF. 1977. Clustering of suspension-feeding macrobenthos near abyssal hydrothermal vents at oceanic spreading centers. *Deep-Sea Res.* 24: 857–63
8. Hessler RR, Smithey WM Jr. 1983. The distribution and community structure of megafauna at the Galapagos Rift hydrothermal vents. In *Hydrothermal Processes at Seafloor Spreading Centers,* ed.

PA Rona, K Boström, L Laubier, KL Smith, pp. 735–70. New York: Plenum
9. Johnson KS, Beehler CL, Sakamoto-Arnold CM, Childress JJ. 1986. In situ measurements of chemical distributions in a deep-sea hydrothermal vent field. *Science* 213:1139–41
10. Cavanaugh CM. 1980. Symbiosis of chemoautotrophic bacteria and marine invertebrates. *Biol. Bull.* 159:457
11. Cavanaugh CM, Gardiner SL, Jones ML, Jannasch HW, Waterbury JB. 1981. Prokaryotic cells in the hydrothermal vent tube worm *Riftia pachyptila*: possible chemoautotrophic symbionts. *Science* 213:340–42
12. Felbeck H. 1981. Chemoautotrophic potential of the hydrothermal vent tube worm *Riftia pachyptila* Jones (Vestimentifera). *Science* 213:336–38
13. Childress JJ. 1987. Uptake and transport of sulfide in marine invertebrates. In *Life in Water and on Land,* ed. P Dejours, L Bolis, CR Taylor, ER Weibel. Fidia Res. Ser. IX:231–39. Padova: Liviana
14. Childress JJ, Felbeck H, Somero GN. 1987. Symbiosis in the Deep Sea. *Sci. Am.* 265:106–12
15. Fisher CR. 1990. Chemoautotrophic and methanotrophic symbiosis in marine invertebrates. *Rev. Aquat. Sci.* 2:399–463
16. Powell MA, Vetter RD, Somero GN. 1987. Sulfide detoxification and energy exploitation by marine animals. In *Life in Water and on Land,* ed. P Dejours, L

Bolis, CR Taylor, ER Weibel. Fidia Res. Ser. IX:241–50. Padova: Liviana

17. Somero GN, Childress JJ, Anderson AE. 1989. Transport, metabolism, and detoxification of hydrogen sulfide in animals from sulfide-rich marine environments. *Crit. Rev. Aquat. Sci.* 1:591–614

18. Vetter RD. 1991. Symbiosis and the evolution of novel trophic strategies: thiotrophic organisms at hydrothermal vents. In *Symbiosis as a Source of Evolutionary Innovation,* ed. L Margulis, R Fester, 16:219–45. Cambridge: MIT Press

19. Bagarinao T. 1992. Sulfide as an environmental factor and toxicant: tolerance and adaptations in aquatic organisms. *Aquat. Toxicol.* 24:21–62

20. Fenchel TM, Riedl RJ. 1970. The sulfide system: a new biotic community underneath the oxidized layer of marine sand bottoms. *Mar. Biol.* 7:225–68

21. Vismann B. 1991. Sulfide tolerance: physiological mechanisms and ecological implications. *Ophelia* 34:1–27

22. Völkel S, Grieshaber MK. 1995. Sulfide tolerance in marine invertebrates. In *Advances in Comparative and Environmental Physiology. Mechanisms of Systemic Regulation: Acid-Base Regulation, Ion Tranfer and Metabolism,* ed. N Heisler, 22:233–57. Berlin/Heidelberg/New York: Springer-Verlag

23. Millero FJ, Plese T, Fernandez M. 1988. The dissociation of hydrogen sulfide in seawater. *Limnol. Oceanogr.* 33:269–74

24. Boutilier RG. 1990. Respiratory gas tensions in the environment. In *Advances in Comparative and Enviromental Physiology,* ed. RG Boutilier, 6:1–13. Berlin/Heidelberg/New York: Springer-Verlag

25. Nedwell DB. 1982. The cycling of sulphur in marine and freshwater sediments. In *Sediment Microbiology,* ed. DB Nedwell, DM Brown, pp. 73–106. London: Academic

26. Jørgensen BB, Fenchel T. 1974. The sulfur cycle of a marine sediment model system. *Mar. Biol.* 24:189–201

27. Jørgensen BB. 1982. Ecology of the bacteria of the sulfur cycle with special reference to anoxic/oxic interface environments. *Philos. Trans. R. Soc. London Ser. B* 298:543–61

28. Jørgensen B. 1977. The sulfur cycle of a coastal marine sediment (Limfjorden, Denmark). *Limnol. Oceanogr.* 22:814–32

29. Nedwell DB, Floodgate GD. 1972. Temperature-induced changes in the formation of sulphide in a marine sediment. *Mar. Biol.* 14:18–24

30. Grieshaber MK, Hardewig I, Kreutzer U, Pörtner HO. 1994. Physiological and metabolic responses to hypoxia in invertebrates. *Rev. Physiol. Biochem. Pharmacol.* 125:43–147

31. Arp AJ, Hansen BM, Julian D. 1992. Burrow environment and coelomic fluid characteristics of the echiurian worm *Urechis caupo* from populations at three sites in northern California. *Mar. Biol.* 113:613–23

32. Völkel S, Grieshaber MK. 1992. Mechanisms of sulfide tolerance in the peanut worm *Sipunculus nudus* (Sipunculida) and in the lugworm *Arenicola marina* (Polychaeta). *J. Comp. Physiol. B* 162:469–77

33. Völkel S, Hauschild K, Grieshaber MK. 1995. Sulfide stress and tolerance in the lugworm *Arenicola marina* during low tide. *Mar. Ecol. Prog. Ser.* 122:205–15

34. Oeschger R. Vetter RD. 1992. Sulfide detoxification and tolerance in *Halicryptus spinulosus* (Priapulida): a multiple strategy. *Mar. Ecol. Prog. Ser.* 86:167–79

35. Johns AR, Taylor AC, Atkinson RJA, Grieshaber MK. 1997. Sulphide metabolism in thalassinidean crustacea. *J. Mar. Biol. Assoc.* 77:127–44

36. Powell E. 1989. Oxygen, sulfide and diffusion: why thiobiotic meiofauna must be sulfide-insensitive first-order respirers. *J. Mar. Res.* 47:887–932

37. Jahn A, Gamenick I, Theede H. 1996. Physiological adaptations of *Cyprideis torosa* (Crustacea, Ostracoda) to hydrogen sulfide. *Mar. Ecol. Prog. Ser.* 142:215–23

38. Julian D, Arp AJ. 1992. Sulfide permeability in the marine invertebrate *Urechis caupo. J. Comp. Physiol.* 162:59–67

39. Hauschild K, Grieshaber MK. 1997. Oxygen consumption and sulfide detoxification in the lugworm *Arenicola marina* (L.) at different ambient oxygen partial pressures and sulfide concentrations. *J. Comp. Physiol.* B167:378–88

40. Groenendaal M. 1981. The adaptation of *Arenicola marina* to sulphide solutions. *Neth. J. Sea Res.* 15:65–77

41. Vismann B. 1996. Sulfide species and total sulfide toxicity in the shrimp *Crangon crangon. J. Exp. Mar. Biol. Ecol.* 204:141–54

42. Nicholls P. 1975. The effect of sulfide on cytochrome aa3. Isosteric and allosteric shifts of the reduced α-peak. *Biochim. Biophys. Acta* 396:24–35

43. Nichol AW, Hendry I, Morell DB, Clezy PS. 1968. Mechanism of formation

of sulphaemoglobin. *Biochim. Biophys. Acta* 156:97–108

44. Park CM, Nagel RL. 1984. Sulfhemoglobinemia. Clinical and molecular aspects. *N. Engl. J. Med.* 310:1579–84

45. Kraus DW, Doeller JE, Powell CS. 1996. Sulfide may directly modify cytoplasmic hemoglobin deoxygenation in *Solemya reidi* gills. *J. Exp. Biol.* 199:1343–52

46. Patel S, Spencer CP. 1963. The oxidation of haem compounds from the blood of *Arenicola marina. J. Mar. Biol. Assoc.* 43:167–75

47. Vismann B. 1990. Sulfide detoxification and tolerance in Nereis (Hediste) diversicolor and *Nereis (Neanthes) virens* (Annelida:Polchaeta). *Mar. Ecol. Prog. Ser.* 59:229–39

48. Hagerman L, Vismann B. 1993. Anaerobic metabolism, hypoxia and hydrogen sulphide in the brackish water isopod *Saduria entomon* (L.). *Ophelia* 38:1–11

49. Vetter RD, Wells ME, Kurtsman AL, Somero GN. 1987 Sulfide detoxification by the hydrothermal vent crab *Bythograeava thermydron* and other decapod crustaceans. *Physiol. Zool.* 60:121–37

50. Zebe E, Schiedek D. 1996. The lugworm *Arenicola marina*: a model of physiological adaptation to life in intertidal sediments. *Helgoländer Meeresunters.* 50:37–68

51. Powell EN, Crenshaw MA, Rieger RM. 1979. Adaptations to sulfide in the meiofauna of the sulfide system. ^{35}S-sulfide accumulation and the presence of a sulfide detoxification system. *J. Exp. Mar. Biol. Ecol.* 37:57–76

52. Powell EN, Crenshaw MA, Rieger RM. 1980. Adaptations to sulfide in sulfide-system meiofauna. Endproducts of sulfide detoxification in three turbellarians and a gastrotrich. *Mar. Ecol. Prog. Ser.* 2:169–77

53. Cline JD, Richards FA. 1969. Oxygenation of hydrogen sulfide in seawater at constant salinity, temperature and pH. *Environ. Sci. Technol.* 3:838–43

54. Almgren T, Hagström I. 1974. The oxidation rate of sulphide in sea water. *Water Res.* 8:395–400

55. Baxter CF, Van Reen R. 1958. Oxidation of sulfide to thiosulfate by metallo-protein complexes and by ferritin. *Biochim. Biophys. Acta* 28:573–78

56. Chen KY, Asce AM, Morris JC. 1972. Oxidation of sulfide by O_2: catalysis and inhibition. *Proc. Am. Soc. Civil Eng.* SA1:215–27

57. Millero FJ, Hubinger S, Fernandez M, Garnett S. 1987. Oxidation of H_2S in seawater as a function of temperature, pH and ionic strength. *Environ. Sci. Technol.* 21:439–43

58. Morse JW, Millero FJ, Cornwell JC, Rickard D. 1987. The chemistry of the hydrogen sulfide and iron sulfide systems in natural waters. *Earth Sci. Rev.* 24:1–42

59. Völkel S, Grieshaber MK. 1994. Oxygen-dependent sulfide detoxification in the lugworm *Arenicola marina. Mar. Biol.* 118:137–47

60. Arp AJ, Menon JG, Julian D. 1995. Multiple mechanisms provide tolerance to environmental sulfide in *Urechis caupo. Am. Zool.* 35:132–44

61. Vismann B. 1991. Physiology of sulfide detoxification in the isopod *Saduria (Mesidotea) entomon. Mar. Ecol. Prog. Ser.* 76:283–93

62. Powell MA, Arp AJ. 1989. Hydrogen sulfide oxidation by abundant nonhemoglobin heme compounds in marine invertebrates from sulfide-rich habitats. *J. Exp. Zool.* 249:121–32

63. Arp AJ. 1991. The role of heme compounds in sulfide tolerance in the echiuran worm *Urechis caupo.* In *Structure and Function of Invertebrate Oxygen Proteins,* ed. SN Vinogradov, OH Kapp, pp. 337–46. Heidelberg/New York: Springer-Verlag

64. Anderson AE, Childress JJ, Favuzzi JA. 1987. Net uptake of CO_2 driven by sulphide and thiosulphate oxidation in the bacterial symbiont-containing clam *Solemya reidi. J. Exp. Biol.* 133:1–31

65. Anderson AE, Felbeck H, Childress JJ. 1990. Aerobic metabolism is maintained in animal tissue during rapid sulfide oxidation in the symbiont-containing clam *Solemya reidi. J. Exp. Zool.* 256:130–34

66. Felbeck H. 1983. Sulfide oxidation and carbon fixation by the gutless clam *Solemya reidi*: an animal-bacteria symbiosis. *J. Comp. Physiol.* 152:3–11

67. Powell MA, Somero GN. 1985. Sulfide oxidation occurs in the animal tissue of the gutless clam, *Solemya reidi. Biol. Bull.* 169:164–81

68. Wilmot DB, Vetter RD. 1992. Oxygen- and nitrogen-dependent sulfur metabolism in the thiotrophic clam *Solemya reidi. Biol. Bull.* 182:444–53

69. Arp AJ, Childress JJ, Vetter RD. 1987. The sulfide-binding protein in the blood of the vestimentiferan tube-worm, *Riftia pachyptila,* is the extracellular haemoglobin. *J. Exp. Biol.* 128:139–58

70. Childress JJ, Fisher CR, Favuzzi JA, Kochevar RE, Sanders NK. 1991. Sulfide-driven autotrophic balance in the bacterial symbiont-containing hydrothermal vent tubeworm, *Riftia pachyptila* Jones. *Biol. Bull.* 180:135–53

71. Felbeck H, Childress JJ, Somero GN. 1981. Calvin-Benson cycle and sulfide oxidation enzymes in animals from sulfide-rich habitats. *Nature* 293:291–93

72. Fisher CR, Childress JJ, Minnich E. 1989. Autotrophic carbon fixation by the chemoautotrophic symbionts of *Riftia pachyptila. Biol. Bull.* 177:372–85

73. Powell MA, Somero GN. 1986. Adaptations to sulfide by hydrothermal vent animals: sites and mechanisms of detoxification and metabolism. *Biol. Bull.* 171:274–90

74. Wilmot DB, Vetter RD. 1990. The bacterial symbiont from the hydrothermal vent tubeworm *Riftia pachyptila* is a sulfide specialist. *Mar. Biol.* 106:273–83

75. Anderson AE. 1995. Metabolic responses to sulfur in lucinid bivalves. *Am. Zool.* 35:121–31

76. Dando PR, O'Hara SCM. 1991. Sulphide and methane rich ecosystems (Symbiosis between bacteria and marine invertebrates). *J. Mar. Biol. Assoc.* 71:953–56

77. Dando PR, Southward AJ, Southward EC. 1986. Chemoautotrophic symbionts in the gills of the bivalve mollusc *Lucinoma borealis* and the sediment chemistry of its habitat. *Proc. R. Soc. London Ser. B* 227:227–47

78. Dando PR, Southward AJ, Southward EC, Terwilliger NB, Terwilliger RC. 1985. Sulphur-oxidizing bacteria and haemoglobin in gills of the bivalve mollusc *Myrtea spinifera. Mar. Ecol. Prog. Ser.* 23:85–98

79. Reid RGB, Brand DG. 1986. Sulfide-oxidizing symbiosis in lucinaceans: implications for bivalve evolution. *Veliger* 29:3–24

80. Powell MA, Somero GN. 1986. Hydrogen sulfide oxidation is coupled to oxidative phosphorylation in mitochondria of *Solemya reidi. Science* 233:563–66

81. O'Brien J, Vetter RD. 1990. Production of thiosulphate during sulphide oxidation by mitochondria of the symbiont-containing bivalve *Solemya reidi. J. Exp. Biol.* 149:133–48

82. Bagarinao T, Vetter RD. 1989. Sulfide tolerance and detoxification in shallow-water marine fishes. *Mar. Biol.* 103:291–302

83. Fahey RC, Newton GL. 1987. Determination of low-molecular-weight thiols using monobromobimane fluorescent labeling and high performance liquid chromatography. *Meth. Enzymol.* 143:85–96

84. Fahey RC, Newton GL, Dorian R, Kosower EM. 1981. Analysis of biological thiols: quantitative determination of thiols at the picomole level based upon derivatization with monobromobimane and separation by cation-exchange chromatography. *Anal. Biochem.* 111:357–65

85. Newton GL, Dorian RC, Fahey RC. 1981. Analysis of biological thiols: derivatization with monobromobimane and separation by reverse-phase high-performance liquid chromatography. *Anal. Biochem.* 114:383–87

86. Vetter RD, Matrai PA, Javor B, O'Brien J. 1989. Reduced sulfur compounds in the marine environment: analysis by HPLC. *Symp. Ser. Am. Chem. Soc.* 393:243–61

87. Gorodezky LA, Childress JJ. 1994. Effects of sulfide exposure history and hemolymph thiosulfate on oxygen-consumption rates and regulation in the hydrothermal vent crab *Bythograea thermydron. Mar. Biol.* 120:123–31

88. Cary SC, Vetter RD, Felbeck H. 1989. Habitat characterization and nutritional strategies of the endosymbiont-bearing bivalve *Lucinoma aequizonata. Mar. Ecol. Prog. Ser.* 55:31–45

89. Vetter RD. 1985. Elemental sulfur in the gills of three species of clams containing chemoautotrophic bacteria: a possible inorganic energy storage compound. *Mar. Biol.* 88:33–42

90. Schiemer F, Novak R, Ott J. 1990. Metabolic studies on thiobiotic free-living nematodes and their symbiotic microorganisms. *Mar. Biol.* 106:129–37

91. Eaton RA, Arp AJ. 1993. Aerobic respiration during sulfide exposure in the marine echiuran worm *Urechis caupo. Physiol. Zool.* 66:1–19

92. Grieshaber MK, Hauschild K, Sommer A, Völkel S. 1995. Anaerobiosis and sulfobiosis in the lugworm, *Arenicola marina* L. In *Biology and Ecology of Shallow Coastal Waters*, ed. A Eleftheriou, AD Ansell, CJ Smith, pp. 131–37. Fredensborg: Olsen & Olsen

93. Lee RW, Kraus D, Doeller JE. 1996. Sulfide-stimulation of oxygen consumption rate and cytochrome reduction in gills of the estuarine mussel *Geukensia demissa. Biol. Bull.* 191:421–30

94. Chen C, Rabourdin B, Hammen CS. 1987. The effect of hydrogen sulfide on the metabolism of *Solemya velum* and enzymes of sulfide oxidation in gill tissue. *Comp. Biochem. Physiol.* 88B:949–52

95. Grieshaber MK, Hardewig I, Kreutzer U, Schneider A, Völkel S. 1992. Hypoxia and sulfide tolerance in some marine invertebrates. *Verh. Dtsch. Zool. Ges.* 85:55–76

96. Pörtner HO, Grieshaber MK. 1993. Critical PO_2(s) in oxyconforming and oxyregulating animals: gas exchange, metabolic rate and the mode of energy production. In *The Vertebrate Gas Transport Cascade. Adaptations to Environment and Mode of Life*, ed. E Bicudo, pp. 330–57. Boca Raton: CRC Press

97. Pörtner HO, Heisler N, Grieshaber MK. 1985. Oxygen consumption and mode of energy production in the intertidal worm *Sipunculus nudus* L.: definition and characterization of the critical PO_2 for an oxyconformer. *Resp. Physiol.* 59:362–77

98. Dubilier N, Giere O, Grieshaber MK. 1994. Concomitant effects of sulfide and hypoxia on the aerobic metabolism of the marine oligochaete *Tubificoides benedii*. *J. Exp. Zool.* 269:287–97

99. Sörbo B. 1972. The pharmacology and toxicology of inorganic sulfur compounds. In *Sulfur in Organic and Inorganic Chemistry*, ed. A Senning, pp. 143–70. New York: Dekker

100. Voegtlin C, Dyer HA, Leonard CS. 1924. On the specificity of the so called arsenic receptor in the higher animals. *J. Pharmacol. Exp. Theor.* 25:297–307

101. Cardozo RH, Edelman IS. 1952. The volume of distribution of sodium thiosulfate as a measure of the extracellular fluid space. *J. Clin. Invest.* 31:280–90

102. Holmes WN, Donaldson EM. 1969. The body composition and distribution of electrolytes. In *Fish Physiology*, ed. WS Hoar, DJ Randall, 1:1–239. New York: Academic

103. Hryniewicz M, Sirko A, Palucha A, Böck A, Hulanicka D. 1990. Sulfate and thiosulfate transport in *Escherichia coli* K-12: identification of a gene encoding novel protein involved in thiosulfate binding. *J. Bacteriol.* 172:3358–66

104. Sirko A, Hryniewicz M, Hulanicka D, Böck A. 1990. Sulfate and thiosulfate transport in *Escherichia coli* K-12: nucleotide sequence and expression of the cys *TWAM* gene cluster. *J. Bacteriol.* 172:3351–57

105. Seto SL, Mason Z, Arp AJ. 1993. Anal vesicle granules accumulate sulfur and iron in *Urechis caupo*. *Am. Zool.* 33:84A (Abstr.)

106. Kelly DP. 1982. Biochemistry of the chemolithotrophic oxidation of inorganic sulphur. *Philos. Trans. R. Soc. London Ser. B* 298:499–528

107. Kelly DP. 1988. Oxidation of sulfur compounds. In *The Nitrogen and Sulphur Cycles*, ed. JA Cole, SJ Ferguson, pp. 65–94. Cambridge: Cambridge Univ. Press

108. Kelly DP. 1989. Physiology and biochemistry of unicellular sulfur bacteria. In *Autotrophic Bacteria*, ed. HG Schlegel, B Bowien. pp. 193–217. Heidelberg: Science Tech; Madison & Springer-Verlag

109. Nelson DC, Hagen KD. 1995. Physiology and biochemistry of symbiotic and free-living chemoautotrophic bacteria. *Am. Zool.* 35:91–101

110. Kraus DW, Doeller JE, Wittenberg JB. 1992. Hydrogen sulfide reduction of symbiont cytochrome c_{552} in gills of *Solemya reidi* (Mollusca). *Biol. Bull.* 182:435–43

111. Scott KM, Fisher CR. 1995. Physiological ecology of sulfide metabolism in hydrothermal vent and cold seep vesicomyid clams and vestimentiferan tube-worms. *Am. Zool.* 35:102–11

112. Somero G. 1987. Symbiotic exploitation of hydrogen sulfide. *News Physiol. Sci.* 2:3–6

113. Vetter RD, Powell MA, Somero GN. 1991. Metazoan adaptation to hydrogen sulphide. In *Metazoan Life Without Oxygen,* ed. C Bryant, pp. 109–28. London: Chapman & Hall

114. Bagarinao T, Vetter RD. 1990. Oxidative detoxification of sulfide by mitochondria of the California killifish *Fundulus parvipinnis* and the speckled sanddab *Citharichthys stigmaeus. J. Comp. Physiol. B* 160:519–27

115. Oeschger R, Vismann B. 1994. Sulphide tolerance in *Heteromastus filiformis* (Polychaeta): mitochondrial adaptations. *Ophelia* 40:147–58

116. Völkel S, Grieshaber MK. 1996. Mitochondrial sulfide oxidation in *Arenicola marina.* Evidence for alternative electron pathways. *Eur. J. Biochem.* 235:231–37

117. Völkel S. 1995. Sulfide tolerance and detoxification in *Arenicola marina* and *Sipunculus nudus. Am. Zool.* 35:145–53

118. Völkel S, Grieshaber MK. 1997. Sulphide oxidation and oxidative phosphorylation in the mitochondria of the lugworm *Arenicola marina. J. Exp. Biol.* 200:83–92

119. Tschischka K, Oeschger R. 1995. Mitochondrial sulphide oxidation in selected marine invertebrates. *Physiol. Zool.* 68:135 (Abstr.)

120. Brock TD, Madigan MT, Martinko JM, Parker J. 1997. *Biology of Microorganisms.* London: Prentice-Hall. 8th ed.

121. Mason J, Kelly DP, Wood AP. 1987.

Chemolithotrophic and autotrophic growth of *Thermothrix thiopara* and some thiobacilli on thiosulphate and polythionates, and a reassessment of the growth yields of *Thx. thiopara* in chemostat culture. *J. Gen. Microbiol.* 113:1249–56

122. Doeller JE. 1995. Cellular energetics of animals from high sulfide environments. *Am. Zool.* 35:154–62

123. Lopez GR, Clough LM. 1993. A dual sulfide and oxygen requirement in a symbiont-free infaunal polychaete. *Am. Zool.* 33:83A (Abstr.)

124. Schneider A. 1996. Metabolic rate of the brackish water polychaete *Marenzelleria viridis* under reducing conditions. *Thermochim. Acta* 271:31–40

125. Haggard HW. 1921. The fate of sulfide in the blood. *J. Biol. Chem.* 49:519–29

126. Sörbo B. 1958. On the formation of thiosulfate from inorganic sulfide by liver tissue and heme compounds. *Biochim. Biophys. Acta* 27:324–29

127. Krebs HA. 1929. Über die Wirkung von Kohlenoxyd und Blausäure auf Hämatinkatalysen. *Biochem. Z.* 204:322–42

128. Haurowitz F. 1941. Katalytische Oxidation von Sulfiden durch Hämin oder Hämoglobin. *Enzymologica* 10:141–45

129. Mangum C. 1976. Primitive respiratory adaptations. In *Adaptation to Environment*, ed. RC Newell, pp. 191–278. London: Butterworths

130. Patel S, Spencer CP. 1962. Studies on the haemoglobin of *Arenicola marina*. *Comp. Biochem. Physiol.* 8:65–82

131. Bagarinao T, Vetter RD. 1992. Sulfidehemoglobin interactions in the sulfidetolerant salt marsh resident, the California killifish *Fundulus parvipinnis*. *J. Comp. Physiol. B* 162:614–24

132. Bogan MR, Arp AJ. 1993. Sulfide oxidation by the tissues of *Urechis caupo* in vitro. *Am. Zool.* 33:47A (Abstr.)

133. Menon JG, Arp AJ. 1992. Morphological adaptations of the respiratory hindgut of a marine echiuran worm. *J. Morphol.* 214:131–38

134. Menon JG, Arp AJ. 1993. The integument of the marine echiuran worm *Urechis caupo*. *Biol. Bull.* 185:440–54

Annu. Rev. Physiol. 1998. 60:55–72

BIOLOGICAL ICE NUCLEATION AND ICE DISTRIBUTION IN COLD-HARDY ECTOTHERMIC ANIMALS

Richard E. Lee, Jr. and Jon P. Costanzo

Department of Zoology, Miami University, Oxford, Ohio 45056;
e-mail: leere@muohio.edu

KEY WORDS: cold hardiness, freeze tolerance, supercooling, cryobiology, inoculative freezing

ABSTRACT

For many ectotherms, overwintering survival depends on the avoidance or regulation of ice nucleation and growth within their body fluids. Freeze avoidance via supercooling plays an important role in the cold hardiness of many small species, particularly terrestrial arthropods, that do not survive the freezing of their body fluids. In contrast, mechanisms that limit supercooling and initiate freezing at relatively high temperatures promote survival of the few invertebrates and vertebrates that tolerate freezing. These mechanisms include inoculative freezing, which results from contact with ice in the environment, and various ice nucleating proteins, microbes, and crystalloid compounds. In freeze-tolerant ectotherms, cold hardiness is influenced by complex, seasonally changing interactions among physiological factors, ice nucleators, and the physical microenvironment. Extraorgan sequestration of ice is a major adaptation of freeze tolerance. For most freeze-tolerant species, ice growth is primarily restricted to extracellular compartments; however, intracellular freezing also occurs in some species.

INTRODUCTION

A review article on the subject of biological ice nucleation and internal ice formation may seem to many physiologists, particularly ones that work with birds and mammals, as a rather bizarre topic with little relevance to the normal function and survival of animals. However, winter survival of many ectotherms critically depends on either avoidance or regulation of ice formation within their bodies.

55

0066-4278/98/0315-0055$08.00

A number of recent reviews have dealt with various aspects of cold tolerance and winter survival; however, here we focus on endogenous and environmental factors that influence or regulate supercooling and ice nucleation within body fluids and compartments. It has become clear in recent years that studying an organism in isolation from its environment can result in major misconceptions about its means for winter survival. Consequently, we use several model systems to illustrate the critical and dynamic role that complex interactions between the organism and its particular microenvironment play in the survival of ectotherms at low temperature. We also examine sites of ice nucleation and growth, and their significance to organismal cold tolerance.

BIOLOGICAL ICE NUCLEATION
AND SUPERCOOLING

A solution that remains unfrozen at temperatures below its equilibrium freezing point (FP_{eq}) is said to be supercooled. Water droplets of a few microliters in volume can supercool to $-40°C$ before spontaneously freezing. The first step in ice nucleation is the aggregation of water molecules to form an embryo; once this cluster reaches a critical size, such that it grows rather than disperses, a nucleus is formed upon which an ice crystal can grow (1).

Ice nuclei may arise by two mechanisms. One, termed homogeneous nucleation, involves only the spontaneous aggregation of water molecules. The chance of an aggregation reaching critical size increases with decreasing temperature and increasing duration of chilling. The other mechanism, heterogeneous nucleation, occurs when some entity other than water forms the template upon which an ice crystal forms. These ice-nucleating agents facilitate the clustering of water molecules and increase the likelihood that embryos reach a critical size.

When exposed to subzero temperatures, many organisms can supercool, sometimes by many degrees, before ice nucleates within their body fluids. The lowest body temperature (T_b) reached before body fluids begin to freeze is called the supercooling point or temperature of crystallization (T_c). Within biological systems, ice nucleation is believed to begin by heterogeneous mechanisms in which nucleating agents catalyze ice nucleation at relatively high subzero temperatures. Organisms realize their innate capacity to supercool only in the absence of these agents. Ice nucleators vary in their potency to initiate freezing, with more efficient ones inducing freezing at higher T_bs. Although an organism may contain a variety of potential ice nucleators, only the most efficient one(s) actually catalyzes an ice nucleation event, because once freezing begins, the ice lattice grows throughout the body. Furthermore, the release of the latent heat of crystallization warms the body and thus decreases the chance that other

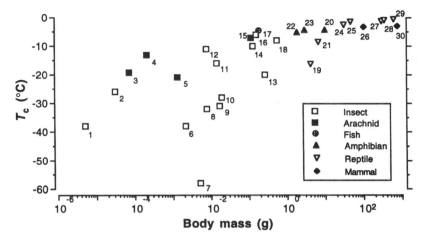

Figure 1   Relationship between body mass and temperature of crystallization (T_c) of animals representing Arthropoda and Vertebrata. Legend: 1. eggs of *Psylla mali* (81); 2. eggs of *Arcynopteryx compacta* (82); 3. *Hygroribates marinus* (6); 4. *Alaskozetes antarcticus* (6); 5. larvae of *Ixodes uriae* (83); 6. larvae of *Diplolepis bicolor* (8); 7. larvae of *Mayetiola rigidae* (8); 8. *Typhlocyba* sp. (8); 9. larvae of *Dendroctonus rufipenis* (8); 10. *Dendroctonus rufipenis* (8); 11. *Hippodamia convergens* (84); 12. *Pterostichus brevicornis* (8); 13. *Nymphalis antiopta* (8); 14. *Leptinotarsa decemlineata* (36); 15. *Ixodes uriae* (83); 16. *Upis ceramboides* (8); 17. juvenile *Carassius carassius* (85); 18. *Danaus plexippus* (86); 19. hatchlings of *Chrysemys picta* (JP Costanzo, JD Litzgus, JB Iverson & RE Lee, unpublished data); 20. *Bufo cognatus, B. woodhousei* (16); 21. *Sphenomorphus kosciuskoi* (26); 22. *Pseudacris triseriata* (16); 23. *Scaphiopus bombifrons* (87); 24. *Egernia saxatilis* (26); 25. *Thamnophis sirtalis* (88); 26. *Rattus norvegicus* (89); 27. *Chrysemys picta* (58); 28. *Terrapene carolina* (90); 29. *Alligator mississippiensis* (28) 30. *Spermophilus parryii* (91).

agents would catalyze freezing. In practice, the T_c measured for a given taxon, individual, or tissue may vary considerably depending on such factors as the quantity and potency of nucleators present, water content, cryoprotectant levels, and amount of freezable water present (2, 3).

The capacity to supercool decreases as body mass increases (Figure 1). This is due, in part, to the higher probability that an ice embryo will spontaneously form or that the larger volume of body fluid will contain a particularly active nucleator. Many insect eggs, springtails, and mites weighing <100 μg supercool extensively, while larger terrestrial arthropods freeze between -5 and $-15°C$. Larger still, most vertebrates supercool relatively little, if at all (4). The relationship between body mass and T_c has been observed intraspecifically (5, 6) and suggests that ontogenetic changes in supercooling capacity may influence the winter survival strategy adopted during different life history stages (e.g. *Ixodes uriae*, *Chrysemys picta*; Figure 1).

It may seem contradictory that any animal could supercool to $\leq -60°C$ (Figure 1), given that the limit of homogeneous nucleation is $-40°C$. Some arthropods achieve exceptional supercooling by accumulating high concentrations of glycerol, sorbitol, or other cryoprotectants, which may reach multimolar levels and comprise up to 25% of their body mass. Several studies (7) indicate that accumulation of such osmolytes effectively reduces T_c by approximately two to three times as much as the FP_{eq} is colligatively depressed ($1.86°C$/osmol). Thus by producing 4.8 M glycerol, the Alaskan willow cone gall fly larva (*Rhabdophaga strobiloides*) achieves a corresponding FP_{eq} of $-19.3°C$ and the capacity to supercool to $-56.1°C$ (8). Vertebrates apparently do not use cryoprotectants for this purpose. Some species undergo a seasonal dehydration that serves to concentrate extant osmolytes and reduce water volume, thus enhancing supercooling capacity (4, 9).

Because most ectotherms do not survive extensive ice formation within body fluids, they must either avoid low temperatures, rely on mechanisms that promote supercooling, or attenuate ice embryos within the blood (e.g. antifreeze proteins in polar fishes; 10). In contrast, a relatively few species of terrestrial insects, intertidal invertebrates, amphibians, and reptiles that overwinter terrestrially survive freezing and do so daily or seasonally. For many of these species, it is critical that extensive supercooling be avoided and that ice nucleation occur at a T_b very near the FP_{eq}. This moderates the rate of ice growth and allows time to physiologically adjust to the osmotic and mechanical stresses associated with freezing. Low rates of ice growth are particularly important for freeze-tolerant vertebrates which, unlike invertebrates that prepare in advance of seasonal cold, initiate cryoprotective responses only after freezing begins. The wood frog (*Rana sylvatica*), for example, mobilizes the cryoprotectant glucose and undergoes protective organ dehydration during the first 12–24 h of freezing (see reviews 11–13); rapid freezing inhibits these cryoprotective responses and is lethal (14, 15). Similarly, the chorus frog *Pseudacris triseriata* readily survives freezing if ice nucleation occurs between -1 and $-2°C$, but mortality increases progressively at lower T_cs (16).

Classes of Ice Nucleators and Inoculative Freezing

Although the actual ice nucleating agent in a given organism is frequently unknown, distinct classes of ice nucleating agents have been identified. These include special proteins produced by the animal and microorganisms that become intimately associated with animals' tissues. In addition, crystalloid inorganic compounds, active in the range of -8 to $-12°C$, were recently discovered in a freeze-tolerant insect (17).

The best known class of biological ice nucleators is comprised of proteins and lipoproteins that occur in a variety of freeze-tolerant insects (see reviews 3, 7). Production of these hemolymph-borne agents, which typically are active in the range of -6 to $-9°C$, coincides with seasonal patterns of cold-hardening. Blood nucleators exhibiting activity at -7 to $-8°C$ occur in various freeze-tolerant vertebrates, although their adaptive significance is unclear because freezing at these temperatures is lethal (18).

The most potent ice nucleators known are an unusual group of bacteria and fungi (19), which were originally reported as epiphytes and often viewed as pathogens, that cause extensive frost damage to crops. Aggregations of ice-nucleating proteins within the bacterial cell wall serve as the nucleus upon which the ice crystal grows, with larger aggregations resulting in greater nucleating activity. The association between microbial ice nucleators and insect cold hardiness was suggested by the fact that gut evacuation frequently enhanced the supercooling capacity and, indeed, strains of the bacteria *Enterobacter taylorae, Enterobacter agglomerans*, and *Erwinia herbicola* expressing ice-nucleating activity as high as $-2°C$ have been isolated from the gut of insects (20, 21). A fungus (*Fusarium* sp.) with ice-nucleating activity matching that of the whole body T_c has been found in a freeze-tolerant moth larva (22); this finding is noteworthy because it suggests a mutualistic relationship in which these normal microbial flora insure protective freezing at high subzero T_bs (23, 24). Ice-nucleating microorganisms, which were recently isolated from a freeze-tolerant frog (25), may also play a role in the winter biology of vertebrate ectotherms. Microbial ice nucleators may be used to artificially elevate the T_c of freeze-intolerant insect pests and thus potentially offer a novel means of biological control (24).

Although some ice-nucleating agents have considerable activity, none matches the potency of ice itself. Ice in the animal's microenvironment may initiate inoculative freezing of body water. Ice apparently gains ingress through alimentary and respiratory orifices (26–28) or by directly permeating the integument (29–31). The moist skin of amphibians is a particularly poor barrier to the inward propagation of ice.

The vast majority of ectotherms do not survive freezing and must behaviorally avoid low temperature and contact with ice. For example, most aquatic freshwater invertebrates are freeze intolerant and have little capacity to supercool or resist inoculative freezing (32). In contrast, with freeze-tolerant animals, ice inoculation is beneficial because it allows freezing to begin when T_b falls to the FP_{eq} with little, if any, prior supercooling. Inoculative freezing is crucial to the survival of the centipede *Lithobius forficatus*, since despite having an ice nucleator active at $-3°C$, it dies if freezing begins after the centipede has supercooled to this temperature (33). When cooled in contact with ice, however, inoculative freezing occurs at $-1°C$ and the animal survives, even at T_bs as low as $-6°C$.

Recent work suggests that the susceptibility to inoculative freezing in some animals depends upon microenvironmental conditions. The likelihood of inoculative freezing increases with decreasing temperature (31) and increasing water potential of the microenvironment (34, 35). Characteristics of the substrate such as texture, water content, water potential, and hydraulic conductivity may be particularly important (36, 37).

Initiation of Freezing: Case Studies

There has been a growing appreciation that ice nucleation is influenced by the complex interplay of endogenous factors (e.g. ice nucleators, water balance, cryoprotectants), but also by interactions between the organism and its microenvironment. Furthermore, both physiological and physical factors influencing cold hardiness may vary seasonally. To illustrate this complexity, we discuss three model systems with which we are particularly familiar: an insect, an amphibian, and a reptile.

GALL-INHABITING FLY LARVA   For approximately 11 months of the year, larvae of the goldenrod gall fly *Eurosta solidaginis* (Tephritidae) live within spherical galls on stems of goldenrod (*Solidago* sp.). This fly ranges from the Gulf of Mexico to central Canada. Because the galls provide little thermal buffering and frequently project above any surrounding snow, larvae often experience fluctuating and extreme temperatures, with the daily range commonly exceeding $25°C$ and occasionally reaching $35°C$ (38).

In the northern United States, first, second, and early third instar larva are intolerant of freezing and typically supercool to $\leq-13°C$ (39). In autumn, larvae become freeze tolerant to $\leq-40°C$ and accumulate cryoprotectants, principally glycerol and sorbitol, in response to low environmental temperatures and desiccation as the surrounding gall tissues senesce (40, 41); supercooling capacity at this time is limited to -8 to $-10°C$ (39). During the subsequent larval-pupal metamorphosis, cold hardiness changes markedly as freeze tolerance is lost and the T_c of pupae decreases to $-18°C$ (17).

The abrupt increase in T_c of larvae associated with the acquisition of freeze tolerance during the autumn suggests the presence of a relatively efficient endogenous ice nucleator. Some data suggest the presence of an ice nucleator in the hemolymph of this species, although a recent study has ascribed these results to contamination by external materials (42). The timing of this seasonal elevation in T_c is consistent with the production and action of ice-nucleating proteins that have been reported in other freeze-tolerant insects; however, proteinaceous nucleators have not been definitively identified in this species.

A recent report describes significant levels of ice-nucleating activity in fat body cells and a crystalloid compound isolated from *E. solidaginis* larvae (17). Fat body cell suspensions had a mean T_c of $-10.9°C$, with some samples freezing high enough ($-6°C$) to explain the T_c of intact larvae. In addition, within the Malpighian tubules of overwintering larvae are 25–45 crystalloid spherules that grow to a diameter of 300 μm. Scanning electron microscopy and X-ray diffraction studies reveal that these spherules are amorphous (i.e. lacking crystalline structure) conglomerates of round particles of tribasic calcium phosphate. As with the fat body cells, these spherules exhibit ice-nucleating activity at temperatures as high as $-6°C$ (mean T_c, $-10.9°C$). Furthermore, during the larval-to-pupal transition, T_c drops to $-18°C$ (17) coincident with the disappearance of these spherules.

Calcium carbonate, uric acid, potassium phosphate, and other crystalloid deposits are present in diapausing and overwintering insects. Commercial preparations of these compounds have ice-nucleating activity in the range of -8 to $-11°C$ (17). These compounds represent a new class of endogenous, heterogeneous nucleators in freeze-tolerant insects that function to ensure that cryoprotective ice nucleation occurs at relatively high subzero T_bs.

Despite the identification of efficient internal ice nucleators in overwintering larvae, this story is not complete without considering interactions between the larva and the gall it inhabits. Layne and colleagues (30) investigated the possibility that ice in the gall tissues might inoculate the larva. In October, field-collected galls (with larvae removed) have a water content of 66%, and a mean T_c of $-4.5°C$. When galls containing larvae were held for 24 h at $\approx-5.5°C$, all the galls and the larvae within them froze. By November, the water content of the galls had fallen to 20%, although the T_c remained the same. When the galls with larvae were again held for 24 h at $-5.5°C$, all the galls froze but only 10% of the larvae did. The susceptibility of larvae to inoculative freezing was confirmed by cooling isolated larvae in contact with moist filter paper. The larvae froze when the external water did, whereas larvae on dry paper remained supercooled.

During early autumn in the northern United States, when galls are green, larvae apparently freeze at T_bs near $0°C$ by inoculation from ice in the surrounding plant tissues. Later in the season, when the plant has senesced and its tissues have dried, the action of internal ice nucleators predominates, causing freezing at lower T_bs of -8 to $-10°C$. Consequently, if only the T_c of isolated larvae and expected environmental temperatures were used to predict the first time that larvae freeze, the estimate would, in fact, be 1–2 months later than the actual first incidence of freezing.

Due to the daily thermoperiod and intermittent periods of warming, larva may undergo many cycles of freezing and thawing during the winter. Furthermore, wetting of galls by rain may result in rehydration of the gall tissue and restoration of the potential to cause inoculative freezing of larvae in mid-winter (38). Consequently, whether a given larva freezes depends on dynamic interactions between a particular overwintering life stage, activity of internal ice-nucleating agents, and the hydration state of the surrounding plant tissues.

TERRESTRIAL HIBERNATION IN THE WOOD FROG   The wood frog *R. sylvatica* is a common resident of mesic forests and ranges from the southern Appalachians north to the Maritime provinces and west to northern Alaska, even to the Arctic Circle (43). Its winter habits are known only from a few anecdotal accounts, which suggest that their hibernacula are shallow burrows in the forest floor, well within the frost zone, overlain by leaves and other organic detritus. In southern Ohio, *R. sylvatica* encounters infrequent freezing episodes that expose frogs to a minimum T_b of -2 to $-4°C$ and may last several days (JP Costanzo, JT Irwin, RE Lee, unpublished data).

Freeze tolerance in *R. sylvatica* (and other vertebrate ectotherms) was reported only recently (44), yet several unique biochemical and physiological adaptations have been discovered (see current reviews, 11, 45–47). Generally, wood frogs can survive (*a*) the freezing of up to 65–70% of their body water, (*b*) a minimum T_b of $-6°C$, and (*c*) uninterrupted freezing for ≥ 4 weeks. Survival in the frozen state is promoted by an accumulation of cryoprotectant (glucose) and redistribution of water among body compartments; these responses mitigate the osmotic, mechanical, and metabolic perturbations of freezing and thawing.

Regulation of T_c is an important problem for freeze-tolerant animals that may suffer injury by spontaneous nucleation of deeply supercooled tissues. The intrinsic supercooling capacity of adult *R. sylvatica,* which weigh 5–20 g depending on geographic origin, is modest (Figure 1), but the smaller juveniles risk cryoinjury if they supercool extensively before nucleating (16). At least two efficient mechanisms ensure that freezing commences at relatively high T_b.

Owing to the highly permeable nature of amphibian skin, inoculative freezing of the body fluids of a supercooled frog commences virtually on contact with environmental ice (29, 30). To keep from desiccating extensively, *R. sylvatica* must hibernate in relatively moist microenvironments, which, during frosts, would provide an abundance of seed crystals. Thus freezing in nature likely occurs under most circumstances very near the FP_{eq}, $-0.4°C$.

Various strains of *Pseudomonas fluorescens, Pseudomonas putida,* and *Enterobacter agglomerans* expressing potent ice-nucleating activity have been cultured from intestines of winter-collected *R. sylvatica,* indicating that such bacteria are retained throughout hibernation (25). Feeding of *P. putida* to another freeze-tolerant frog, *Pseudacris crucifer,* markedly increased its T_c, demonstrating that these agents may promote ice formation in freeze-tolerant frogs. The T_c of intact *R. sylvatica* corresponds closely with that of isolated intestine and skin, organs that likely harbor such bacteria, but not of other body organs, tissues, or fluids (18, 48). The adaptive significance of microbial ice nucleators in their winter biology remains uncertain, although in the absence of ice inoculation they may ensure that freezing begins at a relatively high T_b.

The blood of *R. sylvatica* contains a proteinaceous ice nucleator that retains full activity (-7 to $-8°C$) in 0.2% dilutions (49, 50). Such agents have been suggested to be a critical factor in the evolution of vertebrate freeze tolerance (51). However, there are problems assigning adaptive function to these blood nucleators: (*a*) They are not unique to freeze-tolerant species, but rather may occur in various animals, including mammals; (*b*) some freeze-tolerant vertebrates lack them; (*c*) blood-borne ice nucleators exhibit less activity in vitro than certain tissues (namely, skin and intestine, which may harbor microbial ice nucleators); (*d*) there is poor congruence between activity temperature of blood nucleators and the T_c of intact animals; and (*e*) the activity temperature of blood nucleators is substantially lower than the minimum T_b that can be survived in the frozen state (i.e. -4 to $-6°C$). Collectively these issues cast doubt that blood nucleators are important for initiating protective freezing of *R. sylvatica* or other vertebrates whose supercooling capacity is so limited (18, 52).

OVERWINTERING OF HATCHLING TURTLES   Painted turtles (*Chrysemys picta*) are long-lived residents of quiet, shallow waters, which range from coast to coast in the northern United States and southern Canada. These turtles hatch during late summer but overwinter within the natal nest, only ≈ 10 cm beneath the ground surface, even in northern populations (43). Many emerge in spring after surviving exposure to minimum T_bs of -2 to $-11°C$ (37, 53, 54). In the sandhills of Nebraska, winters are particularly severe and hatchling *C. picta* are intermittently exposed to subzero temperatures from late November through early March. Cooling episodes are usually mild (minimum $T_b > -4°C$) and brief (<24 h), but temperatures of -10 to $-12°C$ occasionally occur (37, 53).

The remarkable cold hardiness of hatchling *C. picta* has been ascribed to supercooling (55, 56), as, indeed, they are among the few cold-hardy vertebrates whose bodies are small enough to permit extensive supercooling (Figure 1). However, these animals are also freeze tolerant (37, 54, 57, 58). Adaptations promoting freeze tolerance in *C. picta* are poorly understood (54, 57). A protein with ice-nucleating activity of -7 to $-8°C$ occurs in its blood; however, as with *R. sylvatica*, it apparently plays no role in cold hardiness (18, 51).

Freeze tolerance and supercooling are generally regarded as dichotomous strategies for cold tolerance, yet both may be effective survival mechanisms in hatchling *C. picta* subject to certain constraints (43, 56). Turtles tolerate freezing at $T_bs \geq -4\ °C$ (37, 54, 57, 58), whereas survival at much lower T_bs (e.g. $\approx -12\ °C$) is possible only if freezing is avoided. Whether supercooling or freeze tolerance is employed during a particular cooling episode depends upon prevailing physiological and microenvironmental conditions (37). According to this model, supercooling predominates during periods of low environmental water potential, since the risk of ice inoculation is reduced and the turtles may partially desiccate. Alternatively, exposure to a damp substrate promotes ice nucleation via inoculation at a T_b near the FP_{eq}, a condition requisite for freezing survival. Although many cooling episodes may be endured by frozen turtles, survival of the extreme temperatures occurring in some nests can only be ascribed to supercooling (37, 53). The factors limiting supercooling capacity are thus of particular interest in the winter life history of this species.

Reptiles such as *C. picta* are much less susceptible to inoculative freezing than the moist-skinned amphibians (4, 18), yet inoculation may occur when external ice contacts mucous membranes of the cloaca, nostrils, or eyes (26, 28), or even the skin (31). The resistance of *C. picta* hatchlings to ice inoculation reportedly varies anatomically, as skin of the head and neck apparently is more impervious to ice than is skin of the inguinal and axial pouches (55). In nature, susceptibility to inoculative freezing depends on hydric characteristics of the substrate. Laboratory trials with Nebraska *C. picta* showed that hatchlings immersed in native sand containing as little as 2.3% moisture (w/w) could not avoid ice inoculation (37), but about half of those tested in "damp clayey soil" resisted inoculation at T_bs as low as $-9°C$ (55). Data provided in a recent field study indicated that survival of hatchlings overwintering in loamy sand (94%) was substantially higher than that (65%) for animals overwintering in nests constructed in fine sand (53). Minimum nest temperatures did not differ between the groups, so one plausible explanation is that animals in the latter substrate were more susceptible to (lethal) inoculative freezing.

Given suitable environmental conditions it seems reasonable that hatchling *C. picta* may supercool as extensively in nature as they do under optimal laboratory conditions. By taking precautions to reduce contamination by free water and nucleating agents, turtles can be readily supercooled to $\approx -12°C$ (55) or even $-20°C$ (JP Costanzo, JD Litgus, JB Iverson & RE Lee, unpublished data). However, laboratory results for meticulously cleaned turtles may overrepresent supercooling capacity in nature because hatchling *C. picta* hibernate in intimate physical contact with soil, which conceivably harbors various ice nucleating agents. Recent work suggests that ice nucleators are indeed normal constituents of the nesting substrates and that they may constrain supercooling of hatchling turtles. For example, turtles hatched from eggs incubated in native sand supercooled much less than turtles hatched and reared on vermiculite (Figure 2). Material sampled in autumn from several nests of Nebraska

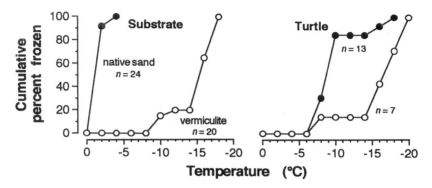

Figure 2 Cumulative freezing distributions of substrate washings (*left*) and hatchling painted turtles (*Chrysemys picta*) (*right*) that were hatched, reared, and cold acclimatized on native substrate (sand) or vermiculite. Substrate washings were cooled in 10-μl aliquots; turtles were individually cooled in dry vessels (10°C/h) after surface moisture was eliminated by evaporation. The data indicate that the substrate in which turtles overwinter contains a potent nucleator that markedly diminishes their supercooling capacity (JP Costanzo, JD Litzgus, JB Iverson & RE Lee, unpublished data).

C. picta contained ice nucleating agents that catalyzed the freezing of water at −3 to −5°C, exhibited increased potency with cold acclimation, and retained full activity in dilutions up to 10^{-3}. To date, ice nucleators have been found in nesting/overwintering substrates in the midwestern United States (Indiana, Nebraska) and Ontario, Canada. The identity of the nucleator is as yet unknown; however, preliminary results indicate that it is heat labile and, therefore, possibly of organic composition (JP Costanzo, JD Litzgus, JB Iverson & RE Lee, unpublished data). This discovery may reconcile some inconsistencies in the contemporary literature. Virtually all studies using animals hatching in natural nests (and thus potentially exposed to syntopic ice nucleators) have reported limited supercooling (e.g. $T_c \geq -4°C$; Reference 18), whereas extensive supercooling ($T_c < -8°C$) is known only in turtles hatched and reared in the laboratory (55).

Because hatchling *C. picta* must nucleate at high T_bs if they are to survive freezing, it is tempting to speculate a commensalistic role for the ice nucleator present in its winter microenvironment. Preliminary data do suggest that the nucleator may function in concert with available substrate water to promote (protective) inoculative freezing. However, under conditions favoring extensive supercooling (e.g. low environmental water potential), the nucleator catalyzes the freezing of turtles at −7 to −10°C, which do not survive. Interpopulational differences in winter survival may reflect not only the regional variation in susceptibility to inoculative freezing associated with soil characteristics (37), but also patchy distributions of potent ice nucleators in the winter microenvironment. These interactions may ultimately influence both regional and local distributions of this species.

DISTRIBUTION OF ICE WITHIN THE BODY

Freeze-tolerant animals can survive the freezing of up to 65–70% of their body water, but only if ice gradually forms within the tissues (11, 13). In both invertebrates and vertebrates, an equilibrium ice content is attained many hours or days after freezing begins (59, 60). Such low rates of ice formation, which are promoted by insulation in the microenvironment (snow cover, organic detritus, etc), allow time for the activation of cryoprotective responses and permit cells to adapt to the ensuing physical and osmotic stresses. Magnetic resonance imaging has revealed that freezing of *C. picta* and *R. sylvatica* begins in peripheral tissues and gradually moves toward the core (61, 62). In contrast, thawing occurs simultaneously throughout the body with deep visceral organs (e.g. liver) melting relatively quickly due to their higher concentrations of cryoprotectant and consequently, lower FP_{eq} (61, 62).

It is believed that freeze tolerance requires ice growth to be restricted to the extracellular spaces (63, 64). One consequence of ice forming in these compartments is that cells, which remain supercooled, are subject to osmotic stress, a primary cause of freezing injury. Because only water molecules join the growing ice lattice, rejected solute accumulates in the as yet unfrozen water; in turn, this hypertonic solution osmotically draws water from within cells. As freezing progresses cells may become dramatically distorted and shrunken. Cryoprotectants mitigate osmotic stress by binding water within cells, increasing intracellular osmolality, and by stabilizing structural elements within cells (64).

Extraorgan Ice Sequestration

Ice formation within body fluids not only poses the threat of excessive cellular dehydration, but also the potential for mechanical injury by the growing ice lattice, particularly in compact and highly structured tissues and organs. Ice fronts may shear and separate tissues, disrupting intercellular communication systems. Within organs, ice forms preferentially in the vascular system (65). A gradual freezing of the blood causes the plasma to become progressively hypertonic, drawing in additional extravascular water. Ultimately, vessels may be damaged by excessive expansion of the ice within them even though surrounding tissues are unharmed. Prevention of this type of cryoinjury is a major challenge to the successful cryopreservation of mammalian organs (65).

Some freeze-tolerant plants are well adapted to avoid excessive ice formation within sensitive structures. Vegetative and flower buds, as well as seeds, survive by translocating water from frost-sensitive tissues to sites were ice crystals grow innocuously (66, 67). This temporary redistribution of water allows tissues to supercool extensively and avoid freezing injury. Because the extracellular fluids of plants are markedly hypotonic with respect to the cytoplasm, the withdrawal and translocation of cell water is affected along a vapor pressure gradient extending from supercooled tissues to the growing ice mass, rather than along an osmotic gradient.

Recent studies reveal that organs of some freeze-tolerant animals are also protected by the translocation of water to other compartments. Dissection of frozen wood frogs reveals a surprising and striking distribution of ice within the body. As frogs freeze, a process that may require >24 h for the crystallization of 65% of the body water, organ water is progressively translocated to subdermal lymph sacs and the coelomic cavity where it freezes (Figure 3). Appendicular skeletal muscles lose 20–30% of their initial water content, whereas the heart, liver, intestine, and peripheral nerves lose >50% (68, 69). Tissues are fully rehydrated within several hours after thawing begins.

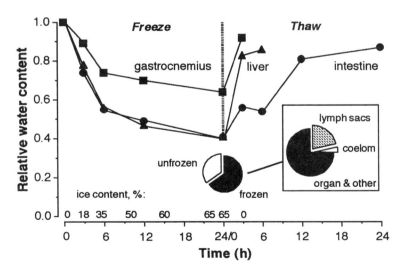

Figure 3 Dynamics of organ water and body ice during a routine 24-h freezing episode to −2.5°C, and subsequent thawing at 5°C, of the freeze-tolerant wood frog (*Rana sylvatica*). As up to 65% of total body water progressively freezes, over half of the water in some organs is relocated to spaces where it freezes innocuously; about 25% of all ice is sequestered within the coelom and lymph sacs. Most organs rapidly rehydrate upon thawing. Adapted from Lee & Costanzo (92).

Although some water inevitably freezes within organs, the partial dehydration apparently functions to reduce potential mechanical damage (69). An added benefit is that cryoprotectant becomes locally concentrated (15, 70). The significance of protective dehydration is evidenced by the fact that rapid freezing, which is lethal, inhibits organ dehydration in *R. sylvatica* (14, 15). In the freeze-tolerant box turtle (*Terrapene carolina*), some structures, particularly nervous tissues, dehydrate during freezing, although others (e.g. liver) do not (45). The freeze-intolerant leopard frog (*Rana pipiens*) also exhibits organ dehydration during freezing, but the amount of organ water lost (9–33%) is relatively low (71). Desiccation tolerance may thus be a chief preadaptation supporting the evolutionary development of freeze tolerance (69, 72).

The sequestration of ice in innocuous locations within the body may be facilitated by a lack of physical barriers and the presence of natural and/or potential voids. However, the specific mechanisms promoting translocation of bulk water and its redistribution are poorly known. The open circulatory system of arthropods and other invertebrates may facilitate the innocuous growth of ice external to compact organs. In *R. sylvatica*, an extended function of the heart, which continues to beat for many hours after freezing begins (73), likely affects the translocation of water from remote tissues. Osmotic forces may be involved, although hyperglycemia (as induced by administration of glucose) does not influence the degree of organ dehydration during freezing (70). Patterns of water loss among organs suggest that the basic mechanism is subordinate to regulation at the organ or tissue level. Extraorgan ice sequestration complements the action of cryoprotectants and plays a critical role in the freeze tolerance of some ectotherms.

Intracellular Ice Formation

Although cryobiologists generally believe that intracellular freezing is lethal to all organisms, some freeze-tolerant species naturally tolerate ice formation within certain cells. Working with *E. solidaginis*, Salt (74, 75) originally reported survival after freezing of cells in the fat body, an organ whose metabolic role is analogous to that of vertebrate liver. Recent investigation reveals that fat body cells are susceptible to inoculative freezing at a relatively high temperature ($-4.6°C$), a characteristic that markedly differs from that of mammalian cells, which resist inoculation at temperatures $< -15°C$ (76). Upon thawing, a radical reorganization of cytoplasmic contents is evident. The formerly dispersed, uniformly distributed lipid droplets coalesce in each cell's center, whereas the remaining organelles, including the nucleus, are displaced to the periphery (77, 78). Salt observed lipid coalescence in fat body cells through the transparent cuticle of previously frozen larvae (that continued normal development to become pupae and adults), which suggests that these cells freeze internally during routine freezing of the organism.

In 1995, Wharton & Ferns (79) provided convincing evidence for survival of intracellular freezing in the nematode *Panagrolaimus davidi*. Using cryomicroscopy and freeze-fracture electron microscopy, they observed freezing within cells of intact individuals which later laid eggs that developed normally. In this species, intracellular freezing may be an adaptation for reducing transmembrane osmotic stress (79). The supernatant from homogenates of this nematode inhibits recrystallization, an action that may promote tolerance of intracellular freezing (80). Future studies using vital dyes, cryomicroscopy, and freeze-fracture electron microscopy are needed to determine whether intracellular freeze tolerance occurs more commonly in freeze-tolerant ectotherms and what special adaptations permit cells to tolerate these stresses.

ACKNOWLEDGMENTS

We thank Jon Kelty and Jackie Litzgus for their comments on the manuscript. The authors gratefully acknowledge grant support for the research described in this review from the National Science Foundation, National Institutes of Health, and the United States Department of Agriculture.

> Visit the *Annual Reviews home page* at
> http://www.AnnualReviews.org.

Literature Cited

1. Vali G. 1995. Principles of ice nucleation. See Ref. 19, pp. 1–28
2. Block W. 1990. Cold tolerance of insects and other arthropods. *Philos. Trans. R. Soc. London Ser. B* 326:613–33
3. Zachariassen KE. 1992. Ice nucleating agents in cold-hardy insects. In *Water and Life*, ed. GN Somero, CB Osmond, CL Bolis, pp. 261–81. Berlin: Springer-Verlag
4. Costanzo JP, Lee RE. 1995. Supercooling and ice nucleation in vertebrate ectotherms. See Ref. 19, pp. 221–37
5. Johnston SL, Lee RE. 1990. Regulation of supercooling and nucleation in a freeze intolerant beetle (*Tenebrio molitor*). *Cryobiology* 27:562–68
6. Pugh PJA. 1994. Supercooling points and water contents in Acari. *Acta Ecol.* 15:71–77
7. Duman JG, Olsen TM, Yeung KL, Jerva F. 1995. The roles of ice nucleators in cold tolerant invertebrates. See Ref. 19, pp. 201–19
8. Miller LK. 1982. Cold-hardiness strategies of some adult and immature insects overwintering in interior Alaska. *Comp. Biochem. Physiol.* 73A:595–604
9. Ring RA, Danks HV. 1994. Desiccation and cryoprotection: overlapping adaptations. *Cryo-Letters* 15:181–90
10. DeVries AL, Cheng C-HC. 1992. The role of antifreeze glycopeptides and peptides in the survival of cold-water fishes. In *Water and Life*, ed. GN Somero, CB Osmond, CL Bolis, pp. 301–15. Berlin: Springer-Verlag
11. Costanzo JP, Lee RE, DeVries AL, Wang T, Layne JR. 1995. Survival mechanisms of vertebrate ectotherms at subfreezing temperatures: applications in cryomedicine. *FASEB J.* 9:351–58
12. Storey KB, Storey JM. 1992. Natural freeze tolerance in ectothermic vertebrates. *Annu. Rev. Physiol.* 54:619–37
13. Storey KB, Storey JM. 1988. Freeze tolerance in animals. *Physiol. Rev.* 68:27–84
14. Costanzo JP, Lee, RE, Wright MF. 1991. Effect of cooling rate on the survival of frozen wood frogs, *Rana sylvatica. J. Comp. Physiol.* 161:225–29
15. Costanzo JP, Lee RE, Wright MF. 1992. Cooling rate influences cryoprotectant distribution and organ dehydration in freezing wood frogs. *J. Exp. Zool.* 261:373–78
16. Swanson DL, Graves BM, Koster KL. 1996. Freezing tolerance/intolerance and

cryoprotectant synthesis in terrestrially overwintering anurans in the Great Plains, USA. *J. Comp. Physiol.* 166:110–19

17. Mugnano JA, Lee RE, Taylor RT. 1996. Fat body cells and calcium phosphate spherules induce ice nucleation in the freeze-tolerant larvae of the gall fly *Eurosta solidaginis* (Diptera, Tephritidae). *J. Exp. Biol.* 199:465–71

18. Costanzo JP, Lee RE. 1996. Mini-review: ice nucleation in freeze-tolerant vertebrates. *Cryo-Letters* 17:111–18

19. Lee RE, Warren GJ, Gusta LV, eds. 1995. *Biological Ice Nucleation and Its Applications.* St. Paul, MN: Am. Phytopathol. Soc. 370 pp.

20. Lee RE, Strong-Gunderson JM, Lee MR, Grove KS, Riga TJ. 1991. Isolation of ice nucleating active bacteria from insects. *J. Exp. Zool.* 257:124–27

21. Kaneko J, Yoshida T, Owada T, Kita K, Tanno K. 1991. *Erwinia herbicola* ice nucleation active bacteria isolated from diamondback moth *Plutella xylostella* L. pupae (in Japanese). *Jpn. J. Appl. Entomol. Zool.* 35:247–51

22. Tsumuki H. 1992. An ice-nucleating active fungus isolated from the gut of the rice stem borer, *Chilo suppressalis* Walker (Lepidoptera: Pyralidae). *J. Insect Physiol.* 38:119–25

23. Lee RE. 1991. Principles of insect low temperature tolerance. In *Insects at Low Temperature,* ed. RE Lee, DL Denlinger, pp. 17–46. New York: Chapman & Hall

24. Lee RE, Lee MR, Strong-Gunderson JM. 1993. Insect cold-hardiness and ice nucleating active microorganisms including their potential use for biological control. *J. Insect Physiol.* 39:1–12

25. Lee MR, Lee RE, Strong-Gunderson JM, Minges SR. 1995. Isolation of ice nucleating active bacteria from the freeze-tolerant frog, *Rana sylvatica. Cryobiology* 32:358–65

26. Spellerberg IF. 1972. Temperature tolerances of southeast Australian reptiles examined in relation to reptile thermoregulatory behavior and distribution. *Oecologia* 9:23–46

27. Steigerwald KA, Lee MR, Lee RE, Marshall JC. 1995. Effect of biological ice nucleators on insect supercooling capacity varies with anatomic site of application. *J. Insect Physiol.* 41:603–8

28. Lowe CH, Lardner PJ, Halpern EA. 1971. Supercooling in reptiles and other vertebrates. *Comp. Biochem. Physiol.* 39A:125–35

29. Layne JR. 1991. External ice triggers freezing in freeze-tolerant frogs at temperatures above their supercooling point. *J. Herpetol.* 25:129–30

30. Layne JR, Lee RE, Huang JL. 1990. Inoculation triggers freezing at high subzero temperatures in a freeze-tolerant frog (*Rana sylvatica*) and insect (*Eurosta solidaginis*). *Can. J. Zool.* 68:506–10

31. Packard GC, Packard MJ. 1993. Delayed inoculative freezing is fatal to hatchling painted turtles (*Chrysemys picta*). *Cryo-Letters* 14:273–84

32. Oswood MW, Miller LK, Irons JG. 1991. Overwintering of freshwater benthic macroinvertebrates. In *Insects at Low Temperature,* ed. RE Lee, DL Denlinger, pp. 360–75. New York: Chapman & Hall

33. Tursman D, Duman JG, Knight CA. 1994. Freeze tolerance adaptations in the centipede, *Lithobius forficatus. J. Exp. Zool.* 268:347–53

34. Holmstrup M, Zachariassen ZE. 1996. Physiology of cold hardiness in earthworms. *Comp. Biochem. Physiol.* 115A: 91–101

35. Forge TA, MacGuidwin AE. 1992. Effects of water potential and temperature on survival of the nematode *Meloidogyne hapla* in frozen soil. *Can. J. Zool.* 70:153–60

36. Costanzo JP, Moore JB, Lee RE, Kaufman PE, Wyman JA. 1997. Influence of soil hydric parameters on the winter cold hardiness of a burrowing beetle, *Leptinotarsa decemlineata* (Say). *J. Comp. Physiol. B* 167:169–76

37. Costanzo JP, Iverson JB, Wright MF, Lee RE. 1995. Cold hardiness and overwintering strategies of hatchlings in an assemblage of northern turtles. *Ecology* 76:1772–85

38. Layne JR. 1993. Winter microclimate of goldenrod spherical galls and its effects on the gall inhabitant *Eurosta solidaginis* (Diptera: Tephritidae). *J. Therm. Biol.* 18:125–30

39. Morrissey RE, Baust JG. 1976. The ontogeny of cold tolerance in the gall fly, *Eurosta solidaginis. J. Insect Physiol.* 22:431–37

40. Rojas RR, Lee RE, Baust JG. 1986. Relationship of environmental water content to glycerol accumulation in the freezing tolerant larvae of *Eurosta solidaginis* (Fitch). *Cryo-Letters* 7:234–45

41. Baust JG, Lee RE. 1982. Environmental triggers to cryoprotectant modulation in separate populations of the gall fly, *Eurosta solidaginis* (Fitch). *J. Insect Physiol.* 28:431–36

42. Bale JS, Hansen TN, Baust JG. 1989. Nucleators and sites of nucleation in the freeze tolerant larvae of the gall fly *Eurosta*

solidaginis (Fitch). *J. Insect Physiol.* 35:291–98

43. Ultsch GR. 1989. Ecology and physiology of hibernation and overwintering among freshwater fishes, turtles, and snakes. *Biol. Rev.* 64:435–516

44. Schmid WD. 1982. Survival of frogs in low temperature. *Science* 512:697–98

45. Costanzo JP, Wright MF, Lee RE. 1993. Physiological responses to freezing in the turtle *Terrapene carolina. J. Herpetol.* 27:117–20

46. Storey KB, Storey JM. 1996. Natural freezing survival in animals. *Annu. Rev. Ecol. Syst.* 27:365–86

47. Layne JR, Lee RE. 1995. Adaptations of frogs to survive freezing. *Climate Res.* 5:53–59

48. Layne JR. 1995. Crystallization temperatures of frogs and their individual organs. *J. Herpetol.* 29:296–98

49. Wolanczyk JP, Baust JG, Storey KB. 1990. Seasonal ice nucleating activity in the freeze tolerant frog *Rana sylvatica. Cryo-Letters* 11:143–50

50. Wolanczyk JP, Storey KB, Baust JG. 1990. Ice nucleating activity in the blood of the freeze-tolerant frog, *Rana sylvatica. Cryobiology* 27:328–35

51. Storey KB, McDonald DG, Duman JG, Storey JM. 1991. Blood chemistry and ice nucleating activity in hatchling painted turtles. *Cryo-Letters* 12:351–58

52. Storey KB. 1985. Freeze tolerance in terrestrial frogs. *Cryo-Letters* 6:115–34

53. Packard GC. 1997. Temperatures during winter in nests with hatchling painted turtles (*Chrysemys picta*). *Herpetologica* 53:89–95

54. Storey KB, Storey JM, Brooks SPJ, Churchill TA, Brooks RJ. 1988. Hatchling turtles survive freezing during winter hibernation. *Proc. Natl. Acad. Sci. USA* 85:8350–54

55. Packard GC, Packard MJ. 1995. The basis for cold tolerance in hatchling painted turtles (*Chrysemys picta*). *Physiol. Zool.* 68:129–48

56. Paukstis GL, Shuman RD, Janzen FJ. 1989. Supercooling and freeze tolerance in hatchling painted turtles (*Chrysemys picta*). *Can. J. Zool.* 67:1082–84

57. Churchill TA, Storey KB. 1992. Natural freezing survival by painted turtles *Chrysemys picta marginata* and *C. picta bellii. Am. J. Physiol.* 262:R530–37

58. Claussen DL, Zani PA. 1991. Allometry of cooling, supercooling, and freezing in the freeze-tolerant turtle *Chrysemys picta. Am. J. Physiol.* 261:R626–32

59. Lee RE, Lewis EA. 1985. Effect of temperature and duration of exposure on tissue ice formation in the gall fly, *Eurosta solidaginis* (Diptera, Tephritidae). *Cryo-Letters* 6:24–34

60. Layne JR, Lee RE. 1987. Freeze tolerance and the dynamics of ice formation in wood frogs (*Rana sylvatica*) from southern Ohio. *Can. J. Zool.* 65:2062–65

61. Rubinsky B, Hong J-S, Storey KB. 1994. Freeze tolerance in turtles: visual analysis by microscopy and magnetic resonance imaging. *Am. J. Physiol.* 267:R1078–88

62. Rubinsky B, Wong STS, Hong J-S, Gilbert J, Roos M, Storey KB. 1994. [1]H magnetic resonance imaging of freezing and thawing in freeze-tolerant frogs. *Am. J. Physiol.* 266:R1771–77

63. Storey KB, Bischof J, Rubinsky B. 1992. Cryomicroscopic analysis of freezing in liver of the free-tolerant wood frog. *Am. J. Physiol.* 263:R185–94

64. Mazur P. 1984. Freezing of living cells: mechanisms and implications. *Am. J. Physiol.* 247:C125–42

65. Pegg DE. 1988. The nature of cryobiological problems. In *Low Temperature Biotechnology: Emerging Applications and Engineering Contributions,* ed. JJ McGrath, KR Diller, pp. 3–21. New York: Am. Soc. Mech. Eng.

66. Quamme HA. 1995. Deep supercooling in buds of woody plants. See Ref. 19, pp. 183–99

67. Sakai A, Larcher W. 1987. *Frost Survival of Plants.* Berlin: Springer-Verlag. 321 pp.

68. Kling KB, Costanzo JP, Lee, RE. 1994. Post-freeze recovery of peripheral nerve function in the freeze-tolerant wood frog (*Rana sylvatica*). *J. Comp. Physiol.* 164:316–20

69. Lee RE, Costanzo JP, Davidson EC, Layne JR. 1992. Dynamics of body water during freezing and thawing in a freeze-tolerant frog (*Rana sylvatica*). *J. Therm. Biol.* 17:263–66

70. Costanzo JP, Lee RE, Lortz PH. 1993. Glucose concentration regulates freeze tolerance in the wood frog *Rana sylvatica. J. Exp. Biol.* 181:145–55

71. Costanzo JP, Lee RE, Lortz PH. 1993. Physiological responses of freeze-tolerant and -intolerant frogs: clues to evolution of anuran freeze tolerance. *Am. J. Physiol.* 265:R721–25

72. Costanzo JP, Wright MF, Lee RE. 1992. Freeze tolerance as an overwintering adaptation in Cope's gray treefrog (*Hyla chrysoscelis*). *Copeia* 1992:565–69

73. Layne JR, Lee RE, Heil TL. 1989. Freezing-induced changes in the heart rate

of wood frogs (*Rana sylvatica*). *Am. J. Physiol.* 257:R1046–49

74. Salt RW. 1959. Survival of frozen fat body cells in an insect. *Nature* 193:1426

75. Salt RW. 1962. Intracellular freezing in insects. *Nature* 193:1207–8

76. Lee RE, McGrath JJ, Morason RT, Taddeo RM. 1993. Survival of intracellular freezing, lipid coalescence and osmotic fragility in fat body cells of the freeze-tolerant gall fly *Eurosta solidaginis*. *J. Insect Physiol.* 39:445–50

77. Morason RT, Allenspach AL, Lee RE. 1994. Comparative ultrastructure of fat body cells of freeze-susceptible and freeze-tolerant *Eurosta solidaginis* larvae after chemical fixation and high pressure freezing. *J. Insect Physiol.* 40:155–64

78. Collins SD, Allenspach AL, Lee RE. 1996. Ultrastructural effects of lethal freezing on brain, muscle and Malpighian tubules from freeze-tolerant larvae of the gall fly, *Eurosta solidaginis*. *J. Insect Physiol.* 43:39–45

79. Wharton DA, Ferns DJ. 1995. Survival of intracellular freezing by the Antarctic nematode *Panagrolaimus davidi*. *J. Exp. Biol.* 198:1381–87

80. Ramlov H, Wharton DA, Wilson PW. 1996. Recrystallization in a freezing tolerant Antarctic nematode, *Panagrolaimus davidi*, and an alpine weta, *Hemideina maori* (Orthoptera; Stenopelmatidae). *Cryobiology* 33:607–13

81. Skanland HT, Somme L. 1981. Seasonal variation in cold-hardiness of eggs of the apple psyllid *Psylla mali* (Schmidb.) in Norway. *Cryo-Letters* 2:86–91

82. Gehrken U, Somme L. 1987. Increased cold hardiness in eggs of *Arcynopteryx compacta* (Plecoptera) by dehydration. *J. Insect Physiol.* 33:987–91

83. Lee RE, Baust JG. 1987. Cold-hardiness in the Antarctic tick, *Ixodes uriae*. *Physiol. Zool.* 60:499–506

84. Bennett VA, Lee RE. 1997. Modeling seasonal changes in intracellular freeze-tolerance of fat body cells of the gall fly, *Eurosta solidaginis* (Diptera: Tephritidae). *J. Exp. Biol.* 200:185–92

85. Kalabukhov NI. 1958. The problem of freezing, undercooling and vitrifying of animal organism. In *Institute of Biology, International Symposium on Freezing and Drying.* pp. 101–18. Oxford: Blackwell Sci. 2nd ed.

86. Larsen KJ, Lee RE. 1994. Cold tolerance including rapid cold-hardening and inoculative freezing in migrant monarch butterflies in Ohio. *J. Insect Physiol.* 40:859–64

87. Swanson DL, Graves BM. 1995. Supercooling and freeze intolerance in overwintering juvenile spadefoot toads (*Scaphiopus bombifrons*). *J. Herpetol.* 29:280–85

88. Costanzo JP, Claussen DL, Lee RE. 1988. Natural freeze tolerance in a reptile. *Cryo-Letters* 9:380–85

89. Andjus RK. 1955. Suspended animation in cooled, supercooled and frozen rats. *J. Physiol.* 128:547–56

90. Costanzo JP, Claussen DL. 1990. Natural freeze tolerance in the terrestrial turtle, *Terrapene carolina*. *J. Exp. Zool.* 254:228–32

91. Barnes BM. 1989. Freeze avoidance in a mammal: body temperatures below 0°C in an Arctic hibernator. *Science* 244:1593–95

92. Lee RE, Costanzo JP. 1993. Integrated physiological responses promoting anuran freeze tolerance. In *Life in the Cold: Ecological, Physiological, and Molecular Mechanisms,* ed. C Carey, G Florant, BA Wunder, B Horwitz, pp. 501–10. Boulder, CO: Westview

Annu. Rev. Physiol. 1998. 60:73–103

THE ROLE OF VITRIFICATION IN ANHYDROBIOSIS

John H. Crowe*, John F. Carpenter #, and Lois M. Crowe*

*Section of Molecular and Cellular Biology, University of California, Davis, California 95616; e-mail: Jhcrowe@ucdavis.edu; #Department of Pharmaceutical Sciences, School of Pharmacy, University of Colorado Health Sciences Center, Denver, Colorado

KEY WORDS: glass, anhydrobiosis, dormancy, cryobiology, protein stabilization, membrane stabilization, freezing, drying

---

ABSTRACT

Numerous organisms are capable of surviving more or less complete dehydration. A common feature in their biochemistry is that they accumulate large amounts of disaccharides, the most common of which are sucrose and trehalose. Over the past 20 years, we have provided evidence that these sugars stabilize membranes and proteins in the dry state, most likely by hydrogen bonding to polar residues in the dry macromolecular assemblages. This direct interaction results in maintenance of dry proteins and membranes in a physical state similar to that seen in the presence of excess water. An alternative viewpoint has been proposed, based on the fact that both sucrose and trehalose form glasses in the dry state. It has been suggested that glass formation (vitrification) is in itself sufficient to stabilize dry biomaterials. In this review we present evidence that, although vitrification is indeed required, it is not in itself sufficient. Instead, both direct interaction and vitrification are required. Special properties have often been claimed for trehalose in this regard. In fact, trehalose has been shown by many workers to be remarkably (and sometimes uniquely) effective in stabilizing dry or frozen biomolecules, cells, and tissues. Others have not observed any such special properties. We review evidence here showing that trehalose has a remarkably high glass-transition temperature (T_g). It is not anomalous in this regard because it lies at the end of a continuum of sugars with increasing T_g. However, it is unusual in that addition of small amounts of water does not depress T_g, as in other sugars. Instead, a dihydrate crystal of trehalose forms, thereby shielding the remaining glassy trehalose from effects of the added water. Thus under less than ideal conditions such as high humidity and temperature, trehalose does indeed have special properties, which may explain the stability and longevity of

73

0066-4278/98/0315-0073$08.00

anhydrobiotes that contain it. Further, it makes this sugar useful in stabilization of biomolecules of use in human welfare.

INTRODUCTION

Both the association of amphiphiles to form phospholipid bilayers and the folding of proteins that results in their tertiary structure are profoundly influenced by the low solubility of hydrocarbons in water (e.g. 1). These molecular arrangements, which are thought to be entropically driven, are lost when the water in which they are formed is removed. For instance, when a biological membrane is dehydrated, irreversible changes occur in its structural and functional integrity (reviewed in 2). Similarly, many labile proteins lose their functional and probably structural integrity when they are desiccated (reviewed in 3). However, evidence has been accumulating that certain sugars may replace the water around polar residues in membrane phospholipids and proteins, thereby maintaining their integrity in the absence of water.

The findings described herein have their roots in investigations over the past two decades on the biochemistry of organisms that are capable of surviving more or less complete dehydration (2). The dry organisms, said to be in a state of anhydrobiosis, may persist without water for decades and, in some cases, centuries (4, 5). When rehydrated, they rapidly resume active metabolism, frequently within minutes. Such organisms often contain large quantities of sugars and sugar alcohols, the presence of which appears to be associated with their survival in the dry state (2).

Many anhydrobiotic organisms, including fungal spores, yeast cells, certain soil-dwelling animals, cysts of the brine shrimp *Artemia* and the desert resurrection plant *Selaginella* contain large quantities (as much as 20% of the dry weight) of trehalose (see 2 for references). The analogue of trehalose in higher plants appears to be sucrose, which may in some cases make up as much as 50% of the dry weight (2). Over 20 years ago (4), we suggested that these sugars replace the water around polar residues in labile macromolecular assemblages such as membranes and proteins, thus stabilizing these structures in the absence of appreciable amounts of water. This idea has seen extensive experimental testing (see 2 for a recent review) and has come to be widely accepted as a principal mechanism for stabilization of dry biomaterials.

In the last few years, however, an alternative viewpoint has emerged that the sugars involved in stabilizing anhydrobiotic organisms do so by virtue of their ability to form glasses. In our view, glass formation (or vitrification) is not mutually exclusive with the water replacement hypothesis. Indeed, we believe and demonstrate in this review that vitrification is often required for stabilization of dry biomolecules, but is in itself insufficient to accomplish that stabilization.

The Properties of Glasses

A glass is a liquid of such high viscosity that it is capable of slowing chemical reactions or even, for all practical purposes, stopping them altogether (6). In so doing, it has been suggested by Bruni & Leopold (7) that the glassy state may assure quiescence and stability in a living system for lengthy periods. The viscous glass can, nevertheless, be readily melted by addition of water, thus restoring conditions permissive for normal metabolism. This latter point is particularly important in considerations on stability of cells in the dry state, as is discussed below. Excellent reviews on the properties of glasses can be found in Slade & Levine (8, 9).

A glass typically is spatially homogeneous, but without any long-range lattice order (10). Glasses show temperature-dependent transitions during which they pass from a glassy mechanical solid to a state with markedly decreased viscosity. This transition, called T_g, is a second order transition (as opposed to a first order transition such as a crystalline melt). It can be detected by a change in heat capacity (10) or by direct measurement of mechanical relaxation of viscosity (8). Operationally, T_g is most often measured with differential scanning calorimetry (DSC), differential mechanical analysis (DMA), electron spin resonance (ESR), or nuclear magnetic resonance (NMR) (9). With DSC, the most widely used method, a change in baseline is seen at T_g, which represents the change in heat capacity (Figure 1).

T_g is strongly affected by the addition of plasticizers such as water. In sucrose glasses, for example, T_g falls from about 70 to $-70°C$ with the addition of water (Figure 2). A diagram of the relationship between T_g and water content, known as a state diagram, has fundamental importance in the study of glasses. Construction of the state diagram for a pure solute requires care, but it is nevertheless a straightforward procedure, involving addition of small amounts of water to the dry glass, with measurements of T_g at each increment. State diagrams for mixed solute systems are considerably more complex; a three-dimensional state diagram has recently been prepared for a ternary system—sucrose, glycine, and water (11)—that yielded a three-dimensional glass transition surface (rather than the two-dimensional state diagram seen in a binary system). Based on such results, it would seem hopeless to attempt to construct state diagrams for sugar-protein mixtures, for example, let alone sugars in intact cells. Nevertheless, it has been possible to do so, possibly because the sugar contents of anhydrobiotic organisms are so high—often exceeding 20 or even 25% and sometimes as much as 50% of the dry weight—thus restricting the participation of other compounds in the glass transition of the predominant sugar.

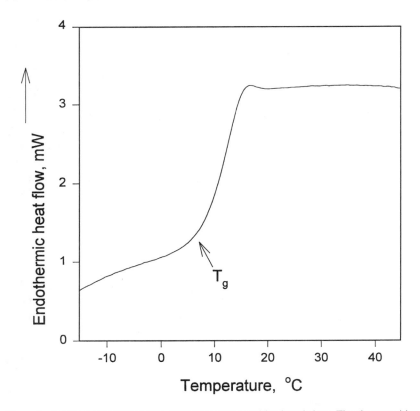

Figure 1   A typical calorimetric scan, showing a glass transition in trehalose. The glass transition is indicated by a change in slope due to a change in heat capacity.

Furthermore, Finegold et al (12) and Orford et al (13) have shown that T_g values for mixtures of mono-, di-, and oligosaccharides can be satisfactorily approximated from a mole fraction-weighted average of the individual T_g values. These findings are particularly reassuring because some anhydrobiotes, notably seeds, often contain such mixtures (14). Thus in such a case it appears feasible for an interpretable state diagram to be found rather than the more complex diagram seen in the mixtures mentioned above.

It seems a priori that if maintenance of the dry cell in an anhydrobiote in the glassy state is required, an elevated T_g would be advantageous. For instance, it is clear from the state diagram for sucrose, shown in Figure 2, that addition of even modest amounts of water results in devitrification of the sample at physiological temperatures. In seeds (14) or pollen (15), which contain large amounts of

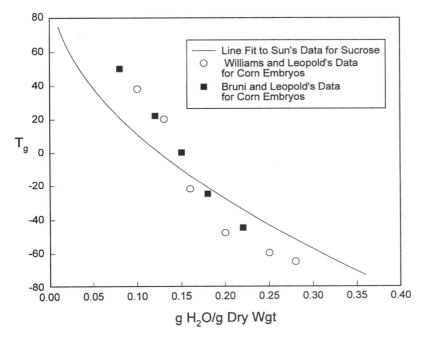

Figure 2   State diagram for sucrose, showing that the glass transition (T_g) increases inversely with water content (data from 24). Also shown are data for glass transitions in corn embryos, obtained by DSC by Williams & Leopold (16) and by ESP by Bruni & Leopold (17).

sucrose, devitrification would clearly appear problematic. One solution might be to add a third compound at high concentrations that would elevate T_g. Good candidates for such additives could be many polymers that have elevated T_gs. T_g varies with molecular weight in a characteristic and predictable fashion; T_g increases nearly linearly with molecular weight of the solute, and some polymers have T_gs exceeding 200°C (reviewed in 9). Thus it seems that such compounds would be found at high concentrations in anhydrobiotic organisms. The fact that they are not, even in cases where maintaining the cell in a glassy state is problematic, suggests that glass formation is not in itself all that is required. We return to this point in the section on trehalose and dry biomaterials.

Do Anhydrobiotes Contain Glasses?

The only published evidence on glass transitions in cells of anhydrobiotes comes from studies on seeds of higher plants, mainly from Leopold and colleagues. The first evidence that intact anhydrobiotes contain glasses was obtained by

Williams & Leopold (16) in studies on corn embryos excised from dry seeds. They were able to detect clear glass transitions with DSC and even produced a state diagram for the dry seeds, which shows a remarkable resemblance to that for sucrose (Figure 2). It is clear from these data that glasses do indeed form in these embryos, but their significance seems doubtful, at least on first examination. With a water content of 13% (not unusual for a seed), T_g is about $-22°C$. In fact, T_g does not exceed room temperature (22°C) unless the water content is maintained below about 10% (0.12 g H_2O/g dry weight). Corn embryos that are dry clearly exist in a glassy state, but addition of even small amounts of water results in devitrification. Subsequently, Bruni & Leopold (17), using ESR, did similar measurements on corn embryos to measure the glass transitions and obtained similar results (Figure 2). However, they pointed out that the standard storage temperature for corn seeds is $-5°C$, at which the embryos would clearly be in a glassy state (cf Figure 2). The same authors (18) obtained similar results with soybean embryos. Furthermore, Bruni & Leopold (18) and Koster (19) reported that desiccation-intolerant embryos showed no evidence of glass transitions; instead, the only transition seen was a crystalline melt coinciding with the melting of water ice. Finally, Sun & Leopold (20) produced from viability studies on seeds a set of equations that predicts the maximum temperature at which seeds will survive at a given water content. They showed that loss of viability closely agrees with the point at which storage temperature exceeds the measured T_g.

The conclusion that follows from this evidence is that maintaining the dry cells of anhydrobiotes in the glassy state is associated with survival. However, additional data are needed on other anhydrobiotic systems before a broad conclusion can be made.

Is Vitrification Sufficient to Preserve Dry Liposomes?

It is difficult to interpret results with intact organisms on a molecular scale; even though correlations between survival and glass formation seem clear, elucidation of the function of the glass in intact cells is very difficult. Thus we have turned to model systems, liposomes (discussed below) and proteins (discussed in the section on dry proteins), for this purpose.

FUSION IN DRY LIPOSOMES   Liposomes composed of pure phospholipids can be preserved in the dry state if they are dried in the presence of disaccharides (21). This finding has had immediate applications in pharmaceutical sciences because liposomes are being used as drug delivery vehicles (22, 23). The requirements for stabilizing dry liposomes are to (a) prevent fusion during drying and storage and (b) avoid phase transitions. Because we have reviewed this field recently (2, 21), extensive discussion is not needed here. Briefly, in the dry state, the liposomes are packed tightly, separated by a sugar matrix. If the liposomes become mobile, they may come in contact with each other and undergo fusion. Fusion is damaging because it not only increases the size of the vesicles, it also often results in leakage during the fusion event.

The most complete study to date on effects of vitrification on stability of dry liposomes is that of Sun et al (24), who studied the effects of storage of liposomes in sucrose glasses as a function of temperature above and below T_g. When retention of carboxyfluorescein, a trapped marker, was recorded, the results seen in Figure 3 were obtained. Only small effects of temperature were seen until the samples were heated above T_g; above that temperature, leakage occurred rapidly. Diameter of the vesicles was recorded under similar conditions, and the results showed essentially no change until the samples were heated above T_g, after which massive fusion was observed (Figure 3). When

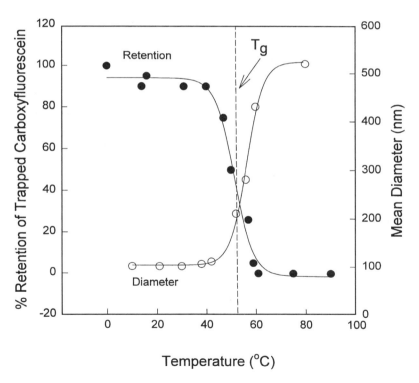

Figure 3   Effects of storage of liposomes dried in the presence of sucrose at the indicated temperatures. The dry liposomes were stored for 2 h at each temperature, after which retention of trapped carboxyfluorescein and average size of the liposomes were determined (data from 24).

we plotted the retention of trapped solute against the size of the vesicles, it became clear that these two parameters are related (Figure 4). In the absence of fusion, no leakage was observed, but once fusion commenced, leakage was seen to increase linearly until all the contents of the liposomes were leaked to the external medium. Thus we suggest that the primary mechanism by which the liposomes are destabilized during devitrification is fusion. It follows that the primary role of vitrification is to prevent the close approach of the liposomes in the dry state, thus preventing fusion. By extension, the role of vitrification in intact cells might well be to prevent close approach of membranes and, in fact, any molecular assemblages that might undergo damage by direct contact with other such assemblages.

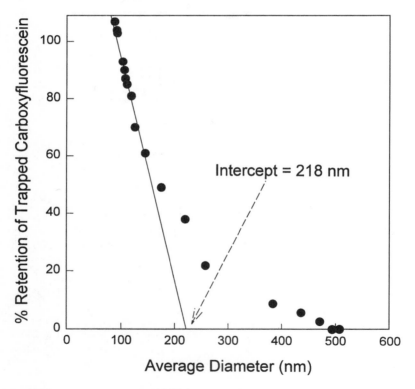

Figure 4   Retention of trapped carboxyfluorescein plotted as a function of fusion (represented as average diameter). Initially, the decay in percent retention is a linear function. A line fit to that linear portion of the curve extrapolates on the abscissa to about 220 nm. Because the vesicles were originally about 100 nm in diameter, one fusion event per vesicle appears to lead to leakage of all the contents (data from 24).

PHASE TRANSITIONS AND STABILITY OF DRY LIPOSOMES   The polar head-groups of phospholipids are hydrated; about 10 water molecules are associ-ated with a typical phosphatidylcholine (PC) headgroup. The physical state of this water is not well understood, but its removal has profound consequences for the physical state of the bilayer (2). These water molecules spatially sepa-rate the polar headgroups, and when they are removed, the packing density of the headgroups increases. This increased packing, in turn, leads to increased opportunities for van der Waals interactions among the hydrocarbon chains. As a result, the temperature at which the chains melt to form the liquid crystalline phase (T_m) increases. For example, fully hydrated egg PC has a transition tem-perature of about $-7°C$. When this phospholipid is fully dehydrated, T_m rises to about 70°C. Thus it is in gel phase at room temperature when it is dry and passes through the phase transition when it is rehydrated.

The significance of this phase transition during rehydration is that when phospholipids pass through such transitions, the bilayer becomes transiently leaky (25). Thus the leakage that normally accompanies this transition must be avoided if the contents of membrane vesicles and whole cells are to be retained. During drying this need not be a problem because T_m is not affected until all the bulk water has been removed. However, during rehydration it is a serious problem; the membranes are placed in water and undergo the phase transition in the presence of excess bulk water.

When phospholipids are dried in the presence of sucrose or trehalose, T_m is depressed to a remarkable degree. In the case of egg PC mentioned above, T_m is driven down as low as $-20°C$, at least 10° lower than T_m for the fully hydrated lipid and about 90°C lower than T_m for the lipid dried without trehalose. Thus such membranes are in liquid crystalline phase, even though they are dry, and do not pass through a phase transition during rehydration.

A summary of this mechanism, shown in cartoon form in Figure 5, has been shown to apply to intact cells (26–28), as well as to the liposomes (21, 29), with which it was first described. For instance, dry yeast cells are known to require rehydration at elevated temperatures, above about 40°C. Leslie et al (27, 28) have shown that membrane lipids in the dry yeast cells have a phase transition between 30 and 38°C. If the cells are rehydrated at lower temperatures, they leak their contents and are killed during the rehydration. But if they are hydrated at 40°C or higher, they do not leak. Leslie et al (28) established that trehalose in the cells depresses T_m from about 70°C to between 30 and 38°C.

IS VITRIFICATION INVOLVED IN DEPRESSION OF T_M?   Koster et al (1994) pro-posed that vitrification of the sugar is in itself sufficient to reduce T_m. The analysis of Koster et al (30), derived from an elegant physical model of Bryant & Wolfe (31), proposes that vitrification inhibits the increase in T_m during

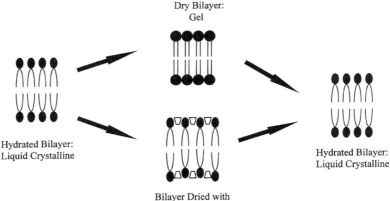

Dry Bilayer:
Gel

Hydrated Bilayer:
Liquid Crystalline

Hydrated Bilayer:
Liquid Crystalline

Bilayer Dried with
Trehalose: Liquid Crystalline

Figure 5 Cartoon illustrating the mechanism of stabilization of liposomes in the dry state by sugars. Similar results have been obtained for intact cells.

dehydration, perhaps by limiting lateral stresses in bilayers during the process. They admit they do not understand how this could lead to depression of T_m below that of the hydrated phospholipid, but nevertheless suggest that while "...specific sugar/lipid interactions may exist,... they probably contribute little to the effect of preventing increases in T_m."

The Bryant-Wolfe model is based on extensive studies on effects of the hydration force that separates membranes in the presence of excess water (31). The essence of the model is that as osmotic shrinkage proceeds during dehydration, lateral stresses develop in the plane of the bilayer, driving up the phase transition. Bryant & Wolfe propose that the presence of sugars between and inside vesicles limits both the close approach of neighboring vesicles and the volume decrease. The latter results in relaxation of the lateral pressure and thus obviates the increase in T_m. This is an interesting idea, supported by an elegant analysis, that could indeed theoretically limit the increase in T_m of phospholipids during dehydration. However, there are several points on which it is inconsistent with experimental evidence: (*a*) Counter to the model, liposomes undergo profound shrinkage and shape changes during dehydration (32). (*b*) The model cannot account for depression of T_m below that of the fully hydrated phospholipid. But T_m is sometimes depressed as much as 25°C below that seen when the phospholipid is in excess water (2). (*c*) The phosphate of the dry phospholipid behaves as if it were fully hydrated when the sugar is present. For example, dipalmitoylphosphatidylcholine (DPPC) shows a P = O vibrational frequency of 1230 cm^{-1} in the hydrated state, which rises to 1260 cm^{-1}

when the lipid is dried without the sugar. When it is dried with trehalose, that frequency drops to 1240 cm^{-1} (33). We see no way for the model to account for this effect, which also depends on the thermal history of the sample. (*d*) Thermal history of the sample plays a large role in its phase behavior, a behavior that the model cannot accommodate. For instance, when DPPC is dried in the presence of trehalose, T_m on the first scan is 60°C. But after the hydrocarbon chains are melted, T_m is depressed to 24°C (33, 34). We interpret these findings as follows: DPPC is in gel phase at room temperature, thus limiting access to the polar headgroups. Under these conditions, the sugar forms an association with the headgroups that partially depresses T_m (Figure 6). Once the hydrocarbon chains are melted, the sugar has free access to the polar headgroups and forms an association that depresses T_m maximally (Figure 6). If the sample is then stored below T_m for even a few minutes, T_m rises again to the 60°C level, suggesting that the sugar is partially forced out again when the lipid is in gel phase (Figure 6). Furthermore, the size of the sugar determines its effect on T_m; glucose gives a stable T_m of about 40°C, whereas trehalose and raffinose give metastable T_ms of 24 and 17°C, respectively (Figure 6). The P = O vibrational frequency parallels these effects on T_m. On the first heating of the sample with trehalose, the PO^{2-} frequency drops from 1240 cm^{-1} to 1225 cm^{-1}. When the sample is stored below T_m for as little as 15 min, the P = O frequency rises again to 1240 cm^{-1}. We cannot reconcile these findings with the Bryant-Wolfe model.

A key finding reported by Koster et al (1994) is that T_g (the glass-transition temperature for the dry sugar) must exceed T_m in order to depress T_m in the dry lipid. Koster et al (30) suggested that the state diagram for the sugar and the phase diagram for the lipid must intersect and cross at some point during dehydration, after which T_g would exceed T_m, and further increases in the transition temperature would be halted. We do not see how this could lead to depression of T_m, even though it could limit further increases in T_m as dehydration progresses, as Koster et al (30) proposed. Even so, there is no ambiguity in the proposal of Koster et al (1994) that T_g must exceed T_m of the hydrated phospholipid in order to depress T_m of the dry phospholipid. This is a boundary condition for the proposed mechanism.

We have tested the validity of this boundary condition through studies of the effects of various carbohydrates on the T_m of dry DPPC (33). This phospholipid has a T_m in the hydrated state of 42°C, which rises to nearly 120°C when the lipid is fully dehydrated. Table 1 shows T_g values for a number of dry carbohydrates, which suggest their predicted effectiveness at depressing T_m in dry DPPC if the Koster et al (30) hypothesis is correct. Glucose, for example, has a T_g of about 30°C, so T_g never exceeds T_m for the lipid, in either the hydrated or dry states. Dextran, by contrast, has a $T_g > 110$°C and is predicted by the

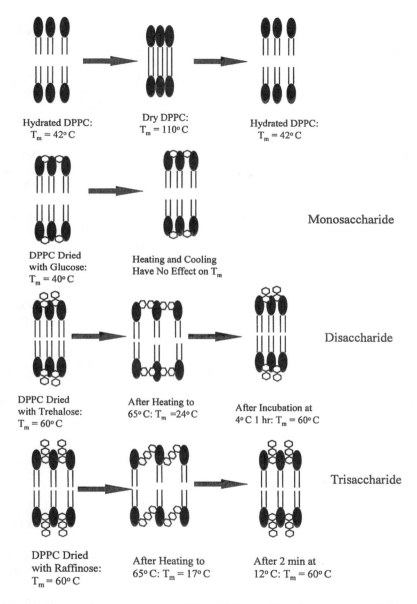

Hydrated DPPC:
$T_m = 42°C$

Dry DPPC:
$T_m = 110°C$

Hydrated DPPC:
$T_m = 42°C$

Monosaccharide

DPPC Dried
with Glucose:
$T_m = 40°C$

Heating and Cooling
Have No Effect on T_m

Disaccharide

DPPC Dried
with Trehalose:
$T_m = 60°C$

After Heating to
$65°C: T_m = 24°C$

After Incubation at
$4°C$ 1 hr: $T_m = 60°C$

Trisaccharide

DPPC Dried
with Raffinose:
$T_m = 60°C$

After Heating to
$65°C: T_m = 17°C$

After 2 min at
$12°C: T_m = 60°C$

Figure 6   Cartoon illustrating the effects of thermal history on T_m in liposomes prepared with the indicated sugars.

Table 1 Glass transition temperatures and effects of the corresponding molecules on T_m in dry dipalmitoylphosphatidylcholine (DPPC)

Solute	T_g (°C)	T_m (°C) (First heating)	T_m (°C) (Second heating)
Control	—	90	90
Glucose	30	40	40
Sucrose	65	60	24
Trehalose	110	60	24
Raffinose	90	60	17
Stachyose	98	60	60
Dextran	>110	90	90
Hydroxyethyl starch	>110	90	—

Data for T_m values from Crowe et al (1996), and references to the T_g values are given in the same paper. The samples were dried with the sugar, heated through the phase transition (First Heating), cooled, and then immediately heated through the transition again (Second Heating).

vitrification hypothesis to be particularly effective at reducing T_m in dry DPPC. The predicted order of effectiveness, based on T_g alone, would be dextran $\geq$ hydroxyethyl starch > stachyose > raffinose > trehalose > sucrose > glucose. Glucose should, in fact, have no effect at all on T_m in the dry lipid.

In fact, the opposite result was obtained. Glucose—predicted to have no effect from the Koster et al (30) hypothesis—has the largest effect of any of the sugars tested without further manipulation. Hydroxyethyl starch—predicted to have the largest effect—has no effect at all (33).

Although we agree that vitrification might possibly limit the rise in T_m as dehydration progresses, it clearly cannot account for depression of T_m.

Is Vitrification Sufficient to Preserve Dry Proteins?

MICROMOLECULAR VERSUS MACROMOLECULAR ADAPTATION TO ANHYDROBIOSIS   Adaptations of organisms to certain environmental stresses (e.g. high temperature or hypersalinity) can involve alterations in protein primary structure that increase the intrinsic capacity of the macromolecule to be stable and functional under extreme conditions (35). In other organisms (e.g. those adapted to osmotic or freezing stresses), accumulation of micromolecular components in the cytosol allows unaltered proteins to survive and function under stressful conditions (35). These compounds include sugars, amino acids, polyols, and methylamines. The data on proteins purified from anhydrobiotic organisms are limited. In one example, phosphofructokinase was purified from *Artemia* embryos and subjected to dehydration stress during air-drying. The enzyme was completely inactive after rehydration (JF Carpenter & SC Hand, unpublished observation), indicating that the protein was not intrinsically resistant to dehydration. This is a key enzyme for the development of the embryos because it regulates glycolytic flux (36) and because development in *Artemia* embryos is fueled solely by carbohydrate catabolism (37). Therefore, if only this enzyme were denatured by dehydration, development could not be continued after rehydration. The *Artemia* embryo phosphofructokinase was stabilized by trehalose during air-drying and rehydration. Thus it appears that in terms of maintenance of protein stability, as is the case for membrane stability, the accumulation of trehalose and sucrose are critical for organismal adaptation to dehydration.

PROTECTION OF PROTEINS DURING DEHYDRATION   Numerous studies with proteins have documented that both sucrose and trehalose are effective at inhibiting protein denaturation and inactivation during dehydration/rehydration processes (38). Only a few studies employed the most biologically relevant process of evaporatively drying samples in air, followed by rehydration. One study from 1935 showed that several blood proteins could be protected by sucrose (39). More recently, it was documented that both trehalose and sucrose protected rabbit skeletal muscle phosphofructokinase (40). Many other studies have used freeze-drying to dehydrate proteins. One reason is that freeze-drying is often used to prepare recombinant protein drugs for shipping and storage and, hence, is an area of great scientific and economic interest. With freeze-drying, both trehalose and sucrose have also been found to inhibit protein denaturation (e.g. 40–43). For our purposes, the effects of dehydration stress on the structure of isolated proteins and the interaction of sugars with dried proteins can be evaluated equally well with proteins that are air-dried or freeze-dried.

MECHANISM FOR PROTEIN PROTECTION IN THE PRESENCE OF BULK WATER   During the final stages of either freeze-drying or air-drying, the protein is subjected to denaturing stress during removal of its hydration shell (42, 43). Below we discuss the evidence for this structural perturbation and the mechanism by which disaccharides prevent damage during this level of water removal. But first, it is important to consider that during dehydration, prior to the removal of the protein's hydration shell, denaturing conditions can arise. These include (*a*) an increase in the concentrations of all solutes, including salts; (*b*) exposure to air-water and other potentially damaging interfaces (e.g. membrane-water); and (*c*) increased concentrations of protein molecules that can foster non-native intermolecular interactions between molecules that are unfolded by the other stresses.

Disaccharides stabilize proteins against these stresses that arise while bulk water and the protein's hydration shell are still present (e.g. 44). The mechanism for this level of protection is different from that occurring during the terminal stages of drying (see below). A single, universal thermodynamic mechanism for stabilization of any protein in aqueous solution by numerous different solutes (e.g. sugars, amino acids, polyols, methylamines and salting-out salts) has been developed and proven by Timasheff and colleagues (reviewed in 45, 46).

Prior to examining the specifics of the Timasheff mechanism, it is instructive to consider the general effects of ligand binding on protein stability. (Detailed quantitative explanations can be found in References 47 and 48.) A two-state model is considered, in which there is an equilibrium between native and denatured states of the protein (N → D). At room temperature and in nonperturbing solvent environments, the native state is favored because it has a lower free energy than the denatured state. The magnitude of the difference in free energy between the two states (i.e. the free energy of denaturation) dictates the relative stability of the native state. Binding of a ligand to either state will reduce the free energy (chemical potential) of that state; thermodynamically, binding can occur only if the free energy of the protein-ligand complex is lower than that for the protein alone. The effect on protein stability depends on the difference in the magnitude of binding between the two states. If more ligand binds to the native than to the denatured state, then the free energy of denaturation will be increased, and the native state will be stabilized. The opposite will be seen if more ligand binds to the denatured state.

Consider next how this general ligand-binding argument relates specifically to the Timasheff mechanism for solute-induced protein stabilization. Detailed, quantitative reviews of the Timasheff mechanism can be found elsewhere (e.g. 45, 46). Relatively high concentrations (≈ >0.2 M) of nonspecific solutes (e.g. sucrose) are needed to affect protein stability. This is because the interactions of the solute (ligand) with the protein are relatively weak. These weak interactions are determined by equilibrium dialysis experiments. Binding measured by this method is actually a measure of the relative affinities of the protein for water and ligand. Therefore, the ligand interaction is referred to as preferential.

Stabilizing solutes (e.g. sugars and polyols) have been found to be preferentially excluded from contact with the surface of the protein, and the protein is said to be preferentially hydrated. Preferential exclusion, in a thermodynamic sense, means that the solute (ligand) has negative binding to the protein. Thus there is an increase in the free energy (chemical potential) of the protein. The degree of exclusion is greater for the denatured state than for the native state because unfolding leads to a greater surface area of contact between the protein and the solvent. Thus even though there is an increase in the free energy of the native state, there is a greater increase in the free energy of the denatured state. The result is an increase in the stability of the native state.

MECHANISM OF PROTECTION OF PROTEINS DURING TERMINAL STAGES OF DRYING   Interactions of the protein with water are critical for formation of the native folded protein (49, 50). The level of hydration routinely achieved during freeze-drying of proteins is low enough (e.g. <0.01 g H_2O/g protein) that the protein's hydration shell is essentially completely removed; i.e. almost all interactions with water are lost. High-resolution Fourier transform infrared (FTIR) spectroscopic analysis of the conformationally sensitive amide I band has shown that most unprotected proteins (i.e. dried in the presence of buffer only) are unfolded in the dried solid (42, 43, 51–54). It has been documented with several proteins that the ability of stabilizers (e.g. disaccharides) to inhibit aggregation and to increase recovery of activity after rehydration correlates directly with their capacity to foster retention of the native structure in the dried solid (42, 43, 51–54). Thus the mechanism by which stabilizing additives (e.g. sugars) minimize loss of activity and aggregation during dehydration/rehydration is by preventing unfolding during dehydration (42, 43, 51–54). Also, unfolding of proteins that refold if immediately rehydrated can be inhibited by stabilizing additives. As is discussed below, it appears crucial that even these proteins must be stabilized against dehydration-induced unfolding, in order to maintain long-term stability in the dried solid (38, 52, 55).

As is the case with membrane preservation, the mechanism by which additives such as sucrose and trehalose protect proteins during the terminal stages of dehydration has been debated. It appears, however, that most researchers agree that protection by compounds such as sucrose and trehalose depends on formation of an amorphous phase with the protein. The importance of an amorphous additive can best be illustrated by what happens to proteins during dehydration in the presence of compounds that crystallize. For example, mannitol readily crystallizes during freeze-drying, but the degree of crystallization can be manipulated by altering formulation components (56–58). In the concentration range where it remains mostly amorphous, mannitol has been shown to protect enzymes during freeze-drying in a concentration-dependent manner (56–58). A relatively high mass ratio of protein:mannitol serves to inhibit mannitol crystallization, whereas with excess mannitol, crystallization and loss of stabilization arise. Similarly, substantial stabilization has been achieved with solutes (including buffer salts) that can crystallize alone, but in combination interfere with each other's crystallization. For example, Izutsu et al (57) found that with a sufficiently high ratio of potassium phosphate:mannitol, mannitol remained amorphous and protected lactate dehydrogenase during freeze-drying. However, when there was excess mannitol, its crystallization eliminated protein protection.

Although it is well established that an amorphous additive is needed to protect proteins during dehydration, the nature of the protective interaction of amorphous solutes with the dried protein has been a matter of contention. There are at least two nonexclusive mechanisms proposed. One mechanism states that proteins are simply mechanically immobilized in the glassy, solid matrix during dehydration (e.g. 59). The restriction of translational and relaxation processes is thought to prevent protein unfolding, and spatial separation between protein molecules (i.e. dilution of protein molecules within the glassy matrix) is proposed to prevent aggregation.

However, simply forming a glassy solid does not assure protein stabilization. First, if only the formation of a glass were needed, then the protein by itself would be stable because proteins form an amorphous phase in the dried solid (60). However, most unprotected proteins are denatured by dehydration (51–54).

One can further qualify the mechanism by proposing that the requisite mechanical restriction to unfolding and aggregation can be achieved only if another amorphous compound is present to provide immobilization and spatial separation of the protein molecules. However, several studies have shown that formation of a glassy phase by an additive is not a sufficient condition for protection of proteins. For example, solutions of 100 mg/ml interleukin-1 receptor antagonist, prepared with sucrose concentrations ranging from 0–10% (wt/vol), all formed a glass during lyophilization and all had T_gs of $66 \pm 2°C$ (55). Yet only in formulations containing $>5\%$ sucrose was dehydration-induced unfolding prevented. Tanaka and colleagues (61) have found that the capacity of carbohydrates to protect freeze-dried catalase decreased with increased carbohydrate molecular weight. Dextrans were the largest and least effective of all the carbohydrates tested, and the larger the dextran molecule the less it stabilized catalase. Although they did not determine whether their dried samples were amorphous, it is well known that as the molecular weight of the carbohydrate is increased, the glassy state is formed more readily (8, 9). Furthermore, recent FTIR spectroscopic studies with several proteins (e.g. lactate dehydrogenase, actin, lysozyme, ribonuclease, and lipase) have shown that proteins dried in the presence of dextran are unfolded in the dried solid, to a degree at least as great as that seen in samples dried with only buffer (SD Allison, L Kreilgaard, T Randolph, M Zhang, S Prestrelski, T Arakawa & J Carpenter, unpublished data). Differential scanning calorimetry documented that the dried samples were amorphous and, as expected with dextran, had a relatively high T_g of greater than 80°C. Thus although it is necessary for stabilizing additives to remain amorphous to protect proteins during dehydration, glass formation alone is not sufficient for stabilization of proteins against removal of their hydration shell.

Several studies support the other mechanism, which is, as with membranes, the water replacement hypothesis. According to this hypothesis, sugars protect proteins during drying by hydrogen bonding to polar and charged groups as water is removed and thus preventing drying-induced denaturation of the protein. For example, in early studies using FTIR spectroscopy, it was found that the band at 1583 cm^{-1} in the infrared spectrum for lysozyme, the result of hydrogen bonding of water to carboxylate groups, was not present in the spectrum for the dried protein (62). When lysozyme was dried in the presence of trehalose or lactose, the carboxylate band was retained in the dried sample, indicating that the sugar was hydrogen bonding in the place of water. Similar results have been obtained with α-lactalbumin and sucrose (42). More recently, it has been documented that the carboxylate band can be titrated back by freeze-drying lysozyme in the presence of increasing concentrations of either trehalose or sucrose (S Allison, T Randolph, B Chang & J Carpenter, unpublished observations). Furthermore, this effect correlates directly with an increased inhibition of protein unfolding in the presence of increasing amounts of sugar.

Tanaka and colleagues (61) have found that the capacity of a saccharide to protect catalase during freeze-drying is inversely related to the size of the saccharide molecule. They suggest that as the size of the saccharide increases, steric hindrance interferes with hydrogen bonding between the saccharide and the dried protein. In support of this contention, recent experiments have shown that the carboxylate band is only minimally detectable in the infrared spectrum of lysozyme freeze-dried in the presence of dextran (SD Allison, T Randolph, B Chang & J Carpenter, unpublished observation). This failure of the dextran to hydrogen bond to the dried protein could account for the inability of the polymer to protect the protein's structure during dehydration.

Similarly, by studying protein structure in the dried solid with FTIR spectroscopy, Prestrelski et al (52) found that as the molecular weight of a carbohydrate additive was increased, the capacity to inhibit unfolding of interleukin-2 during lyophilization decreased, and the level of protein aggregation after rehydration increased. Also, it was clear that protection of the protein did not correlate directly with the formation of a glass (all samples were found to be amorphous) or with the T_g of the sample (the T_g increased as carbohydrate molecular weight increased). Rather, there was a negative correlation between stabilization and molecular weight, which is to be expected if protection during drying is due to the water replacement mechanism.

Some of the most compelling evidence for the water replacement hypothesis comes from studies on the effects of freeze-drying on a model polypeptide, poly-L-lysine (42). This peptide assumes different conformations depending on solution conditions. At neutral pH, poly-L-lysine exists as an unordered peptide. At pH 11.2, the peptide adopts an α-helical conformation. Poly-L-lysine assumes an intermolecular β-sheet conformation (cf. 54) in the dried state, regardless of its initial conformation in aqueous solution. The preference for β-sheet in the dried state appears to compensate for the loss of hydrogen bonding interactions with water. The β-sheet allows for the highest degree of hydrogen bonding in the dried sample. If poly-L-lysine is freeze-dried in the presence of sucrose, the original solution structure is retained in the dried state, because sucrose hydrogen bonds in place of water, obviating the need to form a β-sheet.

Taken together, these studies support the conclusion that the importance of the amorphous behavior of an additive is that it allows for effective hydrogen bonding between the additive and the protein. A glassy additive that does not have this interaction will not protect the protein against dehydration damage.

Vitrified State and Stability of Dry Biomolecules

LIPOSOMES   Molecular motion in a vitrified sample has been assumed to be exceedingly slow, thus precluding events like fusion between membranes. Recent evidence strongly suggests that this is not the case. For example, Hancock et al (63) showed with a variety of glasses that molecular motion continues significantly until the sample is cooled as much as 50°C below T_g. This is not to say that vitrification does not slow the rate of movement; it does, indeed, but movement continues below T_g nevertheless. Sun et al (24) studied such effects on stability of liposomes dried with sucrose. When the dry liposomes were kept at fixed temperatures for varying lengths of time, data such as those shown in Figure 7 were obtained. From the slopes of these decay curves, an Arrhenius plot of the data was made, showing a clear break at T_g (with an accompanying change in activation energy, as one might expect). Nevertheless, the decay continues below T_g, albeit at a much depressed rate. When we calculated the half-life of the samples above and below T_g, we found that this parameter increased by orders of magnitude below T_g. In agreement with Hancock et al (63), the samples had to be cooled well below T_g in order to stop all damage, at least on a reasonable time scale. The point we want to make is that although vitrification can indeed slow the damage, it does not stop it in dry liposomes.

LONG-TERM STABILITY OF DRIED PROTEINS   It has been proposed that all that is needed to assure the long-term stability of dried proteins is to maintain the sample below its T_g (e.g. 59). The rate of diffusion-controlled reactions important for protein degradation, including protein unfolding and chemical degradative processes, should be greatly reduced relative to rates noted above the transition temperature (e.g. 59). Storage of a protein above its T_g, which will lead to greatly increased mobility of the protein, should greatly accelerate reaction rates to a much greater level than expected, based on Arrhenius kinetics. In addition, the farther below the T_g a sample is stored, the greater the protein

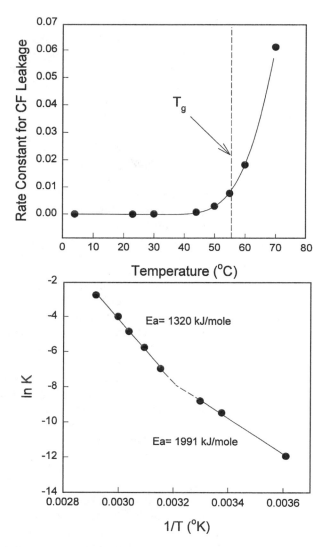

Figure 7   Upper panel: Rate constants for leakage of trapped carboxyfluorescein from liposomes dried with sucrose and stored at various temperatures. *Lower panel:* Arrhenius plot of data from upper panel. The intercept is near T_g. Unexpectedly, while the rate of leakage decreases and activation energy for the leakage (Ea) increases below T_g, leakage does not stop in the glassy state (data from 24).

stability should be. Roy et al (64) found that this mechanism explained the temperature- and residual moisture-dependent changes in storage stability of a lyophilized monoclonal antibody-vinca conjugate. However, more recent studies have shown that simply maintaining protein samples below their T_g is not adequate for long-term storage stability.

First, as noted above, a protein alone will form an amorphous phase in the final dried solid. The transition temperatures of pure protein glasses are relatively high and, as with other glasses, vary inversely with sample water content. For example, dry legumin has a T_g of about 140°C, and in the presence of 10% water (by weight), the T_g is ≈50°C (60). Simply keeping an unprotected protein sample below its T_g is not adequate for storage stability, because proteins dehydrated without stabilizers rapidly degrade in the dried solid, even if they are held at temperatures well below their T_gs. This might be due to, at least in part, the fact that even at a temperature as much as 50°C below T_g there can be significant molecular mobility, which is permissive to degradative reactions (63, 65).

Prestrelski and colleagues (51) first suggested that in addition to storage below T_g, long-term stability could be dependent on retaining the native protein structure in the dried solid. One way of envisioning the importance of native structure is to consider the geometric constraints of chemical degradative reactions. For example, a common degradation process in proteins is methionine oxidation. Even at temperatures well below T_g, diffusion of molecular oxygen in glassy solids is sufficient to allow methionine oxidation, especially on the time scale of months. Thus for any methionine residue exposed on the protein's surface, oxidation is expected, even at storage temperatures below T_g. However, if the residue is buried in the interior of the native protein, access to oxygen is greatly restricted in the dried sample. Conversely, if dehydration induces unfolding, the previously buried residue could be exposed and subjected to reaction. Carpenter and colleagues are currently exploring this possibility with a model protein.

The first published data supporting the importance of native protein structure in long-term stability came from the study of Prestrelski et al in which they found that when freeze-dried from a solution of pH 7, interleukin-2 was unfolded in the dried solid and unstable during storage at 45°C (52). In contrast, lyophilization from a solution with pH 4 led to a native protein and storage stability. This storage temperature was most likely below the sample T_g, because characteristically dried proteins have T_gs > 100°C (60). Using protein in a pH 7 solution, they also compared protection afforded during freeze-drying and storage stability conferred by carbohydrates of increasing molecular weight. As molecular weight increases, the inhibition of unfolding during processing decreases and the formulation T_g increases. The optimum stability during storage at 45°C was noted in samples stabilized with the tetrasaccharide stachyose, in which the dried protein was native and T_g was $>45°C$. The protein degraded in samples with lower molecular weight carbohydrates, which had native protein, but a T_g $<45°C$. (It is important to note that the residual moisture in these samples was relatively high ($\approx 4\%$ by weight), which accounts for the finding that samples with sucrose had a T_g below 45°C.) Thus even with a native protein, stability was dependent on maintaining the temperature below T_g.

In a long-term storage study on interleukin-1 receptor antagonist, it was found, in support of the glass transition theory, that for any given dried formulation (among more than 15 tested), storage above T_g greatly accelerated degradation, which was due to deamidation and aggregation (55). However, in a series of formulations (100 mg/ml protein) with varying initial sucrose concentrations ranging from 0–10% (wt/vol), all of which had a T_g of $66 \pm 2°C$, those with sucrose concentrations $<5\%$ degraded rapidly during storage below T_g at 50°C. In contrast, formulations with higher sucrose concentrations had less than 2% deamidation and no detectable aggregation after 14 months at 50°C. FTIR spectroscopy of samples prior to storage indicated that the stable formulations contained native protein in the dried solid, whereas the protein was unfolded in the unstable formulations. In addition, FTIR analysis of the stored samples showed that the glassy state allowed sufficient mobility for further structural alterations in, and intermolecular interactions between, unfolded protein molecules. In samples prepared with $<1\%$ sucrose, the infrared spectra after 6 months of storage at 50°C were further altered relative to those for the protein immediately after lyophilization. The appearance of bands at 1620 and 1695 cm^{-1}, owing to the presence of an intermolecular β-sheet, indicate that protein aggregation is arising during storage in the dried solid. These interactions were not seen in the preparations containing 5 and 10% sucrose, in which the initial lyophilization-induced protein unfolding was inhibited.

Finally, a recent study with freeze-dried lipase compared the capacities of sucrose, trehalose, and dextran to protect the protein during the freeze-drying process and during subsequent storage in the dried solid at 40 and 60°C (L Kreilgaard & JF Carpenter, unpublished results). It was found that after freeze-drying in the presence of trehalose and sucrose, the protein was native in the dried solid. In contrast, dextran did not protect during freeze-drying and the protein was unfolded to the same degree as seen with buffer alone. Those samples that contained a small amount of water had excellent stability during 3 months of storage [with trehalose (T_g = 80°C) and sucrose (T_g = 68°C)]. The sample prepared with dextran (T_g = 95°C) degraded, even though it had the highest T_g ($>150°C$).

Taken together the results of these studies document that storage of a dried protein formulation below T_g is necessary but not sufficient for stability. It is also necessary to obtain a native protein during the freeze-drying process.

Vitrified Polymers and Stability of Dry Biomaterials

LIPOSOMES   Goodrich et al (66, 67) recently described a procedure for freeze-drying red blood cells involving use of a mixture of hydroxyethyl starch (HES) and glucose. These reports have come under question in some recent publications. Spieles et al (68) attempted to freeze-dry red blood cells in the presence of HES and reported that the cells were completely destabilized during freeze-drying and rehydration. Franks (69) attacked the Goodrich et al (66, 67) results, calling them a "...confidence trick." Curiously, both Spieles et al (68) and Franks (69) ignored the report of Goodrich et al (66, 67) that HES is in itself insufficient for the preservation of red blood cells; a monosaccharide (in practice, glucose) is required as well. In our view, because the studies of Spieles et al (68) were done without glucose, their results do not constitute a fair re-examination of those of Goodrich et al (66, 67). We have recently provided such a re-examination, using liposomes as a model (70). The results, summarized in Figure 8, show the following: Neither HES nor glucose alone prevents leakage from egg PC liposomes in the dry state. The combination of the two, however, is effective at preserving the dry liposomes. HES (which has very high T_g—in

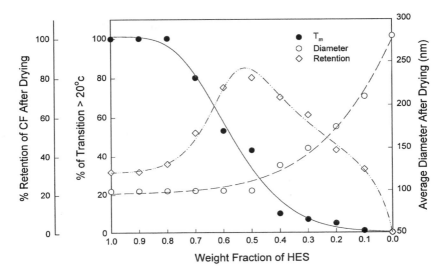

Figure 8   Effects on mixtures of hydroxyethyl starch and glucose on stability of dry liposomes made from egg phosphatidylcholine. At 100% HES and 0% glucose (*left end* of abscissa), fusion is inhibited, but T_m is unaffected. At 100% glucose and 0% HES (*right end* of abscissa), T_m is depressed, but fusion is not inhibited. In the midrange, both T_m is depressed and fusion is inhibited. As a result, the liposomes retain trapped carboxyfluorescein (data from 70).

excess of 150°C) inhibits fusion between liposomes, as expected, based on its T_g. It does not, however, depress T_m in the dry phospholipids. Glucose, by contrast, depresses T_m. It does not depress T_m as effectively as a disaccharide, but the transition temperature is, nevertheless, well below room temperature, so phase transitions during rehydration would be avoided even when glucose is combined with HES in up to an $\approx$1:1 mixture. Glucose has a very low T_g, however, and thus does not inhibit fusion between the dry liposomes. When we measured T_g in mixtures of HES and glucose, we found that a 1:1 mixture of HES and glucose (the ratio that stabilizes dry egg PC liposomes) has a T_g of about 35°C, thus satisfying the apparent requirement that the sample be vitrified. As a result, the combination of the two molecules works reasonably well.

POLYMERS IN ANHYDROBIOTIC CELLS   Based on the findings reported above, one might expect to find polymers, which are good glass formers, in combination with sugars in nature in anhydrobiotes. Recently, we thought we had found such a combination, but the mechanism proved to be a novel finding, rather than one related to vitrification. Potts (reviewed in 5) and his colleagues have for several years been working on the structure of an extracellular polysaccharide (EPS), produced by the cyanobacterium *Nostoc*, in preparation for dehydration. These cells also contain small amounts of a mixture of sucrose and trehalose but probably not enough to stabilize the dry cells. When we measured T_m in the dry cells, it was found to be similar to that of the fully hydrated cells (DR Hill, TW Keenan, RF Helm, M Potts, LM Crowe & JH Crowe, unpublished data). In model systems, we found also that the EPS was not responsible for depressing T_m, which we inferred was due to the presence of the sucrose and trehalose. Based on the discussion above, we expected the EPS to be a good glass former and thus to behave like HES. Instead, we could find no evidence of a glass transition up to the decomposition temperature for the EPS. However, we instead were able to detect a gel-sol transition in this material in the range of 50°C. Based on these findings, we are suggesting that the gel may play a role similar to vitrification, a possibility we are currently investigating.

Similar findings have been made in a study on desiccation in the bacterium *Rhizobium* (AE Oliver, P Perreira & JH Crowe, unpublished data). These bacteria can be freeze-dried in the presence of trehalose with nearly 100% recovery, even when the cells are stored under very adverse conditions such as high humidities and temperatures. By contrast, when the cells were freeze-dried with sucrose, they initially showed high survival but, unlike the samples with trehalose, their viability rapidly decreased when they were exposed to high humidities and temperatures. (The mechanism by which trehalose imparts this remarkable stability is described in the following section.) One strain, however, showed high stability when it was freeze-dried with sucrose and stored under the same unfavorable conditions. Subsequently, this strain, similar to *Nostoc*, appears to produce an extracellular polysaccharide. Like the EPS of *Nostoc*, the one from *Rhizobium* also shows a gel-sol transition, but no evidence of a glass transition. As for *Nostoc*, we propose that the gel may play a role in inhibiting proximity events such as membrane fusion.

It remains to be seen whether polymers that form glasses are indeed found in anhydrobiotes.

Is Trehalose Special for Preservation of Dry Biomaterials?

In our initial studies on stabilization of membranes by trehalose, we reported that trehalose was superior to the other sugars tested (71, 72). That is the case for the membranes with which we worked in those days—sarcoplasmic reticulum isolated from lobster muscle. Subsequently, it was found that these membranes have a transporter for trehalose, which permits the sugar to cross the membrane. Trehalose is a blood sugar in lobsters, so a transporter might be expected. Therefore, the large effect of trehalose on these particular membranes can be explained by the presence of this transport mechanism.

Subsequently, we showed that trehalose is among the most effective sugars tested at stabilizing liposomes during drying (reviewed in 21), although other sugars later proved to be equally effective, particularly at high concentrations. There has been considerable confusion on this point. At elevated concentrations, the differences between the sugars tend to disappear, leading to puzzlement about their relative effectiveness.

Nevertheless, numerous workers have reported that trehalose seems to have special abilities in preserving dry and frozen biological materials (e.g. 73–81). Recently, we found that bacteria freeze-dried in the presence of trehalose show remarkably high survival immediately after freeze-drying (27, 78). Furthermore, we found that the bacteria freeze-dried with trehalose retain a high viability, even after long exposure to moist air. By contrast, when the bacteria are freeze-dried with sucrose, they show lower initial survival and when they are exposed to moist air, viability decreases rapidly.

Using liposomes as a model, we attempted to find a mechanism for the results obtained with bacteria. As with the bacteria, the liposomes exposed to 58% relative humidity rapidly leaked their contents when they were dried with sucrose, but not when they were dried with trehalose. Measurements on fusion of the liposomes showed that they had undergone extensive fusion in the moist air when dried with sucrose, but not with trehalose.

Examination of the state diagram for trehalose provides an explanation for this effect (83). T_g for trehalose is much higher than that for sucrose (Figure 9), in qualitative agreement with previous results of Green & Angell (84). (Green &

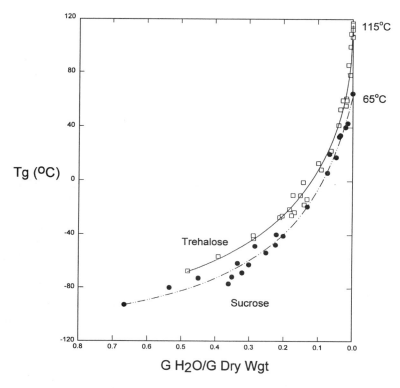

Figure 9   State diagrams for sucrose and trehalose. Note that T_g for dry trehalose is approximately 50°C higher than that for sucrose (data from 83).

Angell reported a significantly lower T_g than we found, almost certainly because of under estimating the water contents of their samples.) As a result, one would expect that addition of small amounts of water to sucrose by adsorption in moist air would decrease T_g to below the storage temperature, whereas at the same water content, T_g for trehalose would be above the storage temperature. This proved to be the case. Furthermore, we point out again that degradation does proceed in samples below T_g, albeit at a slower rate. With trehalose, a sample at 20°C would be nearly 100°C below T_g. By contrast, one dried with sucrose would be only about 45°C below T_g. Under these conditions, one would expect the sample dried with sucrose to be degraded more rapidly.

Aldous et al (85) have suggested an additional interesting property of trehalose, which we were able to confirm. They suggested that because the crystalline structure of trehalose is a dihydrate, some of the sugar might, during adsorption of water vapor, be converted to the crystalline dihydrate, thus sparing the remaining trehalose from contact with the water. This suggestion emerged as correct; with addition of small amounts of water, the crystalline dihydrate immediately appeared, and T_g for the remaining glassy sugar remained unexpectedly high.

We point out, however, that the elevated T_g seen in trehalose is not anomalous, as has been claimed (84). Indeed, trehalose lies at the end of a continuum of sugars that show increasing T_g (83), although the basis for this effect is not understood.

Summary and Conclusions

We believe that vitrification may indeed be required for preservation of the labile components of the cells of anhydrobiotes in the dry state. But we also believe that the bulk of the evidence strongly indicates that vitrification is in itself insufficient to accomplish this stabilization; instead the water replacement hypothesis seems to be more consistent with the data. We stress again, however, that vitrification and the water replacement hypothesis are not mutually exclusive mechanisms; indeed, we believe that both are required. These findings are not only important to our understanding of the mechanisms by which anhydrobiotes escape irreversible damage, they are also coming to have increasing importance in the realm of human welfare, wherever stability of biological materials is required.

We end on a more biological note, with a quotation from our colleague James Clegg (86), who has been party to many of the fundamental discoveries in the field of anhydrobiosis:

"What are we to think of an organism that loses practically all of its cellular water at ordinary temperatures and pressures and ceases to metabolize, but upon being rehydrated resumes all of the characteristics it previously exhibited? In the dried state it cannot easily be considered 'alive' since we are told that the characteristics of living organisms are exhibited through the dynamics of their metabolism. On the other hand, we should be reluctant to call such an organism dead (unless we are willing to entertain the possibility of its resurrection) because it resumes an active life upon simple restoration of water. Thus, either one considers life to be a discontinuous process, or the reversibly-dried organism presents to us a special level of biological organization, apart from any question of its being alive or dead."

We agree with Potts (5) that the ability to undergo anhydrobiosis was probably acquired during the earliest stages of biological evolution. We also believe that water replacement played a key role in that achievement then, as it does now in contemporary anhydrobiotes.

ACKNOWLEDGMENTS

We gratefully acknowledge support of this work by grants IBN 93-08581 and BES 95-05301 from the National Science Foundation.

Visit the *Annual Reviews home page* at
http://www.AnnualReviews.org.

Literature Cited

1. Tanford C. 1978. The hydrophobic effect and the organization of living matter. *Science* 200:1012–18
2. Crowe JH, Crowe LM, Carpenter JF, Prestrelski S, Hoekstra FA, et al. 1997. Anhydrobiosis: cellular adaptation to extreme dehydration. In *Handbook of Physiology,* ed. WH Dantzler, II:1445–78. Oxford: Oxford Univ. Press
3. Carpenter JF. 1994. Interactions of stabilizers with proteins during freezing and drying. In *Formulation and Delivery of Proteins and Peptides,* pp. 134–47. Washington, DC: Am. Chem. Soc.
4. Crowe JH, Clegg JS. 1973. *Anhydrobiosis.* Stroudsburg, PA: Dowden, Hutchinson & Ross
5. Potts M. 1994. Desiccation tolerance of prokaryotes. *Microbiol. Rev.* 58:755–805
6. Franks F. 1985. *Biophysics and Biochemistry at Low Temperatures.* Cambridge: Cambridge Univ. Press
7. Bruni F, Leopold AC. 1991. Glass transitions in soybean seed. Relevance to anhydrous biology. *Plant Physiol.* 96:660–6
8. Levine H, Slade L. 1988. Water as a plasticizer: physico-chemical aspects of low-moisture polymeric systems. In *Water Science Reviews,* ed. F Franks, 3:79–185. Cambridge: Cambridge Univ. Press
9. Slade L, Levine H. 1995. Glass transitions and water-food structure interactions. In *Advances in Food and Nutrition Research,* ed. JE Kinsella, pp. 103–269. San Diego: Academic
10. Wunderlich B. 1990. *Thermal Analysis.* Boston: Academic
11. Shalaev EY, Kanev AN. 1993. Study of the solid-liquid state diagram of the water-glycine-sucrose system. *Cryobiology* 31:374–82
12. Finegold L, Franks F, Hatley RHM. 1990. Glass/rubber transitions and heat capacities of binary sugar blends. *J. Chem. Soc. Faraday Trans.* 85:2945–51
13. Orford PD, Parker R, Ring SG. 1990. Aspects of glass transition behavior of mixtures of carbohydrates of low molecular weight. *Carbo. Res.* 196:11–18
14. Koster KL, Leopold AC. 1988. Sugars and desiccation tolerance in seeds. *Plant Physiol.* 88:829–32
15. Hoekstra FA, Crowe JH, Crowe LM, van Roekel T, Vermeer E. 1992. Do phospholipids and sucrose determine membrane phase transitions in dehydrating pollen species? *Plant Cell Environ.* 15:601–6
16. Williams RJ, Leopold AC. 1989. The glassy state in corn embryos. *Plant Physiol.* 89:977–81
17. Bruni F, Leopold AC. 1992. Cytoplasmic glass formation in maize embryos. *Seed Sci. Res.* 2:251–53
18. Bruni F, Leopold AC. 1991. Glass transitions in soybean seed. *Plant Physiol.* 96:660–63
19. Koster KL. 1991. Glass formation and desiccation tolerance in seeds. *Plant Physiol.* 96:302–4
20. Sun WQ, Irving TC, Leopold AC. 1994. The role of sugar, vitrification and membrane phase transition in seed desiccation tolerance. *Physiol. Plant.* 90:621–28
21. Crowe LM, Crowe JH. 1995. Freeze-dried liposomes. See Ref. 23, pp. 237–72.
22. Gregoriadis G. 1993. *Liposome Technology.* Boca Raton, FL: CRC
23. Peuisieux F, Couvreur P, Delattre J, Devissaguet J-P, eds. 1995. *Liposomes, New Systems and New Trends in Their Appplications.* Paris: Editions de Sante
24. Sun WQ, Leopold AC, Crowe LM, Crowe JH. 1996. Stability of dry liposomes in sugar glasses. *Biophys. J.* 70:1769–76
25. Crowe JH, Crowe LM, Hoekstra FA. 1989. Phase transitions and permeability changes in dry membranes during rehydration. Mini review. *J. Bioenerg. Biomembr.* 21:77–91
26. Hoekstra FA, Crowe JH, Crowe LM. 1992. Germination and ion leakage are linked with phase transitions of membrane lipids during imbibition of *Typha latifolia* pollen. *Physiol. Plant.* 84:29–34
27. Leslie SB, Israeli E, Lighthart B, Crowe JH,

Crowe LM. 1995. Trehalose and sucrose protect both membranes and proteins in intact bacteria during drying. *Appl. Environ. Microbiol.* 61:3592–97

28. Leslie SB, Teter SA, Crowe LM, Crowe JH. 1994. Trehalose lowers membrane phase transitions in dry yeast cells. *Biochim. Biophys. Acta* 1192:7–13

29. Crowe JH, Crowe LM. 1992. Preservation of liposomes by freeze drying. In *Liposome Technology,* ed. G Gregoriadis, pp. 229–52. Boca Raton, FL: CRC. 2nd ed.

30. Koster KL, Webb MS, Bryant G, Lynch DV. 1994. Interactions between soluble sugars and POPC during dehydration: vitrification of sugars alters the phase behavior of the phospholipid. *Biochim. Biophys. Acta* 1193:143–50

31. Bryant G, Wolfe J. 1992. Interfacial forces in cryobiology and anhydrobiology. *Cryo-Letters* 13:23–36

32. Crowe LM, Womersley C, Crowe JH, Reid D, Appel L, Rudolph A. 1986. Prevention of fusion and leakage in freeze-dried liposomes by carbohydrates. *Biochim. Biophys. Acta* 861:131–40

33. Crowe JH, Hoekstra FA, Nguyen KHN, Crowe LM. 1996. Is vitrification involved in depression of the phase transition temperature in dry phospholipids? *Biochim. Biophys. Acta* 1280:187–96

34. Crowe LM, Crowe JH. 1988. Trehalose and dry dipalmitoylphosphatidylcholine revisited. *Biochim. Biophys. Acta* 946:193–201

35. Hochachka P, Somero GN. 1986. *Biochemical Adaptations.* Princeton: Princeton Univ. Press

36. Carpenter JF, Hand SC. 1986. Arrestment of carbohydrate metabolism during anaerobic dormancy and aerobic acidosis in *Artemia* embryos: determination of pH-sensitive control points. *J. Comp. Physiol. B* 156:451–59

37. Clegg JS. 1964. The control of emergence and metabolism by external osmotic pressure and the role of free glycerol in developing cysts of *Artemia salina. J. Exp. Biol.* 41:879–92

38. Carpenter JF, Chang BS. 1996. Lyophilization of protein pharmaceuticals. In *Biotechnology and Biopharmaceutical Manufacturing, Processing and Preservation,* ed. K Avis, V Wu, pp. 199–263. Buffalo Grove, IL: Intep0harm Press

39. Brostreaux J, Ericksson-Quensel I-B. 1935. Etude sur la dessication des proteines. *Arch. Phys. Biol.* 23(4):209–226

40. Carpenter JF, Crowe LM, Crowe JH. 1987. Stabilization of phosphofructokinase with sugars during freeze-drying: characterization of enhanced protection in the presence

of divalent cations. *Biochim. Biophys. Acta* 923:109–15

41. Carpenter JF, Martin B, Crowe LM, Crowe JH. 1987. Stabilization of phosphofructokinase during air-drying with sugars and sugar/transition metal mixtures. *Cryobiology* 24:455–64

42. Prestrelski S, Tedeschi N, Arakawa T, Carpenter JF. 1993. Dehydration-induced conformational changes in proteins and their inhibition by stabilizers. *Biophys. J.* 65:661–71

43. Prestrelski SJ, Arakawa T, Carpenter JF. 1993. Separation of freezing- and drying-induced denaturation of lyophilized proteins by stress-specific stabilization: II. Structural studies using infrared spectroscopy. *Arch. Biochem. Biophys.* 303:465–73

44. Carpenter JF, Crowe JH. 1988. Modes of stabilization of a protein by organic solutes during desiccation. *Cryobiology* 25:459–70

45. Timasheff SN. 1992. Water as ligand: preferential binding and exclusion of denaturants in protein unfolding. *Biochemistry* 31:9857–64

46. Timasheff SN. 1995. Preferential interactions of water and cosolvents with proteins. In *Protein-Solvent Interactions,* ed. RB Gregory, pp. 445–82. New York: Dekker

47. Wyman J. 1964. Linked functions and reciprocal effects in hemoglobin: a second look. *Adv. Protein Chem.* 19:223–86

48. Wyman J, Gill SJ. 1990. *Binding and Linkage. Functional Chemistry of Biological Molecules.* Mill Valley, CA: Univ. Sci. Books

49. Kuntz ID, Kauzman W. 1974. Hydration of proteins and polypeptides. *Adv. Protein Chem.* 28:239–345

50. Edsall JT, McKenzie HA. 1983. Water and proteins II. The location and dynamics of water in protein systems and its relation to their stability and properties. *Adv. Biophys.* 16:53–183

51. Prestrelski SJ, Arakawa T, Carpenter JF. 1994. The structure of proteins in lyophilized formulations using Fourier transform infrared spectroscopy. *Am. Chem. Soc. Symp. Ser.* 567:148–69

52. Prestrelski SJ, Pikal KA, Arakawa T. 1995. Optimization of lyophilization conditions for recombinant human interleukin-2 by dried-state conformational analysis using Fourier transform infrared spectroscopy. *Pharmacol. Res.* 12:1250–59

53. Allison SD, Dong A, Carpenter JF. 1996. Counteracting effects of thiocyanate

and sucrose on chymotrypsinogen secondary structure and aggregation during freezing drying and rehydration. *Biophys. J.* 71:2022–32

54. Dong A, Prestrelski SJ, Allison SD, Carpenter JF. 1995. Infrared spectroscopic studies of lyophilization- and temperature-induced protein aggregation. *J. Pharmacol. Sci.* 84:415–24

55. Chang BS, Beauvais RM, Dong A, Carpenter JF. 1996. Physical factors affecting the storage stability of freeze-dried interleukin-1 receptor antagonist: glass transition and protein conformation. *Arch. Biochem. Biophys.* 331:249–58

56. Izutsu K, Yoshioka S, Teroa T. 1993. Decreased protein-stabilizing effects of cryoprotectants due to crystallization. *Pharmacol. Res.* 10:1232–37

57. Izutsu K, Yoshioka S, Terao T. 1994. Effect of mannitol crystallinity on the stabilization of enzymes during freeze-drying. *Chem. Pharmacol. Bull.* 42:5–8

58. Carpenter JF, Prestrelski SJ, Arakawa T. 1993. Separation of freezing- and drying-induced denaturation of lyophilized proteins by stress-specific stabilization: I. Enzyme activity and calorimetric studies. *Arch. Biochem. Biophys.* 303:456–64

59. Franks F, Hatley RMH, Mathias SF. 1991. Materials science and the production of shelf stable biologicals. *BioPharm* 4:38–55

60. Angell CA. 1995. Formation of glasses from liquids and biopolymers. *Science* 267:1924–35

61. Tanaka T, Takeda T, Miyajama R. 1991. Cryoprotective effect of saccharides on denaturation of catalase during freeze-drying. *Chem. Pharmacol. Bull.* 39:1091–94

62. Carpenter JF, Crowe JH. 1989. Infrared spectroscopic studies on the interaction of carbohydrates with dried proteins. *Biochemistry* 28:3916–22

63. Hancock BC, Shamblin SL, Zografi G. 1995. Molecular mobility of amorphous pharmaceutical solids below their glass transition temperatures. *Pharmacol. Res.* 12:799–806

64. Roy ML, Pikal MJ, Rickard EC, Maloney AM. 1990. The effects of formulation and moisture on the stability of a freeze-dried monoclonal antibody-vinca conjugate: a test of the WLF glass transition theory. *Dev. Biol. Stand.* 74:323–40

65. Pikal MJ. 1994. Freeze-drying of proteins. *Am. Chem. Soc. Symp. Ser.* 567:120–33

66. Goodrich RP, Sowemimo-Coker SO, Zerez CR, Tanaka KR. 1992. Preservation of metabolic activity in lyophilized human erythrocytes. *Proc. Natl. Acad. Sci. USA* 89:967–71

67. Goodrich RP, Williams CM, Franco RS, Weiner M. 1989. Lyophilization of red blood cells. *US Patent No. 4,874,690*

68. Spieles G, Heschel I, Rau G. 1996. An attempt to recover viable human red blood cells after freeze-drying. *Cryo-Letters* 17:43–52

69. Franks F. 1996. Freeze-dried blood: reality or confidence trick? *Cryo-Letters* 17:1

70. Crowe JH, Oliver AE, Hoekstra FA, Crowe LM. 1997. Stabilization of dry membranes by mixtures of hydroxyethyl starch and glucose: the role of vitrification. *Cryobiology.* In press

71. Crowe JH, Crowe LM, Jackson SA. 1983. Preservation of structural and functional activity in lyophilized sarcoplasmic reticulum. *Arch. Biochem. Biophys.* 220:477–84

72. Crowe LM, Mouradian R, Crowe JH, Jackson SA, Womersley C. 1984. Effects of carbohydrates on membrane stability at low water activities. *Biochim. Biophys. Acta* 769:141–50

73. Bando T, Liu CJ, Kosaka S, Yokomise H, Inui K, et al. 1994. Twenty-hour canine lung preservation using newly developed solutions containing trehalose. *Transplantation Proc.* 26:871–72

74. Beattie GM, Crowe JH, Lopez AD, Cirulli V, Ricordi C, Hayek A. 1997. Trehalose: a cryoprotectant that enhances recovery and preserves function of human pancreatic islets after long-term storage. *Diabetes* 46:519–23

75. Hincha DK. 1989. Low concentrations of trehalose protect isolated thylakoids against mechanical freeze-thaw damage. *Biochim. Biophys. Acta* 2670:1–4

76. Hirata T, Fukuse F, Liu T, Muro C, Yokomise H, et al. 1992. Effects of trehalose in canine lung preservation. *Surgery* 115:102–7

77. Hirata T, Yokomise H, Fukuse T, Muro K, Ono N, et al. 1993. Successful 12-hour lung preservation with trehalose. *Transplantation Proc.* 25:1597–98

78. Israeli E, Shaffer BT, Lighthart B. 1993. Protection of freeze-dried *Escherichia coli* by trehalose upon exposure to environmental conditions. *Cryobiology* 30:519–23

79. Mansure JJC, Panek AD, Crowe LM, Crowe JH. 1994. Trehalose inhibits ethanol effects of intact yeast cells and lipsosomes. *Biochim. Biophys. Acta* 1191:309–16

80. Newman YM, Ring SG, Colaco C. 1993. The role of trehalose and other carbohydrates in biopreservation. *Biotechnol. Genet. Eng. Rev.* 11:263–94

81. Roser B. 1991. Trehalose drying: a novel replacement for freeze-drying. *BioPharm* 23:47–55

82. Smorag Z, Heyman Y, Garnier V, Gajda B. 1990. The effect of sucrose and trehalose on viability of one- and two-cell rabbit embryos. *Theriogenology* 33:741–47

83. Crowe LM, Reid DS, Crowe JH. 1996. Is trehalose special for preserving dry biomaterials? *Biophys. J.* 71:2087–93

84. Green JL, Angell CA. 1989. Phase relations and vitrification in saccharide-water solutions and the trehalose anomaly. *J. Phys. Chem.* 93:2880–82

85. Aldous BJ, Auffret AD, Franks F. 1995. The crystallisation of hydrates from amorphous carbohydrates. *Cryo-Letters* 16:181–86

86. Clegg JS. 1986. The physical properties and metabolic status of *Artemia* cysts at low water contents: the "water replacement hypothesis". In *Membranes, Metabolism and Dry Organisms*, ed. AC Leopold, pp. 169–87. New York: Cornell Univ. Press

Annu. Rev. Physiol. 1998. 60:105–19

ROUTES AND MECHANISM OF FLUID TRANSPORT BY EPITHELIA[1]

Kenneth R. Spring

Laboratory of Kidney and Electrolyte Metabolism, National Heart, Lung and Blood Institute, Bethesda, Maryland 20892-1603; e-mail: Springk@fido.nhlbi.nih.gov

KEY WORDS: water permeability, tight junction, standing-osmotic gradient, solvent drag, lateral intercellular space

ABSTRACT

The mechanism of fluid transport by leaky epithelia and the route taken by the transported fluid are in dispute. A consideration of current mathematical models for coupling of solutes and water, as well as the methodologies for the study of fluid transport, shows that local osmosis best accounts for water movement. Although it seems virtually certain that the tight junctions are water permeable, the fraction of absorbed fluid that crosses the tight junction cannot yet be determined with confidence.

INTRODUCTION

Physiologists have long been impressed by the large volumes of fluid absorbed across gastrointestinal and renal epithelia. Surprisingly, nearly one hundred years of investigation have not resulted in a consensus about the mechanism of this transport. Indeed, the widely accepted standing-osmotic gradient model for isosmotic fluid transport proposed by Diamond & Bossert (1) has been recently challenged as the basis for such transport (2). Although considerable progress has been made recently on the identification of proteins in the tight junctional complex (3), far less has been accomplished in the assessment of tight junctional permeability to water and in determination of the physico-chemical properties of the lateral intercellular spaces (LIS) between epithelial cells. The

---

[1] The US Government has the right to retain a nonexclusive, royalty-free license in and to any copyright covering this paper.

methods for defining the fraction of transepithelial fluid crossing cellular and paracellular pathways are somewhat indirect, and a central issue of uncertainty in the field continues to be the determination of the relative magnitudes of the water flows across the two routes.

This review considers the current state of our understanding of epithelial fluid transport, previous methods for the determination of the pathways taken by transported fluid, the measurement limitations imposed by tissue geometry, and possible future experimental strategies.

MODELS OF FLUID TRANSPORT

Fluid absorption by the renal proximal tubule, gallbladder, and small intestine has the following distinguishing characteristics: The reabsorbate is isosmotic to the bathing solution; it is strictly dependent on solute movement; and it remains isosmotic to the bathing solution over a wide range of osmolalities (4–6). The absence of externally detectable gradients in water activity (i.e. osmolality) led to the proposal of the existence of an intraepithelial compartment of increased osmolality (7).[2] Whitlock & Wheeler (6) provided an anatomical counterpart to this cryptic intraepithelial compartment in the LIS (Figure 1). They proposed that transported solutes such as NaCl accumulate in the LIS as a result of active transport to a concentration above that of the bathing solutions. The osmotic driving force created by this solute accumulation would result just in swelling of the LIS unless a vectorial component of solute and water movement existed. The anatomical asymmetry of the paracellular pathway provides a plausible mechanism for such directed movement.

Diamond & Bossert formalized the compartmental model of Curran & MacIntosh (7) and the anatomical observations of Whitlock & Wheeler (6) and Diamond (9) into the standing-osmotic gradient model of osmotic flow in leaky epithelia. As it was originally described, the standing-osmotic gradient model resulted in a near isosmotic absorbate when (a) the tight junctions were impermeable to the transported solute and water; (b) the active transport sites were clustered at the end of the LIS close to the tight junction; (c) the diffusion coefficient for the transported solute was reduced below that in free solution by the tortuosity of the LIS and/or other factors; (d) the water permeability of the lateral cell membranes was relatively low; and (e) a small hydrostatic pressure developed in the LIS leading to swelling of the LIS and hydraulic flow across the basal connective tissue supporting layer.

A review of some of these predictions of the standing-osmotic gradient model gives insight into the sources of the present-day uncertainties about the

---

[2]It is worth noting that even the measurements of osmolality have been questioned because of concerns about the absolute values of osmolality determined in complex biological fluids (8).

Possible Routes for Fluid Flow

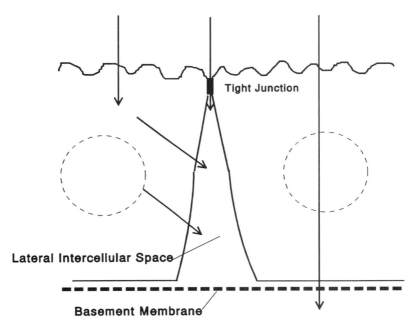

Figure 1   Possible routes for transepithelial fluid transport—wholly paracellular, wholly transcellular, transcellular then paracellular.

mechanism of fluid transport. The water permeabilities of several epithelial-cell basolateral membranes have since been measured and found to be about an order of magnitude higher than the values used in the model calculations (10–15). Although the possibility of a leaky tight junction was not simulated in the original model, subsequent calculations by others (16) showed that while such a leak would not invalidate the model, it would diminish or eliminate the standing-osmotic gradient in solute concentration. More importantly, it became clear from experimental observations that the primary solute transport system in the basolateral membrane, the Na^+, K^+-ATPase, was not concentrated at the tight junctional end of the LIS, as was the best case in the standing-osmotic gradient model, but was uniformly distributed along the LIS (17, 18). The combination of highly water permeable lateral cell membranes, uniform distribution of active transport sites, and leaky tight junctions made it very difficult to envision the formation of a standing-osmotic gradient (19, 20). In a remarkable review of the state of understanding of epithelial fluid transport in 1979,

Diamond (21) pointed out the critical need for additional experimental data before questions about the validity of the standing-osmotic gradient model could be resolved. He noted that it was essential to (a) measure transepithelial water fluxes and tissue water permeability, with adequate time resolution and free of unstirred layer artifacts; (b) partition the transepithelial water flows between the transcellular and paracellular routes; and (c) make direct measurements of the solute concentrations in the LIS.

The complexity of the experimental methods needed to make the critical measurements directly has thwarted development of the field for the last two decades. Concerns about inconsistencies between the data and the predictions of the standing-osmotic gradient model prompted some investigators to propose radically different mechanisms of solute-water coupling during isosmotic fluid transport. The alternative explanations can be divided roughly into two groups—exclusively paracellular or exclusively transcellular fluid transport.

Once it became clear that tight junctions were leaky to solutes (22, 23), it seemed likely that water could also cross the junction. A strictly paracellular route for fluid movement implies that the cellular composition would be unaffected by the reabsorbate. Several imaginative schemes for wholly paracellular transport have been proposed, including electro-osmosis across the junctional complex (24) or peristaltic waves within the tight junction (25). None of these alternatives has been definitively demonstrated to exist or be widely accepted.

A wholly transcellular route for fluid movement requires that the absorbate mix with the cytoplasm, or that it be sequestered in vesicles (26–28), or confined to transcellular channels (29). The vesicular mechanism was rejected long ago because it required an unreasonably high rate of transcytosis, as well as solute selectivity (6). The segregated channel scheme has not been convincingly demonstrated in any epithelium. A strictly transcellular route for transported fluid has recently been proposed for several epithelia, including small intestine, based on the obligate coupling of water to transported solutes such as glucose (2, 30). This mechanism, first proposed by Zeuthen & Stein (31), arises from the speculation that transport proteins (e.g. the sodium-coupled glucose transporter) could engulf water along with the transported solutes during uptake from the *cis* side (e.g. the extracellular fluid) and directionally extrude both solute and water into the *trans* side (e.g. the cytoplasm). The osmolality of the transported fluid would then depend only on the ratio of water to solute in the transport protein active site. Because this co-transport scheme is not based on the local osmotic movement of water, water absorption is independent of cell membrane water permeability and does not even require an epithelium (32). Despite a spate of recent papers purporting to rule out local osmosis and to demonstrate the co-transport of water and solute (33–35), unequivocal

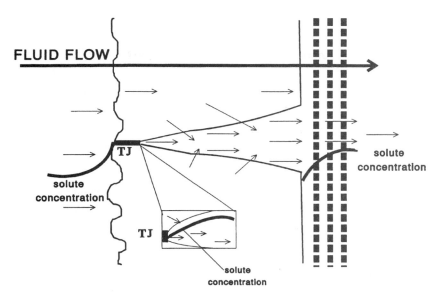

Figure 2   The effects of unstirred layers on predicted solute concentration profiles are shown during volume flow in the absorptive direction. The inset shows the predicted solute concentration profile in the lateral intercellular space adjacent to a water permeable tight junction.

evidence for the uphill movement of water or the non-osmotic production of an isosmotic fluid has not been presented (32, 36).[3]

One of the most significant impediments to the accurate determination of the water permeability and local solute concentration values for fluid transporting tissues is posed by unstirred layers. As has been pointed out repeatedly over a period of three decades (10, 21, 37), extracellular unstirred layers result in solute polarization during transepithelial fluid flow and act to oppose any imposed osmotic gradient and thereby diminish the magnitude of the driving force for fluid movement (Figure 2). Epithelia, by their very architecture, contain

---

[3]The majority of these studies involves the measurement of intracellular ionic activity and epithelial cell volume using ion-sensitive microelectrodes. The authors infer from the rate of change of ion activity and cell volume (usually measured by the rate of change in concentration of a poorly permeant intracellular solute that can be sensed by the electrode) that water movement is uphill and cannot be accounted for by local osmosis. Unstirred layers are assumed to be insignificant, but convincing experimental evidence for the validity of this assumption is not presented. Disregarding local osmosis as the mechanism for the volume flows may be a significant error, as the rate and magnitude of solute accumulation by the transport systems under investigation are readily underestimated with the methods employed. As presently described, this proposed mechanism for epithelial fluid transport cannot result in the observed isosmotic transport and must be considered unproven.

unstirred layers in the LIS, basolateral cell membrane infoldings, and underlying connective tissue (20, 37). Although the thickness of extracellular unstirred layers can be reduced somewhat by vigorous stirring (37) or by reduction in the size of the extracellular baths (14, 38), intraepithelial unstirred layers can not be experimentally altered by stirring of the bathing solutions. Because of external unstirred layers, measurements of transepithelial water permeability in small intestine or gallbladder always underestimate the correct value (21, 37). The magnitude of this underestimate has been the subject of debate for over a decade (37, 39). Most isolated epithelia have a thick (several hundred μm) connective tissue layer underlying the basal epithelial surface. As pointed out as early as 1964 (6), these tissues, in situ, would have blood and lymphatic perfusion to within a few μm of the subepithelial basement membrane. Thus subepithelial unstirred layers are, to a large extent, an artifact of the experimental use of an isolated epithelial tissue. Only in isolated renal tubules can extracellular unstirred layers be reduced to negligible thickness (38).

METHODS FOR MEASUREMENT OF THE FLUID FLOW THROUGH THE PARACELLULAR PATHWAY

In principle, the most straightforward approach to determination of the fraction of water flow through the paracellular pathway is to measure the·rate of transepithelial fluid flow before and after blocking the tight junctions. This approach has proven unsuccessful in many investigations because all functional inhibitors of the tight junction identified to date have been shown to cause substantive changes in the cellular pathway as well. The most recent use of this approach is the application of protamine to the *Necturus* gallbladder (40). A decrease in the rate of fluid absorption in the presence of protamine that could be reversed with heparin was observed, and it was concluded that about 30% of the fluid flow was paracellular. At this time, it is not unequivocally established whether the protamine effects are specific or limited to the tight junctions.

The converse approach, used on isolated rabbit renal proximal tubules (14) is to block the transcellular water pathway with mercurials and measure the resultant diminution in transepithelial water permeability. Two concerns arise: Some aquaporins are mercury insensitive (41), and the inhibitory action of mercurials on junctional proteins is unknown. Using this method, it was concluded that about 50% of the transepithelial water flow across rabbit proximal tubule occurred through the paracellular pathway (14).

In the absence of clean inhibitors of water movement across either pathway, the permeability of the paracellular pathway has been determined indirectly by electrophysiologic, radioactive tracer, or light microscopic methods.

Electrophysiologic Methods

Electrical resistance (measured with a DC current or voltage pulse) or impedance (measured with AC currents or voltages) are measures of transepithelial ionic permeability because electrical currents are carried by ions in aqueous solutions. The transepithelial electrical resistance of a fluid-transporting epithelial monolayer is dominated by the high ionic conductance of the paracellular shunt (22) and is frequently utilized to evaluate the leakiness of the tight junctions and LIS (37). If a leaky epithelium contains only a single cell type and damage to the edges or other regions are avoided, electrical resistance or impedance will be dominated by the ionic conductance of the paracellular pathway. However, as pointed out by Kottra & Frömter (42), a collapse of the LIS from cell swelling will increase the transepithelial resistance or impedance and be misinterpreted as a decrease in tight junctional conductivity (43). Even under the most favorable circumstances, electrical resistance measurements of cultured epithelial cell monolayers are suspect because of heterogeneity of cell type, local areas of damage or desquamation, or leaks at the edges of the preparation (O Kovbasnjuk, U Szmulowicz & KR Spring, submitted for publication).

Another electrophysiologic approach involves measuring the streaming potentials, voltages that develop in response to fluid flow through charged channels. Most leaky epithelia exhibit pseudo-streaming potentials instead of true streaming potentials (21, 37). Pseudo-streaming potentials are generated by solute polarization in unstirred layers adjacent to the cell membranes or within the LIS (37). Although they have been interpreted as indicators of changes in LIS composition, this is model-dependent and thus must be done with caution (44, 45). In sum, these electrophysiologic methods do not yield direct information about the magnitude of water flows across the tight junctions of fluid transporting epithelia.[4]

Radioactive Tracer Methods

The fluxes of radioactive non-electrolyte tracers across the epithelium have been used to estimate the magnitude of the paracellular water flow, as well as the pore size of the tight junctions. The approach utilized by a number of investigators (47–51) involves the determination of the transepithelial unidirectional fluxes of a range of radioactive non-electrolyte tracers of large enough size that they cannot cross the cellular pathway. The apical-to-basal flux of solutes of graded size and molecular weight is measured as a function of molecular size and transepithelial volume flow. Figure 3a illustrates typical results for a leaky

---

[4] Ion-sensitive electrodes have been used in several attempts to measure the ionic composition of the fluid in LIS. The disruption of LIS geometry, the likelihood of leakage of solutes from adjacent cells, the large size of the microelectrode tips, the impossibility of in situ calibration, and the poor selectivity of some of the ion exchangers significantly limit the reliability of the results (see 46).

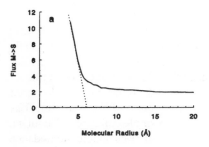
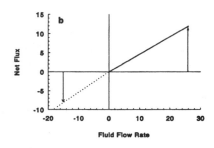

Figure 3   Two experimental approaches to characterizing tight junctional properties, adapted from References 47–51, are shown. Panel *a* shows the unidirectional flux (arbitrary units) of solutes of varying size. The steep initial slope extrapolates to an effective tight junctional pore size of 6 Å. Panel *b* shows the net flux of a solute (arbitrary units) of sufficient size that it is confined to the paracellular pathway, as a function of the rate of transepithelial volume flow (arbitrary units) induced by imposed osmotic gradients.

epithelium—the transepithelial unidirectional flux of non-electrolytes from the apical side diminishes markedly at a critical molecular weight (or molecular radius). This cut-off radius has been used to estimate the equivalent pore or slit size of the selectivity filter in tight junctions (47–51). As shown in Figure 3*b*, when the rate of transepithelial volume flow is altered by imposing an osmotic gradient, the net flux of these solutes is affected (49–51). Several investigators (48–51) have interpreted the alterations in solute flux to be the result of solvent drag across the tight junction and have employed the flux data to deduce the fraction of the volume flow across the tight junction. The fractional paracellular flow derived from these estimates varies considerably from 50 to 100% (48–51). Others (10, 21, 47) have argued that the changes in the non-electrolyte fluxes are not the result of solvent drag but occur because of alterations in the local concentration of solutes in unstirred layers within the LIS, as well as on the extracellular surfaces. Extracellular unstirred layers are less of a concern in the isolated renal tubule experiments (e.g. 47, 49, 51) because of the small dimensions of the tubule lumen and the lack of any significant connective tissue layers on the basal surface (38). Therefore, the results of these experiments may demonstrate a solvent-drag effect.

Because estimates of the fractional water flows derived from the non-electrolyte fluxes are dependent on the parameter values chosen for the cellular and paracellular pathway properties, many of which are undetermined, it is virtually impossible to assess the validity of these estimates. What seems clear from these experiments is that there are substantial transepithelial flows of relatively large solutes that must be confined to the paracellular pathway and that the equivalent pore or slit sizes determined from these experiments would allow water to flow through the same routes.

Optical Microscopic Methods

Optical spectroscopy has been used for over 40 years in the determination of the water permeability of cell membranes.   The values obtained for rat small intestinal cell brush border and basolateral membrane vesicles (15) are about 10% of those measured by the same method in vesicles from rat renal proximal tubule cells. The measured water permeabilities of small intestinal cell basolateral membrane vesicles are still about ten times higher than those used in the original standing-osmotic gradient model calculations. Renal cell membrane water permeabilities, determined by light microscopic methods (see below), are in good agreement with the values determined from spectroscopy.

Measurement of epithelial cell volume by light microscopy provides a direct method for the determination of cell membrane water permeability (38). Recently, several innovative approaches for the measurement of cell volume have been developed with an eye toward improving the accuracy and temporal resolution of the method (52, 53). The rate of cell swelling or shrinkage in an anisosmotic solution, together with the estimated cell surface area, allows a calculation of cell membrane water permeability. Light microscopy has been used to measure the water permeabilities of the apical and basolateral membranes of *Necturus* gallbladder cells (12), rabbit renal proximal tubule cells (14), and rat medullary (11) and rabbit cortical collecting duct cells (54). The apical and basolateral membrane permeabilities of cultured renal cells (MDCK) have also been measured recently (55). Although extracellular unstirred layers were minimized by the chamber design in the *Necturus* gallbladder studies (12), the basolateral membrane water permeability values tended to increase as the osmotic gradient diminished, a sign that unstirred layers due to basal connective tissue were still significant (12). Unstirred layer effects were not evident in the renal tubule studies that utilized multiple osmotic gradients.

As mentioned above, if one knows the water permeability of the cellular pathway and the transepithelial water permeability, it should be possible to calculate the water permeability of the paracellular pathway. The only cases in which this has been done are in the rabbit renal proximal tubule (14) and in the rat medullary collecting duct (56). Measurements of the transepithelial water permeability of flat epithelia, such as gallbladder and intestine, are undoubtedly in error because of unstirred layer effects (21). When the comparison of transepithelial and cellular values was done for the rabbit renal proximal tubule, it was concluded that about 50% of the water flowed through the paracellular pathway (14). A major concern is that the reported values of the proximal tubule cell membrane water permeabilities have been steadily increasing over the years as measurement methods have improved, with a consequential increase in the calculated fraction of water flowing through this pathway (14). In the rat medullary collecting duct studies (56), transepithelial and cell basolateral membrane water permeabilities were measured simultaneously using the same osmotic gradient, and it was concluded that paracellular fluid flux must occur when the tubules are treated with anti-diuretic hormone.[5]

The sensitivity of the dimensions of the LIS of fixed rabbit gallbladder epithelium to active transport and hydrostatic pressure provided early investigators with clues about the site of solute-solvent coupling (6, 58). Light microscopic studies of in vitro *Necturus* gallbladder LIS confirmed the conclusion that the LIS was highly deformable and compliant (59). On the other hand, morphological studies of the rabbit renal proximal tubule were consistent with a poorly deformable LIS of relatively uniform width from tight junction to basement membrane (60). Recently, the LIS of renal (MDCK) cell monolayers was found to be relatively non-compliant in comparison with gallbladder (55), a result consistent with the observations of multiple cross-bridges in the lateral spaces of renal epithelia (61). Thus a compliant LIS is not a mandatory requirement for isosmotic fluid absorption.

The recent development of techniques for loading the LIS of MDCK cell monolayers with fluorescent dyes (62) provided a major technological advance in the study of the mechanisms of fluid transport. Over the last three years, the concentration of Na^+ (63), Cl^- (64), and H^+ (62) in the LIS of MDCK cells grown on glass coverslips has been determined. LIS NaCl concentration was shown to be elevated by about 15 mM above that of the bathing medium during active transport, a result consistent with the local osmotic mechanism of fluid transport.[6]

The rate of transepithelial fluid absorption by MDCK cells, calculated from the measured osmotic gradient and cell membrane water permeabilities, yielded values in good agreement with those measured directly (55). The Na^+ flux across an individual MDCK cell tight junction was quantitated by measurement of the time course of changes in LIS Na^+ concentration after a change in the Na^+ concentration of the apical perfusate (57). The Na^+ permeability of the tight junction was shown to be regulated, increasing with stimulation of protein kinase A and decreasing with inhibition of the kinase. About 20% of the Na^+ extruded into the LIS by active transport from the cell was estimated to leak back into the apical bath across the tight junction (57).[7]

Data on the ionic composition of the LIS are not yet available for intestinal epithelia. Attempts to measure the Na^+ concentration in the interstitium of intestinal epithelia with a fluorescent dye were technical failures (66–69), complicated in part by the complex tissue geometry. A recent, technically successful study of the local pH of colonic crypts using fluorescent dyes revealed substantive changes during secretion (70). Preparations of isolated colonic crypts may prove optically ideal for such studies (71). Studies of the transport by isolated liver cells of fluorescent analogues of bile salts have also provided valuable insights into the rate and ionic dependence of these transporters (72).

To properly characterize a transporting epithelium, it is necessary to know the water and solute permeabilities of the cell membranes and tight junctions, the solute reflection coefficients of both pathways, the diffusion coefficient of solutes in the LIS, and the fluid convection rate within the LIS. Of these variables, solute diffusion and fluid convection in the LIS have received the least experimental attention. The balance between diffusion of transported solutes and osmotically driven water flow is a major determinant of the osmolality of the transported fluid. If solute diffusion out of the LIS is very rapid, water will not equilibrate fully, and the transported fluid may be hypertonic. A reduced rate of solute diffusion allows osmotic equilibration and the production of an isosmotic fluid, as well as the possible development of gradients in solute concentration. A leaky tight junction combined with a reduced rate of solute diffusion in the LIS actually leads to a reversed standing-osmotic gradient with a lower osmolality adjacent to the tight junction than would be present in the middle portion of the LIS (16). Most models for isosmotic transport incorporate a reduced solute diffusion coefficient within the LIS, but only recently has the diffusion coefficient for any substance been determined within the LIS. Fluorescence recovery after photobleaching was used to show that in the LIS of MDCK cells grown on glass coverslips, the diffusion coefficient of BCECF, a fluorescein derivative with four negative charges, was indistinguishable from that in free solution (62). The diffusion rates for cationic species have not been determined, and there is reason to suspect that cation mobility in the LIS may be reduced.

The LIS of MDCK cells grown on permeable supports is acidic to the bathing solutions by about 0.2–0.4 pH units (73). No evidence could be found for proton extrusion from the adjacent cells, and the low pH was attributed to buffering by the fixed negative charges of the glycosylation moieties of the glycocalyx on the lateral cell membranes. This is analogous to the low pH microclimate observed on the apical surface of intestinal epithelia that has been attributed to the buffering effects of mucins (74). Although new approaches have been developed utilizing caged fluorophores and high-speed sampling (P Xia, PM Bungay, CC Gibson & KR Spring, manuscript in preparation), the lack of cationic caged fluorescent dyes is a significant impediment to measurements of cation diffusion in the LIS.

THE CURRENT VIEW

This review has led me to the following conclusions about the present state of our knowledge of fluid transporting epithelia: (*a*) It is widely accepted that the tight junctions of leaky epithelia are permeable to a range of relatively large solutes; therefore water should also cross these junctions. (*b*) The measured water permeabilities of the cell membranes are sufficiently high that only moderate osmotic gradients (<30 mOsm/kg H_2O) are required to produce the observed rates of transport by transcellular osmosis. (*c*) The local osmotic mechanism for fluid absorption remains the only theory that explains the large body of literature on isosmotic fluid transport. (*d*) Until the rates of diffusion and convection in the LIS are known, the question of the existence of standing gradients will remain unresolved. (*e*) The permeability of tight junctions is regulated and the width of the LIS may vary in many, but not all, epithelia. (*f*) The fraction of the transepithelial fluid that flows directly across the tight junction remains to be accurately determined in any leaky epithelium.

The present picture for gastrointestinal epithelia is far less satisfying than that for renal epithelia. Tissue geometry and heterogeneity of cell type make it difficult to study the intestine; the gallbladder offers the most favorable tissue geometry with large, uniform cells.

FUTURE STRATEGIES

Light microscopic methods offer the best prospects for determination of the key variables in fluid transporting epithelia. The number of pieces missing from the puzzle depends on the tissue of interest. The recent studies on MDCK cell cultures provide the most complete picture to date of a fluid-transporting tissue (although the fluid transport rate of MDCK cells is only about 1% of that of the renal proximal tubule). The parameters still needed for that tissue are the diffusion coefficient for Na^+ in the LIS, the convection profiles in the LIS, and transepithelial water permeability.

How can we make the necessary measurements when the number of laboratories in the field can be counted on the fingers of both hands? We can utilize the powerful tools of molecular biology to block the tight junctions with anti-occludin peptides (75, 76), to study the details of the distribution of aquaporins and Na^+ pumps along the basolateral membrane, and to modify the transporters to develop a cultured cell model that transports significant quantities of fluid. We can utilize the power of optical microscopic methods, such as two-photon microscopy (77), to probe deep within complex tissues, to measure rapid changes in LIS ionic composition, to determine rates of convection and solute diffusion, to probe the peculiar microenvironment close to apical and basolateral membranes, and to improve measurements of the functional consequences of perturbation of epithelial tight junctional structure. We can take advantage of the powerful combination of theory and experiment that is offered by collaboration with the developers of mathematical models of transporting epithelia (78). The application of modern tools to an old, unresolved problem will eventually produce a clear picture of the mechanism of an essential physiological process.

Visit the *Annual Reviews home page* at
http://www.AnnualReviews.org.

Literature Cited

1. Diamond JM, Bossert WH. 1967. Standing-gradient osmotic flow. A mechanism for coupling of water and solute transport in epithelia. *J. Gen. Physiol.* 50:2061–83
2. Loo DDF, Zeuthen T, Chandy G, Wright, EM. 1996. Cotransport of water by the Na^+/glucose cotransporter. *Proc. Natl. Acad. Sci. USA* 93:13367–70
3. Anderson JM, Van Itallie CM. 1995. Tight junctions and the molecular basis for regulation of paracellular permeability. *Am. J. Physiol.* 269(32):G467–75
4. Curran PF, Solomon AK. 1957. Ion and water fluxes in the ileum of rats. *J. Gen. Physiol.* 41:143–68
5. Green R, Giebisch G. 1984. Luminal hypotonicity: a driving force for fluid absorption from the proximal tubule. *Am. J. Physiol.* 246(15):F167–74
6. Whitlock RT, Wheeler HO. 1964. Coupled transport of solute and water across rabbit gallbladder epithelium. *J. Clin. Invest.* 48:2249–65
7. Curran PF, MacIntosh JR. 1962. A model system for biological water transport. *Nature* 193:347–48
8. Sweeney TE, Beuchat CA. 1993. Limitations of methods of osmometry: measuring the osmolality of biological fluids. *Am. J. Physiol.* 264(33):R469–80
9. Diamond JM. 1962. The reabsorptive function of the gallbladder. *J. Physiol.* 161:442–73
10. Berry CA. 1983. Water permeability and pathways in the proximal tubule. *Am. J. Physiol.* 245(14):F279–94
11. Flamion B, Spring KR. 1990. Water permeability of apical and basolateral cell membranes of rat inner medullary collecting duct. *Am. J. Physiol.* 259(28):F986–99
12. Persson BE, Spring KR. 1982. Gallbladder

epithelial cell hydraulic water permeability and volume regulation. *J. Gen. Physiol.* 79:481–505
13. Welling LW, Welling DJ, Ochs TJ. 1983. Video measurement of basolateral membrane hydraulic conductivity in the proximal tubule. *Am. J. Physiol.* 245(14):F123–29
14. Carpi-Medina P, Whittembury G. 1988. Comparison of transcellular and transepithelial water osmotic permeabilities (P_{os}) in the isolated proximal straight tubule (PST) of the rabbit kidney. *Pflügers Arch.* 412:66–74
15. Van Heeswijk MPE, Van Os CH. 1986. Osmotic water permeabilities of brush border and basolateral membrane vesicles from rat renal cortex and small intestine. *J. Membr. Biol.* 92:183–93
16. King-Hele JA, Paulson RW. 1977. On the influence of a leaky tight junction on water and solute transport in epithelia. *J. Theor. Biol.* 67:61–84
17. Kyte J. 1976. Immunoferritin determination of the distribution of ($Na^+ + K^+$) ATPase over the plasma membranes of renal convoluted tubules. II. Proximal segment. *J. Cell Biol.* 68:304–18
18. Mills JW, DiBona DR. 1978. Distribution of Na^+ pump sites in the frog gallbladder. *Nature* 271:273–75
19. Hill AE. 1980. Salt-water coupling in leaky epithelia. *J. Membr. Biol.* 55:117–82
20. Sackin H, Boulpaep EL. 1975. Models of coupling salt and water transport. *J. Gen. Physiol.* 66:671–733
21. Diamond JM. 1979. Osmotic water flow in leaky epithelia. *J. Membr. Biol.* 51:195–216
22. Boulpaep EL. 1967. Ion permeability of the peritubular and luminal membrane of the renal tubule cell. In *Transport und Funktion*

Intracellularer Elektrolyte, ed. F Krück, 98–107. Munich: Urban & Schwarzenberg

23. Frömter E. 1972. The route of passive ion movement through the epithelium of *Necturus* gallbladder. *J. Membr. Biol.* 8:259–301

24. Hill AE. 1975. Solute-solvent coupling in epithelia: an electro-osmotic theory of fluid transfer. *Proc. R. Soc. London Ser. B* 190:115–34

25. Hill AE, Shachar-Hill B. 1993. A mechanism for isotonic fluid flow through the tight junctions of *Necturus* gallbladder epithelium. *J. Membr. Biol.* 136:253–62

26. Grim E. 1963. A mechanism for absorption of sodium chloride solutions for the canine gallbladder. *Am. J. Physiol.* 205:247–54

27. Frederiksen O, Leyssac PP. 1977. Effect of cytochalasin B and dimethylsulphoxide on isosmotic fluid transport by rabbit gallbladder in vitro. *J. Physiol.* 265:103–18

28. Leyssac PP, Frederiksen O. 1974. An alternative model for isosmotic water transport. In *Secretory Mechanism of Exocrine Glands,* ed. NA Thorn, OH Petersen, 432–48. Copenhagen: Munksgaard

29. Mollgaård K, Rostgaard J. 1978. Morphological aspects of some sodium transporting epithelia suggesting a transcellular pathway via elements of endoplasmic reticulum. *J. Membr. Biol.* 42:71–89

30. Zeuthen T. 1994. Cotransport of K^+, Cl^-, and H_2O by membrane proteins in choroid plexus epithelium of *Necturus maculosus. J. Physiol.* 478:203–19

31. Zeuthen T, Stein WD. 1994. Cotransport of salt and water in membrane proteins: membrane proteins as osmotic engines. *J. Membr. Biol.* 137:179–95

32. Diamond JM. 1996. Wet transport proteins. *Nature* 384:611–12

33. Zeuthen T. 1991. Secondary active transport of water across ventricular cell membrane of choroid plexus epithelium of *Necturus maculosus. J. Physiol.* 444:153–73

34. Zeuthen T. 1995. Molecular mechanisms for passive and active transport of water. *Intern. Rev. Cytol.* 160:99–161

35. Zeuthen T, Hamann S, la Cour M. 1996. Cotransport of H^+, lactate and H_2O by membrane proteins in retinal pigment epithelium of bullfrog. *J. Physiol.* 497:3–17

36. Reuss L. 1996. 'Active' water transport? *J. Physiol.* 497:1

37. Barry PH, Diamond JM. 1984. Effects of unstirred layers on membrane phenomena. *Physiol. Rev.* 64:763–72

38. Strange K, Spring KR. 1986. Methods for imaging renal tubule cells. *Kidney Inter.* 30:192–200

39. Hill AE. 1980. Salt-water coupling in leaky epithelia. *J. Membr. Biol.* 55:177–82

40. Loeschke K, Bentzel CJ. 1994. Osmotic water flow pathways across *Necturus* gallbladder: role of the tight junction. *Am. J. Physiol.* 266(29):G722–30

41. Knepper MA. 1994. The aquaporin family of molecular water channels. *Proc. Natl. Acad. Sci. USA* 91:6255–58

42. Kottra G, Haase W, Frömter E. 1993. Tight-junction tightness of *Necturus* gall-bladder epithelium is not regulated by cAMP or intracellular Ca^{2+}. *Pflügers Arch.* 425:528–34

43. Duffey ME, Hainan B, Ho S, Bentzel CJ. 1981. Regulation of the epithelial tight junction permeability by cyclic AMP. *Nature* 294:451–53

44. Reuss L, Simon B, Xi Z. 1992. Pseudo-streaming potentials in *Necturus* gallbladder epithelium. I. Paracellular origin of the transepithelial voltage changes. *J. Gen. Physiol.* 99:297–316

45. Reuss L, Simon B, Cotton C. 1992. Pseudo-streaming potentials in *Necturus* gallbladder epithelium. II. The mechanism is a junctional diffusion potential. *J. Gen. Physiol.* 99:317–38

46. Chatton JY, Harris PJ, Spring KR. 1993. Properties of the lateral intercellular spaces of cultured renal epithelial cells. In *Isotonic Transport in Leaky Epithelia,* ed. HH Ussing, J Fischbarg, O Sten-Knudsen, EH Larsen, NJ Willumsen, 34:259–68. Copenhagen: Munksgaard

47. Berry CA, Boulpaep EL. 1978. Nonelectrolyte permeability of the paracellular pathway in *Necturus* proximal tubule. *Am. J. Physiol.* 235(4):F592–604

48. Steward MC. 1982. Paracellular non-electrolyte permeation during fluid transport across rabbit gall-bladder epithelium. *J. Physiol.* 322:419–39

49. Whittembury G, Malnic G, Mello-Aires M, Amorena C. 1988. Solvent drag of sucrose during absorption indicates paracellular water flow in the rat kidney proximal tubule. *Pflügers Arch.* 412:541–47

50. Shachar-Hill B, Hill AE. 1993. Convective fluid-flow through the paracellular system of *Necturus* gall-bladder epithelium as revealed by dextran probes. *J. Physiol.* 468:463–86

51. Sofia Hernandez C, Gonzalez E, Whittembury G. 1995. The paracellular channel for water secretion in the upper segment of the Malpighian tubule of *Rhodnius prolixus. J. Membr. Biol.* 148:233–42

52. Alvarez-Leefmans FJ, Altamirano J, Crowe WE. 1995. Use of ion-selective microelectrodes and fluorescent probes

to measure cell volume. *Meth. Neurosci.* 27:361–91

53. Raat NJH, De Smet P, Van Driessche W, Bindels RJM, Van Os CH. 1996. Measuring volume perturbations of proximal tubular cells in primary culture with three different techniques. *Am. J. Physiol.* 271(40):C235–41

54. Strange K, Spring KR. 1987. Cell membrane water permeability of rabbit cortical collecting duct. *J. Membr. Biol.* 96:27–43

55. Timbs MM, Spring KR. 1996. Hydraulic properties of MDCK cell epithelium. *J. Membr. Biol.* 153:1–11

56. Flamion B, Spring KR, Abramow M. 1995. Adaptation of inner medullary collecting duct to dehydration involves a paracellular pathway. *Am. J. Physiol.* 268(37):F53–63

57. Kovbasnjuk O, Chatton JY, Friauf WS, Spring KR. 1995. Determination of the Na permeability of the tight junctions of MDCK cells by fluorescence microscopy. *J. Membr. Biol.* 148:223–32

58. Tormey JMcD, Diamond JM. 1967. The ultrastructural route of fluid transport in rabbit gall bladder. *J. Gen. Physiol.* 50:2031–60

59. Spring KR, Hope A. 1978. The size and shape of the lateral intercellular spaces in a living epithelium. *Science* 200:54–58

60. Welling LW, Welling DJ. 1975. Surface areas of brush border and lateral cell walls in the rabbit proximal nephron. *Kidney Internat.* 9:385–94

61. Zampighi G, Kreman M. 1985. Intercellular fibrillar skeleton in the basal interdigitations of kidney tubular cells. *J. Membr. Biol.* 88:33–43

62. Harris PJ, Chatton JY, Tran PH, Bungay PM, Spring KR. 1994. pH, morphology, and diffusion in lateral intercellular spaces of epithelial cell monolayers. *Am. J. Physiol.* 266(35):C73–80

63. Chatton JY, Spring KR. 1995. The sodium concentration of the lateral intercellular spaces of MDCK cells: a microspectrofluorimetric study. *J. Membr. Biol.* 144:11–19

64. Xia P, Persson BE, Spring KR. 1995. The chloride concentration in the lateral intercellular spaces of MDCK cell monolayers. *J. Membr. Biol.* 144:21–30

65. Ussing HH, Lind F, Larsen EH. 1996. Ion secretion and isotonic transport in frog skin glands. *J. Membr. Biol.* 152:101–10

66. Naftalin RJ, Pedley KC. 1990. Video enhanced imaging of the fluorescent Na^+ probe SBFI indicates that colonic crypts absorb fluid by generating a hypertonic interstitial fluid. *FEBS Lett.* 260:187–94

67. Pedley KC, Naftalin RJ. 1993. Evidence from fluorescence microscopy and comparative studies that rat, ovine and bovine colonic crypts are absorptive. *J. Physiol.* 460:525–47

68. Naftalin RJ, Pedley KC. 1995. The sodium concentration of lateral intercellular spaces. *J. Membr. Biol.* 147:105–6

69. Chatton JY, Spring KR. 1995. Reply to: the sodium concentration of lateral intercellular spaces. *J. Membr. Biol.* 147:106–7

70. Chu S, Montrose MH. 1995. Extracellular pH regulation in microdomains of colonic crypts: effects of short chain fatty acids. *Proc. Natl. Acad. Sci. USA* 92:3303–7

71. Greger R, Bleich M, Leipziger J, Ecke D, Mall M, Kunzelmann K. 1997. Regulation of ion transport in colonic crypts. *News Physiol. Sci.* 12:62–67

72. Fitz JG, Bass NM, Weisiger RA. 1991. Hepatic transport of a fluorescent stearate derivative: electrochemical driving forces in intact liver. *Am. J. Physiol.* 261(24): G83–91

73. Chatton JY, Spring KR. 1994. Acidic pH of the lateral intercellular spaces of MDCK cells cultured on permeable supports. *J. Membr. Biol.* 140:89–99

74. Daniel H, Neugebauer B, Kratz A, Rehner G. 1985. Localization of acid microclimate along intestinal villi of rat jejunum. *Am. J. Physiol.* 248(11):G293–98

75. Wong V, Gumbiner BM. 1977. A synthetic peptide corresponding to the extracellular domain of occludin perturbs the tight junction permeability barrier. *J. Cell Biol.* 136:399–409

76. Balda MS, Whitney JA, Flores C, González, Cereijido M, Matter K. 1996. Functional dissociation of paracellular permeability and transepithelial electrical resistance and disruption of the apical-basolateral intramembrane diffusion barrier by expression of a mutant tight junction membrane protein. *J. Cell Biol.* 134:1031–49

77. Denk W, Strickler JH, Webb WW. 1990. Two-photon laser scanning fluorescence microscopy. *Science* 248:73–76

78. Green R, Giebisch G, Unwin R, Weinstein AM. 1991. Coupled water transport by rat proximal tubule. *Am. J. Physiol.* 261(30):F1046–54

Annu. Rev. Physiol. 1998. 60:121–42

MOLECULAR ARCHITECTURE OF TIGHT JUNCTIONS

L. L. Mitic and J. M. Anderson[#]*

*Department of Cell Biology, Yale School of Medicine, New Haven, Connecticut 06520; e-mail: laura.mitic@yale.edu; [#]Departments of Internal Medicine and Cell Biology, Yale School of Medicine, New Haven, Connecticut, 06520

KEY WORDS: occludin, ZO-1, ZO-2, actin, adherens junction

ABSTRACT

The tight junction creates a regulated barrier in the paracellular pathway and, together with the actin-rich adherens junction, forms a functional unit called the apical junction complex. A growing number of tight junction–associated proteins have been identified, but functions are defined for only a few. The intercellular barrier is formed by rows of the transmembrane protein occludin, which is bound on the cytoplasmic surface to ZO-1 and ZO-2. These proteins are members of the membrane-associated guanylate kinase (MAGUK) protein family and are likely to have both structural and signaling roles. Junctional plaque proteins without known functions include cingulin, p130, and 7H6; single reports describe ZA-1TJ and symplekin. Many cellular signaling pathways affect assembly and sealing of junctions. Transducing proteins, which localize within the junction, include both heterotrimeric and rho-related GTP-binding proteins, PKC-ζ and nonreceptor tyrosine kinases. Control of perijunctional actin may be the unifying mechanism for regulating paracellular permeability.

INTRODUCTION

Tight junctions create a rate-limiting barrier to diffusion of solutes between vertebrate epithelial and endothelial cells (1, 2). They also act as a fence within the membrane bilayer to separate distinct lipid and protein components of the apical and basolateral surface domains (3, 4). The barrier varies in tightness by several orders of magnitude in resistance between so-called tight and leaky epithelia, shows a slight cation selectivity and, depending on the cell type, has

121

0066-4278/98/0315-0121$08.00

a pore size in the range of 8–20 Å (1, 2). Tight junctions are also controlled within individual cells by a wide variety of physiologically relevant signals (5). By defining the characteristics of paracellular transport, tight junctions help define the overall transport characteristics of each epithelia. The molecular basis of these properties remained, until very recently, completely unknown. There is now a sizeable and growing list of proteins that are components of the tight junction. At present, most remain as markers without known functions or protein associations. In this review, we focus on those proteins whose properties begin to provide a molecular basis for junctional physiology (see Figure 1). These are the transmembrane protein occludin (6) and

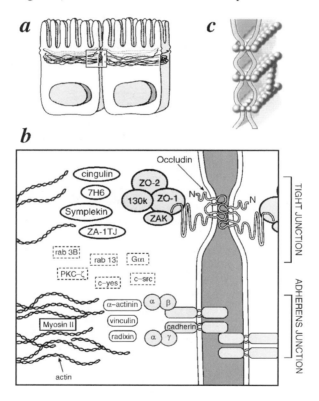

Figure 1   Model depicting the protein components of the apical junction complex, the tight and adherens junctions, in a highly polarized epithelial cell. (*a*) Continuous cell-cell contact is made at the apical end of the lateral interspace where a ring of bidirectional actin filaments is concentrated. (*b*) The boxed region is depicted at higher magnification, showing identified proteins and their protein associations. Some proteins are specific to one junction; others may be shared (*broken boxes*). (*c*) Interpretation of freeze-fracture EM images (see Figure 2) showing barriers formed by the intercellular contact of branching linear polymers of occludin and its cytoplasmic scaffold.

the MAGUK proteins ZO-1 (7–9) and ZO-2 (10, 11), which couple occludin to the cytoplasmic plaque. Other plaque proteins, including many potential signaling proteins, are enumerated, and we speculate on how the plaque is connected to and regulated by the perijunctional ring of actin and myosin. Accompanying reviews in this volume focus more specifically on the physiologic characteristics of the barrier, including its regulation and contribution to cell polarity.

Over a century ago, the barrier between polarized epithelial cells was attributed to an intercellular thickening termed the terminal bar, which was visualized with vital dyes at the apical-lateral cell boundary (Figure 1). This site was thought to contain a secreted cement, which formed an unregulated seal in the paracellular space. In the early part of this century, physiologic studies had demonstrated the barrier was not complete and varied among tissues (3). With the arrival of the electron microscope in the early 1960s, the terminal bar was revealed as several morphologically distinct intercellular junctions. The apical-most contact limited paracellular movement of electron-dense tracer molecules and was named the zonula occludens or tight junction (12). Biochemical description of gap, adherens, tight, and desmosomal junctions has progressed over the last two decades, with the tight junction being, until very recently, the most refractory to molecular description.

Consistent with their role in maintaining barriers, tight junctions form continuous gasket-like contacts between adjacent epithelial cells (Figure 2). In transmission electron micrographs, transverse sections across the region of intercellular contact show a series of spot-like contacts or "kisses" (3, 12). When the intramembrane structure is revealed by freeze-fracture electron microscopy technique, cell-cell contacts coincide with rows of intramembrane particles that form continuous branching fibrils around each cell (Figures 1 and 2). Immuno-electron microscopy and immuno-freeze fracture reveal linear aggregates of the transmembrane protein occludin (13) within the fibrils, which appear to associate between cells and seal the paracellular space. Each contact, or linear barrier, is likely to contribute a resistive element in the paracellular pathway because when tissues are compared, the number of fibrils correlates with the paracellular electrical resistance and impedance to solute flux (1, 14).

The tight junction is invariably positioned next to another continuous circumferential contact zone called the adherens junction (Figure 1). Adherens junctions are formed by members of the cadherin family of Ca^{2+}-dependent homotypic adhesion molecules and their cytoplasmic plaque proteins α-, β-, and γ-catenin. Cadherin is bound directly through α-catenin and indirectly through α-actinin, vinculin, and radixin to a dense belt of bipolar actin filaments (15). Many lines of evidence suggest tight and adherens junctions are two aspects of a single functional unit. The formation of tight junctions both in developing

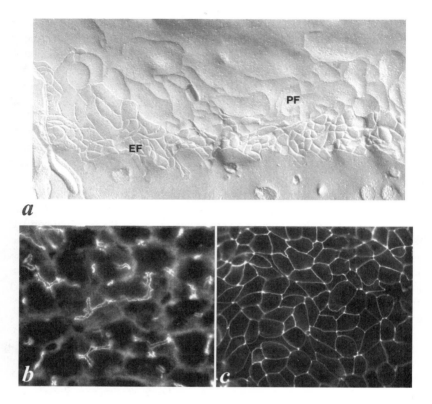

Figure 2   (*a*) Freeze-fracture replica image of a tight junction between bronchial epithelial cells in the rat lung. PF (protoplasmic face) and EF (ectoplasmic face) fracture faces are visible. Note the smooth and continuous fibrils (×55,1000. Figure provided by E Schneeberger). (*b*) Indirect immunofluorescent localization of occludin at the tight junctions between hepatocytes in rat liver, and (*c*) cultured MDCK cells. Each linear contact visible at the light microscope level corresponds, in freeze-fracture electron microscopy images, to a belt of branching fibrils within the membrane bilayer.

embryonic tissues (16) and in cultured cell model systems (17) is dependent on the prior formation of cadherin-based contacts. It has not been resolved whether cadherin initiates intracellular signals used to instruct the assembly of tight junctions, or whether tight junctions use cadherin as a physical scaffold for assembly, or both (18). The former model is consistent with the observation that activators of protein kinase C cause tight junctions to form without a need for cadherin either during compaction in the mouse embryo (19) or in cultured cell models (20). The latter possibility is consistent with the observation that the occludin-binding protein ZO-1 (Figure 1) is reported to transiently bind β-catenin during the initial phase of junction formation in cultured Madin-Darby canine kidney (MDCK) epithelial cells (21). ZO-1 is also a component of cadherin-based contacts in cells that lack occludin, suggesting it could nucleate assembly of tight junctions from adherens junctions (22).

The present challenge to understanding the functional architecture of the tight junction is to define how individual proteins associate and are connected to the cytoskeleton and how assembly and sealing is influenced by the numerous signaling proteins present in the plaque.

PROTEIN COMPONENTS

Occludin

The past year has witnessed major progress in understanding the function of occludin, which is the only known transmembrane protein in the tight junction. Occludin has been shown to localize within the tight junction fibrils, to confer cell-cell adhesion and to function in the permeability barrier (13, 23–25).

Occludin's Cellular Location and Chemistry

Occludin is localized in immuno-gold-labeled thin sections precisely at tight junction contacts (6). It assumes a gasket-like junctional position in intact tissues such as the liver (Figure 2b), where it participates in separating the blood from bile spaces, and is most obvious in monolayers of epithelial-derived tissue culture cell lines, such as the MDCK cells (Figure 2c). By immuno-gold labeling freeze-fracture techniques, Fugimoto (13) showed that antibodies against occludin recognized a protein found within the tight junction fibrils. However, it is not known if occludin is the sole component of the fibrils.

Occludin cDNAs from five species have now been cloned and amino acid sequences deduced (26). An alignment of these five amino acid sequences reveals surprising divergence across species for a protein postulated as crucial in creating such a fundamental property of multicellular animals (Figure 3). For example, the overall identity between chicken and human, rat-kangaroo and human, and chicken and rat-kangaroo occludin is only 39.8, 38.2, and 54.1%, respectively. There is much higher identity between the placental mammals, dog, and human (90.6%) and dog and mouse (85.8%).

Occludin cDNAs from all species predict a protein of approximately 65 kDa, which forms two extracellular loops of approximately 47 amino acids bounded by N- and C-terminal cytoplasmic domains (Figure 4). Consistent with this topological prediction, a monoclonal antibody against the C-terminal tail

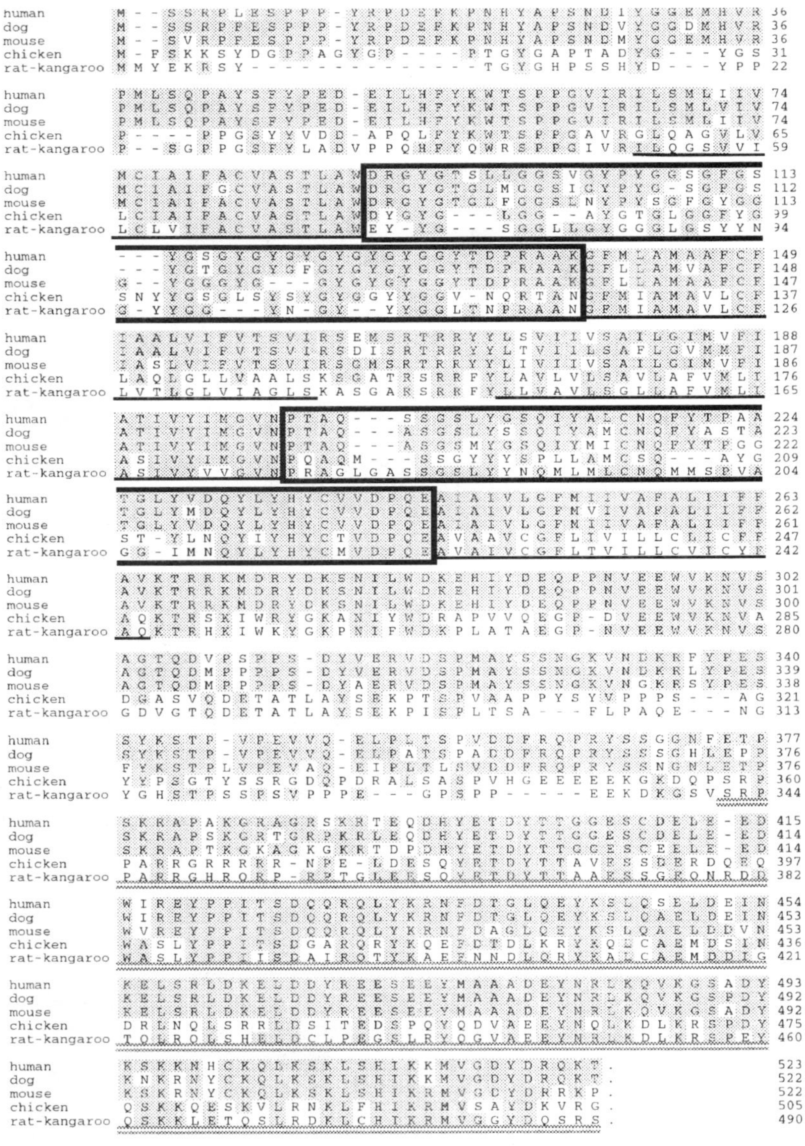

Figure 3   Amino acid alignment of occludin sequences from human, dog, rat, chicken, and rat-kangaroo. Residues conserved across all species are *shaded*. Extracellular loops are *boxed* and transmembrane sequences are *underlined*. Note the high concentration of tyrosine and glycine in the first extracellular loop. The ZO-1 binding domain is *double-underlined*.

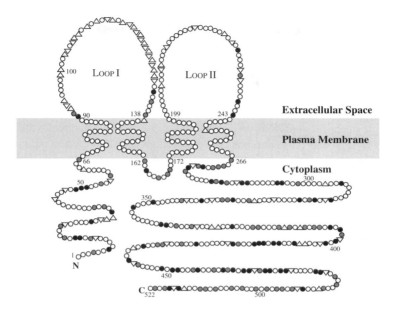

Figure 4 Predicted folding topology of human occludin. Antibody accessibility studies demonstrate Loop I is extracellular and the C-terminal tail is cytoplasmic. Acidic (*solid circle*), basic (*cross-hatch*) and uncharged (*open circle*) residues at neutral pH are indicated. Glycines are represented as (*triangle*) and tyrosines as (*inverted triangle*). Adapted from chicken occludin model of Furuse et al (6).

labeled only the cytoplasmic side of junctions in thin section electron microscopic images (6), whereas an antibody raised against the putative first extracellular loop labeled living nonpermeabilized cultured epithelial cells (27). The function of occludin's extracellular loops has been the subject of much speculation because of their unusual chemistry. Specifically, the first loop has an extremely high content of alternating glycine and tyrosine residues, 36 and 22%, respectively. The loops, as described in detail below, are implicated in the tight junction's barrier function and in cell adhesion, but whether they form homo- or heterotypic interactions remains unknown. In the human sequence, the loops contain a total of only nine charged side chains (Figure 4), suggesting that loops on adjacent cells may interact in the ion-rich paracellular environment simply through energetically favorable hydrophobic contacts. The high glycine content should create a highly flexible structure; the tyrosine side chains may stack. This suggests loops from adjacent cells may interdigitate in a zipper-like fashion to create the paracellular seal. Moreover, proteins with similar membrane topology, such as connexin and synaptophysin, function as homophilic molecular seals, supporting the hypothesis that occludin may also have homotypic interactions.

Determining Occludin's Function at the Tight Junction

The discovery of occludin has initiated a molecular dissection of its function. McCarthy et al (24), using a Lac-inducible vector, showed that expression of chicken occludin in MDCK cells increased transepithelial electrical resistance (TER) by 30–40% , thus demonstrating that occludin is a functional component of the transepithelial electrical barrier. This was associated with a 15% increase in the number of fibrils (24). Similar increases in TER and fibril number were reported by Balda et al (23), who used a butyrate-inducible expression system to overexpress chicken occludin in MDCK cells. These authors also showed that occludin's C-terminal tail is not necessary to induce an electrically tighter seal, because cells stably expressing a chicken occludin construct, which is truncated after the fourth transmembrane domain, also showed increased TER. Thus occludin functions in creating the paracellular barrier, and this property is conferred by the extracellular loops.

In experiments involving forced occludin expression in cultured cells, occludin appears to be the rate-limiting factor in the formation of fibrils and the development of TER because its expression correlates with both (25, 24). In contrast, levels of two of the cytoplasmic tight junction plaque proteins, cingulin and ZO-1, remain relatively constant as occludin levels, fibril content, and TER increase (25). It should be noted, however, that the localization of ZO-1 and cingulin during the establishment of TER was not examined in parallel with immunoblot analysis; their expression may have remained constant, but their concentration at the junction may have increased in response to occludin expression. Translational control of occludin expression could theoretically provide a slow mechanism for regulating TER. In contrast, rapid, massive assembly of tight junction fibrils in cultured cells has been observed in response to some noxious stimuli (28), implying that another, much faster method of regulating tight junction fibril number (and thus dynamics) must also exist. These experiments strongly suggest that a pool of fibril protein exists outside of the fibril, ready to respond immediately to presently unknown signals (28). It will be interesting to determine if occludin is maintained in such a pool, or if the rapid form of assembly observed involves another, yet unidentified, protein component.

Support for the role of occludin's extracellular loops in forming the junctional seal was demonstrated in a study using loop-blocking peptides. Wong & Gumbiner (25) examined whether peptides corresponding to the sequences of the loops could competitively inhibit occludin binding in monolayers of *Xenopus* A6 epithelial cells. A peptide containing the sequence of the second loop (see Figure 4) caused a dramatic loss of occludin localization at the tight junction and a correspondingly significant drop in TER. This effect was specific for Loop II; a peptide corresponding to Loop I had no effect (25). In addition to its role in establishing TER, occludin also functions in the well-characterized solute diffusion barrier. The selective removal of occludin from the tight junction, as seen following the treatment of A6 monolayers with a peptide corresponding to loop II, results in a dramatic increase in flux and a loss of the barrier's size-selectivity (25). Similarly, as observed in vivo during developmental remodeling of the neuroepithelium prior to neural tube closure, the loss of occludin expression in neuroepithelial cells is coincident with a loss of barrier function (29). Hence, occludin localization at the junction is required to maintain TER and the size-selective solute permeability barrier.

In intact epithelia, the electrical tightness of the junctional barrier correlates inversely with the flux of small tracer molecules through the paracellular space; i.e. high TER correlates with low flux. Therefore, one would predict that since increasing occludin expression increases TER, it would simultaneously lower paracellular flux. Surprisingly, two studies have shown that an increase in TER induced by overexpression of occludin results in increased flux (23, 24). This paradox cannot be easily explained by current models of junction organization.

Occludin has recently been shown to function as a cell-cell adhesion molecule, adding additional support to the idea it is directly involved in closing the intercellular space. When human occludin is expressed under an inducible promotor in occludin-null fibroblasts, it confers calcium- and cadherin-independent cell-cell adhesion (27). Adhesiveness is dependent upon colocalization with ZO-1 and can be abolished by adding peptides corresponding to the first extracellular occludin loop (see Figure 4). Because expression of occludin in previously non-adhesive occludin-null fibroblasts was sufficient to confer adhesiveness, it seems likely that occludin may be interacting in a homotypic fashion. Consistent with this model, Furuse et al (30), using a baculovirus expression system, demonstrated that overexpression of occludin in insect cells results in accumulation of intracellular multilamellar structures with tightly adherent membranes. The idea that the tight junction fibril component may be adhesive is not a new one. Early freeze-fracture studies demonstrated in glutaraldehyde-fixed epithelia that fused fibrils evident on the protoplasmic fracture face (P-face) correspond to complementary grooves on the exoplasmic fracture face (E face) of the membrane bilayer (31). In contrast, in unfixed tissue, the tight junction particles preferentially partition to the E-face, suggesting that unless the particles are chemically cross-linked to cytoplasmic components, they have a higher affinity for their counterpart on an adjacent cell (32).

Occludin also appears to participate in maintaining the intramembrane diffusion barrier. Lipid diffusion in the outer, but not inner, leaflet of the bilayer is restricted at the tight junction (33, 4). Expression of an occludin construct lacking the C-terminal tail in MDCK cells results in a discontinuous ring of both truncated occludin and endogenous, full-length occludin. Balda et al (23) showed that 60 min after introducing the fluorescent lipid tracer BODIPY-sphingomyelin into the apical domain, it is also detected on the basolateral cell surface. In nontransfected cells the label is retained apically, suggesting a continuous ring of occludin is necessary to restrict lipid diffusion in the exoplasmic leaflet. How occludin is able to restrict diffusion in one leaflet and not the other remains unclear.

Targeting Occludin to the Tight Junction

Several lines of evidence suggest occludin depends on the plaque proteins for targeting and not vice versa. For example, several studies show that occludin's displacement or absence from the junction does not change the localization of the plaque proteins ZO-1, ZO-2, and cingulin (25, 29). For instance, ZO-1 may act as the scaffold to organize occludin at the junction. When full-length human occludin is transfected into occludin-null fibroblasts, it only localizes at sites of cell-cell contact where ZO-1 is already concentrated. Fibroblast lines that lack cadherin fail to localize ZO-1 at cell contacts, and when occludin is expressed in these fibroblasts, it is diffusely distributed on the cell surface (27). Moreover, human occludin missing the ZO-1-binding domain does not concentrate at ZO-1-containing sites of cell-cell contact in fibroblasts, providing additional evidence that the ZO-1-binding domain is required for localization of occludin (CM Van Itallie, personal communication). Lastly, the ZO-1 binding domain is sufficient to target chimeras containing the connexin-32 transmembrane sequence fused to the last 150 residues of human occludin to the tight junction and to intercalate them into fibrils in MDCK cells, or to ZO-1-containing sites of cell-cell contact in fibroblasts (L Mitic, personal observation).

Other experiments suggest the existence of ZO-1-independent targeting mechanisms for occludin. Balda et al (23) recently reported the localization of a truncated occludin construct at the tight junction despite its lack of a ZO-1-binding site. However, it is likely that this construct was able to associate with other, endogenous, full-length occludin molecules that were capable of binding ZO-1. We have evidence in support of this hypothesis using cotransfection of truncated and full-length occludin in fibroblasts. Occludin without the ZO-1-binding region only localizes at sites of cell contact when it is expressed in fibroblasts also expressing full-length occludin.

ZO-1 may act as an organizational scaffold, whereas lateral occludin-occludin interactions may stabilize and promote assembly of occludin into a linear fibril. In this way, ZO-1 may anchor occludin at the membrane and instruct its polymerization. It will be interesting to investigate whether occludin contains such a putative internal polymerization domain and how this interaction occurs.

ZO-1, ZO-2 Are Members of the Membrane-Associated Guanylate Kinase (MAGUK) Protein Family

The best-studied protein within the cytoplasmic plaque is the 220-kDa phosphoprotein ZO-1 (7, 8, 22, 9). It can be immunoprecipitated in a stable complex with ZO-2, a homologous 160-kDa protein (10, 34) (Figure 5), and less predictably with a 130-kDa protein (20). As described above, ZO-1 binds directly to a 150-amino acid domain at the cytoplasmic tail of occludin (35), and one report suggests it may bind to the actin-binding protein spectrin (22). Similar binding properties are predicted for its homologue ZO-2 but have not been reported. Both ZO-1 and ZO-2 are expressed and colocalize with occludin in all cells that form tight junctions. In contrast, ZO-1 is also expressed in cells lacking tight junctions, such as fibroblasts and cardiac myocytes, where it localizes at cell contacts with members of the cadherin superfamily (22). ZO-1 is also present in at least one junction that lacks both occludin and cadherin: the filtration slit junctions between renal glomerular epithelial cells (36). The functional role of ZO-1 in any of these junctions is still poorly defined.

Based on sequence homologies, ZO-1 and ZO-2 are members of the membrane-associated guanylate kinase (MAGUK) protein family (9). A preliminary report reveals p130 is also a MAGUK protein (37). All MAGUK proteins are associated with the plasma membrane, typically at sites of specialized cell-cell contact. Genetic evidence from invertebrate systems demonstrates a role for ZO-1 and MAGUK proteins in organizing signal transduction, and evidence

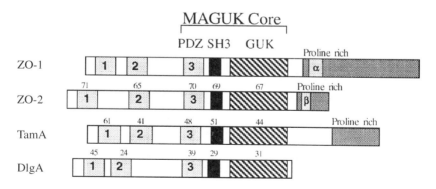

Figure 5 Domain alignments of Drosophila Discs-large tumor suppressor (Dlg-A), mammalian ZO-1 and ZO-2, and Tamou (TamA) the *Drosophila* orthologue of ZO-1. All MAGUK proteins contain PDZ and SH3 domains and a region of homology to guanylate kinase. The proteins shown are a branch of MAGUK, which contain three PDZ domains. ZO-1, ZO-2, and TamA are a closely related subset with proline-rich C-terminal domains. ZO-1 and ZO-2 share alternatively-spliced domains of 80 (α) and 36 (β) amino acids, respectively. Percent identity is indicated between specific domains of human ZO-1 and those in other proteins.

from vertebrate systems demonstrates a structural role in organizing transmembrane protein complexes (9). Other members of this protein family have been studied extensively through genetic, biochemical, and cell biological methods, and insights about their function can be cautiously extrapolated to the tight junction.

MAGUK proteins share a multidomain organization including one or three PDZ domains, an SH3 domain, and a region of homology with the enzyme guanylate kinase (Figure 5). Functions for each of these domains have been postulated and are discussed below in relation to possible analogous functions at the tight junction. PDZ domains are approximately 80–100-amino acid domains named for their expression in the MAGUK proteins: post-synaptic density protein-95 kDa (PSD-95), the *Drosophila* tumor suppressor Discs-large, and ZO-1 (38, 39). They have been described in more than 50 proteins, most of which are not MAGUKs (9). PDZ domains are protein-binding modules that recognize variations on a short peptide motif within their protein targets. In almost all cases, the target sequences have been the last three to five residues at the extreme C terminus of a transmembrane protein (40). For example, the second of three PDZ domains within PSD-95 binds the cytoplasmic C terminus of two synaptic ion channels, i.e. Shaker-type K^+ channels (41) and the NMDA receptor (42). Several lines of evidence strongly suggest the interaction with the PDZ domain is responsible for clustering the channels into synapses. For example, PSD-95 colocalizes in vivo with these channels at synapses in the rat brain and causes the channels to cluster on the plasma membrane when both are expressed in heterologous cultured cell models (41). A related protein in *Drosophila*, Disc-large (Figure 5), is implicated in clustering K^+ channels within neuromuscular junctions because in Dlg-null embryos the channels fail to cluster. Channels cluster on the surface of myocytes when a transgene encoding only the three PDZ domains of Dlg is expressed, although the clusters form outside neuromuscular junctions. Constructs containing only the SH3 and GUK domains localize to junctions but do not cluster channels (43). The implication is that the concatenated PDZ domains cluster channels, whereas another domain of the protein targets the clusters into synapses. Presumably the PDZ domains of ZO-1 and ZO-2 also provide a scaffold to organize several proteins within the junction. Occludin lacks a PDZ-binding consensus at its C terminus and most likely binds outside of the PDZ domains of ZO-1. Presently, protein ligands for the PDZ domains of ZO-1 and ZO-2 remain unknown.

SH3 domains (src homology 3) have been described in numerous cytoskeletal and signaling proteins, where they mediate direct protein-protein binding and direct subcellular localization and formation of multiprotein complexes. Binding partners for the SH3 domains of MAGUKs remain uncharacterized. The exception is a single report of a novel serine kinase activity that can be precipitated from cell lysates through interaction with the SH3 domain of ZO-1 (44). This kinase, termed ZO-1-associated kinase or ZAK, phosphorylates serine residues between the SH3 and GUK domains of ZO-1. It shares the unusual ability with casein kinase II to use both GTP and ATP as phosphoryl donors, yet it is distinct and immunologically unrelated to casein kinase II. It remains unknown what function of ZO-1 is regulated by ZAK.

Guanylate kinase catalyzes conversion of GMP to GDP; however, this activity has never been documented for the GUK domain of any MAGUK protein. MAGUK proteins can be classified into several groups based on whether they maintain specific residues required for binding the phosphoryl donor ATP and acceptor GDP. ZO-1 and ZO-2 have specific deletions at both sites, which suggests that these functions were selected against for their role in tight junctions. Recently, a novel protein of unknown function was identified and cloned based on its association with the GUK domain of PSD-95 (45). Although this guanylate kinase-associated protein (GKAP) also binds the GUK domains of two other synaptic MAGUKs, SAP97 and chapsyn-110, it is not a component of tight junctions, raising the possibility that ZO-1 and ZO-2 may bind a distinct GKAP-related protein.

Analysis of the mutant phenotypes of two invertebrate MAGUKs suggests that tight junction MAGUKs are involved in organizing signal transduction. The first MAGUK cloned was the *lethal (1) discs-large* (DlgA) tumor suppressor of *Drosophila* (Figure 5), which is located on the cytoplasmic surface of septate junctions between epithelial cells as well as at neuromuscular junctions (46). Embryos homozygous for null mutants of the *dlg* gene fail to develop septate junctions between epithelial cells covering imaginal discs. Apical-basal cell polarity and growth regulation are lost, resulting in a proliferation of lethal epithelial tumors on the discs. In contrast, in flies with weaker mutant alleles, such as point mutations in the SH3 or GUK domains, development of septate junctions progresses normally, but lethal tumor growth still occurs (46). These results, as well as the protein's multidomain structure, imply that DlgA is a multifunctional protein, with some domains required for structural organization of the septate junction and other domains for function in signal transduction pathways that influence mitosis. Although septate and tight junctions are morphologically dissimilar, their homologous protein composition and barrier function strongly suggest a common evolutionary relationship. As the molecular architecture of septate junctions is further defined, its similarities and differences should provide insight into both the structure and function of tight junctions. Specifically, could tight junctions be involved in contact inhibition of cell growth?

The LIN-2 protein of *Caenorhabditis elegans* is a second invertebrate MAGUK required for membrane-based signal transduction. LIN-2 mutants interrupt a receptor tyrosine kinase signaling pathway that normally activates ras and induces vulval cell precursors to differentiate (47). In LIN-2-null mutants, the receptor is not properly polarized to the basal cell surface and fails to respond to the diffusible EGF-like signal presented from the basal surface (48). By analogy to Dlg and LIN-2, we can speculate that ZO-1 and ZO-2 may also be used to organize the tight junction architecture to permit propagation of presently undefined signaling pathways.

There are early hints that ZO-1 may have a role in regulation of transcription. Gottardi et al (49) have noted a fraction of ZO-1 localizes in the nucleus of subconfluent, but not confluent, cultured epithelial cells. Nuclear localization is also seen in cells at the edge of wounded monolayers in culture and at the maturation tip of intestinal villi. These authors speculate that the presence of a nuclear pool of ZO-1 may be related to the state of cell differentiation. Stronger, but still circumstantial, evidence comes from cloning what appears to be the *Drosophila* orthologue of ZO-1, a gene called *tamou* (50). The tamou protein is strikingly similar to ZO-1 and ZO-2 in its domain structure and in the presence of a large C-terminal proline-rich region (Figure 5). Tamou (which means hairy in Japanese) mutants exhibit defective development of sensory organs, a structure that includes hair bristles. Sensory organ development is governed by the competing activity of proneural and repressor genes on a cluster of cells called the proneural organ. Loss of repressor gene activity causes enlargement of the proneural organ and additional hair bristles on the adult fly. One such repressor gene, *extramacrochaetae*, requires *tamou* for expression. The tamou protein (TamA) is reported to localize around the periphery of epithelial cells, although its exact subcellular location has not been reported in detail. It is an intriguing idea that TamA and ZO-1 may share a role in regulating transcription, and progress on the mechanism of TamA function will be followed closely by those in the tight junction field.

Both ZO-1 and ZO-2 have proline-rich C-terminal domains containing variably expressed sequences arising from alternative RNA splicing (Figure 5). An 80-amino acid domain, termed α, is found in ZO-1, which is expressed in polarized epithelial cells. The splice-form lacking the α-domain is found in most endothelial cell tight junctions and in the highly plastic contacts formed between Sertoli cells and glomerular epithelial cells (51). ZO-2 contains a nonhomologous 36-amino acid alternatively spliced domain at the same relative position in the protein; its cell type distribution has not been defined (11). Contiguous 7- and 13-amino acid motifs termed $\beta 1$ and $\beta 2$ are found near the C terminus of ZO-1 and also show tissue-specific expression patterns (A Brecher, personal observation). As described below, symplekin and ZA-1TJ are not expressed in endothelial cell junctions. Taken together, these observations reveal a high degree of molecular diversity among different tight junction types. Differential expression of proteins and splice forms presumably underlies variable regulation or barrier properties.

Cingulin and 7H6

Two additional cytoplasmic plaque proteins, cingulin (140kDa) (52) and the 7H6 antigen (155 kDa) (53), have been localized precisely to tight junctions using immuno-electron microscopic techniques (Figure 1). Although used extensively as markers, these proteins remain without known functions or binding interactions.

Cingulin (140 kDa) was identified by Citi et al (52) while attempting to raise monoclonal antibodies to purified intestinal brush-border myosin. Several of its characteristics suggest cingulin probably has a structure similar to the coiled-coil tail of myosin, and it was copurifed as a contaminant with myosin. When the purified protein is viewed in the electron microscope after rotatory shadowing, it appears as a highly extended coiled-coil dimer with a contour length of 130 nm and width of 2–3 nm. These are the dimensions predicted if the protein is all or nearly all α-helical. Its stability in both ethanol and elevated temperatures is also consistent with such a structure. These observations raise the possibility that cingulin is related to another fibrous cytoskeleton protein and organizes or tethers actin in the junctional plaque.

The 7H6 antigen is a 155 kDa phosphoprotein expressed in both epithelial and endothelial cell tight junctions. Preliminary observations suggest 7H6 may be sensitive to the functional state of the junction. In response to cellular ATP depletion, 7H6 reversibly dissociates from the junction, whereas ZO-1 remains attached, and its expression is progressively decreased as cells progress from normal to dysplastic to carcinomatous states (54). A cDNA sequence of 7H6 has been reported, and the deduced amino acid sequence shows homology to the SMC family. These are largely α-helical coiled-coil proteins with a putative ATPase domain. Although the function of SMC proteins is not defined, a role in chromosome movements has been suggested based on the observations that the temperature-sensitive *SMC1* gene in budding yeast is lethal during cell division and that the chicken protein homologue ScII associates with chromosomes (55). The relationship of these observations to 7H6 and the tight junction remains to be defined.

Symplekin and ZA-1TJ

Single publications (56, 58) have, to date, described the existence of two additional tight junctional plaque proteins: symplekin and ZA-ITJ (Figure 1). Neither protein has defined binding interactions or functional properties.

Symplekin is a 126.5-kDa protein identified by monoclonal antibody techniques and cloned from a human colon cDNA library (56). The deduced amino acid sequence is novel. Its localization within the junctional plaque is confirmed at the light and ultrastructural levels. Symplekin reinforces the molecular diversity of junctions as it is found within tight junctions of Sertoli cells but not within endothelial cells. Symplekin may have multiple functions because it is expressed in all cell types regardless of whether they form stable cell-cell contacts. In cultured fibroblasts, symplekin is predominantly found in the nucleus, whereas in epithelial cells, both in culture and in situ, it is nuclear and junctional. Keon et al (56) speculate that symplekin may have a role in controlling nuclear events, such as reporting the functional status of tight junctions contacts. This is reminiscent of the observations of Gottardi et al (49) that ZO-1 can be immuno-localized to the nucleus. A role for tight junction proteins in transcription regulation deserves more study and may have a precedent given the proven role for β-catenin, an adherens junction component and putative ZO-1-binding protein, in regulating the LEF-1 transcription factor (57).

The ZA-1TJ antigen was described by Kapprell et al (58) and, although its molecular weight has not been reported on immunoblots, it is likely to be distinct from other known proteins. Unlike other known proteins, it is absent from both endothelial and Sertoli cell junctions. Using ultrastructural immunogold methods, it is found under the tight junction but slightly farther from the membrane than either cingulin (65 Å) or ZO-1 (20 Å) (59). The distinct subjunctional localization observed for these different proteins suggests a functional subdomain organization that awaits further study.

Perijunctional Actin, Signaling Proteins, and Paracellular Permeability

Many lines of evidence suggest that paracellular permeability is influenced by the state of perijunctional actin. A dense band of bidirectional actin filaments and myosin is visible under the adherens junction. When actin filaments are made more conspicuous in ultrastructural images by decoration with the S1 fragment of myosin, a smaller number of actin filaments are also noted to enter the tight junction and terminate at sites of cell-cell contact, presumably near occludin (Figure 1) (60). Molecules involved in virtually all intracellular signaling pathways have been reported to affect permeability, including tyrosine kinases, Ca^{2+}, protein kinase C, heterotrimeric G proteins, calmodulin, cAMP, lipid second messengers, and phospholipase C (61, 62). Their effects often correlate with changes in actin organization. Other experimental approaches suggest that these signals are used to control assembly and disassembly of the junction (5, and references therein). A number of signaling proteins have been localized to tight junctions; although they could effect assembly, cell growth, differentiation, or aspects of cell physiology, we review their function only in relation to the hypothesis that perijunctional actin regulates paracellular permeability. Perhaps the simplest model for regulating permeability is through myosin-generated cytoskeletal traction on components of the apical junction complex. In nonmuscle cells, myosin ATPase and contraction are activated by phosphorylation of its regulatory light chain by myosin light chain kinase (MLCK). The possibility that a myosin-dependent mechanism exists in the tight junction is supported by the early observations of Mooseker (63) and Rodewald et al (64), who demonstrated in isolated enterocyte membranes that the apical actomyosin ring was capable of ATP-dependent contraction. Several lines of evidence suggest this contraction is regulated through the Ca^{2+}-dependent MLCK. For example, Hecht et al (65) have expressed elevated levels of MLCK using viral vectors in monolayers of MDCK cells and observed elevated light chain phosphorylation that correlates with decreased TER. Similarly, studies in isolated perfused rat livers and isolated hepatocytes treated with ADH, which elevates intracellular Ca^{2+}, report phosphorylation of myosin regulatory light chain with coincident contraction of perijunctional actin and increased para-cellular permeability (66). Enhanced permeability has also been documented in isolated hepatocytes following direct microinjection of a Ca^{2+}-independent fragment of MLCK (67). Exactly how actin is coupled to the tight junction is still unclear but represents an area of intense investigation.

Small GTP-binding proteins of the rho subfamily have been implicated in coordinating the functional state of actin in many systems (68). Presumably in their active GTP-bound state they interact with target proteins that control actin dynamics. One mechanism, based largely on experimental work in fibroblasts, is through activation of a rho-dependent kinase. In the activated rho-GTP state, rho-kinase phosphorylates and inactivates MLC phosphatase. The net effect is to enhance myosin light chain phosphorylation, myosin ATPase activity, and contractile tone. Although rho has not been reported to be specifically concentrated in the apical junction complex, expression of activated rho in cultured MDCK cells induces a synchronous change in junctional actin, dissociation of ZO-1 from the junction, and a fall in TER (68).

Other small GTP-binding proteins, rab13 (69) and rab3B (70), are concentrated in the junction complex; however, their downstream targets have not been identified and, like other members of the rab family, they could also be involved in vesicle targeting instead of regulating actin organization. A role for heterotrimeric G proteins is less well studied at the tight junction, although their activators and inhibitors affect junction assembly (71). $G\alpha_{i2}$ has been shown to be concentrated at tight junctions of MDCK cells where it reportedly immuno-precipitated with ZO-1 (72). Transfection of MDCK cells with constitutively activated forms of $G\alpha_0$ accelerates the formation of TER in monolayer cultures following Ca^{2+}-induced assembly (72). Again, upstream activators and down-stream targets for heterotrimeric G proteins in the junction remain unknown, but preliminary evidence of their involvement at the tight junction provides an exciting avenue for further investigation.

Protein kinases represent additional plausible effectors in the physiologic regulation of junction assembly and actin dynamics. The nonreceptor tyrosine kinases c-src and c-yes (73), p120, the src substrate and β catenin/cadherin-binding protein (74), and the protein kinase C isoform (75) are all concentrated in the apical junction plaque. Enhanced tyrosine phosphorylation of junctional substrates induced by tyrosine phosphatase inhibitors correlates with increased paracellular permeability in many models, including MDCK monolayers (76) and isolated perfused liver (77). Nonselective inhibitors like orthovanadate cause a striking purse string-like contraction of the perijunctional actin ring. A more selective tyrosine phosphatase inhibitor, phenylarsine oxide, causes a drop in paracellular resistance with only subtle morphologic changes to the junctions (76), perhaps mimicking a physiologically relevant effect on actin. The role of protein kinase C pathways in physiologic regulation of the tight junction has received extensive study, and assembly and permeability are responsive to Ca^{2+} and diacylglycerol, both allosteric effectors of PKC. (61). The mechanism by which tyrosine kinase- and PKC-mediated effects control junctional permeability is poorly defined and will require identification of their targets.

CONCLUSIONS AND QUESTIONS

Rapid progress is being made in describing the molecular architecture of tight junctions. This has led to new insights of how the paracellular seal is created and regulated. Identification of occludin as the intercellular barrier-forming protein has provided a significant breakthrough. A major unresolved question is how occludin is organized into competent barriers. Does occludin have an intrinsic ability to polymerize and form seals, or does the cytoplasmic plaque play a central role in organizing and controlling occludin? Is there a pool of occludin that moves in and out of fibrils? Will the signaling and structure functions established for other MAGUKs prove true for ZO-1 and ZO-2? What is the nature and purpose of signal transduction pathways focused in the apical junction complex? Do they control permeability or events like differentiation and cell growth? Future progress will depend on more detailed information about molecular architecture of the junction.

ACKNOWLEDGMENTS

The authors would like to thank Dr. Christina Van Itallie for reviewing the manuscript. JMA is supported by grants from the National Institutes of Health: DK45134 and CA66263, and in part by DK34989 and DK38979.

Literature Cited

1. Reuss L. 1991. Tight junction permeability to ions and water. In *Tight Junctions,* ed. M Cereijido, pp. 49–66. Boca Raton: CRC Press
2. Powell DW. 1981. Barrier function of epithelia. *Am. J. Physiol.* 241:G275–88
3. Cereijido M, ed. 1992. Evolution of ideas on the tight junction. In *Tight Junctions,* pp. 1–13. Boca Raton: CRC Press
4. van Meer G, Simons K. 1986. The function of tight junctions in maintaining differences in lipid composition between the apical and the basolateral cell surface domains of MDCK cells. *EMBO J.* 5:1455–64
5. Anderson JM, Van Itallie CM. 1995. Tight junctions and the molecular basis for regulation of paracellular permeability. *Am. J. Physiol.* 269:G467–75
6. Furuse M, Hirase T, Itoh M, Nagafuchi A, Yonemura S, Tsukita S. 1993. Occludin: a novel integral membrane protein localizing at tight junctions. *J. Cell Biol.* 123:1777–88
7. Stevenson BR, Silicano JD, Mooseker M, Goodenough DA. 1986. Identification of ZO-1: a high molecular weight polypeptide associated with the tight junction (zonula occludens) in a variety of epithelia. *J. Cell Biol.* 103:755–66
8. Willott E, Balda MS, Fanning AS, Jameson B, Van Itallie C, Anderson JM. 1993. The tight junction protein ZO-1 is homologous to the *Drosophila* Discs-large tumor suppressor protein of septate junctions. *Proc. Natl. Acad. Sci. USA* 90:7834–38
9. Fanning AS, Lapierre LA, Brecher AR, Van Itallie CM, Anderson JM. 1996. Protein interactions in the tight junction: the role of MAGUK proteins in regulating tight junction organization and function. *Curr. Topics Membr.* 43:211–35
10. Gumbiner B, Lowenkopf T, Apatira D. 1991. Identification of 160-kDa polypeptide that binds to the tight junction protein ZO-1. *Proc. Natl. Acad. Sci. USA* 88:3460–64
11. Beatch M, Jesaitis LA, Gallin WJ, Goodenough DA, Stevenson BR. 1996. The tight junction protein ZO-2 contains three PDZ (PSD-95/Discs-Large/ZO-1) domains and an alternatively spliced region. *J. Biol. Chem.* 271:25723–26
12. Farquhar M, Palade GE. 1963. Junctional complexes in various epithelia. *J. Cell Biol.* 17:375–412
13. Fujimoto K. 1995. Freeze-fracture replica electron microscopy combined with SDS digestion for cytochemical labeling of integral membrane proteins. Application to the immunogold labeling of intracellular junctional complexes. *J. Cell Sci.* 108:3443–49
14. Claude P. 1978. Morphological factors influencing transepithelial permeability: a model for the resistance of the zonula occludens. *J. Membr. Biol.* 39:219–32
15. Takeichi M. 1990. Cadherins: a molecular family important in selective cell-cell adhesion. *Annu. Rev. Biochem.* 59:237–52
16. Collins JE, Fleming TP. 1995. Epithelial differentiation in the mouse preimplantation embryo: making adhesive contacts for the first time. *Trends Biochem. Sci.* 20:307–12
17. Gumbiner B, Stevenson BR, Grimaldi A. 1988. The role of the cell adhesion molecule uvomorulin in the formation and maintenance of epithelial junctional complex. *J. Cell Biol.* 107:1575–87
18. Anderson JM, Balda MS, Fanning AS. 1993. The structure and regulation of tight junctions. *Curr. Opin. Cell Biol.* 5:772–76
19. Winkel GK, Ferguson JE, Takeichi M, Nuccitelli R. 1990. Activation of protein kinase C triggers premature compaction in the four-cell stage mouse embryo. *Dev. Biol.* 138:1–15
20. Balda MS, Gonzales-Mariscal L, Matter L, Contreras RG, Cereijido M, Anderson JM. 1993. Assembly of the tight junctions: the role of diacylglycerol. *J. Cell Biol.* 123:293–302
21. Rajasekaran AK, Hojo M, Huima T, Rodriguez-Boulan E. 1996. Catenin and zonula occludens-1 form a complex during early stages in the assembly of tight junctions. *J. Cell Biol.* 132:451–63
22. Itoh M, Nagafuchi A, Yonemura S, Kitani-Yasuda T, Tsukita S. 1993. The 220-kD protein colocalizing with cadherins in non-epithelial cells is identical to ZO-1, a tight junction-associated protein in epithelial cells; cDNA cloning and immunolocalization. *J. Cell Biol.* 121:491–502
23. Balda MS, Whitney JA, Flores C, Gonzalez S, Cereijido M, Matter K. 1996. Functional dissociation of paracellular permeability

and transepithelial electrical resistance and disruption of the apical-basolateral intramembrane diffusion barrier by expression of a mutant tight junction membrane protein. *J. Cell Biol.* 134:1031–49

24. McCarthy KM, Skare IB, Stankewich MD, Furuse M, Tsukita S, et al. 1996. Occludin is a functional component of the tight junction. *J. Cell Sci.* 109:2287–98

25. Wong V, Gumbiner BM. 1997. A synthetic peptide corresponding to the extracellular domain of occludin perturbs the tight junction permeability barrier. *J. Cell Biol.* 136:399–409

26. Ando-Akatsuka Y, Saitou M, Hirase T, Kishi M, Sakakibara A, et al. 1996. Interspecies diversity of the occludin sequence: cDNA cloning of human, mouse, dog, and rat-kangaroo homologues. *J. Cell Biol.* 133:43–47

27. Van Itallie CM, Anderson JM. 1997. Occludin confers adhesiveness when expressed in fibroblasts. *J. Cell Sci.* 110:1113–21

28. Kachar B, Pinto da Silva P. 1981. Rapid massive assembly of tight junction strands. *Science* 213:541–44

29. Aaku-Saraste E, Hellwig A, Huttner WB. 1996. Loss of occludin and functional tight junctions, but not ZO-1, during neural tube closure—remodeling of the neuroepithelium prior to neurogenesis. *Dev. Biol.* 180:664–79

30. Furuse M, Fujimoto K, Sato N, Hirase T, Tsukita S. 1996. Overexpression of occludin, a tight junction-associated integral membrane protein, induces the formation of intracellular multilamellar bodies bearing tight junction-like structures. *J. Cell Sci.* 109:429–35

31. Staehlin LA. 1974. Structure and function of intracellular junctions. *Int. Rev. Cytol.* 39:191–282

32. Van Deurs B, Luft JH. 1979. Effects of gluteraldehyde fixation on the structure of tight junctions. *J. Ultrastruct. Res.* 68:160–72

33. Dragsten PR, Blumenthal R, Handler JS. 1981. Membrane asymmetry in epithelia: Is the tight junction a barrier to diffusion in the plasma membrane? *Nature* 294:718–22

34. Jesaitis LA, Goodenough DA. 1994. Molecular characterization and tissue distribution of ZO-2, a tight junction protein homologous to ZO-1 and the *Drosophila* discs-large tumor suppressor protein. *J. Cell Biol.* 124:949–61

35. Furuse M, Itoh M, Hirase T, Nagafuchi F, Yonemura S, Tsukita S. 1994. Direct association between occludin and ZO-1 and its possible involvement in the localization of occludin at tight junctions. *J. Cell Biol.* 127:1617–26

36. Schnabel E, Anderson JM, Farquhar MG. 1990. The tight junction protein ZO-1 is concentrated along slit diaphragms of the glomerular epithelium. *J. Cell Biol.* 111:1255–64

37. Stevenson BR, Haskins J, Hibbard J, Tamber M, Weber D. 1996. P130 is homologous to ZO-1 and ZO-2 and is a novel member of the MAGUK family of proteins. *Mol. Biol. Cell. Suppl.* 7:605a

38. Cho K, Hunt CA, Kennedy MB. 1992. The rat brain postsynaptic density fraction contains a homolog of the *Drosophila* discs-large tumor suppressor protein. *Neuron* 9:929–42

39. Doyle DA, Lee A, Lewis J, Kim E, Sheng M, MacKinnon R. 1996. Crystal structure of a complexed and peptide-free membrane protein-binding domain: molecular basis of peptide recognition by PDZ. *Cell* 85:1067–76

40. Sheng M. 1996. PDZs and receptor/channel clustering: rounding up the latest suspects. *Neuron* 17:575–78

41. Kim E, Niethammer M, Rothschild A, Jan YN, Sheng S. 1995. Clustering of the Shaker-type K^+ channels by direct interaction with the PSD-95/SAP90 family of membrane-associated guanylate kinases. *Nature* 378:85–88

42. Kornau HC, Schenker LT, Kennedy MB, Seeburg PH. 1995. Domain interaction between NMDA receptor subunits and the postsynaptic density protein PSD-95. *Science* 269:1737–40

43. Tejedor FJ, Bokhari A, Rogero O, Gorczyca M, Zhang J, et al. 1997. Essential role for dlg in synaptic clustering of Shaker K^+ channels in vivo. *J. Neurosci.* 17:152–59

44. Balda MS, Anderson JM, Matter K. 1996. The SH3 domain of the tight junction protein ZO-1 binds to a serine protein kinase that phosphorylates a region C-terminal to this domain. *FEBS Lett.* 399:326–32

45. Kim E, Naisbitt S, Hsueh Y, Rao A, Rothschild A, et al. 1997. GKAP, a novel synaptic protein that interacts with the guanylate kinase-like domain of the PSD-95/SAP90 family of channel clustering molecules. *J. Cell Biol.* 136:669–78

46. Woods DF, Bryant PJ. 1991. The *discs-large* tumor suppressor gene of Drosophila encodes a guanylate kinase homolog localized at septate junctions. *Cell* 66:451–64

47. Hoskins R, Hajinal A, Harp S, Kim SK. 1995. The *C. elegans* vulval induction gene *lin-2* encodes a member of the MAGUK

family of cell junction proteins. *Development* 122:97–111

48. Simske JS, Kaech SM, Harp SA, Kim SK. 1996. LET-23 receptor localization by the cell junction protein LIN-7 during C. elegans vulval induction. *Cell* 85:195–204

49. Gottardi CJ, Arpin M, Fanning AS, Louvard D. 1996. The junction-associated protein, zonula occludens-1, localizes to the nucleus before the maturation and during the remodeling of cell-cell contacts. *Proc. Natl. Acad. Sci. USA* 93:10779–84

50. Takahisa M, Togashi S, Suzuki T, Kobayashi M, Murayama A, et al. 1996. The *Drosophila tamou* gene, a component of the activating pathway of extramacrochaetae expression, encodes a protein homologous to mammalian cell-cell junction-associated protein ZO-1. *Genes Dev.* 10:1783–95

51. Balda MS, Anderson JM. 1993. Two classes of tight junctions revealed by ZO-1 isoforms. *Am. J. Physiol.* 264:C918–24

52. Citi S, Sabannay H, Jakes R, Geiger B, Kendrich-Jones J. 1988. Cingulin, a new peripheral component of tight junctions. *Nature* 333:272–75

53. Zhong Y, Saitoh T, Minase T, Sawada N, Enomoto K, Mori M. 1993. Monoclonal antibody 7H6 reacts with a novel tight junction-associated protein distinct from ZO-1, cingulin and ZO-2. *J. Cell Biol.* 120:477–83

54. Zhong Y, Enomoto K, Tobioka H, Konishi Y, Satoh M, Mori M. 1994. Sequential decrease in tight junctions as revealed by 7H6 tight junction-associated protein during rat hepatocarcinogenesis. *Jpn. J. Cancer Res.* 85:351–56

55. Ezoe E, Kokai Y, Konishi Y, Kuwahara K, Zhong Y, et al. 1995. Isolation of cDNA encoding 7H6-reactive polypeptide defines a new class of protein with α-helical coiled-coil structure and DA-box similar to yeast chromosomal segregation proteins. *Tumor Res.* 30:21–36

56. Keon BH, Schafer S, Kuhn C, Grund C, Franke WW. 1996. Symplekin, a novel type of tight junction plaque protein. *J. Cell Biol.* 134:1003–18

57. Peifer M. 1997. B-catenin as oncogene: the smoking gun. *Science* 275:1752–53

58. Kapprell H, Duden R, Owaribe K, Schmelz M, Franke WW, et al. 1990. Subplasmalemmal plaques of intercellular junctions: common and distinguishing proteins. In *Morphoregulatory Molecules,* ed. GM Edelman, BA Cunningham, JP Thiery, pp. 285–314. New York: Wiley & Sons

59. Stevenson BR, Heintzelman MB, Anderson JM, Citi S, Mooseker MS. 1989. ZO-1

and cingulin: tight junction proteins with distinct identities and localizations. *Am. J. Physiol.* 257:C621–28

60. Hirokawa N, Tilney LG. 1982. Interactions between actin filaments and between actin filaments and membranes in quick-frozen and deeply etched hair cells of the chick ear. *J. Cell Biol.* 95:249–61

61. Balda MS, Gonzalez-Mariscal L, Contreras RG, Macias-Silva M, Torres-Marquez ME, et al. 1991. Assembly and sealing of tight junctions: possible participation of G-proteins, phospholipase C, protein kinase C and calmodulin. *J. Membr. Biol.* 122:193–202

62. Madara JL, Parkos C, Colgan S, Nusrat A, Atisook K, et al. 1992. The movement of solutes and cells across tight junctions. *Ann. NY Acad. Sci.* 664:47–60

63. Mooseker M. 1985. Organization, chemistry and assembly of the cytoskeletal apparatus of the intestinal brush border. *Annu. Rev. Cell Biol.* 1:209–41

64. Rodewald RS, Newman SB, Karnovsky MJ. 1976. Contraction of isolated brush borders from the intestinal epithelium. *J. Cell Biol.* 70:541–54

65. Hecht G, Pestic L, Nikcevic G, Koutsouris A, Tripuraneni J, et al. 1996. Expression of the catalytic domain of myosin light chain kinase increases paracellular permeability. *Am. J. Physiol.* 271:C1678–84

66. Yamaguchi Y, Dalle-Molle E, Hardison WGM. 1991. Vasopressin and A23187 stimulate phosphorylation of myosin light chain in isolated rat hepatocytes. *Am. J. Physiol.* 261:G312–19

67. Tsuneo K, Brauneis U, Gatmaitan Z, Arias I. 1991. Extracellular ATP, intracellular calcium and canalicular contraction in rat hepatocyte doublets. *Hepatology* 14:640–47

68. Ridley AJ. 1996. Rho: theme and variations. *Curr. Biol.* 6:1256–64

69. Zahraoui A, Joberty G, Arpin M, Fontaine JJ, Hellio R, et al. 1994. A small rab GTPase is distributed in cytoplasmic vesicles in non-polarized cells but colocalized with the tight junction marker ZO-1 in polarized epithelial cells. *J. Cell Biol.* 124:101–15

70. Weber E, Berta G, Tousson A, St. John P, Gree MW, et al. 1994. Expression and polarization of a Rab3 isoform in epithelial cells. *J. Cell Biol.* 125:583–94

71. Balda MS, Fallon MB, Van Itallie CM, Anderson JM. 1992. Structure, function and pathophysiology of tight junctions in the gastrointestinal tract. In *Current Clinical Perspectives in Gastroenterology,* ed. IM Modlin, pp. 311–22. New Haven: Yale J. Biol. Med.

72. Denker BM, Saha C, Khawaja S, Nigam SK. 1996. Involvement of a heterotrimeric G protein alpha subunit in tight junction biogenesis. *J. Biol. Chem.* 271:25750–53

73. Tsukita S, Itoh M, Nagafuchi A, Yonemura S. 1993. Submembranous junctional plaque proteins include potential tumor suppressor molecules. *J. Cell Biol.* 123:1049–53

74. Reynolds AB, Daniel J, McCrea PD, Wheelock MJ, Wu J, Zhang Z. 1994. Identification of a new catenin: the tyrosine kinase substrate p120^{cas} associates with E-cadherin complexes. *Mol. Cell. Biol.* 14:8333–42

75. Dodane V, Kachar B. 1996. Identification of isoforms of G proteins and PKC that colocalize with tight junctions. *J. Membr. Biol.* 149:199–209

76. Staddon JM, Herrenknecht K, Smales C, Rubin LL. 1995. Evidence that tyrosine phosphorylation may increase tight junction permeability. *J. Cell Sci.* 108:609–19

77. Hadari YR, Geiger B, Nadiv O, Sabany I, Roberts CT Jr, et al. 1993. Hepatic tyrosine-phosphorylated proteins identified and localized following in vivo inhibition of protein tyrosine phosphatases: effects of H_2O_2 and vanadate administration into rat livers. *Mol. Cell. Endocrinol.* 97:9–17

Annu. Rev. Physiol. 1998. 60:143–59

REGULATION OF THE MOVEMENT OF SOLUTES ACROSS TIGHT JUNCTIONS

James L. Madara

Department of Pathology and Laboratory Medicine, Emory University School of Medicine, Atlanta, Georgia 30322

KEY WORDS: tight junctions, permeability, cytoskeleton, epithelia

-----

ABSTRACT

The intercellular tight junction is the rate-limiting barrier in the paracellular pathway for permeation by ions and larger solutes. A variety of widely used electrical and flux approaches are used in the analyses of solute permeation through this pathway; however, each has limitations in practice. It is now clear that solute permeation across tight junctions is dynamically regulated by intracellular events with a common effector mechanism apparently tied to the cytoskeleton. These pathways, which regulate tight junction solute permeability, are targets that produce epithelial barrier dysfunction in a variety of disease states. However, regulation of solute permeation across the junctional barrier may also represent a potential means to improve bioavailability of orally administered bioactive solutes.

INTRODUCTION

Solute transport across monolayers of columnar epithelia in vivo is often quantitatively astounding. The human intestine particularly exemplifies this. For example, consumption of meals and the subsequent osmotic equilibration of this intake in the proximal small intestine, coupled with endogenous secretions of hepatobiliary, gastroduodenal, pancreatic, and salivary origins, result in the delivery of approximately 9 liters of isosmotic fluid daily to this organ. Approximately 90% of this volume is absorbed over the small intestine surface, which correcting for surface amplifications, including villous projections and

0066-4278/98/0315-0143$08.00

microvilli on individual cells, has a surface area of $\approx 2 \times 10^6$ cm^2. Because ≈ 1 liter of fluid that passes the ileocecal valve and enters the colon remains essentially isosmotic, it follows that a vast solute transport occurs across this epithelium. Not only must the intestinal epithelium support such solute transport to assure nutrition, but it must perform this function while simultaneously serving as a barrier restricting free diffusion of potentially noxious environmental molecules.

Historically, a simplified view of this absorptive process was that transcellular movement of nutrients and water via specific pumps, transporters, and channels would account for absorption, while an impermeable tight junction seal adjoining epithelial cells would provide for the requisite barrier function (the biophysical nature of lipid bilayers is such that passive movement of hydrophilic solutes across the transcellular pathway is highly restricted). However, it has become increasingly clear that transjunctional solute movement does occur, that it occurs in a regulated fashion, and that its regulation in certain states may be coupled to transcellular absorptive events. Thus epithelial solute transport and tight junction barrier function cannot be viewed as separate unrelated events, but rather as activities displaying coordinated interplay. This chapter discusses the principles of movement of hydrophilic solutes across tight junctions in qualitative terms. Although the focus is on the intestine, we draw on principles derived from a host of other natural and cultured epithelia.

METHODS TO ANALYZE TIGHT JUNCTION SOLUTE TRANSPORT

Methods to analyze tight junctions solute transport have recently been reviewed by Reuss (1) and Clausen (2). Because these methods are routinely and widely applied in cell biology and medical literature as assays of tight junction permeability, we discuss them here in general conceptual terms rather than in formalized biophysical terms. More biophysical explanations of these methods can be found in other reviews (1–3). Additionally, our discussion centers largely on approaches that can be readily applied to epithelial monolayers and do not require specialized skills such as microelectrode techniques. Analyses of approaches utilizing intracellular recordings are well described elsewhere (1–3).

Measurements of Resistance (Direct Current)

Analysis of transepithelial resistance to passive ion flow relies on simplified equivalent circuit models of epithelia, such as those shown in Figure 1. Such circuit models view the epithelium as a parallel circuit consisting of paracellular and transcellular pathways. In turn, each of these pathways is composed

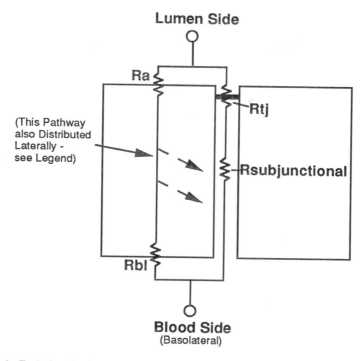

Lumen Side

(This Pathway also Distributed Laterally - see Legend)

Ra

Rtj

Rsubjunctional

Rbl

Blood Side
(Basolateral)

Figure 1   Equivalent circuit model of an epithelium. Two polarized epithelial cells (*rectangles*) are joined apically by a *dark line* representing the circumferential continuous tight junction. The circuit contains two parallel resistive arms. The paracellular arm consists of a tight junction resistance (Rtj) in series with a subjunctional lateral space resistance (Rsubjunctional). Although the resistance of the subjunctional space is often considered minimal in comparison with that of the tight junction, under certain circumstances (where Rtj is low and/or the paracellular space is collapsed as it is when epithelial cells swell), Rsubjunctional may even be dominant. The transcellular arm of the circuit consists of an apical membrane resistance (Ra) in series with a basolateral membrane resistance (Rbl). Rbl will also be distributed, meaning that portions of the current will exit cells along the lateral membrane and thus also be in series with portions of Rsubjunctional.

of resistors in a series: the transcellular pathway as the apical and basolateral membranes in series, and the paracellular pathway as the tight junction and subjunctional intercellular space in series. Cable analyses afforded by microelectrode impalement approaches, which permit assessment of apical, basolateral, and shunt resistances, support the equivalent circuit model shown as a reasonable approximation of the epithelium (4, 5). Because transepithelial resistance of many natural or model epithelia (small intestine, gall bladder, or cell lines such as MDCK and CaCO-2, etc) is small (60–250 ohm cm^2)

relative to usual resistances of biomembranes (>1000 ohm cm^2), variation in measured resistance values are often viewed in overly simplified terms as reflecting paracellular permeability. However this view is also simplified in general use: Because the tight junction is often rate limiting to paracellular solute movement, alterations in transepithelial resistance are often used as an index of tight junction permeability. Thus as used broadly in cell biological studies, a pulse of known amplitude is passed across the epithelium, the corresponding transepithelial voltage deflection is measured, and Ohm's law is used to calculate resistance, corrected for system and fluid resistance.

Although the above approach is useful in conjunction with others, several specific areas outlined below may potentially confound interpretation of such resistance measurements.

Transcellular Influences on Transepithelial Resistance May Be Substantial

Particularly in systems in which transepithelial resistance is greater than that outlined above, activation of membrane channels may lead to large changes in transepithelial resistance. For example, as neutrophils migrate across model intestinal epithelia, which exhibit baseline resistance values of $\approx 1{,}500$ ohm cm^2 (T84 cells) (6), alterations in transepithelial resistance occur that represent complex changes of resistance in both paracellular and transcellular pathways (7). Neutrophil migration across intercellular tight junctions, when occurring at high density (see below), alters junctional permeability as directly determined by analyses of flux of paracellular markers (below) and visualization of solute probes within the junction (8). However, neutrophils migrating across the epithelium also release 5′-AMP as a paracrine factor, which can be converted to adenosine by epithelial CD73. Adenosine is subsequently recognized by epithelial A2b receptors and, via a cAMP-dependent pathway, elicits electrogenic Cl secretion (9). Because this secretory response involves activation of apical Cl channels (and perhaps basolateral K channels) (10), a decrease in resistance due to alterations in transcellular resistance also occurs (7). This latter decrease in resistance, which is transcellular in origin, is several hundred ohm cm^2. Other manipulations that activate these channels but do not change paracellular solute movement also produce substantial decreases in resistance (10). Thus as exemplified by this model, a decrease in transepithelial resistance by itself does not equate with altered paracellular solute transport.

Circuit Models of Epithelial Monolayers

The above paracellular and transcellular components of resistance can be modeled as an equivalent electrical circuit (Figure 1). Given the low cytoplasmic resistance, the transcellular resistance is largely contributed by the two rate-limiting barriers to passive ion flow in this pathway (the apical and ba-solateral membranes in series). The paracellular pathway (shunt pathway) resistance is parallel to the transcellular arm of the equivalent circuit and is often viewed as dominantly reflecting resistance of the intercellular tight junc-tion because the tight junction appears rate limiting in the paracellular shunt pathway. However, even this view of the paracellular pathway is substantially oversimplified, as collapse of the subjunctional space, associated, for example, with an increase in cell volume, may substantially contribute to paracellular resistance, particularly if the junctional resistance is low (11). Collapse of the subjunctional intercellular space would also influence the resistance of the ba-solateral membrane of the transcellular pathway. Although the apical and basal portions of the membranes likely behave as simple series resistors, current ex-iting the lateral membrane could encounter an additional series resistance (the subjunctional intercellular space), and this additional resistance could vary de-pending on the length of intercellular space encountered. More quantitative analyses of these conceptual concerns in interpreting resistance measurements are well described elsewhere (3).

Monolayer Edge Effects

Work with epithelial sheets obtained from various species led investigators to realize that unless special precautions were taken, a significant component of passive paracellular ion flow could be related to artifactual damage of the edge associated with the crush induced by mounting mucosal sheets in the chamber. Such edge effects are usually neglected in studies of monolayers prepared from cultured intestinal epithelial cells, because monolayers are initially seeded on permeable supports that are pre-attached to a hemi-chamber, and thus edges are not crushed during chamber assembly. However, the nature of the resistance seal between the edge of the chamber and the monolayer under such condi-tions is not well understood. Visualization of stained monolayers suggests that (particularly when dealing with tissue culture–treated commercial supports) the monolayer extends 10 to 50 cell positions up the side of the chamber (J Madara, unpublished observations). Cells at the edge appear less columnar than those in the polarized monolayer. Furthermore, in selective surface biotinylation ex-periments, polarization of apically or basolaterally targeted membrane proteins appears to be significantly more complete if the edge of the monolayer is not included in the post-labeling lysate (12). Such observations suggest that either edge-related leakage of biotin and/or significant attenuation of the polarized phenotype (consistent with the morphologic appearance of the edge) are ar-tifacts associated with such edges. The growth of the epithelial monolayer a short distance along the edge of the well appears, by electrical assays, to provide an adequate electrical seal that does not influence electrical readings to a substantial degree (for example, altering the edge/surface ratio by using chamber-mounted filters varying in dimension appears to yield similar resistance values, consistent with the absence of significant edge effects; J Madara, unpublished observations).

Measurements of Impedance (Alternating Current)

If membrane capacitance is accounted for in an equivalent circuit model such as that shown in Figure 1, use of alternating current may permit more sensitive assignment of resistance values to parameters such as the tight junction and subjunctional paracellular space (2, 11). Because current interacts with such circuits in a frequency-dependent manner that can be resolved mathematically, accurate measurement of even low-resistance tight junction components should be possible. A major limitation of this approach, however, is to design a circuit model that accurately represents the monolayer studied, and it is difficult to do this without major uncertainties related to various problems, some of which are mentioned above. One approach to this problem is to subject a proposed circuit model and the impedance data obtained to an independent approach such as morphology (11). For example, if (a) substantial increases in basolateral membrane area (defined morphologically) correspond to expected increases in capacitance, if (b) alterations in junctional structure and solute flux correlate with changes in junctional resistance, and if (c) similar correlations are found with other components of the circuit, then the circuit model is considered a reasonable simplification of the tissue in hand (13). In essence, such approaches (although producing highly reproducible values) will yield data that are only as reliable as the proposed equivalent circuit is reflective of the epithelium studied.

Flux

When morphologically detectable tracers, which can be immobilized after tissue exposure, were utilized to examine the permeability of epithelia, these tracers were impeded from entering the paracellular space from the apical bathing solution (14). When applied basolaterally, such tracers freely permeated the subjunctional intercellular spaces but were again blocked from entering the lumen by the apical tight junction. A smaller undecapeptide, which can be similarly immobilized and visualized, and divalent cations, which can be precipitated and visualized, provided evidence that the tight junction was the rate-limiting barrier to passive transepithelial flux of inert solutes (14). Typically, only cruder forms of injury will result in detectable leak of macromolecules across tight junctions, whereas some movement of small peptides across tight junctions can be induced by physiological stimuli (Figure 2). Corresponding studies of transepithelial flux of hydrophilic solutes of varying hydrodynamic radii indicate that tight junctions are size selective (15). Thus analyses of transepithelial

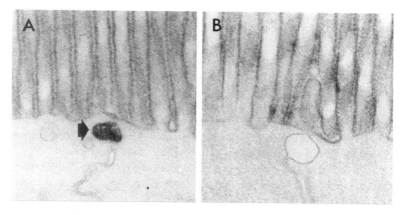

Figure 2   Electron micrographs of tight junctions of small intestinal absorptive cells that respond to activation of apical membrane Na^+-glucose cotransport with the appearance of intrajunctional dilatations and enhanced junctional permeability (see text). (*A*) Leakage of an 11–amino acid peptide, which can be fixed in place and localized by development of a reaction product into a dilatation, is indicated (*arrowhead*), but as shown in (*B*), a macromolecule (horseradish peroxidase) remains excluded from such dilatations ($\approx$x 45,000).

flux of inert solutes such as mannitol, inulin, and dextrans are widely utilized to determine the permeability characteristics of tight junctions (15, 16).

Analyses of solute movement across epithelial and endothelial tight junctions is often reported as a percent of tracer, which moves from one side of the epithelium to the other, rather than as an actual flux, which takes into account activity and is reported in units of mass area^{-1} time^{-1}. A general consideration of these approaches is useful to highlight the pitfall of percent tracer transfer measurements as they are now widely applied. If one places trace inulin ($\approx$5000 M_r; $\approx$11.5 Å radius) above a commercially available permeable support [e.g. a Costar device with an insert of a polycarbonate filter having 5 μm pores and with reservoir volumes as would occur in a 24-well plate ($\approx$1 ml basolaterally and $\approx$200 ul apically)], equilibration will occur over a period of $\approx$2 h. In numerous publications this approach has been used in the presence and absence of plated cells and, if the cell monolayer retards such equilibration substantially (>90%), it is concluded that a biophysically confluent monolayer is formed. However, as cell membranes have very restricted permeability to such tracers, the degree to which cells cover the surface area of the filter is the same degree to which the pathway available for diffusion from one chamber to another becomes restricted. Thus if fibroblasts, which do not form intercellular tight junctions, are grown as a monolayer in which the cells closely abut, the available open paracellular space for diffusion easily can be <95% of the area available on a blank filter. Judging by this criterion then, investigators could erroneously conclude that fibroblasts exhibit functional intercellular tight junctions. More reasonable evidence of biophysically confluent monolayers would be flux rates compatible with confluency (in the range of $nmoles^{-1}$ cm^{-2} for inulin) and size selectivity, including impermeability to macromolecules (confirmed by non-permeability at 18°C, a temperature at which transcytosis is blocked). In general, flux analyses across biophysically confluent monolayers for periods of 1 h result in transfer of a negligible percent of net tracer, and such experiments are ideally performed under conditions where both reservoirs are actively stirred in order that activities are uniform in the bathing solutions.

Consideration of the relationship between flux and resistance provides insight into which test of permeability might best apply to a given cultured epithelial monolayer. Routine analyses of resistance to passive ion flow essentially regard the tight junctions of single cells as individual resistances in parallel. Solutions for such parallel circuits reveal that components of low resistance can dominate the net resistance of such a circuit, even when these components are present at low frequency (Figure 3). In contrast, flux measurements are essentially the sum of fluxes across all junctional pathways (15, 16). As a result, the relationship between transepithelial resistance and solute flux is nonlinear. Given these considerations, one finds that, particularly at values of several hundred ohm

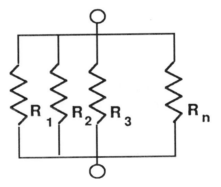

Figure 3   Model of epithelial tight junctions as a circuit of parallel resistors. To consider how total circuit resistance is influenced by a subpopulation of junctions of low resistance, one can substitute resistance values and frequencies for individual components (assuming there are 10 junctions each for R1, R2, and R3, and 70 junctions have the R_n value). In a uniform population of 100 junctions, each having a resistance of 10,000 ohm, the RT is 100 ohm. However if the 10 junctions of the R1 variety have a resistance of 1,000 ohm, RT now approaches half the former value ($\approx$50 ohm). Such considerations reinforce how minor populations of junctions can inordinately influence overall paracellular resistance and in so doing, confound structure-function analyses in a heterogeneous monolayer.

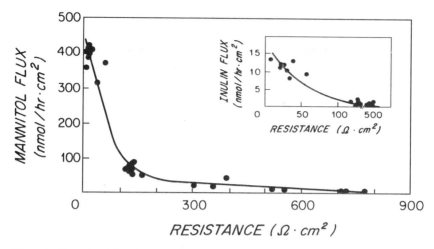

Figure 4   Example of the relationship between flux of a small inert paracellular marker (mannitol, hydrodynamic radius ≈3.6 Å) and transepithelial resistance during maturation of a polarized
columnar epithelial monolayer plated at confluent density. At low-resistance values, flux appears
a more reliable index of changes in junctional permeation. At high-resistance values, flux does
not sensitively measure the very subtle increments in monolayer resistance that might be related
to increased resistance in a minor (previously lower resistance) subpopulation of junctions that
dominate the electrical characteristics of the monolayer (see text).

per cm^2 and above, very small increments in junctional permeability may produce large decreases in resistance. Conversely, at low-resistance values (<200
ohm cm^2), as routinely measured by direct current techniques, relatively large
changes in transjunctional flux of hydrophilic solutes will often be associated
with very modest changes in transepithelial resistance (7). An example of this
relationship between resistance and flux of a paracellular marker is shown in
Figure 4. In low-resistance states, measurement of transepithelial resistance
may have exaggerated errors in systems now commonly applied to cultured
monolayers. For example, it is usual in the cell biology literature to measure
transepithelial resistance of monolayers in 24-well systems plated on permeable
supports. If the resistances of monolayers are high (>500 ohm cm^2), current
densities are likely to be uniform at the monolayer surface even with the low
reservoir volumes (≈200 μl) on the apical side and with the short distances from
apical bridges to the monolayer surface. In contrast, low-resistance monolayers
appear to have significant differences in readings related to the positioning of the
apical bridges, and such variances can influence reproducibility of resistance
values. For these reasons, it is helpful, when characterizing new monolayer
systems, to rely on resistance and flux values of symmetrical Ussing chambers

adapted for cultured cells. These chambers have the advantages of having fixed agar bridges that are distant from the monolayer surfaces and stirring of the solutions (the latter advantage is key for flux analyses). Measurements from simpler systems can then be judged against this standard.

GENERAL CORRELATES BETWEEN TIGHT JUNCTION STRUCTURE AND SOLUTE PERMEABILITY

Claude & Goodenough (18) first recognized a general positive relationship between resistance to passive ion flow and numbers of tight junction strands as revealed in freeze fracture replicas. Claude subsequently reported that as the numbers of tight junction strands increased, the transjunctional resistance values increased exponentially (19)—a finding that led to the suggestion that junctional pores fluctuate between closed and open states. Recently, Balda et al provided further indirect evidence that junctional pores (i.e. the sites of permeation in the otherwise tight seal of the junctional strand) are gated (20). This idea was utilized to explain data obtained from epithelia expressing COOH-terminal truncations of occludin, which suggested that in some states of regulation, junctional permeability to hydrophilic solutes could be enhanced in the absence of a change in junctional resistance. Thus it was suggested that while flux represents net movement of solute across a junction with several pores in series, resistance measurements are detecting a continuous series of pores that are synchronously in the open state across the width of the junction (Figure 5). Although the general relationship between strand number and resistance appears valid, it is now clear that this relationship (a) is likely complicated by considerations such as open probabilities of the permeable pores and (b) is further confounded by cell heterogeneity. For example, given the foregoing discussion it is clear that if an epithelial monolayer is composed of cells with two differing tight junctions, the most permeable phenotype will dominate the paracellular permeability characteristics of the overall monolayer (as judged by electrical assays) even if that phenotype is infrequent (Figure 3). Thus monolayers with two or more junctional phenotypes related to differing positions in the cell cycle in a clonal cell line might have junction permeability heterogeneity. Such features complicate the dissection of general structure/function correlates, although analyses of structural features in such heterogeneous systems using principles of circuit analyses support the relationship suggested by Claude & Goodenough.

Junctional strands, the sites of close membrane-membrane apposition (called kisses) within the tight junction, are the location of the transmembrane protein occludin. Recently, it was shown that a synthetic peptide corresponding to the extracellular domain of occludin is capable of enhancing tight junction permeability, thus verifying that occludin is likely involved in establishing the seal at

Lumen

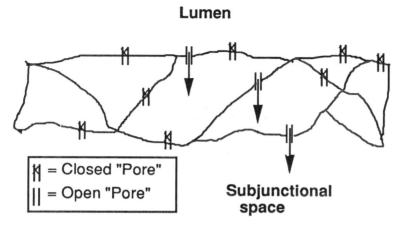

= Closed "Pore"

|| = Open "Pore"

**Subjunctional
space**

Figure 5 Diagrammatic representation of potential means of dissociation of resistance values from measured solute flux across tight junction strands, as proposed by Balda et al (20). The three open pores shown permit solute diffusion from the apical to subjunctional compartment and because a continuous channel is formed across the resistive component of the tight junction, an electrically detectable channel would result. However, if the pores open in a dysynchronous fashion, solute diffusion (which does not require temporal continuity of the transjunctional pathway) might dissociate from the electrical measurement (which would require temporal continuity of the transjunctional pathway).

the sites of junctional strands (22). Occludin, in turn, is linked to peripheral membrane proteins such as ZO-1, ZO-2, and cingulin. The tight junction is also enriched in cytoplasmic/membrane-associated proteins that typically control either vesicular trafficking (rab 13) or signal transduction (src). These specific junction-associated proteins are described in detail by L Mitic & JM Anderson in this volume. In general, the specific contributions of these proteins to junctional permeability is just beginning to be understood, and although evidence of events such as phosphorylation of specific junction-associated proteins are associated with alterations in junctional permeability under specific conditions, it is not yet clear if such changes represent cause-effect relationships.

REGULATION OF TIGHT JUNCTION SOLUTE TRANSPORT

Cytoskeletal Contributions

Aside from the potential for junctional permeability regulation via modulation of the specific junction-associated proteins (see above and L Mitic & JM Anderson, this volume), the influence of the actin-myosin II-based cytoskeleton also exists. Numerous second messenger pathways have been shown capable of influencing perijunctional cytoskeletal organization in concert with changes in junctional permeability (21, 23, 24). However, the changes often vary between specific cell types, and the agonists used to establish this principle were often not physiological.

The perijunctional actin-myosin II ring encircles the apical pole of polarized columnar epithelial cells, and the major interface of this ring with the lateral membrane occurs just below the tight junction at the adherens junction. Given that lateral tension appears capable of influencing tight junctions (25), it has been suggested that tension within the perijunctional actin-myosin II ring may influence solute permeation (24–27). The actin and myosin II filament alignment within the ring allows for contraction and, in fact, the ability of this ring to contract in isolated brush borders of enterocytes was demonstrated some 20 years ago (28). However, F-actin microfilaments projecting from the ring also interface at kiss sites within the tight junction (29) (Figure 6), thus allowing for more direct interactions between the rate-limiting permeability barrier within the junction and the F-actin-based cytoskeleton.

Control of cytoskeletal events by small GTPases rho, rac, and Cdc42 at the leading edge of serum-starved and repleted fibroblasts points to a role for these proteins in the signaling cascades that control dynamic F-actin rearrangement (30). The role of these small G proteins in polarized columnar epithelial cells has been less well studied because the tools used, including a bacterial-derived toxin (C3) that selectively ribosylates rho proteins and uncouples them from their effectors, are often difficult to apply to polarized cells. For example, the C3 toxin does not permeate membranes and thus must be microinjected. A recent strategy utilizing a chimeric toxin, which included a binding subunit that recognizes a cell surface receptor, has permitted uniform intracellular delivery of C3 to polarized monolayers of columnar epithelia (31). In these cells, the dominant influence of rho ribosylation is solation of apical F-actin, including that contained within the F-actin ring. These effects are in parallel with the loss of ZO-1 from the membrane at the site of the tight junction without effects on the distribution of underlying E-cadherin. In parallel, tight junction permeation of hydrophilic solutes occurs. Such data suggest that these crucial cytoskeletal regulatory proteins have a major influence on the structure of the perijunctional cytoskeleton in static polarized confluent monolayers (while having less influence on basal F-actin). Interestingly, the effectors of rho include kinase systems that influence actin-myosin interactions as well as F-actin interactions with the plasma membrane (32).

Evidence supporting physiological agonists that influence junctional permeation via probable effects on the cytoskeleton has also been found. For example, in response to histamine, the endothelial cells retract from each other and become round due to cytoskeletal tension brought about by phosphorylation of myosin light chain (33). Similarly, activation of the receptor for antidiuretic

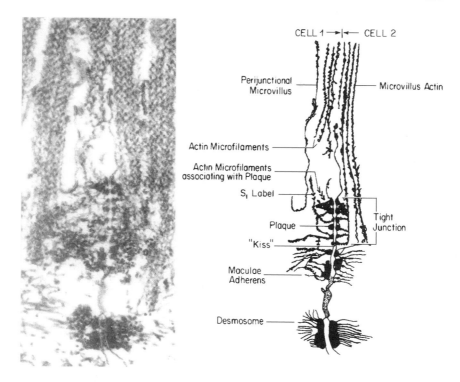

Figure 6   Electron micrograph (*left*) and labeled sketch (*right*) of naked cytoskeleton in a zone of an ideally sectioned absorptive-cell tight junction. Electron-dense plaques intimately associate with intrajunctional kisses on one side and with cytoskeletal elements on the other. Specifically, in sections unlabeled with S_1 actin probe, such cytoskeletal elements appear to be microfilaments (not shown), and in sections labeled with S_1 (shown), such microfilaments are shown to be actin microfilaments by characteristic arrowhead label due to S_1-actin association. $\approx$x115,000.

hormone by its physiological ligand produces a Ca^{2+} signal that is coupled to phosphorylation of myosin light chain and enhanced solute permeability of hepatocyte tight junctions (33). Lastly, activation of enterocyte Na^+-glucose cotransport similarly alters tight junction solute transport in association with condensation of the perijunctional actin-myosin II ring (11, 13). Overexpression of the transport protein (SGLT1) in cultured human intestinal epithelial cell lines permits recovery of this physiologically mediated alteration in junctional solute permeability and is also coupled to enhanced myosin light chain phosphorylation (J Turner, JL Madara, manuscript in preparation).

Other examples of physiological regulation of junctional solute permeability by physiological signals that are even less well understood include epidermal growth factor (34), hepatocyte growth factor (35), interferon-gamma (36), and insulin (37). The last two agonists are also coupled with alterations in perijunctional actin organization but occur over a much longer time course and appear to require new protein synthesis.

PATHOBIOLOGY OF TIGHT JUNCTION PERMEABILITY TO SOLUTES

Several disease-associated states have a pathobiology that effectively alters normal solute permeability of intercellular tight junctions. For example, a toxin derived from *Vibrio cholera*, termed ZO toxin or ZOT, appears to influence junctional solute permeation by influencing one of the second messenger pathways (PKC) previously shown to influence junctional permeation in specific cell types (38). Similarly, toxins derived from *Clostridium difficile* (Toxins A and B) cause profound alterations in tight junction solute permeability of enterocytes and do so in association with solation of the F-actin microfilaments of the perijunctional actin-myosin II ring (39, 40). Rho and the related proteins rac and Cdc42 are now recognized as targets for these latter toxins, which act by glucosylation and, similar to C3 toxin, uncouple these proteins from their effectors (32).

Physiological regulation of tight junction solute transport may also influence tissue pathophysiology in disease states. As discussed above, activation of SGLT1 by luminal glucose alters the permeability of enterocyte tight junctions such that small solutes, potentially including antigens, can cross into the subepithelial space more efficiently. Castro and colleagues (41) have recently shown that intestinal anaphylaxis due to oral challenge with antigen is markedly influenced by the inclusion of glucose with the orally administered antigen. Because inclusion of other sugars, which do not activate SGLT1 (or inclusion of SGLT1 inhibitors), ablates this response, it appears that this form of physiological regulation of junctional solute transport has pathophysiological consequences in certain settings.

Lastly, cell-cell interactions that commonly occur in pathological circumstances can also influence junctional solute permeability. For example, migration of neutrophils across epithelial or endothelial surfaces induces a reversible increase in tight junction permeability, presumably the direct consequence of perturbation of the structural barrier (42). Although the mechanisms underlying such alterations are not clear, studies performed on endothelial monolayers suggest that neutrophil contact with this cell type promotes a cytosolic Ca^{2+} signal that permissively opens junctions via a cytoskeleton-dependent event (43). In this view, the endothelial cell behaves cooperatively with the neutrophil in the transmigration event, and control of junctional permeation appears directly and actively regulated by the endothelial cell. It is not clear if similar events also occur in epithelia.

TIGHT JUNCTION SOLUTE PERMEATION AS A TARGET FOR DRUG DELIVERY

Better understanding of the mechanisms by which solute movement across tight junctions is regulated is of potential pharmacological significance. Orally administered reagents sometimes contain so-called barrier breakers—agents that transiently disrupt the epithelial barrier by nonspecific means (i.e. these epithelia possess attributes that permit rapid repair by flattening, spreading, and migration of individual epithelial cells). Using the same basic principle, junctional permeability can be transiently modified by more physiological means. Thus glucose-elicited activation of SGLT1 causes a reversible alteration in junctional solute permeability that has been utilized as a means for improving oral bioavailability of peptides, such as somatostatin analogues, which have been engineered to resist hepatic degradation by substitution of D-amino acids (44). Those approaches that build on understanding the mechanisms by which tight junction solute permeation is naturally regulated may provide insights into simple everyday problems, including improved bioavailability of orally administered drugs.

Visit the *Annual Reviews home page* at http://www.AnnualReviews.org.

Literature Cited

1. Reuss L. 1992. Tight junction permeability to ions and water. In *Tight Junctions*, ed. M Cereijido, 4:49–66. Boca Raton, FL: CRC Press
2. Clausen C. 1989. Impedance analysis in tight epithelia. *Meth. Enzymol.* 171:628–42
3. Stoddard JS, Reuss L. 1988. Voltage- and time-dependence of apical membrane conductance during current clamp in *Necturus* gallbladder epithelium. *J. Membr. Biol.* 103:91–96
4. Gordon LGM, Kottra G, Fromter E. 1989. Electrical impedance analysis of leaky epithelia: theory, techniques, and leak artifact problems. *Meth. Enzymol.* 171:642–65
5. Clausen C, Lewis SA, Diamond JM. 1979. Impedance analysis of a tight epithelium using a distributed resistance model. *Biophys. J.* 26:291–96
6. Dharmsathaphorn K, Madara JL. 1990. Established intestinal cell lines as model systems for electrolyte transport studies. In *Methods in Enzymology*, ed. S Fleisher, B Fleisher, 19:354–79. Orlando, FL: Academic

7. Parkos CA, Colgan SP, Delp C, Arnaout A, Madara JL. 1992. Neutrophil migration across a cultured epithelial monolayer elicits a biphasic resistance response representing sequential effects on transcellular and paracellular pathways. *J. Cell Biol.* 117:757–64
8. Nash S, Stafford J, Madara JL. 1987. Effects of polymorphonuclear leukocyte transmigration on the barrier function of cultured intestinal epithelial monolayers. *J. Clin. Invest.* 80:1104–13
9. Strohmeier GR, Reppert SM, Lencer WI, Madara JL. 1995. The A2b-adenosine receptor mediates cAMP responses to adenosine receptor agonists in human intestinal epithelia. *J. Biol. Chem.* 270:2387–94
10. Barrett K. 1993. Positive and negative regulation of chloride secretion in T84 cells. *Am. J. Physiol.* 265:C859–68
11. Pappenheimer J, Reiss KZ. 1987. Contribution of solvent drag through intercellular junctions to absorption of nutrients by the small intestine of the rat. *J. Membr. Biol.* 100:123–36

12. Gottardi CJ, Kaplan MJ. 1992. Cell surface biotinylation and the determination of epithelial membrane polarity. *J. Tissue Cult. Meth.* 14:173–80

13. Madara JL, Pappenheimer JR. 1987. The structural basis for physiological regulation of paracellular pathways in intestinal epithelia. *J. Membr. Biol.* 100:149–64

14. Madara JL, Trier JS. 1982. Structure and permeability of goblet cell tight junctions in rat small intestine. *J. Membr. Biol.* 66:145–57

15. van Os CH, de Jong MD, Slegers JFG. 1974. Dimensions of polar pathways through rabbit gallbladder epithelium. The effect of phloretin on nonelectrolyte permeability. *J. Membr. Biol.* 15:363–71

16. Moreno JH, Diamond JM. 1975. Nitrogenous cations as probes of permeation channels. *J. Membr. Biol.* 21:197–203

17. Madara JL, Dharmsathaphorn K. 1985. Occluding junction structure function relationships in a cultured epithelial monolayer. *J. Cell Biol.* 101:2124–33

18. Claude P, Goodenough DA. 1973. Fracture faces of zonulae occludents from "tight" and "leaky" epithelia. *J. Cell Biol.* 58:390–98

19. Claude P. 1978. Morphological factors influencing transepithelial permeability: a model for the resistance of the zonula occludens. *J. Membr. Biol.* 39:219–24

20. Balda MS, Whitney JA, Flores C, González S, Cereijido M, Matter K. 1996. Functional dissociation of paracellular permeability and transepithelial electrical resistance and disruption of the apical-basolateral intramembrane diffusion barrier by expression of a mutant tight junction protein. *J. Cell Biol.* 134:1031–49

21. Balda MS, Gonzáles-Mariscal L, Contreras RG, Macias-Silva M, Torres-Marquez ME, et al. 1991. Assembly and sealing of tight junctions: possible participation of G-proteins, phospholipase C, protein kinase C and calmodulin. *J. Membr. Biol.* 122:193–202

22. Wong V, Gumbiner BM. 1996. A synthetic peptide corresponding to the extracellular domain of occludin perturbs the tight junction permeability barrier. *J. Cell Biol.* 136:399–411

23. Balda MS, Gonzáles-Mariscal L, Matter K, Contreras RG, Cereijido M. 1993. Assembly of the tight junctions: the role of diacylglycerol. *J. Cell Biol.* 123:293–302

24. Madara JL, Parkos CA, Colgan SP, Nusrat A, Atisook K, et al, 1992. The movement of solutes and cells across tight junctions. *Ann. NY Acad. Sci.* 664:47–60

25. Pitelka DR, Taggart B. 1983. Mechanical tension induces lateral movement of intramembrane components of the tight junction: studies on mouse mammary cells in culture. *J. Cell Biol.* 96:606–12

26. Madara JL, Moore R, Carlson S. 1987. Alteration of intestinal tight junction structure and permeability by cytoskeletal contraction. *Am. J. Physiol.* 253:C854–61

27. Mooseker M. 1985. Organization, chemistry, and assembly of the cytoskeletal apparatus of the intestinal brush border. *Annu. Rev. Cell Biol.* 1:209–41

28. Rodewald RS, Newman SB, Karnovsky MJ. 1976. Contraction of isolated brush borders from the intestinal epithelium. *J. Cell Biol.* 70:541–54

29. Madara JL. 1987. Intestinal absorptive cell tight junctions are linked to the cytoskeleton. *Am. J. Physiol.* 253:C171–75

30. Hall A. 1994. Small GTP-binding proteins and the regulation of the actin cytoskeleton. *Annu. Rev. Cell Biol.* 10:31–51

31. Nusrat A, Giry M, Turner JR, Colgan SP, Parkos CA, et al. 1995. Rho regulates tight junctions and perijunctional actin organization in polarized epithelia. *Proc. Natl. Acad. Sci. USA* 92:10629–33

32. Aktories K . 1979. Bacterial toxins that target rho proteins. *J. Cell Biol.* 99:827–29

33. Lum H, Malik AB. 1994. Regulation of vascular endothelial barrier function. *Am. J. Physiol.* 267:L223–41

34. Van Italie CM, Balda MS, Anderson JM. 1995. Epidermal growth factor induces tyrosine phosphorylation and reorganization of the tight junction protein ZO-1 in A431 cells. *J. Cell Sci.* 108:1735–42

35. Nusrat A, Parkos CA, Bacarra AE, Godowski PJ, Delp-Archer C, et al. 1994. Hepatocyte growth factor/scatter factor effects on epithelia. *J. Clin. Invest.* 93:2056–65

36. Madara JL, Stafford J. 1989. Interferon-gamma directly affects barrier function of cultured intestinal epithelial monolayers. *J. Clin. Invest.* 83:724–27

37. McRoberts JA, Aranda R, Riley N, Kang H. 1990. Insulin regulates the paracellular permeability of cultured intestinal epithelial cell monolayers. *J. Clin. Invest.* 85:1127–34

38. Margaretten K, Ding X, Guandalini S, Comstock L, Goldblum SE. 1997. Zonula occludens toxin (ZOT) modulates tight junctions through protein kinase C-dependent actin reorganization, in vitro. *J. Clin. Invest.* In press

39. Hecht G, Pothoulakis C, LaMont T, Madara JL. 1988. *Clostridium difficile* toxin A perturbs cytoskeletal structure and tight

junction permeability of cultured human intestinal epithelial monolayers. *J. Clin. Invest.* 82:1516–24

40. Hecht G, Pothoulakis C, LaMont T, Madara JL. 1992. *Clostridium difficile* toxin B disrupts the barrier function of T84 monolayers. *Gastroenterology* 102:416–23

41. Zhang S, Castro G. 1992. Boosted mucosal immune responsiveness in the rat intestine by actively transported hexose. *Gastroenterology* 103:1162–66

42. Madara JL. 1994. Migration of neutrophils through epithelial monolayers. *Trends Cell Biol.* 4:4–7

43. Huang A, Manning JE, Bandak TM, Tataw MC, Hauser KR, et al. 1993. Endothelial cell cytosolic free calcium regulates neutrophil migration across monolayers of endothelial cells. *J. Cell. Biol.* 120:1371–80

44. Fricker G, Drewe J. 1995. Enteral absorption of octreotide: modulation of intestinal permeability by distinct carbohydrates. *J. Pharmacol. Exp. Ther.* 274:826–32

Annu. Rev. Physiol. 1998. 60:161–77

ROLE OF TIGHT JUNCTIONS IN ESTABLISHING AND MAINTAINING CELL POLARITY

Marcelino Cereijido, Jesús Valdés, Liora Shoshani, and Rubén G. Contreras

Center for Research and Advanced Studies, México D.F., México;
e-mail: mcereiji@fisio.cinvestav.mx

KEY WORDS: MDCK, epithelial cells, sorting, ion channels expression

ABSTRACT

The tight junction (TJ) is not randomly located on the cell membrane, but occupies a precise position at the outermost edge of the intercellular space and, therefore, is itself considered a polarized structure. This article reviews the most common experimental approaches for studying this relationship. We then discuss three main topics. (*a*) The mechanisms of polarization that operate regardless of the presence of TJs: We explore a variety of polarization mechanisms that operate at stages of the cell cycle in which TJs may be already established. (*b*) TJs and polarity as partners in highly dynamic processes: Polarity and TJs are steady state situations that may be drastically changed by a variety of signaling events. (*c*) Polarized distribution of membrane molecules that depend on TJs: This refers to molecules (mainly lipids) whose polarized distribution, although not the direct result of TJs, depends on these structures to maintain such distribution.

INTRODUCTION

Polarity and tight junctions (TJs) are the two fundamental features of the transporting phenotype. Polarity provides the necessary vectoriality for substances to be transported across epithelia toward or away from the lumen. TJs ensure that those substances do not diffuse back through the intercellular space. In the past, TJs were regarded as hermetic, and vectorial movement of substances

161

0066-4278/98/0315-0161$08.00

across epithelia was not considered to obey the laws of thermodynamics.[1] More recently, the use of Na-tracers has demonstrated that, in fact, the unidirectional fluxes of Na^+ may differ by a factor of 20 or more, even in the absence of an external driving force, and Koefoed-Johnsen & Ussing (55) proposed a model whose basic feature was the structural asymmetry of epithelial cells to account for such transport. In turn, it was found that the TJs of some epithelia may be highly leaky (8, 30, 100), but the TJ is still considered hermetic:[2] Its synthesis, structure, and physiological properties are not fully understood.

THE TIGHT JUNCTION

The TJ is a belt of anastomosing strands of proteins and lipids that surrounds the lateral membrane of epithelial cells and seals the outermost end of the intercellular space. For a further description, see the review by L Mitic and JM Anderson in this volume.

POLARITY

In a broad sense, polarity is not an exclusive feature of the cell membrane but is reflected in the position of the nucleus, the Golgi apparatus, microvilli, mitochondria, flagellae, dendrites, axons, microtubules, microfilaments, and the composition of the extracellular matrix, e.g. the basal lamina. However, this review is restricted to the polarity of the cell membrane. Actually, a certain degree of asymmetry, or at least regionality in the distribution of membrane components, is found in most cells, including some that do not have TJs. Thus neurons, spermatozoa, yeasts, skeletal muscle fibers, osteoclasts, and T cells have pumps, channels, carriers, and receptors, and some of them bud daughter cells and bind viruses in restricted domains of the membrane (6, 77, 92, 94, 111, 117).

EXPERIMENTAL APPROACHES TO STUDY THE RELATIONSHIP BETWEEN TJs AND POLARITY

Yeast budding is polarized, either in sites adjacent to the previous budding sites (axial budding pattern) or from the opposite end of the cell (bipolar budding pattern) in response to cues that are spatially and chronologically arranged in a hierarchy of mechanisms: (a) assembly of a signaling apparatus at the

---

[1] At the beginning of this century, when G Galeotti proposed that the electrical potential across the frog skin was due to a higher Na^+ permeability in the inward than in the outward direction, it was argued that such asymmetry would be in violation of the laws of thermodynamics (16, 18).

[2] The original meaning of hermetic, refers to Hermes Trimegistus, the Greek name for the Egyptian god Thoth, founder of alchemy and other occult sciences, and is used to allude to something that remains obscure.

budding site to decode the cue; (*b*) reinforcement of the cue and assembly of the cytoskeleton; and (*c*) propagation of signals controlling the secretory pathway, the actin cables, and microtubules that convey the information to the cytoplasm (34). One of the main advantages offered by yeasts is that they can be easily mutated to individualize genes, such as *Rho1p, cdc24,* and *cdc28,* that participate in the different stages of polarization, acting, e.g., through cyclins, GTP-binding proteins, and protein kinases (33, 40, 56, 113, 129).

Transitions from fertilized egg throughout embryogenesis have been used to study the moment and circumstances in which cells activate a given gene, express specific molecules (e.g. ZO-1, cingulin, E-cadherin), assemble the cytoskeleton, and depend on signals derived from the extracellular matrix, adjacent cells, or remote cells that send growth and differentiation factors (for an extensive review, see 37). Embryogenesis has been used also to understand the steps leading to the expression of TJs and apical/basolateral polarity. The retinal pigment epithelium (RPE), unlike most epithelia, expresses Na^+,K^+-ATPase on the apical rather than basolateral plasma membrane (7, 50, 102) and is a valuable tool for investigating the mechanisms of distribution of this enzyme (65, 82).

Epithelial cells that are harvested and allowed to reaggregate in suspension culture may form closed follicles in which microvilli extend into the lumen, or inverted follicles in which the microvilli are oriented outward, depending on the culture medium used. In both configurations, the TJs separate the apical from the basolateral domain (21, 72, 73, 74, 75, 86, 87).

Cultured monolayers of established cell lines that resemble native epithelia express TJs and polarity (19, 20, 78, 99). When dissociated with trypsin-EDTA, the epithelial cells lose these features, which are recovered in a few hours when seeding is made at confluence, so cells do not have to divide to fill the area available for growing. These preparations offer several advantages: use of a single cell type; can be synchronized; provide a sufficient amount of cells for biochemical studies; easily mutated by changing experimental conditions (media composition, growth factors, extracellular matrix); and large monolayers amenable to measurement of transepithelial fluxes and electrical parameters. To some extent, these methods can also be applied to primary cultures, which offer the advantage that observations can be readily extrapolated to the tissue of origin.

Formation of TJs can be followed through the development of a transepithelial electrical resistance (TER) and through restriction to permeation of extracellular markers (3, 45). Changes in the surface area of apical and basolateral membrane domains can be gauged through changes in the electrical capacity (29, 54, 79, 80, 108). Polarization, in turn, is studied by specifically marking the molecules in a given pole with biotin-avidin (58), antibodies (14), ^{3}H-ouabain (17, 24), and lipid probes (124).

Cramer and coworkers (27, 28) have developed a model system, using cultured monolayers, to study migration of leukocytes through the space between the epithelial cells that involves the opening and resealing of TJs.

Ca^{2+} is one of many agents involved in synthesis and maintenance of TJs and apical/basolateral polarity. Cells plated at confluence and transferred to a calcium-free medium (42, 43), or maintained in a stirred medium without calcium (1, 38, 41, 47, 104, 110, 112, 125), do not polarize or make TJs. However, with the addition of Ca^{2+}, TJs form. Thus calcium is used as a tool (Ca-switch) to trigger both polarization and assembly and sealing of TJs (39, 66, 93).

Ca^{2+} is needed primarily on the extracellular side of the membrane (26, 45), probably to activate E-cadherins (48, 49, 53). During a Ca-switch, La^{3+} inhibits the influx of Ca^{2+} and prevents the increase of its cytosolic concentration, without affecting the sealing of TJs (Figure 1). Cd^{2+} blocks both Ca^{2+} entry and junction formation; however, it cannot trigger junction formation (26). The contact between neighboring cells promoted by Ca^{2+} activates a cascade of intracellular reactions, including phospholipase C (PLC), protein kinase C (PKC), and calmodulin (CaM) (2). Although the participation of PKC in the development of TJs and polarity is well documented (35, 79, 114), some controversy remains about the identity of the protein(s) phosphorylated by PKC (3, 22, 57, 116, 118). TJ assembly and sealing also involve a receptor mediated by two G proteins (2). These reactions are not limited to the establishment of TJs and polarization of membrane molecules, as they also participate in the expression of a variety of other cell-cell contacts (3, 90) and in rearrangement of the cytoskeleton (2, 12, 23).

Inhibitors of transcription and translation block the development of TJs and polarity, depending on when they are added (Figure 2). In some instances, however, protein synthesis is not necessary for restoration of polarized expression of certain specific proteins. Contreras et al (24) have shown that the polarized expression of Na^+,K^+-ATPase in newly plated MDCK cells is prevented by cycloheximide; however, these cells have an intracellular pool of Na^+,K^+-ATPase whose transfer to the plasma membrane depends on the synthesis of other peptide(s).

One of the problems in separating TJ formation from apical/basolateral polarization is that during differentiation, TJ development and apical/basolateral polarization occur simultaneously, and agents that impair the development of one will also block the expression of the other. However, there are significant exceptions. Thus proteolytic enzymes elicit the expression of TJs in HT29 cells (95, 96), and mutations of the basolateral and transcytosis signals impair the polarized distribution or the transcytosis of pIgG receptors without noticeable effects on the TJ (14, 15, 71). [The pIgG receptor has a sequence of amino acids

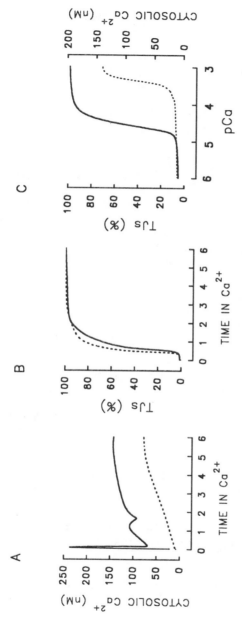

Figure 1 Ca^{2+} acts primarily at an extracellular site. (*A*) Before the Ca-switch, there is a low intracellular calcium concentration. With 1.8 mM Ca^{2+} the concentration rises to a peak, followed by a slow increase to control values (*full line*). The presence of La^{3+} suppresses the peak and markedly slows the increase of cytosolic Ca^{2+} (*dashed line*). (*B*) Time course of TJ sealing following a Ca-switch, in the absence and presence of La^{3+}. Junctions seal in spite of the low cytosolic Ca^{2+} concentration. (*C*) Junctional sealing (*full line*) and cytosolic Ca^{2+} (*dashed line*) following a switch to the concentration of Ca^{2+} in the abscissa. At 0.1 mM Ca^{2+}, the cytosolic Ca^{2+} concentration is essentially the same as before the switch, but TJs are 60% sealed (26, 45).

A   B

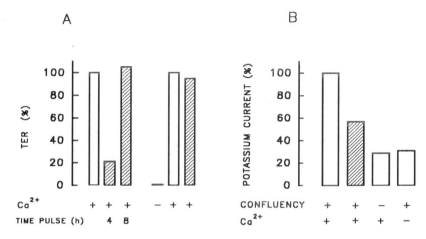

Figure 2   Dependence of tight junction formation and polarization on protein synthesis and Ca^{2+}. (A) Assembly and sealing of TJs is commonly gauged through the development of transepithelial electrical resistance (TER). MDCK cells plated at confluence ($t = 0$) and incubated for more than 15 h reach a maximum value of TER (first column). A pulse of cycloheximide between 2 and 4 h drastically reduces TER (second column). A similar pulse added between 6 and 8 h fails to inhibit the development of TER, suggesting that by this time, the necessary proteins are already synthesized (third column). Monolayers incubated for 20 h without Ca^{2+} do not develop TER (fourth column), but TER reaches a maximum value in 4 h of being transferred to 1.8 mM Ca^{2+} (fifth column) (Ca-switch). The increase in TER following the Ca-switch is not inhibited by cycloheximide (sixth column), which suggests that calcium acts mainly in the last steps of junction formation (17, 44). (B) MDCK cells express K^+ channels in a polarized manner: four types in the apical domain and a fifth in the basolateral domain. These channels are lost upon harvesting with trypsin-EGTA but recovered 8–15 h after plating at confluence (first column). Recovery is less in the absence of cell-cell contacts (second column) or Ca^{2+} (third column). Cycloheximide partially inhibits recovery (fourth column) (97, 120). In A and B, cross-hatching indicates the presence of inhibitor.

that addresses the protein to the basolateral domain and another that is required to send the receptor to the opposite side of the cell (transcytosis).]

MECHANISMS OF POLARIZATION THAT OPERATE REGARDLESS OF THE PRESENCE OF TJs

Early in the studies of polarization, it was assumed that it depended on a sorting signal and an addressing mechanism. Today, for every conceivable mechanism of polarization, there is a clear example of a molecule that depends on it. A thorough review of these mechanisms and signals would not be possible in this article, so we provide only a few examples of each type (Figure 3).

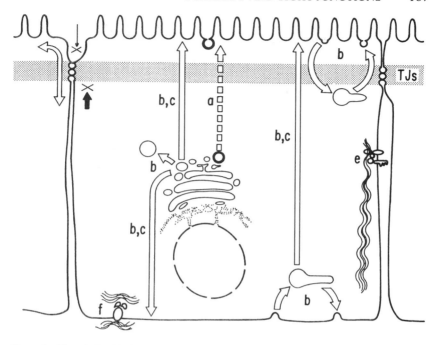

Figure 3 The relationship between TJs and polarity: epithelial cell in which the junctional belt (*dotted area*) separates the apical (*top*) from the basolateral (*bottom*) domain. Letters correspond to polarization mechanisms described in the text.

Anchorage to Glycosyl-Phosphatidylinositol (GPI)

GPI proteins are a class of glycoproteins whose extracellular domain is a polypeptide linked to a phosphatidic molecule of the membrane via an ethanolamine, a glycan, and an inositol. Lisanti et al (59, 60) have shown that GPI proteins owe their polarization to the fact that the lipid moiety is sorted in the *trans*-Golgi network (TGN) and addressed to the apical domain. Addition of a GPI signal to normally basolateral proteins, such as the G protein of the VSV virus, leads to its apical expression (10). GPI-anchored proteins appear to pack together to form lipid rafts in the TGN, which are then delivered to the apical membrane (reviewed in 105).

Other Addressing Signals

Basolateral delivery of numerous proteins depends on coated-pit related signals. These mechanisms are divided into two groups, depending on whether they are related to clathrin (69). For example, the proximal signal of the LDL receptor (68) and of the IgG Fc receptor are related to clathrin. These signals generally rely on a tyrosine residue or on a dileucine motif. Typical examples of coated-pit mechanisms unrelated to clathrin are the distal determinant of the LDL receptor (52, 71) and of transferrin receptor (14). Clustering of other proteins in the membrane occurs through the recognition of carbohydrate moieties by a sorting receptor (36) or, as mentioned above, through a cytosolic protein coat structure.

Default Polarization

Deletion of the tetrapeptide Lys-Asp-Glu-Leu in some proteins normally expressed in intracellular organelles results in their insertion in the plasma membrane or secretion (62, 67, 81, 88, 106).

Hierarchical Signaling

There is now clear evidence of overlapping signals or differential interpretation of the same cue. Thus the LDL and polyimmunoglobulin receptors are expressed on the basolateral membrane by a dominant signal related to clathrin. However, once these receptors are exposed to the basolateral milieu and bind their respective ligands (LD, IgG, or IgM), they are readdressed and transcytosed to the apical domain (70, 15). HA antigen of the influenza virus is sorted to the apical domain, but when a cysteine 543 is mutated to tyrosine, the protein is readdressed to the basolateral domain (9). This suggests either that the tyrosine becomes a basolateral signal that now dominates over the apical signal, or that wild-type HA is being sorted to the apical domain by a default mechanism (until the basolateral signal, tyrosine, is incorporated) (69). The latter interpretation is supported by the fact that few apical determinants have been characterized (see above). Furthermore, Thy-1, a GPI-anchored protein that is addressed to the apical domain, is still delivered there upon removal of the GPI, implying that it must have a second apical signal or that apical delivery is through a default mechanism (98).

Anchoring to the Cytoskeleton

Disruption of microtubules and microfilaments with drugs such as colchicine, nocodazole, and cytochalasin results in missorting or reduction of the degree of polarization of HA proteins of influenza virus, but does not interfere with the delivery of G protein from stomatitis virus to the basolateral surface (101, 107). In most epithelial cells, Na^+,K^+-ATPase is delivered almost exclusively to the basolateral membrane (46) and is retained there through anchoring to ankyrin and fodrin (76, 83, 84, 85, 126).

Interaction with the Extracellular Matrix or with Neighboring Cells

TJs can be formed between different types of epithelial cells (44). Likewise, the junction-associated molecule ZO-1 can be expressed at junctions between cells derived from dog Madin-Darby canine kidney (MDCK) or monkey (Ma104) epithelial cells (Figure 4 is available on the Annual Reviews site in the Supplementary Materials Section; http://www.AnnualReviews.org). On the contrary, MDCK cells express Na^+,K^+-ATPase and E-cadherin in the lateral membrane, provided these proteins are also expressed by the neighboring cell (Figure 4, see above). Intercalated cells (IC) from the collecting duct exist in two interconvertible forms: α-IC, which expresses H^+-ATPase in the apical domain and band 3 in the basolateral domain, and β-IC, which expresses the reversed polarity (109). Changes in pH induce the secretion of hensin, which becomes part of the extracellular matrix and can reverse the polarity of the α and β ICs (51, 119, 122).

Finally, there is clear evidence that some membrane proteins become polarized in the absence of TJs. Thus the newly plated human breast cancer cell line MCF-7, which expresses the antigen MAM-6 on the entire plasma membrane, reaches a 17:1 apical/basolateral polarization 2–6 h after plating, whereas TJs become evident only after 12–20 h (128).

DYNAMIC NATURE OF THE ROLE OF TJs IN EPITHELIAL CELL POLARITY

The cell membrane undergoes a continuous process of retrieval and restoration of molecules but does not randomize its components (91) nor perturb junctional sealing. In this respect, polarity and TJs should not be regarded as stable features, but as highly dynamic steady state configurations:

1. Binding of IgA or IgM to a membrane receptor (pIgR) located at the basolateral domain leads to receptor-ligand internalization followed by transcytosis to the apical membrane (15). In addition, the empty receptor is efficiently transcytosed, providing its serine-604 is phosphorylated (14).

2. Glucose, alanine, or leucine activate Na-cotransporters on the apical side of intestinal cells and elicit a decrease of the electrical resistance of the TJ, accompanied by the development of large dilatations between its strands (63; see review by JL Madara, this volume).

3. ADH triggers the incorporation of water channels in the apical membrane domain of renal collecting duct cells (11).

4. Intercalated cells retarget membrane domain markers in a pH/hensin-dependent manner (51, 119, 122; see above).

5. Leucine aminopeptidase is removed from the apical domain in MDCK cells and reinserted a few minutes later in the same domain (61).

6. The orientation of the apical and basolateral poles of cells in suspended follicles can be experimentally changed by adding serum, collagen, or hormones to the bathing medium. These changes are accompanied by large displacements of the TJ (21, 72, 73, 74, 86, 87).

7. TJs are retained during mitosis; thus cells in a mucosa proliferate, displace, and rearrange in the plane of the epithelium without breaking down its barrier function (5).

8. Additionally, TJs open and reseal to allow the passage of leukocytes during diapedesis (27, 28, 89).

9. TJs between Sertoli cells and between those cells and germ cells in seminiferous epithelium are sufficiently plastic to allow the transit of germ cells toward the lumen of seminiferous tubules without distorting the role of the blood-testis barrier (13).

10. Studies in the retinal pigment epithelium show that molecules such as Na^+,K^+-ATPase, spectrin, ankyrin, and antigen 5A11 polarize by moving at different times and even to opposite poles of the cell (103).

POLARIZED DISTRIBUTION OF MEMBRANE MOLECULES THAT DEPEND ON TJs

At the body temperature of mammals, the hydrophobic moiety of membrane lipids is in a liquid state, and in spite of strong hydrophilic bonds between polar groups and between the surrounding water, molecules can diffuse in the plane of the membrane. However, some lipid species are preferentially confined to a given membrane domain (32, 115, 121–124, 127). Lipid probes such as 5-[N-hexadecanoyl] amino fluorescein, 1-acyl-2-[N-4-nitrobenz-2-oxa-1, 3-diazole]aminocaproyl phosphatidylcholine, and gangliosides added to the apical membrane are unable to pass through the TJ. These molecules have a negligible flip-flopping rate. On the other hand, lipids that can readily flip-flop from the outer to the inner leaflet of the membrane (and back), such as 3, 3'-dihexacylin docarbocyanine iodide and 5-[N-dodecanoyl] aminofluorescein, are able to avoid the TJ and pass from the apical domain, where they were added, to the basolateral region. On this basis, the TJ is interpreted as a fence between the apical and the lateral domain of the outer leaflet only (31, 32).

As described by L Mitic and JM Anderson (this volume), occludin is probably the main protein constituent of the strands. Balda et al (4) found that MDCK cells expressing transfected chicken occludin, in addition to endogenous occludin, show a significant increase of transepithelial resistance (TER) and prevent the apical-to-lateral diffusion of the fluorescent probe BODIPY-FL-sphingomyelin. Cells transfected with C-terminally truncated occludin do not form a continuous junctional belt of occludin or ZO-1, as revealed by immunofluorescence staining of these TJ proteins. Nevertheless, these monolayers exhibit an increased value of TER, indicating that a continuous junctional distribution of occludin is not required for the formation of electrically tight epithelia. Interestingly, in spite of this increase in TER, monolayers of cells transfected with C-terminally truncated occludin were no longer capable of preventing diffusion of the lipid probe from the apical to the basolateral domain (4).

CONCLUSIONS: INFLUENCE OF TJs ON POLARITY, AND OF POLARITY ON TJs

The relationship between TJs and polarity was once thought to be simple: Transport proteins were synthesized and somehow delivered to a given plasma membrane domain, and the TJ was regarded as a fence preventing lateral diffusion and randomization. As summarized above, the picture is now far more complex because membrane molecules can achieve polarization and redistribute in spite of the presence of the TJ. However, the TJ has been confirmed as a barrier that restricts the mixing of some freely diffusing membrane molecules (see, for instance, 64). Ironically, its precise position at the apical/basolateral interface is the result of a polarized insertion of its components. The polarized location of TJs, in principle, serves two functions: (*a*) The obvious one is to meet in register (contact at very specific site) a moiety in the neighboring cell; and (*b*) some of the molecules within the TJ have strong homology with proteins known to participate in signal-transducing cascades; thus signaling events are triggered by TJ components at specific points of the cell surface. TJs and polarity are not static features of cells; rather they represent highly dynamic arrangements of molecules in the plasma membrane that are sensitive to the composition of the extracellular matrix, contacts with neighboring cells, growth and differentiation factors, hormones, pharmacological agents, and cell cycle stages.

ACKNOWLEDGMENTS

This work was supported by the National Research Council of México (CONACYT).

Literature Cited

1. Anderson JM, Van Itallie CM, Peterson MD, Stevenson BR, Carew EA, Mooseker MS. 1989. ZO-1 mRNA and protein expression during tight junction assembly in Caco-2 cells. *J. Cell Biol.* 109:1047–56

2. Balda MS, González-Mariscal L, Contreras RG, Macias-Silva M, Torres-Marquez ME, Garcia Sains JA, Cereijido M. 1991. Participation of a G-protein modulation system in the assembly and sealing of tight junctions. *J. Membr. Biol.* 122:193–202

3. Balda MS, González-Mariscal L, Matter K, Cereijido M, Anderson JM. 1993. Assembly of the tight junctions: the role of diacylglycerol. *J. Cell Biol.* 123:293–302

4. Balda MS, Whitney JA, Flores C, González S, Cereijido M, Matter K. 1996. Functional dissociation of paracellular permeability and electrical resistance and disruption of the apical-basolateral intramembrane diffusion barrier by expression of a mutant membrane protein of tight junctions. *J. Cell. Biol.* 134:1031–49

5. Baker J, Garrod D. 1993. Epithelial cells retain junctions during mitosis. *J. Cell Sci.* 104:415–25

6. Baron R, Neff L, Louvard D, Courtoy PJ. 1985. Cell mediated extracellular acidification and bone resorption: evidence for a low pH in resorbing lacunae and localization of a 100-kDa lysosomal membrane protein at the osteoclast ruffled border. *J. Cell Biol.* 101:2210–22

7. Bok D. 1982. Autoradiographic studies on the polarity of plasma membrane receptors in retinal pigment epithelial cells. In *The Structure of the Eye,* ed. J Hollyfield, pp. 247–56. New York: Elsevier-North Holland

8. Boulpaep EL, Seely JL. 1971. Electrophysiology of proximal and distal tubules in the autoperfused dog kidney. *Am. J. Physiol.* 221:1084–96

9. Brewer CB, Roth MG. 1991. A single amino acid change in the cytoplasmic domain alters the polarized delivery of influenza virus hemagglutinin. *J. Cell Biol.* 114:413–21

10. Brown DA, Cride B, Rose JK. 1989. Mechanism of membrane anchoring affects polarized expression of two proteins in MDCK cells. *Science* 245:1499–501

11. Brown D, Katsura T, Kawashima N, Verknon AS, Sabolic I. 1995. Cellular distribution of the aquaporins: a family of the water channel proteins. *Histochem. Cell. Biol.* 104:1–9

12. Burgstahler AD, Nathanson MH. 1995. NO modulates the apicolateral cytoskeleton of isolated hepatocytes by a PKC-dependent, cGMP-independent mechanism. *Am. J. Physiol.* 269:G789–99

13. Byers S, Pelletier RM. 1991. Sertoli-Sertoli cell tight junctions and the blood-testis barrier. In *Tight Junctions,* ed. M Cereijido, pp. 279–304. Boca Raton: CRC Press

14. Casanova JE, Apodaca G, Mostov KE. 1991. An autonomous signal for basolateral sorting in the cytoplasmic domain of the polymeric immunoglobulin receptor. *Cell* 66:65–75

15. Casanova JE, Breitfeld PP, Ross SA, Mostov KE. 1990. Phosphorylation of the polymeric immunoglobulin receptor required for its efficient transcytosis. *Science* 248:742–45

16. Cereijido M, ed. 1992. Evolution on the ideas of the tight junction. In *Tight Junctions,* pp. 1–13. Boca Raton: CRC Press

17. Cereijido M, Ehrenfeld J, Fernández-Castelo S, Meza I. 1981. Fluxes, junctions and blisters in cultured monolayers of epithelial cells. *Ann. NY Acad. Sci.* 372:422–41

18. Cereijido M, Ponce A, González-Mariscal L. 1989. Tight junctions and apical/basolateral polarity. *J. Membr. Biol.* 110:1–9

19. Cereijido M, Robbins ES, Dolan WJ, Rotunno CA, Sabatini DD. 1978. Polarized monolayers formed by epithelial cells on a permeable and translucent support. *J. Cell Biol.* 77:853–80

20. Cereijido M, Rotunno CA, Robbins ES, Sabatini D. 1978. Polarized epithelial membranes produced in vitro. In *Membrane Transport Processes,* ed. J Hoffman, pp. 433–61. New York: Raven

21. Chambard M, Gabrion J, Mauchamp J. 1981. Influence of collagen gel on the orientation of epithelial cell polarity: follicle formation from isolated thyroid cells and from preformed monolayers. *J. Cell Biol.* 91:157–66

22. Citi S, Denisenko N. 1995. Phosphorylation of the tight junction protein cingulin and the effects of protein kinase inhibitors and activators in MDCK epithelial cells. *J. Cell Sci.* 108:2917–26

23. Citi S, Volberg T, Bershadsky AD,

Denisenko N, Geiger B. 1994. Cytoskeletal involvement in the modulation of cell-cell junctions by the protein kinase inhibitor H-7. *J. Cell Sci.* 107:683–92

24. Contreras RG, Avila G, Gutiérrez C, Bolívar JJ, González-Mariscal L, et al. 1989. Repolarization of Na-K-pumps during establishment of epithelial monolayers. *Am. J. Physiol.* 257:C896–905

25. Deleted in proof

26. Contreras RG, Miller J, Zamora M, González-Mariscal L, Cereijido M. 1992. The interaction of calcium with the plasma membrane of epithelial (MDCK) cells during junction formation. *Am. J. Physiol.* 263:C313–18

27. Cramer EB. 1992. The ability of leucocytes to cross tight junctions. In *Tight Junctions,* ed. M Cereijido, pp. 321–36. Boca Raton: CRC Press

28. Cramer EB, Milks LC, Ojakian GK. 1980. Transepithelial migration of human neutrophils: an in vitro model system. *Proc. Natl. Acad. Sci. USA* 77:4069–73

29. Crowe WE, Ehrenfeld J, Brochiero E, Wills NK. 1995. Apical membrane sodium and chloride entry during osmotic swelling of renal (A6) epithelial cells. *J. Membr. Biol.* 144:81–91

30. Diamond JM. 1974. Tight and leaky junctions of epithelia. *Fed. Proc.* 33:2220–24

31. Dragsten PR, Blumenthal R, Handler JS. 1981. Membrane asymmetry in epithelia: is the tight junction a barrier to diffusion in plasma membrane? *Nature* 94:718–22

32. Dragsten PR, Handler JS, Blumenthal R. 1982. Fluorescent membrane probes and the mechanism of maintenance of cellular asymmetry in epithelia. *Fed. Proc.* 41:48–53

33. Drgonová J, Drgon T, Tanaka K, Kollár R, Chen G-C, et al. 1996. Rho1p, a yeast protein at the interface between cell polarization and morphogenesis. *Science* 272:277–79

34. Drubin DG, Nelson WJ. 1996. Origins of cell polarity. *Cell* 84:335–44

35. Ellis B, Schneeberger E, Rabito CA. 1992. Cellular variability in the development of tight junctions after activation of protein kinase C. *Am. J. Physiol.* 263:F293–300

36. Fiedler K, Simons K. 1995. The role of N-glycans in the secretory pathway. *Cell* 81:309–12

37. Fleming TP, Johnson MH. 1988. From egg to epithelium. *Annu. Rev. Cell Biol.* 4:459–85

38. Forte JG, Naus AH. 1963. Effects of calcium removal on bullfrog gastric mucosa. *Am. J. Physiol.* 205:631–37

39. Franchi E, Camatini M. 1985. Evidence that a Ca^{2+} chelator and calmodulin blocker interfere with the structure of inter-sertoli junctions. *Tissue Cell* 17:13–25

40. Gimeno CJ, Fink GR. 1992. The logic of cell division in the life cycle of yeast. *Science* 257:626

41. González-Mariscal L. 1992. Biosynthesis of the tight junction. In *Tight Junctions,* ed. M Cereijido, pp. 243–55. Boca Raton: CRC Press

42. González-Mariscal L, Borboa L, López-Vancell R, Beaty G, Cereijido M. 1985. Electrical properties of MDCK cells. In *Tissue Cultured in Epithelial Cells,* ed. M Taub, pp. 25–36. New York: Plenum

43. González-Mariscal L, Chávez de Ramírez B, Cereijido M. 1985. Tight junction formation in cultured epithelial cells (MDCK). *J. Membr. Biol.* 86:113–25

44. González-Mariscal L, Chávez de Ramírez B, Lazaro A, Cereijido M. 1989. Establishment of tight junction between cells from different animal species and different sealing capacities. *J. Membr. Biol.* 107:43–56

45. González-Mariscal L, Contreras RG, Bolívar JJ, Ponce A, Chávez de Ramírez B, Cereijido M. 1990. Role of calcium in tight junction formation between epithelial cells. *Am. J. Physiol.* 259:C978–86

46. Gottardi CJ, Caplan MJ. 1993. Delivery of Na^+,K^+-ATPase in polarized epithelial cells. *Science* 260:552–54

47. Griepp EB, Dolan WJ, Robbins ES, Sabatini DD. 1983. Participation of plasma membrane proteins in the formation of tight junctions by cultured epithelial cells. *J. Cell Biol.* 96:693–702

48. Gumbiner B, Simons K. 1986. A functional assay for proteins involved in establishing an epithelial occluding barrier: identification of an uvomorulin-like peptide. *J. Cell Biol.* 102:457–68

49. Gumbiner B, Stevenson B, Grimaldi A. 1988. The role of the cell adhesion molecule uvomorulin in the formation and maintenance of the epithelial junctional complex. *J. Cell Biol.* 107:1575–88

50. Gundersen D, Orlowski J, Rodríguez-Boulán E. 1991. Apical polarity of Na,K-ATPase in retinal pigment epithelium is linked to a reversal of the ankyrin-fodrin submembrane cytoskeleton. *J. Cell Biol.* 112:863–72

51. Hikita C, Takito J, Al-Awqati Q. 1995. Hensin, an ECM protein that reverses the polarity of band 3, is induced by cyclic AMP. *Mol. Biol. Cell* 65:401A

52. Hunziker W, Harter C, Matter K, Mellman I. 1991. Basolateral sorting in MDCK cells requires a distinct cytoplasmic determinant. *Cell* 66:907–20

53. Imhof BA, Vollmers HP, Goodman SL, Birchmeier W. 1983. Cell-cell interaction and polarity of epithelial cells: specific perturbation using a monoclonal antibody. *Cell* 35:667–75

54. Jovov B, Lewis SA, Crowe WE, Berg JR, Wills NK. 1994. Role of intracellular Ca^{2+} in modulation of tight junction resistance in A6 cells. *Am. J. Physiol.* 266:F775–84

55. Koefoed-Johnsen V, Ussing HH. 1958. The nature of the frog skin potential. *Acta Physiol. Scand.* 42:298–308

56. Kron SJ, Styles CA, Fink GR. 1994. Symmetric cell division in pseudohyphae of the yeast *Saccharomyces cerevisiae. Mol. Biol. Cell* 5:1003–22

57. Kurihara H, Anderson JM, Farquhar MG. 1995. Increased tyr phosphorylation of ZO-1 during modification of tight junctions between glomerular processes. *Am. J. Physiol.* 268:F514–24

58. Le Bivic A, Real FX, Rodríguez-Boulán E. 1989. Vectorial targeting of apical and basolateral plasma membrane proteins in a human adenocarcinoma epithelial cell line. *Proc. Natl. Acad. Sci. USA* 86:9313–17

59. Lisanti MP, Caras IW, Davitz MA, Rodríguez-Boulán E. 1989. A glycophospholipid membrane anchor acts as an apical targeting signal in polarized epithelial cells. *J. Cell Biol.* 109:2145–56

60. Lisanti MP, Sargiacomo M, Graeve L, Saltiel AR, Rodríguez-Boulán E. 1988. Polarized apical distribution of glycosyl-phosphatidylinositol-anchored proteins in a renal epithelial cell line. *Proc. Natl. Acad. Sci. USA* 88:9557–61

61. Louvard D. 1980. Apical membrane aminopeptidase appears at sites of cell-cell contact in cultured epithelial cells. *Proc. Natl. Acad. Sci. USA* 77:4132–36

62. Machamer CE, Rose JK. 1987. A specific transmembrane domain of a coronavirus E1 glycoprotein is required for its retention in the Golgi region. *J. Cell Biol.* 105:1205–14

63. Madara JL, Pappenheimer JR. 1987. Structural basis for physiological regulation of paracellular pathways in intestinal epithelia. *J. Membr. Biol.* 100:149–64

64. Mandel LJ, Bacallao R, Zampighi G. 1993. Uncoupling of the molecular "fence" and paracellular "gate" functions in epithelial tight junctions. *Nature* 361:552–55

65. Marrs JA, Anderson-Fisone C, Jeong MC, Cohen-Gould L, Zurzolo C, Nabi IR, et al. 1995. Plasticity in epithelial cell phenotype: modulation by the expression of different cell adhesion molecules. *J. Cell Biol.* 129:507–19

66. Martínez-Palomo A, Meza I, Beaty G, Cereijido M. 1980. Experimental modulation of occluding junctions in a cultured transporting epithelium. *J. Cell Biol.* 87:736–45

67. Matlin KS, Bainton D, Pesonen M, Genty N, Louvard D, Simons K. 1983. Transfer of a viral envelope glycoprotein from the apical to the basolateral plasma membrane of MDCK cells. I. Morphological evidence. *J. Cell Biol.* 97:627–37

68. Matter K, Hunzinker W, Mellman I. 1992. Basolateral sorting of LDL receptor in MDCK cells: The cytoplasmic domain contains two tyrosine-dependent targeting determinants. *Cell* 71:741–53

69. Matter K, Mellman I. 1994. Mechanisms of cell polarity: sorting and transport in epithelial cells. *Curr. Opin. Cell Biol.* 6:545–54

70. Matter K, Whitney JA, Yamamoto EM, Mellman I. 1993. Common signals control LDL receptor sorting in endosomes and the Golgi complex of MDCK cells. *Cell* 74:1053–64

71. Matter K, Yamamoto EM, Mellman I. 1994. Structural requirements and sequence motifs for polarized sorting and endocytosis of LDL and Fc receptors in MDCK cells. *J. Cell Biol.* 126:991–1006

72. Mauchamp J, Chambard M, Gabrion J, Verrier B. 1983. Polarized multicellular structures designed for the in vitro study of thyroid cell function and polarization. *Meth. Enzymol.* 98:477–86

73. Mauchamp J, Charrier B, Takasu N, Margotat A, Chambard M, Dumas D. 1979. Modulation by thyrotropin, prostaglandin E2 and catecholamines of sensitivity to acute stimulation in culture thyroid cells. In *Hormones and Cell Regulation*, ed. JE Dumont, J Nuñez, pp. 51–68. Amsterdam: North-Holland

74. Mauchamp J, Fayet G. 1974. Three-dimensional reorganization of thyroid cells in culture and iodide metabolism. *Endocrinol. Exp.* 8:170

75. Mauchamp J, Margotat A, Chambard M, Charrier B, Remy L, Michel-Bechet M. 1979. Polarity of three-dimensional structures derived from isolated hog thyroid cells in primary culture. *Cell Tissue Res.* 204:417–30

76. Mays RW, Beck KA, Nelson WJ. 1993. Organization and function of the cytoskeleton in polarized epithelial cells: a component of the protein sorting machinery. *Curr. Opin. Cell Biol.* 6:16–24

77. Miledi R. 1960. The acetylcholine sensitivity of frog muscle fibres after complete or partial denervation. *J. Physiol.* 151:1–23

78. Misfeldt DS, Hamamoto ST, Pitelka DR. 1976. Transepithelial transport in cell culture. *Proc. Natl. Acad. Sci. USA* 73:1212–16

79. Mullin JM, McGinn X. 1988. Effects of diacylglycerols on LLC-PK1 renal epithelia: similarity to phorbol ester tumor promoters. *J. Cell. Physiol.* 134:357–66

80. Mullin JM, Snock KV. 1990. Effect of tumor necrosis factor on epithelial tight junctions and transepithelial permeability. *Cancer Res.* 50:2172–76

81. Munro S, Pelham HR. 1987. A terminal signal prevents secretion of luminal ER proteins. *Cell* 48:899–907

82. Nabi IR, Mathews AP, Cohen-Gould L, Gundersen D, Rodríguez-Boulán E. 1993. Immortalization of polarized rat retinal pigment epithelium. *J. Cell Sci.* 104:37–49

83. Nelson WJ, Veshnock P. 1986. Dynamics of membrane-skeleton (fodrin) organization during the development of polarity in Madin-Darby canine kidney epithelial cells. *J. Cell Biol.* 103:1751–65

84. Nelson WJ, Veshnock P. 1987. Ankyrin binding to $(Na^+,K^+)ATPase$ and implications for the organization of membrane domains in polarized cells. *Nature* 328:533–35

85. Nelson WJ, Veshnock P. 1987. Modulation of fodrin (membrane skeleton) stability by cell-cell contact in Madin-Darby canine kidney epithelial cells. *J. Cell Biol.* 104:1527–37

86. Nitsch L, Wollman SH. 1980. Thyrotropin preparations are mitogenic for thyroid epithelial cells in follicles in suspension culture. *Proc. Natl. Acad. Sci. USA* 77:2743–47

87. Nitsch L, Wollman SH. 1980. Ultrastructure of intermediate stages in polarity reversal of thyroid epithelium in follicles in suspension culture. *J. Cell Biol.* 86:875–80

88. Pääbo S, Bhat BM, Wold WSM, Peterson PA. 1987. A short sequence in the COOH-terminus makes an adenovirus membrane glycoprotein a resident of the endoplasmic reticulum. *Cell* 50:311–17

89. Parkos CA, Colgan SP, Madara JL. 1994. Interactions of neutrophils with epithelial cells: lessons from the intestine. *J. Am. Soc. Nephrol.* 5:138–52

90. Pasdar M, Li Z, Chan H. 1995. Desmosome assembly and disassembly are regulated by reversible protein phosphorylation in cultured epithelial cells. *Cell Motil. Cytoskelet.* 30:108–21

91. Patzac A, Winkler H. 1986. Exocytic exposure and recycling of membrane antigens of chromafin granules: ultrastructure evaluation after immunolabeling. *J. Cell Biol.* 102:510–15

92. Peng I, Dennis JE, Rodríguez-Boulán E, Fishman DA. 1987. Epithelial polarity in presumptive myocardial cells. *J. Cell Biol.* 105:2043–51

93. Pitelka DR, Taggart BN, Hamamoto ST. 1983. Effects of extracellular calcium depletion on membrane topography and occluding junctions of mammary epithelial cells in culture. *J. Cell Biol.* 96:613–24

94. Poindexter JS. 1964. Biological properties and classification of the Caulobacter group. *Bacteriol. Rev.* 28:231–95

95. Polack-Charcon S. 1992. Proteases and the tight junction. In *Tight Junctions*, ed. M Cereijido, pp. 257–77. Boca Raton: CRC Press

96. Polack-Charcon S, Shoham JJ, Ben-Shaul Y. 1978. Junction formation in trypsinized cells of human adenocarcinoma cell line. *Exp. Cell Res.* 116:1–13

97. Ponce A, Bolívar JJ, Vega J, Cereijido M. 1991. Synthesis of plasma membrane and potassium channels in epithelial (MDCK) cells. *Cell. Physiol. Biochem.* 1:195–204

98. Powell SK, Lisanti MP, Rodríguez-Boulán EJ. 1991. Thy-1 expresses two signals for apical localization in epithelial cells. *Am. J. Physiol.* 260:C715–20

99. Rabito CA. 1986. Reassembly of the occluding junctions in a renal cell line with characteristics of proximal tubular cells. *Am. J. Physiol.* 250:F734–43

100. Reuss L. 1992. Tight junction permeability to ions and water. In *Tight Junctions*, ed. M Cereijido, pp. 49–66. Boca Raton: CRC Press

101. Rindler MJ, Ivanov IE, Sabatini DD. 1987. Microtubule-acting drugs lead to the nonpolarized delivery of the influenza hemagglutinin to the cell surface of polarized Madin-Darby canine kidney cells. *J. Cell Biol.* 104:231–41

102. Rizzolo LJ. 1990. The distribution of Na^+,K^+-ATPase in the retinal pigmented

epithelium from chicken embryo is polarized in vivo but not in primary cell culture. *Exp. Eye Res.* 51:435–46

103. Rizzolo LJ, Zhou S. 1995. The distribution of Na^+,K^+-ATPase and 5A11 antigen in apical microvilli of the retinal pigment epithelium is unrelated to α-spectrin. *J. Cell Sci.* 108:3623–33

104. Rodríguez-Boulan E, Paskiet KT, Sabatini DD. 1983. Assembly of enveloped viruses in Madin-Darby canine kidney cells: polarized budding from single attached cells and from clusters of cells in suspension. *J. Cell Biol.* 96:866–74

105. Rodríguez-Boulán E, Powell SK. 1992. Polarity of epithelial and neuronal cells. *Annu. Rev. Cell Biol.* 8:395–427

106. Rothman JE. 1987. Protein sorting by selective retention in the endoplasmic reticulum and Golgi stack. *Cell* 50:521–22

107. Salas P, Misek I, Vega-Salas DE, Gundersen D, Cereijido M, Rodríguez-Boulán E. 1986. Microtubules and actin filaments are not critically involved in the biogenesis of epithelial cell surface polarity. *J. Cell Biol.* 102:1853–67

108. Schneeberger EE, Lynch RD. 1992. Structure, function, and regulation of cellular tight junctions. *Am. J. Physiol.* 262:L647–61

109. Schwartz GJ, Barasch J, Al-Awqati Q. 1985. Plasticity of functional epithelial polarity. *Nature* 318:368–71

110. Sedar AW, Forte JG. 1964. Effects of calcium depletion on the junctional complex between oxyntic cells of gastric glands. *J. Cell Biol.* 22:173–88

111. Shapiro L. 1985. Generation of polarity during Caulobacter cell differentiation. *Annu. Rev. Cell Biol.* 1:173–207

112. Siliciano JD, Goodenough DA. 1988. Localization of the tight junction protein, ZO-1, is modulated by extracellular calcium and cell-cell contact in Madin-Darby canine kidney epithelial cells. *J. Cell Biol.* 107:2389–99

113. Simon MN, De Virgilio C, Souza B, Pringle JR, Abo A, Reed SI. 1995. Role of the Rho-family GTPase Cdc42 in yeast mating-pheromone signal pathway. *Nature* 376:702–5

114. Singer KL, Stevenson BR, Woo PL, Firestone GL. 1994. Relationship of serine/threonine phosphorylation/dephosphorylation signaling to glucocorticoid regulation of tight junction permeability and ZO-1 distribution in nontransformed mammary epithelial cells. *J. Biol. Chem.* 269:16108–15

115. Spiegel S, Blumenthal R, Fishman PH, Handler JS. 1985. Gangliosides do not move from apical to basolateral plasma membrane in cultured epithelial cells. *Biochim. Biophys. Acta* 821:310–18

116. Staddon JM, Herrenknecht K, Smales C, Rubin LL. 1995. Evidence that tyrosine phosphorylation may increase tight junction permeability. *J. Cell Sci.* 108:609–19

117. Stowers L, Yelon D, Berg LJ, Chant J. 1995. Regulation of the polarization of T cells toward antigen-presenting cells by Ras-related GTPase cdcC42. *Proc. Natl. Acad. Sci. USA* 92:5027–31

118. Stuart RO, Nigam SK. 1995. Regulated assembly of tight junctions by protein kinase C. *Proc. Natl. Acad. Sci. USA* 92:6072–76

119. Takito J, Hikita C, Al-Awqati Q. 1996. Hensin, a new collecting duct protein involved in the in vitro plasticity of intercalated cell polarity. *J. Clin. Invest.* 98:2324–31

120. Talavera D, Ponce A, Fiorentino R, González-Mariscal L, Contreras RG, Sánchez SH, et al. 1995. Expression of potassium channels in epithelial cells depends on calcium-activated cell-cell contacts. *J. Membr. Biol.* 143:219–26

121. Tournier JF, Lopez A, Gas N, Tocanne JF. 1989. The lateral motion of lipid molecules in the apical plasma membrane of endothelial cells is reversibly affected by the presence of cell junctions. *Exp. Cell Res.* 181:375–84

122. van Adelsberg J, Edwards JC, Takito J, Kiss B, Al-Awqati Q. 1994. An induced extracellular matrix protein reverses the polarity of Band 3 in intercalated epithelial cells. *Cell* 76:1053–61

123. van Meer G, Gumbiner B, Simons K. 1986. The tight junction does not allow lipid molecules to diffuse from one epithelial cell to the next. *Nature* 322:639–41

124. van Meer G, Simons K. 1986. The function of tight junctions in maintaining differences in lipid composition between the apical and the basolateral cell surface domains of MDCK cells. *EMBO J.* 5:1455–64

125. Vega-Salas DE, Salas PJI, Rodríguez-Boulán E. 1987. Modulation of the expression of an apical membrane protein of Madin-Darby canine kidney epithelial cells: Cell-cell interactions control the appearance of a novel intracellular storage compartment. *J. Cell Biol.* 104:1249–59

126. Wang AZ, Ojakian GK, Nelson WJ. 1990. Steps in the morphogenesis of a polarized

epithelium. *J. Cell Sci.* 95:137–51

127. Wong V, Gumbiner B. 1997. A synthetic peptide corresponding to the extracellular domain of occludin perturbs the tight junction permeability barrier. *J. Cell Biol.* 136:399–409

128. Zhao ZS, Leung T, Manser E, Lim L. 1995. Pheromone signalling in *Saccha-romyces cerevisiae* requires the small GTP-binding protein Cdc42 and its activator CDC24. *Mol. Cell. Biol.* 15:5246–57

129. Ziomek CA, Schulman S, Edidin M. 1980. Redistribution of membrane proteins in isolated mouse intestinal epithelial cells. *J. Cell Biol.* 86:849–57

Annu. Rev. Physiol. 1998. 60:179–97

CODEPENDENCE OF RENAL CALCIUM AND SODIUM TRANSPORT

Peter A. Friedman

Department of Pharmacology and Toxicology, Dartmouth Medical School, Hanover, New Hampshire 03755; e-mail: PAF@Dartmouth.Edu

KEY WORDS: calcium channels, Na^+/Ca^{2+} exchange, Na-Cl cotransport, hormones, electrophysiology

ABSTRACT

Calcium and sodium absorption by the kidney normally proceed in parallel. However, a number of physiological, pharmacological, pathological, and genetic conditions dissociate this relation. In each instance, the dissociation can be traced to the distal convoluted tubule, where calcium and sodium transport are inversely related. Based on the identification of the relevant sodium transporters in these cells and on analysis of the mechanism of calcium transport, an explanation for this inverse relation can be developed. Apical membrane calcium entry is mediated by voltage-sensitive calcium channels that are activated upon membrane hyperpolarization. Basolateral calcium efflux is effected primarily by Na^+/Ca^{2+} exchange. According to the model, inhibition of sodium entry through either the Na-Cl cotransporter or the Na^+ channel hyperpolarizes the cell, as does parathyroid hormone, thereby activating the calcium entry channel and increasing the driving force for diffusional entry. Membrane hyperpolarization also increases the driving force of calcium efflux through the Na^+/Ca^{2+} exchanger. Thus sodium-dependent changes of calcium transport are indirect and occur secondarily through effects on membrane voltage.

INTRODUCTION

Renal calcium and sodium absorption, as a whole, proceed in parallel with the excretion of sodium, accompanied by proportional changes of calcium (30, 31, 110, 118). The cellular mechanisms that underlie and account for this

179

0066-4278/98/0315-0179$08.00

pattern of parallel transport differ among the nephron segments primarily involved in calcium absorption, namely the proximal tubule and thick ascending limb of Henle's loop. In the distal nephron, which is the principal site of hormone and pharmacological regulation of renal calcium transport, sodium and calcium absorption are inversely related, with increases of one associated with decreases of the other. The goal of the present chapter is to review sodium-calcium interactions in proximal tubules and thick ascending limbs and to highlight recent progress in understanding distal calcium absorption and the cellular mechanisms responsible for the characteristic dissociation of calcium and sodium absorption.

PARALLEL CALCIUM AND SODIUM ABSORPTION BY PROXIMAL TUBULES AND THICK ASCENDING LIMBS

Proximal Tubules

The major part of calcium and sodium reabsorption occurs in proximal tubules. As noted above and covered elsewhere (30, 31, 110, 118), renal calcium and sodium absorption proceed in parallel under a variety of conditions. Such parallel excretion patterns stem primarily from the transport behavior of proximal tubules, where calcium permeability is high and absorption is largely passive (7, 16, 40, 85, 87, 101, 116). As sodium and fluid are absorbed during their passage through the proximal tubule, the concentration of calcium in the tubular fluid increases (110), thereby enhancing the driving force for its passive absorption. Solvent drag may also contribute to proximal calcium absorption (124). Additionally, tubular fluid traversing late proximal tubules contains more chloride than bicarbonate (96). Because proximal convoluted tubules are more permeable to chloride than to bicarbonate (8), the concentration differences for these anions result in a diffusion voltage that is oriented electropositive in the lumen with respect to the peritubular fluid (5). This positive voltage serves as an additional driving force for passive calcium absorption. In each instance, sodium absorption parallels that of calcium.

Careful analysis of calcium absorption by proximal convoluted tubules under experimental conditions, where the driving forces for passive calcium were eliminated, permitted the identification of a small, active absorptive calcium flux (11, 116). It is not known whether this represents net calcium absorption or the aggregate of individual calcium entry and exit steps as a manifestation of constitutive cellular activity and intracellular homeostasis.

Thick Ascending Limbs

Approximately 20–25% of the calcium initially filtered at the glomerulus is absorbed by medullary and cortical thick ascending limbs of Henle's loop (1, 10, 74, 86, 108). As in proximal tubules, basal, i.e. hormone-independent, calcium absorption is passive. However, the driving forces responsible for passive calcium transport in thick ascending limbs are established by a mechanism different from that in proximal tubules. Sodium absorption by thick limbs renders the tubule lumen electropositive with respect to the serosal or peritubular surface (Figure 1) (54, 55). Calcium permeability is high and the lumen-positive voltage drives calcium absorption between adjoining cells through the paracellular pathway (18). When sodium transport increases, the magnitude of

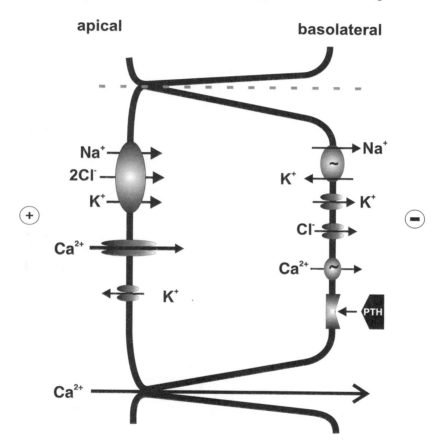

Figure 1   Model of calcium and sodium transport in thick ascending limb cells. The transepithelial voltage is oriented with the lumen electropositive with respect to the serosal surface. The paracellular pathway is denoted by the *dashed line*. Apical membrane sodium entry is mediated by the Na-K-2Cl cotransporter. Resting calcium absorption is passive, driven by the ambient transepithelial voltage through the paracellular pathway. PTH activates transcellular calcium absorption that involves entry through apical membrane calcium channels, followed by extrusion across basolateral plasma membranes. The latter process is probably mediated by a plasma membrane Ca^{2+}-ATPase (PMCA).

the lumen-positive voltage increases pari passu (56), thereby evoking parallel changes in the rate of calcium absorption (41). Conversely, decreases of sodium absorption are accompanied by reductions of the transepithelial voltage and are attended by decreases of calcium absorption.

In single mouse cortical ascending limbs, parathyroid hormone (PTH) stimulates active, cellular calcium absorption (41) under conditions where the electrochemical driving forces for passive transport were eliminated. Sodium absorption was not measured. Di Stefano et al, in contrast, found that under conditions of the ambient, spontaneous transepithelial voltage PTH enhanced both calcium and sodium absorption in mouse cortical thick ascending limbs (33).

DIVERGENT CALCIUM AND SODIUM ABSORPTION BY DISTAL TUBULES

In contrast to transport by proximal tubules and thick ascending limbs, calcium and sodium transport by the distal nephron are characterized by a reciprocal relation; increases of sodium absorption are accompanied by decreases of calcium absorption and conversely, decreases of sodium are attended by increases of calcium. Such reciprocity is apparent during saline loading, administration of thiazide diuretics or amiloride, hormone action by PTH, $1,25(OH)_2$ vitamin D_3, or mineralocorticoids, and in metabolic acidosis (112). Moreover, in each instance the dissociation of calcium and sodium transport is attributable to an alteration in calcium or sodium absorption within the distal nephron. However, the origin of this interaction remains uncertain and controversial. It is certain that the mechanisms and regulation of calcium and sodium absorption at these nephron sites are distinct from one another. The details of calcium and sodium transport by distal nephron segments have been individually and comprehensively surveyed (10, 17, 43, 65, 70, 109). The purpose of the remaining section is to examine the dynamic relations between sodium and calcium absorption in the distal nephron because they are notably interactive. However, before so embarking, a brief note regarding the topology of the distal nephron and an overview of the individual processes involved in sodium and calcium absorption is warranted because an appreciation of the interactive nature of the two processes is predicated on an understanding of the cellular transport mechanisms.

Organization of the Distal Nephron

The distal tubule, once considered a single structural entity, is now recognized to consist of three distinct nephron segments: the distal convoluted tubule per se, the connecting tubule, and the initial portion of the cortical collecting duct. Each has a unique cellular morphology and functional physiology. Distal convoluted tubules (DCT) begin shortly after the macula densa after an intervening segment that, based on the expression of the Na-K-2Cl cotransporter (58, 62), would appear to be an extension of the cortical thick ascending limb. The distal convoluted tubule (DCT) begins abruptly (114) and is formed of a single cell type: the DCT cell. In some nomenclatures, the DCT, which under conventional illumination has a bright appearance, is referred to as the DCT_b (68). The DCT is a short segment of ≈0.3–0.5 mm. In murine species and in humans, the DCT ends in a gradual transition to the connecting tubule (CNT) (69, 81). Recent morphological findings (2, 88) reveal considerable overlap in the expression of the Na-Cl cotransporter and Na^+/Ca^{2+} exchange at the transition of the distal convoluted tubule and connecting tubule in the rat. These findings were interpreted to indicate the presence of a distinct segment, referred to as DCT-2. In the rabbit, the DCT terminates abruptly (61, 81). Insofar as the connecting tubule has a granular appearance, due to the mixture of connecting tubule cells and intercalated cells (84), this segment has also been called the DCT_g. The third segment forming the distal nephron is the initial portion of the cortical collecting duct. It too is composed of two cell types, the principal cell and the intercalated cell.

Sodium Transport

All distal nephron segments are intimately involved in sodium absorption, although different transport mechanisms mediate entry across apical cell membranes: Na-Cl cotransport, conductive amiloride-sensitive Na^+ channels, and parallel Na^+/H^+ and Cl^-/base exchange. These different transport proteins are not uniformly distributed among distal nephron segments. In humans, and in the rat, mouse, and rabbit, the Na-Cl cotransporter is expressed predominantly in distal convoluted tubules (2, 88). The amiloride-sensitive Na^+ channel (ENaC) is also expressed in distal convoluted tubules, as well as in connecting and cortical collecting tubules (24, 25, 35).

Until recently, the specific mechanisms responsible for sodium absorption by distal convoluted tubules were unclear. Much of the uncertainty was a consequence of the complex tubular morphology, as described above, species differences, and the use of functional markers to localize putative transporters. With the recent molecular cloning and mapping of the Na-Cl (2, 57, 88, 91) and Na-K-2Cl (44, 59, 62) cotransporters, and the amiloride-sensitive epithelial Na channel (ENaC) (22, 23, 25, 100), a reasonable picture can now be drawn of the distribution of cellular sodium transport mechanisms along the distal tubule. Taken together, the preponderance of these results supports the view that the DCT exhibits three apical membrane sodium entry mechanisms: an Na-Cl cotransporter, an amiloride-sensitive sodium channel, and Na^+/H^+ exchange in parallel with and coupled to $Cl^-/HCOO^-$ exchange (35, 58, 119). At least half or more of the sodium entry is mediated by Na-Cl cotransport (50), with a correspondingly smaller portion sensitive to and inhibited by the sodium channel blocker, amiloride. The relative fraction of sodium entry mediated by these two proteins appears to differ between species.

Distal Calcium Absorption

The fundamental features of calcium absorption by distal convoluted tubules were characterized by a series of now classical micropuncture and microperfusion experiments (4, 27–29, 36, 38, 39, 45, 52, 75, 78, 85, 93, 111, 123). These studies revealed that the distal nephron is responsible for capturing 8–10% of the calcium filtered at the glomerulus (28, 52, 74). It was further deduced that since transepithelial calcium absorption occurred against an electrochemical gradient, it is metabolically active or dependent and proceeds by a cellular pathway in distal convoluted tubules (28, 29) and connecting tubules (60, 76). In these segments, passive calcium permeability is particularly low (43), and thus backleak from peritubular or interstitial fluid into the tubular lumen is negligible. With the establishment of calcium absorption as transcellular, attention was subsequently focused on defining the mechanisms responsible for apical membrane calcium entry and basolateral efflux. A variety of indirect studies implicated calcium channels in mediating calcium entry (63, 64, 72, 73, 77, 125). These investigations applied blockers of L-type calcium channels, such as dihydropyridine or phenylalkylamine-type inhibitors, to show that they suppressed calcium transport. More direct examination of the participation of calcium channels in mediating entry employed patch-clamp electrophysiological approaches. These studies (92) characterized calcium channels in freshly prepared or primary cultures of DCT cells isolated from the mouse (83), rabbit (92, 102), and the pig (77). Unfortunately, somewhat disparate findings, perhaps attributable to technical differences, preclude drawing a cohesive interpretation. Nonetheless, these studies generally report the presence of a modestly calcium-selective channel (83, 102) with a single-channel conductance ranging from 2 to 30 pS that was inhibited by a variety of inorganic and organic calcium channel blockers.

A defining characteristic of calcium transport in distal convoluted tubules is that PTH hyperpolarizes membrane voltage (48). This macroscopic voltage effect is recapitulated in the behavior of PTH on the calcium channels expressed in mouse DCT cells (83) and in apical membranes of rabbit connecting tubules (113). Different candidate channels may be responsible for hormone-stimulated apical membrane calcium influx. Definitive evidence that any one of these channels mediates calcium entry is lacking.

As noted above, renal sodium excretion normally parallels that of calcium. However, certain physiological (e.g. PTH), pharmacological (thiazide diuretics, amiloride), pathophysiological (phosphate depletion, adrenocortical insufficiency, metabolic acidosis), and genetic (Gitelman's syndrome) conditions reverse this relation. In each instance, calcium and sodium transport are dissociated in the distal convoluted tubule. These correlations suggest that, in the distal convoluted tubule, sodium and calcium absorption are linked. In principle, this linkage could have its origin in direct coupling through a cotransport or countertransport protein, or they could be functionally linked through an indirect mechanism. To uncover the origin of this dissociation, a number of studies examined the interdependence of distal calcium and sodium transport (28, 53, 103).

COUPLING BETWEEN SODIUM AND CALCIUM ABSORPTION

Na^+/Ca^{2+} Exchange

The most parsimonious mechanism by which sodium and calcium entry could be coupled would be through a common transporter. An obvious candidate for such a protein is the Na^+/Ca^{2+} exchanger (90). The exchanger may operate in several different modes: forward and reverse, as well as Ca^{2+}/Ca^{2+} and Na^+/Na^+ self-exchange (89, 95). In the forward direction, the exchanger mediates calcium efflux that is coupled to sodium influx. In this setting, the dissipative energy generated on Na^+ entry is coupled to Ca^{2+} extrusion (43, 90). The stoichiometry of this reaction is generally thought to involve the influx of three sodium ions in exchange for the extrusion of one calcium ion (97). However, other stoichiometries have been described (37). Ca^{2+}/Ca^{2+} self-exchange is catalyzed in an electroneutral fashion with a 1:1 stoichiometry, although the presence of monovalent cations potentiates the rate of exchange (79). The exchanger may also operate in a reverse mode, where calcium influx is coupled to sodium efflux. Such sodium-dependent calcium uptake has been demonstrated in Madin-Darby canine kidney (MDCK) cells (13–15, 106). As is evident from the following discussion, a preponderance of data support the view that the Na^+/Ca^{2+} exchanger is likely to operate in the forward mode in most calcium-absorbing cells under resting conditions.

The magnitude and direction of Na^+/Ca^{2+} exchange is dictated by the ambient electrochemical driving forces according to the following relation:

$$E_m\text{-}E_R = (nE_{Na} - 2E_{Ca})/(n - 2),$$

where E_m is the membrane voltage, E_R is the reversal potential, n is the number of moles of Na^+ exchanged for each mole of Ca^{2+}, and E_{Na} and E_{Ca} are the Nernst equilibrium potentials for Na^+ and Ca^{2+}, respectively.[1] When the membrane voltage (E_m) is greater than the reversal potential (E_R) for the exchanger

---

[1]$E_{Na} = RT/zF \ln (a^o_{Na} - a^i_{Na})$ and $E_{Ca} = RT/zF \ln (a^o_{Ca} - a^i_{Ca})$, where R is the gas constant, T the absolute temperature, F the Faraday constant, z the valence, and $a^o_x - a^i_x$ refer, respectively, to the extracellular and intracellular chemical activities of Na or Ca.

reaction, Na^+/Ca^{2+} exchange proceeds in the forward direction. The greater $\Delta(E_m\text{-}E_R)$, the greater the driving force for sodium-dependent calcium extrusion, i.e. forward Na^+/Ca^{2+} exchange. Conversely, when $E_R > E_m$, Na^+/Ca^{2+} exchange operates in the reverse mode. These relations are depicted schematically in Figure 2. In the course of recent studies of calcium transport by DCT cells, we measured all the determinants of Na^+/Ca^{2+} exchange, both under basal conditions and after challenge with PTH, chlorothiazide or other experimental maneuvers. Resting intracellular Na^+ is 13 mM (46). The resting membrane voltage of DCT cells is -70 mV (47, 48). At this voltage, the exchanger is essentially quiescent, poised slightly in the forward mode with $E_m\text{-}E_R = -1$ to -15 mV. When the cells are stimulated with a maximally effective dose of PTH, $[Ca^{2+}]_i$ increases from 100 to 350 nM, and the membrane voltage hyperpolarizes to -90 mV (48). In this setting, the driving force for Na^+/Ca^{2+}

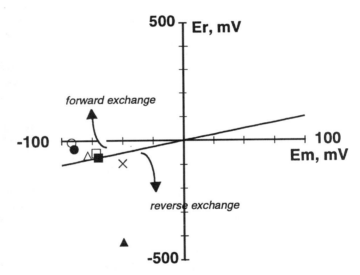

Figure 2   Analysis of Na^+/Ca^{2+} exchange. E_m, the membrane voltage is plotted as a function of E_r, the reversal potential for Na^+/Ca^{2+} exchange. The exchanger can operate in the forward mode, where Na^+ entry is coupled to Ca^{2+} efflux, and in the reverse mode, where Na^+ efflux energizes Ca^{2+} entry. The direction of Na^+/Ca^{2+} exchange is determined by the driving force for the exchanger, $E_m\text{-}E_r$. The *solid line* shows equilibrium, where $E_m = E_r$. The symbols indicate measurements made in single DCT cells: under spontaneous conditions (*solid box*), when the exchanger is close to equilibrium; after treatment with PTH (*solid circle*), which hyperpolarizes membrane voltage and increases $[Ca^{2+}]_i$ (46, 48), thereby increasing the rate of the forward exchange; and after treatment with ouabain (X) or upon removal of extracellular Na^+ (*solid triangle*), which increases intracellular Na^+ and depolarizes membrane voltage (121).

exchange increases dramatically to -70 mV. Comparable results were seen with chlorothiazide, which also hyperpolarized membrane voltage and increased intracellular Ca^{2+}, but reduced intracellular Na^+. Thus maneuvers that enhance calcium entry also increase the driving force for sodium-dependent calcium extrusion through the Na^+/Ca^{2+} exchanger. Hence, even in the absence of specific regulation of the exchanger by phosphorylation or changes of intracellular pH, ATP, or ionic milieu, for example, the rate of exchange would increase as a consequence of the elevated electrochemical driving force acting on the exchanger. Such results are compatible with the view that physiological and pharmacological maneuvers that directly stimulate apical membrane calcium entry in distal tubule cells will inherently augment the rate of basolateral calcium extrusion. Conversely, as shown in Figure 2, when the cells were treated with ouabain, intracellular Na^+ increased with concomitant membrane depolarization (121). Under these conditions the driving forces favor reverse Na^+/Ca^{2+} exchange.

It has been suggested (28, 104) that stimulation of calcium absorption by distal tubules is mediated by a primary increase of Na^+/Ca^{2+} exchange and is responsible for the dissociation of sodium and calcium absorption. According to this scheme, by inhibiting apical membrane sodium entry, thiazide diuretics reduce the intracellular Na^+ concentration, which in turn increases the electrochemical gradient for basolateral sodium entry, thereby augmenting calcium efflux through the Na^+/Ca^{2+} exchanger. The observation that amiloride and chlorothiazide increase free intracellular calcium is contrary to what would be predicted were Na^+/Ca^{2+} exchange the initial event responsible for hormone or diuretic-stimulated calcium absorption by distal convoluted tubules. Furthermore, PTH and calcitonin, which also increase free intracellular calcium, have no effect on intracellular sodium. Thus the coupling between sodium and calcium absorption in distal tubules is likely to arise as an indirect consequence of the dissipative energy generated upon sodium entry rather than by a primary effect on basolateral calcium efflux.

Na^+/Ca^{2+} Exchanger Isoforms

Recent evidence demonstrates that the DCT expresses several isoforms of the NCX1 Na^+/Ca^{2+} exchanger (66, 80, 98, 99). Mouse DCT cells express NACA2, NACA3, and NACA6 isoforms and exhibit sodium-dependent calcium transport. Collapse of the Na^+ gradient with an ionophore abolished calcium transport (121). The Na^+/Ca^{2+} exchanger undergoes alternative splicing within a variable portion of the intracellular loop. Isoform composition is determined by the six exons that comprise this variable region. Exons A and B are mutually exclusive, whereas C-F are cassette-type (67). Exon D is ubiquitous. Thus 16 unique isoforms can be formed. Antisense oligodeoxynucleotides to exon B, present in NACA2 and NACA3, inhibited reverse Na^+/Ca^{2+} exchange in DCT cells (120). Antisense oligodeoxynucleotides to exon C, present in NACA2, but not in NACA3, caused comparable inhibition. Although preliminary, these findings provide good evidence that Na^+/Ca^{2+} exchange attributable to specific exchanger isoforms mediates calcium efflux from DCT cells.

Plasma Membrane Ca^{2+}-ATPase

In addition to expressing one or more isoforms of the Na^+/Ca^{2+} exchanger, the DCT expresses a plasma membrane Ca^{2+}-ATPase (PMCA) (12, 19, 34, 71, 117, 122). It is not known to what extent PMCA also participates in cellular calcium extrusion, nor is it known how or if these processes are hormonally regulated. In view of the earlier theoretical analysis of Na^+/Ca^{2+} exchange, the calculations are consistent with the conclusion that under resting conditions Na^+/Ca^{2+} exchange exerts little if any role in calcium extrusion, which may be mediated by one or more PMCAs. Conversely, when cellular calcium transport is stimulated, Na^+/Ca^{2+} exchange may be the dominant calcium efflux mechanism.

Load Dependence

An important feature of distal nephron electrolyte transport is its load dependence. This term is used to describe the relations between the amount of solute delivered to a nephron site and the corresponding change in its transport. Such load dependence is a well-recognized feature of distal sodium absorption. Load dependence of calcium absorption in distal convoluted tubules was evaluated by two laboratories using somewhat different experimental approaches. Costanzo & Windhager (28) applied an in vivo microperfusion strategy that resembled in vivo conditions, where changes in the load of calcium were achieved by increasing the rate of calcium delivery and not the concentration. Artificial perfusion solutions were introduced into the early distal convoluted tubule, then collected with a second pipette located downstream, and subjected to microchemical analysis for calcium. They found that absolute and fractional calcium absorption increased as the load was elevated. In these experiments, increasing loads were achieved by increasing the rate at which perfusate was introduced into the tubule. No saturation of calcium absorption was observed over a sevenfold range. Furthermore, the rate of calcium absorption increased directly as a function of the rate of sodium absorption. It was proposed (28) that the elevated calcium absorption, in response to the increased delivery, resulted from enhanced passive calcium entry across apical plasma membranes. In our experience (3, 48, 83), calcium entry and calcium channel activity are undetectable in the absence of hormonal stimulation or of a primary change in sodium transport or membrane voltage. Furthermore, increasing the external sodium decreases calcium entry and vice versa (see below).

It is difficult to reconcile the aforementioned results with those of Greger et al (52), who examined the same issue but applied a somewhat different approach. Again, artificial solutions containing ^{45}Ca were introduced into the lumens of distal tubules in a manner similar to that of Costanzo & Windhager (28), but the ipsilateral urine produced by that kidney was collected. Greger et al found that the fractional recovery of calcium in the voided urine increased as the delivered load was elevated. In other words, a reciprocal relation obtained, where the fractional absorption diminished as a function of increased load.

Calcium absorption by distal convoluted tubules leads to the development of a steep transtubular concentration gradient that, in turn, diminishes the electrochemical driving force for entry across apical plasma membranes. It is plausible that an additional component of the inverse relation between sodium and calcium absorption by distal convoluted tubules, and possible explanation for the disparate findings, is a consequence of the flow dynamics. According to this idea, as the load of sodium presented to the distal convoluted tubule is raised by increasing the luminal sodium concentration or the tubular urine flow rate (or both), the point at which this limiting gradient is achieved is deflected further downstream with an attendant increase in the absolute amount of calcium that is reabsorbed.

Vesicle and Cell Studies of Calcium and Sodium Transport

In apical membrane vesicles prepared from rabbit distal tubules, calcium uptake decreases asymptotically as a function of the extravesicular sodium concentration (20). These findings were interpreted by Brunette et al to indicate that sodium interferes with the calcium entry through a competitive or allosteric mechanism. The calcium entry mechanism was deduced to be an electroneutral carrier or voltage-insensitive channel because maneuvers to alter the membrane potential had no effect on the rate of calcium uptake (21). Control experiments demonstrating electrogenic transport of Na^+, however, were not performed, so it is difficult to be certain that the vesicles had a sufficiently high resistance to establish a membrane potential.

Our laboratory explored the relations between calcium and sodium transport in immortalized mouse DCT cells. Similar to Brunette et al's, our results (shown in Figure 3) reveal an inverse relation between the rates of calcium and sodium uptake. However, based on measurement of membrane voltage and of PTH-activated calcium currents that were inhibitable by nifedipine, we deduced that PTH-stimulated calcium entry is mediated by small conductance, modestly selective calcium channels. These channels are unusual in that they are activated upon membrane hyperpolarization, which also enhances the driving force for calcium entry. A working model for calcium transport by DCT cells based on these observations is shown in Figure 4.

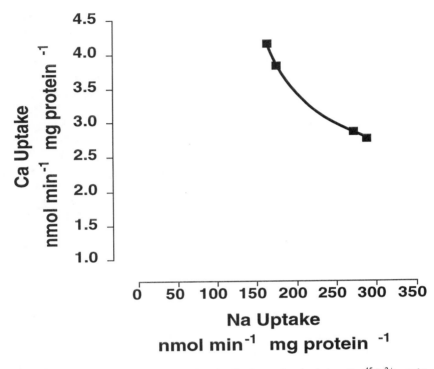

Figure 3   Sodium-dependent calcium uptake by distal convoluted tubule cells. $^{45}Ca^{2+}$ uptake was measured in immortalized mouse DCT cells under conditions where calcium transport was stimulated with PTH (48) or sodium transport was inhibited by amiloride (42).

A Model for Calcium Transport by DCT Cells

The primary features of this model (Figure 4) include the presence of two apical membrane sodium entry pathways: the Na-Cl cotransporter and the amiloride-sensitive epithelial Na^+ channel. Inhibition of either hyperpolarizes the membrane voltage and activates an apical membrane calcium channel. Basolateral calcium efflux is mediated by Na^+/Ca^{2+} exchange and by a plasma membrane Ca^{2+}-ATPase.

The interrelations of sodium on calcium in distal convoluted tubules can be explained by and experimentally tested according to the tenets of this model (Figure 4). The unifying feature of this scheme is that membrane hyperpolarization activates the apical membrane calcium entry channel (83). In the absence of such stimulation, channel activity is undetectable (83). Diminished sodium entry through either the Na-Cl cotransporter (47, 107) or the Na^+

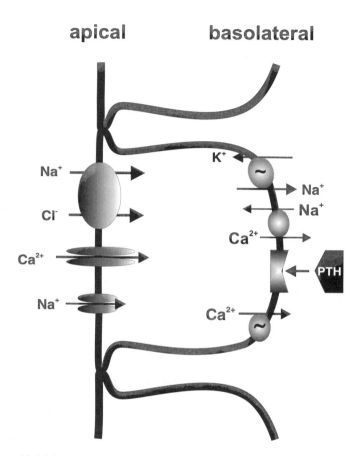

Figure 4   Model for calcium and sodium transport by distal convoluted tubule cells. Calcium absorption proceeds exclusively by a transcellular pathway. Entry of calcium across apical plasma membranes is mediated by a dihydropyridine-sensitive calcium channel that is activated upon membrane hyperpolarization. Basolateral calcium efflux is mediated by Na^+/Ca^{2+} exchange and by the Ca^{2+}-ATPase. Sodium enters the cells through a combination of Na-Cl cotransport and by the epithelial Na^+ channel, ENaC. Inhibition of the former with thiazide diuretics or the latter with amiloride hyperpolarizes membrane voltage, thereby activating the calcium entry channel and augmenting the driving force for diffusional Ca^{2+} entry. Hyperpolarization would also enhance the driving force for calcium efflux through the Na^+/Ca^{2+} exchanger. PTH, acting through its cognate receptor, hyperpolarizes membrane voltage, similarly activating calcium entry.

channel (32, 42, 107) hyperpolarizes the membrane. Likewise, PTH (48, 83) and calcitonin acting thorough their cognate receptors (49) hyperpolarize DCT membrane voltage. Hyperpolarization of membrane voltage by PTH is a direct effect because this action is present even when calcium entry is blocked by nifedipine (48). Directly hyperpolarizing membrane voltage by reducing extracellular potassium concentrations stimulated calcium uptake (47). Thus according to this model, sodium-dependent changes of calcium transport are indirect and occur secondarily through effects on membrane voltage.

INHERITED DISORDERS OF DISTAL CALCIUM ABSORPTION

Bartter's syndrome, which is characterized by salt wasting, volume depletion, and hypokalemic metabolic alkalosis, is accompanied by hypercalciuria and hypermagnesuria (6, 26). A variant of this disease, initially described by Gitelman & Welt (51), shares the same constellation of salt wasting, hypokalemia, and hypermagnesuria but is associated with diminished calcium excretion (9, 51). Pioneering efforts by Lifton and others (82, 105) established that Gitelman's syndrome is attributable to mutations in the *Slc12a3* (the Na-Cl or TSC cotransporter) gene, which is located on human chromosome 16q13. The characteristic hypocalciuria of Gitelman's syndrome can be understood from the model of sodium and calcium absorption in DCT cells shown in Figure 4. Because the magnitude of sodium and calcium absorption are inversely related in distal convoluted tubules, impaired or diminished Na-Cl cotransporter function results in enhanced calcium reabsorption and consequent hypocalciuria. Operationally, Gitelman's syndrome functionally results in the same effect as inhibition of the Na-Cl cotransporter with thiazide diuretics. Not surprisingly, Gitelman's patients show diminished response to the administration of thiazide diuretics, whereas the action of loop diuretics that inhibit the Na-K-2Cl cotransporter is normal (94, 115). In Bartter's syndrome, which is due to mutations in the Na-K-2Cl cotransporter located in thick ascending limbs, salt wasting is accompanied by hypercalciuria, consistent with the parallel nature of sodium and calcium absorption by the thick ascending limb. Patients with Bartter's syndrome evince a normal response to thiazide diuretics but impaired responses to loop diuretics. Thus these two inherited disorders reinforce the conclusions drawn regarding the cellular mechanisms responsible for the parallel transport of calcium and sodium in thick ascending limbs and the inverse codependence of calcium transport in distal tubules.

ACKNOWLEDGMENTS

Original work from our laboratory was supported by NIH National Institute of General Medical Sciences grant GM 34399. The author gratefully acknowledges the invaluable collaborations of Frank Gesek, Bonnie Couter-marsh, Susan Kennedy, and Ken White.

Visit the *Annual Reviews home page* at
http://www.AnnualReviews.org.

Literature Cited

1. Agus ZS, Ziyadeh FN, Kelepouris E. 1986. Mechanisms of calcium transport in the thick ascending limb of the loop of Henle. *Adv. Exp. Med. Biol.* 208:171–75
2. Bachmann S, Velázquez H, Obermüller N, Reilly RF, Moser D, et al. 1995. Expression of the thiazide-sensitive Na-Cl cotransporter by rabbit distal convoluted tubule cells. *J. Clin. Invest.* 96:2510–14
3. Bacskai BJ, Friedman PA. 1990. Activation of latent Ca^{2+} channels in renal epithelial cells by parathyroid hormone. *Nature* 347:388–91
4. Bailly C, Roinel N, Amiel C. 1985. Stimulation by glucagon and PTH of Ca and Mg reabsorption in the superficial distal tubule of the rat kidney. *Pflügers Arch.* 403:28–34
5. Barratt LJ, Rector FC Jr, Kokko JP, Seldin DW. 1974. Factors governing the transepithelial potential difference across the proximal tubule of the rat kidney. *J. Clin. Invest.* 53:454–64
6. Bartter FC, Pronove P, Gill JR, MacCardle RC. 1962. Hyperplasia of the juxtaglomerular complex with hyperaldosteronism and hypokalemic alkalosis. *Am. J. Med.* 33:811–28
7. Bauman K, Holzgreve H, Kolb F, Peters R, Rumrich G, et al. 1966. Unidirektionale Flusse fur ^{24}Na, ^{42}K, ^{45}Ca, ^{38}Cl, ^{82}Br, and ^{131}I im proximalen Konvolut der Rattenniere. *Pflügers Arch.* 289:R77
8. Berry CA, Rector FC Jr. 1978. Relative sodium-to-chloride permeability in the proximal convoluted tubule. *Am. J. Physiol.* 235:F592–604
9. Bettinelli A, Bianchetti MG, Girardin E, Caringella A, Cecconi M, et al. 1992. Use of calcium excretion values to distinguish two forms of primary renal tubular hypokalemic alkalosis: Bartter and Gitelman syndromes. *J. Pediatr.* 120:38–43
10. Bindels RJM. 1993. Calcium handling by the mammalian kidney. *J. Exp. Biol.* 184:89–104
11. Bomsztyk K, Wright FS. 1986. Dependence of ion fluxes on fluid transport by rat proximal tubule. *Am. J. Physiol.* 250:F680–89
12. Borke JL, Minami J, Verma AK, Penniston JT, Kumar R. 1988. Co-localization of erythrocyte Ca^{2+}-Mg^{2+} ATPase and vitamin D-dependent 28-kDa-calcium binding protein. *Kidney Int.* 34:262–67
13. Borle AB. 1981. Control, modulation, and regulation of cell calcium. *Rev. Physiol. Biochem. Pharmacol.* 90:13–153
14. Borle AB. 1988. Na^{+}-Ca^{2+} exchange as a Ca^{2+} influx pathway in kidney cells. In *Cellular Calcium and Phosphate Transport in Health and Disease*, ed. F Bronner, M Peterlik, pp. 53–58. New York: Liss
15. Borle AB, Bender C. 1991. Effects of pH on Ca_i^{2+}, Na_i^{+}, and pH_i of MDCK cells: Na^{+}-Ca^{2+} and Na^{+}-H^{+} antiporter interactions. *Am. J. Physiol.* 261:C482–89
16. Bourdeau JE. 1986. Calcium transport across the pars recta of cortical segment 2 proximal tubules. *Am. J. Physiol.* 251:F718724
17. Bourdeau JE, Attie MF. 1994. Calcium metabolism. In *Maxwell and Kleeman's Clinical Disorders of Fluid and Electrolyte Metabolism*, ed. RG Narins, pp. 243–306. New York: McGraw-Hill. 5th ed.
18. Bourdeau JE, Burg MB. 1979. Voltage dependence of calcium transport in the thick ascending limb of Henle's loop. *Am. J. Physiol.* 236:F357–64
19. Brunette MG, Blouin S, Chan M. 1987. High affinity Ca^{2+}-Mg^{2+} ATPase in the distal tubule of the mouse kidney. *Can. J. Physiol. Pharmacol.* 65:2093–98
20. Brunette MG, Mailloux J, Lajeunesse D. 1992. Calcium transport through the luminal membrane of the distal tubule. I. Interrelationship with sodium. *Kidney Int.* 41:281–88
21. Brunette MG, Mailloux J, Lajeunesse D. 1992. Calcium transport through the luminal membrane of distal tubule: II. Effect of pH, electrical potential and calcium channel inhibitors. *Kidney Int.* 41:289–96

22. Canessa CM, Horisberger JD, Rossier BC. 1993. Epithelial sodium channel related to proteins involved in neurodegeneration. *Nature* 361:467–70

23. Canessa CM, Schild L, Buell G, Thorens B, Gautschi I, et al. 1994. Amiloride-sensitive epithelial Na⁺ channel is made of three homologous subunits. *Nature* 367:463–67

24. Chalfant ML, Peterson-Yantorno K, O'Brien TG, Civan MM. 1996. Regulation of epithelial Na⁺ channels from M-1 cortical collecting duct cells. *Am. J. Physiol.* 271:F861–70

25. Ciampolillo F, McCoy DE, Green RB, Karlson KH, Dagenais A, et al. 1996. Cell-specific expression of amiloride-sensitive, Na⁺-conducting ion channels in the kidney. *Am. J. Physiol.* 271:C1303–15

26. Clive DM. 1995. Bartter's syndrome: the unsolved puzzle. *Am. J. Kidney Dis.* 25:813–23

27. Costanzo LS. 1984. Comparison of calcium and sodium transport in early and late rat distal tubules: effect of amiloride. *Am. J. Physiol.* 246:F937–45

28. Costanzo LS, Windhager EE. 1978. Calcium and sodium transport by the distal convoluted tubule of the rat. *Am. J. Physiol.* 235:F492–506

29. Costanzo LS, Windhager EE. 1980. Effects of PTH, ADH, and cyclic AMP on distal tubular Ca and Na reabsorption. *Am. J. Physiol.* 239:F478–85

30. Costanzo LS, Windhager EE. 1986. Transport functions of the distal convoluted tubule. In *Physiology of Membrane Disorders,* ed. TE Andreoli, JF Hoffman, DD Fanestil, SG Schultz, pp. 727–50. New York: Plenum 2nd ed.

31. Costanzo LS, Windhager EE. 1992. Renal regulation of calcium balance. In *The Kidney: Physiology and Pathophysiology,* ed. DW Seldin, G Giebisch, pp. 2375–93. New York: Raven. 2nd ed.

32. Dai L-J, Friedman PA, Quamme GA. 1997. Mechanisms of amiloride stimulation of Mg²⁺ uptake in immortalized mouse distal convoluted tubule cells. *Am. J. Physiol.* 272:F249–56

33. Di Stefano A, Wittner M, Nitschke R, Braitsch R, Greger R, et al. 1990. Effects of parathyroid hormone and calcitonin on Na⁺, Cl⁻, K⁺, Mg²⁺ and Ca²⁺ transport in cortical and medullary thick ascending limbs of mouse kidney. *Pflügers Arch.* 417:161–67

34. Doucet A, Katz AI. 1982. High-affinity Ca-Mg-ATPase along the rabbit nephron. *Am. J. Physiol.* 242:F346–52

35. Duc C, Farman N, Canessa CM, Bonvalet JP, Rossier BC. 1994. Cell-specific expression of epithelial sodium channel alpha, beta, and gamma subunits in aldosterone-responsive epithelia from the rat: localization by in situ hybridization and immunocytochemistry. *J. Cell Biol.* 127:1907–21

36. Edwards BR, Baer PG, Sutton RAL, Dirks JH. 1973. Micropuncture study of diuretic effects on sodium and calcium reabsorption in the dog nephron. *J. Clin. Invest.* 52:2418–27

37. Eisner DA, Lederer WJ. 1985. Na:Ca exchange: stoichiometry and electrogenicity. *Am. J. Physiol.* 248:C189–202

38. Elalouf JM, Roinel N, de Rouffignac C. 1983. Stimulation by human calcitonin of electrolyte transport in distal tubules of rat kidney. *Pflügers Arch.* 399:111–18

39. Elalouf JM, Roinel N, de Rouffignac C, Segre GV. 1984. Effects of antidiuretic hormone on electrolyte reabsorption and secretion in distal tubules of rat kidney. *Pflügers Arch.* 401:167–73

40. Frick A, Rumrich G, Ullrich KJ, Lassiter WE. 1965. Microperfusion study of calcium transport in the proximal tubule of the rat kidney. *Pflügers Arch.* 286:109–17

41. Friedman PA. 1988. Basal and hormone-activated calcium absorption in mouse renal thick ascending limbs. *Am. J. Physiol.* 254:F62–70

42. Friedman PA, Gesek FA. 1995. Stimulation of calcium transport by amiloride in mouse distal convoluted tubule cells. *Kidney Int.* 48:1427–34

43. Friedman PA, Gesek FA. 1995. Cellular calcium transport in renal epithelia: measurement, mechanisms, and regulation. *Physiol. Rev.* 75:429–71

44. Gamba G, Miyanoshita A, Lombardi M, Lytton J, Lee WS, et al. 1994. Molecular cloning, primary structure, and characterization of two members of the mammalian electroneutral sodium-(potassium)-chloride cotransporter family expressed in kidney. *J. Biol. Chem.* 269:17713–22

45. Garland HO, Phipps DJ, Harpur ES. 1992. Gentamicin-induced hypercalciuria in the rat: assessment of nephron site involved. *J. Pharmacol. Exp. Ther.* 263:293–97

46. Gesek FA. 1993. Stimulation of α2-adrenergic receptors increase Na⁺,K⁺-ATPase activity in distal convoluted tubule cells. *Am. J. Physiol.* 265:F561–68

47. Gesek FA, Friedman PA. 1992. Mechanism of calcium transport stimulated by chlorothiazide in mouse distal convoluted tubule cells. *J. Clin. Invest.* 90:429–38

48. Gesek FA, Friedman PA. 1992. On the mechanism of parathyroid hormone stimulation of calcium uptake by mouse distal convoluted tubule cells. *J. Clin. Invest.* 90:749–58

49. Gesek FA, Friedman PA. 1993. Calcitonin stimulates calcium transport in distal convoluted tubule cells. *Am. J. Physiol.* 264:F744–51

50. Gesek FA, Friedman PA. 1995. Sodium entry mechanisms in distal convoluted tubule cells. *Am. J. Physiol.* 268:F89–98

51. Gitelman HJ, Graham JB, Welt LG. 1966. A new familial disorder characterized by hypokalemia and hypomagnesemia. *Trans. Assoc. Am. Phys.* 79:221–35

52. Greger R, Lang F, Oberleithner H. 1978. Distal site of calcium reabsorption in the rat nephron. *Pflügers Arch.* 374:153–57

53. Gutman Y, Gottschalk CW. 1966. Microinjection study of the effect of calcium on sodium transport in the rat kidney. *Isr. J. Med. Sci.* 2:243–45

54. Hall DA, Varney DM. 1980. Effect of vasopressin on electrical potential difference and chloride transport in mouse medullary thick ascending limb of Henle's loop. *J. Clin. Invest.* 66:792–802

55. Hebert SC, Culpepper RM, Andreoli TE. 1981. NaCl transport in mouse medullary thick ascending limbs. I. Functional nephron heterogeneity and ADH-stimulated NaCl cotransport. *Am. J. Physiol.* 241:F412–31

56. Hebert SC, Friedman PA, Andreoli TE. 1984. Effects of antidiuretic hormone on cellular conductive pathways in mouse medullary thick ascending limbs of Henle: I. ADH increases transcellular conductive pathways. *J. Membr. Biol.* 80:201–19

57. Hebert SC, Gamba G. 1994. Molecular cloning and characterization of the renal diuretic-sensitive electroneutral sodium-(potassium)-chloride cotransporters. *Clin. Investig.* 72:692–94

58. Hebert SC, Gamba G, Kaplan M. 1996. The electroneutral $Na^+-(K^+)-Cl^-$ cotransport family. *Kidney Int.* 49:1638–41

59. Igarashi P, Heuvel GBV, Payne JA, Forbush B III. 1995. Cloning, embryonic expression, and alternative splicing of a murine kidney-specific Na-K-Cl cotransporter. *Am. J. Physiol.* 269:F405–18

60. Imai M. 1981. Effects of parathyroid hormone and N^6,O^2-dibutyryl cyclic AMP on calcium transport across the rabbit distal nephron segments perfused in vitro. *Pflügers Arch.* 390:145–51

61. Kaissling B, Kriz W. 1979. Structural analysis of the rabbit kidney. *Adv. Anat. Embryol. Cell Biol.* 56:1–123

62. Kaplan MR, Plotkin MD, Lee WS, Xu ZC, Lytton J, et al. 1996. Apical localization of the Na-K-Cl cotransporter, *rBSC1*, on rat thick ascending limbs. *Kidney Int.* 49:40–47

63. Kauker ML, Zawada ET, Castle LM, Roman RJ. 1990. Renal hemodynamic and tubular effects of a calcium channel blocker, nislodipine. *Circulation* 82:III–585 (Abstr.)

64. Kawahara K, Matsuzaki K. 1992. Activation of calcium channel by shear-stress in cultured renal distal tubule cells. *Biochem. Biophys. Res. Commun.* 184:198–205

65. Koeppen BM, Stanton BA. 1992. Sodium chloride transport: distal nephron. In *The Kidney, Physiology and Pathophysiology,* ed. DW Seldin, G Giebisch, pp. 2003–40. New York: Raven. 2nd ed.

66. Kofuji P, Lederer WJ, Schulze DH. 1993. Na/Ca exchanger isoforms expressed in kidney. *Am. J. Physiol.* 265:F598–603

67. Kofuji P, Lederer WJ, Schulze DH. 1994. Mutually exclusive and cassette exons underlie alternatively spliced isoforms of the Na/Ca exchanger. *J. Biol. Chem.* 269:5145–49

68. Kriz W, Bankir L. 1988. A standard nomenclature for the structures of the kidney. *Am. J. Physiol.* 254:F1–8

69. Kriz W, Kaissling B. 1992. Structural organization of the mammalian kidney. In *The Kidney: Physiology and Pathophysiology,* ed. DW Seldin, G Giebisch, pp. 707–77. New York: Raven. 2nd ed.

70. Kumar R. 1995. Calcium transport in epithelial cells of the intestine and kidney. *J. Cell. Biochem.* 57:392–98

71. Kumar R, Penniston JT, Borke JL. 1988. $Ca^{2+}-Mg^{2+}$-ATPase calcium pumps in the kidney. *News Physiol. Sci.* 3:219–22

72. Lajeunesse D, Bouhtiauy I, Brunette MG. 1994. Parathyroid hormone and hydrochlorothiazide increase calcium transport by the luminal membrane of rabbit distal nephron segments through different pathways. *Endocrinology* 134:35–41

73. Lajeunesse D, Bouhtiauy I, Mailloux J, Brunette MG. 1991. Parathyroid hormone (PTH) opens calcium (Ca^{2+}) channels in the luminal membrane (LUM) from rabbit distal tubules (DT). *J. Am. Soc. Nephrol.* 2:638 (Abstr.)

74. Lassiter WE, Gottschalk CW, Mylle M. 1963. Micropuncture study of renal tubular reabsorption of calcium in normal rodents. *Am. J. Physiol.* 204:771–75

75. Lau K, Agus ZS, Goldberg M, Goldfarb S. 1979. Renal tubular sites of altered calcium transport in phosphate depleted rats. *J. Clin. Invest.* 64:1681–87

76. Lau K, Bourdeau JE. 1995. Parathyroid hormone action in calcium transport in the distal nephron. *Curr. Opin. Nephrol. Hypertens.* 4:55–63

77. Lau K, Quamme G, Tan S. 1991. Patch-clamp evidence for a Ca channel in apical membrane of cortical thick ascending limb (cTAL) and distal tubule (DT) cells. *J. Am. Soc. Nephrol.* 2:775 (Abstr.)

78. Le Grimellec C, Roinel N, Morel F. 1974. Simultaneous Mg, Ca, P, K, Na and Cl analysis in rat tubular fluid. III. During acute Ca plasma loading. *Pflügers Arch.* 346:171–88

79. Ledvora RF, Hegyvary C. 1983. Dependence of Na$^+$-Ca^{2+} exchange and Ca^{2+}-Ca^{2+} exchange on monovalent cations. *Biochim. Biophys. Acta* 729:123–36

80. Lee S-L, Yu ASL, Lytton J. 1994. Tissue-specific expression of Na$^+$-Ca^{2+} exchanger isoforms. *J. Biol. Chem.* 269:14849–52

81. Madsen KM, Tisher CC. 1986. Structure-functional relationships along the distal nephron. *Am. J. Physiol.* 250:F1–15

82. Mastroianni N, De Fusco M, Zollo M, Arrigo G, Zuffardi O, et al. 1996. Molecular cloning, expression pattern, and chromosomal localization of the human Na-Cl thiazide-sensitive cotransporter (SLC12A3). *Genomics* 35:486–93

83. Matsunaga H, Stanton BA, Gesek FA, Friedman PA. 1994. Epithelial Ca^{2+} channels sensitive to dihydropyridines and activated by hyperpolarizing voltages. *Am. J. Physiol.* 267:C157–65

84. Morel F, Chabardès D, Imbert M. 1976. Functional segmentation of the rabbit distal tubule by microdetermination of hormone-dependent adenylate cyclase activity. *Kidney Int.* 9:264–77

85. Murayama Y, Morel F, Le Grimellec C. 1972. Phosphate, calcium and magnesium transfers in proximal tubules and loops of Henle, as measured by single nephron microperfusion experiments in the rat. *Pflügers Arch.* 333:1–16

86. Ng RCK, Peraino RA, Suki WN. 1982. Divalent cation transport in isolated tubules. *Kidney Int.* 22:492–97

87. Ng RCK, Rouse D, Suki WN. 1984. Calcium transport in the rabbit superficial

proximal convoluted tubule. *J. Clin. Invest.* 74:834–42

88. Obermüller N, Bernstein P, Velázquez H, Reilly R, Moser D, et al. 1995. Expression of the thiazide-sensitive Na-Cl cotransporter in rat and human kidney. *Am. J. Physiol.* 269:F900–10

89. Philipson KD. 1985. Sodium-calcium exchange in plasma membrane vesicles. *Annu. Rev. Physiol.* 47:561–71

90. Philipson KD, Nicoll DA. 1992. Sodium-calcium exchange. *Curr. Opin. Cell Biol.* 4:678–83

91. Plotkin MD, Kaplan MR, Verlander JW, Lee WS, Brown D, et al. 1996. Localization of the thiazide sensitive Na-Cl cotransporter, *rTSCl*, in the rat kidney. *Kidney Int.* 50:174–83

92. Poncet V, Merot J, Poujeol P. 1992. A calcium-permeable channel in the apical membrane of primary cultures of the rabbit distal bright convoluted tubule. *Pflügers Arch.* 422:112–19

93. Poujeol P, Chabardès D, Roinel N, de Rouffignac C. 1976. Influence of extracellular fluid volume expansion on magnesium, calcium and phosphate handling along the rat nephron. *Pflügers Arch.* 365:203–11

94. Puschett JB, Greenberg A, Mitro R, Piraino B, Wallia R. 1988. Variant of Bartter's syndrome with a distal tubular rather than loop of Henle defect. *Nephron* 50:205–11

95. Quabius ES, Murer H, Biber J. 1996. Expression of proximal tubular Na-P$_i$ and Na-SO$_4$ cotransporters in MDCK and LLC-PK1 cells by transfection. *Am. J. Physiol.* 270:F220–28

96. Rector FC Jr. 1983. Sodium, bicarbonate, and chloride absorption by the proximal tubule. *Am. J. Physiol.* 244:F461–71

97. Reeves JP, Hale CC. 1984. The stoichiometry of the cardiac sodium-calcium exchange system. *J. Biol. Chem.* 259:7733–39

98. Reilly RF, Shugrue CA. 1992. cDNA cloning of a renal Na$^+$-Ca^{2+} exchanger. *Am. J. Physiol.* 262:F1105–9

99. Reilly RF, Shugrue C, Philipson K, Biemesderfer D. 1992. Immunolocalization of the Na$^+$/Ca^{2+} exchanger in rat kidney. *J. Am. Soc. Nephrol.* 3:689 (Abstr.)

100. Roudier-Pujol C, Rochat A, Escoubet B, Eugène E, Barrandon Y, et al. 1996. Differential expression of epithelial sodium channel subunit mRNAs in rat skin. *J. Cell Sci.* 109:379–85

101. Rouse D, Ng RCK, Suki WN. 1980. Calcium transport in the pars recta and thin descending limb of Henle of rabbit

perfused in vitro. *J. Clin. Invest.* 65:37–42

102. Saunders JCJ, Isaacson LC. 1990. Patch clamp study of Ca channels in isolated renal tubule segments. In *Calcium Transport and Intracellular Calcium Homeostasis,* ed. D Pansu, F Bronner, pp. 27–34. Berlin: Springer-Verlag

103. Shareghi GR, Stoner LC. 1978. Calcium transport across segments of the rabbit distal nephron in vitro. *Am. J. Physiol.* 235:F367–75

104. Shimizu T, Nakamura M, Yoshitomi K, Imai M. 1991. Interaction of trichlormethiazide or amiloride with PTH in stimulating calcium absorption in the rabbit connecting tubule. *Am. J. Physiol.* 261:F36–43

105. Simon DB, Nelson-Williams C, Bia MJ, Ellison D, Karet FE, et al. 1996. Gitelman's variant of Bartter's syndrome, inherited hypokalaemic alkalosis, is caused by mutations in the thiazide-sensitive Na-Cl cotransporter. *Nat. Genet.* 12:24–30

106. Snowdowne KW, Borle AB. 1985. Effects of low extracellular sodium on cytosolic ionized calcium. Na^+-Ca^{2+} exchange as a major calcium influx pathway in kidney cells. *J. Biol. Chem.* 260:14998–5007

107. Stanton BA. 1990. Cellular actions of thiazide diuretics in the distal tubule. *J. Am. Soc. Nephrol.* 1:832–36

108. Suki WN. 1979. Calcium transport in the nephron. *Am. J. Physiol.* 237:F1–6

109. Suki WN, Rouse D. 1991. Renal transport of calcium, magnesium, and phosphorous. In *The Kidney,* ed. BM Brenner, FC Rector, Jr. pp. 380–423. Philadelphia: Saunders. 4th ed.

110. Sutton RAL, Dirks JH. 1975. The renal excretion of calcium: a review of micropuncture data. *Can. J. Physiol. Pharmacol.* 53:979–88

111. Sutton RAL, Wong NLM, Dirks JH. 1976. Effects of parathyroid hormone on sodium and calcium transport in the dog nephron. *Clin. Sci. Mol. Med.* 51:345–51

112. Sutton RAL, Wong NLM, Dirks JH. 1979. Effects of metabolic acidosis and alkalosis on sodium and calcium transport in the dog kidney. *Kidney Int.* 15:520–33

113. Tan S, Lau K. 1993. Patch-clamp evidence for calcium channels in apical membranes of rabbit kidney connecting tubules. *J. Clin. Invest.* 92:2731–36

114. Tisher CC, Madsen KM. 1991. Anatomy of the kidney. In *The Kidney,* ed. BM Brenner, FC Rector, Jr. pp. 3–75. Philadelphia: Saunders. 4th ed.

115. Tsukamoto T, Kobayashi T, Kawamoto K, Fukase M, Chihara K. 1995. Possible discrimination of Gitelman's syndrome from Bartter's syndrome by renal clearance study: report of two cases. *Am. J. Kidney Dis.* 25:637–41

116. Ullrich KJ, Rumrich G, Kloss S. 1976. Active Ca^{2+} reabsorption in the proximal tubule of the rat kidney. Dependence on sodium- and buffer transport. *Pflügers Arch.* 364:223–28

117. van Baal J, Yu AL, Hartog A, Fransen JAM, Willems PHGM, et al. 1996. Localization and regulation by vitamin D of calcium transport proteins in rabbit cortical collecting system. *Am. J. Physiol.* 271:F985–93

118. Walser M. 1961. Calcium clearance as a function of sodium clearance in the dog. *Am. J. Physiol.* 200:1099–104

119. Wang T, Agulian SK, Giebisch G, Aronson PS. 1993. Effects of formate and oxalate on chloride absorption in rat distal tubule. *Am. J. Physiol.* 264:F730–36

120. White KE, Gesek FA, Friedman PA. 1995. Exon-specific antisense inhibition of Na/Ca exchange in distal convoluted tubule cells. *J. Am. Soc. Nephrol.* 6:356 (Abstr.)

121. White KE, Gesek FA, Friedman PA. 1996. Structural and functional analysis of Na^+/Ca^{2+} exchange in distal convoluted tubule cells. *Am. J. Physiol.* 271:F560–70

122. White KE, Gesek FA, Nesbitt T, Drezner MK, Friedman PA. 1997. Molecular dissection of Ca^{2+} efflux in immortalized proximal tubule cells. *J. Gen. Physiol.* 109:217–28

123. Winaver J, Sylk DB, Robertson JS, Chen TC, Puschett JB. 1980. Micropuncture study of the acute renal tubular transport effects of 25-hydroxyvitamin D_3 in the dog. *Miner. Electrolyte Metab.* 4:178–88

124. Wright FS, Bomsztyk K. 1986. Calcium transport by the proximal tubule. *Adv. Exp. Med. Biol.* 208:165–70

125. Yu A, Saltzberg SN, Hebert SC, Lytton J. 1991. Multiple voltage-dependent Ca^{2+} channels (VDCC) are expressed in rodent kidney. *J. Am. Soc. Nephrol.* 2:756 (Abstr.)

Annu. Rev. Physiol. 1998. 60:199–220

AQUAPORIN-2 AND -3: Representatives of Two Subgroups of the Aquaporin Family Colocalized in the Kidney Collecting Duct

S. Sasaki, K. Ishibashi, and F. Marumo

Internal Medicine II, Tokyo Medical and Dental University, Tokyo 113, Japan;
e-mail: ssasaki.med2@med.tmd.ac.jp

KEY WORDS: water channel, kidney, collecting duct, vasopressin, urinary concentration

ABSTRACT

Since the molecular identification of the first aquaporin in 1992, the number of proteins known to belong to this family has been rapidly increasing. These members may be separated into two subgroups based on gene structure, sequence homology, and function. Regulation of the water permeability of the collecting ducts of the kidney is essential for urinary concentration. Aquaporin-2 and -3, which are representative of these subgroups, are colocalized in the collecting ducts. Understanding these subgroups will elucidate the differences between aquaporin-2 and -3. Aquaporin-2 is a vasopressin-regulated water channel located in the apical membrane, and aquaporin-3 is a constitutive water channel located in the basolateral membrane. In contrast to aquaporin-3, which appears to be less well regulated, many studies have now identified multiple regulational mechanisms at the gene, protein, and cell levels for aquaporin-2, thus reflecting its physiological importance. Evidence of the participation of aquaporin-2 in the pathophysiology of water-balance disorders is accumulating.

INTRODUCTION

Since the milestone discovery of water channel function in a red cell membrane protein (CHIP28) (1, 2), which had been cloned and identified as a member of the MIP family (named after the family's first identified member, major intrinsic protein of lens fiber cells in the eye), many members of the MIP family have been

0066-4278/98/0315-0199$08.00

cloned, and some have been shown to have water channel function. Once an MIP protein has been shown to have this function, it is called aquaporin (AQP) to distinguish it from other members of the MIP family with nonwater channel or unknown functions. The number of AQP proteins is rapidly increasing. Accumulating evidence indicates that the MIP/AQP family may be separated into two subgroups. In this review, we discuss the kidney collecting duct AQPs, AQP2 and AQP3 (3), each of which represents one of these subgroups, and show how they differ. Although AQP2 and AQP3 are colocalized in the kidney collecting duct cells and contribute to urine concentration, their characteristics, physiological roles, and responses to vasopressin are different. Extensive studies of AQP2 have demonstrated its physiological importance by unmasking its multiple regulational mechanisms at the gene, protein, and cell levels, whereas AQP3 is apparently less regulated. Detailed comparison of AQP2 and AQP3 will determine what is needed to gain such regulation mechanisms.

STRUCTURE AND FUNCTION OF AQP2 AND AQP3

Although AQP2 and AQP3 were cloned as members of the MIP family, AQP3 differs from other mammalian AQPs in four primary aspects: (a) different gene structure; (b) low homology to other mammalian AQPs and close homology to a bacterial MIP member, the glycerol facilitator of *Escherichia coli* (GlpF); (c) existence of extra amino acids in the two extracellular loops; and (d) permeation of small solutes such as glycerol and urea in addition to water. Analysis of these differences between AQP2 and AQP3 will shed light on the structure-function relationship of AQPs and validate the separation of the MIP/AQP family members into two subgroups.

Gene Structure

The gene locus of human AQP2 was assigned by fluorescence in situ hybridization (FISH) to chromosome 12q13 (4, 5), the same locus to which the MIP(AQP0) (6) gene had been assigned (7). Subsequent studies have shown that the genes of newly identified AQPs, AQP5 and hKID/AQP6 (8), are also assigned to this locus. Although assigned to the same locus, more careful examination using two-color FISH indicates that MIP(AQP0) and AQP2 are 500 kb apart on the genome. A recent report suggests that the genes for AQP2 and AQP6 are located within 200 kb of each other (9). Thus more studies will determine whether these AQP genes and other unknowns exist here as a true cluster. The presence of these multiple AQP genes in a narrow region strongly suggests that they have evolved from the same ancestor. The AQP3 gene has been assigned to chromosome 9p13, a locus to which no other AQPs

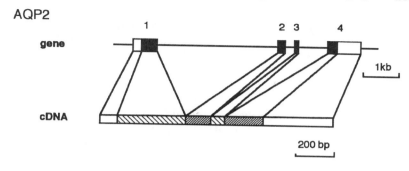

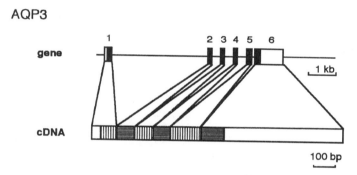

Figure 1 The gene structure of AQP2 and AQP3. The coding regions of AQP2 and AQP3 are coded by 4 and 6 exons, respectively. Both genes are relatively small, spanning 5–7 kb in the genome (from References 15, 16).

are assigned nor to which any hereditary human disease has been linked (10). AQP1 has been mapped to chromosome 7p14 (11, 12), and AQP4 to chromosome 18 (13, 14). In our laboratory, another mammalian AQP (AQP7), which shows a closer homology to AQP3 than other AQPs, has been isolated. It is of interest to determine whether the gene locus of this AQP locates close to that of AQP3.

The AQP2 gene is relatively small, spanning about 7 kb in the genome (Figure 1). The coding region is coded by 4 exons separated by 3 introns, and all splice sites conform to the GT-AG rule (15). The AQP3 gene is also a small gene, but it is coded by 6 exons (Figure 1) (16). When the gene structures of mammalian AQPs (AQP0-AQP6) are compared, all AQPs except AQP3 have 4 exons, each with a conserved size (the sizes of the introns are variable). Accordingly, the exon-intron boundaries are at the same positions in all mammalian AQPs except AQP3. These data suggest that AQP0, AQP1, AQP2, and AQP4-AQP6 are evolutionarily close, whereas AQP3 is distinct from the others.

Amino Acid Sequence: Phylogenetic Analysis

The number of known MIP/AQP proteins has been increasing dramatically, and members of this family have been identified in almost every organism. This explosive discovery has been attained by the presence of the signature sequence (NPA box, see below) found in their amino acid sequence (17). Recently, a thorough review of the phylogenetic analysis of the MIP/AQP family proteins has been published (18). When AQP3 was cloned, its amino acid identity surprisingly was shown to be closer to GlpF (42%) than to other mammalian AQPs ($\approx$35%) that had been identified (19). Since then, all subsequent mammalian AQPs discovered have shown a higher homology to AQP0/AQP1/AQP2 than to AQP3. Very recently, we cloned AQP7, a new AQP from rat that has a 48% homology to AQP3 (20). Figure 2 shows a phylogenetic tree of the MIP/AQP members, including all the mammalian AQPs. Recently, it was discovered that

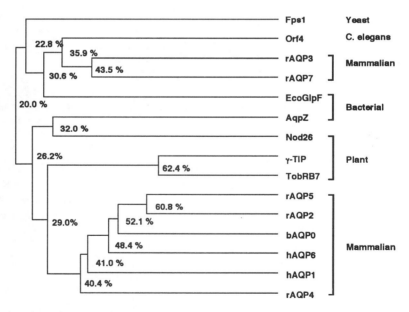

Figure 2 Phylogenetic analysis of the MIP/AQP family members. The family members distribute widely from bacteria to mammals. Amino acid sequences are aligned and analyzed by computer using Clustal V. See text for abbreviations. r, b, and h preceding the gene symbols represent rat, bovine, and human, respectively.

an AQP in *E. coli* (Aqp-Z) (21, 22) may be a counterpart of another MIP protein, GlpF, in that organism. Aqp-Z is a water channel, and GlpF functions as a channel specific for glycerol, a neutral small solute. Based on amino acid sequence homology, the MIP/AQP kingdom can be divided into two large subgroups (glp and aqp) with GlpF and Aqp-Z as the prototypes for each (Figure 2) (18, 23). All mammalian AQPs except AQP3 and AQP7 belong to the aqp group. A large number of MIP/AQP members have been isolated from plants (more than 35) and all belong to the aqp group. In contrast to this abundance in the aqp group, the number of proteins in the glp group is relatively small: AQP3 and AQP7 in mammals, two proteins in yeast, GlpF in bacteria, and four proteins in *Caenorhabditis elegans*. This separation of the MIP/AQP family is also supported by differences in topology and function, as discussed below. It is noteworthy that Aqp-Z and GlpF, two prototypes with distinct differences in sequences (homology 30%) and functions (water channel versus glycerol facilitator), already exist in the genome of *E. coli*. This indicates that the division in the two subfamilies was a very old event.

Topology

The members of the MIP/AQP family show the same topology, namely, six-membrane-spanning domains, N and C termini in the cytoplasm, and a conserved Asp-Pro-Ala motif (NPA box) twice in the sequence (17, 24) (Figure 3). A careful comparison shows some difference between AQP2 and AQP3. In hydrophilic Loops C and E, AQP3 has 15–20 more amino acids than AQP2 (Figure 3, *dotted lines* indicate the extra amino acids) (25). Ishibashi et al (23) have extended this comparison to all MIP/AQP members, and surprisingly, the presence of these extra amino acids in Loops C and E are observed in all glp

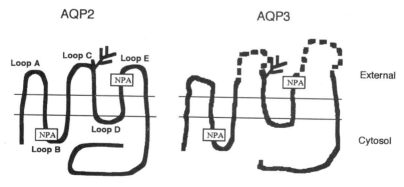

Figure 3   Topologies of AQP2 and AQP3. Basic shape is the same in both, but extra 15–20 amino acids (*dotted lines*) are present in Loops C and E of AQP3. NPA boxes are shown.

group members, but they are not found in aqp members. Thus the separation of these two subfamilies is validated not only by the homology discussed above but also by this topological difference. If there are differences in the functions between the aqp and glp groups, these domains might therefore be the sites of such differences.

Both AQP2 and AQP3 are *N*-glycosylated at loop C (5, 19, 26), but the physiological significance of these glycosylations remains unknown at present. For AQP2, water permeability was the same in the oocytes expressing either a wild-type or mutated glycosylation-lacking AQP2 (27).

Function

Functions of the MIP/AQP proteins have been examined in many systems including their natural host cells: *Xenopus* oocytes, yeast (28), cultured cells (29–31), and lipid bilayers/liposomes (32, 33). The data reported so far are not necessarily consistent among researchers even for the oocyte expression system, and careful studies using different systems are required to provide critical answers (34).

The function of AQP2 has been extensively examined in the oocyte expression system and found to be a water channel. Most researchers agree that it permeates neither small solutes, such as glycerol and urea, nor ions (35, 36). This basic characteristic, i.e. exclusive selectiveness to water, seems a common feature for the aqp group. This distinct functional characteristic may come from the aqp's prototype, Aqp-Z. Aqp-Z permeates only water and excludes glycerol and other neutral solutes, as well as ions (22). Few studies, however, have presented different results. Abrami et al have reported that AQP1, AQP2, and FA-CHIP (toad homologue of AQP1) permeate glycerol, ethylene glycol, and 1,3-propanediol, in addition to water, but do not permeate urea in the oocyte system and liposomes (37, 38). The reason for this apparent difference is not readily clear, but methodology may account for it. Recently, Yool et al (39) examined the attractive possibility that certain stimulation will unmask channel functions other than a water-selective channel. They showed that phosphorylation by cAMP-dependent protein kinase (PKA) makes AQP1 permeable to ions. However, this study has not been repeated by others (40). We examined such a possibility for AQP2 and could not find any effect other than the stimulation of water permeability (see below) (41, 42).

The other prototype, GlpF, permeates only glycerol and excludes water (43, 44), which has been confirmed by other researchers (37). Permeation of small solutes by AQP3 is easily conceivable because it is a member of the glp group. AQP3, however, is unique in that it also permeates water. The water channel function of AQP3 has been demonstrated by two research groups (19, 45), but a third group was unable to detect it (46). We further confirmed a water channel function in both human and rat AQP3 (47). A recently cloned mammalian glp protein, AQP7, permeates both small solutes and water (as does AQP3), strongly supporting the notion that mammalian glp proteins have a loose channel feature (permeating solutes and water) (20). Although GlpF does not show any water channel function, it is interesting to speculate on when glp group proteins acquired water channel function in their evolution. Thus far only a very limited number of glp proteins have been examined for their function. Recently, a yeast member (Fps1) was tested for its function and found to be a glycerol facilitator, but its water channel function was not directly examined (28). Further functional studies of other members of glp proteins are needed to identify the evolution of water channel function in the glp group.

LOCALIZATION AND PHYSIOLOGICAL ROLES OF AQP2 AND AQP3

Good antibodies against both AQP2 and AQP3 have been easily obtained, and the relative ease in obtaining these antibodies may be a common feature for the MIP/AQP family, as such antibodies have been reported for almost all members. Antibodies against C termini were especially easy to obtain. Using these antibodies, we and many others have performed extensive research, and many excellent reviews have been published (3, 48–52).

AQP2

Northern blot analysis of systemic organs for the expression of AQP2 mRNA clearly shows a selective expression only in the kidney, and immunohistochemistry, using specific antibodies, further narrows its localization to the apical region of kidney collecting ducts (26). Subsequent immunohistochemical and electronmicroscopic studies (53–55) have shown that (a) localization of AQP2 is limited to the kidney; (b) inside the kidney, AQP2 is present in principal cells of cortical collecting ducts, inner medullary collecting duct cells, and connecting tubule cells; (c) AQP2 is abundant in the vesicles located near the apical membrane; (d) AQP2 is also present in the apical membrane, and its abundance is under regulational control (see next section); and (e) AQP2 is occasionally observed in the basolateral membrane of collecting duct cells, but its abundance is greatly limited compared with that in the apical membrane. A possible age-dependent basolateral localization of AQP2 has been suggested (56).

The localization of AQP2 in the urinary concentrating nephron segments strongly indicates that AQP2 is the vasopressin-regulated water channel; this has been hypothesized for some time (for review, 57). Regulation of its subcellular localization and abundance by hydration conditions further strengthens this speculation. A direct demonstration for this speculation came from human genetics. Deen et al reported a patient with nephrogenic diabetes insipidus (NDI), who had two heterocompound mutations in the AQP2 gene (58). Thus AQP2 was demonstrated to be the vasopressin-regulated water channel. Importantly, AQP2 may be the only AQP whose physiological function has been clearly demonstrated. Numerous AQP members are present in many tissues in the body where water transport is high, but direct demonstration of their function is still lacking (59). Subjects who do not express AQP1 have been found, but surprisingly, no clinical abnormality has been observed, leaving the physiological function of AQP1 unknown (60). Mutations in the mouse AQP0 gene cause cataracts, although the underlying mechanism is not known (61).

AQP3

A Northern blot analysis of AQP3 clearly showed that its expression is found in the kidney (strongly in medulla) and other tissues such as the gastrointestinal tract and the spleen (19). An in situ hybridization study showed its localization in medullary collecting ducts (45). Immunohistochemical studies have shown that, like AQP2, its localization in the kidney is limited to the collecting ducts (47). The cell types positive for AQP3 staining are identical to the AQP2-positive cells. However, subcellular localization is the reverse; AQP3 is localized in the basolateral membrane, and AQP2 is localized in the apical region. AQP3 is predominantly localized in the basolateral membrane and is rarely localized in the cytoplasmic vesicles (62, 63). Outside the kidney, AQP3 localizes in the basal membrane of tracheal epithelial cells, conjunctival epithelium, the basolateral membrane of villus epithelial cells in the colon, and brain ependymal cells (64). Interestingly, co-expression of AQP3 and AQP4 was noted in some of these tissues, including kidney collecting duct cells. The physiological significance of this unexpected colocalization of AQP3 and AQP4 in several tissues remains unknown (64).

The physiological function of AQP3 in the body is entirely open to speculation at present. As described above, its localization coincides with the sites where water transport takes place. AQP3 and AQP4 likely contribute to water exit across the basolateral membrane of collecting duct cells, a membrane whose water permeability (per area corrected for infoldings) has been reported to be four times higher than that of the apical membrane (65–67). This high water permeability could be accounted for by the constitutive presence of AQP3 and AQP4. In an antidiuretic condition, where massive amounts of water flow through the cells, the high water permeability of the basolateral membrane of collecting duct cells is critically important to protect intracellular compartments from dilution (66). The presence of AQPs does not necessarily assure their physiological function in the body; thus knockout mouse models and a search for gene mutations in clinical disorders are required to clarify the physiological role of AQP3.

REGULATION OF AQP2 AND AQP3

The factors known to affect urinary concentrating ability possibly exert their effect by modulating AQP2 and/or AQP3. The best-known factor is vasopressin, which increases collecting duct water permeability very rapidly (68). Additional factors that cause clinical nephrogenic diuresis or antidiuresis are hypokalemia, hypercalcemia, ureteral obstruction, and certain drugs such as lithium and demeclocycline (69). Water deprivation of humans or animals for several days is known to induce an adaptive increase in kidney-concentrating ability that is independent of a high circulating vasopressin level (70, 71). This change, so-called long-term regulation, may be induced by a mechanism other than the rapid antidiuretic effect of vasopressin.

Molecular identification of AQPs has opened a new field in this research area. Extensive studies have now shown that the alterations of AQP2 (AQP3 on some occasions) are involved in almost all situations where diuresis/antidiuresis occurs. Regulational mechanisms of any protein may be divided into three steps; i.e. gene level, protein level, and cell level. AQP2 is dramatically regulated in each of these steps (Figure 4), whereas regulation of AQP3 is less prominent.

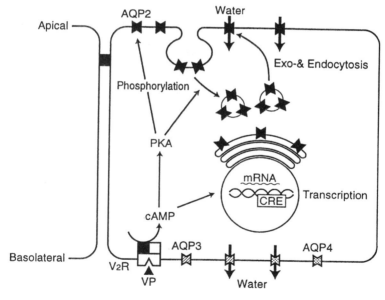

Figure 4 Multiple mechanisms of AQP2 regulation by vasopressin in kidney collecting duct cells. Vasopressin acts on the V2 receptor located on the basolateral membrane and increases intracellular cAMP, which in turn stimulates gene transcription of AQP2, protein phosphorylation of AQP2, and trafficking of AQP2. As a result, the water permeability of the apical membrane dramatically increases, and the entered water exits the basolateral membrane through AQP3 and AQP4.

In the following discussion, we mainly deal with the effects of vasopressin on AQP2 at these three regulational levels. The many regulational mechanisms at different levels by a single molecule, e.g vasopressin, indicate that AQP2 is a typical example of a multi-regulational transport protein.

Gene Level

AQP2   Initial Northern blot and in situ hybridization studies showed two important characters of AQP2 gene expression; i.e. strictly limited expression only in the kidney collecting duct and upregulation by dehydration (26, 35). Limited expression in the kidney indicates that its function is specific to the kidney, in this case, urinary concentration. This strictly limited expression is likely mediated by transcription of the gene. Isolation and analysis of the 5′ flanking region of the human AQP2 gene (Figure 5) showed the presence of a TATA box, GATA motifs, a cyclic AMP-responsive element (CRE), an AP-1 site, an AP-2 site, and E boxes (15, 72). When the 5′ regions (up to −600 bp) of the AQP2 genes of human, rat, and mouse were aligned, nucleotide identity was more than 60%, and major canonical consensus sequences such as a TATA box, GATA motifs, and a CRE were conserved (Figure 5), indicating the importance of these *cis*-elements (73). Elements found in the human sequence such as AP-1, AP-2, and Sp-1 are not conserved in other species, which leaves their physiological roles open to question. Immediately after the transcription initiation site, a GA-rich motif is present in all three species. It is interesting that similar sequences have been found in other kidney-specific genes, i.e. the Na-K-Cl cotransporter gene and the vasopressin V2 receptor gene (74, 75), suggesting that this sequence

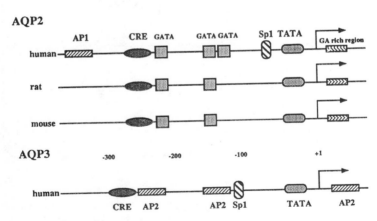

Figure 5   The 5′ flanking region of the human, rat, and mouse AQP2 genes, and the human AQP3 gene. There are many canonical consensus sequences of *cis*-motifs. Some of them are conserved among different species (from References 15, 16, 73).

might work as a kidney-specific *cis*-element. Other elements important for kidney-specific expression may be the GATA motif (76) and E box.

The reporter gene assay using the 5′ region fragment of the AQP2 gene was the next step to examine each *cis*-element's role. This technique requires cultured cells that naturally express AQP2. The search for such cells was unsuccessful; even a primary culture of innermedullary collecting duct cells lost its ability to transcribe AQP2 (77). Recently, however, candidates of naturally expressing cells have been reported (29, 78). Nevertheless, the reporter gene assay for AQP2 has been performed in nonexpressing cells, and several *cis*-elements that negatively regulate the transcription have been identified (73, 77). Clearly, many more studies, including those of transgenic mice, will be required to determine the kidney-specific gene expression of AQP2.

The conserved presence of a CRE in the 5′ flanking region of the AQP2 gene has attracted the interest of many researchers. Because vasopressin increases intracellular cAMP though the V2 receptor/adenylate cyclase system, it is quite conceivable that this element contributes to the gene transcription of AQP2. Reporter gene assay systems such as CAT and luciferase assays using the 5′ flank of the AQP2 gene were performed in kidney-derived cell lines. The results have clearly shown that cAMP increases the promoter activity two- to threefold and that this effect is dependent on the CRE motif (72, 78). It was suggested that other *cis*-elements (AP2 site or SP1 site) may cooperate to confer full cAMP inducibility to the AQP2 gene (72). However, the absence of these *cis*-elements in rat and mouse raises some doubt about this possibility. Examination of the effect of phorbol esters using the same reporter gene assay system failed to show any discernible effect, indicating that the protein kinase C (PKC)-mediated signaling pathway does not affect the promoter activity of the AQP2 gene (78).

The above CRE-dependent stimulation of the transcription of the AQP2 gene may explain the increased amount of AQP2 mRNA and protein in the collecting duct cells of dehydrated animals. The signal stimulating AQP2 gene transcription in dehydration could be vasopressin, because upregulation of AQP2 mRNA was observed with vasopressin treatment, and this effect was completely reversed by simultaneous V2 receptor antagonist administration (79, 80). These vasopressin-administration studies also indicate that the AQP2 gene is rapidly regulated. Induction after vasopressin stimulation was observed within 90 min in rats (80). When the stimulation was withdrawn in dehydrated rats by forced water drinking, stimulated mRNA levels decreased very rapidly (50% reduction at 20 min), indicating accelerated degradation of the mRNA (81).

Dehydration or vasopressin administration undoubtedly increases the kidney interstitial osmolality to some extent, and this hypertonicity may possibly increase the transcription of the AQP2 gene. Such effects of hypertonicity and a corresponding *cis*-element have been reported for the betaine transporter gene (82). In OMCD cells, experiments using RNase protection assay showed an upregulation of AQP2 mRNA by medium hypertonicity (77), suggesting that such a regulatory mechanism also works on the AQP2 gene. At present, cis-elements that mediate upregulation have not been determined.

Increased AQP2 mRNA levels in collecting duct cells in dehydrated states could lead to stimulated production of AQP2 protein. Indeed, abundant expression of AQP2 protein in collecting duct cells has been repeatedly demonstrated in dehydrated rats (55, 83–86). This abundant expression of AQP2 mostly localized in the apical region may explain the long-term regulation of the collecting duct in dehydration. High expression of AQP2 in the apical membrane can maintain a high water permeability of this membrane irrespective of circulating vasopressin levels.

AQP3   Regulation of the AQP3 gene is less well characterized than that of the AQP2 gene. As shown in Figure 5, the 5′ flanking region of the AQP3 gene has a TATA box, a Sp1 sequence, a CRE motif, two AP2 sites, and other components (16). Luciferase reporter assay in A549 cells (lung-carcinoma-derived cell line naturally expressing AQP3) showed that the 5′ flanking region has a promoter activity that is upregulated fourfold by phorbol ester but not affected by cAMP. These results may explain the upregulation of AQP3 mRNA and protein in the kidney of dehydrated animals (47, 63, 84), although the induction of AQP3 mRNA was not prominent compared with that of AQP2 (87). In Brattleboro rats, which lack endogenous vasopressin, infusion of vasopressin caused induction of AQP3 expression, as well as that of AQP2 (84), indicating that the signal molecule for AQP3 is vasopressin. It may be possible that vasopressin activates the vasopressin V1 receptor coupled to the Ca^{2+}/PKC system. Presence of the V1 receptor in collecting duct cells has been reported (88). Activation of the Ca^{2+}/PKC system would then stimulate the transcription of the AQP3, possibly via AP2. In such a case, vasopressin would exert its effects in the same collecting duct cells through two different signaling systems to stimulate the transcription of the AQP2 and AQP3 genes.

Protein Level

Little is known about the regulation of AQPs at the protein level. Phosphorylation by protein kinases is an important mechanism in the alteration of transport protein function (89, 90). Among mammalian AQPs, AQP2, AQP4, and AQP5 have typical consensus sequences for phosphorylation by PKA and/or PKC. Rat AQP2 has consensus sequences for PKA, PKC, and casein kinase II (26). These sequences are conserved in human, although the PKC site moves slightly (5, 58). Kuwahara et al (41) showed that cAMP treatment indeed phosphorylated AQP2 proteins expressed in oocytes or naturally present in rat collecting tubule cells. They further showed that Ser256, the expected site in the sequence, was phosphorylated. The effect of this phosphorylation on function was examined in the oocyte. Application of cAMP increased the water permeability of AQP2-expressing oocytes by about 50%. A possible trafficking, induced by cAMP, of AQP2 protein from cytosol to the plasma membrane in the oocytes was ruled out because the amount of AQP2 on the oocyte surface membrane did not change after cAMP treatment (41). These results indicate that PKA-dependent phosphorylation increases water channel function of AQP2s. Stimulated water channel function by PKA has been reported for other AQPs. Maurel et al (91) showed that PKA-dependent phosphorylation of α-TIP, an AQP in plants, stimulates its water channel function by 80–100%. They showed a lack of such effect in a homologous AQP, γ-TIP, suggesting the specificity of the phosphorylation effect. Protein kinase-dependent phosphorylation has been reported for other members of the MIP/AQP family (92).

This attractive possibility of regulation of the AQP2 water channel function by PKA was examined by Lande et al (93) using kidney medulla-derived AQP2-rich endosomes (94). They confirmed the phosphorylation of AQP2 by PKA but did not observe the stimulation of the water permeability in their preparation. A similar negative result was reported in the oocyte expression system (35), but the presence of a cAMP-inducible water channel has been suggested using the same oocyte system (95). Thus further studies are needed to settle whether phosphorylation itself directly alters AQP2 water channel function.

Although AQP3 lacks consensus phosphorylation sequences, the possible phosphorylation by PKA or PKC in AQP3 cannot excluded. AQP1 does not have the consensus sequence for PKA, but it has been shown to be phosphorylated by PKA (39). From the physiological point of view, a rapid regulation of the AQP3 water channel may not be necessary because the water permeability of the collecting duct basolateral membrane is not stimulated by vasopressin (65).

Clearly, much more work is left for future studies of the regulation at the protein level. What are the mechanisms for the degradation of AQPs? What is the life span of AQPs, and is it regulated? What is the role of N-glycans, and are there proteins that directly interact with AQPs and alter their functions? We are just entering the protein world of AQPs, and new technologies such as electron crystallography (96, 97) will help our understanding.

Cell Level: Trafficking

AQP2   When antibodies against AQP2 became available, one of the most exciting studies was a direct demonstration of the shuttle hypothesis, the proposed explanation for the drastic change of the water permeability in vasopressin-responsive epithelia (98). It predicted that vesicles containing vasopressin-regulated water channels move between the apical membrane and cytoplasm by exo- and endocytosis via stimulation and withdrawal of vasopressin. This thesis was based on morphological studies; primarily freeze-fracture electron microscopy studies where the appearance of membrane particles assumed to be water channels correlated to vasopressin-stimulated water permeability (99–102). The antibodies against AQP2 have opened a new approach to this thesis. Immunohistochemical and immunogold labeling studies in Brattleboro rats (62, 103) and normal rats (104) have shown that administration of vasopressin increases the number of AQP2 proteins in the apical membrane of collecting duct cells five- to sixfold, demonstrating an exocytotic translocation of AQP2 to the apical membrane. Nielsen et al also showed in isolated perfused collecting ducts that the number of apical membrane AQP2s was reduced after withdrawal of AVP, demonstrating the retrieval of the apical membrane AQP2 (104). These changes in the content of AQP2 proteins in the apical membrane paralleled the water permeability of the same segments (104). Retrieval of apical-localized AQP2 to the intracellular compartment was also shown in dehydrated rats after forced water drinking (105). Brown and his associates (106) have developed a cell culture model in which stably transfected AQP2 could be translocated to the plasma membrane (basolateral membrane) after vasopressin or forskolin treatment. They further showed in the same system that AQP2 could be recycled between intracellular vesicles and the plasma membrane in the total absence of de novo protein synthesis (107). AQP2 translocation to the apical membrane after cAMP addition was also demonstrated in another cell culture system (29). Taken together, these studies have validated the long-lasting shuttle hypothesis.

The next step is the identification of the components that constitute the sorting events: transferring, docking, fusing, and retrieval of AQP2-containing vesicles to and from the plasma membrane (108). It has been pointed out that there are many resemblances between the exocytotic events in neurotransmitter-releasing neuronal cells and AVP-induced vesicle trafficking in collecting duct cells (109, 110). Studies following this speculation have shown that several proteins known to be involved in synaptic vesicle trafficking are colocalized with AQP2 in the collecting ducts (111–113), and in endosomes isolated from renal papilla (114, 115). This circumstantial evidence supporting the involvement of these factors should be directly evaluated in future studies.

Although the cell culture model described above (106, 107) showed that cAMP triggers trafficking, the interactions between vasopressin-induced intracellular cAMP accumulation and AQP2 trafficking remain unknown. Using a similar cell culture (LLCPK1 cells) model, Fushimi et al showed that cAMP treatment led the phosphorylation of AQP2 and translocation of AQP2 to the plasma membrane. This cAMP-elicited AQP2 trafficking was abolished by the introduction of the mutation to the PKA phosphorylation site (Ser256). This result indicates that sorting of AQP2-containing vesicles is dependent on the PKA-mediated phosphorylation of its own major passenger, AQP2 (116). This phosphorylation could be an initial step of many sequential events that ultimately lead to the shuttle trafficking of AQP2. Many exciting results can be expected in the near future.

AQP3   Subcellular localization of AQP3 has not been shown to be greatly regulated after long-term dehydration (47) or after acute vasopressin administration (56). Near-selective localization in the basolateral membrane and scarce presence in cytoplasmic vesicles are consistent with a lack of dynamic subcellular translocation of AQP3.

AQP2 AND AQP3 IN HEALTH AND DISEASE

As stated, mutations in the AQP2 gene cause hereditary nephrogenic diabetes insipidus (NDI). Figure 6 summarizes the mutations so far reported (58, 117–120). This information is critically important in understanding the structure-function relationship of AQP2. Because AQP2 protein may exist as homotetramers in biological membranes, and because each molecule transports water in the same manner as AQP1 (121), a recessive type of inheritance can be expected for the AQP2-defected NDI. Indeed, reported inheritance patterns are an autosomal-recessive type, and the discovered mutations are homozygotes for a single mutation or compound heterozygotes for pairs of different mutations. Thirteen

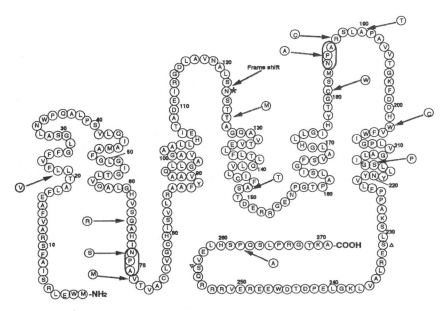

Figure 6 Reported mutations of the human AQP2 gene, which cause nephrogenic diabetes insipidus (from References 58, 117–120).

missense mutations and one frameshift mutation have been reported. Half of the mutations are present in the NPA boxes and their surrounding regions (G64S, N68S, V71M, C181W, P185A, R187C, A190T; Figure 6), supporting the notion that the NPA boxes and their surrounding regions contribute to the pore formation of the AQP channel (122). However, missense mutations exist in other places including the C terminus (P262L). The mutations in Loops C and D (T126M, A147T) are also interesting, because in our structure-function analysis of AQP2 (27), the functional importance of these two loops was shown by site-directed mutagenesis and chimeric replacements—a neat coincidence of clinical data and basic laboratory work.

These NDI-causing mutations were expressed in *Xenopus* oocytes and found to have a decreased water permeability. Immunohistochemistry of oocytes and Western blot analysis of membrane fractions of oocytes indicate that the underlying defect is misrouting of AQP2, inhibiting the surface appearance of AQP2 (119, 123). However, these expression studies were done only in oocytes, so further studies in mammalian epithelial cells will be necessary to confirm these results. Our studies of the PKA-dependent trafficking of AQP2 indicate that it can be demonstrated in mammalian epithelial cells (LLCPK1 cells) (116) but not in oocytes (41).

To address the contributions of AQP2 in several pathophysiological states where water balance is disturbed, AQP2 expression in the kidney has been examined in many experimental models. Increased expression of AQP2 mRNA and protein were observed in liver cirrhosis and SIADH models in rats for examination of an antidiuretic state. Lithium treatment (124), hypokalemia (125), ureteral obstruction (126), and low-protein diet (127) were examined as diuretic states, and decreased expression of AQP2 was observed in all cases. These data indicate that disturbed metabolism of AQP2 causes the disturbance of water balance of the body.

AQP immunostaining was used to estimate the percentage of the cysts derived from the collecting ducts in the kidneys of autosomal-dominant polycystic kidney disease, and 8–30% of total cysts were positive for AQP2 staining (128–130). The polarity of the AQP2-positive cells in the cysts was normal with respect to AQP2 and AQP3 staining (128). Immunostaining of AQP1 and AQP2 was also used to determine the cell origin of renal cell carcinoma, and the result confirms the idea of proximal or descending tubule origin of this carcinoma (131). Surprisingly, AQP2 is present in human urine, and about half of it exists in a membrane-bound form. More importantly, the amount of excretion is responsive to vasopressin, demonstrating once more that AQP2 is the vasopressin-regulated water channel (132). The benefit of this measurement in clinical situations is now under evaluation (133–135), and some degree of usefulness in the diagnosis of central diabetes insipidus has been reported (136).

ACKNOWLEDGMENTS

We are grateful to our colleagues, Drs. K Fushimi, S Uchida, N Inase, and M Kuwahara for their help. This work was supported by Grants-in-Aid for Scientific Research from the Ministry of Education, Science, and Sports.

NOTE ADDED IN PROOF

Another aqp member (AQP8) was recently cloned by us (*Biochem. Biophys. Res. Commun.* 232:714–18). AQP8 is a water-selective mercury-sensitive aquaporin.

Visit the *Annual Reviews home page* at
http://www.AnnualReviews.org.

Literature Cited

1. Preston GM, Carroll TP, Guggino WB, Agre P. 1992. Appearance of water channels in *Xenopus* oocytes expressing red cell CHIP28 protein. *Science* 256:385–87

2. Preston GM, Agre P. 1991. Isolation of the cDNA for erythrocyte integral membrane protein of 28 kilodaltons: member of an ancient channel family. *Proc. Natl. Acad. Sci. USA* 88:11110–14

3. Sasaki S, Fushimi K, Ishibashi K, Marumo F. 1995. Water channels in the kidney collecting duct. *Kidney Int.* 48:1082–87

4. Deen PM, Weghuis DO, Sinke RJ, Geurs van Kessel A, Wieringa B, et al. 1994. Assignment of the human gene for the water channel of renal collecting duct Aquaporin 2 (AQP2) to chromosome 12 region q12→q13. *Cytogen. Cell Genet.* 66:260–62

5. Sasaki S, Fushimi K, Saito H, Saito F, Uchida S, et al. 1994. Cloning, characterization, and chromosomal mapping of human aquaporin of collecting duct. *J. Clin. Invest.* 93:1250–56

6. Mulders SM, Preston GM, Deen PM, Guggino WB, van Os CH, et al. 1995. Water channel properties of major intrinsic protein of lens. *J. Biol. Chem.* 270:9010–16

7. Sparkes RS, Mohandas T, Heinzmann C, Gorin MB, Horwitz J, et al. 1986. The gene for the major intrinsic protein (MIP) of the ocular lens is assigned to human chromosome 12cen-q14. *Invest. Ophthalmol. Vis. Sci.* 27:1351–54

8. Ma T, Yang B, Kuo WL, Verkman AS. 1996. cDNA cloning and gene structure of a novel water channel expressed exclusively in human kidney: evidence for a gene cluster of aquaporins at chromosome locus 12q13. *Genomics* 35:543–50

9. Ma T, Umenishi F, Yang B, Verkman AS. 1996. Isolation of a 200 kb YAC clone derived from chromosome 12q13 which contain genes for AQP2 and an homologous aquaporin, hKID. *J. Am. Soc. Nephrol.* 7:1269 (Abst.)

10. Mulders SM, Weghuis DO, van Boxtel JA, van Kessel AG, Echevarria M, et al. 1996. Localization of the human gene for aquaporin 3 (AQP3) to chromosome 9, region p21→p12, using fluorescent in situ hybridization. *Cytogen. Cell Genet.* 72:303–5

11. Moon C, Preston GM, Griffin CA, Jabs EW, Agre P. 1993. The human aquaporin-CHIP gene. Structure, organization, and chromosomal localization. *J. Biol. Chem.* 268:15772–78

12. Deen PM, Weghuis DO, Geurs van Kessel A, Wieringa B, van Os CH. 1994. The human gene for water channel aquaporin 1 (AQP1) is localized on chromosome 7p15→p14. *Cytogen. Cell Genet.* 65:243–46

13. Yang B, Ma T, Verkman AS. 1995. cDNA cloning, gene organization, and chromosomal localization of a human mercurial insensitive water channel. Evidence for distinct transcriptional units. *J. Biol. Chem.* 270:22907–13

14. Lu M, Lee MD, Smith BL, Jung JS, Agre P, et al. 1996. The human AQP4 gene: definition of the locus encoding two water channel polypeptides in brain. *Proc. Natl. Acad. Sci. USA* 93:10908–12
15. Uchida S, Sasaki S, Fushimi K, Marumo F. 1994. Isolation of human aquaporin-CD gene. *J. Biol. Chem.* 269:23451–55
16. Inase N, Fushimi K, Ishibashi K, Uchida S, Ichioka M, et al. 1995. Isolation of human aquaporin 3 gene. *J. Biol. Chem.* 270:17913–16
17. Reizer J, Reizer A, Saier MJ. 1993. The MIP family of integral membrane channel proteins: sequence comparisons, evolutionary relationships, reconstructed pathway of evolution, and proposed functional differentiation of the two repeated halves of the proteins. *Crit. Rev. Biochem. Mol. Biol.* 28:235–57
18. Park JH, Saier MJ. 1996. Phylogenetic characterization of the MIP family of transmembrane channel proteins. *J. Membr. Biol.* 153:171–80
19. Ishibashi K, Sasaki S, Fushimi K, Uchida S, Kuwahara M, et al. 1994. Molecular cloning and expression of a member of the aquaporin family with permeability to glycerol and urea in addition to water expressed at the basolateral membrane of kidney collecting duct cells. *Proc. Natl. Acad. Sci. USA* 91:6269–73
20. Ishibashi K, Kuwahara M, Gu Y, Kageyama Y, Tohsaka A, et al. 1997. Cloning and functional expression of a new water channel abundantly expressed in the testis also permeable to glycerol and urea. *J. Biol. Chem.* 272:20782–86
21. Fushimi K, Bai L, Marumo F, Sasaki S. 1997. Isolation of a gene encoding nodulin-like intrinsic protein of *Escherichia coli. Biochem. Mol. Biol. Int.* 41:995–1003
22. Calamita G, Bishai WR, Preston GM, Guggino WB, Agre P. 1995. Molecular cloning and characterization of AqpZ, a water channel from *Escherichia coli. Biol. Chem.* 270:29063–66
23. Ishibashi K, Sasaki S. 1997. The dichotomy of MIP family suggests the two separate origins of water channels. *News Physiol. Sci.* In press
24. Gorin MB, Yancey SB, Cline J, Revel JP, Horwitz J. 1984. The major intrinsic protein (MIP) of the bovine lens fiber membrane: characterization and structure based on cDNA cloning. *Cell* 39:49–59
25. Echevarria M, Windhager EE, Frindt G. 1996. Selectivity of the renal collecting duct water channel aquaporin-3. *J. Biol. Chem.* 271:25079–82
26. Fushimi K, Uchida S, Hara Y, Hirata Y, Marumo F, et al. 1993. Cloning and expression of apical membrane water channel of rat kidney collecting tubule. *Nature* 361:549–52
27. Bai L, Fushimi K, Sasaki S, Marumo F. 1996. Structure of aquaporin-2 vasopressin water channel. *J. Biol. Chem.* 271:5171–76
28. Luyten K, Albertyn J, Skibbe WF, Prior BA, Ramos J, et al. 1995. Fps1, a yeast member of the MIP family of channel proteins, is a facilitator for glycerol uptake and efflux and is inactive under osmotic stress. *EMBO J.* 14:1360–71
29. Valenti G, Frigeri A, Ronco PM, D'Ettorre C, Svelto M. 1996. Expression and functional analysis of water channels in a stably AQP2-transfected human collecting duct cell line. *J. Biol. Chem.* 271:24365–70
30. Ma T, Frigeri A, Tsai ST, Verbavatz JM, Verkman AS. 1993. Localization and functional analysis of CHIP28 water channels in stably transfected Chinese hamster ovary cells. *J. Biol. Chem.* 268:22756–64
31. Delporte C, O'Connell BC, He X, Ambudkar IS, Agre P, et al. 1996. Adenovirus-mediated expression of aquaporin-5 in epithelial cells. *J. Biol. Chem.* 271:22070–75
32. Zeidel ML, Ambudkar SV, Smith BL, Agre P. 1992. Reconstitution of functional water channels in liposomes containing purified red cell CHIP28 protein. *Biochemistry* 31:7436–40
33. van Hoek AN, Verkman AS. 1992. Functional reconstitution of the isolated erythrocyte water channel CHIP28. *J. Biol. Chem.* 267:18267–69
34. Agre P, Brown D, Nielsen S. 1995. Aquaporin water channels: unanswered questions and unresolved controversies. *Curr. Opin. Cell Biol.* 7:472–83
35. Ma T, Hasegawa H, Skach WR, Frigeri A, Verkman AS. 1994. Expression, functional analysis, and in situ hybridization of a cloned rat kidney collecting duct water channel. *Am. J. Physiol.* 266:C189–97
36. Fushimi K, Sasaki S, Yamamoto T, Hayashi M, Furukawa T, et al. 1994. Functional characterization and cell immunolocalization of AQP-CD water channel in kidney collecting duct. *Am. J. Physiol.* 267:F573–82
37. Abrami L, Tacnet F, Ripoche P. 1995. Evidence for a glycerol pathway through

aquaporin 1 (CHIP28) channels. *Pflügers Arch.* 430:447–58

38. Abrami L, Berthonaud V, Deen PM, Rousselet G, Tacnet F, et al. 1996. Glycerol permeability of mutant aquaporin 1 and other AQP-MIP proteins: inhibition studies. *Pflügers Arch.* 431:408–14

39. Yool AJ, Stamer WD, Regan JW. 1996. Forskolin stimulation of water and cation permeability in aquaporin 1 water channels. *Science* 273:1216–18

40. Agre P, Lee MD, Davidas S, Guggino WB. 1997. Aquaporins and ion conductance. *Science* 275:1490

41. Kuwahara M, Fushimi K, Terada Y, Bai L, Marumo F, et al. 1995. cAMP-dependent phosphorylation stimulates water permeability of aquaporin-collecting duct water channel protein expressed in *Xenopus* oocytes. *J. Biol. Chem.* 270:10384–87

42. Sasaki S, Uchida S, Kuwahara M, Fushimi K, Marumo F. 1997. Aquaporins and ion conductance. *Science* 275:1490–91

43. Maurel C, Reizer J, Schroeder JI, Chrispeels MJ. 1993. The vacuolar membrane protein gamma-TIP creates water specific channels in *Xenopus* oocytes. *EMBO J.* 12:2241–47

44. Maurel C, Reizer J, Schroeder JI, Chrispeels MJ, Saier MJ. 1994. Functional characterization of the *Escherichia coli* glycerol facilitator, GlpF, in *Xenopus* oocytes. *J. Biol. Chem.* 269:11869–72

45. Echevarria M, Windhager EE, Tate SS, Frindt G. 1994. Cloning and expression of AQP3, a water channel from the medullary collecting duct of rat kidney. *Proc. Natl. Acad. Sci. USA* 91:10997–1001

46. Ma T, Frigeri A, Hasegawa H, Verkman AS. 1994. Cloning of a water channel homolog expressed in brain meningeal cells and kidney collecting duct that functions as a stilbene-sensitive glycerol transporter. *J. Biol. Chem.* 269:21845–49

47. Ishibashi K, Sasaki S, Fushimi K, Yamamoto T, Kuwahara M, et al. 1997. Immunolocalization and effect of dehydration on AQP3, a basolateral water channel of kidney collecting ducts. *Am. J. Physiol.* 272:F235–41

48. Brown D, Katsura T, Kawashima M, Verkman AS, Sabolic I. 1995. Cellular distribution of the aquaporins: a family of water channel proteins. *Histochem. Cell Biol.* 104:1–9

49. Knepper MA, Wade JB, Terris J, Ecelbarger CA, Marples D, et al. 1996. Renal aquaporins. *Kidney Int.* 49:1712–17

50. Nielsen S, Marples D, Frokiaer J, Knepper M, Agre P. 1996. The aquaporin family of water channels in kidney: an update on physiology and pathophysiology of aquaporin-2. *Kidney Int.* 49:1718–23

51. Nielsen S, Agre P. 1995. The aquaporin family of water channels in kidney. *Kidney Int.* 48:1057–68

52. Verkman AS, van Hoek AN, Ma T, Frigeri A, Skach WR, et al. 1996. Water transport across mammalian cell membranes. *Am. J. Physiol.* 270:C12–30

53. Kishore BK, Mandon B, Oza NB, DiGiovanni SR, Coleman RA, et al. 1996. Rat renal arcade segment expresses vasopressin-regulated water channel and vasopressin V2 receptor. *J. Clin. Invest.* 97:2763–71

54. Nielsen S, DiGiovanni SR, Christensen EI, Knepper MA, Harris HW. 1993. Cellular and subcellular immunolocalization of vasopressin-regulated water channel in rat kidney. *Proc. Natl. Acad. Sci. USA* 90:11663–67

55. Yamamoto T, Sasaki S, Fushimi K, Kawasaki K, Yaoita E, et al. 1995. Localization and expression of a collecting duct water channel, aquaporin, in hydrated and dehydrated rats. *Exp. Nephrol.* 3:193–201

56. Yamamoto T, Sasaki S, Fushimi K, Ishibashi K, Yaoita E, et al. 1997. Expression of AQP family in rat kidneys during the development and maturation. *Am. J. Physiol.* 272:F198–204

57. Verkman AS. 1992. Water channels in cell membranes. *Annu. Rev. Physiol.* 54:97–108

58. Deen PM, Verdijk MA, Knoers NV, Wieringa B, Monnens LA, et al. 1994. Requirement of human renal water channel aquaporin-2 for vasopressin-dependent concentration of urine. *Science* 264:92–95

59. King LS, Agre P. 1996. Pathophysiology of the aquaporin water channels. *Annu. Rev. Physiol.* 58:619–48

60. Preston GM, Smith BL, Zeidel ML, Moulds JJ, Agre P. 1994. Mutations in aquaporin-1 in phenotypically normal humans without functional CHIP water channels. *Science* 265:1585–87

61. Shiels A, Bassnett S. 1996. Mutations in the founder of the MIP gene family underlie cataract development in the mouse. *Nature Genet.* 12:212–15

62. Yamamoto T, Sasaki S, Fushimi K, Ishibashi K, Yaoita E, et al. 1995. Vasopressin increases AQP-CD water channel in apical membrane of collecting duct cells in Brattleboro rats. *Am. J. Physiol.* 268:C1546–51

63. Ecelbarger CA, Terris J, Frindt G, Echevarria M, Marples D, et al. 1995. Aquaporin-3 water channel localization and regulation in rat kidney. *Am. J. Physiol.* 269:F663–72

64. Frigeri A, Gropper MA, Turck CW, Verkman AS. 1995. Immunolocalization of the mercurial-insensitive water channel and glycerol intrinsic protein in epithelial cell plasma membranes. *Proc. Natl. Acad. Sci. USA* 92:4328–31

65. Strange K, Spring KR. 1987. Cell membrane water permeability of rabbit cortical collecting duct. *J. Membr. Biol.* 96:27–43

66. Strange K, Spring KR. 1987. Absence of significant cellular dilution during ADH-stimulated water reabsorption. *Science* 235:1068–70

67. Flamion B, Spring KR. 1990. Water permeability of apical and basolateral cell membranes of rat inner medullary collecting duct. *Am. J. Physiol.* 259:F986–99

68. Kuwahara M, Verkman AS. 1989. Pre-steady-state analysis of the turn-on and turn-off of water permeability in the kidney collecting tubule. *J. Membr. Biol.* 110:57–65

69. Robertson GL, Berl T. 1996. Pathophysiology of water metabolism. In *The Kidney,* ed. B. Brenner, 1:873–928 Philadelphia: Saunders. 5th ed.

70. Lankford SP, Chou CL, Terada Y, Wall SM, Wade JB, et al. 1991. Regulation of collecting duct water permeability independent of cAMP-mediated AVP response. *Am. J. Physiol.* 261:F554–66

71. Epstein FH, Kleeman CR, Hendrikx A. 1957. The influence of bodily hydration on the renal concentrating process. *J. Clin. Invest* 36:629–34

72. Hozawa S, Holtzman EJ, Ausiello DA. 1996. cAMP motifs regulating transcription in the aquaporin 2 gene. *Am. J. Physiol.* 270:C1695–702

73. Rai T, Uchida S, Furuno M, Marumo F, Sasaki S. 1997. Cloning of rat and mouse aquaporin-2 gene promoters and identification of a negative *cis*-regulatory element. *Am. J. Physiol.* 273:F264–73

74. Igarashi P, Whyte DA, Li K, Nagami GT. 1996. Cloning and kidney cell-specific activity of the promoter of the murine renal Na-K-Cl cotransporter gene. *J. Biol. Chem.* 271:9666–74

75. Mandon B, Bellanger AC, Elalouf JM. 1995. Inverse PCR-mediated cloning of the promoter for the rat vasopressin V2 receptor gene. *Pflügers Arch.* 430:12–18

76. Uchida S, Matsumura Y, Rai T, Sasaki S, Marumo F. 1997. Regulation of aquaporin-2 gene transcription by GATA-3.

Biochem. Biophy. Res. Commun. 232: 65–68

77. Furuno M, Uchida S, Marumo F, Sasaki S. 1996. Repressive regulation of the aquaporin-2 gene. *Am. J. Physiol.* 271:F854–60

78. Matsumura Y, Uchida S, Furuno M, Marumo F, Sasaki S. 1997. Cyclic AMP and hypertonicity increase AQP-2 transcription through their responsive element. *J. Am. Soc. Nephrol.* 8:861–67

79. Fujita N, Ishikawa SE, Sasaki S, Fujisawa G, Fushimi K, et al. 1995. Role of water channel AQP-CD in water retention in SIADH and cirrhotic rats. *Am. J. Physiol.* 269:F926–31

80. Hayashi M, Sasaki S, Tsuganezawa H, Monkawa T, Kitajima W, et al. 1996. Role of vasopressin V2 receptor in acute regulation of aquaporin-2. *Kidney Blood Press. Res.* 19:32–37

81. Sachs AB. 1993. Messenger RNA degradation in eukaryotes. *Cell* 74:413–21

82. Takenaka M, Preston AS, Kwon HM, Handler JS. 1994. The tonicity-sensitive element that mediates increased transcription of the betaine transporter gene in response to hypertonic stress. *J. Biol. Chem.* 269:29379–81

83. DiGiovanni SR, Nielsen S, Christensen EI, Knepper MA. 1994. Regulation of collecting duct water channel expression by vasopressin in Brattleboro rat. *Proc. Natl. Acad. Sci. USA* 91:8984–88

84. Terris J, Ecelbarger CA, Nielsen S, Knepper MA. 1996. Long-term regulation of four renal aquaporins in rats. *Am. J. Physiol.* 271:F414–22

85. Kishore BK, Terris JM, Knepper MA. 1996. Quantitation of aquaporin-2 abundance in microdissected collecting ducts: axial distribution and control by AVP. *Am. J. Physiol.* 271:F62–70

86. Hayashi M, Sasaki S, Tsuganezawa H, Monkawa T, Kitajima W, et al. 1994. Expression and distribution of aquaporin of collecting duct are regulated by vasopressin V2 receptor in rat kidney. *J. Clin. Invest.* 94:1778–83

87. Umenishi F, Verkman AS, Gropper MA. 1996. Quantitative analysis of aquaporin mRNA expression in rat tissues by RNase protection assay. *DNA Cell Biol.* 15:475–80

88. Terada Y, Tomita K, Nonoguchi H, Yang T, Marumo F. 1993. Different localization and regulation of two types of vasopressin receptor messenger RNA in microdissected rat nephron segments using reverse transcription polymerase chain reaction. *J. Clin. Invest.* 92:2339–45

89. Edelman AM, Blumenthal DK, Krebs EG. 1987. Protein serine/threonine kinases. *Annu. Rev. Biochem.* 56:567–613

90. Levitan IB. 1994. Modulation of ion channels by protein phosphorylation and dephosphorylation. *Annu. Rev. Physiol.* 56:193–212

91. Maurel C, Kado RT, Guern J, Chrispeels MJ. 1995. Phosphorylation regulates the water channel activity of the seed-specific aquaporin alpha-TIP. *EMBO J.* 14:3028–35

92. Ehring GR, Lagos N, Zampighi GA, Hall JE. 1992. Phosphorylation modulates the voltage dependence of channels reconstituted from the major intrinsic protein of lens fiber membranes. *J. Membr. Biol.* 126:75–88

93. Lande MB, Jo I, Zeidel ML, Somers M, Harris HJ. 1996. Phosphorylation of aquaporin-2 does not alter the membrane water permeability of rat papillary water channel-containing vesicles. *J. Biol. Chem.* 271:5552–57

94. Harris HJ, Zeidel ML, Jo I, Hammond TG. 1994. Characterization of purified endosomes containing the antidiuretic hormone-sensitive water channel from rat renal papilla. *J. Biol. Chem.* 269:11993–2000

95. Echevarria M, Frindt G, Preston GM, Milovanovic S, Agre P, et al. 1993. Expression of multiple water channel activities in *Xenopus* oocytes injected with mRNA from rat kidney. *J. Gen. Physiol.* 101:827–41

96. Mitra AK, van Hoek AN, Wiener MC, Verkman AS, Yeager M. 1995. The CHIP28 water channel visualized in ice by electron crystallography. *Nat. Struct. Biol.* 2:726–29

97. Walz T, Typke D, Smith BL, Agre P, Engel A. 1995. Projection map of aquaporin-1 determined by electron crystallography. *Nat. Struct. Biol.* 2:730–32

98. Wade JB, Stetson DL, Lewis SA. 1981. ADH action: evidence for a membrane shuttle mechanism. *Ann. NY Acad. Sci.* 372:106–17

99. Brown D. 1989. Membrane recycling and epithelial cell function. *Am. J. Physiol.* 256:F1–12

100. Handler JS. 1988. Antidiuretic hormone moves membranes. *Am. J. Physiol.* 255:F375–82

101. Harris HW, Strange K, Zeidel ML. 1991. Current understanding of the cellular biology and molecular structure of the antidiuretic hormone stimulated water transport pathway. *J. Clin. Invest.* 88:1–8

102. Verkman AS. 1989. Mechanisms and regulation of water permeability in renal epithelia. *Am. J. Physiol.* 257:C837–50

103. Sabolic I, Katsura T, Verbavatz JM, Brown D. 1995. The AQP2 water channel: effect of vasopressin treatment, microtubule disruption, and distribution in neonatal rats. *J. Membr. Biol.* 143:165–75

104. Nielsen S, Chou CL, Marples D, Christensen EI, Kishore BK, et al. 1995. Vasopressin increases water permeability of kidney collecting duct by inducing translocation of aquaporin-CD water channels to plasma membrane. *Proc. Natl. Acad. Sci. USA* 92:1013–17

105. Saito T, Ishikawa S, Sasaki S, Fujita N, Fushimi K, et al. 1997. Alteration in water channel AQP-2 by removal of AVP stimulation in collecting duct cells of dehydrated rats. *Am. J. Physiol.* 271:F183–91

106. Katsura T, Verbavatz JM, Farinas J, Ma T, Ausiello DA, et al. 1995. Constitutive and regulated membrane expression of aquaporin 1 and aquaporin 2 water channels in stably transfected LLC-PK1 epithelial cells. *Proc. Natl. Acad. Sci. USA* 92:7212–16

107. Katsura T, Ausiello DA, Brown D. 1996. Direct demonstration of aquaporin-2 water channel recycling in stably transfected LLC-PK1 epithelial cells. *Am. J. Physiol.* 270:F548–53

108. Rothman JE. 1994. Mechanisms of intracellular protein transport. *Nature* 372:55–63

109. Brown D, Stow JL. 1996. Protein trafficking and polarity in kidney epithelium: from cell biology to physiology. *Physiol. Rev.* 76:245–97

110. Hays RM, Franki N, Simon H, Gao Y. 1994. Antidiuretic hormone and exocytosis: lessons from neurosecretion. *Am. J. Physiol.* 267:C1507–24

111. Franki N, Macaluso F, Schubert W, Gunther L, Hays RM. 1995. Water channel-carrying vesicles in the rat IMCD contain cellubrevin. *Am. J. Physiol.* 268:C792–97

112. Nielsen S, Marples D, Birn H, Mohtashami M, Dalby NO, et al. 1995. Expression of VAMP-2-like protein in kidney collecting duct intracellular vesicles. Colocalization with aquaporin-2 water channels. *J. Clin. Invest.* 96:1834–44

113. Mandon B, Chou CL, Nielsen S, Knepper MA. 1996. Syntaxin-4 is localized to the apical plasma membrane of rat renal collecting duct cells: possible role in aquaporin-2 trafficking. *J. Clin. Invest.* 98:906–13

114. Jo I, Harris HW, Amendt RA, Majewski RR, Hammond TG. 1995. Rat kidney papilla contains abundant synaptobrevin

protein that participates in the fusion of antidiuretic hormone-regulated water channel-containing endosomes in vitro. *Proc. Natl. Acad. Sci. USA* 92:1876–80

115. Liebenhoff U, Rosenthal W. 1995. Identification of Rab3-, Rab5a- and synaptobrevin II-like proteins in a preparation of rat kidney vesicles containing the vasopressin-regulated water channel. *FEBS Lett.* 365:209–13

116. Fushimi K, Sasaki S, Marumo F. 1997. Phosphorylation of the serine 256 is required for cAMP-dependent regulatory exocytosis of aquaporin 2 water channel. *J. Biol. Chem.* 272:14800–4

117. van Lieburg AF, Verdijk MA, Knoers VV, van Essen AJ, Proesmans W, et al. 1994. Patients with autosomal nephrogenic diabetes insipidus homozygous for mutations in the aquaporin 2 water-channel gene. *Am. J. Hum. Genet.* 55:648–52

118. Oksche A, Moller A, Dickson J, Rosendahl W, Rascher W, et al. 1996. Two novel mutations in the aquaporin-2 and the vasopressin V2 receptor genes in patients with congenital nephrogenic diabetes insipidus. *Hum. Genet.* 98:587–89

119. Mulders SM, Knoers NVAM, Van Lieburg AF, Monnens LAH, Leumann E, et al. 1997. New mutations in the AQP2 gene in nephrogenic diabetes insipidus resulting in functional but misrouted water channels. *J. Am. Soc. Nephrol.* 8:242–48

120. Bichet DG, Arthus MF, Lonergan M, Balfe W, Skorecki K, et al. 1995. Autosomal dominant autosomal recessive nephrogenic diabetes insipidus: novel mutations in AQP2 gene. *J. Am. Soc. Nephrol.* 6:717 (Abstr.)

121. Agre P, Preston GM, Smith BL, Jung JS, Raina S, et al. 1993. Aquaporin CHIP: the archetypal molecular water channel. *Am. J. Physiol.* 265:F463–76

122. Jung JS, Preston GM, Smith BL, Guggino WB, Agre P. 1994. Molecular structure of the water channel through aquaporin CHIP. The hourglass model. *J. Biol. Chem.* 269:14648–54

123. Deen PM, Croes H, van Aubel RA, Ginsel LA, van Os CH. 1995. Water channels encoded by mutant aquaporin-2 genes in nephrogenic diabetes insipidus are impaired in their cellular routing. *J. Clin. Invest.* 95:2291–96

124. Marples D, Christensen S, Christensen EI, Ottosen PD, Nielsen S. 1995. Lithium-induced downregulation of aquaporin-2 water channel expression in rat kidney medulla. *J. Clin. Invest.* 95:1838–45

125. Marples D, Frokiaer J, Dorup J, Knepper MA, Nielsen S. 1996. Hypokalemia-induced downregulation of aquaporin-2 water channel expression in rat kidney medulla and cortex. *J. Clin. Invest.* 97:1960–68

126. Frokiaer J, Marples D, Knepper MA, Nielsen S. 1996. Bilateral ureteral obstruction downregulates expression of vasopressin-sensitive AQP-2 water channel in rat kidney. *Am. J. Physiol.* 270:F657–68

127. Sands JM, Naruse M, Jacobs JD, Wilcox JN, Klein JD. 1996. Changes in aquaporin-2 protein contribute to the urine concentrating defect in rats fed a low-protein diet. *J. Clin. Invest.* 97:2807–14

128. Hayashi M, Yamaji Y, Monkawa T, Yoshida T, Tsuganezawa H, et al. 1997. Expression and localization of the water channels in human autosomal dominant polycystic kidney disease. *Nephron* 75:321–26

129. Bachinsky DR, Sabolic I, Emmanouel DS, Jefferson DM, Carone FA, et al. 1995. Water channel expression in human ADPKD kidneys. *Am. J. Physiol.* 268:F398–403

130. Devuyst O, Burrow CR, Smith BL, Agre P, Knepper MA, et al. 1996. Expression of aquaporins-1 and -2 during nephrogenesis and in autosomal dominant polycystic kidney disease. *Am. J. Physiol.* 271:F169–83

131. Kageyama Y, Sasaki S, Yamamura Y, Oshima H, Ikawa Y. 1996. Water channel protein subtype suggests the origin of renal cell carcinoma. *J. Urol.* 156:291–95

132. Kanno K, Sasaki S, Hirata Y, Ishikawa S, Fushimi K, et al. 1995. Urinary excretion of aquaporin-2 in patients with diabetes insipidus. *N. Engl. J. Med.* 332:1540–45

133. Rai T, Sekine K, Kanno K, Hata K, Miura M, et al. 1997. Urinary excretion of aquaporin-2 water channel protein in human and rat. *J. Am. Soc. Nephrol.* In press

134. Elliot S, Goldsmith P, Knepper M, Haughey M, Olson B. 1996. Urinary excretion of aquaporin-2 in humans: a potential marker of collecting duct responsiveness to vasopressin. *J. Am. Soc. Nephrol.* 7:403–9

135. Deen PM, van Aubel RA, van Lieburg AF, van Os CH. 1996. Urinary content of aquaporin 1 and 2 in nephrogenic diabetes insipidus. *J. Am. Soc. Nephrol.* 7:836–41

136. Saito T, Ishikawa S, Sasaki S, Nakamura T, Rokkaku K, et al. 1997. Urinary excretion of aquaporin-2 in the diagnosis of central diabetes insipidus. *J. Clin. Endocr. Metab.* 82:1823–27

Annu. Rev. Physiol. 1998. 60:221–42

MOLECULAR MECHANISMS OF PROSTAGLANDIN TRANSPORT

Victor L. Schuster

Departments of Medicine and Physiology and Biophysics, Albert Einstein College of Medicine, Bronx, New York 10461; e-mail: schuster@aecom.yu.edu

KEY WORDS: eicosanoids, carrier proteins, biological transport, molecular cloning

ABSTRACT

Despite the fact that prostaglandins (PGs) have low intrinsic permeabilities across the plasma membrane, they must cross it twice: first upon release from the cytosol into the blood, and again upon cellular uptake prior to oxidation. Until recently, there were no cloned carriers that transported PGs. PGT is a broadly-expressed, 12-membrane-spanning domain integral membrane protein. When heterologously expressed in HeLa cells or *Xenopus* oocytes, it catalyzes the rapid, specific, and high-affinity uptake of PGE_2, $PGF_{2\alpha}$, PGD_2, 8-iso-$PGF_{2\alpha}$, and thromboxane B_2. Functional studies indicate that PGT transports its substrate as the charged anion. The PGT substrate specificity and inhibitor profile match remarkably well with earlier in situ studies on the metabolic clearance of PGs by rat lung. Because PGT expression is especially high in this tissue, it is likely that PGT mediates the membrane step in PG clearance by the pulmonary circulation. Evidence is presented that PGT may play additional roles in other tissues and that there may be additional PG transporters yet to be identified molecularly.

INTRODUCTION

Prostaglandins (PGs) and thromboxanes (Txs) play fundamental roles in health and disease and, increasingly, as therapeutic agents. Examples of these broad roles include gastric protection and peptic ulcer formation; pregnancy, labor, delivery, abortion, luteolysis, and menstruation; glaucoma; blood pressure control; intestinal fluid secretion; liver protection and damage; airway resistance and asthma; fever; and modulation of inflammatory cells (2, 7, 9, 28, 31, 52, 70, 71, 76, 93, 99, 104, 106, 115, 116, 126, 131).

PG Synthesis and Release

PGs are synthesized from arachidonic acid by prostaglandin endoperoxide H synthases (PGHS) types 1 and 2 (PGHS-1 and PGHS-2, also referred to as cyclooxygenases, or COX-1 and COX-2) (118). Both enzymes catalyze the formation of PGH_2 from arachidonic acid, and both are inhibited by non-steroidal anti-inflammatory drugs such as aspirin. PGHS-1 is generally constitutively active, whereas PGHS-2 is induced by growth factors, cytokines, and tumor promoters (118). PGH_2 is converted to any of several other PGs including PGE_2 and $PGF_{2\alpha}$.

Both PGHS-1 and -2 have been localized immunocytochemically to the lumen of the endoplasmic reticulum (ER) and the outer nuclear envelope (88), which implies that the site of PG synthesis is intracellular. This is further supported by two observations. First, the enzymes that metabolize PGH_2 to thromboxane and PGE have been immunocytochemically localized to the cytosolic face of the ER (111, 119). Second, the introduction of surrogate fluorescent PGHS substrates into cells has clearly revealed PGHS enzymatic activity within the cytosol (88, 89). These data have led to a model in which polar PGs (e.g. PGE_2 and $PGF_{2\alpha}$) are formed in the ER and then rapidly gain access to the cytosol, after which they exit the cell across the plasma membrane (118).

In some respects, this model poorly explains some of the available data. When labeled arachidonate or PGH_2 was added to intact endothelial cells, radioactivity rapidly appeared in the surrounding medium as PGI_2, PGE_2, and other prostanoids (82), but the endothelial cells themselves contained no label (118). Because diffusional efflux of PG from the cytosol through the plasma membrane would require an outwardly directed concentration gradient, the cell should have contained at least some label. Similarly, when rabbit renal slices were incubated with tracer arachidonate, tracer PGE_2 and $PGF_{2\alpha}$ appeared in the surrounding medium but no labeled prostanoids were found intracellularly (39). Because no cell-surface PGHS has been found immunocytochemically (WL Smith, personal communication), it is curious that the enzyme behaves as if at least some of it were functionally present at the cell surface (18). An alternative explanation is that the rate of efflux in these experiments was so great that there was no label left intracellularly.

PG Diffusion Across Cell Membranes

If polar PGs (e.g. PGE_2 and $PGF_{2\alpha}$) are formed in the cytosol, the plasma membrane must be highly permeable so that they can rapidly efflux. It is often assumed that protonated PGs are highly permeant, but in fact, this is not the case.

PGs are organic anions with a pK_a of ≈ 5. At physiological pH, they exist primarily as the charged species (5, 110, 124). Baroody & Bito reported that rabbit erythrocytes have a very low influx permeability to tracer PGE_1, PGE_2, $PGF_{2\alpha}$, PGI_2, 6-keto-$PGF_{1\alpha}$ and TxB_2 (8, 21). Similarly, Garcia-Perez & Smith reported that in monolayers of cultured canine kidney cortical collecting ducts, diffusion of tracer PGE_2 across the monolayer was equal to that of inulin, but was much lower than that of Na^+, suggesting that PGE_2 crossed the monolayer via the tight junctions at a very low rate (55).

Our laboratory has also examined the permeabilities of several tracer prostanoids by measuring their influx into cultured HeLa cells. Although arachidonic acid has a high permeability, most other prostanoids do not (64, 69, 80). We addressed more directly the issue of PG efflux using native *Xenopus* oocytes. Efflux resulting from injecting tracer PGE_2 varied linearly as a function of the amount of tracer PGE_2 injected, suggesting simple diffusion. Both influx and efflux permeability coefficients for PGE_2 were $\approx 1 \times 10^{-6}$ cm/sec (B Chan & VL Schuster, unpublished observations). In absolute terms, these values are comparable to those for the influx of urea (130) and for the efflux of taurocholate (87) in native oocytes. Thus in the absence of a carrier, most PGs diffuse poorly across biological membranes.

Metabolic Clearance of PGs

PGs must also cross the plasma membrane after they have finished their job. Newly released PGE_2 and $PGF_{2\alpha}$ are autacoids: They bind to specific receptors on the same or nearby cells, signaling a wide variety of events through any of several G protein–coupled cascades (36). The signal must be terminated locally, because a single type of molecule (e.g. PGE_2) can signal diverse biological events, depending upon the cell type. Without local termination, a stray PGE_2 molecule, such as one released by the renal papilla for purposes of modulating vasa recta blood flow or medullary tubular salt transport, might inappropriately modulate uterine contraction or gastric acid production.

There is considerable evidence that extracellular PGs are taken up by a carrier-mediated transport process and degraded in the cytosol. Experiments in the 1960s and 1970s showed that, although PGE_1 and PGE_2 are readily metabolized by tissues to the corresponding 15-keto PG, there is little or no PG 15 dehydrogenase activity in the blood or plasma of humans, dogs, or cats (38, 53, 56, 62, 83, 95, 117, 128). However, when cells are ruptured, an intracellular PG dehydrogenase is revealed that is capable of oxidizing many diverse prostanoids (4, 94). Similarly, bromcresol green (BCG) has no effect on PG metabolism by cell-free rat homogenates, but it inhibits PG metabolism by intact tissue (20, 23). Taken together, these data indicate that metabolic clearance occurs via two steps: (*a*) selective PG uptake across the plasma membrane and (*b*) nonselective oxidation inside the cell.

ACTIVE TRANSPORT OF PGs

Many papers beginning in the late 1960s presented evidence consistent with carrier-mediated PG transport, which can be considered in three groups: (a) transport and metabolic clearance by the lung, (b) transport by non-lung tissues that metabolize PGs, and (c) transport by tissues that do not metabolize PGs.

Transport by the Lung: High Specificity

The perfused lung serves as an excellent model of PG uptake and oxidation. When PGE_1, PGE_2, PGD_2, or $PGF_{2\alpha}$ are injected into perfusate of the isolated lung, there is rapid, essentially single-pass metabolic clearance that can be modeled kinetically as carrier-mediated (37, 38, 40, 41, 53, 77, 78, 84, 102, 108). There is substantially less clearance of PGA (23, 84, 102) and essentially none of PGI_2 or 6-keto $PGF_{1\alpha}$ (49, 86, 108, 122).

An extensive series of investigations by Eling and co-workers revealed the precise structural requirements for PG uptake by the rat lung (Figure 1). These include a carboxyl group at the 1-position, a 15-OH group in the S configuration, an oxygen group at position 11, and a double bond at positions 13–14 (51) (these specificities will be considered further below).

Several inhibitors of pulmonary PG metabolic clearance have been identified; among the most effective are indocyanine green (ICG) and BCG (23, 103). The degree of inhibition depends, to some extent, on the presence or absence of protein or blood in the perfusate (41).

Metabolites, primarily 15-keto PG and the 13,14 dihydro 15-keto PG, appear in the pulmonary venous effluent promptly upon infusion of the native PG (4, 38, 43, 122). As with transport, the appearance of metabolites depends on whether blood and/or proteins are present in the perfusate (4, 37, 38, 59). The site of metabolism appears to be the type II alveolar cells (43). Inhibitors of pulmonary transport inhibit the appearance of these metabolites (20, 23), a finding consistent with the two-step model. Of interest, the uptake (transport) of metabolites such as 15-keto $PGF_{2\alpha}$ and 13,14 dihydro 15-keto PGE_1 is low (4, 108). Because the latter has the same albumin binding and oil-water partition coefficient (lipophilicity) as PGE_1 (108), it appears that there is an entry carrier for the native PGs but not for their metabolites. These metabolic pathways appear to be operative in humans: On infusion of tracer PGE_1 intravenously, the 15-keto PG and 13,14 dihydro metabolites appear rapidly in the circulation (33, 113). The mechanism by which metabolites exit the lung cell and enter the circulation remains unclear.

Transport by Non-Lung Tissues That Metabolize PGs

Other tissues also exhibit uptake and metabolism of PGs. The most convincing evidence for concentrative, carrier-mediated PG transport in any system was

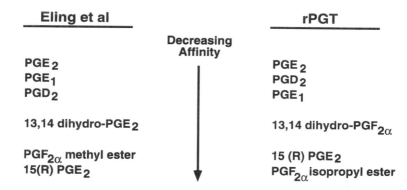

A

B

Eling et al	Decreasing Affinity	rPGT
PGE$_2$		PGE$_2$
PGE$_1$		PGD$_2$
PGD$_2$		PGE$_1$
13,14 dihydro-PGE$_2$		13,14 dihydro-PGF$_{2\alpha}$
PGF$_{2\alpha}$ methyl ester		15 (R) PGE$_2$
15(R) PGE$_2$		PGF$_{2\alpha}$ isopropyl ester

Figure 1 (*A*) Structure of PGE$_2$ as a representative PG. Selected carbons are numbered. (*B*) Selected comparison of the rank order of substrate specificities obtained by Eling et al using the isolated, perfused rat lung preparation (4, 50, 51, 59) versus that of rat PGT expressed heterologously in vitro in HeLa cells (64). PGs are grouped as having high affinity (PGE$_1$, PGE$_2$, and PGD$_2$), moderate affinity (13,14 dihydro PGE$_2$), or low affinity (15-R PGE$_2$ and the 1-position esters of PGE$_2$ or PGF$_{2\alpha}$).

adduced by Bito's laboratory using the rabbit vagina. When the vagina was studied as an isolated, in vitro transporting epithelium with controlled solutions on each side of the preparation, tracer PGF$_{2\alpha}$ exhibited a large mucosa-to-serosa flux, but a negligible serosal-to-mucosal flux. Eversion of the vaginal sac reversed the direction of the fluxes (16). These data clearly indicate active transport. About one-third of the transported PGF$_{2\alpha}$ was converted to metabolites, a finding that does not detract from the conclusion that active transport occurred. Interestingly, vaginal PG transport is not found in the cat or rat (30).

The liver and kidney cortex also take up and metabolize PGE and PGF (12, 13, 17, 25, 29, 42, 85). Hepatic uptake takes place almost exclusively in hepatocytes (120), and degradation occurs via the peroxisomal cytochrome P-450 system (46–48, 74). In the kidney, the proximal straight tubule takes up

PGE_2 via a basolateral concentrative step and then secretes either native PGE_2 or its metabolites into the lumen (63).

Although human HL-60 cells rapidly convert PGE_2 to 15-keto PGE_2 (1), PGE/F uptake is not observed in muscle (29).

As opposed to the negligible extraction of PGI_2 by the lung, there is clear PGI_2 extraction by the kidney, liver, and hindquarters (49, 122), although the renal metabolism is much less for PGI_2 than for PGE_2 (32).

Transport by Tissues That Do Not Metabolize PGs

Some tissues transport PGs but do not metabolize them. For example, the brain does not effectively metabolize PGE and PGF (96, 101), and it does not take them up when injected directly into the carotid or vertebral arteries (61). Thus the blood-brain barrier is tight to these PGs. On the other hand, $PGF_{2\alpha}$ injected into the cerebrospinal fluid is rapidly transported out and appears in the venous blood (24, 57). The isolated choroid plexus takes up PGE_1 (13, 25), suggesting that this is the site of the transporter. $PGF_{2\alpha}$ taken up by rabbit choroid plexus was shown to migrate as authentic $PGF_{2\alpha}$, i.e. it was not metabolized (19).

A similar picture has emerged for the iris-ciliary process (13, 19, 25). Here the data suggest that PGs are removed from the vitreous body and posterior chamber by a carrier in the ciliary process (13, 26). Strong similarities of the PG transport systems in the choroid plexus and the anterior uvea indicate that they are functionally related (44). The observations suggest that these tissues terminate PG signaling by transporting unmetabolized PGs into the blood. Final metabolism would then occur via sequential uptake and oxidation in other tissues, e.g. the lung.

THE FIRST CLONED PG TRANSPORTER: PGT

The Organic Anion Transporter oatp

We did not set out to clone a PG transporter. Rather, a few years ago our laboratory, in collaboration with that of Wolkoff's, was studying a novel organic anion transporter called oatp that had been expression-cloned by Jacquemin et al and shown to transport taurocholic acid (TCA) and related bile salts (65). We found that oatp mRNA and protein were strongly expressed in rat kidney; that the protein expression was restricted to the apical membrane of the S3 proximal tubule; that conjugated steroid anions, especially estradiol 17 β-D glucuronide ($E_2$17G), were excellent substrates; and that the oatp mRNA in kidney was under strong androgen control (10, 67, 68, 81). We hypothesized that conjugation of estradiol within the cell to the sulfate or glucuronide conjugate would result in intracellular anion trapping and that apical oatp would provide a passive apical exit route through which the charged conjugate could diffuse down its concentration gradient through the lipid bilayer. As part of these studies on oatp, we carried out a homology search.

Matrin F/G

Genbank/EMBL search using the oatp cDNA revealed 37% amino acid identity with a previously published sequence called matrin F/G (58). This cDNA was cloned by Hakes & Berezney from a rat liver λ cDNA expression library using a polyclonal antibody raised to a purified nuclear protein known as matrin F. The deduced protein, as originally published, was interpreted to encode a zinc-fingered nuclear protein. However, no function was demonstrated for matrin F/G (58).

When we re-examined the open reading frame (ORF) of the matrin F/G cDNA, we found that the first ATG (#88) encountered, starting from the 5' end, was an excellent Kozak consensus sequence for translation initiation (72). The resulting predicted protein has a M_r of 70.5. The hydropathy profiles of oatp versus matrin F/G showed that both have 12 regions of sufficient hydrophobicity over a length of 20 or more residues, each qualifying as an α-helical membrane spanning segment (66). In fact, the degree of similarity of the hydrophobicity profiles of oatp and matrin F/G was characteristic of those published for siblings of transporter gene families, such as the anion exchangers (AE1-3) (3) and Na/H^+ exchangers (NHE1-4) (121). We postulated that matrin F/G had been mischaracterized as a nuclear matrix protein and was, instead, another member of the 12-span transporter family. Indeed, modeling using standard algorithms indicated that matrin F/G resembles a standard 12-membrane-spanning transporter (Figure 2). This model predicts that there are at least three charged residues residing within transmembrane spans, i.e. E78, R561, and K614. These residues are discussed further below.

Prostanoid Transport by PGT

To test this hypothesis directly, we obtained the full-length matrin F/G cDNA and expressed it transiently, either in HeLa cells using the vaccinia-T7 expression system (54) or in *Xenopus* oocytes. We empirically tested the transport of a number of radioactive organic anions, including bromosulfophthalein, bilirubin monoglucuronide, unconjugated bilirubin, glutathione, corticosterone, p-aminohippurate, $E_2$17G, taurocholate, arachidonate, and uric acid. None of these was transported at a rate above that seen with the control plasmid.

However, during this screening we found that the matrin F/G-mediated PGE_2 transport at either 37° or room temperature was extremely rapid and saturated

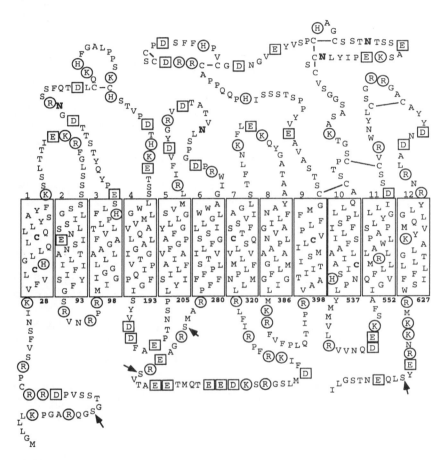

Figure 2 Model of matrin F/G (rat PGT) based on hydropathy analysis. There are 12 regions of hydrophobicity (membrane spans) that have been modeled as α-helices. Four consensus sites for asparagine-linked glycosylation are shown (*bold*) and are extracytoplasmic (*top*), whereas four consensus sites for serine phosphorylation are cytoplasmic (*bottom, arrows*). Placement of extracytoplasmic disulfide bonds is purely conjectural. Several intramembrane cysteines that might be responsible for inhibition by MTSES are shown (*bold*). (We discovered a sequencing error in matrin F/G: The correct sequence, incorporated here, brings the rPGT amino acid sequence closer to hPGT and adds one amino acid. Q502 through A512 of matrin F/G should be substituted by AKTGSCPTSCAQ).

quickly at ≈ 150-fold over that of monolayers expressing control plasmids. Because the matrin F/G cDNA clearly encoded a PG transporter, we renamed it PGT (for prostaglandin transporter) (69). I refer here to the rat cDNA as rPGT and the human cDNA as hPGT.

Examination of the substrate specificity revealed that the initial ≈ 1-min rPGT-mediated uptake rates in HeLa cells had the profile: $PGE_1 \simeq PGE_2 \simeq PGF_{2\alpha} > TxB_2 \gg$ 6-keto $PGF_{1\alpha} \simeq$ iloprost (a PGI_2 analogue) (69, 80). This is very similar to the published rank order of PG clearance by the rat lung (Figure 1): $PGE_1 \simeq PGE_2 \simeq PGF_{2\alpha} > TxB_2 > PGI_2$ (4, 29, 49–51, 53, 59, 84, 102, 103, 109).

The affinity for these substrates is quite high: K_m values are 50–95 nM for PGE_1, PGE_2, and $PGF_{2\alpha}$, and ≈ 400 nM for TxB_2 (64, 69). PG concentrations as presented to the transporter in tissues are probably at least this high. In human lung, for example, the PGE_2 concentration is about 25 ng/gram tissue, or ≈ 70 nM; in human semen this value is ≈ 25 μg/ml, or $\approx 70\mu$M (127). On the other hand, plasma PGE and PGF concentrations in humans are about 0.25 ng/ml, or 0.7 nM (132). Assuming that PGT is the mechanism for re-uptake of PGs after their release, this plasma concentration would represent the residual from the PGT-mediated clearance.

We further explored the hypothesis that PGT might play a role in the carrier-mediated membrane pathway by which at least some PGs are metabolized, with a more detailed analysis of the substrate specificity of rPGT and a comparison with in vivo and in situ data on PG metabolic clearance.

PGT Substrate Specificity Matches PG Clearance by the Isolated, Perfused Lung

We determined the timed uptake of tracer PGE_2 in the presence of various concentrations of unlabeled prostanoids (64). The resulting inhibitory constants (K_i) were calculated by curve-fitting. PGE_2 and $PGF_{2\alpha}$, both known to be transported by rPGT, had similar affinities (K_i 49–50 nM). The strongest interaction (K_i 13–19 nM) was obtained with prostanoids lacking the 9- or 11-position oxygen groups. Structural modifications that produced a moderately reduced affinity relative to that of PGE_2 (K_i 56–286 nM) included reduction of the C5-C6 double bond, addition of a benzene group at position C18, and isomerization at position C8. Substantially weaker interaction ($K_i > 700$ nM) was seen when the 1-position COO^- anionic group was neutralized, or when the 15(S)-OH group was changed to the 15(R)-OH or to 15-keto (64).

These results compare quite favorably with those on prostanoid clearance obtained by Eling, Anderson and co-workers using the isolated perfused rat lung preparation (4, 50, 51, 59). Figure 1 shows a simplified comparison of the data of Eling et al and our data using rPGT. In the isolated, perfused rat lung the rank order of inhibitory capacity was $PGE_2 > PGE_1 > PGD_2 > 13,14$ dihydro-$PGE_{1\alpha} > PGD_1 \simeq PGF_{2\alpha}$ methyl ester $\gg 15(R)$ PGE_2 (51). Our sequence is only slightly different: $PGE_2 > PGD_2 \simeq PGE_1 > PGD_1 > 13,14$ dihydro-$PGE_{2\alpha} > 15$ (R) $PGE_2 > PGF_{2\alpha}$ isopropyl ester. Our rank order also compares favorably with the more limited study of Robinson & Hoult (108). In this regard, at least in the rat, rPGT mRNA expression is strongest in the lung (69).

One striking result of this analysis is the large difference in affinity when PGE_2, which has a C15-OH in the S configuration, is compared with either 15(R)-PGE_2 (24-fold decrease in affinity) or 15-keto-PGE_2 (>100-fold decrease in affinity) (64). It is likely that differences in surface potential of the substrate molecules play a role in these varying affinities, perhaps via electrostatic interactions with a conserved charged residue(s) in the transporter (see below). Note that the lack of affinity of 15-keto PGs fits with the poor uptake of these compounds by the isolated, perfused rat lung (4, 108). It is also of note that neutralizing the anionic charge at position-1 abolishes the affinity of the transporter for the substrate (64), suggesting that the latter may be transported as the anion.

Taken together, our functional data indicate that it is very likely that PGT mediates the carrier step by which PGs such as PGE_2 and $PGF_{2\alpha}$ cross the lung plasma membrane prior to intracellular enzymatic oxidation. This interpretation does not, of course, preclude other roles in PG transport.

Isoprostanes

Isoprostanes are stereoisomers in which the side chains are oriented *cis* in relation to the cyclopentane ring, as opposed to cyclooxygenase-derived prostaglandins in which the side chains are exclusively oriented *trans* (90). Isoprostanes are formed, for the most part, by free radical–catalyzed peroxidation of arachidonic acid independent of the cyclooxygenase enzyme (92, 105). The F_2 isoprostanes have been implicated as markers of oxidative injury in vivo, and 8-iso-$PGF_{2\alpha}$ has vasoconstrictive activity (92). Because free F_2 isoprostanes and their metabolites are found in plasma and in urine in significant concentrations (91, 92), they presumably undergo clearance and metabolism; yet little is known about these pathways. We found that 8-iso-PGE_2 had an affinity for PGT about 1.3-fold lower that of the usual (α 8-position) PGE_2 (K_i 62.3 versus 48.7 nM). Similarly, 8-iso-$PGF_{2\alpha}$ had an affinity about 3.5-fold lower than that of $PGF_{2\alpha}$ (177 versus 50 nM). This suggests that 8-iso-PGE_2 and/or 8-iso-$PGF_{2\alpha}$ represent substrates for the transporter. Upon direct testing, tracer 8-iso-$PGF_{2\alpha}$ was transported at about 13% the rate of PGE_2 (64).

The Human PGT cDNA and Gene

To search for human homologues of rat PGT, we examined adult human kidney RNA by northern blotting with an rPGT antisense RNA probe at high stringency. This revealed two strong bands of 2.3 and 4.2 kb (80), suggesting that there was a human PGT homologue, with perhaps several PGT transcripts expressed in human kidney. We subsequently cloned a full-length hPGT cDNA from a human kidney library. From the consensus hPGT cDNA sequence derived from five clones, the deduced hPGT protein was 82% identical to that of the rat (see legend to Figure 2 for details on the rPGT sequence).

In Figure 3A, the protein sequences of rPGT and hPGT are compared with those of several other recently cloned organic anion transporters: rat oatp (65); human oatp (73) (this may represent an oatp-like transporter rather than the exact human equivalent of rat oatp); and OAT-K1, a rat kidney methotrexate transporter (112). The five proteins exhibit 24% overall amino acid identity. As expected, 73% of the overall identity is clustered within putative transmembrane spans, which constitute only 43% of the protein mass. Figure 3B shows that rPGT and hPGT are very closely related; rOATP and hOATP are more distantly related and are similar to rOAT-K1; and the OATP/OAT-K1 family is more distantly related to the PGTs. Three charged residues in rPGT and hPGT (in rat: E77, R561, and K614), which are predicted to lie within putative membrane spans, are highly conserved among hPGT, rPGT, OAT-K1, and oatp (K614 is an R in oatp and OAT-K1) (65), suggesting that these amino acids play an important role in substrate translocation and/or structure.

Northern blot analysis of human tissue poly A+ RNA with a hPGT RNA probe revealed strongly hybridizing RNA bands of 1.8 to 2.0 kb in skeletal muscle, prostate, testis, ovary, small intestine, and colon; 2.5 to 2.9 kb in heart and skeletal muscle; 4.0 kb in ovary; 4.4 to 5.1 kb in heart, whole brain, placenta, lung, liver, skeletal muscle, kidney, spleen, thymus, prostate, testis, ovary, small intestine, colon, and peripheral blood leukocytes; 8.8 kb in testis and colon; and 10.1 kb in testis. In human fetal tissues, transcripts were 2.1 kb in brain, lung, liver, and kidney; 2.5 kb in lung; 4.8 to 5.1 kb in brain, lung, liver, and kidney; 6.1 kb in liver; and 10 kb in lung and liver (80). Thus hPGT is broadly expressed, but with large variability in mRNA size, likely due to variable posttranscriptional processing (splicing) or use of alternative promoters.

Because the rPGT and hPGT cDNAs are ≈4 kb in length and thus represent only one of the many mRNAs observed, we cloned the hPGT gene in order to obtain insights into the origin of the other transcripts. Spread out over nearly 100 kb, the hPGT gene has 14 exons (79). For the most part, the introns interrupt the ORF in areas of the protein predicted to be either extra- or intracytoplasmic. The three sites at which introns disrupt the ORF in hydrophobic regions

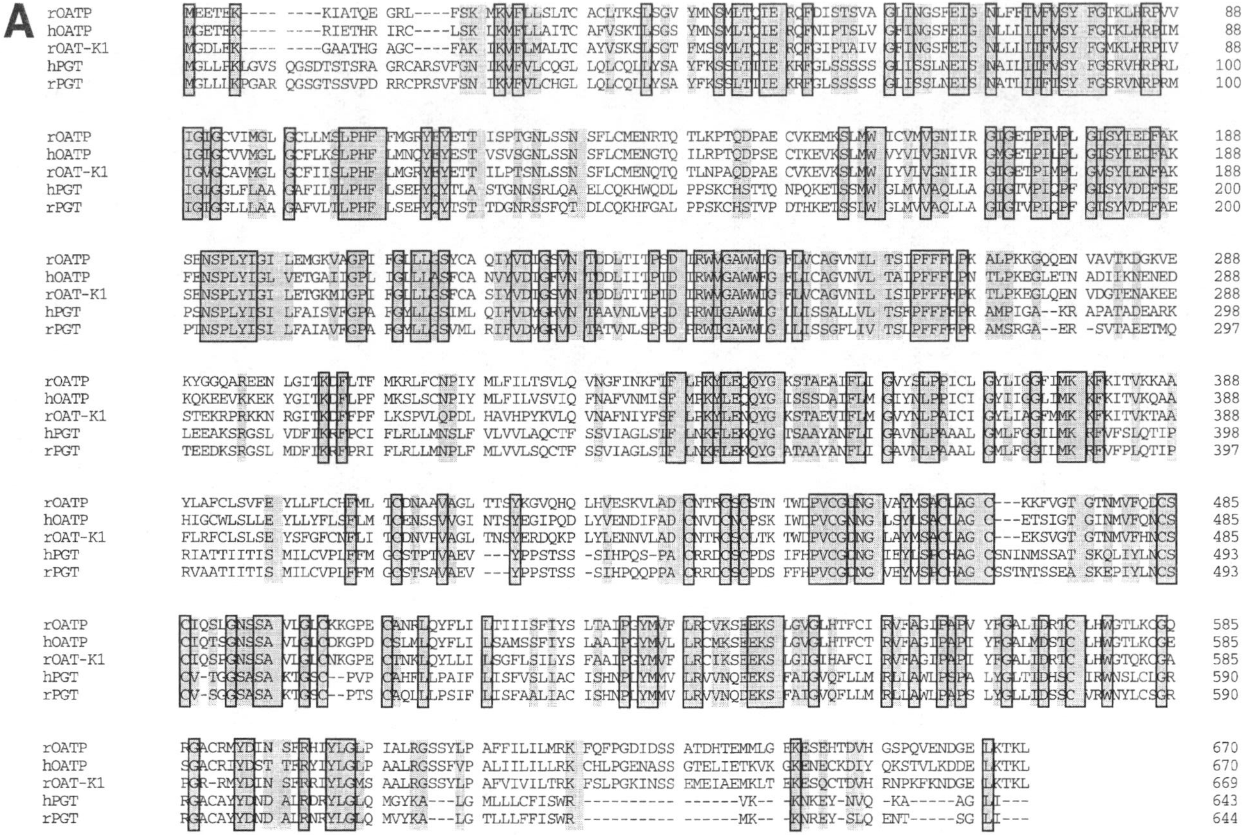

A

Figure 3 (A) Amino acid sequence alignments of several related organic anion transporters: rat oatp (rOATP) (65); human oatp (hOATP) (73); rat OAT-K1 (rOAT-K1) (112); and rPGT and hPGT (69, 80). Identical residues are *boxed*; similar residues are *shaded*.

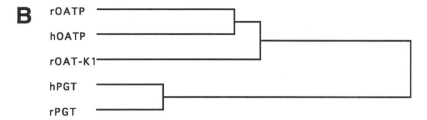

Figure 3 *(Continued)* *(B)* Similarity plot of the same transporters. Length of the lines is proportional to relatedness. Rat and human PGT are closely related. Both PGTs are more distantly related to the OATPs and to OAT-K1.

(membrane spans) occur within a few amino acids of the three conserved intramembrane charged residues (E78, R561, and K614) (79). Knowledge of the intron-exon structure should permit characterization of the various transcripts seen by northern blotting.

As of this writing, we have identified ≈3 kb of 5′ flanking DNA that, when cloned upstream of a luciferase promoter and transfected into lung epithelial A549 cells, gives activity significantly above background, i.e. this region contains the hPGT promoter (R Lu & VL Schuster, unpublished observations). Further characterization of this region should permit insights into possible factors controlling transcription of the PGT gene.

TRANSPORT MECHANISMS

Our early experiments using short-duration ion substitutions in the HeLa cell expression system clearly demonstrated that rPGT transport is Na^+, Cl^-, and H^+ independent (69). Further experiments using the *Xenopus* oocyte expression system have provided evidence that PGT can carry out concentrative (i.e. uphill) PG transport and that transport is sensitive to the metabolic state of the cell; e.g. treatment of PGT-expressing oocytes with iodoacetate and nitrogen gas significantly reduces PGE_2 uptake (B Chan & VL Schuster, unpublished observations). Recent experiments from our laboratory indicate that PG accumulation results from anion exchange-mediated uphill transport (35).

General Transport Inhibitors

ICG, BCG, indomethacin, furosemide, *p*-aminohippurate (PAH), and probenecid inhibit PG transport when applied to intact tissue (17, 22, 25, 27, 45, 51, 63, 85, 103, 107). Some, but not all, of these agents also inhibit transport by the cloned PGT. For example, both rPGT and hPGT are significantly inhibited by furosemide but not by probenecid or indomethacin (69, 80). We have also shown that rPGT is inhibited by BCG and ICG (69). Because PAH, indomethacin, and probenecid have no effect on PGT, it is likely that these agents could act at a separate step(s) in two-step transepithelial PG transport, i.e. they might inhibit a separate PG transporter(s) not yet cloned.

For those agents that do inhibit PGT and also inhibit tissue PG transport or uptake, the inhibition constants (K_i) are similar to those reported in the literature: BCG, 2-4 μM (17, 22, 25, 27, 51); ICG, 16 μM (103); and furosemide, 25–80 μM (22, 27).

Anion Transport Inhibitors

As discussed above, elimination of the 1-position carboxylate group on PGT substrates abolishes their affinity for the transporter, which suggests that the substrate is recognized by PGT as the anion. In accordance with this hypothesis, we found that PGT-mediated tracer PGE$_2$ flux was irreversibly inhibited by the disulfonic stilbenes H$_2$DIDS and DIDS ($K_i \simeq 20$–30 μM) (35).

PGT is also inhibited by the anionic, sulfhydryl-reactive agent Na-(2-sulfona-toethyl) methanethiosulfonate (MTSES), but not by MTSEA, the cationic version (114), again consistent with electrostatic attraction of the anionic compound into the transporter. Finally, rPGT is also inhibited by the anionic transport inhibitor niflumic acid (B Chan & VL Schuster, unpublished observations). Taken together, these data strongly suggest that the PG is transported as the anion.

Amino Acid Modifying Agents and Site-Directed Mutagenesis

To further test this hypothesis, HeLa cells transiently expressing the wild-type transporter were treated with the following amino acid modifying reagents: arginine-specific phenylglyoxal (PGO); lysine-specific trinitrobenzene sulfonic acid (TNBS); histidine-specific diethyl-pyrocarbonate (DEPC); or Woodward's Reagent K (WRK), which neutralizes negatively charged residues (E, D). Only agents directed at positively charged amino acids resulted in inhibition of PG transport. DEPC abolished function completely, whereas PGO and TNBS caused a reduction in transport to $5 \pm 2.5\%$ and $44 \pm 14\%$ of control, respectively. On the other hand, treatment with WRK had no effect (34).

To begin to address the role of specifically charged residues, we have individually mutagenized the conserved cationic amino acids of rPGT: R561 (to asparagine) and K614 (to glutamine). When transiently expressed in HeLa cells, both mutants reach the cell surface, but neither is functional (34). Further experiments are under way to determine whether conservative substitutions at these sites can rescue function. Taken with the data above on stilbenes, MTSES, and other inhibitors, these results are also consistent with PGT functioning as an anion transporter.

PHYSIOLOGICAL INTEGRATION

Infusion of Indocyanine Green into Rats

To definitively test the role of PGT in the whole organism, one would like to selectively inhibit its function. At present, this is not possible; however, a set of interesting experiments has been reported by Pitt et al (103). These investigators infused ICG into rabbits to achieve steady state (known) concentrations and determined the effect on metabolic clearance of tracer PGE_1 across the pulmonary vascular bed. Interestingly, pulmonary PGE_1 clearance was inhibited by 50% at a plasma ICG concentration of 80 μM, a K_i remarkably close to that of the cloned rPGT of 35 μM (69). Furthermore, ICG infusion resulted in significant lowering of arterial blood pressure. The hypotensive effect was probably due to endogenous vasodilatory PGs that escaped pulmonary clearance and reached the arterial circulation (103). These data, taken with ours, strongly suggest that PGT, at least in the lung, plays an active role under normal physiological conditions to prevent PGs in the venous circulation from reaching the arterial side.

Comparison of PGT and Tissue PG Transport

There are many similarities between PGT transport and PG transport described in various tissues. Most have already been mentioned. In addition, like PGT-mediated PG transport in *Xenopus* oocytes, PG transport by the choroid plexus, anterior uvea, and kidney cortex are quite sensitive to the removal of oxygen and the addition of iodoacetate, i.e. to metabolism (25, 44, 45). On the other hand, in many cases the tissue distribution and substrate specificity of PGT simply do not explain all of the data extant on PG transport in cells and tissues.

PGT seems unlikely to mediate renal PG clearance for three reasons. First, renal PG clearance and metabolism clearly take place in the cortex, apparently as part of the proximal tubule organic anion secretory pathway (12, 13, 17, 22, 25, 60, 63, 85, 125), yet the zonal distribution of PGT mRNA in the rat kidney is papilla > medulla > cortex (69). Moreover, PG 15-dehydrogenase has been generally localized to the cortex, not to the papilla (75, 123, 129). Thus the distribution of PGT mRNA seems inappropriate for a primary role in renal PG extraction from the circulation. Second, in the isolated, perfused rabbit kidney there are major differences in substrate affinity compared with PGT; 15-keto-$PGF_{2\alpha}$ interacts very strongly to inhibit that system, yet this compound interacts poorly, if at all, with rPGT (22, 64). Third, renal PG uptake is strongly inhibited by indomethacin (27, 85, 107), whereas PGT is essentially insensitive (69, 80).[1]

As stated above, transport by rPGT is clearly Na^+ independent (69; B Chan & VL Schuster, unpublished observation). In contrast, PG transport by the

[1] See note added in proof.

anterior uvea (44), choroid plexus (45), and ileum (11) is completely or partially Na^+ dependent. It is difficult to see how PGT can be mechanistically Na^+ independent in one cell and Na^+ dependent in another; therefore, there is probably a Na^+-dependent PG transporter(s) yet to be discovered.

The low transport rate exhibited by PGT toward PGI_2 means that extraction of the latter by the kidney, liver, and hindquarters, and the uptake of PGI_2 by the choroid plexus, remain to be molecularly understood (45, 49, 122).

PGA_1 uptake has been described in rat brain, diaphragm, heart, kidney cortex, liver, lung, testis, seminal vesicle, ovary, and uterus (12). There are also several descriptions of PGA_2 uptake by murine L-1210 cells (97, 98, 100). Given the relatively low affinity of rPGT for PGA (64), it seems unlikely that PGT could mediate all of this PGA transport, which raises the possibility that there are PGT homologues for PGA transport. It is of interest that concentrative PGA transport was seen by Bito et al in various tissues of lower animals, such as the gills, choroid plexus, liver, kidney, and stomach of elasmobranchs, teleost fishes, and of lower marine vertebrates such as bivalves (12). For example, the scallop gill concentrated tracer PGA_1 over 200-fold compared with the surrounding medium but concentrated $PGF_{2\alpha}$ only 13-fold (12). The preference for PGA_1 transport by marine tissues, as opposed to PGE_2 and $PGF_{2\alpha}$ by PGT, is interesting and suggests that more than one PG transporter may exist.

SUMMARY AND CONCLUSIONS

We have identified and cloned the first known PG transporter. An exact understanding of its role in PG metabolism remains unclear. We have postulated three possible roles (69): First, PGT might mediate the efflux of newly synthesized PGs from cells. At the beginning of this review, I summarized the evidence that PGs do gain access to the cytoplasmic compartment. It remains unclear whether a carrier is necessary for their subsequent efflux into the extracytoplasmic space. Preliminary immunocytochemical localization of rPGT in our laboratory using a monoclonal antibody is consistent with this proposed role (6), but this clearly remains work in progress. Second, PGT might mediate epithelial PG transport. To date we have no direct evidence either for or against this hypothesis. Third, PGT could mediate PG clearance and degradation. Our data strongly suggest that PGT mediates this function in at least some tissues, such as the lung, but probably not in others, such as the kidney.

Future immunological studies, cell culture model systems, and expression- and homology-cloning efforts should result in expansion of our understanding of the molecular mechanisms of prostanoid transport, in general, and the role of PGT, in particular.

ACKNOWLEDGMENTS

Work from the author's laboratory was supported by grants from the National Institutes of Health (DK 49688), the National Kidney Foundation, and the American Heart Association (New York City Affiliate).

NOTE ADDED IN PROOF

Since submission of this manuscript, a paper appeared describing the expression cloning of a novel rat organic anion transporter (OAT1). OAT1 exchanges α-ketoglutarate for a variety of organic anions, including PGE_2. OAT1 appears to be expressed in the proximal straight tubule of the rat kidney. It is therefore likely that this transporter mediates, at least in part, PGE_2 secretion by the kidney. (Sekine T, Watanabe N, Hosoyamada M, Kanai Y, Endou H. 1997. Expression cloning and characterization of a novel multispecific organic anion transporter. *J. Biol. Chem.* 272:18526–29)

> Visit the *Annual Reviews home page* at
> http://www.AnnualReviews.org.

Literature Cited

1. Agins AP, Delhagen JE. 1997. Metabolism of prostaglandin E2 by human HL-60 leukemia cells. *Agents Actions* 21:400–2
2. Alm A, Villumsen J, Tornquist P, Mandahl A, Airaksinen J, et al. 1993. Intraocular pressure-reducing effect of PhXA41 in patients with increased eye pressure. A one-month study. *Ophthalmology* 100:1312–16
3. Alper SL. 1991. The band 3-related anion exchanger (AE) gene family. *Annu. Rev. Physiol.* 53:549–64
4. Anderson MW, Eling TE. 1976. Prostaglandin removal and metabolism by isolated perfused rat lung. *Prostaglandins* 11:645–77
5. Avdeef A, Box KJ, Takacs-Novak K. 1995. pH-metric log P. 6. Effects of sodium, potassium, and N-CH3-D-glucamine on the octanol-water partitioning of prostaglandins E1 and E2. *J. Pharmacol. Sci.* 84:523–29
6. Bao Y, Chan B, Lu R, Schuster VL. 1996. Immunological characterization of the rat prostaglandin transporter "PGT". *J. Am. Soc. Nephrol.* 7:A1980 (Abstr.)
7. Bardhan KD, Walker R, Hinchliffe RF, Bose K, Morris P, et al. 1991. Gastric ulcer healing: a comparison of enprostil versus

ranitidine. *J. Clin. Gastroenterol.* 13:157–62
8. Baroody RA, Bito LZ . 1981. The impermeability of the basic cell membrane to thromboxane-B2, prostacyclin and 6-keto-PGF 1 alpha. *Prostaglandins* 21:133–42
9. Bates EJ. 1995. Eicosanoids, fatty acids, and neutrophils: their relevance to the pathophysiology of disease. *Prostaglandins Leukot. Essent. Fatty Acids* 53:75–86
10. Bergwerk AJ, Shi XY, Ford AC, Kanai N, Jacquemin E, et al. 1996. Immunologic distribution of an organic anion transport protein in rat liver and kidney. *Am. J. Physiol.* 271:G231–38
11. Bikhazi AB, Lakkis NM, Abu-Chehade KD. 1991. Sodium-dependent retention of prostaglandins in rat ileum. *J. Pharmacol. Sci.* 80:1110–13
12. Bito LZ. 1972. Comparative study of concentrative prostaglandin accumulation by various tissues of mammals and marine vertebrates and invertebrates. *Comp. Biochem. Physiol.* 43A:65–82
13. Bito LZ. 1972. Accumulation and apparent active transport of prostaglandins by some rabbit tissues in vitro. *J. Physiol.* 221:371–87

14. Bito LZ. 1973. Absorptive transport of prostaglandins from intraocular fluids to blood: a review of recent findings. *Exp. Eye Res.* 16:299–306

15. Bito LZ. 1974. The effects of experimental uveitis on anterior uveal prostaglandin transport and aqueous humor composition. *Invest. Ophthalmol. Vis. Sci.* 13:959–66

16. Bito LZ. 1975. Saturable, energy-dependent, transmembrane transport of prostaglandins against concentration gradients. *Nature* 256:134–36

17. Bito LZ. 1976. Inhibition of renal prostaglandin metabolism and excretion by probenecid, bromcresol green, and indomethacin. *Prostaglandins* 12:639–46

18. Bito LZ. 1997. Are prostaglandins intracellular, transcellular, or extracellular autocoids? *Prostaglandins* 9:851–56

19. Bito LZ, Baroody RA. 1974. Concentrative accumulation of ^{3}-H-prostaglandins by some rabbit tissues in vitro: the chemical nature of the accumulated ^{3}-H-labelled substances. *Prostaglandins* 7:131–40

20. Bito LZ, Baroody RA. 1975. Inhibition of pulmonary prostaglandin metabolism by inhibitors of prostaglandin biotransport (probenecid and bromcresol green). *Prostaglandins* 10:633–39

21. Bito LZ, Baroody RA. 1975. Impermeability of rabbit erythrocytes to prostaglandins. *Am. J. Physiol.* 229:1580–84

22. Bito LZ, Baroody RA. 1978. Comparison of renal prostaglandin and *p*-aminohippuric acid transport processes. *Am. J. Physiol.* 234:F80–88

23. Bito LZ, Baroody RA, Reitz ME. 1977. Dependence of pulmonary prostaglandin metabolism on carrier-mediated transport processes. *Am. J. Physiol.* 232:E382–87

24. Bito LZ, Davson H, Hollingsworth JR. 1976. Facilitated transport of prostaglandins across the blood-cerebrospinal fluid and blood-brain barriers. *J. Physiol.* 256:273–85

25. Bito LZ, Davson H, Salvador EV. 1976. Inhibition of in vitro concentrative prostaglandin accumulation by prostaglandins, prostaglandin analogues and by some inhibitors of organic anion transport. *J. Physiol.* 256:257–71

26. Bito LZ, Salvador EV. 1972. Intraocular fluid dynamics. III. The site and mechanism of prostaglandin transfer across the blood intraocular fluid barriers. *Exp. Eye Res.* 14:233–41

27. Bito LZ, Salvador EV. 1976. Effects of anti-inflammatory agents and some other drugs on prostaglandin biotransport. *J.*

28. Bito LZ, Stjernschantz J. 1989. The ocular effects of prostaglandins and other eicosanoids. *Prog. Clin. Biol. Res.* 312:1–514

29. Bito LZ, Wallenstein MC. 1977. Transport of prostaglandins across the blood-brain and blood-aqueous barriers and the physiological significance of these absorptive transport processes. *Exp. Eye Res.* 25:229–43 (Suppl.)

30. Bito LZ, Wallenstein MC, Baroody RA. 1976. The role of transport processes in the distribution and disposition of prostaglandins. *Adv. Prostaglandin Thromboxane Leukot. Res.* 1:297–303

31. Blatteis CM, Sehic E. 1997. Fever: How may circulating pyrogens signal the brain? *News Physiol. Sci.* 12:1–9

32. Bugge JF, Vikse A, Dahl E, Kiil F. 1987. Renal degradation and distribution between urinary and venous output of prostaglandins E2 and I2. *Acta Physiol. Scand.* 130:467–74

33. Cawello W, Schweer H, Muller R, Bonn R, Seyberth HW. 1994. Metabolism and pharmacokinetics of prostaglandin E1 administered by intravenous infusion in human subjects. *Eur. J. Clin. Pharmacol.* 46:275–77

34. Chan B, Bao Y, Itoh S, Lu R, Schuster VL. 1996. Role of charged residues in the function of the prostaglandin transporter "PGT". *J. Am. Soc. Nephrol.* 7:A0252 (Abstr.)

35. Chan B, Kanai N, Satriano JA, Lu R, Bao Y, et al. 1995. The prostaglandin transporter PGT is an anion exchanger. *J. Am. Soc. Nephrol.* 6:753 (Abstr.)

36. Coleman RA, Smith WL, Narumiya S. 1994. VIII. International union of pharmacology classification of prostanoid receptors: properties, distribution, and structure of the receptors and their subtypes. *Pharmacol. Rev.* 46:205–29

37. Cozzini BO, Dawson CA. 1977. Further identification of PGE1 metabolites formed in the cat lung. *Can. J. Physiol. Pharmacol.* 55:311–13

38. Cozzini BO, Dawson CA. 1977. The role of the blood in the metabolism of prostaglandin E1 in the cat lung. *Prostaglandins* 13:587–97

39. Crowshaw K. 1973. The incorporation of [1-14C] arachidonaic acid into the lipids of rabbit renal slices and conversion to prostaglandins E2 and F2α. *Prostaglandins* 3:607–20

40. Dawson CA, Cozzini BO, Lonigro AJ. 1975. Metabolism of [2-14C] prostaglandin E1 on passage through the

pulmonary circulation. *Can. J. Physiol. Pharmacol.* 53:610–15

41. Dawson CA, Linehan JH, Rickably DA, Roerig DL. 1984. Influence of plasma protein on the inhibitory effects of indocyanine green and bromcresol green on pulmonary prostaglandin E1 extraction. *Br. J. Pharmacol.* 81:449–55

42. Dawson W, Jessup SJ, McDonald-Gibson W, Ramwell PW, Shaw JE. 1970. Prostaglandin uptake and metabolism by the perfused liver. *Br. J. Pharmacol.* 39:585–98

43. Devereux TR, Fouts JR, Eling TE. 1987. Metabolism of prostaglandin PGF2 alpha by freshly isolated alveolar type II cells from lungs of adult male or pregnant rabbits. *Prostaglandins Leukot. Med.* 27:43–52

44. DiBenedetto FE, Bito LZ. 1980. The kinetics and energy dependence of prostaglandin transport processes. I. In vitro studies on the rate of PGF2α accumulation by the rabbit anterior uvea. *Exp. Eye Res.* 30:175–82

45. DiBenedetto FE, Bito LZ. 1986. Transport of prostaglandins and other eicosanoids by the choroid plexus: its characterization and physiological significance. *J. Neurochem.* 46:1725–31

46. Diczfalusy U. 1994. Beta-oxidation of eicosanoids. *Prog. Lipid Res.* 33:403–28

47. Diczfalusy U, Alexson SE. 1990. Identification of metabolites from peroxisomal beta-oxidation of prostaglandins. *J. Lipid Res.* 31:307–14

48. Diczfalusy UG, Alexson SE. 1992. Role of peroxisomes in the degradation of prostaglandins. *Prog. Clin. Biol. Res.* 375:253–61

49. Dusting GJ, Moncada S, Vane JR. 1978. Recirculation of prostacyclin (PGI2) in the dog. *Br. J. Pharmacol.* 64:315–20

50. Eling TE, Anderson MW. 1976. Studies on the biosynthesis, metabolism and transport of prostaglandins by the lung. *Agents Actions* 6:543–46

51. Eling TE, Hawkins HJ, Anderson MW. 1977. Structural requirements for, and the effects of chemicals on, the rat pulmonary inactivation of prostaglandins. *Prostaglandins* 14:51–60

52. Epstein M, ed. 1986. *Prostaglandins and the Kidney. Am. J. Med.* 80.No1A:84. New York: Tech. Pub.

53. Ferreira SH, Vane JR. 1967. Prostaglandins: their disappearance from and release into the circulation. *Nature* 216:868–73

54. Fuerst TR, Niles EG, Studier FW, Moss B. 1986. Eukaryotic transient expression system based on recombinant vaccinia virus that synthesizes bacteriophage T7 RNA polymerase. *Proc. Natl. Acad. Sci. USA* 83:8122–26

55. Garcia-Perez A, Smith WL. 1984. Apical-basolateral membrane asymmetry in canine cortical collecting tubule cells. Bradykinin, arginine vasopressin, prostaglandin E2 interrelationships. *J. Clin. Invest.* 74:63–74

56. Golub MS, Zia PK, Horton R. 1974. Metabolism of prostaglandins A1 and A2 by human whole blood. *Prostaglandins* 8:13–20

57. Hagen AA, Gerber JN, Sweeley CC, White RP, Robertson JT. 1977. Levels and disappearance of prostaglandin F2α in cerebral spinal fluid: a clinical and experimental study. *Stroke* 8:672–75

58. Hakes DJ, Berezney R. 1991. Molecular cloning of matrin F/G: a DNA binding protein of the nuclear matrix that contains putative zinc finger motifs. *Proc. Natl. Acad. Sci. USA* 88:6186–90

59. Hawkins HJ, Wilson AG, Anderson MW, Eling TE. 1977. Uptake and metabolism of prostaglandins by isolated perfused lung: species comparisons and the role of plasma protein binding. *Prostaglandins* 14:251–59

60. Haylor J, Lote CJ, Towers JD. 1988. Tubular mechanisms determining the urinary excretion of tritiated prostaglandin E2 in the anaesthetized rat. *J. Physiol.* 403:1–14

61. Holmes SW, Horton EW. 1968. The distribution of tritium-labelled prostaglandin E1 injected in amounts sufficient to produce central nervous effects in cats and chicks. *Br. J. Pharmacol.* 34:32–37

62. Holmes SW, Horton EW, Stewart MJ. 1968. Observations on the extraction of prostaglandins from blood. *Life Sci.* 7:349–54

63. Irish JM. 1979. Secretion of prostaglandin E2 by rabbit proximal tubules. *Am. J. Physiol.* 237:F268–73

64. Itoh S, Lu R, Bao Y, Morrow RD, Roberts LJ, et al. 1996. Structural determinants of substrates for the prostaglandin transporter PGT. *Mol. Pharmacol.* 50:736–42

65. Jacquemin E, Hagenbuch B, Stieger B, Wolkoff AW, Meier PJ. 1994. Expression cloning of a rat liver Na$^+$-independent organic anion transporter. *Proc. Natl. Acad. Sci. USA* 91:133–37

66. Jahnig F. 1990. Structure predictions of membrane proteins are not that bad. *Trends Biochem. Sci.* 15:93–95

67. Kanai N, Lu R, Bao Y, Wolkoff AW,

Schuster VL. 1996. Transient expression of the organic anion transporter "oatp" in mammalian cells: identification of candidate substrates. *Am. J. Physiol.* 270:F319–25

68. Kanai N, Lu R, Bao Y, Wolkoff AW, Vore V, et al. 1996. Estradiol 17-β D-glucuronide is a high-affinity substrate for the organic anion transporter "oatp." *Am. J. Physiol.* 270:F326–31

69. Kanai N, Lu R, Satriano JA, Bao Y, Wolkoff AW, et al. 1995. Identification and characterization of a prostaglandin transporter. *Science* 268:866–69

70. Kobayashi K, Arakawa T, Higuchi K, Nakamura H. 1991. Gastric cytoprotection by ornoprostil, a PGE1 analogue, in human subjects. *J. Clin. Gastroenterol.* 13:1:S32–36 (Suppl.)

71. Konturek SJ, Kwiecien N, Obtulowicz W, Maczka J, Hebzda Z, et al. 1991. Effects of nocloprost on gastric functions in man. *Scand. J. Gastroenterol.* 26:1145–51

72. Kozak M. 1989. The scanning model for translation: an update. *J. Cell Biol.* 108:229–42

73. Kullak-Ublick GA, Hagenbuch B, Stieger B, Schteingart CD, Hofmann AF, et al. 1995. Molecular and functional characterization of an organic anion transporting polypeptide cloned from human liver. *Gastroenterology* 109:1274–82

74. Kupfer D, Holm KA. 1989. Prostaglandin metabolism by hepatic cytochrome P-450. *Drug Metab. Rev.* 20:753–64

75. Larsson C, Anggard E. 1973. Regional differences in the formation and metabolism of prostaglandins in the rabbit kidney. *Eur. J. Pharmacol.* 21:30–36

76. Levine L, ed. 1988. *Arachidonate Metabolism in Immunologic Systems.* New York: Karger. 214 pp.

77. Linehan JH, Dawson CA. 1979. A kinetic model of prostaglandin metabolism in the lung. *J. Appl. Physiol.: Resp. Environ. Exercise Physiol.* 47:404–11

78. Linehan JH, Dawson CA, Wagner-Weber VM. 1981. Prostaglandin E1 uptake by isolated cat lungs perfused with physiological salt solution. *J. Appl. Physiol.: Resp. Environ. Exercise Physiol.* 50:428–34

79. Lu R, Frank M, Schuster VL. 1996. Genomic cloning of the human prostaglandin transporter "PGT" gene. *J. Am. Soc. Nephrol.* 7:A1997 (Abstr.)

80. Lu R, Kanai N, Bao Y, Schuster VL. 1996. Cloning, in vitro expression, and tissue distribution of a human prostaglandin transporter cDNA (hPGT). *J. Clin. Invest.* 98:1142–49

81. Lu R, Kanai N, Wolkoff AW, Schuster VL. 1996. Regulation of renal oatp expression by testosterone. *Am. J. Physiol.* 270:F332–37

82. Marcus AJ, Weksler BB, Jaffe EA. 1978. Enzymatic conversion of prostaglandin endoperoxide H2 and arachidonic acid to prostacyclin by cultured human endothelial cells. *J. Biol. Chem.* 253:7138–41

83. McDonald-Gibson WJ, McDonald-Gibson RG, Greaves MW. 1972. Prostaglandin E1 metabolism by human plasma. *Prostaglandins* 2:251–63

84. McGiff JC, Terragno NA, Strand JC, Lee JB, Lonigro AJ, et al. 1969. Selective passage of prostaglandins across the lung. *Nature* 223:742–45

85. Melendez E, Reyes JL. 1982. Renal handling of indomethacin and its relationship with the secretory pathway of prostaglandins. *J. Pharm. Pharmacol.* 34:648–52

86. Moncada S, Korbut K, Bunting S, Vane JR. 1978. Prostacyclin is a circulating hormone. *Nature* 273:767–68

87. Mori M, Izumi T, Shimizu T. 1993. Energy-dependent export of leukotriene B4 in *Xenopus* oocytes. *Biochim. Biophys. Acta* 1168:23–29

88. Morita I, Schindler M, Regier MK, Otto JC, Hori T, et al. 1995. Different intracellular locations for prostaglandin endoperoxide H synthase-1 and -2. *J. Biol. Chem.* 270:10902–8

89. Morita I, Smith WL, DeWitt DL, Schindler M. 1995. Expression-activity profiles of cells transfected with prostaglandin endoperoxide H synthase measured by quantitative fluorescence microscopy. *Biochemistry* 34:7194–99

90. Morrow JD, Awad JA, Boss HJ, Blair IA, Roberts LJ II. 1995. Non-cyclooxygenase-derived prostanoids (F2-isoprostanes) are formed in situ on phospholipids. *Proc. Natl. Acad. Sci. USA* 89:10721–25

91. Morrow JD, Frei B, Longmire AW, Gaziano JM, Lynch SM, et al. 1995. Increase in circulating products of lipid peroxidation (F2 isoprostanes) in smokers. Smoking as a cause of oxidative injury. *N. Engl. J. Med.* 332:1198–203

92. Morrow JD, Roberts LJ II. 1995. The isoprostanes. Current knowledge and directions for future research. *Biochem. Pharmacol.* 51:1–9

93. Murphy RC, Fitzpatrick FA, eds. 1990. *Arachidonate Related Lipid Mediators. Methods in Enzymology*, Vol. 187. San Diego: Academic. 683 pp.

94. Nakano J, Angaard E, Samuelsson B. 1969. 15-hydroxy-prostaglandin dehydrogenase. Prostaglandins as substrates and inhibitors. *J. Biochem.* 11:386–89

95. Nakano J, Monatague B, Darrow B. 1971. Metabolism of prostaglandin E1 in human plasma, uterus and placenta, in swine ovary and in rat testicle. *Biochem. Pharmacol.* 20:2512–14

96. Nakano J, Pracan AV, Meese SE. 1972. Metabolism of prostaglandin E1 in cerebral cortex and cerebellum of the dog and rat. *Brain Res.* 39:545–48

97. Narumiya S, Fukushima M. 1986. Site and mechanism of growth inhibition by prostaglandins. I. Active transport and intracellular accumulation of cyclopentenone prostaglandins, a reaction leading to growth inhibition. *J. Pharmacol. Exp. Ther.* 239:500–5

98. Narumiya S, Fukushima M. 1987. Active transport and cellular accumulation of cyclopentenone prostaglandins: a mechanism of prostaglandin-induced growth inhibition. *Adv. Prostaglandin Thromboxane Leukot. Res.* 17B:972–75

99. Neri Serneri GG, ed. 1985. *Platelets, Prostaglandins, and the Cardiovascular System. Advances in Prostaglandin, Thromboxane, and Leukotriene Research,* Vol. 13. New York: Raven. 393 pp.

100. Ohno K, Hirata M. 1993. Characterization of the transport system of prostaglandin A2 in L-1210 murine leukemia cells. *Biochem. Pharmacol.* 46:661–70

101. Pace-Asciake CR, Rangaraj G. 1976. Prostaglandin biosynthesis and catabolism in the developing fetal sheep brain. *J. Biol. Chem.* 251:3381–85

102. Piper PJ, Vane JR, Wyllie JH. 1970. Inactivation of prostaglandins by the lungs. *Nature* 225:600–4

103. Pitt BR, Forder JR, Gillis CN. 1983. Drug-induced impairment of pulmonary [3H]prostaglandin E1 removal in vivo. *J. Pharmacol. Exp. Ther.* 227:531–37

104. Poyser NL. 1997. The control of prostaglandin production by the endometrium in relation to luteolysis and menstruation. *Prostaglandins Leukot. Essent. Fatty Acids* 53:147–95

105. Pratico D, Lawson JA, Fitzgerald GA. 1995. Cyclooxygenase-dependent formation of the isoprostane, 8-epi prostaglandin F2α. *J. Biol. Chem.* 270:9800–8

106. Quiroga J, Prieto J. 1993. Liver cytoprotection by prostaglandins. *Pharmacol. Therap.* 58:67–91

107. Rennick BR. 1977. Renal tubular transport of prostaglandins: inhibition by probenecid and indomethacin. *Am. J. Physiol.* 233:F133–37

108. Robinson C, Hoult JRS. 1982. Inactivation of prostaglandins in the perfused rat lung. *Biochem. Pharmacol.* 31:633–38

109. Robinson C, Peers SH, Waddell KA, Blair IA, Hoult JR. 1982. Thromboxane B2 uptake and metabolism in isolated perfused lung. Identification and comparison with prostaglandin F2α. *Biochim. Biophys. Acta* 712:315–25

110. Roseman TJ, Yalkowsky SH. 1973. Physicochemical properties of prostaglandin F2α (tromethamine salt): solubility behavior, surface properties, and ionization constants. *J. Pharmacol. Sci.* 62:1680–85

111. Ruan KH, Wang LH, Wu KK, Kulmacz RJ. 1993. Amino-terminal topology of thromboxane synthase in the endoplasmic reticulum. *J. Biol. Chem.* 268:19483–90

112. Saito H, Masuda S, Inui KI. 1996. Cloning and functional characterization of a novel rat organic anion transporter mediating basolateral uptake of methotrexate in the kidney. *J. Biol. Chem.* 271:20719–25

113. Samuelsson B, Hamberg M. 1971. On the metabolism of prostaglandins E and E2 in man. *J. Biol. Chem.* 22:6713–21

114. Satriano JA, Kanai N, Lu R, Bao Y, Schuster VL. 1994. "OATP-2", a novel prostaglandin transporter: identification of SH groups near the substrate binding site. *J. Am. Soc. Nephrol.* 5:320 (Abstr.)

115. Segal MB, ed. 1992. *Barriers and Fluids of the Eye and Brain.* Boca Raton: CRC Press. 219 pp.

116. Silverstein FE, Graham DY, Senior JR, Davies HW, Struthers BJ, et al. 1995. Misoprostol reduces serious gastrointestinal complications in patients with rheumatoid arthritis receiving nonsteroidal anti-inflammatory drugs. A randomized, double-blind, placebo-controlled trial [see comments]. *Ann. Int. Med.* 123:241–49

117. Smith JB, Silver MJ, Ingerman CM, Kocsis JJ. 1975. Uptake and inactivation of A-type prostaglandins by human red cells. *Prostaglandins* 9:135–45

118. Smith WL, DeWitt DL. 1996. Prostaglandin endoperoxide H synthases-1 and -2. *Adv. Immunol.* 62:167–215

119. Tanaka Y, Ward SL, Smith WL. 1987. Immunochemical and kinetic evidence for two different prostaglandin H-prostaglandin E isomerases in sheep vesicular gland microsomes. *J. Biol. Chem.* 262:1374–81

120. Tran-Thi TA, Gyufko K, Henninger H, Busse R, Decker K. 1987. Studies on synthesis and degradation of eicosanoids by

rat hepatocytes in primary culture. *J. Hepatol.* 5:322–31

121. Tse M, Levine S, Yun C, Brant S, Counillon LT, et al. 1993. Structure/function studies of the epithelial isoforms of the mammalian Na^+/H^+ exchanger gene family. *J. Membr. Biol.* 135:93–108

122. Tsunoda S, Jackson EK, Branch RA, Gerkens JF. 1982. Comparison of the pulmonary, hepatic and renal extraction of PGI2 and 6-keto-PGE1. *Eur. J. Pharmacol.* 77:147–51

123. Uchida S, Nonoguchi H, Endou H. 1985. Localization and properties of NAD^+-dependent 15-hydroxyprostaglandin dehydrogenase activity in the rat kidney. *Pflügers Arch.* 404:278–84

124. Uekama K, Hirayama F, Tanaka H, Takematsu K. 1978. Partition behaviour and ion pair formation of some prostaglandins. *Chem. Pharmacol. Bull.* 26:F58

125. Ullrich KJ, Rumrich G, Papavassiliou F, Kloss S, Fritzsch G. 1991. Contraluminal *p*-aminohippurate transport in the proximal tubule of the rat kidney. VII. Specificity: cyclic nucleotides, eicosanoids. *Pflügers Arch.* 418:360–70

126. Ulmann A, Silvestre L, Chemama L, Rezvani Y, Renault M, et al. 1992. Medical termination of early pregnancy with mifepristone (RU 486) followed by a prostaglandin analogue. Study in 16,369 women. *Acta Obstet. Gynecol. Scand.* 71:278–83

127. von Euler US, Eliasson R, eds. 1967. *Prostaglandins.* New York: Academic. 164 pp.

128. Willman EA. 1971. The extraction of prostaglandin E1 from human plasma. *Life Sci.* 10:1181–91

129. Wright JT, Corder CN. 1979. NAD^+-15-hydroxyprostaglandin dehydrogenase distribution in rat kidney. *J. Histochem. Cytochem.* 27:657–64

130. You G, Smith CP, Kanai Y, Lee W-S, Stelzner M, et al. 1993. Cloning and characterization of the vasopressin-regulated urea transporter. *Nature* 365:844–47

131. Ziai N, Dolan JW, Kacere RD, Brubaker RF. 1993. The effects on aqueous dynamics of PhXA41, a new prostaglandin F2 alpha analogue, after topical application in normal and ocular hypertensive human eyes. *Arch. Ophthalmol.* 111:1351–58

132. Zusman RM, Spector D, Caldwell BV, Speroff L, Schneider G, et al. 1973. The effect of chronic sodium loading and sodium restriction on plasma prostaglandin A, E, and F concentrations in normal humans. *J. Clin. Invest.* 52:1093–98

Annu. Rev. Physiol. 1998. 60:243–66

ORGANIC CATION TRANSPORTERS IN INTESTINE, KIDNEY, LIVER, AND BRAIN

H. Koepsell

Anatomisches Institut der Bayerischen Julius-Maximilians-Universität, 97070 Würzburg, Germany; e-mail: anat010@rzbox.uni-wuerzburg.de

KEY WORDS: cation excretion, cation reabsorption, polyspecific transporters, drug transporters

ABSTRACT

This review focuses on sodium-independent transport systems for organic cations in small intestine, liver, kidney, and brain. The roles of P-glycoproteins (MDR) and anion transporters (OATP) in organic cation transport are reported, and two members of the new transporter family OCT are described. The OCT transporters belong to a superfamily that includes multidrug-resistance proteins, facilitative diffusion systems, and proton antiporters. They mediate electrogenic transport of small organic cations with different molecular structures, independently of sodium and proton gradients. The current knowledge of the distribution and functional properties of cloned cation transport systems and of cation transport measured in intact plasma membranes is used to postulate identical or homologous transporters in intestine, liver, kidney, and brain.

INTRODUCTION

Organic molecules with a transient or permanent positive net charge are categorized as organic cations. They include cationic drugs and xenobiotics, some vitamins, and a variety of endogenous compounds such as choline, as well as monoamine neurotransmitters. The homeostasis of such organic cations is determined by their endogenous production, their absorption in the small intestine, and their excretion by the intestine, liver, and kidney. Organic cations have many important biological functions. They are transported into cells where they act as essential nutrients or have other influences on cell metabolism. Transport of

243

organic cations is mediated by substrate-specific, sodium-dependent transporters (1–3) and by less specific sodium-independent transporters (4–7). Sodium-independent cation transport systems have been described in liver, kidney, small intestine, and brain. In small intestine, liver, and kidney, these transporters mediate the absorption and excretion of organic cations. These functions are mediated by two transport processes in series: cation translocation from the extracellular space into epithelial cells, which may be driven by the membrane potential, followed by cation transport out of the cells in which the membrane potential must be overcome.

This review is focused on polyspecific transport systems for organic cations that are independent of sodium. The functional characterization of these transport systems in small intestine, liver, kidney, and the nervous system are described. I attempt to identify cation transporters in the different organs that may be identical or homologous. Therefore, this review also contains some recent information on cation transport by cloned P-glycoproteins (8) and the anion transporter OATP (9). In addition, two subtypes of a recently identified family of cation transporters are described (10–15).

TRANSPORT MEASUREMENTS IN SMALL INTESTINE

Absorption and secretion of organic cations has been reported from studies in the small intestine (16, 17). For example at low plasma concentrations of N^1-methylnicotineamide (NMN) and tetraethylammonium (TEA), net secretion of these cations was observed. With high luminal concentrations of the cations, a net flux into the blood occurred. Figure 1 summarizes the presently identified sodium-independent cation transport systems in small intestine. In uptake measurements with brush-border membrane vesicles, a high-affinity uptake system for thiamine with an apparent K_m of 0.8 μM was detected that was independent of sodium and inhibited by choline (system 1 in Figure 1) (18). Unfortunately, this transport system was not investigated for its dependence on the membrane potential and proton gradients. This system is different from the putative proton/thiamine antiporter in hepatocytes, which has a higher K_m and is not inhibited by choline (19). Because the thiamine concentration in the small intestinal lumen is less than 2 μM (20), this transporter may be responsible for the first step in thiamine absorption. The intestinal brush-border membrane also contains two relatively unspecific sodium-independent cation transport systems. One system is potential dependent and translocates tyramine and tryptamine (21, 22). It may mediate the first step in the absorption of small cations (system 2 in Figure 1). The other system is not dependent on membrane potential and proton gradients and translocates choline, tetramethylammonium (TMA), and NMN but does not interact with TEA (system 3 in Figure 1)

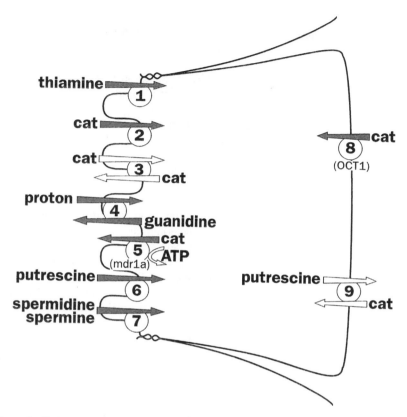

Figure 1 Cation transport systems in enterocytes of small intestine. The transport systems 1–3, 5–9 have been described in rat and other species, whereas system 4 has only been described in rabbit. The *open arrows* in 3 and 9 indicate speculative transport mechanisms.

(23, 24). For the uptake of choline, apparent K_ms of 80 and 160 μM have been determined. This electroneutral transporter is probably also engaged in organic cation secretion: It may perform cation exchange as speculated in Figure 1. In brush-border membranes from rabbit small intestine, a proton/cation antiporter has been described that translocates guanidine (system 4 in Figure 1) (25). This transport system was also detected in renal brush-border membranes (system 4 in Figure 3) and differs from the polyspecific proton/cation antiporter that was observed in brush-border membranes from renal proximal tubules (system 10 in Figure 3), because it does not interact with choline, TEA, or NMN, the classical substrates for the proton/cation antiporter (4, 5, 26).

P-glycoprotein (MDR1 in human, mdr1a in mouse) may also be involved in organic cation secretion across the brush-border membrane (system 5 in Figure 1) (27–30). It is an ATP-dependent, polyspecific export pump that translocates hydrophobic, mostly anionic, solutes. A role for this transporter in organic cation transport was suggested by the observation that the cytotoxicity of *Vinca* alkaloids was increased by the cation verapamil and by demonstrating that ATP hydrolysis was stimulated by cationic drugs in MDR overexpressing cells (31). In Sf9 insect cells, which were transfected with the gene for the mouse P-glycoprotein mdr1b, cation transport was demonstrated directly (32).

In brush-border membrane vesicles of small intestine, transport of polyamines has also been described. The absorption of polyamines in the gut plays an important role in the homeostasis of polyamines that are engaged in the control of cellular growth and differentiation. These agents are formed in many eukaryotic cells, but their extracellular concentration is mainly determined by the amount of polyamines produced by bacteria in the colon and subsequently absorbed. The absorbed polyamines are delivered to the small intestine by hepatobiliary excretion. They are taken up by the enterocytes and stimulate the regeneration and growth of the mucosa (33, 34). The intracellular concentration of polyamines is regulated by the activity of metabolizing enzymes and of polyamine transporters (35–38). Polyamine uptake has been measured in various mammalian cells. In intestinal brush-border membranes, transport of spermine, spermidine, and putrescine has been demonstrated (38–42), with distinct species differences described. In the rat, an energy-dependent system translocates spermidine with an apparent K_m of 2.5 μM. This may be different from the high-affinity transport system for putrescine, which has a K_m in the pmolar range (systems 6 and 7 in Figure 1) (39, 43–45). However, in the rabbit, putrescine and spermine are probably transported by the same system (40).

In contrast to data about transport of cations at the apical membrane, limited functional data are available concerning organic cation transporters in the basolateral membrane of small intestinal enterocytes. By analogy to the kidney and liver, it is possible also that the basal membrane contains a polyspecific, electrogenic cation transporter that mediates the first step of cation secretion (system 8 in Figure 1). This transport is probably mediated by the recently cloned organic cation transporter rOCT1 (10, 11) (see below). The uptake of polyamines across the basolateral membrane (46–48) may be mediated by the same transporter. For the basolateral efflux of cations, evidence suggests the presence of an electroneutral transporter that accepts putrescine (46) (system 9 in Figure 1).

TRANSPORT MEASUREMENTS IN LIVER

The liver plays a central role for the homeostasis of cationic drugs and endogenous organic cations (for reviews, see 6, 31). Organic cations are taken up from the portal vein into hepatocytes where they are metabolized and excreted into the bile or transported back into the blood. Hepatic cation transport has been studied (*a*) in whole animals, (*b*) with perfused livers, (*c*) with cultivated hepatocytes, and (*d*) with hepatocyte membrane vesicles, and cation transport has been analyzed at varying levels of complexity. For example, in whole-animal studies, biliary excretion of tertiary and quaternary ammonium compounds has been demonstrated. The involvement of energy-dependent transport was apparent when after intraveneous injection of procainamide ethobromide (PAEB), a hundredfold higher concentration of the drug was observed in the bile, and biliary excretion was inhibited by other organic cations (49, 50). Subsequent pharmacokinetic studies with a series of quaternary ammonium compounds revealed that their hepatic clearance correlated with lipophilicity (51). Further studies with isolated hepatocytes suggested the existence of two different uptake systems with different substrate specificities (52–54). One system (type 1) transports relatively small and more hydrophilic cations such as TEA and PAEB; a separate system (type 2) transports larger more hydrophobic organic cations such as vecuronium and quinine. The type 1 system was inhibited by type 2 cations but not by taurocholate and certain cardiac glycosides such as *k*-strophantoside, whereas the type 2 system was inhibited by taurocholate and *k*-strophantoside but not by type 1 cations. Measurements of polyspecific cation uptake performed in isolated cells or isolated perfused organs may not distinguish between similar transporters because the interaction with endogenous cations and intracellular effects of the transported cations cannot be excluded. Technical limitations of such preparations may impose additional problems. For example, the observed inhibition by taurocholate and *k*-strophantoside may be due to intracelluar effects because both compounds are transported into the hepatocytes (55, 56). Only after methods were developed to prepare canalicular and basolateral membranes from the hepatocytes (see, for example 57) was it possible to distinguish and characterize the hepatic cation transport systems more unambiguously.

Electroneutral proton/TEA antiport has been demonstrated in canalicular membranes from rat liver (system 10 in Figure 2) (58, 59). Similar to the proton/cation antiporter in the brush-border membrane of renal proximal tubules (60), TEA uptake was *trans* stimulated by TEA. Uptake was inhibited by *cis* concentrations of type 1 cations TEA and PAEB and by the type 2 cation vecuronium. Whether the type 2 cations were also transported was not investigated. Pharmacokinetic studies in canalicular membrane vesicles demonstrated a K_m of 0.6 mM for proton/TEA antiport. This value is similar to the K_m of 0.8 mM that was obtained for electroneutral TEA uptake into brush-border membrane vesicles from rat kidney (61). However, proton/TEA antiport in rat liver canalicular membrane vesicles was not inhibited by 1 mM NMN. This indicates that the affinity of this proton/cation antiporter for NMN is low, as has been shown

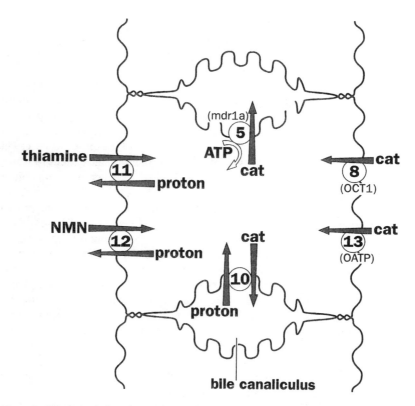

Figure 2   Transport systems for cations in canalicular and basolateral membranes of hepatocytes. The depicted systems have been distinguished in rat. Systems 5 and 8 may be identical to the respective transporters described in small intestine (Figure 1). Systems 5, 8, and 10 may be also present in renal proximal tubules (see Figure 3).

for proton/cation antiport in renal proximal tubules where a K_i value of 8.3 mM for NMN was estimated (62). Taken together, the data suggest that the proton/cation antiporter in the canalicular membrane of the hepatocytes is identical to the proton/cation antiporter in the luminal membrane of the proximal tubule (system 10 in Figures 2 and 3). The transporter appears to be different from the proton/guanidine antiporter in the brush-border membrane of small intestine, which has a higher affinity for NMN and does not interact with TEA (system 4 in Figure 1).

Expression of P-glycoprotein has been observed in liver. MDR1 (human) and mdr1a (mouse) were localized to the canalicular membrane of hepatocytes (system 5 in Figure 2) (28, 30, 63, 64). These P-glycoprotein isoforms may play a physiological role in liver transport of organic cations. The isoforms mdr2 (mouse) and MDR 3 (human), which are also expressed in liver, may function as a phospholipid translocator and as a transporter, respectively, for hydrophobic anions (for review, see 31).

Several organic cation transport systems have been also described in the sinusoidal membrane of hepatocytes. Proton/cation antiporters (systems 11 and 12 in Figure 2), a potential-dependent uptake system (system 8 in Figure 2), and the multispecific uptake system OATP (system 13 in Figure 2) (65, 66) have been identified. The direction of transport by the proton/cation antiporters may be defined by the transmembrane proton gradient that, among others, is mediated by the sodium/proton exchanger (67). Two proton/cation antiporters have been described: a proton/thiamine antiporter (19) and a proton/NMN antiporter (59) (systems 11 and 12 in Figure 2). Thiamine transport measured in sinusoidal membrane vesicles was *trans* stimulated by protons but was independent of sodium and membrane potential (19). This system is different from the thiamine transporter in small intestine because it is inhibited by choline and has a higher K_m, about 30 μM (19, 68–70). However, a second high-affinity K_m of 1.3 μM has also been determined for the transport in measurements with intact hepatocytes (19, 69). This probably reflects the substrate dependence of intracellular thiamine pyrophosphorylation. The apparent sodium dependence reported for transport studies with hepatocytes may be from sodium effects on proton gradients or from inhibitory effects of the substituted cations (68–70). In contrast to the thiamine transporter, the proton/NMN antiporter could be inhibited by various cations, including spermine and monoamine neurotransmitters (59). For proton/NMN antiport, a K_m of 12 μM was determined. This is three orders of magnitude lower than the K_m for NMN transport by the proton/cation antiporter in the canalicular membrane. In sinusoidal membrane vesicles, potential-dependent TEA uptake was also determined. This uptake could be *trans* stimulated by the type 1 cation TEA and was *cis* inhibited by type 1 and type 2 cations (58). It is probably identical to the cation transporter OCT1 (system 8 in Figure 2). Some uptake of type 2 cations into hepatocytes is likely mediated by the transporter OATP in the sinusoidal membrane (system 13 in Figure 2). This transporter has been cloned from rat and human and was originally described as a sodium-independent anion transporter (9, 71). However, recent transport measurements show that OATP is also able to translocate cardiac glycosides, steroids, and the type 2 cation N-(4, 4-azo-n-pentyl)2-1-deoxy ajmalinium (APD-ajmalinium) (65, 66). Therefore, OATP has been redefined as multivalent amphiphilic substrate transporter. Whether the sinusoidal membrane contains another transporter for type 2 cations is yet to be determined.

TRANSPORT MEASUREMENTS IN KIDNEY

The excretion of endogenous organic cations, cationic drugs, and xenobiotics is often controlled by the kidney (4, 5). Organic cations are ultrafiltrated in the glomeruli and/or secreted in proximal tubules. Ultrafiltration occurs readily for hydrophilic cations but is not efficient for hydrophobic ones, which are bound to plasma proteins and therefore scarcely permeate the filtration barrier. Renal clearance of ultrafiltrated endogenous cations such as choline, NMN, or monoamine neurotransmitters is controlled by reabsorption in proximal tubules and in more distal nephron segments (72–76). Some organic cations may be synthesized in the kidney; for example, L-dopamine is formed from L-dopa in the proximal tubule (77).

Cation transport in the kidney has been studied in various species although most data have been obtained from experiments performed in the proximal tubule of rat and rabbit. The cation transport measurements were performed with intact kidneys (75, 78, 79), with slices (80), by microperfusion experiments (72, 74, 81), by uptake measurements with isolated tubules or cells (73, 76, 82), and by uptake measurements with membrane vesicles of brush-border and basolateral membranes (83–91). Figure 3 depicts six cation transport systems in proximal tubules.

The first step in organic cation secretion—cation uptake across the basolateral membrane—is mediated by polyspecific uptake systems. One system performs potential-dependent uptake of type 1 cations such as TEA, NMN, choline, procainamide, cimetidine, and morphine (61, 73, 74, 81, 85–87, 92, 93). This transporter is independent of sodium and proton gradients and appears to be identical to the recently cloned transporter rOCT1 (10, 11; see below). For TEA uptake in rat, K_ms of 2.5 mM (61) and 0.16 mM (81) were determined from studies using voltage-clamped basolateral membrane vesicles and microperfused tubules. The rabbit transporter has a higher affinity for TEA, with K_ms of 0.37 and 0.07 mM determined from membrane vesicles and isolated tubules (73, 86). The different values obtained with the two methods may be partially explained by the potential dependence of the K_m values (11). Further studies suggest that the transporter may operate in both directions, although the transport rates and substrate affinities in either direction may be different (93). The transporter is inhibited by transported type 1 cations but also by nontransported type 2 cations (see below) (81). Basolateral uptake of type 2 cations in the proximal tubule is less well characterized and is probably smaller than in the liver. It may be mediated by a transport system that has not been characterized or identified, and/or by the basolateral PAH transporter, which can be inhibited by cations (94).

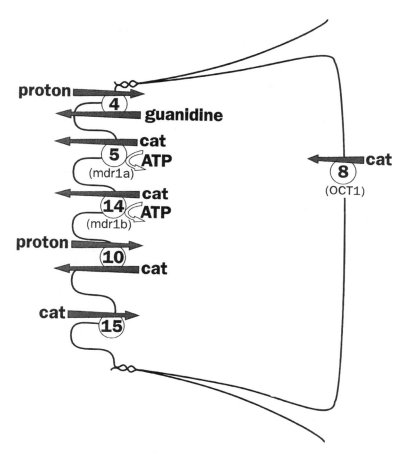

Figure 3 Transport sytems for cations in renal proximal tubules. With the exception of system 4, which has only been identified in rabbit, all transport systems have been demonstrated in the rat.

The second step of secretion—cation transport over the brush-border membrane—is performed by three transport systems: a polyspecific proton/cation antiporter that may be identical to the proton/cation antiporter in canalicular liver membranes (system 10 in Figures 2 and 3); a more specific proton/cation antiporter that transports guanindine (system 4 in Figure 3) (26); and the P-glycoproteins MDR1 (human), mdr1a, mdr1b (mouse) (systems 5 and 14 in Figure 3) (28, 30, 95). By tracer uptake and *trans*-stimulation experiments, TEA, TMA, NMN, choline, mepiperphenidol, procainamide, cimetidine, MPP, and aminocephalosporins have been identified as substrates of the proton/cation antiporter (60, 62, 85–87, 89, 96–100). In brush-border membrane vesicles from rat and rabbit, K_m values of 0.8 and 0.15 mM were determined for TEA influx by this transporter, which may be partially driven by the sodium/proton exchanger (61, 86, 101). In rabbit brush-border membranes, an additional proton/cation antiporter has been described that mediates the efflux of guanidine but does not interact with TEA and NMN (system 4 in Figure 3) (26). This system has also been detected in rabbit small intestine (25). In renal proximal tubules, the efflux of some organic cations across the brush-border membrane may be also performed by P-glycoproteins, which have been detected by immunological methods (systems 5 and 14 in Figure 3) (28, 30, 95). Functional activity of P-glycoproteins in the proximal tubule has been described for rat, dog, and fish (102–105).

Organic cations may also be reabsorbed in the renal nephron, thereby preventing the loss of ultrafiltered physiologically relevant cations like monoamine neurotransmitters and choline. Reabsorption may be partly responsible for the nephrotoxicity of some ultrafiltered cationic xenobiotics. Bidirectional transport of choline in the renal nephron has been demonstrated in chicken, dog, and rat (72, 75). At normal plasma choline concentrations, which do not exceed 25 μM (92), most of the ultrafiltered choline is reabsorbed in the proximal tubule. The first step in the reabsorption is mediated by an electrogenic cation transporter in the brush-border membrane. In rabbit, this transporter has a relatively high affinity for choline and is therefore designated a choline transporter (84). However, more recent micropuncture experiments with rat proximal tubules suggest that this transporter is not specific for choline, because luminal choline uptake is *cis* inhibited by many different cations (106). For inhibition by TEA and TMA, much lower affinities were estimated than with the luminal proton/cation antiporter or the basolateral potential-dependent cation transporter. A significantly higher affinity was determined for *cis*-inhibition by 4-(4-Dimethylamino-styryl)-*N*-methyl-pyridinium (4-Di-1-ASP). For luminal potential-dependent choline uptake, K_m values of 0.2 and 0.8 mM were estimated from measurements with perfused tubules and brush-border membrane vesicles, respectively (106, 107). By immunohistochemistry the multivalent amphiphilic substrate transporter OATP has also been demonstrated in brush-border membranes of S3 segments (66, 108). The physiological role of OATP in this location is not understood.

Elaborate studies have attempted to define the structural requirements for cation transport via different cation transporters in the proximal tubule (62, 81, 84, 106, 109). A weak positive correlation between hydrophobicity and charge of cations and their affinity to the transporters was observed. However, these factors were not sufficient to predict substrate affinity.

TRANSPORT MEASUREMENTS IN THE NERVOUS SYSTEM

Sodium-dependent and -independent transporters for organic cations have been described in the peripheral and central nervous systems. The sodium-coupled transporters are mainly localized at nerve terminals, where they mediate high-affinity uptake of released neurotransmitters (1–3, 110). For example, a high-affinity sodium- and chloride-coupled uptake system for choline is concentrated at cholinergic nerve terminals (3). Several sodium-independent transport systems for organic cations have been described in the nervous tissue, and a saturable high-affinity uptake of thiamine has been observed in brain slices (111). In homogenates and plasma membrane vesicles from brain, low-affinity choline uptake with apparent K_m values between 20 and 200 μM has been described (112–115). This transporter is probably localized at the somata of nerve cells and may supply the cells with choline for the synthesis of phospholipids and acetylcholine (116). It may be polyspecific and play a role in the homeostasis of monoamine neurotransmitters (H Koepsell, unpublished data).

Sodium-independent transporters for organic cations have also been described in glial cells. A high-affinity, sodium-independent noradrenaline uptake system with a K_m of 0.3 μM has been detected in primary cultured astrocytes (117, 118). Recently, low-affinity, sodium-independent noradrenaline uptake has also been demonstrated in the human glial cell line SG-MG-1 (119). This transporter is polyspecific and has a high affinity for corticosterone. It may be identical to the earlier-defined extraneuronal noradrenaline uptake system 2, which was detected primarily in myocardium and smooth muscle. This transporter is also sodium independent, polyspecific, potential dependent, and corticosterone sensitive (7). For noradrenaline uptake by this system, high K_ms between 0.22 and 0.45 mM were determined; however, much lower K_ms were determined for cations other than noradrenaline. The noradrenaline uptake 2 system shows large species differences and is very similar to the polyspecific, potential-dependent cation transporters in intestine, kidney, and liver, which belong to the OCT family (10, 11). Therefore, the noradrenaline uptake 2 systems in muscle and brain are most probably members of this family.

Sodium-independent transporters for organic cations have also been described in the blood-brain barrier, which is formed by the endothelial cells of small blood vessels. These transporters are important for brain homeostasis of choline and thiamine and for the permeation of cationic drugs and xenobiotics. In the blood-brain barrier, high-affinity uptake systems for thiamine and choline, a low-affinity choline transporter, and P-glycoprotein have been described. K_m values between 3 and 30 μM (120–122) have been estimated for high-affinity transport of choline, K_ms between 0.2 and 3 μM for thiamine transport (123, 124). Both transporters may be sodium independent. The thiamine transporter could be identical to the thiamine uptake system in small intestine (Figure 1, system 1) (18). In the blood-brain barrier, low-affinity transport of choline has also been described that is inhibited by various cations (122, 125). For choline uptake, K_m values between 0.2 and 0.44 mM were estimated (122, 126). This system may be homologous or even identical to one of the polyspecific, sodium-independent cation transporters described in small intestine, liver, and kidney. From immunohistochemical studies, P-glycoprotein was detected in brain capillaries from rat and human. It may play a role in the homeostasis of type 2 cations in brain (30, 95).

IDENTIFICATION OF A FAMILY OF CATION TRANSPORTERS

Primary Structure

Through expression cloning we isolated a polyspecific cation transporter from rat kidney (rOCT1) that contains 556 amino acids and belongs to a new transporter family (10). It is expressed in kidney, liver, and small intestine. A homologous transporter from rat named rOCT2 (11, 12) and two from human (hOCT1 and hOCT2) (14), a homologous gene product from mouse (mOCT1) (13), and a homologous transporter from pig (pOCT2) (15) were isolated by homology screening. rOCT1 is localized on chromosome 1q11-12 (127), hOCT2 on chromosome 6q25-26 (H Koepsell, unpublished data), and mOCT1 on chromosome 17 (13). In rOCT1 and mOCT1, and in rOCT1 and hOCT1, 95 and 78% of the amino acids are identical, respectively. Amino acids between rOCT1 and rOCT2 or between hOCT1 and hOCT2 were found to be 70% identical. rOCT2 and hOCT2 contain 81% identical amino acids. Two mammalian gene products with unknown function, NLT (128) and NKT (129), have been isolated from kidney and liver, respectively, which contain 30% amino acid identity with rOCT1.

Figure 4 shows a schematic representation of the membrane topology of rOCT1. Conserved amino acids between the six cloned OCT transporters are indicated in black. OCT transporters may contain twelve transmembrane α-helices. The OCT transporters contain four short motifs with five amino acid residues (130) (see Figure 4), which suggests that the OCT family is a member of the superfamily MFS (131). The MFS superfamily includes (a) drug-resistant proteins, (b) facilitative diffusion systems for sugars, (c) facilitative diffusion systems of Krebs cycle intermediates, (d) phosphate ester/phosphate antiporters, and (e) proton/oligosaccharide symporters. The first large hydrophilic loop of rOCT1 may be extracellular because it contains two conserved potential glycosylation sites, whereas the second large hydrophilic

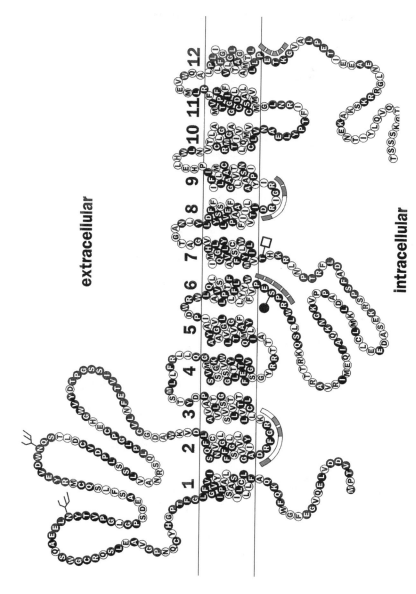

Figure 4 The primary sequence and proposed topology of *rOCT1*. Amino acids that are conserved between *rOCT1*, *mOCT1*, *hOCT1*, *rOCT2*, *hOCT2*, and *pOCT2* are shown in *black*. Four short intracellular consensus sequences with nutrient transporters from the MFS superfamily (*solid-open curved boxes*) and two conserved potential glycosylation sites (*fork*) are marked. One conserved protein kinase C-dependent phosphorylation site (*solid circle*) and one conserved protein kinase A-dependent phosphorylation site (*open box*) are indicated.

loop may be intracellular. This loop contains two conserved potential phosphorylation sites. One site is protein kinase C dependent and may be functional because TEA transport in rabbit proximal tubules is altered by activation of protein kinase C (132). In the first extracellular loop, 66% of the amino acid residues are conserved. The loop contains several stretches of conserved amino acids and seven conserved negatively charged amino acid residues. It also contains six conserved cysteine residues, which may be involved in conformational changes of the transporter (133). Four of these are conserved in the *NKT* and *NLT* gene products. Three negatively charged amino acid residues in the middle of the putative membrane-spanning domains 4, 8, and 11 are conserved in the *OCT* genes, which may be involved in cation translocation.

Tissue and Cellular Distribution

Marked species difference for the transcription of *OCT1* and *OCT2* in rat and human have been observed. In rat, large amounts of *rOCT1* mRNA have been found in kidney, liver, and small intestine, whereas in human, large quantities of *hOCT1* mRNA have been observed only in liver. By performing RT-PCR, a basal transcription of *rOCT1* and *hOCT1* has been detected in many different tissues from rat and human, which suggests a housekeeping function for these transporters. RT-PCR with *rOCT1* was performed in different microdissected parts of the rat nephron (H Koepsell, unpublished data). mRNA of *rOCT1* was detected in proximal tubules, in glomeruli, and in cortical collecting ducts, but not in distal tubules. By immunohistochemistry rOCT1 was localized to the basolateral membrane of small intestinal enterocytes, hepatocytes, and S1 segments of proximal renal tubules (H Koepsell, unpublished data).

The expression of *OCT2* is more tissue specific. In Northern blots the mRNA of *rOCT2* and *hOCT2* was detected only in the kidney. By RT-PCR in rat, small amounts of *rOCT2* mRNA were also found in colon, stomach, and brain (15; H Koepsell, unpublished data). In human, small amounts of *hOCT2* mRNA were found in brain, small intestine, spleen, and placenta (14). RT-PCR experiments with microdissected rat nephron segments showed that *rOCT2* is transcribed in glomeruli, proximal tubules, distal tubules, and cortical collecting ducts. By immunohistochemistry, *rOCT2* was localized to the basolateral membrane of S2 and S3 segments of proximal tubules (H Koepsell, unpublished data). At variance in the human kidney, hOCT2 was localized to the luminal membrane of distal tubules (14). In situ hybridization with human brain showed that *hOCT2* is also transcribed in neurons (H Koepsell, unpublished data).

Functional Properties

Cation transport mediated by the OCT-type transporters was investigated after expression in *Xenopus laevis* oocytes and in the human embryonic kidney cell line HEK 293 (10–12, 14, 15, 134, 135). Following expression of *rOCT1, rOCT2, hOCT1,* and *hOCT2* in *Xenopus* oocytes, uptake of radioactively labeled TEA was induced, which could be inhibited by organic cations of different molecular structure. The uptake was pH and sodium independent and was reduced when the membrane potential was decreased. After stable transfection of HEK 293 cells with *rOCT1, hOCT1,* and *hOCT2,* the expressed uptake of TEA or MPP was linear for only about 1 s (135; H Koepsell, unpublished data). The uptake characteristics were similar to those obtained in the oocytes. In measurements with monolayers, the expressed uptake is linear for several minutes and probably represents transcellular cation movement (15, 134). We were unable to detect potential dependence of uptake in the monolayers, but an apparent dependence on proton gradients has been described (15). Detailed functional studies were performed with *rOCT1, rOCT2,* and *hOCT2.* After expression of these transporters in *Xenopus* oocytes, the influx of ^{14}C TEA was inhibited by cations such as cyanine 863, quinine, *d*-tubocurarine, procainamide, *O*-methyl-isoprenaline, NMN, MPP, choline, dopamine, noradrenaline, serotonin, and TMA. Saturable uptake was demonstrated for TEA, NMN, choline, MPP, and dopamine (10, 11, 14, 135; H Koepsell, unpublished data). Tracer uptake by rOCT1 was also shown for thiamine, noradrenaline, histamine, and spermine but not for putrescine. Table 1 shows apparent K_m values determined

Table 1 Comparison of K_m and IC_{50} values determined for cation transport expressed by *rOCT1* and *rOCT2*

Substrate (inhibitor)	Apparent K_m values or IC_{50} values (μM)	
	rOCT1	rOCT2
MPP	19	17
dopamine	51	650
TEA	95	500
NMN	340	800
choline	620	600
(cyanine 863)	(0.13)	(8.5)
(decynium)	(0.36)	(0.45)
(quinine)	(0.9)	(14)
(desipramine)	(2.8)	(10)
(procainamide)	(13)	(1500)
(3-*O*-methylisoprenaline)	(43)	(2100)
(tetramethylammonium)	(1000)	(770)
(corticosterone)	(160)	(5)

The transporters were expressed in *Xenopus laevis* oocytes and influx measurements with radioactively labeled cations were performed (10, 11; H Koepsell, unpublished data). The apparent K_m values and IC_{50} values were determined as described in the text. Inhibitors and IC_{50} values are shown in parentheses. The standard deviations of the presented data were less than 30%.

for rOCT1 and rOCT2 and IC_{50} values estimated for inhibition of TEA influx by some cations. For rOCT2, significantly higher K_ms were obtained with dopamine, TEA, and NMN, and much higher IC_{50} values were estimated for many cationic inhibitors. In contrast, a much lower IC_{50} value was determined for corticosterone.

The cation transport by rOCT1, rOCT2, and hOCT2 was tested for symmetry and *trans*-stimulation by measuring the efflux of radioactively labeled MPP from *Xenopus* oocytes. MPP efflux was observed when no cations were in the bath (*trans*-zero), suggesting that the transporters may function as uniporters. MPP efflux was *trans* stimulated by both TEA and MPP. However, the efflux of MPP was *trans* inhibited by quinine and cyanine 863, categorized under the type 2 cations that have been classified for liver transport (54). Because the *trans*-inhibition of MPP efflux by quinine and cyanine 863 suggests that these cations are not transported, we also performed tracer influx experiments with ^{14}C quinine in *Xenopus* oocytes and HEK 293 cells expressing rOCT1. The experiments showed that ^{14}C quinine is not transported (H Koepsell, unpublished data). To elucidate whether quinine interacts with the substrate-binding site or with an allosteric cation-binding site of rOCT1, ^{14}C TEA influx was measured at different TEA concentrations and was inhibited by various concentrations of NMN or quinine. As expected, a competitive type of inhibition was found for NMN. In contrast, quinine proved to be a noncompetitive inhibitor. This indicates that rOCT1 contains an allosteric cation-binding site for type 2 cations.

Additional studies focused on electrophysiological measurements performed with *Xenopus* oocytes injected with mRNAs of *rOCT1, rOCT2,* and *hOCT2* (11, 14, 135; H Koepsell, unpublished data). In mRNA-injected, voltage-clamped oocytes, positive inward currents were induced when TEA, NMN, choline, dopamine, or MPP were added to the bath. In water-injected oocytes, no significant currents were induced. In rOCT1- or rOCT2-expressing oocytes, positive inward currents were also induced by TEA or choline when the membrane potential was clamped to zero. This indicates that the chemical gradient may serve as a driving force. When the membrane potential was clamped to −50 mV, the positive inward currents induced by TEA or choline increased about twofold. They increased further when the membrane potential was clamped to more negative (inside) values. The inward currents induced by rOCT1, rOCT2, and hOCT2 were not altered when the pH in the bath was changed between pH 6.5 and 8.5, and when NaCl in the bath was replaced by LiCl or D-glucose. The data show that cation transport by rOCT1, rOCT2, and hOCT2 is electrogenic and is independent of sodium and proton gradients.

When nontransported inhibitory cations such as cyanine 863, quinine, or d-tubocurarine were added to the bath of rOCT1- and rOCT2-expressing oocytes clamped at −50 mV, small positive inward currents were also measured (11;

H Koepsell, unpublished data). In early experiments we interpreted these currents as indicative of transport. Recent experiments show, however, that these currents are generated by the inhibition of electrogenic efflux of endogenous cations via the expressed transporters. For example, the currents increased when the oocytes were preincubated with choline. They decreased with increasing negative membrane potential and could no longer be observed when the membrane potential was clamped to -100 mV.

Prospective Function in Small Intestine, Liver, Kidney, and Brain

The data strongly suggest that the OCT1 and OCT2 transporters are electrogenic, sodium-independent and pH-independent facilitated diffusion systems responsible for the uptake of organic cations into the cells. If organic cations are accumulated in epithelial cells by other transporters, they may also mediate some cation efflux that plays a role in transcellular cation movements. In small intestine, liver, and segments of rat kidney proximal tubules, OCT1 is localized in the basolateral membranes of polarized epithelial cells where it may mediate the first step in the excretion of type 1 cations. Whether hOCT1 in the human is similarily localized has to be elucidated. OCT2 is a kidney-specific transporter subtype that also shows some expression in brain. The rat homologue rOCT2 is localized in the basolateral membrane of S2 and S3 segments of renal proximal tubules. It may engage in excretion of type 1 cations. The human homologue hOCT2 likely has a different distribution and function. hOCT2 is localized in the luminal membranes of distal tubules where it may be responsible for the first step in the reabsorption of some types of cations. Recently, we isolated *hOCT2* from human brain, and in situ hybridization experiments showed that *hOCT2* is expressed in pyramidal cells of the neocortex and hippocampus. Because the cellular localization of *hOCT2* expression in neurons is different from the localization of sodium-dependent monoamine transporters, we propose that hOCT2 in brain may help to reduce the background concentration of basic neurotransmitters and their metabolites.

CONCLUDING REMARKS

Endogenous and exogenous cations are absorbed and excreted by the combined action of polyspecific transporters in small intestine, liver, and kidney. The final distribution of these cations between the extracelluar and intracellular space is determined by the activity of these transporters in different tissues. With the observation that cations may be transported by P-glycoproteins and by the anion transporter OATP, and with the identification of the OCT transporter family, the molecular characterization of organic cation transport has begun.

The functional characterization and cellular localization of two OCT subtypes help to better understand transport measurements that have been carried out with intact membranes. However, we are still far from understanding transcellular cation transport. Therefore, all the cation transporters involved will need to be identified and functionally characterized, with their underlying transport mechanisms further defined and their substrate specificities, symmetry, and in vivo activity determined. In addition, we have to understand how the expression and activity of the different cation transporters is regulated. After the cloning of polyspecific cation transporters, the next challenge will be to determine the three-dimensional structure that provides high-velocity transport for cations with different molecular structures.

ACKNOWLEDGMENT

This work was supported by the Deutsche Forschungsgemeinschaft grant A22 SFB 176.

> Visit the *Annual Reviews home page* at
> http://www.AnnualReviews.org.

Literature Cited

1. Schloss P, Mayser W, Betz H. 1992. Neurotransmitter transporters—a novel family of integral plasma membrane proteins. *FEBS Lett.* 307:76–80
2. Kanner BI, Schuldiner S. 1987. Mechanism of transport and storage of neurotransmitters. *Crit. Rev. Biochem.* 22:1–38
3. Ducis I. 1988. The high-affinity choline uptake system. In *Handbook of Experimental Pharmacology*, ed. VB Whittker, 86:409–45. Berlin/Heidelberg/New York: Springer
4. Roch-Ramel F, Besseghir K, Murer H. 1992. Renal excretion and tubular transport of organic anions and cations. In *Handbook of Physiology (a Critical, Comprehensive Presentation of Physiological Knowledge and Concepts)*, ed. EE Windhager, 48:2189–262. New York/Oxford: Oxford Univ. Press
5. Ullrich KJ. 1994. Specificity of transporters for 'organic anions' and 'organic cations' in the kidney. *Biochim. Biophys. Acta* 1197:45–62
6. Elferink RPJO, Meijer DKF, Kuipers F, Jansen PLM, Groen AK, Groothuis GMM. 1995. Hepatobiliary secretion of organic compounds; molecular mechanisms of membrane transport. *Biochim.*

Biophys. Acta 1241:215–68
7. Trendelenburg U. 1988. The extraneural uptake and metabolism of catecholamines. In *Handbook of Experimental Pharmacology. Catecholamines I*, ed. U Trendelenburg, N Weiner, 90:279–319. Berlin/Heidelberg/New York/ London/Tokyo:Springer
8. Gottesman MM, Pastan I. 1993. Biochemistry of multidrug resistance mediated by the multidrug transporter. *Annu. Rev. Biochem.* 62:385–427
9. Jacquemin E, Hagenbuch B, Stieger B, Wolkoff AW, Meier PJ. 1994. Expression cloning of a rat liver Na⁺-independent organic anion transporter. *Proc. Natl. Acad. Sci. USA* 91:133–37
10. Gründemann D, Gorboulev V, Gambaryan S, Veyhl M, Koepsell H. 1994. Drug excretion mediated by a new prototype of polyspecific transporter. *Nature* 372:549–52
11. Busch AE, Quester S, Ulzheimer JC, Waldegger S, Gorboulev V, et al. 1996. Electrogenic properties and substrate specificity of the polyspecific rat cation transporter rOCT1. *J. Biol. Chem.* 271: 32599–604
12. Okuda M, Saito H, Urakami Y, Takano

M, Inui K. 1996. cDNA cloning and functional expression of a novel rat kidney organic cation transporter, OCT2. *Biochem. Biophys. Res. Commun.* 224:500–7

13. Schweifer N, Barlow DP. 1996. The *Lx1* gene maps to mouse chromosome 17 and codes for a protein that is homologous to glucose and polyspecific transmembrane transporters. *Mammal. Genome* 7:735–40

14. Gorboulev V, Ulzheimer JC, Akhoundova A, Ulzheimer-Teuber I, Karbach U, et al. 1997. Cloning and characterization of two polyspecific organic cation transporters from man. *DNA Cell. Biol.* 16:871–81

15. Gründemann D, Babin-Ebell J, Martel F, Ording N, Schmidt A, Schömig E. 1997. Primary structure and functional expression of the apical organic cation transporter from kidney epithelial LLC-PK1 cells. *J. Biol. Chem.* 272:10408–13

16. Turnheim K, Lauterbach FO. 1977. Absorption and secretion of monoquaternary ammonium compounds by the isolated intestinal mucosa. *Biochem. Pharmacol.* 26:99–108

17. Turnheim K, Lauterbach F. 1980. Interaction between intestinal absorption and secretion of monoquaternary ammonium compounds in guinea pigs—a concept for the absorption kinetics of organic cations. *J. Pharmacol. Exp. Ther.* 212:418–24

18. Casirola D, Ferrari G, Gastaldi G, Patrini C, Rindi G. 1988. Transport of thiamine by brush-border membrane vesicles from rat small intestine. *J. Physiol.* 398:329–39

19. Moseley RH, Vashi PG, Jarose SM, Dickinson CJ, Permoad PA. 1992. Thiamine transport by basolateral rat liver plasma membrane vesicles. *Gastroenterology* 103:1056–65

20. Hoyumpa AMJ, Middleton HN III, Wilson FA, Schenker S. 1975. Thiamine transport across the rat intestine. I. Normal characteristics. *Gastroenterology* 68:1218–27

21. Iseki K, Sugawara M, Saitoh N, Miyazaki K. 1993. The transport mechanisms of organic cations and their zwitterionic derivatives across rat intestinal brush-border membrane. II. Comparison of membrane potential effect on the uptake by membrane vesicles. *Biochim. Biophys. Acta* 1152:9–14

22. Ruifrok PG. 1981. Uptake of quaternary ammonium compounds into rat intestinal brush border membrane vesicles. *Biochem. Pharmacol.* 30:2637–41

23. Kessler M, Acuto O, Storelli C, Murer H, Müller M, Semenza G. 1978. A modified procedure for the rapid preparation of efficiently transporting vesicles from small intestinal brush border membranes: their use in investigating some properties of D-glucose and choline transport systems. *Biochim. Biophys. Acta* 506:136–54

24. Saitoh H, Kobayashi M, Sugawara M, Iseki K, Miyazaki K. 1992. Carrier-mediated transport system for choline and its related quaternary ammonium compounds on rat intestinal brush-border membrane. *Biochim. Biophys. Acta* 1112:153–60

25. Miyamoto Y, Ganapathy V, Leibach FH. 1988. Transport of guanidine in rabbit intestinal brush-border membrane vesicles. *Am. J. Physiol.* 255:G85–92

26. Miyamoto Y, Tiruppathi C, Ganapathy V, Leibach FH. 1989. Multiple transport systems for organic cations in renal brush-border membrane vesicles. *Am. J. Physiol.* 256:F540–48

27. Hsing S, Gatmaitan Z, Arias IM. 1992. The function of Gp170, the multidrug-resistance gene product, in the brush border of rat intestinal mucosa. *Gastroenterology* 102:879–85

28. Thiebaut F, Tsuruo T, Hamada H, Gottesman MM, Pastan I, Willingham MC. 1987. Cellular localization of the multidrug-resistance gene product P-glycoprotein in normal human tissues. *Proc. Natl. Acad. Sci. USA* 84:7735–38

29. Croop JM, Raymond M, Haber D, Devault A, Arceci RJ, et al. 1989. The three mouse multidrug resistance (mdr) genes are expressed in a tissue-specific manner in normal mouse tissues. *Mol. Cell. Biol.* 9:1346–50

30. Schinkel AH, Smit JJM, Van Tellingen O, Beijnen JH, Wagenaar E, et al. 1994. Disruption of the mouse *mdr1a* P-glycoprotein gene leads to a deficiency in the blood-brain barrier and to increased sensitivity to drugs. *Cell* 77:491–502

31. Meijer DKF, Smit JW, Müller M. 1997. Hepatobiliary elimination of cationic drugs: the role of P-glycoproteins and other ATP-dependent transporters. *Adv. Drug Delivery Rev.* 25:159–200

32. Müller M, Mittenbühler K, Mayer R, Wallstab A, Silverman JA, et al. 1994. ATP-dependent transport of amphiphilic cations across the canalicular membrane mediated by P-glycoprotein. In *Transport in the Liver*, ed. D Keppler, K Jungermann, pp. 156–65. Dordrecht/Boston/London: Kluwer

33. Osborne DL, Seidel ER. 1990. Gastrointestinal luminal polyamines: cellular

accumulation and enterohepatic circulation. *Am. J. Physiol.* 258:G576–84

34. Wang J-Y, McCormack SA, Viar MJ, Johnson LR. 1991. Stimulation of proximal small intestinal mucosal growth by luminal polyamines. *Am. J. Physiol.* 261:G504–11

35. Tabor CW, Tabor H. 1984. Polyamines. *Annu. Rev. Biochem.* 53:749–90

36. Lessard M, Zhao C, Singh SM, Poulin R. 1995. Hormonal and feedback regulation of putrescine and spermidine transport in human breast cancer cells. *J. Biol. Chem.* 270:1685–94

37. Alhonen-Hongisto L, Seppänen P, Jänne J. 1980. Intracellular putrescine and spermidine deprivation induces increased uptake of the natural polyamines and methylgloxal bis(guanylhydrazone). *Biochem. J.* 192:941–45

38. Seiler N, Delcros JG, Moulinoux JP. 1996. Polyamine transport in mammalian cells. An update. *Int. J. Biochem. Cell. Biol.* 28:843–61

39. Iseki K, Kobayashi M, Miyazaki K. 1991. Spermine uptake by rat intestinal brush-border membrane vesicles. *Biochim. Biophys. Acta* 1068:105–10

40. Brachet P, Debbabi H, Tomé D. 1995. Transport and steady-state accumulation of putrescine in brush-border membrane vesicles of rabbit small intestine. *Am. J. Physiol.* 269:G754–62

41. Stein J, Milovic V, Lembcke B, Caspary WF. 1992. Characteristics of putrescine uptake by human brush border membrane vesicles. *Z. Gastroenterol.* 30:841–45

42. Kobayashi M, Iseki K, Sugawara M, Miyazaki K. 1993. The diversity of Na^+-independent uptake systems in rat intestinal brush-border membrane vesicles. *Biochim. Biophys. Acta* 1151:161–67

43. Kumagai J, Jain R, Johnson LR. 1989. Characteristics of spermidine uptake by isolated rat enterocytes. *Am. J. Physiol.* 256:G905–10

44. Kobayashi M, Iseki K, Saitoh H, Miyazaki K. 1992. Uptake characteristics of polyamines into rat intestinal brush-border membrane. *Biochim. Biophys. Acta* 1105:177–83

45. Kumagai J, Johnson LR. 1988. Characteristics of putrescine uptake in isolated rat enterocytes. *Am. J. Physiol.* 254:G81–86

46. Scemama J-L, Grabié V, Seidel ER. 1993. Characterization of univectorial polyamine transport in duodenal crypt cell line. *Am. J. Physiol.* 265:G851–56

47. Bardocz S, Brown DS, Grant G, Pusztai A. 1990. Luminal and basolateral polyamine uptake by rat small intestine stimulated to grow by *Phaseolus vulgaris* lectin phytohaemagglutinin in vivo. *Biochim. Biophys. Acta* 1034:46–52

48. Bardocz S. 1992. The role of basolateral polyamine uptake in intestinal adaptation. In *Polyamines in the Gastrointestinal Tract,* ed. RH Dowling, UR Fölsch, C Löser, pp. 409–16. Dordrecht: Kluwer

49. Schanker LS, Solomon HM. 1963. Active transport quaternary ammonium compounds into bile. *Am. J. Physiol.* 204:829–32

50. Meijer DKF, Bos ES, Van der Laan KJ. 1970. Hepatic transport of mono and bisquaternary ammonium compounds. *Eur. J. Pharmacol.* 11:371–77

51. Neef C, Meijer DKF. 1984. Structure-pharmacokinetics relationship of quaternary ammonium compounds—correlation of physicochemical and pharmacokinetic parameters. *Naunyn-Schmiedeberg's Arch. Pharmacol.* 328:111–18

52. Mol WEM, Fokkema GN, Weert B, Meijer DKF. 1988. Mechanisms for the hepatic uptake of organic cations. Studies with the muscle relaxant vecuronium in isolated rat hepatocytes. *J. Pharmacol. Exp. Ther.* 244:268–75

53. Steen H, Oosting R, Meijer DKF. 1991. Mechanisms for the uptake of cationic drugs by the liver: a study with tributylmethylammonium (TBuMA). *J. Pharmacol. Exp. Ther.* 258(2):537–43

54. Steen H, Merema M, Meijer DKF. 1992. A multispecific uptake system for taurocholate, cardiac glycosides and cationic drugs in the liver. *Biochem. Pharmacol.* 44(12):2323–31

55. Ohkuma S, Kuriyama K. 1982. Uptake of cholic acid by freshly isolated rat hepatocytes: presence of a common carrier for bile acid transports. *Steroids* 39:7–19

56. Eaton DL, Klaassen CD. 1978. Carrier-mediated transport of ouabain in isolated hepatocytes. *J. Pharmacol. Exp. Ther.* 205:480–88

57. Meier PJ, Sztul ES, Reuben A, Boyer JL. 1984. Structural and functional polarity of canalicular and basolateral plasma membrane vesicles isolated in high yield from rat liver. *J. Cell. Biol.* 98:991–1000

58. Moseley RH, Jarose SM, Permoad P. 1992. Organic cation transport by rat liver plasma membrane vesicles: studies with tetraethylammonium. *Am. J. Physiol.* 263:G775–85

59. Moseley RH, Morrissette J, Johnson TR. 1990. Transport of N^1-methylnicotinamide by organic cation-proton exchange in rat liver membrane vesicles. *Am. J. Physiol.* 259:G973–82

60. Lazaruk KDA, Wright SH. 1990. MPP$^+$ is transported by the TEA$^+$-H$^+$ exchanger of renal brush-border membrane vesicles. *Am. J. Physiol.* 258:F597–605

61. Takano M, Inui K-I, Okano T, Saito H, Hori R. 1984. Carrier-mediated transport systems of tetraethylammonium in rat renal brush-border and basolateral membrane vesicles. *Biochim. Biophys. Acta* 773:113–24

62. David C, Rumrich G, Ullrich KJ. 1995. Luminal transport system for H$^+$/organic cations in the rat proximal tubule. Kinetics, dependence on pH; specificity as compared with the contraluminal organic cation-transport system. *Pflügers Arch.* 430:477–92

63. Kamimoto Y, Gatmaitan Z, Hsu J, Arias IM. 1989. The function of Gp170, the multidrug resistance gene product, in rat liver canalicular membrane vesicles. *J. Biol. Chem.* 264:11693–98

64. Buschman E, Arceci RJ, Croop JM, Che M, Arias IM, et al. 1992. *mdr2* encodes P-glycoprotein expressed in the bile canalicular membrane as determined by isoform-specific antibodies. *J. Biol. Chem.* 267:18093–99

65. Bossuyt X, Müller M, Hagenbuch B, Meier PJ. 1996. Polyspecific steroid and drug clearance by an organic anion transporter of mammalian liver. *J. Pharmacol. Exp. Ther.* 276:891–96

66. Dubuisson C, Cresteil D, Desrochers M, Decimo D, Hadchouel M, Jacquemin E. 1996. Ontogenic expression of the Na$^+$-indepedent organic anion transporting polypeptide (oatp) in rat liver and kidney. *J. Hepatol.* 25:932–40

67. Henderson RM, Graf J, Boyer JL. 1987. Na-H exchange regulates intracellular pH in isolated rat hepatocyte couplets. *Am. J. Physiol.* 252:G109–13

68. Yoshioka K, Nishimura H, Himukai M, Iwashima A. 1985. The inhibitory effect of choline and other quaternary ammonium compounds on thiamine transport in isolated rat hepatocytes. *Biochim. Biophys. Acta* 815:499–504

69. Yoshioka K. 1984. Some properties of the thiamine uptake system in isolated rat hepatocytes. *Biochim. Biophys. Acta* 778:201–9

70. Lumeng L, Edmondson JW, Schenker S, Li T-K. 1979. Transport and metabolism of thiamine in isolated rat hepatocytes. *J. Biol. Chem.* 254:7265–68

71. Kullak-Ublick GA, Hagenbuch B, Stieger B, Schteingart CD, Hofmann AF, et al. 1995. Molecular and functional characterization of an organic anion transporting polypeptide cloned from human liver. *Gastroenterology* 109:1274–82

72. Acara M, Roch-Ramel F, Rennick B. 1979. Bidirectional renal tubular transport of free choline: a micropuncture study. *Am. J. Physiol.* 236:F112–18

73. Schäli C, Schild L, Overney J, Roch-Ramel F. 1983. Secretion of tetraethylammonium by proximal tubules of rabbit kidneys. *Am. J. Physiol.* 245:F238–46

74. McKinney TD. 1982. Heterogeneity of organic base secretion by proximal tubules. *Am. J. Physiol.* 243:F404–7

75. Acara M, Rennick B. 1973. Regulation of plasma choline by the renal tubule: bidirectional transport of choline. *Am. J. Physiol.* 225:1123–28

76. Bevan C, Kinne RKH. 1990. Choline transport in collecting duct cells isolated from the rat renal inner medulla. *Pflügers Arch.* 417:324–28

77. Lee MR. 1993. Dopamine and the kidney: ten years on. *Clin. Sci.* 84:357–75

78. Okudaira N-I, Sawada Y, Sugiyama Y, Iga T, Hanano M. 1989. Effect of procainamide on renal tubular transport of cimetidine in the isolated perfused rat kidney. *Biochim. Biophys. Acta* 981:1–7

79. Hug CC Jr, Mellett LB, Cafruny EJ. 1965. Stop-flow analysis of the renal excretion of tritium-labeled dihydromorphine. *J. Pharmacol. Exp. Ther.* 150:259–69

80. Soares-da-Silva P. 1993. Kinetic study of the tubular dopamine outward transporter in the rat and dog kidney. *Br. J. Pharmacol.* 109:577–80

81. Ullrich KJ, Papavassiliou F, David C, Rumrich G, Fritzsch G. 1991. Contraluminal transport of organic cations in the proximal tubule of the rat kidney: I. Kinetics of N^1-methylnicotinamide and tetraethylammonium, influence of K$^+$, HCO$^-$stack$_3$, pH; inhibition by aliphatic primary, secondary and tertiary amines, and mono- and bisquarternary compounds. *Pflügers Arch.* 419:84–92

82. Hawk CT, Dantzler WH. 1984. Tetraethylammonium transport by isolated perfused snake renal tubules. *Am. J. Physiol.* 246:F476–87

83. Holohan PD, Ross CR. 1980. Mechanisms of organic cation transport in kidney plasma membrane vesicles: 1. coun-

tertransport studies. *J. Pharmacol. Exp. Ther.* 215:191–97

84. Wright SH, Wunz TM, Wunz TP. 1992. A choline transporter in renal brush-border membrane vesicles: energetics and structural specificity. *J. Membr. Biol.* 126:51–65

85. Kinsella JL, Holohan PD, Pessah NI, Ross CR. 1979. Transport of organic ions in renal cortical luminal and antiluminal membrane vesicles. *J. Pharmacol. Exp. Ther.* 209:443–50

86. Wright SH, Wunz TM. 1987. Transport of tetraethylammonium by rabbit renal brush-border and basolateral membrane vesicles. *Am. J. Physiol.* 253:F1040–50

87. Takano M, Inui K-I, Okano T, Hori R. 1985. Cimetidine transport in rat renal brush border and basolateral membrane vesicles. *Life Sci.* 37:1579–85

88. Gisclon L, Wong FM, Giacomini KM. 1987. Cimetidine transport in isolated luminal membrane vesicles from rabbit kidney. *Am. J. Physiol.* 253:F141–50

89. McKinney TD, Kunnemann ME. 1985. Procainamide transport in rabbit renal cortical brush border membrane vesicles. *Am. J. Physiol.* 249:F532–41

90. McKinney TD, Kunnemann ME. 1987. Cimetidine transport in rabbit renal cortical brush-border membrane vesicles. *Am. J. Physiol.* 252:F525–35

91. Rafizadeh C, Roch-Ramel F, Schäli C. 1987. Tetraethylammonium transport in renal brush border membrane vesicles of the rabbit. *J. Pharmacol. Exp. Ther.* 240:308–13

92. Besseghir K, Pearce LB, Rennick B. 1981. Renal tubular transport and metabolism of organic cations by the rabbit. *Am. J. Physiol.* 241:F308–14

93. Kim YK, Dantzler WH. 1996. Specificity of basolateral organic cation transport in snake renal proximal tubules. *Am. J. Physiol.* 270:R1025–30

94. Ullrich KJ, Rumrich G, David C, Fritzsch G. 1993. Bisubstrates: substances that interact with renal contraluminal organic anion and organic cation transport systems: I. Amines, piperidines, piperazines, azepines, pyridines, quinolines, imidazoles, thiazoles, guanidines and hydrazines. *Pflügers Arch.* 425:280–99

95. Thiebaut F, Tsuruo T, Hamada H, Gottesman MM, Pastan I, Willingham MC. 1989. Immunohistochemical localization in normal tissues of different epitopes in the multidrug transport protein P170: evidence for localization in brain capillaries and crossreactivity of one antibody with a muscle protein. *J. Histochem. Cytochem.* 37:159–64

96. Jung JS, Kim YK, Lee SH. 1989. Characteristics of tetraethylammonium transport in rabbit renal plasma-membrane vesicles. *Biochem. J.* 259:377–83

97. Inui K-I, Takano M, Okano T, Hori R. 1985. H^+ gradient-dependent transport of aminocephalosporins in rat renal brush border membrane vesicles: role of H^+/organic cation antiport system. *J. Pharmacol. Exp. Ther.* 233:181–85

98. Wright SH. 1985. Transport of N^1-methylnicotinamide across brush border membrane vesicles from rabbit kidney. *Am. J. Physiol.* 249:F903–11

99. Sokol PP, Holohan PD, Ross CR. 1985. Electroneutral transport of organic cations in canine renal brush border membrane vesicles (BBMV). *J. Pharmacol. Exp. Ther.* 233:694–99

100. Ott RJ, Hui AC, Yuan G, Giacomini KM. 1991. Organic cation transport in human renal brush-border membrane vesicles. *Am. J. Physiol.* 261:F443–51

101. Aronson PS. 1983. Mechanisms of active H^+ secretion in the proximal tubule. *Am. J. Physiol.* 245:F647–59

102. Hori R, Okamura N, Aiba T, Tanigawara Y. 1993. Role of P-glycoprotein in renal tubular secretion of digoxin in the isolated perfused rat kidney. *J. Pharmacol. Exp. Ther.* 266:1620–25

103. Okamura N, Hirai M, Tanigawara Y, Tanaka K, Yasuhara M, et al. 1993. Digoxin-cyclosporin a interaction: modulation of the multidrug transporter P-glycoprotein in the kidney. *J. Pharmacol. Exp. Ther.* 266:1614–19

104. Miller DS. 1995. Daunomycin secretion by killifish renal proximal tubules. *Am. J. Physiol.* 269:R370–79

105. De Lannoy IAM, Mandin RS, Silverman M. 1994. Renal secretion of vinblastine, vincristine and colchicine in vivo. *J. Pharmacol. Exp. Ther.* 268:388–95

106. Ullrich KJ, Rumrich G. 1996. Luminal transport system for choline$^+$ in relation to the other organic cation transport systems in the rat proximal tubule. Kinetics, specificity: alkyl/arylamines, alkylamines with OH, O, SH, NH_2, ROCO, RSCO and H_2PO_4-groups, methylaminostyryl, rhodamine, acridine, phenanthrene and cyanine compounds. *Pflügers Arch.* 432:471–85

107. Takano M, Katsura T, Tomita Y, Yasuhara M, Hori R. 1993. Transport mechanism of choline in rat renal brush-border membrane. *Biol. Pharm. Bull.* 16:889–94

108. Bergwerk AJ, Shi X, Ford AC, Kanai N, Jacquemin E, et al. 1996. Immunologic distribution of an organic anion transport protein in rat liver and kidney. *Am. J. Physiol.* 271:G231–38

109. Wright SH, Wunz TM, Wunz TP. 1995. Structure and interaction of inhibitors with the TEA/H$^+$ exchanger of rabbit renal brush border membranes. *Pflügers. Arch.* 429:313–24

110. Blakely RD, De Felice LJ, Hartzell HC. 1994. Molecular physiology of norepinephrine and serotonin transporters. *J. Exp. Biol.* 196:263–81

111. Sharma SK, Quastel JH. 1965. Transport and metabolism of thiamine in rat brain cortex in vitro. *Biochem. J.* 94:790–800

112. Yamamura HI, Snyder SH. 1972. Choline: high-affinity uptake by rat brain synaptosomes. *Science* 178:626–28

113. Yamamura HI, Snyder SH. 1973. High affinity transport of choline into synaptosomes of rat brain. *J. Neurochem.* 21:1355–74

114. Carroll PT, Goldberg AM. 1975. Relative importance of choline transport to spontaneous and potassium depolarized release of ACh. *J. Neurochem.* 25:523–27

115. Hemsworth BA, Darmer KI Jr, Bosmann HB. 1971. The incorporation of choline into isolated synaptosomal and synaptic vesicle fractions in the presence of quaternary ammonium compounds. *Neuropharmacology* 10:109–19

116. Jope RS. 1979. High affinity choline transport and acetylCoA production in brain and their roles in the regulation of acetylcholine synthesis. *Brain Res. Rev.* 1:313–44

117. Paterson IA, Hertz L. 1989. Sodium-independent transport of noradrenaline in mouse and rat astrocytes in primary culture. *J. Neurosci. Res.* 23:71–77

118. Pelton EW, Kimelberg HK, Shipherd SV, Bourke RS. 1981. Dopamine and norepinephrine uptake and metabolism by astroglial cells in culture. *Life Sci.* 28:1655–63

119. Streich S, Brüss M, Bönisch H. 1996. Expression of the extraneuronal monoamine transporter (uptake$_2$) in human glioma cells. *Naunyn-Schmiedeberg's Arch. Pharmacol.* 353:328–33

120. Galea E, Estrada C. 1992. Ouabain-sensitive choline transport system in capillaries isolated from bovine brain. *J. Neurochem.* 59:936–41

121. Shimon M, Egozi Y, Kloog Y, Sokolovsky M, Cohen S. 1988. Kinetics of choline uptake into isolated rat forebrain microvessels: evidence of endocrine modulation. *J. Neurochem.* 50:1719–24

122. Kang YS, Terasaki T, Ohnishi T, Tsuji A. 1990. In vivo and in vitro evidence for a common carrier mediated transport of choline and basic drugs through the blood-brain barrier. *J. Pharmacobiol. Dyn.* 13:353–60

123. Reggiani C, Patrini C, Rindi G. 1984. Nervous tissue thiamine metabolism in vivo. I. Transport of thiamine and thiamine monophosphate from plasma to different brain regions of the rat. *Brain Res.* 293:319–27

124. Greenwood J, Love RE, Pratt OE. 1982. Kinetics of thiamine transport across the blood-brain barrier in the rat. *J. Physiol.* 327:95–103

125. Oldendorf WH. 1970. Measurement of brain uptake of radiolabeled substances using a tritiated water internal standard. *Brain Res.* 24:372–76

126. Cornford EM, Braun LD, Oldendorf WH. 1978. Carrier mediated blood-brain barrier transport of choline and certain choline analogs. *J. Neurochem.* 30:299–308

127. Koehler MR, Gorboulev V, Koepsell H, Steinlein C, Schmid M. 1996. Roct1, a rat polyspecific transporter gene for the excretion of cationic drugs, maps to chromosome 1q11–12. *Mammal. Genome* 7:247–48

128. Simonson GD, Vincent AC, Roberg KJ, Huang Y, Iwanij V. 1994. Molecular cloning and characterization of a novel liver-specific transport protein. *J. Cell. Sci.* 107:1065–72

129. Lopez-Nieto CE, You G, Bush KT, Barros EJG, Beier DR, Nigam SK. 1997. Molecular cloning and characterization of NKT, a gene product related to the organic cation transporter family that is almost exclusively expressed in the kidney. *J. Biol. Chem.* 272:6471–78

130. Gingrich JA, Andersen PH, Tiberi M, El Mestikawy S, Jorgensen PN, et al. 1992. Identification, characterization, and molecular cloning of a novel transporter-like protein localized to the central nervous system. *FEBS Lett.* 312:115–22

131. Marger MD, Saier MH Jr. 1993. A major superfamily of transmembrane facilitators that catalyse uniport, symport and antiport. *Trends Biochem. Sci.* 18:13–20

132. Hohage H, Mörth DM, Querl IU, Greven J. 1994. Regulation by protein kinase C of the contraluminal transport system for organic cations in rabbit kidney S2 prox-

imal tubules. *J. Pharmacol. Exp. Ther.* 268:897–901

133. Zimmerman WB, Byun E, McKinney TD, Sokol PP. 1991. Sulfhydryl groups are essential for organic cation exchange in rabbit renal basolateral membrane vesicles. *J. Biol. Chem.* 266:5459–63

134. Martel F, Vetter T, Russ H, Gründemann D, Azevedo I, et al. 1996. Transport of small organic cations in the rat liver: the role of the organic cation transporter OCT1. *Naunyn-Schmiedeberg's Arch. Pharmacol.* 354:320–26

135. Busch AE, Quester S, Ulzheimer JC, Gorboulev V, Akhoundova A, et al. 1996. Monoamine neurotransmitter transport mediated by the polyspecific cation transporter rOCT1. *FEBS Lett.* 395:153–56

Annu. Rev. Physiol. 1998. 60:267–86

ROLE OF CARDIAC NEURAL CREST CELLS IN CARDIOVASCULAR DEVELOPMENT

Tony L. Creazzo, Robert E. Godt*, Linda Leatherbury, Simon J. Conway, and Margaret L. Kirby

Institute of Molecular Medicine and Genetics, Developmental Biology Program, and
*Department of Physiology and Endocrinology, Medical College of Georgia, Augusta,
Georgia 30912-2640; e-mail: tcreazzo@mail.mcg.edu

KEY WORDS: heart defect, excitation-contraction coupling, hemodynamics, contractility, heart
development

ABSTRACT

The discovery in the chick embryo that a specific region of the neural crest, termed the cardiac neural crest, is essential for septation of the cardiac outflow tract and for aortic arch artery development has led to the classification of a whole series of human cardiac defects as neural crest-associated. Recently, several mouse genetic models have been effectively employed to yield new insights into the relationship between cardiac neural crest and structural heart development. In all the animal models of neural crest-related heart defects, prenatal mortality is too high to be attributed to structural defects of the heart alone, and there are obvious signs of severe cardiac dysfunction. The evidence indicates that poor viability is from impaired cardiac excitation-contraction coupling and contractile function at the myocyte level. The continued study of experimental and genetically defined models with neural crest-associated heart defects will prove useful in identifying the common pathways by which the neural crest contributes to normal heart development.

INTRODUCTION

Cardiac conotruncal anomalies comprise a major category of congenital heart disease in which there are defects of the ventricular outflow tract (1) (Figure 1). Outflow tract defects have a prevalence of 4 per 10,000 births (2) and are

267

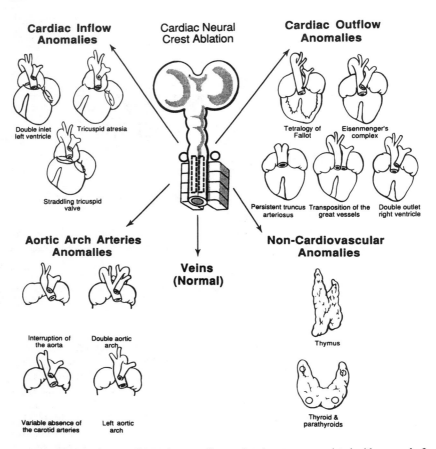

Figure 1   Illustrated are cardiac and non-cardiovascular phenotypes associated with removal of the cardiac neural crest. Figure taken from Reference 3.

well-known as part of the DiGeorge syndrome. Many cardiac outflow tract defects appear to have a specific embryonic pathogenesis, involving the neural crest cell lineage. The role of the neural crest in cardiac development has been most extensively studied in the chick embryo in which the premigratory cardiac neural crest is ablated. The discovery in the chick embryo that a specific region of the neural crest, termed the cardiac neural crest, is essential for septation of the cardiac outflow tract and for aortic arch artery development has led to the classification of a whole series of human cardiac defects as neural crest-associated (3–5) (Figure 1). More recently, several mouse genetic models have been effectively employed to yield new insights into the cardiac neural crest and structural heart development. Interestingly, observations in these models have raised some intriguing questions regarding the possible role of the neural crest and development of myocardial function. As previously noted, prenatal mortality in animal models of neural crest-related heart defects is too high to be attributed to structural defects of the heart alone. Moreover, there are obvious signs of severe cardiac dysfunction that appear to be from impaired function at the myocyte level. These observations are unexpected because there is no oxygenated pulmonary circulation in embryonic mouse and chick (or human), and therefore, prenatally, all the cardiac output is shunted systemically via fetal shunts. Thus it appears that the cardiac neural crest contributes in some way to the development of normal myocardial function.

What follows is an introduction of the role of the cardiac neural crest in development of the aortic arch arteries, the cardiac outflow tract, and cardiac function, along with a discussion of the genetic aspects of neural crest and congenital heart disease. We conclude with an examination of cardiac function in models of such diseases.

THE NEURAL CREST ABLATION MODEL OF CONGENITAL HEART DEFECTS

Neural Crest and Heart Development

Although the myocardium and at least a portion of the endocardium differentiate from the cardiogenic mesoderm near the pharynx of all vertebrate embryos, several elements of the heart are generated from extracardiac cell populations (4, 6). The epicardium grows in from the sinus venosus/liver to cover the heart, while the innervation and cells that organize the outflow septum migrate from the neural folds. The outflow tract itself is generated from the original tubular heart, and neural crest cells contribute to the outflow septum but do not contribute to the myocardium or endocardium of the tubular outflow tract. The neural crest provides an insignificant number of cells to the heart in comparison with the large contribution from the cardiogenic plate; however, the presence of these cells in the outflow tract is essential for normal development.

The neural crest extends along the neural axis from the mid-diencephalon to the caudal-most extent of the embryo. Cells that originate from the caudal hindbrain (rhombomeres 6, 7, and 8) migrate into the caudal pharyngeal arches (3, 4, 6), and a subset continues to migrate into the cardiac outflow tract where it will organize the outflow septum and form cholinergic cardiac ganglia of the parasympathetic plexus (7, 8). If these cells are removed prior to migration, several predictable phenotypes are seen after development of the heart and great arteries is complete. These phenotypes are collectively referred to as the neural

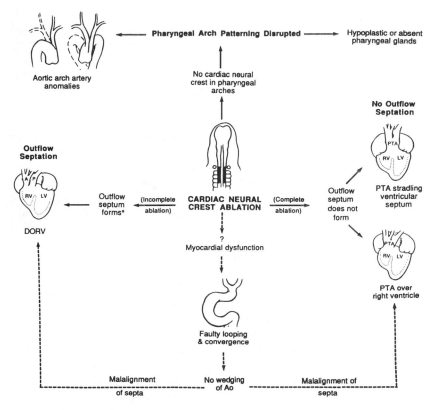

Figure 2 Flow diagram illustrating the effects of cardiac neural crest ablation on early and late cardiovascular development. See the text for detailed discussion. Ao signifies aorta. Other abbreviations are self-explanatory or are defined in the text. Figure taken from Reference 5.

crest ablation model of defective heart development (Figure 2). The defects include, but are not limited to, persisting truncus arteriosus, overriding aorta, ventricular septal defect, and variable regression of the great arteries.

The most severe conotruncal anomaly and the easiest defect to understand etiologically in the neural crest spectrum is persisting truncus arteriosus (PTA). PTA occurs when a threshold number of neural crest cells does not reach the cardiac outflow tract to divide the common truncal outflow vessel into an aorta and pulmonary artery (9). Overriding aorta or double outlet right ventricle is less easily explained in the context of neural crest ablation. This malformation can be produced experimentally by a variety of early interventions and teratogens, and its association with a reduced population of neural crest cells is less obvious.

Double outlet right ventricle has been seen following venous or arterial ligature (10), retinoic acid (11) or phenobarbital treatment (12), electric shock (13), and a number of single gene mutations (14). Overriding aorta is associated with looping, convergence, and wedging, which occur earlier in heart development than outflow septation.

LOOPING, CONVERGENCE AND WEDGING   After midline fusion of the endocardial tubes, the single cardiac tube loops to the right under control of a number of genes that are associated with right-left asymmetry (15, 16). Looping is necessary to bring the outflow and inflow portions of the tube together, which is a prerequisite for developing a four-chambered heart (Figure 2). As the outflow and inflow portions of the tube converge toward one another both craniocaudally and mediolaterally, the loop produced is positioned to become the future left and right ventricles. The outflow vessel must be positioned over these prospective ventricular chambers in such a configuration as to receive blood from both chambers (convergence). During the final adjustment of the outflow tract, the portion of the vessel that will be the aorta nestles between the atrioventricular valves in the process of wedging. If convergence and wedging occur incompletely or incorrectly, the aorta overrides the ventricular septum to varying degrees. Depending on the amount of the aortic base overriding, the defect can be classified as overriding aorta if it is not severe, or double outlet right ventricle if more than 50% of the aortic blood is from the right ventricle. Neural crest ablation and all the other interventions mentioned above can result in overriding aorta, which must originate from some abnormality occurring during the wedging process. Currently, we do not understand the factors that disrupt this process.

OUTFLOW SEPTATION   The outflow septum has three identifiable components: the aorticopulmonary septum, which is most cranial and forms in the aortic sac; the truncal septum, which is just caudal to the aorticopulmonary septum and forms the partition between the aortic and pulmonary semilunar valves; and the conal septum, which is the most inferior portion of the outflow septum and is important for closure of the ventricular septum. Neural crest-derived cells from the pharyngeal arches constitute the aorticopulmonary septum by forming a shelf of cells in the posterior wall of the aortic sac between arches 4 and 6. Thus the aorticopulmonary septum will form the facing walls of the aorta and pulmonary trunk in the supravalvular region of the adult heart. Two columns or prongs of neural crest-derived cells extend into the truncal cushions of the truncus arteriosus, and these columns organize the cells already present to form the truncal septum. A less well-organized group of neural crest-derived cells extends into the conal cushions and will orchestrate partitioning of the conus to form the left ventricular aortic vestibule and the right ventricular pulmonary infundibulum. Finally, the ventricular septum closes using mesenchyme from the conal cushions, the atrioventricular cushions, and the free edge of the ventricular septum (K Waldo, S Miyagawa-Tomita, D Kumiski & M Kirby, manuscript submitted).

Neural Crest and Aortic Arch Patterning

The aortic arch arteries are a series of large vessels that carry blood from the heart through the neck to the dorsal aorta, which supplies blood to the embryonic head and trunk (17). A total of five paired arch arteries develop sequentially on either side of the prospective neck (pharyngeal) region. The first two arteries that develop regress as the caudal three are developing. Arch arteries 3, 4, and 6 are permanent and develop into the carotid arteries, the aorta and base of the right subclavian artery, and the ductus arteriosus. The stability and final pattern of these arteries is dependent on the presence of neural crest, such that in the ablation model, variable regression of the arteries occurs leaving the derivatives unpredictably present or absent (4). Hox information carried by the neural crest cells may provide molecular cues to support the persistence of these vessels (18). Using antisense hox oligomers, it is possible to uncouple aortic arch patterning from outflow tract septation showing that arch anomalies do not necessarily lead to defective outflow septation.

GENETIC ASPECTS OF NEURAL CREST-ASSOCIATED CARDIOVASCULAR DEVELOPMENT

Splotch (Sp^{2H}) Mouse Mutant

Recently, several mammalian models of outflow defects have been described. These mammalian models incorporate a genetically based etiology, which provides a basis for molecular analysis of neural crest function. Currently, the *Splotch* (Sp^{2H}) mouse mutant appears to provide one of the best genetic model systems with a phenotype remarkably similar to the cardiac neural crest ablation in the chick embryo. *Splotch* mutant alleles have long been known to disrupt neural crest development, resulting in defects of neural crest derivatives (19). The *Splotch* (Sp^{2H}) mutant mouse contains a 32–base pair deletion of the DNA-binding transcription factor *Pax3* (19, 20). It has also been demonstrated that *Splotch* (Sp^{1H}) homozygotes (21) and *Splotch* (Sp^{2H}) homozygotes (S Conway, unpublished observations) die in utero and that lethality correlates with the presence of conotruncal heart defects including PTA. *Splotch* embryos additionally exhibit defects of neural tube closure and of the limb musculature (19, 22).

The *Splotch* (Sp^{2H}) mutant mouse provides some of the best direct evidence for the existence of a cardiac neural crest subpopulation in mammals (23).

When the pattern of neural crest cell migration was analyzed using a variety of genetic and molecular markers, the *Splotch* (Sp²ᴴ) mutant mouse had a marked deficiency or complete absence of cardiac neural crest cells traversing the aortic arches and entering the cardiac outflow tract. This evidence indicates that *Pax3* function is essential for the normal migration of the cardiac neural crest to the outflow tract. Additionally, it appears that *Pax3* serves as a marker of the cardiac neural crest cells in the mouse embryo (23).

Other Genetic Models with Neural Crest-Associated Heart Defects

Currently, there is an increasing list of different gene mutations associated with different combinations of neural crest-related defects. In the mouse, cardiac neural crest development also appears to involve the platelet-derived growth factor receptor alpha gene (*PDGF-α*), neurofibromatosis-1 (*NF-1*), endothelin-1 (*ET-1*), and retinoic acid receptors (RARs). The *Patch* mutation lacks the *PDGF-α* receptor gene (24). The phenotype of the *Patch* mouse is more extensive (25); this receptor is expressed in a larger variety of cell types than is *Pax3* and involves another gene, *c-kit*, that may be important in neural crest migration. A targeted mutation in the *NF-1* gene gives rise to double outlet right ventricle (26, 27), and a similar defect is seen in a small percentage of the mice carrying a targeted mutation of the *ET-1* gene (28). Both *NF-1* and *ET-1* knockout mutations may affect the neural crest. The homozygous double knockout RAR $\alpha\beta2$ and $\alpha\gamma$ mice also exhibit neural crest-related outflow tract and aortic arch artery defects (see review by H Sucov, this volume). All the RAR subtypes are expressed in the neural crest (29, 30).

In addition to cardiac outflow tract defects, disturbed development of the neural crest is associated with cranio-facial skeletal defects, abnormalities of pharyngeal derivatives (thymus, thyroid, and parathyroids), sensorineural deafness, pigmentation disturbances, and aganglionic bowel (Hirschsprung's disease) [reviewed by Leatherbury & Kirby (31)]. These neural crest-related defects can coexist in various combinations in humans: DiGeorge syndrome (craniofacial, pharyngeal, and cardiac); Waardenburg syndrome (craniofacial, pigmentation, and deafness) (32); CHARGE association; Goldberg-Sprintzen syndrome (craniofacial, cardiac, and Hirschsprung's); LEOPARD syndrome (craniofacial, cardiac, and deafness); and ABCD syndrome (pigmentation, deafness, and Hirschsprung's). Thus in different etiological groupings, different aspects of neural crest development can be dysfunctional, whereas other aspects appear unaffected. By relating the function of genes such as *Pax3* to the emergence and migration of particular neural crest subpopulations, it should be possible in the future to gain insight into the mechanisms underlying the role of cardiac neural crest cells in cardiovascular development.

NEURAL CREST AND FUNCTIONAL DEVELOPMENT OF THE MYOCARDIUM

The growth effects of cardiac neural crest ablation have been studied in the embryonic chick embryo at embryonic age day 11 (E11) (33). The wet and dry weights of ventricles from hearts with PTA are not different from those of normal hearts from either the sham-operated groups or from unopened control eggs. However, the embryos with PTA weigh less than embryos with normal hearts. The mean ratios of the ventricle to embryo weight are 19 and 58% greater in embryos with PTA for wet and dry weights, respectively. The greater difference between sham-operated and PTA when comparing dry weight ratios indicates that the embryos with PTA are edematous. This evidence of heart failure at these later ages is supported by recent echocardiographic examination, which indicates significantly reduced ejection fractions as well as marked pericardial effusion in many of the embryos with PTA at E15 and older (34, 35). The *Splotch* (Sp^{2H}) mouse embryos with PTA are similarly reduced in size, and regions of necrosis are often seen in the left ventricle in dying embryos at 13.5–14.5 days post coitum (S Conway, unpublished observations). These observations provided the rationale for a series of detailed studies of myocardial function in the chick cardiac neural crest ablation model and, more recently, in *Splotch* (Sp^{2H}) mice.

Hemodynamic Function

Hemodynamic abnormalities in the chick embryo have been documented after neural crest ablation both in very early cardiogenesis, before structural heart defects are present, and after the cardiovascular system is mature, prior to hatching. Indices of decreased contractility have been measured early in cardiogenesis using microcinephotography (36) and late in development using echocardiography (34, 35). Thus far, the majority of the hemodynamic assessment has been carried out during early cardiogenesis when the heart is a looped tube. In embryos that have undergone neural crest ablation, the outflow segment of the ventricle shows significantly depressed contractility by real-time microcinephotography, as indicated by a decreased ejection fraction and other measurements. The embryos compensate for decreased contractility by ventricular dilation in order to maintain their cardiac output in the normal range for survival (37). Several studies have been performed in an effort to determine the cause of this decreased contractility. The high incidence of an interrupted aorta at maturity and an absence of the aortic precursor, the right fourth aortic arch, during this early period of development suggests that an increased pressure gradient might exist across the sum of aortic arch arteries. However, although a systolic gradient does exist across the total sum of aortic arch arteries, it is not different between the neural crest-ablated and the sham embryos (38). A second study similarly failed to provide evidence for an increased afterload presented to the outflow segment of the ventricle in that there is no increase in the systemic resistance, which is measured as a sum of the embryonic and vitelline vasculatures (39). In another series of experiments, it was found that laser ablation of the right aortic arch arteries did not produce hearts with decreased contractility of the outflow segment ventricle; again, suggesting that increased afterload or aortic arch artery anomalies themselves do not directly cause the decreased ventricular contractility (M Crapanzano, R Tran & L Leatherbury, unpublished data). It should also be noted that the pattern of increased wall stresses in the neural crest-ablated embryos is similar to that seen in humans with primary dilated cardiomyopathy (38). Thus the decreased contractility observed with microcinephotography suggests a primary myocardial dysfunction in embryos with cardiac neural crest ablation in early cardiogenesis, prior to the period when outflow septation would normally be expected to occur.

The extent of cardiac neural crest ablation correlates with the timing and severity of ventricular dysfunction and dilation (40). Removal of the entire cardiac neural crest results in depressed contractility earlier (stage 16) and more severely than removal of a portion of the cardiac neural crest. However, both groups have similar, severely depressed contractility by stage 18. The embryos with the poorest contractility have a greater degree of ventricular dilation presumably to maintain a cardiac output compatible with viability. Incomplete looping associated with ventricular dilation may impede appropriate convergence of the inflow and the outflow segments of the looped cardiac tube and result in overriding aorta (41). A correlation exists between incomplete looping and dextroposition of the persisting truncus arteriosus with respect to the right ventricle (42). Presumably, the same factors function to produce overriding aorta when the outflow septum forms but is malaligned with respect to the ventricles.

Contractile Properties Ca^{2+} and Handling in the Myocardium

Contraction of the myocardium is initiated by depolarization of the surface membrane, followed by net entry of calcium through voltage-gated Ca^{2+} channels. In the adult heart, this calcium causes a further release of calcium from the sarcoplasmic reticulum (SR) via a mechanism termed Ca^{2+}-induced Ca^{2+} release (CICR). The subsequent rise in intracellular Ca^{2+} activates cyclic interactions between the contractile proteins myosin and actin, which lead to force production and shortening of the muscle cell. Relaxation of the cell is caused by a decrease in the intracellular level of Ca^{2+}, primarily the result of active uptake of Ca^{2+} back into the SR. The processes linking depolarization of the membrane and the ensuing rise in intracellular Ca^{2+} is termed excitation-contraction (EC) coupling [reviewed by Bers (43)].

In mammals, the SR content is considered sparse at birth and undergoes most of its development postnatally (44). This appears to be true in rabbit and rat hearts (45, 46) but is not the case in guinea pigs, which have a fully developed SR at birth (47). Thus there is variation among mammalian species with respect to the degree of maturity of SR at birth. In the chick, SR morphology and function is well developed by hatching. CICR in chick develops early and is detectable well before hatching, probably by E4–5 (48). The chick heart begins beating at approximately E1.5, at which time SR is present but very sparse. As the myocardium develops, SR and contractile proteins proliferate and myofibrils are formed. After E5, the myofibrils are abundant and are aligned parallel to one another in the cell (49). As the content of myofibrils increases, the force of contraction increases apace (50). In the early chick heart, relaxation is caused primarily by removal of Ca^{2+} from the cell by Na^+/Ca^{2+} exchange proteins in the sarcolemma. With development, the SR begins to play a larger role in control of intracellular Ca^{2+}, such that from around the time of hatching and beyond, Na^+/Ca^{2+} exchange is subsidiary to the SR (51).

The most likely explanations for the apparent reduced contractility in the myocardium of hearts following neural crest ablation are (a) a defect in the contractile apparatus and/or (b) a defect in one or more of the steps involved in the cardiac EC coupling process. Both possibilities are considered in detail in the following discussion.

CONTRACTILE APPARATUS IN EMBRYONIC CHICK MYOCARDIUM   Isometric force measurements can easily be made using small strips from the ventricles of embryonic chick hearts. Increasing extracellular Ca^{2+} leads to an increase of twitch force, which reaches a maximum for Ca^{2+} between 10 and 20 mM (50, 52). Ablation of the neural crest leads to a roughly 50% decrease in twitch force at any level of extracellular Ca^{2+} at E7 and E15, relative to age-matched normal hearts from sham-operated embryos (53) (Figure 3A). These differences could reflect defects at the level of the contractile apparatus and/or in the excitation-contraction coupling process. To distinguish changes of the contractile apparatus, the membranes were removed from ventricular strips using Triton X-100 detergent treatment (i.e. the preparations were "skinned" by the detergent). This allows the contractile apparatus to be activated directly by Ca^{2+} levels under complete experimental control. The maximal Ca^{2+}-activated force (F_{max}) from skinned preparations at E15 was not significantly different between sham-operated and experimental embryos (54). At E7, however, F_{max} was reduced by approximately 50% in skinned preparations from experimental embryos (53). These data suggest that in the experimental embryonic heart

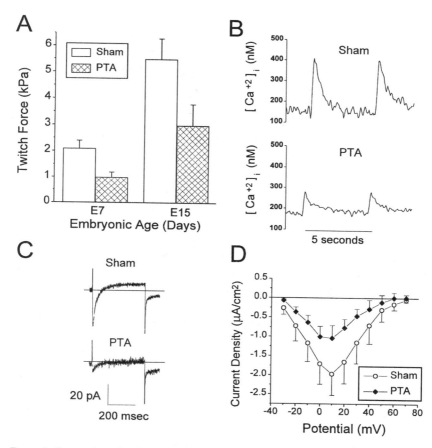

Figure 3 llustrated are the effects of cardiac neural crest ablation on ventricular function in the chick embryo. (*A*) Twitch force (kilo-Pascals) is decreased in left ventricular strips from hearts from embryos with complete cardiac neural crest ablation (PTA) compared with normal hearts from sham-operated embryos at both E7 and E15. (*B*) Field-stimulated Ca^{2+} transients are reduced in isolated ventricular myocytes from hearts with PTA at E15. The data from PTA in this illustration were signal averaged to better view the transient above background noise. Signal averaging was not necessary in normal hearts from sham-operated embryos. (*C*) Examples of L-type Ca^{2+} currents measured with perforated patch-clamp technique at E15. Note that the current is reduced in myocytes from hearts with PTA. The voltage step was from -40 mV to $+10$ mV, and the horizontal lines indicate zero current. The current records were not corrected for leak current. (*D*) Shown are the complete current-voltage relationships for peak L-type Ca^{2+} currents in Sham and PTA. Note that the current is reduced at every test potential in hearts with PTA. Similar results were obtained in *Splotch* (Sp^{2H}) embryos with PTA (see text and reference 67a). This figure was constructed using published data from References 35, 54, 67.

there is a defect of the contractile apparatus at E7 but not at E15 (but see below).

A decrease in F_{max} could involve abnormality in the assembly or orientation of the myofibrils, or a reduction in the concentration of myofibrils within the preparations. Electron-micrographic studies show that the organization and orientation of the myofibrils, as well as their general appearance, is similar in experimental and control ventricles (53; M Kirby, D Bockman, R Fogaça & R Godt, unpublished observations). The content of the major myofibrillar proteins—myosin heavy chain, actin, and tropomyosin—determined from polyacrylamide gel electrophoresis (PAGE) and Coomassie Blue staining and normalized to total protein, was not different in experimental and control ventricles at E7. At E15, however, normalized content of these proteins was roughly doubled in experimental ventricles (R Godt & J Chu, unpublished observations). These data on contractile protein content suggest a possible defect of the contractile apparatus at both E7 and E15. At E7, the myofibrillar content, as reflected in the levels of myosin, actin, and tropomyosin, is the same in control and experimental preparations, whereas F_{max} is about half in the experimental hearts. At E15, F_{max} is similar in control and experimental ventricles, whereas myofibrillar content is markedly increased. The nature of this defect remains to be elucidated.

The Ca^{2+} sensitivity of the contractile apparatus can be determined in skinned preparations by transfer of the preparation between baths containing known concentrations of Ca^{2+} while measuring isometric force (50). At E15, there is no significant difference between the force-Ca^{2+} relation of control and experimental preparations (54). At E8, however, the Ca^{2+} sensitivity of the contractile apparatus in experimental preparations is slightly but significantly decreased relative to control preparations (T Nosek & R Godt, unpublished observations).

Could differences in non-contractile proteins play a role in the contractile differences observed between control and experimental hearts? Specifically, could an increased content of microtubules depress force in the experimental hearts, as has been suggested to explain the reduced shortening of ventricular cells in pressure-overloaded cat heart (55). This does not seem likely for the following reasons. Total tubulin content, determined using PAGE and Western blotting for β-tubulin, was not significantly different between control and experimental ventricles (56). Moreover, there was no correlation between tubulin content and ejection fraction, determined with echocardiography in the same control or experimental hearts, suggesting that increased microtubules do not play a major role in the reduction of ejection fraction observed after neural crest ablation (56). Furthermore, we have found that tubulin content of detergent-skinned preparations decreases with time as the microtubules depolymerize (57). If microtubules inhibit force production, one would expect F_{max} to increase with time as microtubules depolymerize. However, 1 h after skinning, when about 10% of total tubulin remains in the preparation, F_{max} of control preparations was not significantly different from F_{max} determined initially. In experimental preparations, F_{max} actually declined significantly after an hour (58). Thus we conclude that excess microtubules are probably not responsible for the depression of force or ejection fraction observed with neural crest ablation.

POSSIBLE MECHANISMS OF CONTRACTILE ABNORMALITIES ASSOCIATED WITH OUTFLOW TRACT DEFECTS   A possible mechanism for the contractile defect observed following neural crest ablation may be aberrant expression of myosin light chains, as suggested from human studies. Normally, the atrial isoform of the essential or alkali myosin light chain (MLC1e/a) is expressed in the whole heart of the human embryo but becomes confined to the atria during early postnatal development (59–62). It has been reported, however, that the hypertrophied right ventricle of children with Tetralogy of Fallot (comprised of a spectrum of neural crest-associated defects) expresses large amounts of MLC1e/a, which persist into adulthood (63). To determine if persistence of these isoforms might have functional consequences on the contractile process, Morano et al (64) obtained small samples of right ventricular infundibular tissue from patients undergoing repair of congenital heart defects. Patients included in the study ranged in age from newborn through 55 years of age and displayed Tetralogy of Fallot, double outlet right ventricle, or infundibular pulmonary stenosis. The ventricular content of MLC-1e/a ranged from 0 to 27% of total ventricular MLC-1. Mechanical studies to investigate possible influences on cross-bridge cycling kinetics were carried out in detergent-skinned preparations from these samples. The maximal shortening velocity at saturating Ca^{2+} (thought to reflect cross-bridge turnover rate) was significantly correlated with MLC-1e/a content and was nearly double in patients with the highest levels of MLC-1e/a relative to those with no detectable MLC-1e/a. Another measure of cross-bridge cycling kinetics was the time course of tension development when contraction was initiated with ATP release in ATP-free solutions (with saturating Ca^{2+}) using caged ATP. The half time of tension development decreased 1.85-fold with increasing MLC-1e/a content. These data suggest that the anomalous expression of MLC-1e/a in congenitally defective ventricle leads to an acceleration of the cross-bridge cycling rate.

L-TYPE Ca^{2+} CURRENT IS REDUCED IN HEARTS WITH PTA Ca^{2+} channel activity in hearts with PTA following complete cardiac neural crest ablation has been extensively evaluated at E11 in the chick embryo. Ventricular myocytes from hearts with PTA at this age have about a 50% reduction in L-type Ca^{2+} current when comparing the magnitudes of the current at the peak of the current-voltage relationships with sham-operated controls (65, 66). The reduction in current occurs without a change in the voltage dependencies of activation and inactivation, in the time to recovery from inactivation, in the time constants for decay of the current, and in the number of dihydropyridine receptors (66). Similar studies indicate a reduction in L-type Ca^{2+} current at E15 (35) (Figure 3C,D). These observations indicate a reduction in the number of functional L-type channels. Further preliminary studies in very young embryos prior to the period of normal outflow septation indicate that hearts with complete cardiac neural crest ablation that are destined to develop PTA have reduced L-type Ca^{2+} current ($i_{Ca,L}$) as early as E3, which is 2 days before neural crest cells arrive in the outflow tract (35). This result is consistent with reports from microcinegraphic studies indicating reduced ventricular ejection fractions in these hearts (36, 37). These findings demonstrate a marked impairment of a critical component of the cardiac EC coupling process in embryonic hearts with neural crest-related defects. A reduction in Ca^{2+} current may be particularly critical for the early embryo because the SR is sparse and a larger proportion of the Ca^{2+} required for contractile activation enters from the extracellular space.

Ca^{2+} TRANSIENTS ARE REDUCED IN HEARTS WITH PTA   A reduced L-type Ca^{2+} current in hearts with PTA indicates that there is probably less cytosolic Ca^{2+} available for contraction during a single beat. This assumption was verified by comparing Ca^{2+} transients induced by field stimulation in fura-2 loaded myocytes from normal hearts with hearts with PTA. As expected, Ca^{2+} transients were depressed in hearts with PTA when measured at both E11 and E15 of incubation and were often not observable above background noise (35, 67) (Figure 3B). Similar results were obtained in fura-2 loaded trabeculae from E15 hearts (54). Treatment with the β-adrenergic receptor agonist isoproterenol could restore $i_{Ca,L}$ to the level found in normal hearts but could only partially restore the Ca^{2+} transient (35, 67). This suggests that the reduced transients were not solely the result of reduced Ca^{2+} entry via L-type channels. The results further suggest that there is impaired Ca^{2+} release and/or uptake from the sarcoplasmic reticulum in addition to a reduction of $i_{Ca,L}$ in hearts with PTA. This conclusion is supported by recent experiments showing that caffeine-stimulated release of Ca^{2+} is not only greatly reduced in myocytes from hearts with PTA, but the peak time and the decay time are slowed (35, 67). Moreover, experiments in saponin-skinned trabeculae show that CICR is dramatically reduced in neural crest-ablated animals (see below).

We have recently identified a similar impaired EC coupling in hearts with PTA from the *Splotch* (Sp^{2H}) mouse (67a). High-speed digital video imaging of living embryos in utero revealed a twofold reduction in the left ventricular ejection fraction in hearts with PTA at 13.5 days post coitum, when compared with normal hearts from wild-type and heterozygous embryos. Contraction in skinned ventricular muscle strips was normal, indicating no obvious problem with the contractile apparatus. However, the magnitude of the Ca^{2+} current was reduced more than threefold in ventricular myocytes from hearts with PTA, as was the intracellular Ca^{2+} transient, indicating impaired EC coupling. Thus disruption of the neural crest, either with experimental ablation in chick or in a genetically defined mutant mouse, results in similar phenotypes with respect to both septation of the outflow tract and myocardial function.

Interestingly, about 15% of the *Splotch* (Sp^{2H}) embryos that were used in the study described above did not have PTA. This indicates that sufficient neural crest cells migrated to the heart and participated in normal septation of the outflow tract in these embryos. The *Splotch* (Sp^{2H}) embryos without PTA survived until birth and had normal EC coupling (67a). Because the neural crest from all *Splotch* (Sp^{2H}) embryos lack a functional pax3 protein, impairment of EC coupling in those embryos with PTA must occur secondarily to the *Pax3* mutation.

Ca^{2+} HANDLING BY THE SARCOPLASMIC RETICULUM IN EMBRYONIC CHICK HEART
Calcium uptake and release by the sarcoplasmic reticulum (SR) can be studied in ventricular preparations from embryonic chick heart using techniques employed in adult mammalian heart (68). The surface membrane is made permeable with saponin, which at appropriate concentrations spares the SR membranes. Calcium uptake and release are measured indirectly by observing the tension transient associated with Ca^{2+} released from the SR by treatment with high concentrations of caffeine. This approach requires that the Ca^{2+} sensitivity of the contractile apparatus is the same in control and experimental preparations, which has precluded its application to SR Ca^{2+} handling at E8. At E15, however, where Ca^{2+} sensitivity is the same in control and experimental ventricle, it can be shown that neural crest ablation has no effect on the half time of Ca^{2+} loading into the SR. However, it slightly reduced the Ca^{2+} sensitivity of Ca^{2+} uptake by the SR. Its most dramatic effect was to markedly inhibit the CICR from the SR (54). These effects on Ca^{2+} handling by the SR, especially the reduction of CICR, explain, in part, the reduction in the Ca^{2+} transient and twitch force in experimental hearts.

MECHANISMS OF NEURAL CREST REGULATION ON THE DEVELOPMENT OF CAR-
DIAC FUNCTION   Although it is clear that the failure of normal cardiac neural crest function results in myocardial dysfunction, the mechanisms remain elusive. As already discussed, a divided outflow is not necessary for normal

cardiovascular function in the embryo. A few years ago, we considered the possibility that there was an alteration of parasympathetic innervation to the heart that leads to abnormal heart function. The cardiac neural crest also supplies the postganglionic parasympathetic cardiac ganglion neurons to the heart (7). However, in the absence of the cardiac neural crest, cells from the nodose placode migrate to the heart and differentiate into parasympathetic neurons (69), which function normally to reduce heart rate in response to field stimulation (70). Moreover, the reduction in L-type Ca^{2+} current was observed whether the nodose placodes were ablated along with the cardiac neural crest (65, 66). Finally, the reduction in contractility and Ca^{2+} current is observed by the third day of development, well before the neural crest reaches the heart (35). Thus neurotrophic influences are not a likely cause of impaired EC coupling in hearts with PTA.

A final consideration is that the cardiac neural crest has a direct effect on normal heart development, which is disrupted following neural crest ablation. This suggests the existence of a factor produced by the cardiac neural crest essential for normal myocardial development. The hemodynamic studies described above argue against an effect of afterload, at least during early cardiogenesis, and thus support the existence of a neural crest-specific factor. It remains possible that increased afterload plays a role in myocardial dysfunction later in development after the period when outflow septation would normally occur and when the hearts with complete cardiac neural crest ablation have PTA, but this remains to be determined.

SUMMARY AND CONCLUSIONS

Much has been learned from the chick ablation model about the role of the neural crest in the development of the aortic arch arteries and in septation of the cardiac outflow. The recent advent of genetically defined mouse models with neural crest-related heart defects promises to yield new insights at the molecular level on the role of the neural crest in heart development. Surprisingly, the neural crest not only plays a critical role in structural development of the cardiac outflow tract, it is essential for the normal development of myocardial function. Both mouse and chick embryos with PTA have reduced contractility related to impairment of EC coupling and decreased force production by the contractile apparatus. The deficit in myocardial function in these models of neural crest-associated defects is an unexpected finding because a divided outflow should not be a requisite for normal cardiac function in the embryo. Interestingly, work in the chick neural crest ablation model indicates that the contractility deficit and decrease in Ca^{2+} current are present in the very early tubular heart, at a time when the neural crest cells would normally have migrated only as far as the pharyngeal arches and would not be present in the outflow tract. Moreover, the contractility deficit appears not to be associated with changes in cardiac afterload or elevated impedance in the aortic arch arteries. Therefore, we conclude that there must be a factor, either diffusible or passed from cell to cell, that influences myocardial development.

The mechanisms by which the neural crest influences structural and functional development of the heart, as well as the identification of a neural crest factor, remain to be determined. From the discussion in this review, it is important to note that a variety of environmental, experimental, and genetic manipulations give rise to very similar phenotypes. Thus there appears to be a final common pathway that is initiated by these different sources. The continued study of genetically defined mouse models with neural crest-associated heart defects will prove useful in identifying the common pathway by which the neural crest contributes to normal heart development.

The final and most important question is whether cardiac functional deficits are a significant factor in humans with neural crest-associated congenital heart disease. Whether there are EC coupling and contractile defects is an important consideration in the treatment of infants. A recent report of data from individuals with Tetrology of Fallot (discussed above) indicates that there is a problem at least with the contractile apparatus. From the work discussed in this review, it is clear that more data on humans with neural crest-associated congenital heart disease are needed.

Visit the *Annual Reviews home page* at
http://www.AnnualReviews.org.

Literature Cited

1. Bartelings MM, Gittenberger-de Groot AC. 1991. Morphogenetic considerations on congenital malformations of the outflow tract. Part 1: Common arterial trunk and tetralogy of Fallot. *Int. J. Cardiol.* 32:213–30

2. Edmonds LD, James LM. 1993. Temporal trends in the birth prevalence of selected congenital malformations. Birth Defects Monitoring Program/Commission on Professional and Hospital Activities, 1979–1989. *Teratology* 48:647–49

3. Kirby ML, Waldo KL. 1990. Role of neural crest in congenital heart disease. *Circulation* 82:332–40

4. Kirby ML, Waldo KL. 1995. Neural crest and cardiovascular patterning. *Circ. Res.* 77:211–15

5. Kirby ML, Creazzo TL. 1995. Cardiovascular development: neural crest and new perspectives. *Cardiol. Rev.* 3:226–35

6. Yutzey KE, Bader D. 1995. Diversification of cardiomyogenic cell lineages during early heart development. *Circ. Res.* 77:216–19

7. Kirby ML, Stewart DE. 1983. Neural crest origin of cardiac ganglion cells in the chick embryo: identification and extirpation. *Dev. Biol.* 97:433–43

8. Kirby ML, Gale TF, Stewart DE. 1983. Neural crest cells contribute to normal aorticopulmonary septation. *Science* 220:1059–61

9. Nishibatake M, Kirby ML, Van Mierop LHS. 1987. Pathogenesis of persistent truncus arteriosus and dextroposed aorta in chick embryo after neural crest ablation. *Circulation* 75:255–64

10. Rychter Z. 1962. Experimental morphology of the aortic arches and the heart loop in chick embryos. *Adv. Morphogen.* 2:333–71

11. Bouman HGA, Broekhuizen MLA, Mieke A, Baasten J, Gittenberger-de Groot AC, Wenink ACG. 1995. Spectrum of looping disturbances in stage 34 chicken hearts after retinoic acid treatment. *Anat. Rec.* 243:101–8

12. Nishikawa T, Bruyere JHH, Takagi Y, Gilbert EF. 1986. The teratogenic effect of phenobarbital on the embryonic chick heart. *J. Appl. Toxicol.* 6:91–94

13. Chon Y, Ando M, Takao A. 1980. Spectrum of hypoplastic right ventricle in chick experimentally produced by electrical shock. In *Etiology and Morphogenesis of Congenital Heart Disease,* ed. R Van Praagh, A Takao, pp. 249–64. Mt. Kisco, NY: Futura

14. Olson EN, Srivastava D. 1996. Molecular pathways controlling heart development. *Science* 272:671–76

15. Stalsberg H. 1970. Mechanism of dextral looping of the embryonic heart. *Am. J. Cardiol.* 25:265–71

16. Hoyle C, Brown NA, Wolpert L. 1992. Development of left/right handedness in the chick heart. *Development* 115:1071–78

17. Waldo K, Kirby ML. 1997. Development of the great arteries. In *Heart Development,* ed. MV de la Cruz, New York: Academic. In press

18. Kirby ML, Hunt P, Wallis KT, Thorogood P. 1997. Normal development of the cardiac outflow tract is not dependent on normal patterning of the aortic arch arteries. *Dev. Dyn.* 208:34–47

19. Auerbach R. 1954. Analysis of the developmental effects of a lethal mutation in the house mouse. *J. Exp. Zool.* 127:305–29

20. Goulding M, Sterrer S, Fleming J, Balling R, Nadeau J, et al. 1997. Analysis of the *Pax-3* gene in the mutant mouse *Splotch. Genomics* 17:355–63

21. Franz T. 1989. Persistent truncus arteriosus in the *Splotch* mutant mouse. *Anat. Embryol.* 180:457–64

22. Franz T, Kothary R. 1993. Characterization of the neural crest defect in *Splotch* (Sp (1H)) mutant mice using a lacZ transgene. *Dev. Brain Res.* 72:99–105

23. Conway SJ, Henderson DJ, Copp AJ. 1997. *Pax3* is required for cardiac neural crest migration in the mouse: evidence from *Splotch* (Sp^{2H}) mutant. *Development* 124:505–14

24. Smith EA, Seldin MF, Martinez L, Watson ML, Choudhury GG, et al. 1991. Mouse platelet-derived growth factor receptor alpha gene is deleted in W19H and patch mutations on chromosome 5. *Proc. Natl. Acad. Sci. USA* 88:4811–15

25. Schatterman GC, Motley ST, Effman EL, Bowen-Pope DF. 1995. Platelet-derived growth factor receptor alpha subunit deleted in Patch mouse exhibits severe cardiovascular dysmorphogenesis. *Teratology* 51:351–66

26. Brannan CI, Perkins AS, Vogel KS, Ratner N, Nordlund ML, et al. 1994. Targeted disruption of the neurofibromatosis type-1 gene leads to developmental abnormalities in heart and various neural crest-derived tissues. *Genes Dev.* 8:1019–29

27. Jacks T, Shih TS, Schmitt EM, Bronson RT, Bernards A, Weinberg RA. 1994. Tumor predisposition in mice heterozygous for a targeted mutation in NF1. *Nat. Genet.* 7:353–61

28. Kurihara Y, Kurihara H, Oda H, Maemura K, Nagai R, et al. 1995. Aortic arch malformations and ventricular septal defect in mice deficient in endothelin-1. *J. Clin. Invest.* 90:293–300

29. Ruberte E, Dolle P, Chambon P, Morris-Kay G. 1991. Retinoic acid receptors and cellular retinoid binding proteins. II. Their differential pattern of transcription during early morphogenesis in mouse embryos. *Development* 111:45–60

30. Rowe A, Sarkar S, Brickell PM, Thorogood P. 1997. Differential expression of RAR-beta and RXR-gamma transcripts in cultured cranial neural crest cell. *Roux's Arch. Dev. Biol.* 203:445–49

31. Leatherbury L, Kirby ML. 1996. Cardiac development and perinatal care of infants with neural crest-associated conotruncal defects. *Semin. Perinatol.* 20:473–81

32. Baldwin CT, Hoth CF, Amos JA, Da-Silva EO, Milunsky A. 1992. An exonic mutation in the HuP2 paired domain gene causes Waardenburg's syndrome. *Nature* 355:637–38

33. Creazzo TL, Burch J, Redmond S, Kumiski D. 1994. Myocardial enlargement in defective heart development. *Anat. Rec.* 239:170–76

34. Lutin WA, Creazzo TL, Connuck DM. 1996. Congestive heart failure in embryos with persistent truncus arteriosus. *Pediatr. Res.* 39:32A (Abstr.)

35. Creazzo TL, Brotto MAP, Lutin WA, Aliff CL. 1995. Excitation-contraction coupling in cardiac dysmorphogenesis. *J.*

Physiol. 487:16P
36. Leatherbury L, Gauldin HE, Waldo K, Kirby ML. 1990. Microcinephotography of the developing heart in neural crest-ablated chick embryos. *Circulation* 81:1047–57
37. Leatherbury L, Connuck DM, Gauldin HE, Kirby ML. 1991. Hemodynamic changes and compensatory mechanisms during early cardiogenesis after neural crest ablation in chick embryos. *Pediatr. Res.* 30:509–12
38. Leatherbury L, Braden DS, Tomita H, Gauldin HE, Jackson WF. 1990. Hemodynamic changes-wall stresses and pressure gradients in neural crest-ablated chick embryos. *Ann. NY Acad. Sci.* 588:305–13
39. Leatherbury L, Connuck DM, Kirby ML. 1993. Neural crest ablation versus sham surgical effects in a chick embryo model of defective cardiovascular development. *Pediatr. Res.* 33:628–31
40. Leatherbury L, Davis J, Rhoden DK, Connuck DM. 1994. Partial versus complete neural crest ablation in a chick embyro model of heart defects. *Cardiol. Young* 4:195 (Abstr.)
41. Leatherbury L, Yun JS, Wolfe R. 1996. Association of abnormal configuration of heart tube with depressed contractility after cardiac neural crest ablation. *Pediatr. Res.* 39:62A (Abstr.)
42. Tomita H, Connuck DM, Leatherbury L, Kirby ML. 1991. Relation of early hemodynamic changes to final cardiac phenotype and survival after neural crest ablation in chick embryos. *Circulation* 84:1289–95
43. Bers DM. 1991. *Excitation-Contraction Coupling and Cardiac Contractile Force.* Boston: Kluwer
44. Nakanishi T, Jarmakani JM. 1984. Developmental changes in myocardial mechanical function and subcellular organelles. *Am. J. Physiol.* H615–25
45. Seguchi M, Harding J, Jamrmakani J. 1986. Developmental change in the function of sarcoplasmic reticulum. *J. Mol. Cell. Cardiol.* 18:189–95
46. Nakanishi T, Seguchi M, Takao A. 1992. Developmental changes in myocardial mechanical function and subcellular organelles. *Experientia* 44:936–44
47. Goldstein MA, Traeger L. 1985. Ultrastructural changes in postnatal development of the cardiac myocyte. In *The Developing Heart*, ed. ML Legato, pp. 1–20. Boston: Nijhoff
48. Dutro SM, Airey JA, Beck CF, Sutko JL, Trumble WR. 1993. Ryanodine receptor expression in embryonic avian cardiac

muscle. *Dev. Biol.* 155:431–41
49. Manasek FJ. 1970. Histogenesis of the embryonic myocardium. *Am. J. Cardiol.* 25:149–68
50. Godt RE, Fogaça RTH, Nosek TM. 1991. Changes in force and calcium sensitivity in the developing avian heart. *Can. J. Physiol. Pharmacol.* 69:1692–97
51. Vetter R, Will H. 1986. Sarcolemmal Na-Ca exchange and sarcoplasmic reticulum calcium uptake in developing chick heart. *J. Mol. Cell. Cardiol.* 18:1267–75
52. Godt RE, Fogaça RTH, Kassouf Silva I, Nosek TM. 1993. Contraction of developing avian heart muscle. *Comp. Biochem. Physiol. A* 105A:213–218
53. Fogaça RTH, Warren KS, Lin J-C, Nosek TM, Godt RE. 1993. Contractile alterations during myocardial development in the chick subsequent to ablation of cardiac neural crest. *J. Cell. Biochem.* 17D:211 (Abstr.)
54. Nosek TM, Fogaça RTH, Hatcher CJ, Brotto MAP, Godt RE. 1997. Cardiac neural crest ablation (CNCA) decreases calcium uptake and release by the cardiac sarcoplasmic reticulum. *Am. J. Physiol.* 273:H1464–71
55. Tsutsui H, Ishihara K, Cooper IVG. 1993. Cytoskeletal role in the contractile dysfunction of hypertrophied myocardium. *Science* 260:682–87
56. Godt RE, Chu JC, Merry EH, Lutin WA. 1997. Depressed ventricular contractility in an experimental heart defect in the embryonic chick is not associated with an elevated microtubule content. In *The Developing Heart*, ed. B Ostadal, M Nagano, N Takeda, NS Dhalla, pp. 373–83. Philadelphia: Lippincott-Raven
57. Godt RE, Fogaça RTH, Zhelamsky SV, Shu JC, Kirby ML, Nosek TM. 1995. Depressed myocardial contraction associated with a heart defect: possible involvement of microtubules. *Biophys. J.* 68:A170 (Abstr.)
58. Greene CJ, Godt RE, Nosek TM. 1996. An effect of microtubules on F_{max} is not responsible for depressed twitch force in embryonic chick hearts with persistent truncus arteriosus. *FASEB J.* 10:A393 (Abstr.)
59. Price KM, Littler WA, Cummins P. 1980. Human atrial and ventricular myosin light chain subunits in the adult and during development. *Biochem. J.* 191:571–80
60. Barton P, Buckingham ME. 1985. The myosin alkali light chain proteins and their genes. *Biochem. J.* 231:249–61

61. Cummins P, Lambert SJ. 1986. Myosin transitions in the bovine and human heart. A developmental and anatomical study of heavy and light subunits in the atrium ventricle. *Circ. Res.* 58:846–58

62. Schiaffino S, Reggiani C. 1996. Molecular diversity of myofibrillar proteins: gene regulation and functional significance. *Physiol. Rev.* 76:371–423

63. Auckland LM, Lambert SJ, Cummins P. 1986. Cardiac myosin light and heavy chain isotypes in Tetralogy of Fallot. *Cardiovasc. Res.* 20:828–63

64. Morano M, Zacharzowski U, Maier M, Lange PE, Alexi-Meskishvili V, et al. 1996. Regulation of human heart contractility by essential myosin light chain isoforms. *J. Clin. Invest.* 98:467–73

65. Creazzo TL. 1990. Reduced L-type calcium current in the embryonic chick heart with persistent truncus arteriosus. *Circ. Res.* 66:1491–98

66. Aiba S, Creazzo TL. 1992. Calcium currents in hearts with persistent truncus arteriosus. *Am. J. Physiol.* 262:H1182–90

67. Creazzo TL, Burch JL, Brotto MA P. 1997. Excitation-contraction coupling cardiac dysmorphogenesis. In *The Developing Heart,* ed. B Ostadal, M Nagano, N Takeda, NS Dhalla, pp. 313–24. Philadelphia: Lippincott-Raven

67a. Conway SJ, Godt RE, Hatcher CJ, Leatherbury L, Zolotouchnikov VV, et al. 1997. Neural crest is involved in development of abnormal cardiac function. *J. Mol. Cell. Cardiol.* In press

68. Zhu Y, Nosek TM. 1991. Inositol trisphosphate enhances Ca^{2+} oscillations but not Ca^{2+}-induced Ca^{2+} release from cardiac sarcoplasmic reticulum. *Pflügers Arch.* 418:1–6

69. Kirby ML. 1988. Nodose placode contributes autonomic neurons to the heart in the absence of cardiac neural crest. *J. Neurosci.* 8:1089–95

70. Kirby ML, Creazzo TL, Christiansen JL. 1989. Chronotropic responses of chick atria to field stimulation after various neural crest ablations. *Circ. Res.* 65:1547–54

Annu. Rev. Physiol. 1998. 60:287–308

MOLECULAR INSIGHTS INTO CARDIAC DEVELOPMENT

Henry M. Sucov

Department of Cell and Neurobiology, Institute for Genetic Medicine, University of Southern California School of Medicine, 2250 Alcazar Street, IGM 240, Los Angeles, California 90033; e-mail: sucov@zygote.hsc.usc.edu

KEY WORDS: cardiogenesis, cardiac morphogenesis

ABSTRACT

Recent discoveries have led to a greater appreciation of the diverse mechanisms that underlie cardiac morphogenesis. Genetic strategies (primarily gene targeting approaches in mice) have significantly broadened research in cardiovascular developmental biology by illuminating new pathways involved in heart development and by allowing the genetic evaluation of pathways that have previously been implicated in these events. Advances have also been made using biochemical and cell- and tissue-based approaches. This review summarizes the author's interpretation of current trends in the effort to understand the molecular basis of cardiac development, with an emphasis on insights obtained from genetic models.

Specification and Initial Differentiation of the Cardiomyocyte Lineage

In all metazoan animals with a circulatory system, the heart (or its homologue) is a mesodermal organ. In vertebrate embryos, aggregates of cardiomyocyte progenitor cells become allocated from the mesodermal population at or shortly after gastrulation. These clusters of cells are initially bilaterally organized and are brought together at the midline to form a single linear heart tube comprised of an inner layer, or endocardium, surrounded by an outer layer of myocardium, with the two layers separated by a space containing an extracellular matrix material known as cardiac jelly. The endocardium soon becomes continuous with the endothelium of the peripheral vasculature. The vertebrate heart tube lies along the ventral midline, along the rostral-caudal axis, and within the pericardial portion of the embryonic coelom.

0066-4278/98/0315-0287$08.00

The *Drosophila* heart (also known as the dorsal vessel) is a component of an open circulatory system, in which the beating heart forces the distribution of lymphatic fluid (hemolymph) without the use of vasculature. The *Drosophila* heart lacks endocardium, which is consistent with the absence of peripheral vasculature. The *Drosophila* heart is located along the dorsal midline, which contrasts with the ventral position of the vertebrate heart but is consistent with an overall inversion of embryonic dorsal/ventral orientation between *Drosophila* and vertebrates (1, 2). The myogenic cells of the *Drosophila* heart are similar to vertebrate cardiomyocytes at the ultrastructural level and in the protein components of the contractile apparatus. In addition, at a molecular level, the regulatory programs responsible for allocation of cells into the cardiogenic lineage are conserved between flies and vertebrates, as described below.

In *Drosophila* embryos, the gene *decapentaplegic* (*dpp*) is one of many required for allocation of mesodermal cells to the cardiac lineage (3). Dpp is a member of the TGFβ family of secreted factors and is widely utilized in development in many different tissues, such that *dpp* mutants show global disruption of axial patterning. Within the cardiac lineage, *dpp* promotes the expression of *tinman* (3), a transcription factor of the NK homeobox protein family. The expression of *tinman* in wild-type *Drosophila* embryos is restricted to the heart and some adjacent musculature, and mutations of *tinman* prevent the formation of these structures (4); thus *tinman* is a definitive marker of the cardiac lineage and is required for the establishment of this lineage. Mutation of the gene *heartless* (5, 6), which encodes a fibroblast growth factor receptor, leads to a phenotype very similar to that seen in the absence of *tinman,* suggesting that dpp- and FGF-type signaling are both required for allocation of cells into the *Drosophila* cardiac lineage. Several other genes are required for *Drosophila* cardiac development as well (7), in pathways that ultimately regulate the expression of *tinman*.

The cells that will constitute the vertebrate heart are allocated from mesoderm at the anterior (rostral) domain of the embryo. Explant assays using chick embryonic tissue have indicated that the anterior endoderm secretes factors that initiate the cardiogenic program in the adjacent mesoderm (8–10). In the explant assay, FGF4 can substitute for anterior endoderm in maintaining cardiogenesis in isolated anterior mesoderm. By virtue of its proximity to anterior endoderm, anterior mesoderm is already specified to become cardiogenic; FGF4 does not convert posterior mesoderm (which is not normally cardiogenic) to a cardiac fate. A combination of BMP2 and FGF4, however, does convert posterior mesoderm to the cardiac lineage (11). BMP2 is a member of the TGFβ family and appears to be the most abundantly expressed member of this family in the anterior endoderm. These results are consistent with a model in which BMP2 functions to allocate unspecified mesodermal cells to the cardiac lineage, and

FGF4 promotes the proliferation and survival of these already specified cells (11). This model is also consistent with the paradigm from *Drosophila*, where both TGFβ and FGF signaling pathways (i.e. *dpp* and *heartless*) are involved in the specification of the cardiomyocyte lineage.

Because growth factors and their receptors have overlapping specificities, it is not clear from a genetic standpoint that BMP2 and FGF4 are the cardiogenic factors secreted by anterior endoderm in vertebrate embryos, or that these gene products are required in vivo for cardiogenesis. Because many critical regulatory proteins are represented by multigene families in vertebrates, several BMPs or TGFβ family members could collectively or interchangeably function in the initial allocation of the vertebrate cardiac lineage. By using a biological antagonist (called noggin) of BMP function (12), it has recently been demonstrated that cardiogenesis requires BMP activity, although both BMP2 and BMP4 have equivalent cardiogenic activities in this assay. The mouse *BMP2* gene has been mutated by homologous recombination (13), with early amnion defects killing the majority of mutant embryos. The small percentage of mutant embryos that survive this stage go on to die at the linear heart tube stage with a defect in heart morphogenesis: The heart tube forms, but in the exocoelomic space rather than within the pericardial cavity. It is unclear if the heart malformation is a primary consequence of the lack of BMP2 function, or if the heart is secondarily misplaced and malformed because of a more broad disruption of embryonic organization. Mutation of the mouse *BMP4* (14) and *FGF4* (15) genes results in early embryonic lethality prior to a stage where the roles of these factors in cardiogenesis can be evaluated. Thus although there is a strong implication that BMP2/BMP4 and FGF4 are involved in the initial aspects of cardiogenesis, the mutational approach in mouse is not yet conclusive as to the in vivo role of these gene products. Additional factors have also been shown to be bioactive at various levels of vertebrate cardiac specification (16), primarily from results of explant culture assays, and could augment or supplant the roles of BMP2/4 and FGF4.

In vertebrates, several genes are expressed throughout the cardiomyocyte population prior to the fusion of the linear heart tube (i.e. shortly after allocation of mesodermal cells into the cardiac lineage) and remain expressed thereafter. These genes include *Nkx-2.5* (a vertebrate homologue of *Drosophila tinman*), *MEF2C* (encoding a transcription factor), *cardiac actin, desmin,* and several others (17). Thus well before the assembly of sarcomeres, these cells express cardiomyocyte markers and are specified to a cardiogenic fate.

The mouse *Nkx-2.5* gene, a homologue of *Drosophila tinman*, has been mutated (18), with heart development arrested at the looping stage (discussed in more detail below). This is a much different phenotype than the *tinman* phenotype would predict (i.e. absent heart), but *Nkx-2.5* is one of at least seven vertebrate Nkx-2 genes. The initial allocation of cells into the cardiogenic pathway may therefore be subject to regulation by other members of the NK2 family in conjunction with or independent of *Nkx-2.5*. *Nkx-2.5* is the earliest of the known mammalian and avian Nkx-2 genes to be expressed in the cardiogenic region, although a newly discovered *Nkx-2.7* gene in zebrafish precedes *Nkx-2.5* in expression (19) and may be responsible for the initial commitment of cells to the cardiac lineage in a manner analogous to *Drosophila tinman*. The observation that embryo-wide expression of *Nkx-2.3* or *-2.5* in *Xenopus* (20) or zebrafish (21) causes enlargement of the embryonic heart by expansion of the number of cardiac muscle cells suggests that one role of the Nkx genes is to recruit cells to the cardiac lineage. However, phenotypes are not seen in other tissues of these embryos, despite the ectopic expression of these Nkx gene products in these tissues, suggesting that the Nkx genes can only fulfill this recruitment function within a field of cells that are already predisposed to becoming cardiac, i.e. the heart morphogenic field. Presumably, other positive and negative processes establish the domain within which Nkx factors can act, possibly including BMP/TGFβ and/or FGF family members secreted by the anterior endoderm, as described above.

Specification of the Endocardium

The vertebrate endocardium has a developmental origin distinct from the vascular endothelium even though both are functionally similar and become physically continuous. The endocardium is allocated at the edge of the cardiogenic field under the influence of the anterior endoderm (22, 23) and becomes sandwiched within the linear heart tube. Analysis in the chick embryo with a retroviral lineage marker (24) indicates that the endocardial and myocardial lineages are distinct within the cardiogenic mesoderm prior to the fusion of the heart tube and appear not to derive from a common precursor cell (except in the sense that both are mesodermal). This is in contrast to the cardiac conduction system (Purkinje cell) lineage, which can be shown by the same technique to derive from the cardiomyocyte lineage (25).

Mutation of the *cloche* gene in zebrafish (26) results in a complete lack of endocardium, with no endocardium seen at the earliest time points after fusion of the linear heart tube, although the myocardium and the peripheral vascular endothelium both form. The *cloche* gene functions in the endocardium (i.e. functions cell-autonomously) and presumably is involved in the initial allocation of cells to the endocardium lineage. Although the vascular endothelium forms in *cloche* mutant embryos, it is not normal in this background. The *cloche* gene product may therefore have a role not only in the initial establishment of the endocardial lineage, but also in the mature endocardial/endothelial phenotype. The *cloche* gene has not yet been cloned.

By genetic means, the zebrafish *cloche* gene can be demonstrated to be up-stream of *flk-1* in an epistatic pathway (27). Flk-1 is one of four receptor tyrosine kinases expressed in the endothelium and endocardium. In mouse, mutation of *flk-1* results in an absence of the endothelium and endocardium (28). A reasonable interpretation is that although the endocardial and endothe-lial lineages arise independently, genetic programs (i.e. *cloche* and *flk-1*) that allow their specification and differentiation are shared.

Regionalization of the Heart Tube

Formation of the linear heart tube from the bilaterally aggregated cardiomy-ocyte precursors is under genetic control. In embryos lacking the transcription factor GATA4 (28a, b), these precursors fail to assemble at the ventral midline and ultimately differentiate in situ to form laterally paired heart tubes contain-ing differentiated cardiomyocytes. As noted above, differentiation markers are expressed in the early cardiomyocytes prior to formation of the linear heart tube. GATA4 is therefore not necessary for cardiomyocyte specification, but rather has a role in morphogenic processes that promote the assembly of car-diomyocytes into the heart tube at the ventral midline (Figure 1).

The heart tube is organized from the time of its formation with a rostral-caudal polarity, with the rostral end fated to become the outflow region of the mature heart and the caudal end fated to become the inflow region. The early heart tube is demarked into (from rostral to caudal) the aortic sac, the bulbus cordis (the future conotruncus and right ventricle), the future left ventricular chamber, the future atrial chamber(s), and the sinus venosus. The aortic sac connects the early heart to the aortic arch arteries, which in turn connect to the dorsal aortae and peripheral circulation. The sinus venosus collects blood from the umbilical, cardinal, and vitelline veins (originating from the placenta, embryo proper, and yolk sac, respectively).

As the linear heart tube grows, it becomes looped out into the pericardial space. Looping is not a consequence of growth per se, but rather is a mor-phogenic process intrinsic to the embryonic heart (29). The consequence of looping is that the atrial chamber assumes a relative rostral and dorsal position, and the ventricular and proximal outflow tract regions assume a relative caudal and ventral position. Looping of the heart is the first of several morphological features that distinguish the left-right embryonic axis, although dorsal-ventral and anterior-posterior axes are specified (and visibly evident) substantially ear-lier in development of all vertebrate embryos. For the purposes of this overview, looping brings the domains of the linear heart tube that have already been speci-fied (i.e. outflow tract, right ventricle, left ventricle, atrial chamber, and inflow) into their mature relative positions, although these compartments are still in an immature state.

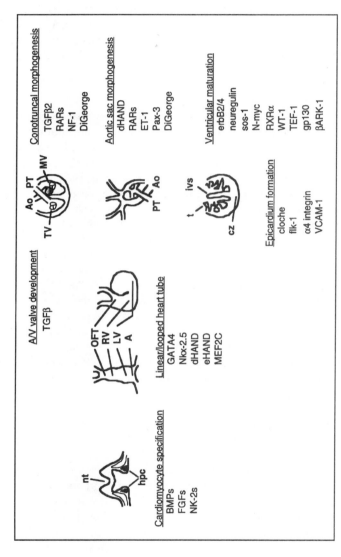

Figure 1 Molecular and genetic components of key steps in vertebrate cardiogenesis. A diagrammatic representation of cardiac anatomy at various stages of development is shown, along with the genes or gene products that have been implicated in the development of the corresponding structures (as described in the text). A cross section through the anterior portion of the vertebrate embryo is shown (*left*), with the heart precursor cells (hpc) indicated as the *filled region* within the splanchnic mesoderm. The folds of the dorsal neural tube (nt) are also indicated. (*Center*) A ventral perspective of the linear and looped heart is shown. The domains of the outflow tract (OFT), right and left ventricles (RV, LV), and atrial chamber (A) are specified by the linear heart tube stage and are maintained as the heart tube loops. The atrial chamber of the looped heart is dorsal to the ventricular chambers and is not in view in this diagram. (*Right*) Several different aspects of later cardiac development are shown from the ventral perspective. The ascending aorta (Ao), pulmonary trunk (PT), mitral and tricuspid inflow valves (MV, TV), the interventricular septum (ivs), and the trabecular layer and compact zone (t, cz) of the myocardium are indicated.

Two genes encoding transcription factors of the bHLH class, identified as *dHAND* and *eHAND,* are expressed in a compartment-specific manner in the early mouse heart (30). Both genes are expressed throughout the early linear heart tube and remain coexpressed in the conotruncus in later embryos. At the time of looping, *dHAND* expression becomes downregulated in the future left ventricle (although not completely so), and *eHAND* becomes completely excluded from the future right ventricle. The ventricular expression patterns of *dHAND* (RV > LV) and *eHAND* (LV only) are therefore complementary. These two genes represent the earliest markers of chamber-specific regionalization within the heart tube.

The *dHAND* gene has been mutated in mice (30), with embryonic lethality seen at the looping stage. By morphological analysis, the ventricular *dHAND* mutant phenotype is consistent with a complete absence of the right ventricle. The *dHAND* gene therefore appears to be required in mice for the specification of the future right ventricle in the linear heart tube. It is unclear if the cells that would normally be right ventricular cardiomyocytes become mis-specified in mutant embryos and are incorporated into the left ventricle or the conotruncus, or if these cells fail to survive or are otherwise ablated from the heart. The *eHAND* gene has not yet been mutated in mice.

Interestingly, the chick homologues of *dHAND* and *eHAND* are expressed in an overlapping pattern, without left-right regionalization. Therefore, it is necessary in chick embryos to suppress the expression (by antisense oligonucleotide approaches) of both genes together to recover a phenotype, rather than either alone (31). The phenotype that results in chick is superficially analogous to the *dHAND* mutant phenotype in mice, i.e. arrest at the looping stage with possible absence of the right ventricle. This suggests that left-right specificity is generated through regulatory mechanisms that in the chick are more complex than an asymmetric expression of the two known HAND genes.

The MEF2 class of transcription factors is required for the expression of a number of terminal cardiomyocyte genes, such as *desmin, myosin light chain 2v,* and *myosin heavy chain β.* By mutational analysis (32), the single *Drosophila* MEF2 gene (*Dmef2*) is not required for initial specification of cardiac cells, as the dorsal vessel forms normally in the correct place. However, in the absence of *Dmef2,* the terminally differentiated muscle phenotype is not elaborated, as evidenced by the lack of MHC expression. In vertebrates, there are four MEF2 genes (identified as A through D). *MEF2C* is the first to be expressed in the heart tube, seen prior to the formation of the linear heart tube, although the other MEF genes become active in an overlapping pattern shortly thereafter (33).

In mice, mutation of the *MEF2C* gene (34) results in arrest at the looping stage, with a phenotype very similar to the *dHAND* mutation described above (i.e. no right ventricle). In fact, *dHAND* expression is substantially reduced in *MEF2C* mutants. *MEF2C* and *dHAND* may both be required components of a single pathway that specifies the right ventricular fate. Alternatively, the *MEF2C* mutation could affect an independent aspect of ventricular development, with the reduction of *dHAND* expression simply reflecting the absence of right ventricular tissue. If the two genes are part of a common pathway, it is clear that *MEF2C* controls other aspects of ventricular development as well: The *MEF2C* mutation is embryonic lethal approximately half a day earlier than the *dHAND* mutation, and there is a distinct spectrum of cardiomyocyte structural protein genes that are differentially expressed in the two mutant backgrounds. The *MEF2B* gene has been mutated without cardiovascular consequences (34).

Several transgenic mouse lines that express reporter genes under the regulatory control of cardiomyocyte structural protein gene promoters have been established. Transgenic expression of the *desmin* and *MLC-2v* gene promoters (35, 36), which are known to be regulated by MEF2 factors, is restricted in the embryonic heart to the right ventricle and outflow tract, in the same pattern identified as the domain of action of *MEF2C*. This would be consistent with a right ventricular expression domain controlled by *MEF2C* at promoter MEF2-binding sites. However, the endogenous *desmin* and *MLC-2v* genes are uniformly expressed in both ventricles, and the other MEF2 proteins are present in these transgenic embryos in the left ventricle. Presumably, the transgenic context, in which only a portion of each gene's promoter is present and is placed in an ectopic location in the genome, has isolated MEF2 dependence to the right ventricle and through unknown mechanisms suppresses expression in the left ventricle. In contrast to desmin and MLC-2v, the cardiac actin promoter in a transgenic context is expressed higher in the left ventricle than the right (37), and other transgenic promoters have illustrated a variety of expression patterns. A surprising degree of regulatory complexity, therefore, appears to underlie gene expression in the left versus right side of the embryonic ventricle, despite the relative similarity in morphology.

As noted above, mutation of the *Nkx-2.5* gene causes arrest at the looping stage. The mechanisms that cause *Nkx-2.5* mutant mouse embryos to arrest remain unclear, although this phenotype does not appear to simply represent the ablation of the left or right ventricles. Because looping is an intrinsic morphogenic property of the heart tube, the *Nkx-2.5* phenotype cannot be ascribed to a nonspecific arrest in growth or proliferation, but rather must be an interruption of one or more morphogenic processes. In *Nkx-2.5* mutant embryos, the expression of *eHAND* (38, 39) and *MLC-2v* (18) are suppressed, as is another nuclear transcription factor (*CARP*) of unknown function (40), although several other molecular markers are properly expressed. One intriguing insight comes from *Drosophila*, where *tinman* (the *Drosophila* homologue of verte-brate Nkx-2 genes) directly transcriptionally activates *DMef2* expression (41). However, *MEF2C* expression appears to be unaffected in *Nkx-2.5* mutants (18), such that the interruption of looping in the *Nkx-2.5* mutants cannot be ascribed simply to epistatic regulation of *MEF2C*. Furthermore, right ventricular fate seems to be normally specified in *Nkx-2.5* mutant embryos, as a transgenic MLC-2v promoter is properly regulated (i.e. RV and conotruncus expression) in this background (35).

Ventricular Maturation

The primitive left ventricle and a portion of the bulbus cordis, structures present at the looping stage, will become the mature left and right ventricles, respec-tively, with the bulboventricular groove demarking the axis of the future in-terventricular septum. Maturation of the ventricular chambers requires several developmental processes: elaboration of the trabecular layer within the ventric-ular lumen, growth and thickening of the outer ventricular chamber wall (the compact zone), and growth of the interventricular septum.

In mice, mutation of the *neuregulin* (also known as glial growth factor) gene or the genes that encode two of the three known neuregulin receptors (erbB2 and erbB4) results in embryonic lethality with a failure to elaborate the trabecular layer (42–44). Neuregulin signaling is transduced by heterodimeric combina-tions of erbB2, B3, and B4, which are receptor tyrosine kinases most closely re-lated to the EGF receptor. Neuregulin is expressed in the endocardium, whereas erbB2 and erbB4 are expressed in the myocardium, suggesting that outgrowth of the trabecular layer from the inner surface of the ventricular chamber wall is induced by a neuregulin signal from the endocardium. The *neuregulin, erbB2,* and *erbB4* mutant backgrounds are embryonic lethal at the same time (day 9.5) and with the same phenotype (absent trabeculation), which would be expected if all are part of a common molecular pathway. Lethality might be a consequence of the lack of trabecular outgrowth, as the trabecular layer has been proposed to be responsible for early cardiac contractions (45). At the same time, neuregulin is known to regulate sodium channels and acetylcholine receptor levels in other cell types (46), suggesting the possibility that embryonic lethality might be a result of altered cardiac contractility.

A mouse mutation in the *sos-1* gene has been established (47), with ho-mozygous embryos dying at around E11.5 with a variable degree of trabecular disorganization. The sos protein is involved in mediating signal transduction between cell surface receptors and ras and can be demonstrated by genetic means to interact in vivo with the EGF receptor in epithelium (47). Because a mouse mutation in the EGF receptor gene does not have an obvious cardiac component (48), and because the neuregulin receptors are closely related to the EGF receptor, the *sos-1* trabecular phenotype may result from an impairment of neuregulin signaling in the myocardium.

In zebrafish embryos, the *cloche* gene is required for allocation of the endocardium lineage (26), as noted above. Embryos lacking *cloche* have no endocardium and also fail to develop trabeculation within the ventricle, consistent with an instructive role for the endocardium in directing myocardial ingrowth of the trabecular layer.

A surprising number of mutations in mice give rise to an underdeveloped hypoplastic ventricular chamber, with embryonic lethality seen in the E13-16 period. These include the genes that encode the transcription factors N-myc (49), RXRα (50, 51), WT-1 (52), and TEF-1 (53); the cell surface receptor gp130 (54); and the G protein–coupled receptor kinase βARK-1 (55). The common phenotype seen in these mutant backgrounds generally involves a deficiency in the expansion of the population of cardiomyocytes in the compact zone of the ventricular chamber wall, with a corresponding deficiency in the ventricular septum. This phenotype is biventricular, although in some there is a trend toward a greater deficiency in one or the other chamber. These mutations therefore probably interrupt programs of ventricular cardiomyocyte development. Although there may be some deficiency in the organization and mass of the trabecular layer as well, these embryos survive the E9.5 period when trabecular function appears to be required (as defined by the *neuregulin/erbB2/erbB4* mutations described above). This suggests that the physiological requirement for a thickening ventricular chamber wall at E13 and beyond is associated with the dramatic growth of the embryo as a whole which is evident at this developmental time. Embryonic lethality can be demonstrated to result from insufficient cardiac performance (56).

In some cases, the known biochemistry of the protein products is helpful in understanding the phenotypes that result from mutation of these genes. The *N-myc* gene is easiest to understand, in that myc genes are known to be positive regulators of the cell cycle (57), the *N-myc* gene is expressed in the cardiomyocyte population (49), and the mutant phenotype is consistent with a failure of cardiomyocytes to proliferate. The other genes cited above presumably regulate gene expression pathways and/or cytoplasmic signal transduction pathways that impact on cardiomyocyte maturation at various levels. It remains to be demonstrated whether any of these genes are components of common epistatic genetic pathways, or if these genes independently represent numerous different and required aspects of ventricular maturation.

Even though the hypoplastic phenotype is manifest in the cardiomyocyte population, it is worth noting that these genes may not all function in the cardiomyocyte population. Signals from the endocardium (as described above) or from the epicardium (see below) might initiate proliferative or other responses in the cardiomyocyte population, with the above-mentioned genes required not in cardiomyocytes but in the endocardium or epicardium. The *WT-1* gene, for example, is more abundantly expressed in the epicardium, although a lower level of expression in the myocardium cannot be ruled out. In the case of *N-myc*, further genetic analysis proves a requirement for this gene in the cardiomyocyte population: A transgene (58) that expresses myc only in cardiomyocytes rescues the cardiac defects and the midgestation embryonic lethality of the *N-myc* mutant background (J Rossant, personal communication). However, this transgene does not rescue the *RXRα* mutant phenotype (HM Sucov, unpublished observations), which might indicate that *RXRα* gene function is not required in cardiomyocytes, or alternatively that *RXRα* and *N-myc* are components of different pathways that are both required for ventricular maturation.

Development of the Epicardium

The epicardium is the outermost layer of the heart and contributes to the population of cells that form the vascular and connective tissues within the heart. The epicardium originates as a motile population of cells from near the sinus venosus that migrate to cover the developing heart. This population also involutes into the ventricular chamber wall to form the vessels of the coronary arteries. Absence of the cell adhesion molecules α4 integrin (59) or VCAM-1 (60, 61) result in a failure of the epicardium to adhere to the myocardium, and thereby the disintegration of the epicardium. VCAM-1 is expressed by the myocardium, whereas α4 integrin is expressed in the epicardium, and VCAM-1 protein physically interacts with α4 integrin. The physical adherence of the epicardium to the myocardium therefore depends on the integrity of the α4 integrin/VCAM-1 interaction. The myocardium in either mutant background is hypoplastic and reminiscent of what is seen in the mutant backgrounds that compromise maturation of the compact zone. Because the epicardium is responsible for the development of the coronary arteries, the hypoplastic nature of the myocardium suggests that vascularization is necessary for growth of the compact layer of the ventricular chamber wall, either in the provision of blood-borne mitogenic factors or for the facilitation of nutritional and waste exchange (which becomes less possible as the chamber wall thickens and becomes compact). The epicardium might actively signal to the myocardium as well. Metabolic labeling studies (62) have indicated that the greatest rate of proliferation of compact zone cardiomyocytes is at the outer edge of the myocardium, i.e. the region in closest proximity to the epicardium.

Atrial Maturation

The most prominent and clinically relevant aspect of atrial chamber maturation is the formation of two sequential septa that together form the atrial septum. The atrial septum in the embryo remains open so that oxygenated blood from the placenta reaches the right atrium and is then shunted to the left atrial chamber, where it is then passed to the left ventricle and pumped to peripheral circulation. The interatrial opening (called the foramen ovale) closes after birth, when the pulmonary system exchanges gases and returns oxygen-rich blood directly to the left atrium.

Although atrial septal defects are a prominent class of human congenital heart malformation, there are few insights into the genes responsible for atrial chamber maturation. This is especially noteworthy relative to the number of genes that are implicated in ventricular maturation (as described above). Several explanations may account for this relative lack of genetic insight. First, atrial septal defects involving a persistence of the foramen ovale are often subclinical and not recognized in humans (63) and would likely not be recognized in mutant mice even if present. Second, the physiological significance of atrial chamber septation is not manifest until after birth. The atrial role of genes that are also involved in processes in the very early embryo or in the development of the ventricular chambers would not be observable if there were a lethal phenotype prior to birth. At the same time, it is clear that several genes are expressed in an atrial-specific pattern (i.e. *ANF, MLC-1a,* etc). Therefore, there is an atrial-specific program of transcriptional regulation that, in principle, is subject to genetic manipulation. Zebrafish genetic screens have identified loci that are involved in normal atrial chamber maturation (64, 65), although the molecular nature of these loci has not yet been determined. A mutation in the human transcription factor gene *TBX5* has been demonstrated to cause Holt-Oram syndrome (66), which includes atrial septal defects as a prominent cardiac malformation. This gene was identified by positional cloning, and given the prominence of atrial septal defects in human congenital syndromes, it is possible that similar strategies using human patient material will identify other genes involved in atrial maturation.

Atrioventricular Canal Formation

The junction between the ventricular and atrial chambers in the looped heart stage is demarked by a morphologically recognizable constriction, representing the atrioventricular (A/V) canal. In this region, a thickened volume of cardiac jelly separates the myocardium from the endocardium and extends the endocardium into the lumen of the A/V canal. Signals from the myocardium or from the cardiac jelly induce an epithelial to mesenchymal transformation in the endocardium, with the mesenchymal cells migrating into the region occupied by the cardiac jelly and proliferating there (67). This process forms what are known as endocardial cushions, which fuse in the midline to partition the A/V canal into right and left sides. These orifices ultimately become the tricuspid and mitral inflow valves that connect the septated atrial chambers to the septated ventricular chambers. Defects in the formation of the endocardial cushions or in their fusion lead to a persistence of the A/V canal, also known as atrioventricular septal defect. This phenotype involves free communication between all four chambers of the heart, and as such is a serious pediatric entity.

The epithelial-mesenchymal transformation of the endocardium is under the influence of TGFβ signaling. TGFβ is expressed by the myocardium, and receptors for TGFβ are found in the endocardium (68). In vitro, explanted chick endocardium can be induced to undergo an epithelial-mesenchyme transformation by application of TGFβ, and antibodies against the TGFβ receptor block this induction (68). Individual mutation in mice of the three TGFβ genes (69) does not appear to compromise formation of the A/V canal or of the inlet valves. It is therefore possible that two of the TGFβ members interchangeably function in the morphogenesis of the A/V canal. In *TGFβ2*-deficient mice (69), a low percentage of embryos have atrioventricular septal defects, but this may be secondary to general disruption of cardiac morphogenesis. The *TGFβ2* mutation causes an aberrant positioning of the inflow valves, resulting in a double inlet left ventricle, but this is likely to be a consequence of looping abnormalities.

The most frequent event that causes persistent A/V canal in humans is Downs syndrome (trisomy 21). The A/V canal is relatively rare in the non-trisomic population, but the high frequency of Downs syndrome in humans causes this phenotype to be a relatively more common congenital heart defect. It is presumed that one or more genes present on chromosome 21 are quantitatively involved in endocardial cushion growth, such that three copies cause a deficiency in the growth and fusion of the cushions. This phenotype is replicated in a mouse model of Downs syndrome, in which trisomy of mouse chromosome 16 (portions of which are syntenous with human chromosome 21) also leads to persistent A/V canal (70). The gene or genes on these chromosomes responsible for this phenotype have not yet been identified.

Outflow Tract Development

Different terminology has been used to describe the structures that carry ventricular ejection to the peripheral vasculature. Pexieder and others (71) define the conotruncus region of the outflow tract from the vestibule (infundibulum) of the ascending aorta and of the pulmonary trunk (deep within what externally would appear to be ventricular tissue) to, at the distal side, the location of the aortic and pulmonary outflow valves (the semilunar valves). The conotruncus is lined by endocardium and is surrounded by myocardium. The aortic sac begins above the semilunar valves and encompasses the proximal portions of the externally visible ascending aorta and pulmonary trunk, although its distal boundary varies as the outflow tract is reorganized. The aortic sac contains smooth muscle rather than myocardium and is lined by endothelium derived from splanchic mesoderm rather than endocardium. The aortic sac connects to the aortic arch arteries, which in turn are connected to the dorsal aortae and peripheral circulation. The term outflow tract is used here in a general sense to encompass the conotruncus and the aortic sac.

The conotruncus is initially an undivided structure that derives from the distal portion of the bulbus cordis at the looped heart stage. Conotruncal septation into the proximal portions of the aorta and pulmonary trunk involves the growth of endocardial cushions in much the same way that the A/V canal is divided. During the process of looping, the conotruncal cushions migrate from the right ventricle to a medial position so that the cushions come to overlie the axis of the ventricular septum. In the process, the cushions assume a spiral orientation that directs aortic outflow to pass dorsal to the pulmonary trunk as each exits the heart. The lower domain of the conotruncus grows downward and ultimately fuses with the ventricular septum to completely separate the left and right ventricular chambers.

Morphogenesis of the aortic sac and the aortic arch arteries is initiated by mesenchymal cells derived from the neural crest, which migrate between the vascular endothelium and the pharyngeal mesoderm from the pharyngeal arches and thereby envelop the vessel (72). The neural crest population is not required for the initial formation of the aortic arch arteries (the endothelium of which is mesodermally derived) but is required for the maintenance of these vessels (72). The ultimate fate of the neural crest–derived cells is to form the smooth muscle layer of the vasculature adjacent to the heart. In addition, these cells also have an instructional role in forming the aorticopulmonary (A/P) septum, which forms as a wedge of tissue between the fourth and sixth aortic arch arteries and which directs aortic outflow to the left fourth aortic arch artery and pulmonary outflow to the left sixth artery. In chick embryo experiments (73), the appropriate region of neural crest can be experimentally removed such that the A/P septum fails to form, resulting in a phenotype termed persistent truncus arteriosus (PTA). This same domain of neural crest is also required for development of the thymus and parathyroids and the parafollicular cells of the thyroid. When this domain is ablated in chick embryos, hypoplasia or agenesis of these organs results. The extent to which neural crest–derived cells migrate below the level of the semilunar valves is uncertain, although it is clear that the neural crest influences conotruncal development. For example, in the chick neural crest ablation studies, conotruncal defects such as double outlet right ventricle and Tetralogy of Fallot (which represent misalignments of the conotruncal cushions with the ventricular septum) are also recovered. The development of the neural crest is also discussed elsewhere in this volume (T Creazzo et al).

The *dHAND* gene, which is required for specification of the right ventricle at the time of looping (described above), is also expressed in the neural crest–derived mesenchyme that infiltrates the heart. In the absence of *dHAND* expression (30), the aortic arch arteries fail to form, resulting in a blind-ended aortic sac that does not connect to peripheral circulation. In principle, this malformation could be a consequence of very early events connecting the developing heart to peripheral circulation, prior to the formation of the neural crest. Alternatively, because the neural crest is required for maintenance of the aortic arch arteries, the *dHAND* mutation may indicate a role for neural crest mesenchyme in the very early stages of maintenance of these vessels.

A syndrome of human pediatric malformations in the heart and several other tissues (74) has been identified as resulting from microdeletions in chromosome 22. The cardiac component of this syndrome primarily includes conotruncal defects. This syndrome, identified as DiGeorge, velo-cardio-facial, and CATCH-22 syndrome, is a haploinsufficient (dominant heterozygous) phenotype with incomplete and variable penetrance,which suggests that one or several genes that are deleted within chromosome 22 are required in the correct gene dosage for normal cardiac development. The critical DiGeorge region, mapped by aligning chromosome 22 markers to the chromosomes of affected patients, spans a length of approximately 250 kb. Several genes lie within this domain (75, 76), although none has yet been confirmed as functionally involved in cardiogenesis. It is also possible that several genes from this chromosomal interval act together during the course of cardiac development, with no single gene being responsible for the DiGeorge syndrome phenotype. Because the DiGeorge phenotype is variably penetrant, even within pedigrees, it is also clear that other unlinked genes modify the penetrance of this syndrome, although how these act is unknown. The DiGeorge syndrome also includes hypoplasia or agenesis of the thymus and parathyroids (74), which suggests that the cardiovascular component of the DiGeorge syndrome results from alterations in the fate of the cardiac neural crest population.

Mutation of the *TGFβ2* gene (69) results in a failure of the muscular component of the outflow arteries to form, with these vessels surrounded instead by mesenchyme. It is speculated (69) that lack of TGFβ2 signaling may allow the proliferation of mesodermally derived mesenchymal cells at the expense of the neural crest–derived cells in the developing outflow tract, with the former population unable to properly differentiate. PTA is not a component of the TGFβ2 mutant phenotype, indicating that formation of the aorticopulmonary septum represents a different aspect of neural crest differentiation that may not be subject to TGFβ regulation.

Perturbation of the retinoic acid (RA; the active form of vitamin A) signal transduction pathway causes several types of outflow tract defects. An excess of RA given on an experimental basis in rodents (77), or inadvertently taken for pharmaceutical purposes by pregnant women (78), causes a spectrum of conotruncal malformations, depending on the time of exposure. Mutation of several of the RA receptor genes (79, 80), or a dietary deficiency of vitamin A (81), result in a partially overlapping spectrum of malformations, but these tend to be more biased toward aortic sac defects rather than conotruncal malformations. Mutation of RA receptor genes causes PTA, but without a significant degree of thymic, thyroid, or parathyroid hypoplasia (80, 82). Possibly, the RA receptor gene mutations affect secondary migration of crest cells specifically into the aortic sac or their terminal differentiation once therein. This is consistent with the temporal requirement for vitamin A in cardiovascular morphogenesis (83), which is during the period when neural crest cells are already resident within the aortic sac. Because the retinoic acid receptors are transcriptional regulators, the different spectrum of defects that occur after RA excess or RA deficiency (or RA receptor deficiency) can be understood by recognizing that RA excess induces ectopic gene expression, whereas RA deficiency interferes with endogenous gene expression. The extent to which common or different downstream target genes are sensitive to these manipulations is unknown.

Mutation of the *neurofibromatosis 1 (NF-1)* gene in mice causes double outlet right ventricle (84, 85). *NF-1* is a negative regulator of cytoplasmic signal transduction through the ras pathway, arguing that an external inductive signal is received and transduced through ras pathways during the course of conotruncal morphogenesis, although the nature of this signal remains undetermined.

Several additional genetic perturbations result in PTA and/or abnormalities of the aortic arch artery, including mutations of the genes encoding the signaling peptide endothelin-1 (ET-1) (86) and the transcription factor *Pax-3 (Splotch)* (87). *ET-1* is expressed in the endothelium of the aortic sac and may be a signal that is interpreted by the arriving neural crest. *Pax-3* is a transcription factor that is broadly expressed in the neural tube and in the initial population of migratory neural crest. By using molecular markers of the neural crest, it was recently shown (88) in the *Pax-3* mutant background that the initial migration of neural crest cells away from the neural tube occurs normally, but that secondary migration into the aortic sac fails to occur. *Pax-3* is therefore likely to function in the neural crest lineage, although through unknown mechanisms.

Normal formation of the A/P septum requires neural crest that originates from the appropriate region of the neural tube, i.e. ectopically transplanted trunk neural crest can contribute cells to the outflow tract but cannot instruct the formation of the A/P septum (89). This suggests that the relevant region of the neural tube contains the appropriate positional information to initiate this aspect of development. The Hox genes are known to be required for establishing positional identity along the rostral-caudal embryonic axis. Of the numerous mutations available in the Hox genes, only one has a relevant phenotype: disruption of the *HoxA3* gene results in deficient development of the thymus, thyroid, and parathyroids, although without extensive cardiac phenotypes (90). By extension from the description above, it would appear that this mutation alters the ability of neural crest cells to either migrate away from the neural tube or to infiltrate these organs. The greatest cellular contribution to the formation of the A/P septum originates from a lower level of the neural tube compared with the domain of action of *HoxA3*. The available single and combination mutations in the Hox-4 and -5 paralogs do not result in PTA or any similar outflow tract malformation (91). This may be because of overlap in expression and function—loss of one does not compromise A/P septal formation—or might indicate that the role of Hox genes in cardiovascular development is more complex than appears. Thus a role for the *Hox* genes in cardiovascular development remains to be elucidated.

Conclusions

A summary of the key steps of cardiogenesis and the genes or gene products that have been implicated in these steps is shown in Figure 1. The modern trend in the analysis of cardiac development is to elucidate the molecules and mechanisms that underlie the morphogenic processes forming the heart. The genetic approach in mice has clearly been an enormous influence in defining new pathways of cardiac development; in many cases the cardiac phenotypes that have emerged in knockout strategies have not been expected. Given the ever-increasing number of genes subject to mutational analysis, this trend is likely to continue. Screens in zebrafish embryos for genes with cardiovascular morphogenic roles have not yet been a prominent source of molecular insight, but this is certain to change as the genes identified by these screens are cloned and characterized. In fact, the zebrafish genetic screens have a major advantage over targeted mouse mutations because the former are done without bias as to the type of gene identified, whereas the aggregate effort of the mouse mutational community tends to emphasize regulatory over structural genes. The molecular characterization of human loci that are established to cause cardiovascular malformations will also continue to yield new genetic paradigms.

While the list of genes involved in various aspects of cardiac development is growing, and while insights exist that might explain the roles of some of these genes, it has only occasionally been possible to unify these genes into epistatic pathways. The elucidation of these pathways is certain to be a major effort in the near future. The *Drosophila* paradigm of heart development will be insightful in this regard, perhaps not so much in the identification of new genes but more in the assembly of these genes into pathways of morphogenesis.

At the same time, in vitro tissue-based studies will continue to represent a fruitful avenue for functionally testing the role of various gene products in cardiac development. This has been particularly evident to date in the analysis of secreted growth factors and with gene transfer approaches, it is likely to continue to be an attractive model system.

In many ways, the field that studies cardiac development is similar in its present status to the proverbial blind men touching different parts of the elephant. The outline of the animal is becoming apparent, but for the moment we can only appreciate how big of an elephant it is likely to be. Nonetheless, given the prominence of congenital cardiovascular malformations in the human population, it is clearly an important creature to better understand.

> **Visit the *Annual Reviews* home page at**
> **http://www.AnnualReviews.org.**

Literature Cited

1. Lacalli TC. 1995. Dorsoventral axis inversion. *Nature* 373:110–11
2. Ferguson EL. 1996. Conservation of dorsal-ventral patterning in arthropods and chordates. *Curr. Opin. Genet. Dev.* 6:424–31
3. Frasch M. 1995. Induction of visceral and cardiac mesoderm by ectodermal Dpp in the early *Drosophila* embryo. *Nature* 374:464–67
4. Bodmer R. 1993. The gene *tinman* is required for specification of the heart and visceral muscles in *Drosophila*. *Development* 118:719–29
5. Beiman M, Shilo BZ, Volk T. 1996. Heartless, a *Drosophila* FGF receptor homolog, is essential for cell migration and establishment of several mesodermal lineages. *Genes Dev.* 10:2993–3002
6. Gisselbrecht S, Skeath JB, Doe CQ, Michelson AM. 1996. *heartless* encodes a fibroblast growth factor receptor (DFR1/DFGF-R2) involved in the directional migration of early mesodermal cells in the *Drosophila* embryo. *Genes Dev.* 10:3003–17
7. Wu X, Golden K, Bodmer R. 1995. Heart development in *Drosophila* requires the segment polarity gene *wingless*. *Dev. Biol.* 169:619–28
8. Schultheiss TM, Xydas S, Lassar AB. 1995. Induction of avian cardiac myogenesis by anterior endoderm. *Development* 121:4203–14
9. Nascone N, Mercola M. 1995. An inductive role for the endoderm in *Xenopus* cardiogenesis. *Development* 121:515–23
10. Sugi Y, Lough J. 1994. Anterior endoderm is a specific effector of terminal cardiac myocyte differentiation of cells from the embryonic heart forming region. *Dev. Dyn.* 200:155–62
11. Lough J, Barron M, Brogley M, Sugi Y, Bolender DL, et al. 1996. Combined BMP-2 and FGF-4, but neither factor alone, induces cardiogenesis in nonprecardiac embryonic mesoderm. *Dev. Biol.* 178:198–202
12. Schultheiss TM, Burch JBE, Lassar AB. 1997. A role for bone morphogenic proteins in the induction of cardiac myogenesis. *Genes Dev.* 11:451–62
13. Zhang H, Bradley A. 1996. Mice deficient for BMP2 are nonviable and have defects in amnion/chorion and cardiac development. *Development* 122:2977–86
14. Winnier G, Blessing M, Labosky PA, Hogan BL. 1995. Bone morphogenetic protein-4 is required for mesoderm formation and patterning in the mouse. *Genes Dev.* 9:2105–16
15. Feldman B, Poueymirou W, Papaioannou VE, DeChiara TM, Goldfarb M. 1995. Requirement of FGF-4 for postimplantation mouse development. *Science* 267:246–49
16. Sugi Y, Lough J. 1995. Activin-A and FGF-2 mimic the inductive effects of anterior endoderm on terminal cardiac myogenesis in vitro. *Dev. Biol.* 168:567–74
17. Lyons GE. 1994. In situ analysis of the

cardiac muscle gene program during embryogenesis. *Trends Cardiovasc. Med.* 4:70–77

18. Lyons I, Parsons LM, Hartley L, Li R, Andrews JE, et al. 1995. Myogenic and morphogenetic defects in the heart tubes of murine embryos lacking the homeobox gene *Nkx2–5. Genes Dev.* 9:1654–66

19. Lee KH, Xu Q, Breitbart RE. 1996. A new tinman-related gene, *nkx2.7*, anticipates the expression of *nkx2.5* and *nkx2.3* in zebrafish heart and pharyngeal endoderm. *Dev. Biol.* 180:722–31

20. Cleaver OB, Patterson KD, Krieg PA. 1996. Overexpression of the tinman-related genes *XNkx-2.5* and *XNkx-2.3* in *Xenopus* embryos results in myocardial hyperplasia. *Development* 122:3549–56

21. Chen JN, Fishman MC. 1996. Zebrafish tinman homolog demarcates the heart field and initiates myocardial differentiation. *Development* 122:3809–16

22. Lee RK, Stainier DY, Weinstein BM, Fishman MC. 1994. Cardiovascular development in the zebrafish. II. Endocardial progenitors are sequestered within the heart field. *Development* 120:3361–66

23. Sugi Y, Markwald RR. 1996. Formation and early morphogenesis of endocardial endothelial precursor cells and the role of endoderm. *Dev. Biol.* 175:66–83

24. Cohen-Gould L, Mikawa T. 1996. The fate diversity of mesodermal cells within the heart field during chicken early embryogenesis. *Dev. Biol.* 177:265–73

25. Gourdie RG, Mima T, Thompson RP, Mikawa T. 1995. Terminal diversification of the myocyte lineage generates Purkinje fibers of the cardiac conduction system. *Development* 121:1423–31

26. Stainier DY, Weinstein BM, Detrich H III, Zon LI, Fishman MC. 1995. *cloche*, an early acting zebrafish gene, is required by both the endothelial and hematopoietic lineages. *Development* 121:3141–50

27. Liao W, Bisgrove BW, Sawyer H, Hug B, Bell B, et al. 1997. The zebrafish gene *cloche* acts upstream of a *flk-1* homologue to regulate endothelial cell differentiation. *Development* 124:381–89

28. Shalaby F, Rossant J, Yamaguchi TP, Gertsenstein M, Wu XF, et al. 1995. Failure of blood-island formation and vasculogenesis in Flk-1-deficient mice. *Nature* 376:62–66

28a. Kuo CT, Morrisey EE, Anandappa R, Sigrist K, Lu MM, et al. 1997. GATA4 transcription factor is required for ventral morphogenesis and heart tube formation. *Genes Dev.* 11:1048–60

28b. Molkentin JD, Lin Q, Duncan SA, Olson EN. 1997. Requirement for transcription factor GATA4 for heart tube formation and ventral morphogenesis. *Genes Dev.* 11:1061–72

29. Taber LA, Lin IE, Clark EB. 1995. Mechanics of cardiac looping. *Dev. Dyn.* 203:42–50

30. Srivastava D, Thomas T, Lin Q, Brown D, Olson EN. 1997. Regulation of cardiac mesodermal and neural crest development by the bHLH transcription factor dHAND. *Nat. Genet.* 16:154–60

31. Srivastava D, Cserjesi P, Olson EN. 1995. A subclass of bHLH proteins required for cardiac morphogenesis. *Science* 270:1995–99

32. Bour BA, O'Brien MA, Lockwood WL, Goldstein ES, Bodmer R, et al. 1995. *Drosophila* MEF2, a transcription factor that is essential for myogenesis. *Genes Dev.* 9:730–41

33. Edmondson DG, Lyons GE, Martin JF, Olson EN. 1994. MEF2 gene expression marks the cardiac and skeletal muscle lineages during mouse embryogenesis. *Development* 120:1251–63

34. Lin Q, Schwarz J, Olson EN. 1997. Control of cardiac morphogenesis and myogenesis by the myogenic transcription factor MEF2C. *Science* 276:1404–7

35. Ross RS, Navankasattusas S, Harvey RP, Chien KR. 1996. An HF-1α/HF-1β/MEF-2 combinatorial element confers cardiac ventricular specificity and establishes an anterior-posterior gradient of expression. *Development* 122:1799–809

36. Kuisk IR, Li H, Tran D, Capetanaki Y. 1996. A single MEF2 site governs desmin transcription in both heart and skeletal muscle during mouse embryogenesis. *Dev. Biol.* 174:1–13

37. Biben C, Hadchouel J, Tajbakhsh S, Buckingham M. 1996. Developmental and tissue-specific regulation of the murine cardiac actin gene in vivo depends on distinct skeletal and cardiac muscle-specific enhancer elements in addition to the proximal promoter. *Dev. Biol.* 173:200–12

38. Harvey RP. 1996. NK-2 homeobox genes and heart development. *Dev. Biol.* 178:203–16

39. Biben C, Harvey RP. 1997. Homeodomain factor Nkx2–5 controls left/right asymmetric expression of bHLH gene *eHAND* during murine heart development. *Genes Dev.* 11:1357–69

40. Zou Y, Evans S, Chen J, Kuo HC, Har-

vey RP, et al. 1997. CARP, a cardiac ankyrin repeat protein, is downstream in the Nkx2–5 homeobox gene pathway. *Development* 124:793–804

41. Gajewski K, Kim Y, Lee YM, Olson EN, Schulz RA. 1997. *D-mef2* is a target for Tinman activation during *Drosophila* heart development. *EMBO J.* 16:515–22

42. Meyer D, Birchmeier C. 1995. Multiple essential functions of neuregulin in development. *Nature* 378:386–90

43. Lee KF, Simon H, Chen H, Bates B, Hung MC, et al. 1995. Requirement for neuregulin receptor erbB2 in neural and cardiac development. *Nature* 378:394–98

44. Gassmann M, Casagranda F, Orioli D, Simon H, Lai C, et al. 1995. Aberrant neural and cardiac development in mice lacking the ErbB4 neuregulin receptor. *Nature* 378:390–94

45. Sedmera D, Thomas PS. 1996. Trabeculation in the embryonic heart. *BioEssays* 18:607

46. Loeb JA, Fischbach GD. 1997. Neurotrophic factors increase neuregulin expression in embryonic ventral spinal cord neurons. *J. Neurosci.* 17:1416–24

47. Wang DZM, Hammond VE, Abud HE, Bertoncello I, McAroy JW, et al. 1997. Mutation in *sos1* dominently enhances a weak allele of the EGFR, demonstrating a requirement for *sos1* in EGFR signaling and development. *Genes Dev.* 11:309–20

48. Threadgill DW, Dlugosz AA, Hansen LA, Tennenbaum T, Lichti U, et al. 1995. Targeted disruption of mouse EGF receptor: effect of genetic background on mutant phenotype. *Science* 269:230–34

49. Moens CB, Stanton BR, Parada LF, Rossant J. 1993. Defects in heart and lung development in compound heterozygotes for two different targeted mutations at the N-myc locus. *Development* 119:485–99

50. Sucov HM, Dyson E, Gumeringer CL, Price J, Chien KR, et al. 1994. RXR alpha mutant mice establish a genetic basis for vitamin A signaling in heart morphogenesis. *Genes Dev.* 8:1007–18

51. Kastner P, Grondona JM, Mark M, Gansmuller A, LeMeur M, et al. 1994. Genetic analysis of RXR alpha developmental function: convergence of RXR and RAR signaling pathways in heart and eye morphogenesis. *Cell* 78:987–1003

52. Kreidberg JA, Sariola H, Loring JM, Maeda M, Pelletier J, et al. 1993. WT-1 is required for early kidney development. *Cell* 74:679–91

53. Chen Z, Friedrich GA, Soriano P. 1994. Transcriptional enhancer factor 1 disruption by a retroviral gene trap leads to heart defects and embryonic lethality in mice. *Genes Dev.* 8:2293–301

54. Yoshida K, Taga T, Saito M, Suematsu S, Kumanogoh A, et al. 1996. Targeted disruption of gp130, a common signal transducer for the interleukin 6 family of cytokines, leads to myocardial and hematological disorders. *Proc. Natl. Acad. Sci. USA* 93:407–11

55. Jaber M, Koch WJ, Rockman H, Smith B, Bond RA, et al. 1996. Essential role of β-adrenergic receptor kinase 1 in cardiac development and function. *Proc. Natl. Acad. Sci. USA* 93:12974–79

56. Dyson E, Sucov HM, Kubalak SW, Schmid-Schonbein GW, DeLano FA, et al. 1995. Atrial-like phenotype is associated with embryonic ventricular failure in *RXRα-/-* mice. *Proc. Natl. Acad. Sci. USA* 92:7386–90

57. Evan GI, Littlewood TD. 1993. The role of c-myc in cell growth. *Curr. Opin. Genet. Dev.* 3:44–49

58. Swain JL, Stewart TA, Leder P. 1987. Parental legacy determines methylation and expression of an autosomal transgene: a molecular mechanism for parental imprinting. *Cell* 50:719–27

59. Yang JT, Rayburn H, Hynes RO. 1995. Cell adhesion events mediated by alpha 4 integrins are essential in placental and cardiac development. *Development* 121:549–60

60. Kwee L, Baldwin HS, Shen HM, Stewart CL, Buck C, et al. 1995. Defective development of the embryonic and extraembryonic circulatory systems in vascular cell adhesion molecule (VCAM-1) deficient mice. *Development* 121:489–503

61. Gurtner GC, Davis V, Li H, McCoy MJ, Sharpe A, et al. 1995. Targeted disruption of the murine *VCAM1* gene: essential role of VCAM-1 in chorioallantoic fusion and placentation. *Genes Dev.* 9:1–14

62. Tokuyasu KT. 1990. Co-development of embryonic myocardium and myocardial circulation. In *Developmental Cardiology: Morphogenesis and Function*, ed. EB Clark, A Takao, pp. 205–18. Mt. Kisco, NY: Futura

63. Cheitlin MD. 1996. Congenital heart disease, including unrepaired lesions in the adult. In *Cardiology for the Primary Care Physician*, ed. JS Alpert, pp. 241–52. St. Louis: Mosby

64. Stainier DY, Fouquet B, Chen JN, Warren KS, Weinstein BM, et al. 1996. Mutations affecting the formation and function of

the cardiovascular system in the zebrafish embryo. *Development* 123:285–92

65. Chen JN, Haffter P, Odenthal J, Vogelsang E, Brand M, et al. 1996. Mutations affecting the cardiovascular system and other internal organs in zebrafish. *Development* 123:293–302

66. Basson CT, Bachinsky DR, Lin RC, Levi T, Elkins JA, et al. 1997. Mutations in human *TBX5* cause limb and cardiac malformation in Holt-Oram syndrome. *Nat. Genet.* 15:30–35

67. Eisenberg LM, Markwald RR. 1995. Molecular regulation of atrioventricular valvuloseptal morphogenesis. *Circ. Res.* 77:1–6

68. Brown CB, Boyer AS, Runyan RB, Barnett JV. 1996. Antibodies to the Type II TGFβ receptor block cell activation and migration during atrioventricular cushion transformation in the heart. *Dev. Biol.* 174:248–57

69. Sanford LP, Ormsby I, Gittenberger-de Groot AC, Sariola H, Friedman R, et al. 1997. TGFβ2 knockout mice have multiple developmental defects that are nonoverlapping with other TGFβ knockout phenotypes. *Development.* 124:2659–70

70. Webb S, Anderson RH, Brown NA. 1996. Endocardial cushion development and heart loop architecture in the trisomy 16 mouse. *Dev. Dyn.* 206:301–9

71. Pexieder T. 1995. Conotruncus and its septation at the advent of the molecular biology era. In *Developmental Mechanisms of Heart Disease*, ed. EB Clark, RR Markwald, A Takao, pp. 227–47. Armonk, NY: Futura

72. Waldo KL, Kumiski D, Kirby ML. 1996. Cardiac neural crest is essential for the persistence rather than the formation of an arch artery. *Dev. Dyn.* 205:281–92

73. Kirby ML, Waldo KL. 1990. Role of neural crest in congenital heart disease. *Circulation* 82:332–40

74. Greenberg F. 1993. DiGeorge syndrome: an historical review of clinical and cytogenetic features. *J. Med. Genet.* 30:803–6

75. Budarf ML, Collins J, Gong W, Roe B, Wang Z, et al. 1995. Cloning a balanced translocation associated with DiGeorge syndrome and identification of a disrupted candidate gene. *Nat. Genet.* 10:269–78

76. Gong W, Emanuel BS, Collins J, Kim DH, Wang Z, et al. 1996. A transcription map of the DiGeorge and velo-cardiofacial syndrome minimal critical region on 22q11. *Hum. Mol. Genet.* 5:789–800

77. Shenefelt RE. 1972. Morphogenesis of malformations in hamsters caused by retinoic acid: relation to dose and stage at treatment. *Teratology* 5:103–18

78. Lammer EJ, Chen DT, Hoar RM, Agnish ND, Benke PJ, et al. 1985. Retinoic acid embryopathy. *N. Engl. J. Med.* 313:837–41

79. Kastner P, Mark M, Chambon P. 1995. Nonsteroid nuclear receptors: What are genetic studies telling us about their role in real life? *Cell* 83:859–69

80. Lee RY, Luo J, Evans RM, Giguere V, Sucov HM. 1997. Compartment-selective sensitivity of cardiovascular morphogenesis to combinations of retinoic acid receptor gene mutations. *Circ. Res.* 80:757–64

81. Wilson JG, Warkany J. 1949. Aortic arch and cardiac anomalies in the offspring of vitamin A deficient rats. *Am. J. Anat.* 85:113–55

82. Mendelsohn C, Lohnes D, Decimo D, Lufkin T, LeMur M, et al. 1994. Function of the retinoic acid receptors (RARs) during development. (II) Multiple abnormalities at various stages of organogenesis in RAR double mutants. *Development* 120:2749–71

83. Wilson JG, Roth CB, Warkany J. 1953. An analysis of the syndrome of malformations induced by maternal vitamin A deficiency. Effects of restoration of vitamin A at various times during gestation. *Am. J. Anat.* 92:189–217

84. Brannan CI, Perkins AS, Vogel KS, Ratner N, Nordlund ML, et al. 1994. Targeted disruption of the neurofibromatosis type-1 gene leads to developmental abnormalities in heart and various neural crest-derived tissues. *Genes Dev.* 8:1019–29

85. Jacks T, Shih TS, Schmitt EM, Bronson RT, Bernards A, et al. 1994. Tumour predisposition in mice heterozygous for a targeted mutation in *Nf1*. *Nat. Genet.* 7:353–61

86. Kurihara Y, Kurihara H, Oda H, Maemura K, Nagai R, et al. 1995a. Aortic arch malformations and ventricular septal defect in mice deficient in endothelin-1. *J. Clin. Invest.* 96:293–300

87. Franz T. 1989. Persistent truncus arteriosus in the *Splotch* mutant mouse. *Anat. Embryol.* 180:457–64

88. Conway SJ, Henderson DJ, Copp AJ. 1997. Pax3 is required for cardiac neural crest migration in the mouse: evidence from the *Splotch* (Sp2H) mutant. *Development* 124:505–14

89. Kirby ML. 1989. Plasticity and predetermination of mesencephalic and trunk neu-

ral crest transplanted into the region of the cardiac neural crest. *Dev. Biol.* 134:402–12

90. Chisaka O, Capecchi MR. 1991. Regionally restricted developmental defects resulting from targeted disruption of the mouse homeobox gene *hox-1.5. Nature* 350:473–79

91. Horan GS, Ramirez-Solis R, Featherstone MS, Wolgemuth DJ, Bradley A, et al. 1995. Compound mutants for the paralogous *hoxa-4, hoxb-4,* and *hoxd-4* genes show more complete homeotic transformations and a dose-dependent increase in the number of vertebrae transformed. *Genes Dev.* 9:1667–77

Annu. Rev. Physiol. 1998. 60:309–25

NORMAL AND ABNORMAL CONSEQUENCES OF APOPTOSIS IN THE HUMAN HEART

Thomas N. James

World Health Organization Cardiovascular Center, Department of Medicine and Department of Pathology, University of Texas Medical Branch, Galveston, Texas 77555-0129; e-mail: jandee@utmb.edu

KEY WORDS: sinus node, AV node, right ventricular involution, Uhl's anomaly

---

ABSTRACT

Knowledge about apoptosis has become essential for understanding many aspects of cardiac structure and function. In the human heart there are major periods of morphogenesis that begin only after birth, and some of these processes recur intermittently for many years. Although the exact mechanisms by which these events are initiated or terminated remain poorly understood, it is clear that their benefits may be mirrored in destructive effects. In this review, selected examples include normal morphogenesis of the cardiac conduction system and the normal postnatal involution of the right ventricle, both of which are mediated by apoptosis. Destructive counterparts include familial heart block ending in fatal arrhythmias, similar results in the long QT syndrome, and the pathogenesis of both Uhl's anomaly and arrhythmogenic right ventricular dysplasia; in each apoptosis is an important factor.

INTRODUCTION

Although apoptosis remains an unfamiliar word and concept for some physicians and scientists, an understanding of apoptosis has already become essential in explaining many fundamental biological processes such as those by which a variety of cardiovascular functions and diseases emerge and evolve. The word apoptosis was introduced by Kerr, Wyllie & Currie (1) to explain a generally ignored form of cell death very different from necrosis. It is an original Greek

0066-4278/98/0315-0309$08.00

word referring to a quiet dropping out process similar to leaves falling from a tree, an image resembling most histologic examples of apoptosis. An excellent history of earlier morphological descriptions of this type over the past century has recently been published by Majno & Joris (2), but the broad significance of apoptosis to explain many normal biological functions, such as morphogenesis and the pathogenesis of a variety of immunological and malignant diseases, only began to be recognized more widely through several perceptive interpretations by Wyllie and his colleagues (3–5).

Regrettable delay in the appreciation of major opportunities for understanding the pathogenesis of disease is nothing new. For example, the pioneering reports of Glucksmann (6), Saunders (7), and Pexeider (8), in which they emphasized that cell death was not only normal but an essential component of morphogenesis, did not receive the attention of scientists or physicians that those reports warranted. Familiar examples of useful morphogenesis include the crucial role of cell death (by apoptosis) in the fetal transformation of interdigital webs into fingers and toes, and the postnatal death of enormous numbers of neurons in the development of useful signaling pathways during normal maturation of the brain.

When I first suggested that cell death was ubiquitous and also normal in the postnatal maturation of the AV (atrioventricular) node and His bundle and that it could pose a hazard for crib death (9), given certain concurrent factors present by chance (10), the idea was harshly criticized (11–13) for a variety of stated reasons. Some said that cell death was never normal, some said that they did not see examples of such cell death in the conduction system of the heart, while still others said yes they saw exactly what I described but that it was a normal phenomenon and not one of cell death because "there was no evidence of necrosis." Apoptosis was presumably an unfamiliar or unacceptable phenomenon for these critics. But as recently emphasized in my refutations of those criticisms, cell death is a normal component of postnatal morphogenesis of the human cardiac conduction system, and apoptosis is a major and possibly the principal mechanism by which this occurs (14).

However, the fact that apoptotic cell death may very often be useful does not mean that apoptosis is always a beneficial process. This seeming paradox— in some respects the yin and yang of cardiology—is better understood when one considers the multitude of different promoters or inhibitors of apoptosis, each of which has a progression that in some circumstances may be reversible, but at a later stage becomes irreversible, thus committing the cell inevitably to die. Unsurprisingly, the balance between promotion and inhibition of apoptosis often changes with time, or as a consequence of associated metabolic or toxic influences, and it differs in different organs of the mammalian body and differs to some degree between species. Whether apoptosis in the human heart is beneficial or harmful depends significantly upon when it happens and how long it lasts. It is the purpose of this review to examine both beneficial and harmful effects of apoptosis in the human heart and to briefly discuss their clinical significance.

ILLUSTRATIVE EXAMPLES OF NORMAL AND ABNORMAL CONSEQUENCES OF APOPTOSIS IN THE HUMAN HEART

Postnatal Morphogenesis of the Cardiac Conduction System

Both the sinus node and the AV conduction system (node, His bundle, and branches) can readily be recognized by the middle of the first trimester of fetal development (15, 16), but they remain essentially unchanged thereafter until one or two weeks following birth. Then the postnatal sinus node begins to be transformed (Figure 1, see color insert) from a mass of P cells, distributed about the large artery around which the sinus node is formed, into a more intricate network of slender transitional cells connecting many small groups of P cells (17, 18). The time when the sinus node achieves its adult configuration varies among individuals but is usually complete in the first few years of life. The sinus node in old age normally contains an increased volume of collagen (19), and this is sometimes misinterpreted as a pathological fibrosis. However, if the increasing fibrosis remains symmetrically distributed and the nodal myocytes similarly dispersed, this is not only normal but may even represent certain physiological advantages for impulse formation and its orderly extranodal distribution.

Also within the first week or two after birth, the fetal AV node and His bundle change morphologically very little. But an elegant experimental study by Preston, McFadden & Moe (20) some years ago demonstrated a physiological or functional immaturity of the AV conduction tissues in the very young of three different mammalian species, from which the investigators proposed a mechanism for electrical vulnerability leading to sudden unexpected death of human infants.

At about the age of two weeks, an orderly morphogenesis begins in which the irregular shape of the left side of the human AV node and His bundle [Figures 2 (see color insert) and 3] becomes transformed into a smooth border by a process of non-inflammatory resorptive degeneration (14, 18, 21). This process has now been demonstrated to include, and possibly be fully mediated by, apoptosis (14, 22). In every heart, this transforming process shapes and molds the AV node and His bundle through recurring bouts of apoptosis—weeks or months apart and not as a massive single event—and is normally complete by adolescence. Another possible morphogenetic influence in this postnatal morphogenesis is

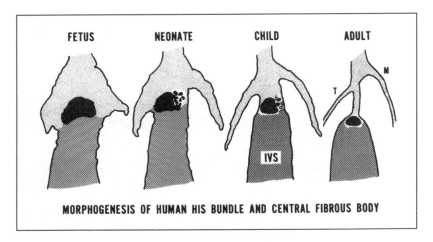

Figure 3   This cartoon displays stages of the postnatal morphogenesis of the human His bundle. The fetal central fibrous body is normally a thick gelatinous mass, whereas the adult counterpart is a thinner tough sheet of collagen.

the extracellular matrix (23–25). Actually, the sinus node is normally encased in a periarterial collagen framework, and both the AV node and His bundle are normally bounded at their margins by the collagenous central fibrous body.

The fact that the sinus node is normally encased in a collagen framework surrounding the sinus node artery led Söderström (26) to suggest that the sinus node resembles an enormous adventitia of its artery. Postnatal morphogenesis of the sinus node certainly includes apoptosis in a selectively distributed pattern with interweaving collagen, but it is uncertain whether that collagen acts to some degree as an inducer of apoptosis or whether there are genetically programmed or targeted nodal cells for primary apoptosis not causally related to the extracellular matrix. Just as there may be an electromechanical servomechanism (27, 28) influencing sinus impulse formation (mediated by the collagen frame of the node being attached to the sinus node artery), we can also consider the possibility that this anatomical arrangement influences how the apoptosis occurs in producing the eventual exquisite geometry of the adult sinus node's configuration. The mature interwoven pattern of a collagen matrix for the nodal myocytes (P cells and transitional cells) could be guided by physical motion determined with each phasic systolic distention (pulse) of the sinus node artery; stretch, for example, has been shown to induce apoptosis (29).

When cut in cross section (Figures 2 and 3), the fetal AV node and His bundle normally have an irregular or shaggy configuration that includes a wide dispersion of bands and clumps of their myocytes throughout the neighboring central fibrous body (18, 21). It was this disproportionately large mass of special myocytes that led Keith & Flack to refer to both structures in the fetal heart as relatively enormous (30). The orderly pruning of this surplus tissue, primarily accomplished by apoptosis (14, 22), normally leaves the AV node and His bundle as smoothly defined structures and almost certainly renders them physiologically safer for their critically important electrical function.

If fronds of normal tissue persist in the central fibrous body adjacent to the AV node, they can become the anatomical substrate for sites of either spontaneous automatic rhythm such as parasystole, or re-entrant (reciprocating) tachycardia (31). Failure in this normal molding and shaping of the AV node and His bundle may also cause unstable and hazardous electrical function there and even sudden death (32). It has recently been demonstrated that AV nodal re-entry is nearly always the specific basis of human fetal tachycardia (33). The lethal hazard of persistent fetal dispersion (in the central fibrous body) of the AV node and His bundle (32) is also supported by experimental evidence of a special postnatal electrical vulnerability of an immature AV transmission system (20).

Selective Apoptotic Destruction of the Sinus Node and AV Node Plus the Internodal and Interatrial Pathways

Gradually progressive development of heart block ending with fatal arrhythmias has been described as a familial problem in South Africa (34, 35). Colleagues and I have conducted postmortem examination of the entire cardiac conduction system of a young woman who had gradually progressive development of complete heart block ending in fatal arrhythmias (22), and we found total absence of the AV node (Figure 4, see color insert) to explain the heart block, but she also had virtually no cardiac myocytes in the internodal and interatrial pathways (Figure 5) and extensive destruction of the sinus node (Figure 6, see color insert). In each of these structures there was abundant apoptosis (Figure 7, see color insert), whereas the His bundle and the myocardium of both ventricles were normal.

As part of that same investigation (22), we examined two other hearts from five brothers with a strong family history of heart block and fatal arrhythmias, where we found similar selective apoptotic destruction of the sinus node, AV node, internodal and interatrial pathways, with sparing of the His bundle and all the ventricular myocardium. Two surviving brothers in that family were successfully treated with implanted automatic cardioverter-defibrillators, without which it seems likely that they would have died as well.

Selectivity of the apoptosis in these three hearts and the sparing of ventricular myocardium and the His bundle is perplexing, as is apparent from the following descriptions of different selectivity patterns for harmful apoptosis in other subjects with fatal arrhythmias. On the other hand, the selective destruction

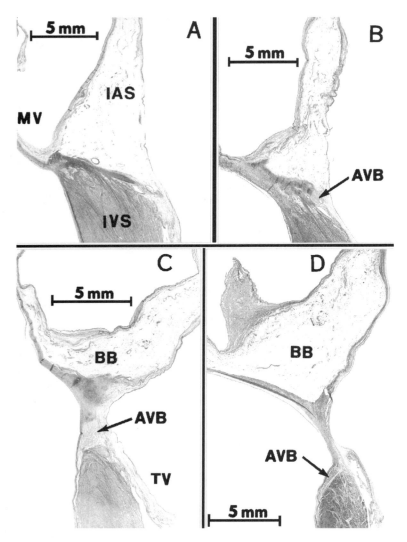

Figure 5   In addition to the absence of AV node (22), there is also absence of myocytes in the entire interatrial septum. These four sections were made about 5 mm apart and show the empty appearance of the IAS. The region of the absent AV node is in *A*. In *B*, the proximal end of the normally preserved His bundle (AVB) is indicated with an *arrow*. In *C*, the AVB is beginning to divide, and in *D* only the left bundle branch portion of the AVB is shown. Note the normal myocardium of interventricular septum. In *C*, the interatrial myocardial band (BB), which marks the anterior margin of the IAS as well as the anterior internodal pathway, is devoid of myocytes.

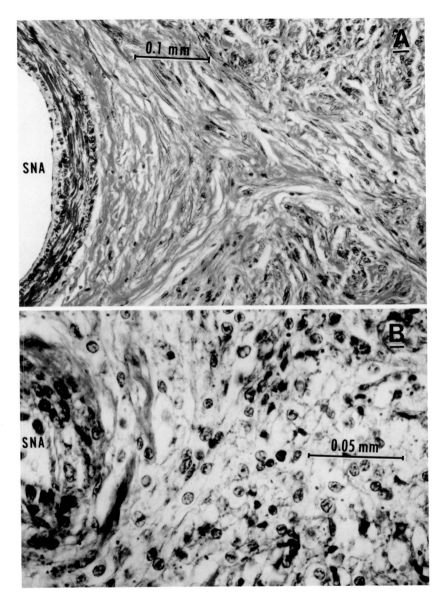

Figure 1 Postnatal morphogenesis of the human sinus node is illustrated here. The adult sinus node *(A)* contains a distinct collagen framework *(blue/green)* attached to the sinus node artery (SNA). Within the collagen frame there is a mixture of small rounded P cells and slender transitional cells (see text for discussion). The sinus node in *(B)* is typical of that in the human fetus and the newborn. It contains much less collagen and the nodal myocytes are almost entirely P cells. Goldner trichrome stain is used here and in other figures except where indicated otherwise. Magnification in each figure is indicated with reference bars.

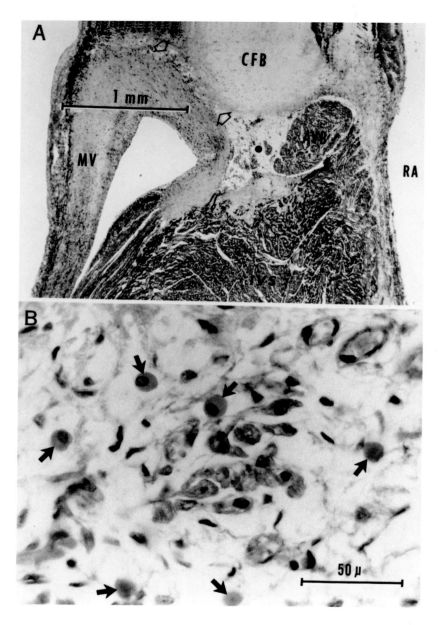

Figure 2 Shortly after birth, the human His bundle (AVB) undergoes selective apoptotic destruction of much of its left half, here centered with a *black dot* in *A*. In *B*, the myocytes of that area exhibit pyknotic nuclei, and there is an evenly spaced distribution of scavenging macrophages *(black arrows)*. MV, mitral value; RA, right atrium; CFB, central fibrous body; and IVS, interventricular septum. The two *small arrows* indicate a fusing seam between the CFB and the anchor of the MV.

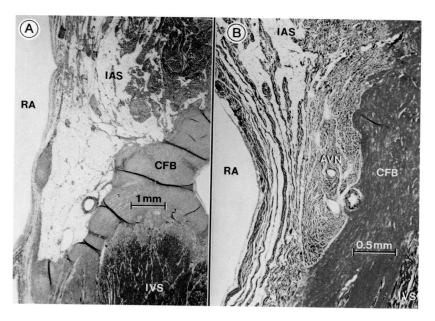

Figure 4 In a study of three cases of progressive development of heart block ending in fatal arrhythmias *(22),* the AV node was found to be absent *(A).* Normal AV node from the heart of a young individual (same age) is shown in *(B).* An orienting mark to compare *A* with *B* is the small artery of the AV node seen in both veiws. IAS, inter-atrial septum.

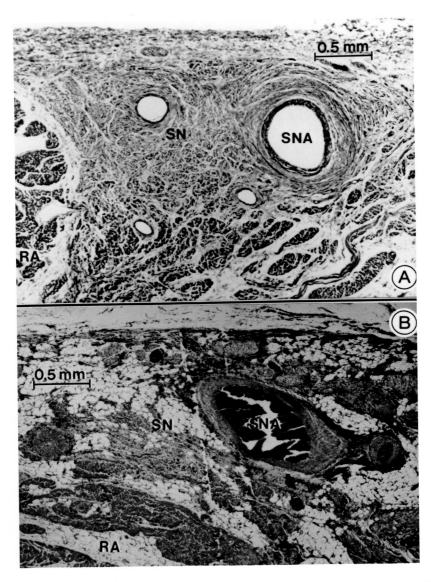

Figure 6 This picture compares a normal sinus node in (*A*) with the shredded fragments of sinus node *(B)* filled with foci of fatty-fibrous residuum from apoptosis, typical of the three hearts discussed in Reference 22. See also Figures 4, 5, and 7.

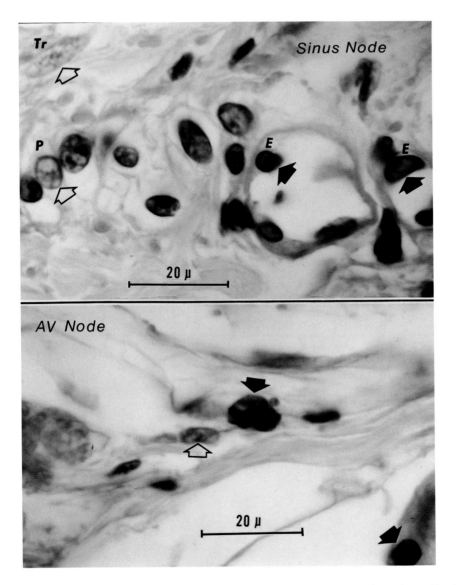

Figure 7 Samples of the apoptotic destruction of both sinus node and AV node in three human hearts (described in text and Reference 22) are shown (TUNEL stain). In the sinus node, one normal *(blue)* nucleus from a non-apoptotic P cell *(open arrow)* is bracketed by two adjacent apoptotic *brown* nuclei. E, endothelial cells; Tr, transitional cells. The AV node example is from a section adjacent to the one shown in Figure 4*A*, where tiny fragments of surviving AV nodal cells can be seen adjacent to the central fibrous body.

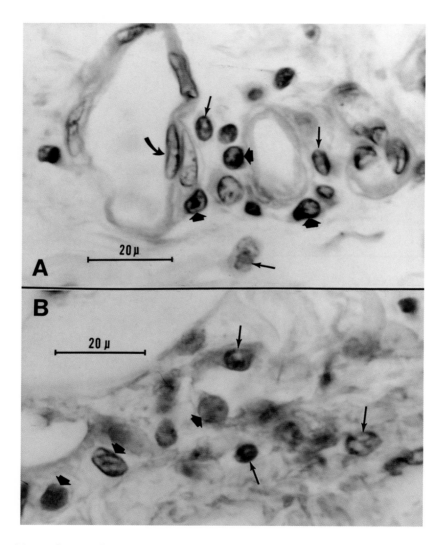

Figure 9 Apoptosis present in the sinus node of one patient with long QT syndrome (51, 53) is demonstrated by the TUNEL stain. *Curved arrow* in *A* marks a smooth muscle cell in the wall of a small artery. *Slender black arrows* mark *blue* nuclei of normal cells, and *short black arrows* mark *brown* apoptotic nuclei. *A* is from the margin of sinus node, and *B* is from the center of the node.

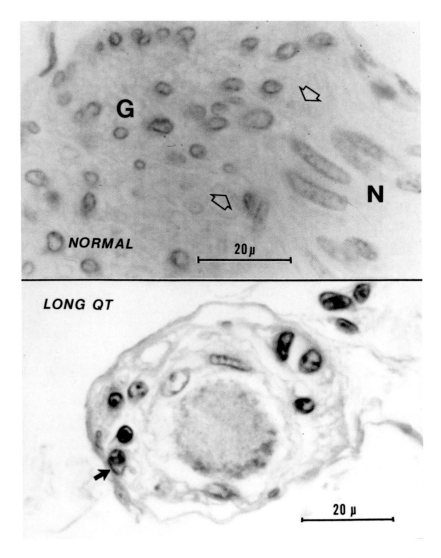

Figure 10 Apoptosis is evident in neural elements in and near the sinus nodes of patients with long QT syndrome (51, 53). *Top panel:* TUNEL staining of a normal heart demonstrates a normal ganglion (G) and connected nerve (N) (the junction is indicated by *open arrows*). *Lower panel:* Ganglion from a patient with long QT syndrome. All nuclei in the ganglion are apoptotic *(brown)* except one *(blue)* marked with *black arrow*.

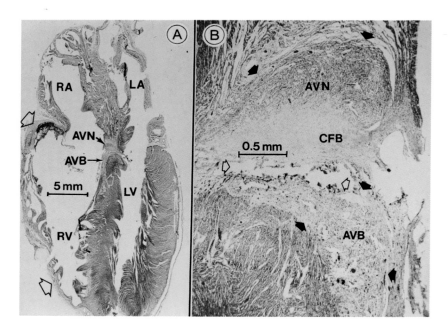

Figure 11 These pictures of a frontal plane section of whole infant heart illustrate apoptotic destruction of the right ventricle *(A; two open arrows)* in Uhl's anomaly. All the other myocardium was essentially normal except that in the His bundle (AVB). In *B*, the normal AVN is marked with two *black arrows* and contrasts with the apoptotic His bundle (AVB, *black arrows*) below. Two *open arrows* indicate an artifactual tear through the CFB just above the AVB.

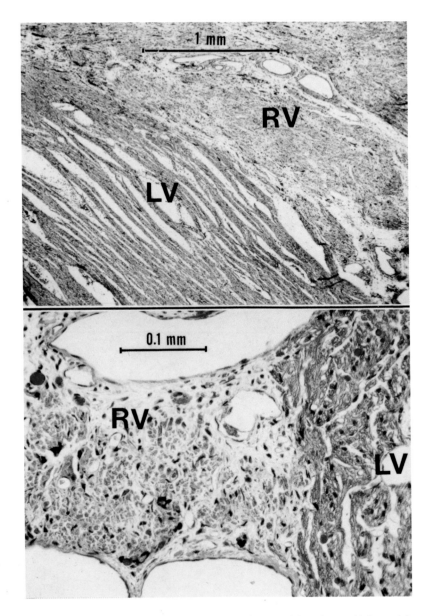

Figure 12 The sharply demarcated margins between apoptotic right ventricle and normal left ventricle are shown in these two examples from the case of Uhl's anomaly (54). Note the absence of inflammation at these margins. The *top* example is from the junction between RV and LV near the apex of the heart, and the *bottom* example is from a midpoint of interventricular septum.

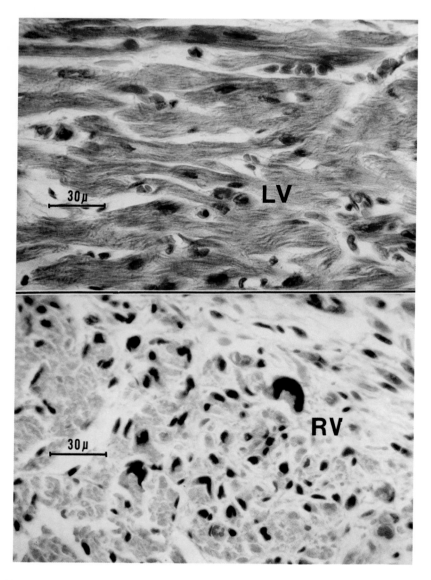

Figure 13 Normal myocytes from the left ventricle (LV) of the case of Uhl's anomaly (54) are compared with the apoptotic destruction of the right ventricle (RV) at the same magnification. See also Figure 14.

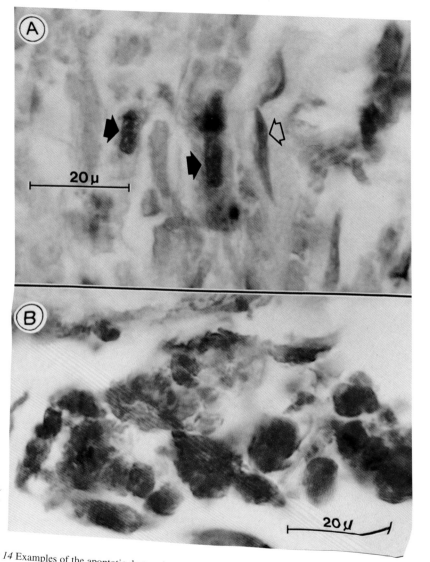

Figure 14 Examples of the apoptotic destruction (TUNEL stain) of myocytes, fibroblasts, and other tissue in the right ventricle of the case of Uhl's anomaly are seen in A. *Blue* nuclei *(open arrow)* are sparse among the apoptotic *brown* nuclei *(black arrows).* In many areas there was a mass of apoptotic debris as shown in B.

(from archival files) sinus node tissue embedded in paraffin in five of the eight cases previously reported with cardioneuropathy (51). In each of those sinus nodes, there was apoptotic destruction (Figures 9, 10, see color insert), not only of myocytes, but also of vascular endothelial and smooth muscle cells and of both nerves and ganglia in and near the sinus node (53).

For many years, patients with long QT syndrome have presented an enigma because they include individuals who are congenitally deaf, as well as those who hear normally (53). In the deafness associated with the long QT syndrome, it was uncertain whether these findings were independent or somehow causally related. Two recent investigations have not only clarified the inheritance pattern for both deaf and non-deaf long QT patients, but also demonstrated that a genetic mutation is responsible for both the cardiac and auditory problems (53a,b). Furthermore, the faulty gene (KVLQT1) also controls an abnormal potassium channel underlying the problems in the heart as well as in the ear. Because the same potassium channel governs impulse information in excitable tissue (53c,d), the sinus node abnormalities typical of the long QT syndrome (53) become an especially intriguing component of the entire long QT mosaic. A fuller understanding of this molecular misbehavior by KVLQT1 could lead to improved diagnosis and treatment of a remarkable array of other disorders of cardiac rhythm, conduction, and repolarization.

Massive Apoptotic Destruction of the Right Ventricle and Its Crista Supraventricularis as well as of the His Bundle in a Two-Month Old Baby, and Its Significance Relevant to Understanding the Pathogenesis of Uhl's Anomaly and of Arrhythmogenic Right Ventricular Dysplasia

A two-month old child died of intractable right ventricular failure associated with complete heart block known to have been present in utero (54). Although I was asked to study the heart mainly because of the congenital heart block, it was already known that the right ventricle was electrically inexcitable and was thin and "abnormal in appearance" at the time that an electronic pacemaker had been placed just after birth.

The unexpected major abnormality we found in that heart was a selective and virtually total destruction of the right ventricular myocardium (Figures 11–14, see color insert) caused by apoptosis. The His bundle was similarly destroyed by apoptosis, but in serial sections the histologically normal AV node was separated from the apoptotic His bundle by a dense band of collagen probably present there for a long time and responsible for complete heart block even before apoptosis destroyed the His bundle. Based on ultrasonographic studies during fetal development in this child, we believe that the complete heart block occurred about the fifth month of gestation (54). By contrast to the devastated right ventricle and His bundle, the sinus node, AV node, internodal and interatrial pathways, and all the working myocardium of both atria and the left ventricle were normal.

The sites of selective apoptotic destruction in this case are a distinct contrast to those of the two preceding abnormalities (progressive development of fatal heart block, and the long QT syndrome). The logical interpretation is that every component of the conduction system can be vulnerable to apoptosis, as can the right ventricle, but the vulnerability may be manifest in a variety of anatomical distributive patterns. Future studies, by us and others, are needed to determine whether these are only rarely encountered clusters or more prevalent than may be thought, and also whether there are still other examples of abnormal anatomical clusters, either analogous to or completely different from the type we found in these three clinically different syndromes.

It is simple to see how this single case (54) is a new example of exactly what Uhl found in his own single case of a patient of the same age who also died of right ventricular failure (55). The one major difference is that in Uhl's case, the patient did not have heart block. However, on careful review of other reported cases, we found that heart block has been seen in Uhl's anomaly in an exceptionally well-studied case in which the conduction system was examined (56) and, furthermore, that heart block is not all that rare in arrhythmogenic right ventricular dysplasia (57, 58), although conduction system studies have been reported in which no anatomical abnormalities were found (59). How all of this may be linked for both Uhl's anomaly and arrhythmogenic right ventricular dysplasia is discussed below.

DISCUSSION

Understanding the general nature of apoptosis (as briefly reviewed in the Introduction) is essential for interpreting how and why apoptosis happens in the human heart, as well as its functional and anatomical consequences. Although many valuable studies (1–5, 52) have examined how apoptosis is signaled to begin, what may or may not prevent its happening, and what the mechanisms may be by which it is terminated, most have been in experimental animals or cell cultures. Much less is known about these switches in human tissues and organs, a situation especially true at the present time about the human heart.

A characteristic residuum of apoptotic cell death in the myocardium is focal noninflammatory destruction causing a paucity or complete absence of myocytes in an area where myocytes are normally expected to be present, leaving small fatty foci or loose areolar tissue composed of empty-appearing spaces arranged in a lacy pattern of thin collagen strands held together by scattered fibroblasts. The lacy foci include assorted cells undergoing apoptosis in and near the conduction system, but these lacy foci are also characteristic of the histologic appearance of the myocardium in arrhythmogenic right ventricular dysplasia (60–62).

The classic morphology of apoptosis is often difficult to capture, for two principal reasons. First, the absence of tissue reaction such as inflammation, useful in identifying areas of necrosis, makes the typically small foci of apoptosis less easy to suspect and tempting to misinterpret as normal. The second reason is the rapidity of both the apoptotic process and prompt phagocytosis, which makes the apoptotic cell available for only a short time in order to be recognized and demonstrated. The duration of time from onset of apoptosis until death and removal of the cell is often only a few minutes.

It has been reported that molecules of phosphatidylserine, normally found on the inner surface of the plasmalemma, move to the outer (extracellular) surface of an apoptotic cell where they then serve to attract macrophages and other scavengers (63, 64), including similar cells such as neighboring myocytes in the heart (14, 40). Details of the process of phagocytosis will probably be found to differ somewhat in various tissues of different species and by the presence of associated biological events such as ischemia or infection.

A great deal has been learned about biochemical triggers for apoptosis, including those associated with viral infection (65–67) or immunological responses (68–70), but it is important to remember that the human heart is unusual (but not unique) in its properties of electrical activation and phasic contraction, two separate functions that are intricately related. One may logically suspect that electrical activity and mechanical contraction of the heart could directly or indirectly also play either a separate or a combined role in triggering apoptosis. I have earlier indicated how the pulse and impulse relationship in the sinus node (27, 28) could play a mechanical role in the apoptotic morphogenesis leading to the ultimate and remarkable normal geometry of the mature sinus node.

In the heart of the young woman with progressive development of heart block cited earlier and described in detail elsewhere (22), two things are notable in the context being considered: she had complete absence of both her interatrial and internodal pathways, and the left atrium was so thin-walled that the appendage was aneurysmal. There was no mitral valve disease. Elimination of her interatrial and internodal pathways precluded any possible normal electrical stimulation of the left atrium, because a sinus impulse had no route by which to get there, and the same tissue damage (by apoptosis) precluded any possible retrograde conduction of an electrical impulse from the AV node to the left atrium. There may have been some unidentified separate process selectively affecting the left atrium, but because the right atrium was not only normal but actually hypertrophied, and the myocardium of both ventricles was normal, it seems more reasonable to consider that the absence of electrical stimulation may have been the basis for atrophy (by apoptosis) of the left atrium.

A different situation exists for the postnatal right ventricle, beginning precisely at the time of birth, because the opening of the pulmonary circulation immediately and substantially diminishes the pressure against which the right ventricle must pump. Teleologically, one would anticipate that nature would not tolerate retention of a mass of right ventricular myocardium, which is far in excess of that needed for its normal postnatal work (contractile function), and apoptosis typically serves valuably in many organs to actively remove cells that are no longer needed. Experimentally, Kajstura et al have demonstrated that apoptotic removal of such cells is a uniform occurrence, especially in the right ventricle, in the postnatal rat heart (71), whereas Katz et al (72) found that right ventricular size and mass begins to diminish immediately in adult patients after lung transplantation to treat severe pulmonary hypertension.

These illustrative examples demonstrate how absence of electrical activation on the one hand or a sharp reduction in pressure-work on the other could cause apoptosis to happen in the heart. However, it is logical to presume that some form of biochemical mediation of either trigger remains necessary for apoptosis to commence. As emphasized by Kroemer et al (52), the situation is most often a mixture of apoptotic triggers or inducer events combined with loss of normal apoptotic-inhibiting factors, and it is the suitable convergence of these events and factors that leads irreversibly to cell death by apoptosis.

Although the modern recognition of apoptosis as a second form of cell death has led to major advances in our understanding of many diseases, particularly in the fields of immunology, oncology, hematology, and normal morphogenesis of many organs in the body (including the heart), there are some confusing overlaps in both the morphology and causal mechanisms for either necrosis or apoptosis. For example, the cellular responses to injury by ischemia, hyperthermia, or radiation differ significantly depending directly upon the severity of the injury: With mild to moderate ischemia or hyperthermia or radiation, the tissue response is characteristically apoptosis, but with more severe injury due to the same type of trauma in the same tissue, the cellular response becomes one of necrosis (73).

As examples familiar to all cardiologists, in either the natural or experimental production of myocardial ischemia and infarction, there is always a histological mixture of dead, dying, and surviving cells depending upon the severity of the injury (74–76), and it should not be surprising that the margins of an infarct may have mainly apoptosis and the central regions necrosis. Furthermore, if apoptotic cells are for some reason not swiftly removed by phagocytosis, the remaining membrane-bound degenerating fragments (apoptotic bodies) eventually disintegrate and elicit inflammatory and other tissue response indistinguishable from necrosis. Nevertheless, when considered in the context of histological appearance (i.e. in situ) in contrast to cytological appearance (in cell culture or flow cytometry), the presence or absence of an inflammatory reaction remains one of the most useful features differentiating apoptosis from necrosis.

In addition to the examples of apoptosis in the human heart already illustrated and discussed, there is growing attention to the role of apoptosis in the pathogenesis of coronary artery disease. This includes not only atherosclerosis but also the restenosis following balloon or other angioplasty (77–79). An especially intriguing role has been reported in the transformation (remodeling) of coronary anastomoses to optimize the effectiveness of collateral circulation (80). New information is also emerging about the role of apoptosis in the remodeling of ventricular myocardium under the stresses imposed by hypertension or after a myocardial infarction. It is likely that we will eventually find that apoptosis participates in almost any injurious effect and the subsequent repair of virtually all diseases of the human heart.

An arrhythmogenic effect by apoptosis may be mediated several ways. In the process of dying, a myocyte passes through phases of increased excitability or becomes automatic, at least until it is dead. Furthermore, from a random grouping of several such dead cells, the process of normal activation in that area of the heart must be deranged and redirected in a way that would provide a suitable anatomical substrate for re-entrant arrhythmias. Additionally, the apoptotic death of nerves or ganglia or arterial cells in the heart may all have their own influence on the function of both dying and surviving cardiac myocytes. There are still other putative possibilities for arrhythmogenesis by apoptosis, but perhaps the main lesson is that we should now include a different and heretofore unconsidered cause of arrhythmias, especially those occurring in cases where other plausible explanations are not available. In addition to coronary spasm, myocardial ischemia, or infarction, or focal myocarditis and similar currently familiar considerations as the cause of unexpected arrhythmias or heart block, we must add apoptosis to the standard differential diagnosis.

My suggestion for the pathogenesis of both the clinical picture and the anatomical findings in Uhl's anomaly and arrhythmogenic right ventricular dysplasia is as follows: Uhl's anomaly represents apoptotic destruction of the right ventricle to an extent much greater than usually occurs in arrhythmogenic right ventricular dysplasia, but the fundamental cause in both diseases is apoptosis, except it is of different duration and distribution. In Uhl's anomaly, the normal postnatal right ventricular apoptosis that beneficially reduces the newly excessive right ventricular myocardial mass, as both experimental studies in animals (71) and clinical observations in human subjects (72) now suggest must occur, simply continues too long unchecked until little or no right ventricular myocardium remains. In arrhythmogenic right ventricular dysplasia, the problem is that this same normal process, having been stopped correctly once in infancy, some years later begins to recur and stop, recur and stop, each time being associated with bouts of right ventricular tachycardia.

If my proposed explanation for the pathogenesis of arrhythmogenic right ventricular dysplasia is correct, i.e. that it is most often and perhaps always mediated primarily by episodic but currently unpredictable bouts of apoptosis, then it becomes necessary to reconsider certain forms of treatment that are intended to excise, cauterize, or otherwise destroy the arrhythmogenic site (81, 82). It could be expected, for example, that many other sites in the right ventricular myocardium (especially including the crista supraventricularis) would sooner or later be involved by subsequent bouts of episodic focal apoptosis. In fact, a recent multicenter study has reported that arrhythmogenic right ventricular dysplasia is indeed a progressive heart muscle disease (83). Consequently, there can be no assurance that physically eliminating a presently active arrhythmogenic site would prevent the later periodic emergence of new sites.

What will eventually be far more useful would be to find and block the apoptotic trigger, or prevent the loss of an apoptosis inhibitor, or to determine if both of these influences might coexist in arrhythmogenic right ventricular dysplasia. Of course, even if such an apoptotic trigger could be found, therapy by blocking it may have undesirable effects elsewhere in the heart or other organs if the therapy were administered systematically. There are obviously many daunting challenges and fascinating questions yet to be answered.

ACKNOWLEDGMENT

This work was supported by the Pegasus Fund of the University of Texas Medical Branch.

> Visit the *Annual Reviews home page* at
> http://www.AnnualReviews.org.

Literature Cited

1. Kerr JRF, Wyllie AH, Currie AR. 1972. Apoptosis: a basic biological phenomenon with wide-ranging implications in tissue kinetics. *Br. J. Cancer* 26:239–57
2. Majno G, Joris I. 1995. Apoptosis, oncosis, and necrosis. An overview of cell death. *Am. J. Pathol.* 146:3–15
3. Wyllie AH. 1987. Apoptosis: cell death under homeostatic control. *Arch. Toxicol.* 11:3–10
4. Searle J, Kerr JRF, Bishop CJ. 1982. Necrosis and apoptosis: distinct modes of cell death with fundamentally different significance. *Pathol. Annu.* 17:229–59
5. Arends MJ, Wyllie AH. 1991. Apoptosis: mechanisms and roles in pathology. *Int. Rev. Exp. Pathol.* 32:223–54
6. Glucksmann A. 1950. Cell deaths in normal vertebrate ontogeny. *Biol. Rev.* 26:59–86
7. Saunders JW Jr. 1966. Death in embryonic systems. Death in cells is the usual accompaniment of embryonic growth and differentiation. *Science* 154:604–12

8. Pexieder T. 1975. Cell death in the morphogenesis and teratogenesis of the heart. *Adv. Anat. Embryol. Cell Biol.* 51:3–100

9. James TN. 1968. Sudden death in babies: new observations in the heart. *Am. J. Cardiol.* 22:479–506

10. James TN. 1983. Chance and sudden death. *J. Am. Coll. Cardiol.* 1:164–83

11. Valdes-Dapena MA, Greene M, Basavanand N, Catherman R, Truex RC. 1973. The myocardial conduction system in sudden death in infancy. *N. Engl. J. Med.* 289:1179–80

12. Anderson RH, Bouton J, Burrow CT, Smith A. 1974. Sudden death in infancy: a study of cardiac specialized tissue. *Br. Med. J.* 2:135–39

13. Hackel DB, Reimer KA. 1993. *Sudden Death. Cardiac and Other Causes.* Durham, NC: Carolina Acad. Press. 72 pp.

14. James TN. 1994. Normal and abnormal consequences of apoptosis in the human heart: from postnatal morphogenesis to paroxysmal arrhythmias. *Circulation* 90:556–73

15. Duckworth JWA. 1952. *The development of the sinu-atrial and atrioventricular nodes of the human heart.* MD thesis. Univ. Edinburgh

16. Boyd JD. 1965. Development of the heart. In *Handbook of Physiology*, ed. WF Hamilton, P Dow, Vol. III, Sec. 2:2511–43. Washington DC: Am. Physiol. Soc.

17. James TN. 1977. The sinus node. *Am. J. Cardiol.* 40:965–86

18. James TN. 1970. Cardiac conduction system: fetal and postnatal development. *Am. J. Cardiol.* 25:213–26

19. Lev M. 1954. Aging changes in the human sinoatrial node. *J. Gerontol.* 9:1–9

20. Preston JB, McFadden S, Moe GK. 1959. Atrioventricular transmission in young mammals. *Am. J. Physiol.* 197:236–40

21. James TN. 1983. Structure and function of the AV junction. The Mikamo Lecture for 1982. *Jpn. Circ. J.* 47:1–47

22. James TN, St Martin E, Willis PW III, Lohr TO. 1996. Apoptosis as a possible cause of gradual development of complete heart block and fatal arrhythmias associated with absence of the AV node, the sinus node and the internodal pathways. *Circulation* 93:1424–38

23. Lin CQ, Bissell MJ. 1993. Multi-faceted regulation of cell differentiation by extracellular matrix. *FASEB J.* 7:737–43

24. Lee KKH, Chan WY, Sze LY. 1993. Histogenetic potential of rat hind-limb interdigital tissues prior to and during the onset of programmed cell death. *Anat. Rec.* 236:568–72

25. Taipale J, Keski-Oja J. 1997. Growth factors in the extracellular matrix. *FASEB J.* 11:51–59

26. Söderström N. 1948. Myocardial infarction and mural thrombosis in the atria of the heart. *Acta Med. Scand.* 132:1–114

27. James TN. 1967. Pulse and impulse in the sinus node. *Henry Ford Hosp. Med. J.* 15:275–99

28. James TN. 1973. The sinus node as a servomechanism. *Circ. Res.* 32:307–13

29. Cheng W, Li B, Kajstura J, Li P, Wolin MS, et al. 1995. Stretch-induced programmed myocyte cell death. *J. Clin. Invest.* 96:2247–59

30. Keith A, Flack MW. 1906. The auriculoventricular bundle of the human heart. *Lancet* 2:359–64

31. James TN. 1985. Normal and abnormal variations in anatomy of the atrioventricular node and His bundle and their relevance to the pathogenesis of reentrant tachycardias and parasystolic rhythms. In *Cardiac Electrophysiology and Arrhythmias*, ed. DP Zipes, J Jalife, pp. 301–10, New York: Grune & Stratton

32. James TN, Marshall TK. 1976. De Subitaneis Mortibus. XVIII. Persistent fetal dispersion of the atrioventricular node and His bundle within central fibrous body. *Circulation* 53:1026–34

33. Naheed ZJ, Strasburger JF, Deal BJ, Benson W Jr, Gidding SS. 1996. Fetal tachycardia: mechanisms and predictors of hydrops fetalis. *J. Am. Coll. Cardiol.* 27:1736–40

34. Brink A, Torrington M. 1977. Progressive familial heart block—two types. *S. Afr. Med. J.* 52:53–59

35. Brink PA, Farriery A, Moolman JC, Weymar HW, van der Merwe P-L, et al. 1995. Gene for progressive familial heart block type I maps to chromosome 19q13. *Circulation* 91:1633–40

36. James TN. 1963. The connecting pathways between the sinus node and A-V node and between the right and left atrium in the human heart. *Am. Heart J.* 66:498–508

37. Sherf L, James TN. 1979. Fine structure of cells and their histologic organization within internodal pathways of the heart: clinical and electrocardiographic implications. *Am. J. Cardiol.* 44:345–69

38. Wagner ML, Lazzara R, Weiss RM, Hoffman BF. 1966. Specialized conducting fibers in the interatrial band. *Circ. Res.* 18:502–18

39. Hariman RJ, Chen C-M. 1983. Effects of hyperkalaemia on sinus nodal function in dogs: sino-ventricular conduction. *Cardiovasc. Res.* 17:509–17

40. James TN, Terasaki F, Pavlovich ER, Vikhert AM. 1993. Apoptosis and pleomorphic micromitochondriosis in the sinus nodes surgically excised from five patients with the long QT syndrome. *J. Lab. Clin. Med.* 122:309–23

41. Bokeriia LA, Belokon' NA, Buziashvili I, Krugliakov IV, Baturkin L. 1988. The current approach to the surgical treatment of Jervell and Lange-Nielsen syndrome (in Russian). *Kardiologia* 28:105–6

42. Crawford MH, Karliner JS, O'Rourke RA, Friedman WF. 1975. Prolonged QT interval syndrome. Successful treatment with combined ventricular pacing and propranolol. *Chest* 68:369–73

43. Eldar M, Griffin JC, Van Hare GF, Witherell C, Bhandari A, et al. 1992. Combined use of beta-adrenergic blocking agents and long-term cardiac pacing for patients with the long QT syndrome. *J. Am. Coll. Cardiol.* 20:830–37

44. Furman S. 1992. Prevalence, circumstances, mechanisms, and risk stratification of sudden cardiac death in artificial ventricular pacing. *Circulation* 85:843–44

45. Zehender M, Buchner C, Meinertz T, Just H. 1992. Prevalence, circumstances, mechanisms, and risk stratification of sudden cardiac death in unipolar single-chamber ventricular pacing. *Circulation* 85:596–605

46. Fraser GR, Froggatt P, James TN. 1964. Congenital deafness associated with electrocardiographic abnormalities, fainting attacks and sudden death. A recessive syndrome. *Q. J. Med.* 33:361–85

47. Han J, Millet D, Chizzonitti B, Moe GK. 1966. Temporal dispersion of recovery of excitability in atrium and ventricle as a function of heart rate. *Am. Heart J.* 71:481–87

48. Han J, Moe GK. 1969. Cumulative effects of cycle length on refractory periods of cardiac tissues. *Am. J. Physiol.* 217:106–9

49. Jervell A, Lange-Nielsen F. 1957. Congenital deaf-mutism, functional heart disease with prolongation of the Q-T interval, and sudden death. *Am. Heart J.* 54:59–68

50. Levine SA, Woodworth CR. 1958. Congenital deaf-mutism, prolonged QT interval, syncopal attacks and sudden death. *N. Engl. J. Med.* 259:412–17

51. James TN, Froggatt P, Atkinson WJ Jr, Lurie PR, McNamara DG, et al. 1978. De Subitaneis Mortibus. XXX. Observations on the pathophysiology of the long QT syndromes with special reference to the neuropathology of the heart. *Circulation* 57:1221–31

52. Kroemer G, Petit P, Zamzami N, Vayssiére J-L, Mignotte B. 1995. The biochemistry of programmed cell death. *FASEB J.* 9:1277–87

53. James TN. 1996. Long reflections on the QT interval. The Sixth Annual Gordon K. Moe Lecture. *J. Cardiovasc. Electrophysiol.* 7:738–59

53a. Neyroud N, Tesson F, Denjoy I, Leibovici M, Donger C, et al. 1997. A novel mutation in the potassium channel gene KVLQT1 causes the Jervell and Lange-Nielsen cardioauditory syndrome. *Nat. Genet.* 15:186–89

53b. Splawski I, Tomothy KW, Vincent GM, Atkinson DL, Keating MT. 1997. Molecular basis of the long-QT syndrome associated with deafness. *N. Engl. J. Med.* 336:1562–67

53c. Ackerman MJ, Clapham DE. 1997. Ion channels—basic science and clinical disease. *N. Engl. J. Med.* 336:1575–86

53d. Hoffman EP, Gardner K. 1997. Ion channels—molecular divining rods hit their clinical mark. *N. Engl. J. Med.* 336:1599–1600

54. James TN, Nichols MM, Sapire, DW, DiPatre PL, Lopez SM. 1996. Complete heart block and fatal right ventricular failure in an infant. *Circulation* 93:1588–600

55. Uhl HSM. 1972. A previously undescribed congenital malformation of the heart: almost total absence of the myocardium of the right ventricle. *Bull. Johns Hopkins Hosp.* 91:107–209

56. Bharati S, Ciraulo DA, Bilitch M, Rosen KM, Lev M. 1978. Inexcitable right ventricle and bilateral bundle branch block in Uhl's disease. *Circulation* 57:636–44

57. Kullo IJ, Edwards WD, Seward JB. 1995. Right ventricular dysplasia: the Mayo Clinic experience. *Mayo Clin. Proc.* 70:541–48

58. Gerlis LM, Schmidt-Ott SC, Ho SY, Anderson RH. 1993. Dysplastic conditions of the right ventricular myocardium: Uhl's anomaly vs. arrhythmogenic right ventricular dysplasia. *Br. Heart J.* 69:142–50

59. Corrado D, Thiene G, Basso C, Rossi L. 1995. The conducting tissues in arrhythmogenic right ventricular cardiomyopathy. *Circulation* 92(8):I-470 (Abstr.)

60. Marcus FI, Fontaine GH, Guiraudon G, Frank R, Laurenceau JL, et al. 1982. Right

ventricular dysplasia: a report of 24 adult cases. *Circulation* 65:384–98

61. Thiene G, Nava A, Corrado D, Rossi L, Pennelli N. 1988. Right ventricular cardiomyopathy and sudden death in young people. *N. Engl. J. Med.* 318:129–33

62. Fontaine G, Fontaliran F, Lascault G, Aouate P, Tonet J, et al. 1995. Arrhythmogenic right ventricular dysplasia. In *Cardiac Electrophysiology From Cell to Bedside*, ed. DP Zipes, J Jalife, pp. 754–69, Philadelphia: Saunders

63. Bennett MR, Gibson DF, Schwartz SM, Tait JF. 1995. Binding and phagocytosis of apoptotic vascular smooth muscle cells is mediated in part by exposure of phosphatidylserine. *Circ. Res.* 77:1136–42

64. Naito M, Nagashima K, Mashima T, Tsuruo T. 1997. Phosphatidylserine externalization is a downstream event of interleukin-1β-converting enzyme family protease activation during apoptosis. *Blood* 89:2060–66

65. Laurent-Crawford AG, Krust B, Muller S, Riviere Y, Rey-Cuille M-A, et al. 1991. The cytopathic effect of HIV is associated with apoptosis. *Virology* 185:829–39

66. McCabe MJ Jr, Orrenius S. 1992. Deletion and depletion: the involvement of viruses and environmental factors in T-lymphocyte apoptosis. *Lab. Invest.* 66:403–6

67. Gougeon M-L, Montagnier L. 1993. Apoptosis in AIDS. *Science* 260:1269–70

68. Golstein P, Ojcius DM, Young JD-E. 1991. Cell death mechanisms and the immune system. *Immunol. Rev.* 121:29–65

69. Cohen JJ. 1991. Programmed cell death in the immune system. *Adv. Immunol.* 50:55–85

70. Baixeras E, Bosca L, Stauber C, Gonzalez A, Carrera AC, et al. 1994. From apoptosis to autoimmunity: insights from the signaling pathways leading to proliferation or to programmed cell death. *Immunol. Rev.* 142:53–91

71. Kajstura J, Mansukhani M, Cheng W, Reiss K, Krajewski S, et al. 1995. Programmed cell death and expression of the protooncogene bcl-2 in myocytes during postnatal maturation of the heart. *Exp. Cell Res.* 219:110–21

72. Katz WE, Gasior TA, Quinlan JJ, Lazar JM, Firestone L, et al. 1996. Immediate effects of lung transplantation on right ventricular morphology and function in patients with variable degrees of pulmonary hypertension. *J. Am. Coll. Cardiol.* 27:384–91

73. Baxter GD, Lavin MF. 1992. Specific protein dephosphorylation in apoptosis induced by ionizing radiation and heat shock in human lymphoid tumor lines. *J. Immunol.* 148:1949–54

74. Misao J, Hayakawa Y, Ohno M, Kato S, Fujiwara T, et al. 1996. Expression of bcl-2 protein, an inhibitor of apoptosis, and bax, an accelerator of apoptosis, in ventricular myocytes of human hearts with myocardial infarction. *Circulation* 94:1506–12

75. Suzuki H, Wildhirt SM, Dudek RR, Narayan KS, Bailey AH, et al. 1996. Induction of apoptosis in myocardial infarction and its possible relationship to nitric oxide synthase in macrophages. *Tissue Cell* 28:89–97

76. Kajstura J, Cheng W, Reiss K, Clark WA, Sonnenblick EH, et al. 1996. Apoptotic and necrotic myocyte cell deaths are independent contributing variables of infarct size in rats. *Lab. Invest.* 74:86–107

77. Bennett MR, Evan GI, Schwartz SM. 1995. Apoptosis of human vascular smooth muscle cells derived from normal vessels and coronary atherosclerotic plaques. *J. Clin. Invest.* 95:2266–74

78. Isner JM, Kearney M, Bortman S, Passeri J. 1995. Apoptosis in human atherosclerosis and restenosis. *Circulation* 91:2703–11

79. Simari RD, San H, Rekhter M, Ohno T, Gordon D, et al. 1996. Regulation of cellular proliferation and intimal formation following balloon injury in atherosclerotic rabbit arteries. *J. Clin. Invest.* 98:225–35

80. Schaper W, Ito WD. 1996. Molecular mechanisms of coronary collateral vessel growth. *Circ. Res.* 79:911–19

81. Fontaine G, Frank R, Rougier I, Tonet JL, Gallais Y, et al. 1989. Electrode catheter ablation of resistant ventricular tachycardia in arrhythmogenic right ventricular dysplasia: experience of 13 patients with a mean follow-up of 45 months. *Eur. Heart J.* 10:74–81

82. Nimkhedkar K, Hilton CJ, Furniss SS, Bourke JP, Glenville B, et al. 1992. Surgery for ventricular tachycardia associated with right ventricular dysplasia: disarticulation of right ventricle in 9 of 10 cases. *J. Am. Coll. Cardiol.* 19:1079–84

83. Corrado D, Basso C, Camerini F, Davies MJ, Fontaine G, et al. 1995. Is arrhythmogenic right ventricular dysplasia/cardiomyopathy a progressive heart muscle disease? A multicenter clinicopathologic study. *Circulation* 92(8):I-470 (Abstr.)

Annu. Rev. Physiol. 1998. 60:327–46

ELECTRICAL AND CALCIUM SIGNALING IN DENDRITES OF HIPPOCAMPAL PYRAMIDAL NEURONS

Jeffrey Magee[1], Dax Hoffman[2], Costa Colbert[3], and Daniel Johnston[2]

[1]Neuroscience Center, Louisiana State University Medical Center, New Orleans, Louisiana 70112; [2]Division of Neuroscience, Baylor College of Medicine, Houston, Texas 77030; [3]Department of Biology and Biochemistry, University of Houston, Houston, Texas 77204; e-mail: dan@mossy.bcm.tmc.edu

KEY WORDS: sodium channels, potassium channels, calcium channels, excitability, long-term potentiation

ABSTRACT

This review discusses recent data regarding the different types of voltage-gated Na^+, Ca^{2+}, and K^+ channels in dendrites of CA1 pyramidal neurons and their function for synaptic integration and plasticity. Na^+ and Ca^{2+} channels are uniformly distributed throughout the dendrites, although Na^+ channels in the soma and proximal dendrites differ in their inactivation properties from Na^+ channels in more distal regions. Also, different regions of the neuron express different subtypes of Ca^{2+} channels. K^+ channels are unevenly distributed, with the distal dendrites expressing a more than fivefold greater density of a transient A-type K^+ channel than proximal regions. These K^+ channels exert profound control over the excitability of the pyramidal neurons and the spread of synaptic potentials throughout the dendrites. The ways in which the active properties of dendrites may contribute toward the induction and maintenance of long-term synaptic plasticity are discussed.

INTRODUCTION

Pyramidal neurons receive tens of thousands of excitatory and inhibitory synaptic inputs onto their dendrites. The dendrites dynamically alter the strengths

327

of these synapses and coordinate them to produce an output in ways that are not well understood. For many years, dendrites were presumed to be passive, cable-like structures in which the electrical signals of the dendrites, i.e. the synaptic potentials, spread to the soma by way of the well-known linear membrane properties of resistance and capacitance (for review, see 25). Elaborate computer models of neurons have been constructed based on these passive cable properties and on exquisitely detailed anatomical reconstructions of dendrites in an effort to understand how the electrical signals spread in dendrites and how synaptic information is integrated by the neuron (31, 44, 56).

Because of recent technical advances, there has been an explosion of new information about the active properties of dendrites. It is now clear that dendrites are anything but passive cables, and instead possess a rich variety of voltage-gated ion channels (perhaps more so than the axon itself!) that bestow upon them very active properties. These active properties allow for the propagation of Na^+-dependent action potentials into the dendrites from their initiation site in the axon (called back-propagation) and, under certain conditions, Na^+-dependent action potentials may even be initiated in the dendrites. Dendritic action potentials and synaptic potentials can also elicit large increases in the concentration of intracellular Ca^{2+} by way of voltage-gated Ca^{2+} channels. Finally, the voltage-gated Na^+ and Ca^{2+} channels in dendrites may produce amplification or boosting of distal synaptic inputs to minimize the attenuation that would otherwise occur from passive cable properties.

These active properties play important functional roles for synaptic integration, synaptic plasticity, and neuronal excitability. In a previous review (25), we focused on the types and distribution of voltage-gated Na^+ and Ca^{2+} channels in dendrites and gave a historical perspective for the study of dendrites over the last hundred years. In the present review, we focus more on the functional implications of the active properties of dendrites. Furthermore, we discuss recent information about voltage-gated K^+ channels. We have found that a particular type of K^+ channel, a transient, A-type K^+ channel, is expressed at a very high density in dendrites of hippocampal CA1 pyramidal neurons. These channels exert profound control over dendritic excitability and may help explain why dendrites were thought to be passive for so many years.

VOLTAGE-GATED ION CHANNELS IN HIPPOCAMPAL DENDRITES

Na^+ Channels

Na^+ channels are found throughout the dendritic arbor at a fairly constant density (at least up to about 350 μm from the soma) (see 38). With at least one key exception, the basic properties of these channels appear quite uniform. The channels have conductances of about 15 pS, rapid activation and inactivation kinetics, and voltage ranges of activation and inactivation that are similar to most neuronal type Na^+ channels. Na^+ channels from both the somatic and dendritic membrane possess a separate inactivation state that requires seconds instead of milliseconds for full recovery (14). Interestingly, the fraction of channels that enter this slow inactivation state is much greater in dendrites compared with that of the soma, and the time for recovery from this inactivation is longer for channels in dendrites than in the soma. This feature of dendritic Na^+ channels helps determine the amplitude of action potentials during a train (see below). Preliminary evidence suggests that the differences between the channel populations in soma and dendrites may be the result of differing levels of phosphorylation (69, 13a). Alternatively, there may be two separate channel types with different inactivation properties. Westenbroek et al (72a) reported a differential distribution of Na^+-channel subtypes RI and RII in the CA1 region of the hippocampus. They showed that CA1 pyramidal somata were primarily labeled with antibodies specific for the RI Na^+ channel subtype, whereas the highest immunoreactivity for RII subtype channels was found in the stratum radiatum. From these data, they suggested that CA1 somata contain mainly subtype RI and that the high RII labeling observed in the stratum radiatum corresponds to a high density of the RII subtype found in the axons. It is possible, however, that part of the RII labeling in the radiatum is from labeling CA1 dendrites. If this were the case, then a differential distribution of Na^+ channel subtypes, with somata containing mainly RI and axons and dendrites containing mainly RII, would exist in CA1 pyramidal neurons. Possible differences in Na^+ channel subtypes between soma and dendrites are important and require further study.

Ca^{2+} Channels

From recordings of single Ca^{2+} channels in cell-attached patches and from fluorescence imaging studies, there appears to be a heterogeneous distribution of Ca^{2+} channel subtypes within the dendrites (11, 38). Most, if not all, of the known types of Ca^{2+} channels (i.e. L-, N-, P/Q-, R-, and T-types) are present in dendrites, and the total Ca^{2+} channel density is fairly uniform. However, the density of the individual channel subtypes varies between the proximal and distal regions of the cell. For example, in the more proximal regions (<100 μm from the soma) the L- and N-types predominate, whereas in the more distal regions, the density of T- and R-types is greater. Recent, whole-cell recordings from acutely isolated dendrites (27) support these general observations, although a higher density of N- and P/Q-types was reported for the isolated dendrites than for the cell-attached patch recordings. Possible explanations for the differences include age of the animals, location along the dendrites where the recordings were made, and voltage-dependency of channel block by conotoxin (64). However, a substantial population of N- and P/Q-type channels within hippocampal dendrites does fit with immunohistochemical studies that found staining for the α_{1A} (P/Q-type) and α_{1B} (N-type) Ca^{2+}-channel subunits in CA1 dendrites (45, 72, 73). α_{1C} (L-type) Ca^{2+} channel subunits have also been reported to be present in the proximal dendritic shafts as well as dendritic spines of CA1 neurons (20, 71). The L-type Ca^{2+} current in these neurons has a component that is activated at voltages near rest and contributes to the resting concentration of intracellular Ca^{2+} (4, 36; see below).

Low-Voltage-Activated Ca^{2+} Currents

Subthreshold EPSPs in dendrites open the T-type Ca^{2+} channels and induce a local increase in intracellular $[Ca^{2+}]_i$ (37). These transient Ca^{2+} channels are about 50% inactivated at rest and can be de-inactivated (and thus their activation increased) by prior hyperpolarizations such as from IPSPs and afterhyperpolarizations (38, 39). In addition to the T-type current, however, there is also a sustained Ca^{2+} current that is activated near the resting membrane potential (-50 to -70 mV). This sustained current provides a significant contribution to the resting $[Ca^{2+}]_i$ in CA1 pyramidal neurons (36). The data suggest that a non-inactivating, dihydropyridine-sensitive Ca^{2+} channel is responsible for this current and that these channels appear to be present throughout the neuron with their highest density at the soma and proximal (initial 100 μm) apical dendrites. Because of this channel distribution, it is possible that dendritic voltage-gated Ca^{2+} channels establish a gradient of $[Ca^{2+}]_i$ across the soma-dendritic axis, with $[Ca^{2+}]_i$ highest in the more proximal regions. This has obvious implications for the various Ca^{2+}-dependent processes that occur throughout the neuron. In addition to contributing to the resting $[Ca^{2+}]_i$, however, these channels may also be activated further by EPSPs and subthreshold signals producing localized increases in $[Ca^{2+}]_i$ and boosting the amplitudes of depolarizing events (see below).

K^+ Channels

Our studies of the dendritic distribution of K^+ channels in hippocampal neurons brought some surprises, the biggest of which was the huge difference in K^+ channel density between soma and distal dendrites (22). Cell-attached patch recordings from CA1 dendrites revealed a high density of outward current that was separated into two main components. The first component is transient, showing rapid activation and a time constant of inactivation that increases with voltage. The second or sustained component inactivates much more slowly. The recorded density of the transient component increases linearly with distance from the soma (slope = 12.5 pA/100 μm). The peak current density of transient channels (for steps from -85 to 55 mV) increases from an average of 8.32 ± 1.38 pA/patch (mean ± SEM) in the soma to 51.56 ± 9.47 pA 350 μm away in the distal dendrites—a more than fivefold increase! The current density of the sustained component, however, remains relatively constant with an average of 8.39 ± 1.46 pA/patch in the soma and 9.55 ± 1.84 pA/patch in the distal dendrites. Steady state activation and inactivation curves indicate that the transient component activates at slightly more hyperpolarized potentials than the sustained component and that significant transient-channel activation will occur at relatively hyperpolarized potentials. Transient channels located in the distal dendrites have an activation curve that is shifted 10–15 mV hyperpolarized compared with that from the soma/proximal (up to 100 μm) dendrites. The increased density of the transient current, along with a more hyperpolarized activation range, increases the impact that these channels have on the electrical properties of the distal dendrites (see below).

The transient component possesses voltage-dependent and pharmacological properties most similar to those generally ascribed to low-voltage-activated A-type K^+ channels (5, 6, 19, 30, 51, 54, 55, 59, 65, 74). The elevated density of dendritic A-type channels reported here agrees with immunohistochemical studies that found an increased density of the transient K^+ channel subtype Kv4.2 in the distal dendrites of CA1 pyramidal neurons (41, 58). Another recent study has found Kv4.2 clustered on the postsynaptic membrane directly apposed to the presynaptic terminal (1). The voltage dependency of activation and steady state inactivation, the 4-AP sensitivity, and the time course of inactivation of Kv4.2 expressed in *Xenopus* oocytes match well with those recorded in CA1 dendrites (5, 6, 22, 57). However, there is no voltage-dependency to the time course of inactivation for the expressed channels in oocytes as there is for the native channels in dendrites. This discrepancy may be due to the presence of β-subunits with the native channels or to differences in the phosphorylation state of the channel in the two recording conditions. β-subunits have been found to modulate the inactivation properties of transient K^+ channels (16, 50, 57).

Finally, the sustained component has voltage-dependent and pharmacological properties similar to delayed-rectifier-type K^+ channels. Delayed-rectifier polypeptides Kv2.1, 2.2, and 1.5 have all been localized to CA1 somata and dendrites (41).

Ratio of Inward to Outward Current Density

Most action potential properties, such as threshold, amplitude, duration, and repetitive firing characteristics, are determined by the relative densities of inward (Na^+ and Ca^{2+}) and outward (K^+) currents located within the membrane. This important ratio changes quite profoundly with distance from the soma along the dendrites of CA1 pyramidal neurons. Because the Na^+ and Ca^{2+} channel densities are maintained fairly constant throughout the neuron, whereas the transient outward component increases more than fivefold, there is a large shift from an inward-dominated current ratio in the proximal regions of the neuron to a predominantly outward-dominated current in the more distal regions (see Figure 1a, b). As is discussed in detail below, this gradient of channel densities determines that under normal conditions the proximal regions of the neuron are more excitable than the more distal regions, even though the potential for full excitability (the large inward current density) is present in the distal dendrites.

DENDRITIC EXCITABILITY

The properties and distribution of voltage-gated ion channels in the axon, soma, and dendrites largely determine the initation and propagation of electrical signals (action and synaptic potentials) in neurons. From the preceding brief review it is clear that dendrites are not passive, but instead possess a complex set of voltage-gated conductances. The functional significance of these dendritic conductances for electrical and Ca^{2+} signaling is discussed more fully in the following sections.

Action Potential Initation and Propagation

There has been much debate in the literature about the site of initiation of the action potential in pyramidal neurons (see 66). Recent data suggest that under most conditions the action potential does not initiate in either the dendrites or the axon hillock/initial segment but instead farther out on the axon, perhaps at

--→

Figure 1   The ratio of total voltage-activated inward current to outward current changes considerably across the dendritic axis. (A) Cell-attached patch recordings of composite currents (no channel blockers in patch pipette) that were evoked by a 80 mV voltage step from a holding potential that was near the resting potential (≈-70 mV). In the trace recorded from the proximal dendrite (*left trace*), the predominant current is the inward, voltage-gated Na^+ current, with a smaller outward K^+ current. In the trace on the *right* (distal dendrite), the predominant current is the outward, voltage-gated K^+ current, with a smaller inward Na^+ current. (B) The ratio of inward to outward current decreases with distance because the A-type K^+ channel density increases approximately fivefold, whereas the Na^+-channel density remains constant. (C) Composite currents from another patch on a different neuron, located ≈170 μm from the soma. Here the amplitude of the inward Na^+ current decreases with repetitive stimulation, whereas the amplitude of the outward K^+ current is unchanged. The voltage protocol was a train of nine, 5 ms, 70 mV voltage steps from the resting potential. This demonstrates that Na^+ channels undergo an inactivation process during repetitive stimulation that is not observed in K^+ channels. This channel inactivation is more pronounced in dendritic Na^+ channels than in those found in the soma and has been hypothesized to underlie the activity-dependent propagation of action potentials observed in CA1 dendrites (14).

A Proximal dendritic recording (20 μm)   Distal dendritic recording (280 μm)

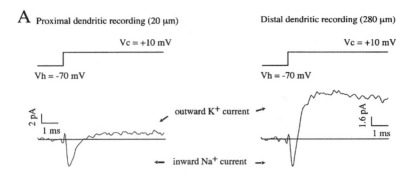

B

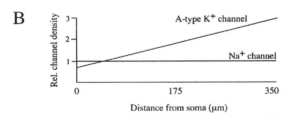

C

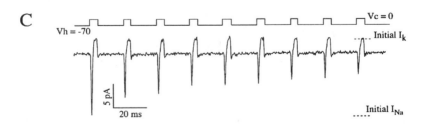

the first node of Ranvier (13). For reasons that are not understood, this site has a lower threshold than anywhere else in the neuron. The lower threshold may be due to a high density of Na^+ channels, a lower voltage range of activation of the Na^+ channels, a low density of outward K^+ channels, or some combination thereof. There are some situations, however, when the action potential does appear to initiate first in the dendrites. These include instances of strong synaptic input to the dendrites or when the threshold at the usual initation site is higher than normal (e.g. from inhibitory input to the axon/soma region or from a somatic leak caused by a microelectrode) (2, 60, 61, 70). It is also possible for the threshold in the dendrites to be lowered by inactivating or blocking dendritic K^+ channels (22), and this would result in a more favorable situation for dendritic spike initiation.

Once initiated at the normally low-threshold site in the axon, the action potential propagates both along the axon toward the terminals and into the soma and dendrites. The latter is called back-propagation and has been shown to occur both in vitro and in vivo (8, 61, 67). The extent of back-propagation, however, is very temperature sensitive and dependent on the age of the animal. It has been known for some time that the back-propagating action potential in the dendrites becomes progressively smaller in amplitude the farther it travels from the soma, and the action potential may actually fail to propagate beyond certain distal branch points (3, 40, 61, 70). The first hypothesis put forth to explain this behavior was that there is a declining density of Na^+ channels in the dendrites. Several groups, however, found no evidence for this and instead the data support a fairly uniform density of Na^+ channels in the soma and dendrites (38, 62). The explanation for the declining amplitude of the dendritic action potential appears to be due to the increasing density of the A-type K^+ channels. These channels activate very rapidly and prevent the action potential from reaching full amplitude. For example, in the presence of 4-AP, which blocks these K^+ channels, the amplitude of the action potential is fairly constant from the soma to at least 300 μm into the dendrites. Thus the elevated A-channel density not only acts to severely reduce the excitability of the dendrites by raising threshold, but it also limits the dendritic propagation of action potentials. Without this elevated channel density, action potentials can be generated locally in the dendrites, and they are capable of invading even the most distal dendritic elements at nearly full amplitude (22).

The action potential firing that occurs during K^+ channel blockade is quite extreme. Typically, the application of mM concentrations of 4-AP causes single action potentials to be transformed into bursts of two to three spikes or plateau potentials that lead to a nearly constant depolarization in the dendrites and continuous repetitive firing in the soma (22). This type of firing behavior results in very large elevations in intracellular $[Ca^{2+}]_i$ from influx through voltage-gated

Ca^{2+} channels. The elevated density of dendritic A-channels thus allows single action potentials (at reduced amplitude) to be propagated into the dendrites but prevents bursting or continuous repetitive firing.

Frequency-Dependent Action Potential Propagation

During repetitive (10–50 Hz) firing, dendritic action potentials display a marked and prolonged voltage- and frequency-dependent decrease in amplitude that is not apparent in the soma (9, 61). The amplitude drop-off in the dendrites is such that by the tenth action potential in a train, the amplitude is reduced by over 60% compared with less than 5% in the soma. The available data suggest that regional differences in Na^+ and K^+ channels can account for this activity-dependent decline in dendritic action potentials.

The increased inactivation with slow recovery observed for dendritic Na^+ channels (compared with soma) plays a primary role in this electrical behavior (Figure 1c) (14, 25a). Because the inward current density decreases substantially during repetitive stimulation and takes seconds to fully recover, the ability of the dendrites to maintain action potential amplitude during repetitive activity is severely limited. The hypothesis that Na^+ channel inactivation is responsible for the decrease in amplitude was tested by giving large membrane hyperpolarizations between action potentials (a manipulation that hastens recovery from inactivation). The frequency-dependent decline in amplitude of the action potentials was largely removed by these hyperpolarizations, supporting an important role for this form of channel inactivation. Also playing a secondary but nevertheless critical role in this phenomenon is the heightened A-channel density in the dendrites. Because of the decreased Na^+/K^+ permeability ratio of the distal dendrites, any decrease in Na^+ current becomes directly manifest in action potential amplitude. In support of this idea, the amount of amplitude decline observed in the different compartments can be manipulated by pharmacologically changing the Na^+/K^+ permeability ratio. Blockade of K^+ channels by 4-AP reduces the amplitude drop-off (particularly in the distal dendrites), whereas decreasing Na^+ channel density by tetrodotoxin (TTX) application increases the severity of the amplitude decrease (particularly in the proximal regions) (14). Therefore, the relatively high density of A-type K^+ channels and the relatively high degree of slow recovery from inactivation of Na^+ channels in the dendrites determine that back-propagation of action potentials into the dendritic arborization will be severely reduced during repetitive firing.

Modulation of Dendritic Action Potential Amplitude

As mentioned above, back-propagating action potentials decline in amplitude with distance from the soma and can fail to propagate beyond certain distal branch points during repetitive firing. It has been observed that pairing of axonally initiated action potentials with subthreshold depolarizations (either dendritic current injection or evoked EPSPs) increases dendritic action potential amplitude and the associated Ca^{2+} influx (40). In fact, the increase in $[Ca^{2+}]_i$ during paired EPSPs and action potentials is significantly larger than the simple sum of the two independent Ca^{2+} signals. The degree of the pairing-induced increase in action potential amplitude and Ca^{2+} influx also increases progressively with distance from the cell body. No observable changes in action potential amplitude occur in the soma and proximal dendritic regions, whereas large, supra-linear increases are recorded from more distal regions. This signal amplification is particularly prominent in areas where it appears that back-propagating action potentials have become non-regenerative (Figure 2). Here

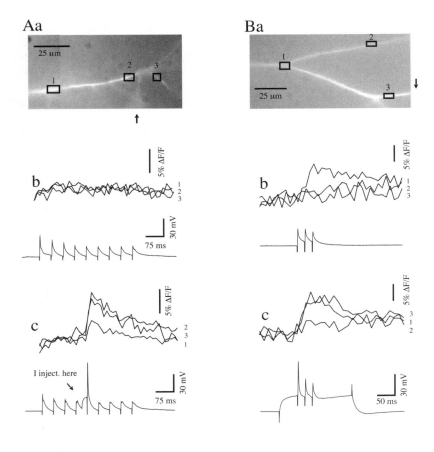

dendritic action potential amplitude has attenuated to such a degree that it is nearly too small to gate dendritic Na^+ and Ca^{2+} channels. In these regions, pairing EPSPs with action potentials increases action potential amplitudes by approximately twofold, whereas the associated rise in $[Ca^{2+}]_i$ is increased three- to fourfold. The propagation of action potentials into the dendritic arbor can, therefore, be modulated by simultaneous synaptic input, with the largest action potentials occurring in the regions of the dendrites that are closest to the active synapses.

We can look again to the types and distribution of dendritic ion channels for a mechanistic explanation of this phenomenon. Because the transient, A-type K^+ channel density increases with distance out into the dendrites, instead of the Na^+ channel density decreasing, the inward current required for the generation of large amplitude action potentials is always available even though it is normally counterbalanced by the high outward current density. What is required for the generation of large amplitude dendritic action potentials is a reduction in the dendritic K^+ current. Because A-type K^+ channels exhibit rapid inactivation at potentials near the resting potential, moderate depolarization provided by synaptic activity can rapidly reduce the available population of A-channels through inactivation. In this scheme, synaptic activity can function to release

---

Figure 2 Localized dendritic action potential boosting. (*Aa*) Fura-filled CA1 pyramidal dendrite with patch electrode (*arrow*) located ≈290 μm from the soma. The image is oriented so that the more proximal regions of the neuron are located toward the left. (*Ab*) Optical recordings (average $\Delta F/F$) from regions of the neuron delimited by the numbered boxes in *Aa*, with dendritic voltage trace shown below. A train of nine antidromically stimulated action potentials (*bottom line Ab*) induces a very small influx of Ca^{2+} into the distal dendrites. (*Ac*) A 40 ms, 0.3 nA current injection causes an increase in dendritic action potential amplitude and associated Ca^{2+} influx. The largest Ca^{2+} influx is located nearest the dendritic pipette suggesting that the largest increase in action potential is likewise near the point of current injection. A trace with only the current injection was used to correct for bleaching and for any small influx of Ca^{2+} (<1% $\Delta F/F$) caused by the current injection. (*Ba*) Another fura-filled CA1 pyramidal dendrite with patch electrode located ≈50 μm farther out the labeled (*arrow*) branch, for a total of ≈280 μm from the soma. Major branch point is ≈150 μm away from the soma. (*Bb*) Optical recordings (average $\Delta F/F$) from regions of the neuron delimited by the numbered boxes in (*Ba*), with dendritic voltage trace shown below. A train of three antidromically stimulated action potentials (*bottom line Bb*) induces an influx of Ca^{2+} that is primarily located in the regions of the dendrite proximal to the branchpoint. (*Bc*) A simultaneous 0.2 nA current injection causes an increase in the amplitude of the first dendritic action potential and associated Ca^{2+} influx. The largest Ca^{2+} influx is located in the dendritic branch that has received the current injection, whereas very little influx occurs in the other branch. This profile suggests that coincident synaptic input can influence back-propagating action potentials to preferentially invade synaptically active regions of the dendrite. The current injection by itself did not induce any influx of Ca^{2+} into the displayed regions.

local regions of the dendrite from the dampening effect of the high A-channel density. This permits action potentials occurring during EPSPs to increase in amplitude in a spatially restricted region of the neuron. The distribution of dendritic channels thus limits the overall excitability of the dendrites while at the same time allowing restricted regions that are synaptically active to propagate large-amplitude action potentials (22).

Integration and Propagation of Synaptic Potentials

Synaptic activity within the dendrites opens voltage-gated Na^+, K^+, and Ca^{2+} channels that are located near the site of input (22, 37, 39). The final outcome of this combined channel activation can be an EPSP that is either magnified or reduced in both amplitude and duration (depending on whether the inward or outward currents prevail) compared with that occurring under completely passive conditions. As a result of this channel activation, the efficacy of any given EPSP is not simply the result of transmitter release or receptor properties, but also of the active properties of the dendrites.

For single EPSPs in adult animals, the activation of transient K^+ channels appears to predominate over the activation of inward Na^+ and Ca^{2+} channels (22, but see also 17, 33, 53). This results in a reduction in the amplitude of EPSPs in the soma compared with purely passive propagation. The relative amount of attenuation from dendrites to soma is approximately the same, however. For example, in CA1 pyramidal neurons, EPSP amplitude is decreased between 50 and 75% upon reaching the soma from a dendritic branch about 250 μm away, and this value is maintained regardless of the channel availability (22). This suggests that channel activation is restricted to a local region of the dendrite that is near the synaptic input. As a result, channel activation increases or decreases the EPSP amplitude, depending on channel availability, but once the input has left this local area, it then spreads basically as in a passive cable. Obviously, any channel clustering near areas of synaptic input would be most effective in shaping EPSPs. Such clustering has been seen for Kv4.2 channels in magnocellular neurons of the supraoptic nucleus and also in hippocampal neurons (1).

For spatial and temporal summation of EPSPs, however, the situation is somewhat different. Here the kinetics of activation and inactivation of the voltage-gated channels, the location of the spatially summed inputs, and the temporal relationship among the inputs become critical parameters, and these issues have not yet been fully explored. Based on initial modeling studies, however, we can make some predictions. One hypothesis is that because the rapidly inactivating A-type K^+ channel dominates in the distal regions of the neuron, input that arrives a few milliseconds following other input would encounter a reduced population of activatable A-channels and therefore be less severely attenuated in amplitude and more likely to activate inward Na^+ and Ca^{2+} channels and NMDA receptors. In this scheme, previously occurring synaptic input would inactivate K^+ channels, releasing later occurring input from the attenuating effect of the high dendritic A-channel density. The same situation would apply for spatially distributed input as long as the distribution imposed a temporal offset. In this way, the types and distribution of dendritic channels would favor the propagation of more temporally and spatially distributed input over input that is highly synchronized. This hypothesis suggests that there could be supra-linear summation of slightly asynchronous or temporally summated events—a sort of non-coincidence detection—because of less K^+ current and greater inward current. However, this type of interaction would depend on the relative proximity of the inputs to each other, the rate of inactivation of the K^+ channels, and the voltage range of activation of the inward currents. With the great diversity of voltage-gated K^+ channels (23, 51), one can easily imagine how different cell types would have different tuning properties for synaptic interactions, depending on the type of K^+ channel expressed in their dendrites.

FUNCTIONAL ASPECTS OF CHANNEL DISTRIBUTIONS

The above discussion illustrates how the types and distribution of dendritic voltage-gated channels determine the manner in which electrical signals such as EPSPs and action potentials spread throughout the soma and dendrites. Below we discuss how the propagation of these signals may play a role in synaptic plasticity and learning and memory.

Associative Synaptic Plasticity

Back-propagating action potentials play a critical role in the induction of LTP and LTD in CA1 neurons by allowing the output region of the neuron (axon) to communicate with the dendrites (12, 40, 42). It has been reported by several groups that the probability of LTP induction is reduced when action potential generation and/or propagation is inhibited (40, 52). Presumably, the action potential provides the synaptically active region of the neuron with the depolarization required for the gating of NMDA receptors and voltage-gated Ca^{2+} channels, thereby increasing the local influx of Ca^{2+}. The Ca^{2+}, in turn, activates the various Ca^{2+}-dependent signaling pathways that are thought to be involved in LTP induction and maintenance (29, 34). The back-propagating action potentials thus provide the synaptic input region of a pyramidal neuron with a feedback signal that an output has occurred. Such a feedback signal is ideally suited for Hebbian modifications of synaptic strength.

Dendritic Na^+ and Ca^{2+} channels provide the means for action potentials to back-propagate into the dendrites and raise local intracellular $[Ca^{2+}]_i$. If left unchecked, however, the inward currents would lead to excessive membrane depolarization and unrestricted Ca^{2+} influx, both of which would be detrimental to neuron viability and function. The biophysical characteristics of the dendritic, A-type K^+ channels are ideally suited for both depressing this undesirable behavior while at the same time allowing locally large depolarizations and Ca^{2+} influx to occur at the appropriate place and time. The inactivation of A-channels by EPSPs and the subsequent amplification of the action potential and evoked Ca^{2+} influx provides a plausible biophysical explanation for the Hebbian associativity that is observed in the more distal dendritic regions of these neurons (40). In fact, the elevated density of dendritic A-channels actually heightens the associativity provided by the back-propagating action potentials. Because A-current density is reduced by local synaptic depolarization, full amplitude action potentials capable of evoking significant Ca^{2+} influx into the more distal dendrites only occur in synaptically active regions of the dendritic arbor (Figure 2A). Thus dendritic A-channels provide a dampening effect on dendritic excitability, which in turn strengthens the available associative link between the input and output regions of the neuron.

Local Dendritic Computations Mediated by Transient K^+ Channels

Following the above discussion on the role of back-propagating action potentials for synaptic plasticity, we speculate a bit here on how the local inactivation of the dendritic K^+ channels by synaptic input could provide spatially restricted induction rules for LTP and LTD. Back-propagating action potentials are large in proximal dendrites and small to nonexistent in distal regions of the neuron. EPSPs on proximal dendrites, therefore, have little effect on the amplitude of action potentials paired with the EPSPs. The associativity and timing relationship between EPSPs and action potentials may thus be different for proximal versus distal inputs. For example, the pairing of distal EPSPs and back-propagating action potentials has a tremendous effect on the local amplitude of the action potentials (40). In fact, failure of action potentials to propagate into certain branches can be overcome when the action potential is paired with EPSPs on that particular branch (the opposite would be true for IPSPs; 68). For this to occur, we predict that the timing relationship between the EPSP and action potential is critical, i.e. the action potential must arrive at the branch point at the appropriate time following the EPSP when significant inactivation of the K^+ channels is present. We further speculate that such interactions could provide an additional source for synapse specificity, because only the synapses on the active branch would experience the increased action potential amplitude and Ca^{2+} influx (Figure 2B). This might be a substrate for both Hebbian and anti-Hebbian interactions leading to LTP (for the active) and LTD (for inactive) synapses on the branch invaded by the action potential.

Our modeling results support these speculations (22), but whether they are important under physiological conditions remains to be determined. Although synapse specificity and the timing of associative interactions among synaptic inputs are determined largely by the unique properties of NMDA receptors, we speculate that the high density of transient K^+ channels in dendrites provides an additional mechanism. Synapse specificity for the induction of both LTP and LTD and for the forward-reverse pairing requirements of associative plasticity and classical conditioning (see, for example, 18, 28, 32, 42) could be established, in part, by the active properties of dendrites. Furthermore, we predict that there will be differences in these plasticity rules for synapses at different locations in the dendrites (e.g. proximal versus distal), leading to a further computational complexity for the neuron.

The Importance of Bursts

Reduction of dendritic, A-type K^+ currents in CA1 pyramidal neurons results in a switch from a firing mode of single action potentials to a burst firing mode in which two to three action potentials are initiated over a 10–20 ms interval (22). The reduction in dendritic outward current produces larger and longer duration action potentials and even the initiation of dendritic Ca^{2+} spikes. There are many reports of CA1 neurons firing bursts, complex spikes, or sharp waves in vivo and in vitro (26, 46, 48, 49, 75), with about 20% of the total number of action potentials recorded in vivo being bursts under certain conditions (43). Sharp waves have even been suggested to be critical for learning (7).

This change in firing mode is representative of a dramatic change in the way in which signals are processed by neurons. If a certain input causes a neuron to fire a burst of multiple action potentials instead of a single action potential, the associated Ca^{2+} influx into all regions of the neuron, including both the dendritic arbor and the synaptic terminal, would be greatly enhanced (22). As a result, there would be an increase in both the probability of induction of some form of long-term synaptic plasticity, as well as the probability of transmitter release (40, 63). In fact, an incoming burst of synaptic input could also be enhanced in amplitude relative to a synchronous input, by way of the previously described supra-linear summation taking place post-synaptically. Furthermore, such an enhanced input will be more likely to produce a burst of action potentials in the post-synaptic neuron because of the local inactivation of the transient K^+ channels. Thus an incoming signal can be transformed from one with a relatively low probability of being transmitted to a signal whose impact on the post-synaptic cell is greatly enhanced over an extended period of time. Because of these aspects of bursting, some investigators have suggested that action potential bursts are more important units of information than single action potentials (reviewed in 35). For example, the well-known place-fields of a CA1 pyramidal neuron are more precisely defined if only the burst of action potentials is considered instead of the overall firing rate (47). By altering the action potential firing mode of neurons, dendritic voltage-gated channels may thus be able to regulate components of learning and memory (10).

SUMMARY

In this review we have briefly summarized the rapidly changing field surrounding the active properties of dendrites. First, there are numerous voltage-gated Na^+, Ca^{2+}, and K^+ channels in dendrites. Second, there are, in some cases, different subtypes of these channels in dendrites than in the soma. Third, many of the channels in the dendrites have properties different from their counterparts in the soma. Not surprisingly, the presence of these channels in dendrites has a tremendous influence on the spread of synaptic potentials to the soma and other parts of the neuron and on the initiation and propagation of action potentials.

The role of dendritic active properties for the spread of synaptic signals is poorly explored. In principle, inward currents in dendrites could enhance the magnitude of distal synaptic events. This would reduce the spatial variability of EPSP amplitude and could lead to an increase in the information storage capability of a neuronal network (15). On the other hand, the high density of K^+ channels in the dendrites will reduce this amplification for synchronous inputs but less so for temporally dispersed inputs. The amount of amplification of distal EPSPs will thus depend on the properties of the K^+ channels, the timing and spatial relationships among the inputs, and the properties of the Na^+ and Ca^{2+} channels in the dendrites.

The voltage-gated Ca^{2+} channels in dendrites are activated by subthreshold EPSPs and by the back-propagating action potentials. EPSPs produce a local rise in $[Ca^{2+}]_i$ near the site of input, whereas the action potential elicits a more general increase throughout at least the proximal portion of the dendrites. Changes in $[Ca^{2+}]_i$ thus provide a spatially inhomogeneous signal to mark the location of the input, as well as to characterize the output firing of the neuron (21, 24). The extent of the back-propagation of action potentials into the dendrites is also dependent on the transient K^+ channels and the slow recovery from inactivation of the Na^+ channels. Dendritic K^+ channels provide a mechanism for modulating the amplitude of dendritic action potentials. Inactivation of the channels allows for an increase in the amplitude of dendritic action potentials, and this may play a role in the induction of Hebbian and anti-Hebbian plasticity of inputs that are located at the more distal regions of the dendrites.

Our view of electrical and Ca^{2+} signaling in dendrites has changed dramatically in the past few years. Roles for various events such as back-propagating action potentials are becoming more clear and lend themselves to testable hypotheses about neural function. This new information must now be considered when trying to understand the ways in which information is processed and stored by single cortical neurons. These neurons are not simple relays for passing electrical signals from one area of the brain to another, but are instead complex processing units of neural events.

ACKNOWLEDGMENTS

This work was supported by National Institutes of Health grants NS11535, MH44754, and MH48432, by the Human Frontiers Science Program, and the Hankamer Foundation. We thank Dr. Richard Gray for computer help.

Visit the *Annual Reviews home page* at
http://www.AnnualReviews.org.

Literature Cited

1. Alonso G, Widmer H. 1997. Clustering of KV4.2 potassium channels in postsynaptic membrane of rat supraoptic neurons: an ultrastructural study. *Neuroscience* 77:617–21

2. Andersen P. 1960. Interhippocampal impulses II. Apical dendritic activation of CA1 neurons. *Acta Physiol. Scand.* 48:178–208

3. Andreasen M, Lambert JD C. 1995. Regenerative properties of pyramidal cell dendrites in area CA1 of the rat hippocampus. *J. Physiol.* 483:421–41

4. Avery RB, Johnston D. 1996. Multiple channel types contribute to the low-voltage-activated calcium current in hippocampal CA3 pyramidal neurons. *J. Neurosci.* 16:5567–82

5. Baldwin TJ, Tsaur M-L, Lopez GA, Jan YN, Jan LY. 1991. Characterization of a mammalian cDNA for an inactivating voltage-sensitive K+ channel. *Neuron* 7:471–83

6. Blair TA, Roberts SL, Tamkun MM, Hartshorne RP. 1991. Functional characterization of RK5, a voltage-gated K+ channel cloned from the rat cardiovascular system. *Fed. Eur. Biochem. Soc.* 295:211–13

7. Buzsaki G. 1989. Two-stage model of memory trace formation: a role for "noisy" brain states. *Neuroscience* 31:551–70

8. Buzsaki G, Penttonen M, Nadasdy Z, Bragin A. 1996. Pattern and inhibition-dependent invasion of pyramidal cell dendrites by fast spikes in the hippocampus in vivo. *Proc. Natl. Acad. Sci. USA* 93:9921–25

9. Callaway JC, Ross WN. 1995. Frequency dependent propagation of sodium action potentials in dendrites of hippocampal CA1 pyramidal neurons. *J. Neurophysiol.* 74:1395–403

10. Cattaneo A, Maffei L, Morrone C. 1981. Two firing patterns in the discharge of complex cells encoding different attributes of the visual stimulus. *Exp. Brain Res.* 43:115–18

11. Christie BR, Eliot LS, Ito KI, Miyakawa H, Johnston D. 1995. Different Ca^{2+} channels in soma and dendrites of hippocampal pyramidal neurons mediate spike-induced Ca^{2+} influx. *J. Neurophysiol.* 73:2553–57

12. Christie BR, Magee JC, Johnston D. 1996. The role of dendritic action potentials and Ca^{2+} influx in the induction of homosynaptic long-term depression in hippocampal CA1 pyramidal neurons. *Learn. Mem.* 3:160–69

13. Colbert CM, Johnston D. 1996. Axonal action-potential initiation and Na+ channel densities in the soma and axon initial segment of subicular pyramidal neurons. *J. Neurosci.* 16:6676–86

13a. Colbert CM, Johnston D. 1998. Protein kinase C activation decreases activity-dependent attenuation of dendritic Na^+ current in hippocampal CA1 pyramidal neurons. *J. Neurophysiol.* In press

14. Colbert CM, Magee JC, Hoffman D, Johnston D. 1997. Slow recovery from inactivation of Na^+ channels underlies the activity-dependent attenuation of dendritic action potentials in hippocampal CA1 pyramidal neurons. *J. Neurosci.* 17:6512–21

15. Cook EP, Johnston D. 1997. Active dendrites reduce location-dependent variability of synaptic input trains. *J. Neurophysiol.* 78:2116–28

16. Covarrubias M, Wei A, Salkoff L, Vyas TB. 1994. Elimination of rapid potassium channel inactivation by phosphorylation of the inactivation gate. *Neuron* 13:1403–12

17. Gillessen T, Alzheimer C. 1997. Amplification of EPSPs by low Ni^{2+}-and amiloride-sensitive Ca^{2+} channels in apical dendrites of rat CA1 pyramidal neurons. *J. Neurophysiol.* 77:1639–43

18. Gustafsson B, Wigström H, Abraham WC, Huang Y-Y. 1987. Long-term potentiation in the hippocampus using depolarizing current pulses as the conditioning stimulus to single volley synaptic potentials. *J. Neurosci.* 7:774–80

19. Halliwell JV, Othman IB, Pelchen-Matthews A, Dolly JO. 1986. Central action of dendrotoxin: selective reduction of a transient K^+ conductance in hippocampus and binding to localized acceptors. *Proc. Natl. Acad. Sci. USA* 83:493–97

20. Hell JW, Westenbroek RE, Breeze LJ, Wang KKW, Chavkin C, Catterall WA. 1996. N-methyl-D-aspartate receptor-induced proteolytic conversion of postsynaptic class C L-type calcium channels in hippocampal neurons. *Proc. Natl. Acad. Sci. USA* 93:3362–67

21. Helmchen F, Imoto K, Sakmann B. 1996. Ca^{2+} buffering and action potential-evoked Ca^{2+} signaling in dendrites of pyramidal neurons. *Biophys. J.* 70:1069–81

22. Hoffman D, Magee JC, Colbert CM, Johnston D. 1997. K^+ channel regulation of signal propagation in dendrites of hippocampal pyramidal neurons. *Nature* 387:869–75

23. Jan LY, Jan YN. 1997. Cloned potassium channels from eukaryotes and prokaryotes. *Annu. Rev. Neurosci.* 20:91–123

24. Johnston D. 1996. The calcium code. *Biophys. J.* 70:1095–95

25. Johnston D, Magee JC, Colbert CM, Christie BR. 1996. Active properties of neuronal dendrites. *Annu. Rev. Neurosci.* 19:165–86

25a. Jung H-Y, Mickus T, Spruston N. 1997. Prolonged Na^+ channel inactivation contributes to dendritic action potential attenuation in hippocampal pyramidal neurons. *J. Neurosci.* 17:6639–46

26. Kandel ER, Spencer WA. 1961. Electrophysiology of hippocampal neurons. II. After-potentials and repetitive firing. *J. Neurophysiol.* 24:243–59

27. Kavalali ET, Zhuo M, Bito H, Tsien RW. 1997. Dendritic Ca^{2+} channels characterized by recordings from isolated hippocampal dendritic segments. *Neuron* 18:651–63

28. Kelso SR, Brown TH. 1986. Differential conditioning of associative synaptic enhancement in hippocampal brain slices. *Science* 232:85–87

29. Kennedy MB. 1989. Regulation of neuronal function by calcium. *Trends Neurosci.* 12:417–20

30. Klee R, Ficker E, Heinemann U. 1995. Comparison of voltage-dependent potassium currents in rat pyramidal neurons acutely isolated from hippocampal regions CA1 and CA3. *J. Neurophysiol.* 74:1982–95

31. Koch C, Segev I, eds. 1989. *Methods in Neuronal Modeling.* Cambridge: MIT Press

32. Levy WB, Steward O. 1983. Temporal contiguity requirements for long-term associative potentiation/depression in the hippocampus. *Neuroscience* 8:791–97

33. Lipowsky R, Gillessen T, Alzheimer C. 1996. Dendritic Na^+ channels amplify EPSPs in hippocampal CA1 pyramidal cells. *J. Neurophysiol.* 76:2181–91

34. Lisman J. 1994. The CaM kinase II hypothesis for the storage of synaptic memory. *Trends Neurosci.* 17:407–12

35. Lisman JE. 1997. Bursts as a unit of neural information: making unreliable synapses reliable. *Trends Neurosci.* 20:38–43

36. Magee JC, Avery RB, Christie BR, Johnston D. 1996. Dihydropyridine-sensitive, voltage-gated Ca^{2+} channels contribute to the resting intracellular Ca^{2+} concentration of hippocampal CA1 pyramidal neurons. *J. Neurophysiol.* 76:3460–70

37. Magee JC, Christofi G, Miyakawa H, Christie B, Lasser-Ross N, Johnston D. 1995. Subthreshold synaptic activation of voltage-gated Ca^{2+} channels mediates a localized Ca^{2+} influx into the dendrites of hippocampal pyramidal neurons. *J. Neurophysiol.* 74:1335–42

38. Magee JC, Johnston D. 1995. Characterization of single voltage-gated Na$^+$ and Ca^{2+} channels in apical dendrites of rat CA1 pyramidal neurons. *J. Physiol.* 487:67–90

39. Magee JC, Johnston D. 1995. Synaptic activation of voltage-gated channels in the dendrites of hippocampal pyramidal neurons. *Science* 268:301–4

40. Magee JC, Johnston D. 1997. A synaptically controlled, associative signal for Hebbian plasticity in hippocampal neurons. *Science* 275:209–13

41. Maletic-Savatic M, Lenn NJ, Trimmer JS. 1995. Differential spatiotemporal expression of K$^+$ channel polypeptides in rat hippocampal neurons developing in situ and in vitro. *J. Neurosci.* 15:3840–51

42. Markram H, Luebke J, Frotscher M, Sakmann B. 1997. Regulation of synaptic efficacy by coincidence of postsynaptic Aps and EPSPs. *Science* 275:213–15

43. McHugh TJ, Blum KI, Tsien JZ, Tonegawa S, Wilson MA. 1996. Impaired hippocampal representation of space in CA1-specific NMDAR1 knockout mice. *Cell* 87:1339–49

44. McKenna T, Davis J, Zornetzer SF, eds. 1992. *Single Neuron Computation.* Boston: Academic

45. Mills LR, Niesen CE, So AP, Carlen PL, Spigelman I, Jones OT. 1994. N-type Ca^{2+} channels are located on somata, dendrites, and a subpopulation of dendritic spines on live hippocampal pyramidal neurons. *J. Neurosci.* 14:6815–24

46. O'Keefe J. 1979. A review of the hippocampal place cells. *Prog. Neurobiol.* 13:419–39

47. Otto T, Eichenbaum H, Wiener SI, Wible CG. 1991. Learning-related patterns of CA1 spike trains parallel stimulation parameters optimal for inducing hippocampal long-term potentiation. *Hippocampus* 1:181–92

48. Pavlides C, Winson J. 1989. Influences of hippocampal place cell firing in the awake state on the activity of these cells during subsequent sleep episodes. *J. Neurosci.* 9:2907–18

49. Ranck JB, Feder R. 1973. Studies on single neurons in dorsal hippocampal formation and septum in unrestrained rats. *Exp. Neurol.* 41:461–555

50. Rettig J, Heinemann SH, Wunder F, Lorra C, Parcej DN, et al. 1994. Inactivation properties of voltage-gated K$^+$ channels altered by presence of β-subunit. *Nature* 369:289–94

51. Rudy B. 1988. Diversity and ubiquity of K channels. *Neuroscience* 25:729–49

52. Scharfman HE, Sarvey JM. 1985. Postsynaptic firing during repetitive stimulation is required for long-term potentiation in hippocampus. *Brain Res.* 331:267–74

53. Schwindt PC, Crill WE. 1995. Amplification of synaptic current by persistent sodium conductance in apical dendrite of neocortical neurons. *J. Neurophysiol.* 74:2220–24

54. Segal M, Barker JL. 1984. Rat hippocampal neurons in culture: potassium conductances. *J. Neurophysiol.* 51:1409–33

55. Segal M, Rogawski M, Barker J. 1984. A transient potassium conductance regulates the excitability of cultured hippocampal and spinal neurons. *J. Neurosci.* 4:604–9

56. Segev I, Rinzel J, Shepherd GM, eds. 1995. *The Theoretical Foundation of Dendritic Function.* Cambridge: MIT Press

57. Serodio P, Kentros C, Rudy B. 1994. Identification of molecular components of A-type channels activating at subthreshold potentials. *J. Neurophysiol.* 72:1516–29

58. Sheng M, Tsaur ML, Jan, J-N, Jan LY. 1992. Subcellular segregation of two A-type K$^+$-channel proteins in rat central neurons. *Neuron* 9:271–84

59. Solc CK, Zagotta WN, Aldrich RW. 1987. Single-channel and genetic analyses reveal two distinct A-type potassium channels in *Drosophila. Science* 236:1094–98

60. Spencer WA, Kandel ER. 1961. Electrophysiology of hippocampal neurons: IV. Fast prepotentials. *J. Neurophysiol.* 24:272–85

61. Spruston N, Schiller Y, Stuart G, Sakmann B. 1995. Activity-dependent action potential invasion and calcium influx into hippocampal CA1 dendrites. *Science* 268:297–300

62. Spruston N, Stuart G, Sakmann B. 1995. How do voltage-activated channels shape EPSPs in hippocampal CA1 neurons? *Soc. Neurosci. Abstr.* 21:584

63. Stevens CF, Wang Y. 1995. Facilitation and depression at single central synapses. *Neuron* 14:795–802

64. Stocker JW, Nadasdi L, Aldrich RW, Tsien RW. 1997. Preferential interaction of ω-conotoxins with inactivated N-type Ca^{2+} channels. *J. Neurosci.* 17:3002–13

65. Storm JF. 1988. Temporal integration by a slowly inactivating K$^+$ current in hippocampal neurons. *Nature* 336:379–81

66. Stuart G, Spruston N, Sakmann B, Haeusser M. 1997. Action potential initiation and backpropagation in neurons of the mammalian CNS. *Trends Neurosci.* 20:125–31

67. Svoboda K, Denk W, Kleinfeld D, Tank DW. 1997. In vivo dendritic calcium dynamics in neocortical pyramidal neurons. *Nature* 385:161–65

68. Tsubokawa H, Ross WN. 1996. IPSPs modulate spike backpropagation and associated $[Ca^{2+}]_i$ changes in the dendrites of hippocampal CA1 pyramidal neurons. *J. Neurophysiol.* 76:2896–906

69. Tsubokawa H, Ross WN. 1997. Muscarinic modulation of spike backpropagation in the apical dendrites of hippocampal CA1 pyramidal neurons *J. Neurosci.* 15:5782–91

70. Turner RW, Meyers DER, Richardson TL, Barker JL. 1991. The site for initiation of action potential discharge over the somatodendritic axis of rat hippocampal CA1 pyramidal neurons. *J. Neurosci.* 11:2270–80

71. Westenbroek RE, Ahlijanian MK, Catterall WA. 1990. Clustering of L-type Ca^{2+} channels at the base of major dendrites in hippocampal pyramidal neurons. *Nature* 347:281–84

72. Westenbroek RE, Hell JW, Warner C, Dubel SJ, Snutch TP, Catterall WA. 1992. Biochemical properties and subcellular distribution of an N-type calcium channel α_1 subunit. *Neuron* 9:1099–115

72a. Westenbroek RE, Merrick DK, Catterall WA. 1989. Differential subcellular localization of R_I and R_{II} Na^+ channel subtypes in central neurons. *Neuron* 3:695–704

73. Westenbroek RE, Sakurai T, Elliott EM, Hell JW, Starr TVB, et al. 1995. Immunochemical identification and subcellular distribution of the α_{1A} subunits of brain calcium channels. *J. Neurosci.* 15:6403–18

74. Wu R-L, Barrish ME. 1992. Two pharmacologically and kinetically distinct transient potassium currents in cultured embryonic mouse hippocampal neurons. *J. Neurosci.* 12:2235–46

75. Ylinen A, Soltész I, Bragin A, Penttonen M, Sik A, Buzsáki G. 1995. Intracellular correlates of hippocampal theta rhythm in identified pyramidal cells, granule cells, and basket cells. *Hippocampus* 5:78–90

Annu. Rev. Physiol. 1998. 60:347–63

THE SYNAPTIC VESICLE CYCLE

W. J. Betz and J. K. Angleson

Department of Physiology and Biophysics/C-240, University of Colorado Medical
School, Denver, Colorado 80262

KEY WORDS: fusion pore, exocytosis, endocytosis, trafficking, secretion

ABSTRACT

The ins and outs of the synaptic vesicle cycle are being examined in increasing
detail with diverse investigative tools in a variety of cell types, particularly those
with large granules. The cycle begins with the opening of a fusion pore that connects the vesicle lumen to the extracellular fluid. Sensitive electrophysiological
techniques reveal the often-stuttering behavior of single pores in non-neuronal
cells, through which small molecules trickle until the fusion pore expands and
the remaining contents erupt from the vesicle. The granule membranes are then
retrieved by multiple processes that appear to act in parallel and that are distinguished from each other kinetically and ultrastructurally. Following endocytosis,
synaptic vesicles are then shuttled back into the vesicle pool, where they briefly
mix with other vesicles, become immobilized, and remain gelled with their neighbors, even while moving en masse again to the presynaptic membrane as a prelude
for another round of exocytosis.

INTRODUCTION

The quantal theory and the vesicular hypothesis, the two major ideas about
presynaptic function, are now more than forty years old. Proof of secretion
via multimolecular quantal packets came early (25). The vesicular hypothesis,
however, resisted definitive analysis; while abundant evidence consistent with
the theory accumulated for several decades, it was not until the 1990s that the
combined application of patch-clamp capacitance and amperometry provided
virtual proof that transmitter secretion is indeed coincident with exocytosis
(2, 13). Now, the entire vesicle cycle can be studied more intensively, thanks
largely to new tools of molecular analysis, electrophysiological monitoring,

and optical imaging. Various aspects of the cycle, including the identification of molecules involved in docking and exocytosis and the role of calcium in the vesicle cycle, have been reviewed recently (4, 56, 67). Here we focus on three aspects of the cycle: the behavior and fate of the fusion pore, the nature of endocytosis, and the properties of intracellular trafficking of recycling vesicles. Our understanding of the first two events in presynaptic terminals has been informed by experiments on non-synaptic cells, particularly adrenal chromaffin and other neuroendocrine cells, mast cells, and other leukocytic cells. The reasons for this are twofold: technically, the non-synaptic cells can be patch clamped and therefore studied with the capacitance technique; biologically, the non-synaptic cells secrete from large granules that give larger capacitance and amperometric signals than small, clear synaptic vesicles. The increasing application of these techniques to neurons is beginning to allow direct comparisons. Capacitance monitoring has been performed with posterior pituitary nerve terminals (24, 31, 48), goldfish retinal bipolar cells (17, 60, 61), photoreceptors (46, 47), and saccular hair cells (43), and amperometry has been applied to leech neurons (9) and mammalian superior cervical ganglion cells (27, 65).

THE FUSION PORE

Flickers, Feet, and Spikes

Elegant and sensitive recording techniques have revealed beautiful details of the fitful and unpredictable lives of fusion pores. Electrical properties of individual fusion pores have been studied most thoroughly in cells that contain relatively large granules. Fusion pores open abruptly to conductances typically of several hundred pS (2, 53). Their subsequent fate is unpredictable. They may flicker between closed and open states for a variable period that can last for several seconds, and then explode open or snap shut (53). Two examples of such behavior, monitored with different recording techniques, are illustrated in Figure 1. Four foot-spike events recorded by amperometry (63) from a bovine adrenal chromaffin cell are shown in Figure 1A (66). In this sensitive technique, a carbon fiber electrode, clamped at a potential of about +800 mV, is positioned close to the cell. Catecholamines released during single exocytic events strike the electrode and are oxidized or reduced, generating the amperometric signals. These traces illustrate how small amounts of catecholamines may dribble through a nascent fusion pore (the foot) for more than 100 ms before the pore explodes open to release the remaining contents of the granule (the spike). During the foot, the signal may fluctuate, as if the fusion pore size were rapidly wavering. These amperometric flickers are considerably faster than capacitance flickers described above. In chromaffin cells, 50 to 70% of all spikes are preceded by a foot that lasts about 50 ms and releases about 10% of the total contents of the

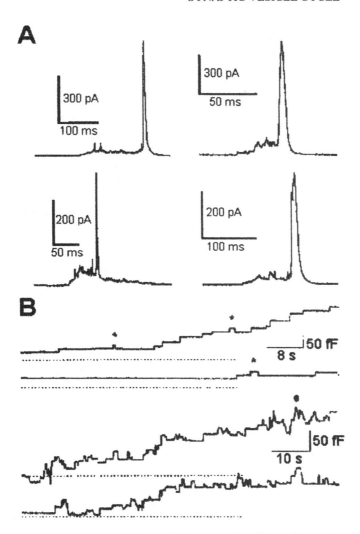

Figure 1 Fusion pore kisses and flickers. *A*. Four examples of foot-spike events recorded by amperometry from an adrenal chromaffin cell (66). The signal shows the current produced when secreted catecholamines strike a carbon electrode positioned near the cell. In each case, a low level of signal (foot), probably representing leakage of catecholamines through a small flickering fusion pore, precedes a spike that results from the rapid dilation of the fusion pore. *B*. Whole-cell capacitance recordings from a normal mast cell (*top pair* of traces) and from a ruby-eye mutant mouse mast cell (*lower pair* of traces) (42). Each step reflects the exocytosis of a single secretory granule. Only three steps (marked) are transient (i.e. reverse promptly) in the normal cell, whereas the mutant cell shows many more transients.

granule. About one third of all feet show distinct flickers; on average each foot flickers 2.7 times at a frequency of about 170 Hz before the spike. Elevation of $[Ca^{2+}]_i$ increases the number and frequency of flickers (66).

Some feet are not followed by a spike. In these foot-alone events, the average duration of the foot is longer by a factor of two (to about 100 ms) than in foot-spike events. The evident explanation of foot-alone events is that the fusion pore opens, flickers awhile, and closes. Although other explanations, such as the controlled release from a granular matrix (44) cannot be ruled out with certainty at present, this is, of course, strong evidence for the phenomenon known colloquially as kiss-and-run exocytosis.

Reversible openings of fusion pores can also be recorded with the whole-cell capacitance technique. This technique tracks the increase in plasma membrane surface area that accompanies exocytosis, and the decrease in area that reflects endocytosis (40). Sensitivity is lower than for amperometry, so that cells with large granules, such as mast cells, must typically be studied for detection of single exocytotic and endocytotic events. The top two traces of Figure 1B were recorded from a normal mast cell as it underwent exocytosis. Each upward step reflects the exocytosis of a single granule. In three cases (marked with *asterisk*), the events were transient and reversed abruptly after ≈200 ms. The lower pair of traces in Figure 1B were recorded from a mast cell from a mutant (ruby-eye) mouse (42). The traces are far more complex than those from the wild-type mouse (*upper pair* of traces), with many more examples of transient events. The molecular basis of this mutant behavior is not known.

Combined amperometry and capacitance of ruby-eye mouse mast cells has revealed further interesting behavior. During the prolonged exocytic burst evoked by a stimulant, the initial amperometric spikes are relatively small. Over time (a few minutes), the amperometric spikes become larger, even though the capacitance jumps remain unchanged. These results suggest that all granules are the same size (no change in capacitance step size over time), but that the first granules to undergo exocytosis contain less serotonin (the normal transmitter) than do the later ones. Such a situation could have arisen if the originally docked granules had become partially depleted of stores owing to spontaneous transient openings of the fusion pore before the exocytic stimulus was applied—a sort of granular incontinence. This hypothesis was confirmed by preincubating cells in serotonin, which restored the initial amperometric events to normal amplitude, presumably by preventing leakage during the spontaneous openings that preceded the experimental recordings (42).

Do studies like these provide definitive proof of kiss-and-run exocytosis? In each case, it is possible to imagine alternative explanations. The real force of the evidence comes from complementary results obtained using different techniques. In addition to amperometry and whole-cell capacitance, other approaches offer promise. For example, exocytosis of single granules ($\approx$1 μm in diameter) in sea urchin eggs can be visualized directly with the light microscope (62). These granules secrete large amounts of protein, and thus their fusion pores must dilate. Fluorescent dye labeling showed that endosomes formed after exocytosis are the same size as the secretory granules. Moreover, serial application of different colors of dyes did not give endosomes with mixed colors, suggesting that the endosomes did not form by coalescence of smaller vesicles, but pinched-off whole (62). These observations, of course, suggest that endosomes form directly as dilated fusion pores shrink and close. This preparation affords an opportunity to test directly this hypothesis by observing single-stained granules over time while monitoring (perhaps with dyes of different colors) the fusion pore patency.

Other new techniques offer additional exciting possibilities. Patch amperometry (1) provides a significant increase in capacitance sensitivity owing to the cell-attached recording configuration (34, 40), and with the carbon fiber placed inside the patch pipette, every exocytic event that occurs in the patch is detected amperometrically. Evanescent wave microscopy offers a means to visualize single-stained granules that lie close to (within about 300 nm) of the plasma membrane (54). Serotonin-containing granules can be visualized in unstained cells by using multiphoton microscopy (35). Luminescent fusion proteins (synaptolucins) inside synaptic vesicles light up after exocytosis (37).

Fat or Meat?

The molecular structure of the fusion pore is not known with certainty. It is natural to consider its behavior to be like that of an ion channel or a gap junction, e.g. proteins that are initially gated open to a conductance of up to several hundred pS (same as a fusion pore) and that may transiently flicker and close (32). The normal full dilation of the fusion pore would require that the protein subunits burst apart when the fusion pore explodes open and the lipids of the granule and plasma membranes coalesce. Some evidence is consistent with this idea (32). For example, the behavior of fusion pores of single, 100-nm diameter granules in human neutrophils has been studied using the cell-attached recording mode, which increases more than tenfold the sensitivity of capacitance recordings compared with the whole-cell mode (34). In about half of the exocytic events, a discrete value of fusion pore conductance can be resolved (the pore opens abruptly to this level, then hovers for a few hundred milliseconds before dilating). The average conductance ($\approx$150 pS, which was independent of the capacitance step, i.e. granule size) is similar to that for an ion channel (34), although the recorded range was large (coefficient of variation $\approx$ 0.6) compared with most ion channel recordings. Considerable variability in fusion pore conductance has also been observed in mast cells (53).

Alternatively, one can envision that the initial fusion pore is lined not with proteins but with lipids, and that the proteins play other roles in catalyzing and regulating interactions between the lipids of the granule and the lipids of the plasma membrane (12, 39). Evidence in support of this view includes the observation that lipidic pores can shut and open. For example, capacitance recordings have revealed transient openings that close to a lower capacitance value than that preceding the opening, as if membrane had flowed from the surface into the granule while the fusion pore was open (38). The rate of lipid flux can be high, sufficient to replace the fusion pore lipids every millisecond. Similarly, fusion pores with conductances much greater than any known ion channel (up to several nS) can flicker (53). If such lipid-containing pores can close and then reopen, it seems reasonable to consider this a plausible or even likely mode of operation during the first opening event.

Hemifusion

Although it is clear that both protein and lipid components of membranes play a role in the final steps of secretory membrane fusion, the contribution of each type of component to the structure of the fusion pore is still uncertain. Vesicle fusion in protein-free systems using synthetic phospholipid vesicles and bilayers demonstrated the formation of hemifusion structures in which the lipids in the outer leaflet of the vesicle bilayer mixed with the lipids in the target bilayer before complete fusion of the two bilayers was observed (11). Hemifusion structures play a central role in several lipidic models of formation of fusion pores (12, 32, 39). The ability of hemifusion and complete fusion to occur in the in vitro system could be modified by addition of different lipids (11). Interestingly, the same lipids appear to have similar effects on several biological fusion events (12). Future reconstitution experiments with well-defined components should prove useful in dissecting the contribution of various proteins and lipids to exocytotic fusion events.

Granules and Vesicles

The studies of single-granule exocytosis are of interest in their own right, and the ability to extend these studies to single synaptic vesicles is of great interest to neurobiologists. The instrumentation sensitivity necessary to record the exocytosis of a single, 50-nm diameter synaptic vesicle (about 0.1 fF capacitance change) has recently been approached with cell-attached capacitance monitoring (34). At present, however, one can only speculate about the fate of a synaptic vesicle after exocytosis, drawing on knowledge of secretion from larger granules. That many of the molecules identified as participants in docking and exocytosis are contained in both cell types suggests close parallels in secretory mechanisms. Moreover, theoretical calculations show that a brief

(1 ms) opening of a small (1 nm diameter) fusion pore would be sufficient to cause the release of virtually all ($\approx$99%) of the acetylcholine contained in a synaptic vesicle (53, 55), which could then refill with the transmitter in several seconds and be ready again to participate fully in an exocytic event.

Despite these parallels, and despite the intuitive appeal of such a conceptually simple mechanism, there exists no quantitative, direct evidence to support the notion that small synaptic vesicles ever flicker transiently open. On the contrary, electron microscopic evidence gives strong evidence that synaptic vesicles can and do collapse into the plasma membrane and many seconds later are reinternalized at relatively remote sites (about 1 μm from the exocytic sites) (22). Moreover, measurements of the rates of uptake of FM1-43 (a styryl dye) after stimulation offer no evidence of a rapid (subsecond) process in hippocampal (51) and frog motor (64) nerve terminals. However, several observations are difficult to explain. For example, frog motor nerve terminals, fixed immediately after intense stimulation, fail to stain extensively with antibodies to synaptophysin (a vesicle membrane protein). The intense stimulation should have shifted quantities of vesicle membrane to the surface if endocytosis is slow; the lack of staining suggests that the synaptophysin-containing membrane was reinternalized relatively quickly (59). In addition, some vesicular structures stained with FM1-43 or other dyes do not destain as readily as expected under some conditions [e.g. frog motor nerve terminals treated with staurosporine (19), hippocampal cultures treated with ruthenium red (P Haydon, personal communication), mammalian primary afferent terminals (M Chua & CC Hunt, personal communication)].

This situation produces something of a paradox: compelling evidence for rapid kiss-and-run exocytosis exists where it is not particularly effective in secreting the contents of the exocytosing granule (e.g. amperometric feet release only a few percent of the total contents), and virtually no solid evidence for kiss-and-run exocytosis exists where it would be entirely sufficient to rid a vesicle of all of its transmitter molecules (e.g. a small, clear synaptic vesicle). The paradox is at least partly resolved by noting that secretion of small amounts of granular content may be physiologically important—perhaps partial secretion is useful in permitting a finer level of control than all-or-nothing exocytosis. Moreover, the slower, more complex and laborious route of recycling evidently followed by synaptic terminals would not be the first example of Nature eschewing apparent parsimony. Finally, it is sometimes assumed that dense core granules secrete their own dense cores, which requires fusion pore dilation. This is undeniably true for cells whose main secretory product is protein, such as insulin secreted by pancreatic beta cells. More recently, evidence has emerged that granules containing small secretory molecules, such as catecholamines in adrenal chromaffin cells and serotonin in mast cells, contain a matrix that is probably not destined for secretion. Instead, the matrix comprises at least some molecules acting as an ion exchange resin that functions to maximize the amount of small transmitter molecules contained in the granule (44); for example, a kind of serotonin sponge in mast cell granules. Recycling, rather than secreting such a commodity could clearly be beneficial during granule recycling. If fusion pore dilation increases the risk of loss of such a matrix, then the utility of kiss-and-run exocytosis is evident.

ENDOCYTOSIS

Secretory granules show clear evidence that they possess fusion pore assemblies that can, on occasion, open briefly and then close—kiss-and-run exocytosis in its purest form. Most often, however, the fusion pore explodes open and dilates. The subsequent fate of the granule is nearly as big a mystery as that of a postexocytic synaptic vesicle. The range of possible destinies after a fusion pore dilates is abundant; issues of both essence and substance of a vesicle are involved. For example, a vesicle might retain its ultrastructural appearance after exocytosis (essence intact), even while the flux of lipids and other membrane constituents through the fusion pore changes entirely its molecular composition (substance altered). At the opposite extreme, the vesicle might collapse and disappear and stream as unit to a remote site of endocytosis, its essence thereby vanishing, while its substance remains unaltered. Many plausible intermediate routes also exist, and it appears increasingly likely that at least two different, parallel routes of endocytosis exist.

Capacitance studies in several cell types, including nerve terminals of the goldfish retinal bipolar cell (60, 61), have consistently revealed a relatively rapid endocytic process (time constant of a few seconds) that is tightly coupled to preceding exocytosis (see Figure 2A). It is tempting to suppose that the rapidly internalized membrane is the same as that which underwent exocytosis, which would almost certainly require that it be mediated by what is conventionally envisioned as kiss-and-run exocytosis (clathrin-mediated endocytosis would be slower). However, it is also possible that the captured membrane is entirely different from the exocytic vesicle membrane, and that the two events just happen to be tightly coupled in time. In fact, evidence for such a linkage exists: Under some conditions, a phenomenon called primed endocytosis is observed in capacitance studies of adrenal chromaffin cells. This takes the form of an extremely fast, short latency endocytic event (primed endocytosis), so fast that it masks, or even reverses the stimulus-evoked exocytic capacitance jump (41, 52, 58). Primed endocytosis probably results from exocytic events that occur long before the stimulus is delivered; these exocytosed granules move slowly along a morphologically and functionally obscure pathway, which leads

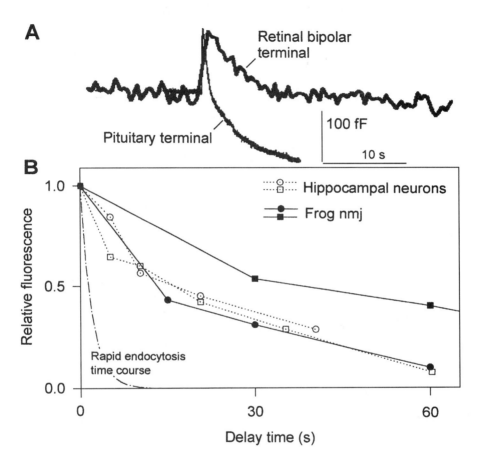

Figure 2   Fast endocytosis seen with capacitance recordings is not observed with FM1-43 measurements of endocytosis kinetics. *A*. Whole-cell capacitance recordings obtained from pituitary (58) and goldfish retinal bipolar (60) cell terminals. A short stimulus (not shown) evoked the abrupt increases in capacitance, which were followed by rapid decreases, probably reflecting endocytosis. Scale bars = 10 s and 100 fF. *B*. Endocytosis measured by the uptake of FM1-43 was slower in hippocampal neurons (51) and frog motor nerve terminals (64). Each point was obtained by stimulating a preparation for a certain period of time, and after a delay time ranging from 0 to 60 s in different experiments, FM1-43 was applied and taken up by any remaining endocytic activity. The brightness of the terminals was then measured. The decay in brightness with increasing delay time provides a measure of endocytic rate. The shortest time constant was ≈20 s, about 10 times longer than rapid endocytosis shown in Panel *A* (*dashed line*).

ultimately to endocytosis, and accumulate at the last station along the route, poised for quick pinch-off. The applied stimulus then provides the trigger for that last internalizing step. It is possible that rapid endocytosis is a slower version of primed endocytosis, and that in both cases the membrane being retrieved is not the same as that which was exocytosed.

Most of the time endocytosis proceeds in steps that are too small to be resolved individually with whole-cell capacitance recording, although in several studies individual abrupt drops in capacitance have been clearly resolved (34, 40, 48). The final rate of closure of such fission pores is slow compared with fusion pore opening (48). The circumference decreases at a final rate of about 25 nm/s, which corresponds to the removal every 15–20 ms of ≈10% of the pore-lining lipids (48). In addition to fission rates, the amplitudes of endocytic steps have been measured, and the observed values vary widely in different capacitance studies. For example, in pituitary nerve terminals studied in the whole-cell capacitance mode, single exocytic events were not resolvable, whereas some single endocytic events were large enough to be detected (most endocytic events, however, were also too small to be resolved individually) (48). Thus at least some endocytic events involved the internalization of amounts of membrane greater than that contained in secretory granules. Such events, which also have been observed in chromaffin cells (40), are most commonly seen after intense, perhaps nonphysiological stimulation of exocytosis. Human neutrophils examined with the high-resolution cell-attached capacitance technique gave a different result (34). Most increases and decreases in capacitance were resolvable as discrete steps (although not the same granules; endocytic steps were especially prevalent during the initial stages of recording, exocytic steps later, after the addition of ionomycin). The average endocytic step was only about half as large as the average exocytic step, suggesting that granules were retrieved piecemeal after exocytosis and fusion pore dilation—a fragmented run following a protracted kiss.

Other synaptic terminals that secrete via small clear vesicles have been examined optically (Figure 2B). Two recent studies using the uptake of FM1-43 applied after tetanic nerve stimulation have shown that the endocytic process in nerve terminals is relatively slow; the fastest time constants observed were ≈20 s (51, 64), approximately 10 times slower than fast endocytosis observed with capacitance recordings in goldfish bipolar nerve terminals (60, 61), pituitary nerve terminals (24, 58), and neuroendocrine cells (3, 18, 41, 58).

The *Drosophila* temperature-sensitive mutant *shibire* has been invaluable for investigation of endocytosis (28). Its mutant protein, dynamin, mediates a final step in endocytosis, the pinching-off of the endosome. In fact, none of the many proteins identified as players in the synaptic vesicle cycle is better understood than dynamin (15). At elevated temperature, endocytosis is completely arrested, suggesting that dynamin is essential for any and all membrane internalization (28, 45). The situation, however, evidently does not involve a single pathway because clear evidence of two parallel pathways of membrane internalization has been described (26) (Figure 3). One pathway is relatively slow, occurs at sites remote from the exocytic sites (active zones), and involves the generation of plump, branched tubules from which coated vesicles bud; this pathway evidently corresponds to the clathrin-mediated route originally described by Heuser & Reese (22). The second pathway is relatively fast and arises at sites adjacent to active zones as unbranched, flat cisternae that extend into the terminal cytoplasm. The two morphologically distinct routes naturally raise the possibility that two distinct types of recycled vesicles are generated (26). Although some evidence is consistent with this idea, the optical and ultrastructural observations made with FM1-43 do not suggest the presence of more than a single functional type of vesicle in significant numbers (5, 20).

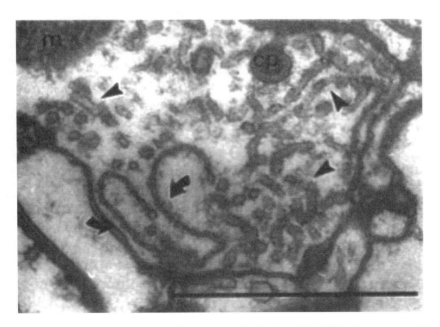

Figure 3 Two parallel routes of synaptic vesicle recyling in *Drosophila shibire* photoreceptor cell (26). Terminals were depleted of synaptic vesicles by stimulating with light at 29°C for 30 s, and then allowed to recover for 5 min at 26°C. *Arrowheads* point to branching, tubule-like endocytic structures that arise slowly at locations remote from exocytic sites. *Arrows* point to long, unbranching cisternae that emerge quickly at locations adjacent to exocytic sites (the dense body between cisternae is an exocytic site). Scale bar, 1 μm; m, mitochondrian; cp, capitate projection.

The great value of *shibire* for studying the mechanisms of endocytosis lies in its selectivity and reversibility. Recently, a technique—intracellular acidification—has been shown to reduce endocytosis reversibly and selectively in lizard motor nerve terminals (33). This clearly could become a valuable investigative tool, although the lack of effects of intracellular acidification on rapid endocytosis in adrenal chromaffin cells (3, 10) and pituitary nerve terminals (58) indicates that it is not applicable to all cell types.

TRAFFICKING

The trafficking of endosomes and the mechanisms that guide the regeneration of synaptic vesicles is the least understood aspect of the vesicle cycle (8). One of the main reasons for our relative ignorance concerns a lack of investigative tools to study the process. In addition, cells that secrete via dense core granules may be less informative on this aspect of the cycle, because the trafficking route of recycling granules may be vastly different than that for synaptic vesicles. This is especially so if granules lose their protein matrix during secretion, for recycling would then require that they acquire new matrix proteins via communication with the Golgi apparatus. A recycling synaptic vesicle can be separated from its Golgi apparatus by a vast distance and can be refilled easily with small neurotransmitter molecules that are synthesized locally in the cytoplasm of the nerve terminal.

The trafficking route of recycling vesicles can be divided into three phases: the endocytic phase, which begins with the pinching-off of an endocytic vesicle; the steady state phase, which describes the situation for mature vesicles in a resting nerve terminal; and the mobilization phase, by which nerve activity moves a vesicle to the presynaptic membrane as a prelude to docking and exocytosis. Each of these can be profitably studied with imaging techniques; according to studies using FM1-43, it takes about a minute for a vesicle to pass through the complete cycle from exocytosis to exocytosis (5, 6, 8, 50).

The Endocytic Phase

In non-neural cells, the components of early endosomes are sorted into different physical pathways by a series of selective vesicular fusions and fissions (36). By analogy, it was thought that recycling synaptic vesicles follow a similar course, although more recent data have suggested that no intracellular fusions are involved, that as soon as a clathrin-coated recycling synaptic vesicle is uncoated it is ready to reenter the vesicle pool (57).

Three different studies have examined the question of whether recently recycled vesicles are sequestered, for example, at the front or back of the cluster of reserve vesicles, or not at all. All three studies have reached the same conclusion: Recycled vesicles mix randomly within the pool of existing vesicles (5, 29, 50).

The Resting Phase

The observed mixing of recycling vesicles during the early stages of recycling naturally suggests a picture of fish in a bowl—vesicles moving, if not churning, constrained to a cluster perhaps by some sort of cytoskeletal cage. On the other hand, considerable evidence has accumulated for more than a decade suggesting that synaptic vesicle motion in resting terminals is constrained. Electron microscopy shows clear signs of vesicles connected by filamentous cross-links, which are likely to include the protein synapsin I (23, 30). Recently, two studies investigated vesicle mobility in living, resting nerve terminals. Each involved the fluorescence recovery after photobleaching (FRAP) technique, and each gave the same result; little or no recovery from photobleaching occurred in resting terminals, suggesting that the vesicles are not mobile (21, 29).

The Mobilization Phase

During repetitive nerve stimulation, vesicles move to the presynaptic membrane as a prelude to docking and exocytosis. What frees them from their resting bonds, and how do they get to the membrane? In regard to mobilization, in vitro studies have shown that phosphorylation by calcium-calmodulin kinase II of synapsin I reduces its affinity for synaptic vesicles (14). Perhaps, synapsin I phosphorylation is the normal in vivo mechanism for freeing vesicles from their resting bonds. The next process—how the vesicles get to the membrane—is more of a mystery. A single FRAP study has dealt with this issue. Vesicle clusters stained with FM1-43 were viewed from above, and small spots were bleached with a laser. Then the nerve was stimulated and the terminals destained. The bleached spots did not recover during the destaining, suggesting that as vesicles moved to the membrane, their lateral movements were sharply constrained (21).

The simplest explanation of this result is that synaptic vesicles are glued to their neighbors (perhaps by synapsin I), and that they are passively pulled toward the presynaptic membrane as docked vesicles exocytose and collapse into the surface membrane. In considering more complex mechanisms, attention is naturally drawn to the cytoskeleton, particularly actin [microtubules are excluded from synaptic vesicle clusters (23, 30)]. Synapsin I interacts with actin in vitro (14), raising the possibility that similar reactions, perhaps involving a molecular motor tugging a vesicle along an actin track, occur in vivo [although recycling rate is not affected in synapsin I knockout mice (49)]. A key unanswered question concerns the morphological disposition of actin filaments in nerve terminals in general, and in vesicle clusters in particular. Unfortunately, the presence, much less arrangement, of actin filaments in vesicle clusters is not clear. Ultrastructural studies are not in complete agreement (23, 30). Light microscopic studies of actin in motor nerve terminals (where vesicle clusters are largest) are difficult to perform owing to the large background signal from muscle actin. A promising development is the work of Connor and colleagues (16), who abolished background muscle fluorescence by killing muscle fibers without damaging nerve terminals. Their observations suggest that actin is not co-distributed with synaptic vesicle clusters and do not rule out the possibility that actin may be excluded from vesicle clusters.

Clear evidence of active movements of synaptic vesicles has been documented. Okadaic acid, a protein phosphatase inhibitor, disrupts synaptic vesicle clusters in resting terminals, evidently by unmasking powerful and widespread vesicle translocators. In frog motor nerve terminals stained with FM1-43, vesicles can be seen to stream from clusters in both directions, moving at rates of a few micrometers per minute ($\approx$50 nm/s) (7). Do these motors normally transport vesicles to the presynaptic membrane? The answer is not known. Nerve stimulation does not ordinarily disrupt vesicle clusters the way that okadaic acid does, suggesting that if these motors are involved, they must be activated selectively by nerve stimulation.

CONCLUSION

Progress toward the holy grail (for neurobiologists) of capacitance studies—the detection of a single synaptic vesicular event—has been steady, and although the techniques are arduous to implement and challenging to refine, the pace seems to be accelerating as success draws nearer. Studies of endocytosis have revealed further information about the multiple, parallel cellular pathways by which membrane is internalized following exocytosis. For both exocytosis and endocytosis, our understanding of synaptic events has been greatly informed by studies of non-neuronal cells. As further information is obtained for different secretory cells and neurons, we will be able to determine the level of conservation and variation between different biological systems. Finally, studies of intracellular trafficking of recycling synaptic vesicles have barely begun to identify and characterize the mechanisms that regulate the movement of vesicles, a field that seems poised for further advancements.

Visit the *Annual Reviews home page* at
http://www.AnnualReviews.org.

Literature Cited

1. Albillos A, Dernick G, Horstmann H, Almers W, Alvarez de Toledo G, Lindau M. 1997. The exocytotic event in chromaffin cells revealed by patch amperometry. *Nature* 389:509–12
2. Alvarez de Toledo G, Fernández-Chacón R, Fernández JM. 1993. Release of secretory products during transient vesicle fusion. *Nature* 363:554–58
3. Artalejo CR, Henley JR, McNiven MA, Palfrey HC. 1995. Rapid endocytosis coupled to exocytosis in adrenal chromaffin cells involves $Ca[2+]$, GTP, and dynamin but not clathrin. *Proc. Natl. Acad. Sci. USA* 92:8328–32
4. Bajjalieh SM, Scheller RH. 1995. The biochemistry of neurotransmitter secretion. *J. Biol. Chem.* 270:1971–74
5. Betz WJ, Bewick GS. 1992. Optical analysis of synaptic vesicle recycling at the frog neuromuscular junction. *Science* 255:200–3
6. Betz WJ, Bewick GS. 1993. Optical and electrophysiological monitoring of transmitter release and synaptic vesicle recycling at the frog neuromuscular junction. *J. Physiol.* 87:193–202
7. Betz WJ, Henkel AW. 1994. Okadaic acid disrupts clusters of synaptic vesicles in frog motor nerve terminals. *J. Cell Biol.* 124:843–54
8. Betz WJ, Wu L-G. 1995. Kinetics of synaptic-vesicle recycling. *Curr. Biol.* 5:1098–101
9. Bruns D, Jahn R. 1995. Real-time measurement of transmitter release from single synaptic vesicles. *Nature* 377:62–65
10. Burgoyne RD. 1995. Fast exocytosis and endocytosis triggered by depolarisation in single adrenal chromaffin cells before rapid $Ca[2+]$ current run-down. *Pflügers Arch.* 430:213–19
11. Chernomordik L, Chanturiya A, Green J, Zimmerberg J. 1995. The hemifusion intermediate and its conversion to complete fusion: regulation by membrane composition. *Biophys. J.* 69:922–29
12. Chernomordik L, Kozlov MM, Zimmerberg J. 1995. Lipids in biological membrane fusion. *J. Membr. Biol.* 146:1–14
13. Chow RH, von Rüden L, Neher E. 1992. Delay in vesicle fusion revealed by electrochemical monitoring of single secretory events in adrenal chromaffin cells. *Nature* 356:60–63
14. De Camilli P, Benfenati F, Valtorta F, Greengard P. 1990. The synapsins. *Annu. Rev. Cell Biol.* 6:433–60
15. De Camilli P, Takei K. 1996. Molecular mechanisms in synaptic vesicle endocytosis and recycling. *Neuron* 16:481–86
16. Dunaevsky A, Bloch R, Ko C-P, Connor EA. 1997. F-actin and β-fodrin at the frog neuromuscular junction. *Soc. Neurosci. Abstr.* 23:36
17. Heidelberger R, Heinemann C, Neher E, Matthews G. 1994. Calcium dependence of the rate of exocytosis in a synaptic terminal. *Nature* 371:513–15
18. Henkel AW, Almers W. 1996. Fast steps in exocytosis and endocytosis studied by capacitance measurements in endocrine cells. *Curr. Opin. Neurobiol.* 6:350–57
19. Henkel AW, Betz WJ. 1995. Staurosporine blocks evoked release of FM1–43 but not acetylcholine from frog nerve terminals. *J. Neurosci.* 15:8246–58
20. Henkel AW, Lübke J, Betz WJ. 1996. FM1–43 ultrastructural localization in and release from frog motor nerve terminals. *Proc. Natl. Acad. Sci. USA* 93:1918–23
21. Henkel AW, Simpson LL, Ridge RMAP, Betz WJ. 1996. Synaptic vesicle movements monitored by fluorescence recovery after photobleaching in nerve terminals stained with FM1–43. *J. Neurosci.* 16:3960–67
22. Heuser JE, Reese TS. 1973. Evidence for recycling of synaptic vesicle membrane during transmitter release at the frog neuromuscular junction. *J. Cell Biol.* 57:314–44
23. Hirokawa N, Sobue K, Kanda K, Harada A, Yorifuji H. 1989. The cytoskeletal architecture of the presynaptic terminal and molecular structure of synapsin I. *J. Cell Biol.* 8:111–26
24. Hsu S-F, Jackson MB. 1996. Rapid exocytosis and endocytosis in nerve terminals of the rat posterior pituitary. *J. Physiol.* 4942:539–53
25. Katz B. 1966. *Nerve, Muscle, and Synapse.* pp. 129–41. New York: McGraw-Hill
26. Koenig JH, Ikeda K. 1996. Synaptic vesicles have two distinct recycling pathways. *J. Cell Biol.* 135:797–808
27. Koh D-S, Hille B. 1997. Modulation by neurotransmitters of catecholamine secretion from sympathetic ganglion neurons detected by amperometry. *Proc. Natl. Acad. Sci. USA* 94:1506–11
28. Kosaka T, Ikeda K. 1983. Possible temperature-dependent blockage of single synaptic vesicle recycling induced by

a single gene mutation in *Drosophila. J. Neurobiol.* 14:207–25

29. Kraszewski K, Daniell L, Mundigl O, De Camilli P. 1996. Mobility of synaptic vesicles in nerve endings monitored by recovery from photobleaching of synaptic vesicle-associated fluorescence. *J. Neurosci.* 16:5905–13

30. Landis DM, Hall AK, Weinstein LA, Reese TS. 1988. The organization of the cytoplasm at the presynaptic active zone of a central nervous system synapse. *Neuron* 1:201–9

31. Lim NF, Nowycky MC, Bookman RJ. 1990. Direct measurement of exocytosis and calcium currents in single vertebrate nerve terminals. *Nature* 344:449–51

32. Lindau M, Almers W. 1995. Structure and function of fusion pores in exocytosis and ectoplasmic membrane fusion. *Curr. Opin. Cell Biol.* 7:509–17

33. Lindgren CA, Emery DG, Haydon PG. 1997. Intracellular acidification reversibly reduces endocytosis at the neuromuscular junction. *J. Neurosci.* 17:3074–84

34. Lollike K, Borregaard N, Lindau M. 1995. The exocytotic fusion pore of small granules has a conductance similar to an ion channel. *J. Cell Biol.* 129:99–104

35. Maiti S, Shear JB, Williams RM, Zipfel WR, Webb WW. 1997. Measuring serotonin distribution in live cells with three-photon excitation. *Science* 275:530–32

36. Mellman I. 1996. Endocytosis and molecular sorting. *Annu. Rev. Cell Dev. Biol.* 12:575–625

37. Miesenböck G, Rothman JE. 1997. Patterns of synaptic activity in neural networks recorded by light emission from synaptolucins. *Proc. Natl. Acad. Sci. USA* 94:3402–7

38. Monck JR, Alvarez de Toledo G, Fernández JM. 1991. Tension in secretory granule membranes causes extensive membrane transfer through the exocytotic fusion pore. *Proc. Natl. Acad. Sci. USA* 88:2035

39. Monck JR, Fernández JM. 1994. The exocytotic fusion pore and neurotransmitter release. *Neuron* 12:707–16

40. Neher E, Marty A. 1982. Discrete changes of cell membrane capacitance observed under conditions of enhanced secretion in bovine adrenal chromaffin cells. *Proc. Natl. Acad. Sci. USA* 79:6712–16

41. Neher E, Zucker RS. 1993. Multiple calcium-dependent processes related to secretion in bovine chromaffin cells. *Neuron* 10:21–30

42. Oberhauser AF, Fernández JM. 1996. A fusion pore phenotype in mast cells of the ruby-eye mouse. *Proc. Natl. Acad. Sci. USA* 93:14349–54

43. Parsons TD, Lenzi D, Almers W, Roberts WM. 1994. Calcium-triggered exocytosis and endocytosis in an isolated presynaptic cell: capacitance measurements in saccular hair cells. *Neuron* 13:875–83

44. Rahamimoff R, Fernández JM. 1997. Pre- and postfusion regulation of transmitter release. *Neuron* 18:17–27

45. Ramaswami M, Krishnan KS, Kelly RB. 1994. Intermediates in synaptic vesicle recycling revealed by optical imaging of *Drosophila* neuromuscular junctions. *Neuron* 13:363–75

46. Rieke F, Schwartz EA. 1994. A cGMP-gated current can control exocytosis at cone synapses. *Neuron* 13:863–73

47. Rieke F, Schwartz EA. 1996. Asynchronous transmitter release: control of exocytosis and endocytosis at the salamander rod synapse. *J. Physiol.* 493.1:1–8

48. Rosenboom H, Lindau M. 1994. Exo-endocytosis and closing of the fission pore during endocytosis in single pituitary nerve terminals internally perfused with high calcium concentrations. *Proc. Natl. Acad. Sci. USA* 91:5267–71

49. Ryan TA, Li L, Chin L-S, Greengard P, Smith SJ. 1996. Synaptic vesicle recycling in synapsin I knock-out mice. *J. Cell Biol.* 134:1219–27

50. Ryan TA, Reuter H, Wendland B, Schweizer FE, Tsien RW, Smith SJ. 1993. The kinetics of synaptic vesicle recycling measured at single presynaptic boutons. *Neuron* 11:713–24

51. Ryan TA, Smith SJ, Reuter H. 1996. The timing of synaptic vesicle endocytosis. *Proc. Natl. Acad. Sci. USA* 93:5567–71

52. Smith CB, Betz WJ. 1996. Simultaneous independent measurement of endocytosis and exocytosis. *Nature* 380:531–34

53. Spruce AE, Breckenridge LJ, Lee AK, Almers W. 1990. Properties of the fusion pore that forms during exocytosis of a mast cell secretory vesicle. *Neuron* 4:643–54

54. Steyer JA, Horstmann H, Almers W. 1997. Transport, docking and exocytosis of single secretory granules in live chromaffin cells. *Nature* 388:474–77

55. Stiles JR, Van Helden D, Bartol TM, Salpeter EE, Salpeter MM. 1996. Miniature endplate current rise times < 100 μs from improved dual recordings can be modeled with passive acetylcholine diffusion from a synaptic vesicle. *Proc. Natl.*

Acad. Sci. USA 93:747–52
56. Südhof TC, Rizo J. 1996. Synaptotagmins: C2-domain proteins that regulate membrane traffic. *Neuron* 17:379–88
57. Takei K, Mundigl O, Daniell L, De Camilli P. 1996. The synaptic vesicle cycle: a single vesicle budding step involving clathrin and dynamin. *J. Cell Biol.* 133:1237–50
58. Thomas P, Lee AK, Wong JG, Almers W. 1994. A triggered mechanism retrieves membrane in seconds after Ca[2+]-stimulated exocytosis in single pituitary cells. *J. Cell Biol.* 124(5):667–75
59. Valtorta F, Jahn R, Fesce R, Greengard P, Ceccarelli B. 1988. Synaptophysin (p38) at the frog neuromuscular junction: its incorporation into the axolemma and recycling after intense quantal secretion. *J. Cell Biol.* 107:2717–27
60. von Gersdorff H, Matthews G. 1994. Dynamics of synaptic vesicle fusion and membrane retrieval in synaptic terminals. *Nature* 367:735–39
61. von Gersdorff H, Matthews G. 1994. Inhibition of endocytosis by elevated internal calcium in a synaptic terminal. *Nature* 370:652–55

62. Whalley T, Terasaki M, Cho M-S, Vogel SS. 1995. Direct membrane retrieval into large vesicles after exocytosis in sea urchin eggs. *J. Cell Biol.* 131:1183–95
63. Wightman RM, Jankowski JA, Kennedy RT, Kawagoe KT, Schroeder TJ, et al. 1991. Temporally resolved catecholamine spikes correspond to single vesicle release from individual chromaffin cells. *Proc. Natl. Acad. Sci. USA* 88:10754–58
64. Wu L-G, Betz WJ. 1996. Nerve activity but not intracellular calcium determines the time course of endocytosis at the frog neuromuscular junction. *Neuron* 17:769–79
65. Zhou Z, Misler S. 1995. Amperometric detection of stimulus-induced quantal release of catecholamines from cultured superior cervical ganglion neurons. *Proc. Natl. Acad. Sci. USA* 92:6938–42
66. Zhou Z, Misler S, Chow RH. 1996. Rapid fluctuations in transmitter release from single vesicles in bovine adrenal chromaffin cells. *Biophys. J.* 70:1543–52
67. Zucker RS. 1996. Exocytosis: a molecular and physiological perspective. *Neuron* 17:1049–55

Annu. Rev. Physiol. 1998. 60:365–84

SURFACTANT PROTEINS: Molecular Genetics of Neonatal Pulmonary Diseases

Joanna Floros[*,#] *and Padma Kala*[*]

*Department of Cellular and Molecular Physiology and [#]Department of Pediatrics, Pennsylvania State University College of Medicine, Hershey, Pennsylvania 17033; e-mail: jfloros@cmp.hmc.psu.edu

KEY WORDS: SP-A, SP-B, respiratory distress syndrome, congenital alveolar proteinosis, complex diseases

ABSTRACT

Genetic and phenotypic complexity has been described for diseases of varied etiology. Groups of patients with varied phenotype can be used in association studies as an initial approach to identify contributing loci. Although association studies have limitations, their value is enhanced by using candidate genes with functions related to disease. Surfactant proteins have been studied in the etiopathogenesis of neonatal pulmonary diseases. SP-A and SP-B polymorphisms are found at a higher frequency in certain groups of patients with respiratory distress syndrome (RDS), and SP-B mutations are linked to the pathogenesis of congenital alveolar proteinosis (CAP). Phenotypic heterogeneity is observed for both CAP and RDS. The available data suggest that a number of factors contribute to the etiology of CAP and RDS and, therefore, a multidisciplinary approach of clinical, genetic, epidemiologic, and statistical considerations is necessary for an in-depth understanding of the pathophysiology of these and other pulmonary diseases.

INTRODUCTION

Recent advances have revealed that a genetic disorder, when thoroughly analyzed, often exhibits complexity regardless of whether it was initially thought to be of a single (1) or multigenic/multifactorial etiology (2). Complexity can arise in several ways. It may be due to (*a*) locus heterogeneity, where mutations in one of several genes result in the disease phenotype (3–7) or (*b*) allelic heterogeneity, where different mutations at a given locus correlate with various

365

unrelated disorders (8) or with differences in disease severity (9, 10). Complexity may also arise from incomplete penetrance, where a given allele may predispose to the disease, but this gene is not sufficient for the disease manifestation; interaction with other genes, environment, sex, or age may determine the disease phenotype (11–13). (c) Finally, complexity may be due to polygenic inheritance, where the simultaneous presence of mutations in multiple genes determine the disease phenotype.

The phenotype of polygenic etiology may be a discrete trait or a quantitative trait. Examples of a discrete phenotype include retinitis pigmentosa (14) and Hirschsprung's disease (15), and of a quantitative trait include hypertension (16) and airway hyperresponsiveness (17). The interaction of quantitative trait loci may be additive or synergistic (epistasis) (17–20). Phenotypic diversity in polygenic disease may arise from the presence of additional modifier mutations [e.g. cystic fibrosis (21) and Gaucher disease (22)], or polymorphisms [e.g. Creutzfeldt-Jakob disease versus familial fatal insomnia (23)] in the same gene, or mutations/polymorphisms at other genetic loci [e.g. sickle cell anemia (1)]. Recently, linkage was found between asthma and various susceptibility loci in different ethnic groups (24). Furthermore, the importance of genetic background in determining phenotypic effects of genetic mutations has been demonstrated in animal models (18, 19, 25, 26). Thus, dissection of processes underlying genetic disorders requires an appreciation for the heterogeneity at the clinical and genetic levels.

A diagramatic representation of the impact of interactions among disease-causing genes, modifier genes, and environment on the disease phenotype is shown in Figure 1. Because different sets of interactions may contribute to the disease phenotype, differences in the phenotype itself (e.g. severity) can exist. Moreover, the mechanism(s) that underlies each set of interactions is likely to differ. Therefore, in this scenario it is important to identify the various disease subgroups (using clinical and/or genetic markers) in order to facilitate identification of the contributing factors. Of note, the distinction among subgroups of clinical phenotype may be a function of the stage of the disease at which comparisons are made. This notion is illustrated in Figure 1, where the overlap among subgroups of phenotype corresponds to the merging of the distinguishing features at certain disease stages. These considerations indicate it is necessary to understand the mechanisms underlying each subgroup of a given phenotype in order to target the appropriate therapy to each disease subgroup and thus increase efficacy of treatment. In the context of Figure 1, the surfactant proteins, because of their importance in surfactant physiology/biology (see below), are considered to be some of the contributors to the etiopathogenesis of certain pulmonary diseases. These diseases include those where the amounts of surfactant proteins are reduced, and the composition and/or

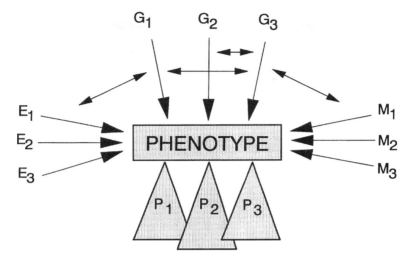

Figure 1   Schematic representation of potential interactions and contributors to the disease pheno-type(s). G_1, G_2, G_3 represent disease-causing genes; E_1, E_2, E_3 represent different environments; M_1, M_2, M_3 represent genes that modify the expression of disease-causing genes; P_1, P_2, P_3 represent disease subgroups of varied phenotype. The *triangles* and their overlap indicate that the distinction among these subgroups may be a function of the stage of disease at which comparisons are made and that this distinction may progressively diminish and/or merge at certain disease stages.

function of surfactant is deranged, as well as diseases where mechansisms of host defense and inflammatory processes of the lung are involved.

PULMONARY SURFACTANT

A biochemical hallmark of lung maturity is the presence of a lipoprotein complex called pulmonary surfactant. Pulmonary surfactant is essential for normal lung function; it lowers the surface tension at the air-liquid interface of the alveolus and thus prevents lung collapse at low lung volumes. In 1959, Avery & Mead (27) suggested that deficiency of surfactant leads to respiratory distress syndrome (RDS) in the prematurely born infant. Lack of surfactant activity that may lead to a variety of pulmonary diseases, including RDS, could result from reduced amounts of surfactant or from functionally impaired surfactant. To date, reduced levels of surfactant and genetic variations or mutations in the surfactant protein (SP-) genes A and B have been associated with respiratory disease in neonates. Deranged surfactant composition and increased or reduced levels of certain surfactant components, particularly of SP-A, have been observed in a number of adult pulmonary diseases (28–32). Because genetic variations (polymorphisms, mutations) associated with or linked to respiratory diseases have been observed only for SP-A and SP-B, the present review is focused on recent and relevant information of SP-A and SP-B.

MOLECULAR ASPECTS OF SP-A AND SP-B

The human SP-A locus is on the long arm of chromosome 10, q21-q24 (33) and consists of two functional genes, *SP-A1* and *SP-A2*, and a pseudogene (reviewed in 34). Recent findings indicate that the SP-A locus is linked to the surfactant protein D (SP-D) locus, and the order of their location from the centromere is SP-D, SP-A2, pseudogene, SP-A1, telomere. In addition, recent data revealed the orientation of the three SP-A genomic sequences— SP-A2 and pseudogene are in the same transcriptional orientation but opposite to that of SP-A1—pointing to the possibility of shared regulatory elements between SP-A1 and SP-A2 (35). The genomic organization of each SP-A gene is similar and consists of seven transcribed regions, as shown in Figure 2A. The

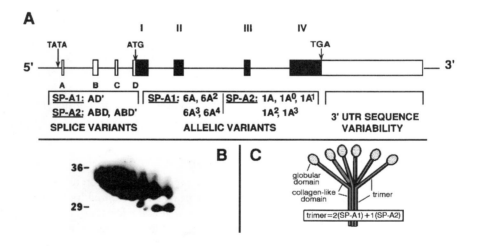

Figure 2 Complexity of human SP-A. *Panel A*: The structural organization of the *SP-A* gene is shown. The four *solid boxes*, labeled I-IV, are coding regions. The 5′ *open boxes* labeled A, B, C, D are 5′UTR, and the 3′ *open box* is the 3′UTR. The major splice variants (AD′, ABD, and ABD′) for each *SP-A* gene and the known allelic variants (6A, $6A^2$, $6A^3$, $6A^4$ for SP-A1 and 1A, $1A^0$, $1A^1$, $1A^2$, $1A^3$ for SP-A2) are noted. The D and D′ regions differ by 3 nucleotides with D′ being shorter (for more details, see 38). Sequence variability at the 3′UTR between *SP-A1* and *SP-A2* genes and among SP-A alleles has been observed. *Panel B* depicts the two-dimensional electrophoretic profile of SP-A (49). The numbers on the left indicate molecular mass of 29 and 36 kDa. *Panel C* depicts the organization of native SP-A. SP-A consists of six trimers; each trimer consists of two SP-A1 and one SP-A2 gene products (after Voss et al, Reference 52).

5′ untranslated regions (5′UTRs) splice in different configurations to give rise to different transcripts (36, 37). The major transcript for SP-A1 is the AD′ type, and for SP-A2 the ABD and ABD′ types. The D and D′ splice sites differ by three nucleotides (36, 38). These SP-A transcripts are translated in vitro (36) and in vivo (39).

In 1986, SP-A cDNA sequences denoted 6A and 1A were cloned (41) for each of the two SP-A primary translation products identified previously (40). The 6A sequence represents the *SP-A1* gene (42) and the 1A sequence represents the *SP-A2* gene (43). Subsequent cloning of SP-A transcripts revealed a number of alleles for each SP-A gene (37, 38, 44). These alleles are classified as to differences within coding sequences. Based on availability of complete coding sequences and on experimental verification of the various human SP-A sequence differences (44), at present there are four SP-A1 alleles (6A, $6A^2$, $6A^3$, $6A^4$) and five SP-A2 alleles (1A, $1A^0$, $1A^1$, $1A^2$, $1A^3$) (Figure 2A). Recently, we characterized two additional alleles, one for each SP-A gene—$1A^4$ and $6A^5$ (J Floros, unpublished observations). Sequence variability at the 3′UTR has also been observed among SP-A sequences (43–46). In addition to 3′UTR divergence, Katyal et al (43) observed high divergence between the two SP-A genes in the 5′UTR, intron 1, and coding exon II (noted as exon III in Reference 43). The higher degree of divergence in these regions suggests that these regions impart important functional and/or regulatory properties that differ between the two SP-A genes. In fact, exon II contains invariant nucleotides that distinguish *SP-A1* from *SP-A2* genes and their corresponding alleles (36). On the other hand, high divergence in noncoding regions may account for mechanisms involved in the differential regulation of the two SP-A genes (47, 48) and perhaps in differential regulation of SP-A alleles.

Mature SP-A found in the bronchoalveolar lavage material (BAL) is extensively co- and post-translationally modified (49, 50), resulting in numerous isoforms with differences in molecular weight and charge, as shown by two-dimensional gel electrophoretic analysis (Figure 2B). Furthermore, the native human SP-A consists of six trimers with a "bouquet of tulips" arrangement shown in Figure 2C (51). It is suggested that each SP-A trimer consists of two SP-A1 molecules and one SP-A2 (52).

The *SP-B* gene is located on 2p12→(p11.2 (53), and its genomic structural organization consists of 11 exons (54); the precursor SP-B protein is encoded by the first 10 exons. A small 5′UTR is part of the first exon, and the 11th exon encodes a 3′UTR (34, 55). A number of SP-B alleles have been identified, and the frequency of these alleles differs among various populations (56, 57). The mature human SP-B is a single gene product and is derived from a precursor molecule of 42 kDa (58) that undergoes amino- and carboxy-terminal cleavages of 200 and 102 amino acids, respectively. The mature SP-B, the form found in

BAL, is a 79 amino acid (8 kDa) hydrophobic peptide encoded by exons 6 and 7. Processing of the human pro SP-B (381 amino acids) occurs intracellularly in the multivesicular body (59), in a type II cell-type-specific manner (60). Targeting the SP-B precursor to the secretory granules is not cell-type-specific and does not require the carboxy-terminal peptide (60).

Function and Importance of SP-A and SP-B

SP-A   Many reports have attributed multiple functions to SP-A. It has been implicated in the metabolism, structure, and the surface tension–lowering properties of surfactant, as well as in local host defense and inflammatory processes of the lung. Studies of the SP-A knockout mouse (61, 62) suggest either that SP-A is not involved in the metabolism of surfactant in vivo or that redundant mechanisms take over in the absence of SP-A. On the other hand, in vitro studies (63, 64), as well as the data from the SP-A ($-/-$) mouse, indicate that SP-A is important for the formation of tubular myelin (TM), an extracellular morphologic form of surfactant. Moreover, information obtained from in vitro (65) and in vivo studies (61) suggests that the role of SP-A in the surface tension–lowering properties of surfactant becomes important primarily under conditions where concentrations of surfactant components (e.g. lipids) or other molecules (e.g. Ca^{2+}) are not optimal. SP-A, when combined with low concentrations of BAL lipid extract surfactant (LES), enhances adsorption dramatically and also appears to enrich the surfactant monolayer with dipalmitoylphosphatidyl choline. However, at high concentrations of LES, SP-A supplementation shows no additional effect on surface activities when compared with measurements obtained with LES alone (65). LES contains surfactant phospholipids, SP-B, and SP-C. Similarly, the surface tension lowering activity of LES obtained from 7–8-week-old SP-A ($-/-$) mice was significantly reduced at low LES concentrations in the absence of Ca^{2+}, compared with comparable concentrations of LES obtained from wild-type mice. The activities of LES obtained from both groups of mice, however, were similar at high LES concentrations. The surface tension lowering ability of surfactant obtained from fetal lungs of either wild-type or SP-A ($-/-$) mice and the survival rate of prematurely delivered SP-A ($-/-$) pups are currently unknown. In addition, a modest increase in the surfactant pool size was shown in 8-week-old SP-A ($-/-$) mice compared with their wild-type counterparts (62).

Another major function of SP-A is in the host defense and inflammatory processes of the lung. These functions of SP-A became apparent over the last several years. The cDNA cloning of SP-A led to subsequent discovery of structural similarities with mannose-binding protein (an acute phase reactant) and C1q (involved in complement cascade). SP-A (like SP-D) is a collagenous C-type lectin or collectin and, similar to the other members of the collectin family, is involved in various functions of host defense (66, 67). SP-A contains a carbohydrate recognition domain that may bind to macrophage membrane proteins (68) and a collagenous domain that may bind C1q (69). Several studies have shown that surfactant plays an important role in the regulation of immune cells in the alveolus (reviewed in 70). The predominant surfactant lipids have an inhibitory effect on immune cell function, whereas SP-A, SP-D, and some of the minor lipids (sphingomyelin, phosphatidylethanolamine) have a stimulatory effect (71). It appears that in the normal lung a delicate balance exists between inhibition and stimulation of immune cells through the maintenance of an appropriate ratio of the various surfactant components (71). An imbalance may occur in lung injury; for example, the level of the minor (stimulatory) lipids or SP-A is increased in BAL from smokers and patients with interstitial lung diseases and hypersensitivity pneumonitis (30, 72). The stimulatory effects of SP-A include, but are not limited to, macrophage chemotaxis (73), phagocytosis (74, 75), immune cell proliferation (76), and production of proinflammatory cytokines (77, 78). Surfactant lipids inhibit all of these processes.

SP-B   Many in vitro and in vivo studies have demonstrated an essential role for SP-B in normal lung/surfactant function. In vitro studies indicate SP-B accelerates the rate of adsorption and spreading of surfactant phospholipids into a surface monolayer, the functional form of surfactant (79; reviewed in 55). Addition of SP-B to surfactant phospholipids or to a mixture of synthetic phospholipids improves the in vivo function of surfactant lipids to levels comparable to those of natural surfactant (80). SP-B, along with SP-A, is essential for the in vitro formation of TM, a morphologic form of sufactant (63, 64). Well-structured TM is absent in lungs of infants who died from RDS (81) and in lungs of SP-A (−/−) mice (61). Furthermore, instillation of a monoclonal antibody (MAb) against SP-B into the trachea of near-term newborn rabbits induces severe respiratory failure (82), and the addition of anti-SP-B MAb to porcine surfactant destroys the surface-active properties of surfactant (83). Deficiency of SP-B in human neonates results in fatal congenital alveolar proteinosis (CAP) (84). The importance of SP-B in surfactant function is clearly exemplified in studies of SP-B knockout mouse and of humans with SP-B deficiency. Although the lungs of SP-B (−/−) mice develop normally, they remain atelectatic and the newborn mice die from severe respiratory failure; the heterozygotes (+/−) appear normal (85). Although adult SP-B (+/−) mice have no clinical consequences from decreased levels of SP-B, they show decreased lung compliance and increased residual lung volume (86). The functional significance and mechanisms underlying these changes in the heterozygous (+/−) mice are not known.

RESPIRATORY DISTRESS SYNDROME (RDS)

RDS is caused by a deficiency in pulmonary surfactant in prematurely born infants (27). Prematurity and low birth weight are important predisposing factors for RDS (87–89). Race and sex are additional risk factors of RDS (88, 90–97). Despite a higher incidence of prematurity in blacks, black infants show a lower incidence of RDS than white infants (92) at each gestational age (93) that is not accounted for by changes in lecithin/sphingomyelin ratio (93, 94) or by changes in TDx fetal lung maturity surfactant-to-albumin assay (96). Whereas the incidence of RDS is not different between the sexes, several studies have shown an increased risk for mortality due to RDS in males (95, 97–99).

A number of studies suggest a genetic component in the etiology of RDS (100–103). Mothers who delivered low birth weight (LBW) babies could be divided into two groups: one group with LBW babies who seldom develop RDS (3%) and another group with LBW infants with a high incidence (90%) of RDS (100, 101). Of note is the observation that the mortality and morbidity rates of full-term infants of the high-risk mothers were similar to those in the general population (100). Pedigree analysis revealed a higher incidence of RDS in the LBW infants of female relatives of high-risk mothers and in maternal half-sibs compared to paternal half-sibs. A genetically determined maternal factor was suggested to explain the findings of this study (102). A study of twins showed an 85% concordance of RDS among monozygotic twins compared with a 44% concordance among dizygotic twins (103). Furthermore, familial trends in LBW, a known predisposing factor for RDS, have been reported (104, 105). Thus, these studies together suggest a multigenic and/or multifactorial etiology for RDS.

Consistent with the association of low levels of SP-A and lack of TM with RDS (81, 106, 107) is a recent finding that an SP-A2 allele ($1A^0$) is found in significantly higher frequency in the RDS population of unrelated white infants of >28 weeks gestation (108). This observation is intriguing in view of a recent report that the $1A^0$ allele associates with low levels of SP-A mRNA in human lung tissues of unrelated individuals (38). Furthermore, as noted above, the surface tension–lowering properties of surfactant from the SP-A ($-/-$) postnatal pup are compromised when the concentration of surfactant components (e.g. lipids) or other molecules (e.g. Ca^{2+}) are not optimal. The similarities and the differences between the studies of the SP-A ($-/-$) mouse and babies who died from RDS (61, 81, 106, 107) are intriguing. In both cases, there is a correlation between absence (or very low levels of SP-A) and lack of the highly ordered structures of TM. The difference in phenotype observed in the two studies may be explained by differences in the composition of other surfactant components. In the full-term or postnatal SP-A ($-/-$) pup the composition of surfactant components is similar to that of the wild-type, whereas the composition in prematurely born infants that died from RDS may differ from that in term infants or in prematurely born infants free of disease. Currently, the precise concentrations of various surfactant components at different lung developmental stages (from 24 weeks of gestation to term), and the range of concentrations of surfactant components at a given gestational age of an infant born prematurely with or without RDS are not entirely known, although reduced levels or altered surfactant composition in babies with or at risk for RDS has been shown (109–112). Therefore, data from varied studies (human RDS, in vitro functional studies, knockout mouse) suggest that the physiological role of SP-A with regards to the surface tension lowering function of surfactant becomes essential when developmental processes and concentrations of surfactant constituents are suboptimal.

An SP-B variant that correlates with RDS has also been described (57). An insertion or deletion in the number of copies of a motif that consists of two elements, a 20-bp conserved sequence and a variable number of $(CA)_n$ repeats in intron 4, constitutes the variant. This SP-B variant appears with a significantly higher frequency in the RDS population (29.3 versus 16.8%, $p < 0.05$). Because not all infants with RDS carried the $(CA)_n$ variant, additional genetic alterations associated with RDS must exist. Whether this variation in the SP-B gene compromises SP-B mRNA processing or other processes remains to be established. Moreover, the frequency for the combination of $1A^0$ allele and the SP-B intron 4 variant is significantly higher in the RDS compared with either locus alone (108). The synergistic interaction of SP-A and SP-B variants with RDS in >28 weeks white population is interesting because the SP-A and SP-B proteins interact functionally, e.g. both are essential for the in vitro formation of TM (63, 64) and both contribute to the adsorption of phospholipids to the surfactant layer at the alveolar air-liquid interface (reviewed in 113). The simultaneous presence of mutations in two unlinked, yet functionally interactive, photoreceptor-specific genes has been observed in some cases of retinitis pigmentosa (14).

CONGENITAL ALVEOLAR PROTEINOSIS (CAP) AND SP-B

CAP is a rare, fatal disease of term neonates characterized clinically by severe, persistent, and progressive respiratory distress, and histologically by accumulation of lipoproteinaceous material, macrophages, and desquamated type II cells in the alveolar spaces. The initial report of CAP in a family suggested an autosomal-recessive mode of inheritance (114). Genetic defects associated with SP-B deficiency have been characterized in a number of patients, the most common being a homozygous mutation of an insertion (121ins2) in exon 4 of the

Table 1   Mutations and polymorphisms in the human *SP-B* gene

Designation	Location	Type of change	Disease	Reference
121 ins2[a]	Exon 4, codon 121	Insertion: C→GAA (frameshift)	CAP	84, 115, 116
R236C	Exon 7, codon 236	Substitution: C→T (Arginine→Cysteine)	CAP	117
Intron 4 variant	Intron 4	Insertion/deletion of a $(CA)_n$-containing motif	RDS	57

[a]Associated mRNA alterations: Exon 7 deletion and exon 8 splice variations.

SP-B gene (Table 1) (84, 115–117). CAP also occurs in the absence of known SP-B mutations, suggesting that as yet unidentified SP-B mutations exist, or that CAP may also be caused by mutations in other genetic loci (116). Thus CAP is a genetically heterogeneous disease entity. Phenotypic diversity that includes variations in SP-B protein and mRNA levels, as well as in the pattern of distribution of *SP-B* mRNA, is also observed in CAP (117, 118). Of interest, two siblings with homozygous mutations of 121ins2 showed phenotypic differences (118), suggesting other genetic or nongenetic influences modify the given phenotype of SP-B deficiency.

The 121ins2 is a frameshift mutation of codon 121 of the *SP-B* cDNA, resulting in the premature termination of translation after codon 214; the mature protein is derived from 201–279 of the 381-amino acid proprotein. The presence of nonsense codons has been associated with decreased levels of transcripts (115). Additional splice abnormalities were detected in cDNA clones derived from two affected siblings. These include deletions of exon 7 and the use of a cryptic splice site 12 bp 3' of the reported exon 8 splice junction. The significance of these abnormalities is not known. Parents and siblings heterozygous for 121ins2 were asymptomatic (115). A case of partial deficiency of SP-B in an infant who was a compound heterozygote for 121ins2, as well as another SP-B point mutation (R236C), has been reported (Table 1) (117). The authors concluded that R236C mutation did not affect transcription or mRNA stability, but decreased efficiency of translation and/or altered processing of the primary translation product. This patient (117) has an apparent response to dexamethasone therapy, in contrast to the homozygous 121ins2 patient (119), whose respiratory function deteriorated despite dexamethasone treatment. Further, the 121ins/R236C heterozygous patient was dependent on dexamethasone therapy, as seen by the worsening of his respiratory status each time the investigators attempted to withdraw steroid therapy. Because steroid therapy increases SP-B production (55), it was inferred that steroids can increase the production of SP-B from the R236C-containing allele (117). Thus SP-B allelic differences may have an impact on the severity of illness and response to treatment.

Additional defects in CAP include abnormalities in SP-A distribution (84, 116, 118), absence of phosphatidylglycerol in lavage fluid or lung tissue (119), absence of TM, presence of aberrantly processed SP-C (84, 116), possible loss of directional surfactant secretion, desquamation of type II cells (116, 118), and increased vascular permeability (119). Exogenous administration of SP-B does not alter the course of CAP (84, 115–117, 119) suggesting that endogenous SP-B is required for surfactant and/or type II cell function. This suggestion is consistent with the recent observation that pulmonary surfactant function and SP-B are within the normal range (120) following lung transplantation in CAP patients. Although the significance of these associated abnormalities is not known, it is likely that some of the observed heterogeneity of CAP involves the interaction of specific SP-B mutations and other genetic/nongenetic factors underlying these associated defects.

ADULT RESPIRATORY DISEASES (ARDS)

Abnormalities in surface tension–lowering properties and/or host defense functions secondary to changes in SP-A levels have been implicated in the pathophysiology of ARDS (28, 31, 121), hypersensitivity pneumonitis (30), idiopathic pulmonary fibrosis (122, 123), pulmonary alveolar proteinosis (29, 124), *Pneumocystis carinii* pneumonia (125), and sarcoidosis (30; reviewed in 70, 126); specific genetic defects have not been identified. In a study of a small group of ARDS patients and healthy control individuals, the SP-B intron 4 polymorphism occurred at a significantly higher frequency in the ARDS group (126a). The significance of this observation in terms of disease susceptibility remains unclear. Of note, SP-A and SP-B levels were found to be reduced in BAL from ARDS patients (28). For a disease such as ARDS, with a known multifactorial etiology (126b,c), the susceptibility factors may be different in different phenotypic subgroups, and this difference may have an impact on the success of various therapeutic modalities. Recently, linkage has been reported between asthma, a phenotypically heterogeneous disorder, and different susceptibility loci in different racial populations (24). Thus a comprehensive approach including characterization of discrete clinical subgroups, well-structured studies of the genetics and the epidemiology of disease, and further advances in the molecular biology of the lung can facilitate a better understanding of pulmonary diseases.

PERSPECTIVE

Several studies have provided evidence for a genetic component in the etiology of RDS (100–103, 127). Although it is possible that genetic factors in combination with maternal/perinatal factors lead to the disease phenotype, specific genetic defects, i.e. mutations both necessary and sufficient for RDS, have not been identified. There is evidence, however, that certain alleles/polymorphisms in SP genes associate with RDS, at least in certain subgroups of patients (57, 108). Association implies the locus is in linkage disequilibrium with the actual disease gene or that the allele itself has pathogenetic effects. Limitations of association studies include false positives secondary to population admixture and nonrandom mating, as well as the inability to distinguish between necessary loci and susceptibility loci (128, 129). However, the value of an association study is enhanced if the candidate gene has functional implications related to the disease (2, 129).

Indirect evidence for the possible role of SP-A as a disease modifier comes from the following data. The $1A^0$ allele correlates with low levels of SP-A mRNA in unrelated adults (38) and is observed at a significantly higher frequency in the RDS population compared with controls (108). A correlation between severity of RDS and SP-A levels is also reported (111, 130). Studies of the SP-A-deficient mouse and in vitro studies suggest SP-A is important for lowering surface tension at low phospholipid concentrations, especially in the absence of Ca^{2+} (61, 65). It is conceivable that under compromised conditions, such as surfactant deficiency due to prematurity or other factors, the role of SP-A in maintaining surfactant function and alveolar integrity becomes critical. In this circumstance, the levels of SP-A in prematurely born infants with $1A^0$ genotype may not be sufficient to maintain normal lung function. Consistent with this notion is the clinical observation that the rates for morbidity and mortality of full-term infants of high risk mothers (delivering LBW babies with RDS) are similar to those observed in the general population (100). Moreover, an apparently synergistic interaction of SP-A and SP-B alleles with RDS has been observed (108), further implicating these two unlinked but functionally interactive loci in the etiology of RDS.

Neonatal respiratory disease appears to exhibit heterogeneity in both clinical and underlying genetic processes. The development of CAP in the absence of currently known mutations suggests either the presence of yet unknown mutations in SP-B gene or the involvement of other genetic loci in the etiology of CAP. Observations of the occasional occurrence of RDS in term infants, as well as in babies with normal L/S ratios, the increased incidence of RDS in the second born twin, the development of RDS in babies several hours after birth (with normal respiration in the first few hours), and the observation that not all premature infants develop RDS suggest heterogeneity in the etiology of RDS (98). In addition, there is a greater incidence of RDS in LBW infants of female relatives of high-risk mothers and in maternal half-sibs, suggesting the involvement of a maternal risk factor unrelated to LBW (101, 102). Furthermore, race and gestational age have an impact on the incidence, severity, response to treatment, and outcome of RDS. Although clinical trials have clearly demonstrated beneficial effects of the use of antenatal steroids on the incidence and outcome of RDS (131–133), RDS develops in certain newborns despite antenatal steroid treatment, i.e. there are responders and non-responders to steroid treatment. Together, these observations further support the notion that a number of factors are involved in the etiology of neonatal respiratory disease, and these factors either singly or in combination contribute to the formation of disease subgroups with varied phenotype.

Various epidemiologic strategies could greatly facilitate elucidation of the etiopathogenesis of neonatal respiratory diseases. For example, stratification based on race, sex, age, multiple-affected siblings, severity, clinical outcomes, and steroid responsiveness versus non-responsiveness is likely to enhance detection of etiologic factors of RDS. The elucidation of genetic factors of other complex diseases has been greatly facilitated by phenotype stratifications. Examples include subgrouping based on age of onset for Alzheimer's disease (3, 4, 134, 135) and family history for breast cancer (11). Even if an entirely homogeneous subgroup is not identified, the power of genetic studies is increased with increasing homogeneity of the study population (2, 136).

RDS does not have a clear pattern of inheritance, and large family pedigrees with RDS are not available, thus making the use of traditional linkage studies difficult. Therefore, affected sib-pair analysis of the high-risk families and studies of twins provide effective approaches to the study of genetics of RDS. These approaches detect main effects of genes, i.e. effects of a particular locus independent of other loci. On the other hand, with these approaches it would be difficult to elucidate truly polygenic diseases when the individual effects of the susceptibility loci are small. Transmission/disequilibrium tests (TDT) could be used to identify susceptibility genes with modest effects (128, 137). The major advantage of TDT compared with affected sib-pair analysis is that it does not require families with multiple-affected siblings (128) and is based on the notion that a parent heterozygous for an associated allele and a non-associated allele should preferentially transmit the associated allele to the affected offspring. Because the non-transmitted parental allele serves as an internal control, TDT overcomes the problems of using unrelated controls in population association studies (128). Further, this test has been extended for multi-allele marker loci to accommodate the possibility that each marker allele may be associated to a different extent with the disease (138). The chances of identifying etiologic factors with these approaches is improved by the use of markers within or linked to functionally relevant candidate genes.

The study of the neonatal respiratory diseases—RDS and CAP—has involved a systematic approach to the biology and genetics of the surfactant proteins. Further advances could be facilitated by an appreciation for the clinical heterogeneity as well as for the complex interactions of genetic and/or environmental determinants underlying these diseases. A multidisciplinary approach including clinical, genetic, epidemiologic, and statistical analyses is required for the in-depth understanding of pulmonary pathophysiology.

ACKNOWLEDGMENTS

The authors thank Drs. David S Phelps and Rebecca Bascom and Mr. John Wert for their contributions, and Holly Donaldson for typing. This work is supported by National Institutes of Health grant HL34788.

Visit the *Annual Reviews home page* at
http://www.AnnualReviews.org.

Literature Cited

1. Powars D, Hiti A. 1993. Sickle cell anemia: β^s gene cluster haplotypes as genetic markers for severe disease expression. *Am. J. Dis. Child.* 147:1197–202

2. Lander ES, Schork NJ. 1994. Genetic dissection of complex traits. *Science* 265:2037–48

3. St George-Hyslop PH, Haines JL, Farrer LA, Polinsky R, Van Broeckhoven C, et al. 1990. Genetic linkage studies suggest that Alzheimer's disease is not a single homogeneous disorder. *Nature* 347:194–97

4. Pericak-Vance MA, Bebout JL, Gaskell PC Jr, Yamaoka LH, Hung WY, et al. 1991. Linkage studies in familial Alzheimer's disease: evidence for chromosome 19 linkage. *Am. J. Hum. Genet.* 48(6):1034–50

5. Froguel P, Vaxillaire M, Sun F, Velho G, Zouali H, et al. 1992. Close linkage of glucokinase locus on chromosome 7p to early-onset non-insulin-dependent diabetes mellitus. *Nature* 356:162–64

6. Yamagata K, Oda N, Kaisaki PJ, Menzel S, Furuta H, et al. 1996. Mutations in the hepatocyte nuclear factor-1α gene in maturity-onset diabetes of the young (MODY3). *Nature* 384:455–58

7. Yamagata K, Furuta H, Oda N, Kaisaki PJ, Menzel S, et al. 1996. Mutations in the hepatocyte nuclear factor-4α gene in maturity-onset diabetes of the young (MODY1). *Nature* 384:458–60

8. Romeo G, McKusick VA. 1994. Phenotypic diversity, allelic series and modifier genes. *Nat. Genet.* 7:451–53

9. Okano Y, Eisensmith RC, Güttler F, Lichter-Konecki U, Konecki DS, et al. 1991. Molecular basis of phenotypic heterogeneity in phenylketonuria. *N. Engl. J. Med.* 324:1232–38

10. Collins FS. 1992. Cystic fibrosis: molecular biology and therapeutic implications. *Science* 256:774–79

11. Newman B, Austin MA, Lee M, King MC. 1988. Inheritance of human breast cancer: evidence for autosomal dominant transmission in high-risk families. *Proc. Natl. Acad. Sci. USA* 85:3044–48

12. Easton D, Ford D, Pete J. 1993. Inherited susceptibility to breast cancer. *Cancer Surv.* 18:95–113

13. Ford D, Easton DF, Bishop DT, Narod SA, Goldgar DE, et al. 1994. Risks of cancer in BRCA1-mutation carriers. *Lancet* 343:692–95

14. Kajiwara K, Berson EL, Dryja TP. 1994. Digenic retinitis pigmentosa due to mutations at the unlinked peripherin/RDS and ROM1 loci. *Science* 264:1604–7

15. Puffenberger EG, Kauffman ER, Bolk S, Matise TC, Washington SS, et al. 1994. Identity-by-descent and association mapping of a recessive gene for Hirschsprung disease on human chromosome 13q22. *Hum. Mol. Genet.* 3(8):1217–25

16. Lifton RP, Jeunemaitre X. 1993. Finding genes that cause human hypertension. *J. Hypertens.* 11:231–36

17. DeSanctis GT, Merchant M, Beier DR, Dredge RD, Grobholz JK, et al. 1995. Quantitative locus analysis of airway hyperresponsiveness in A/J and C57BL/6J mice. *Nat. Genet.* 11:150–54

18. Fijneman RJA, de Vries SS, Jansen RC, Demant P. 1996. Complex interactions

of new quantitative trait loci, *Sluc1*, *Sluc2*, *Sluc3*, and *Sluc4*, that influence the susceptibility to lung cancer in the mouse. *Nat. Genet.* 14:465–67

19. van Wezel T, Stassen APM, Moen CJA, Hart AAM, van der Valk MA, Demant P. 1996. Gene interaction and single gene effects in colon tumour susceptibility in mice. *Nat. Genet.* 14:468–70

20. Moisan MP, Courvoisier H, Bihoreau MT, Gauguier D, Hendley ED. 1996. A major quantitative trait locus influences hyperactivity in the WKHA rat. *Nat. Genet.* 14:471–73

21. Kieswetter S, Macek M Jr, Davis C, Curristin SM, Chu CS, et al. 1993. A mutation in CFTR produces different phenotypes depending on chromosomal background. *Nat. Genet.* 5:274–78

22. Latham T, Grabowski GA, Theophilus BDM, Smith FI. 1990. Complex alleles of the acid β-glucosidase gene in Gaucher disease. *Am. J. Hum. Genet.* 47:79–86

23. Goldfarb LG, Petersen RB, Tabaton M, Brown P, LeBlanc AC, et al. 1992. Fatal familial insomnia and familial Cruetzfeldt-Jakob disease: disease phenotype determined by a DNA polymorphism. *Science* 258:806–8

24. Collaborative Study on the Genetics of Asthma (CSGA). 1997. A genome-wide search for asthma susceptibility loci in ethnically diverse populations. *Nat. Genet.* 15:389–92

25. Threadgill DW, Dlingos ZAA, Hansen LA, Tennenbaum T, Lichti U, et al. 1995. Targeted disruption of mouse EGF receptors: effect of genetic background on mutant phenotype. *Science* 269:230–38

26. Zhang Y, Lamm WJE, Albert RK, Chi EY, Henderson WR Jr, Lewis DB. 1997. Influence of the route of allergen administration and genetic background on the murine allergic pulmonary response. *Am. J. Respir. Crit. Care Med.* 155:661–69

27. Avery ME, Mead J. 1959. Surface properties in relation to atelectasis and hyaline membrane disease. *Am. J. Dis. Child.* 97:517–23

28. Gregory TJ, Longmore WJ, Moxley MA, Whitsett JA, Reed CR, Fowler AA, et al. 1991. Surfactant chemical composition and biophysical activity in acute respiratory distress syndrome. *J. Clin. Invest.* 88:1976–81

29. Honda Y, Takahashi H, Shijubo N, Kuroki Y, Akino T. 1993. Surfactant protein-A concentration in bronchoalveolar lavage fluids of patients with pulmonary alveolar proteinosis. *Chest* 103:496–99

30. Hamm H, Luhrs J, Guzman y Rotaeche J, Costabel U, Fabel H, et al. 1994. Elevated surfactant protein A in bronchoalveolar lavage fluids from sarcoidosis and hypersensitivity pneumonitis patients. *Chest* 106:1766–70

31. Veldhuizen RAW, McCaig LA, Akino T, Lewis JF. 1995. Pulmonary surfactant subfractions in patients with the acute respiratory distress syndrome. *J. Respir. Crit. Care Med.* 152:1867–71

32. Günther A, Siebert C, Schmidt R, Ziegler S, Grimminger F. 1996. Surfactant alterations in severe pneumonia, acute respiratory distress syndrome, and cardiogenic lung edema. *Am. J. Respir. Crit. Care Med.* 153:176–84

33. Bruns G, Stroh H, Veldman GM, Latt SA, Floros J. 1987. The 35 kD pulmonary surfactant-association protein is encoded on chromosome 10. *Hum. Genet.* 76:58–62

34. Floros J, Karinch AM. 1995. Human SP-A: then and now. *Am. J. Physiol.* 268(12):L162–65

35. Hoover RR, Floros J. 1997. Organization of the human SP-A and SP-D loci at 10q22-23. Physical and radiation hybrid mapping reveals gene order and orientation. *Am. J. Respir. Cell Mol. Biol.* In press

36. Karinch AM, Floros J. 1995. 5′ splicing and allelic variants of the human pulmonary surfactant protein A genes. *Am. J. Respir. Cell Mol. Biol.* 12:77–88

37. McCormick SM, Boggaram V, Mendelson CR. 1994. Characterization of mRNA transcripts and organization of human SP-A1 and SP-A2 genes. *Am. J. Physiol.* 266(10):L354–66

38. Karinch AM, deMello DE, Floros J. 1997. Effect of genotype on the levels of surfactant protein-A mRNA and on the SP-A2 splice variants in adult humans. *Biochem. J.* 321:39–47

39. Karinch AM, Floros J. 1995. Translation in vivo of 5′ untranslated-region splice variants of human surfactant protein A. *Biochem. J.* 307(2):327–330

40. Floros J, Phelps DS, Taeusch HW. 1985. Biosynthesis and in vitro translation of the major surfactant-associated protein from human lung. *J. Biol. Chem.* 260:495–500

41. Floros J, Steinbrink R, Jacobs K, Phelps D, Kriz R, et al. 1986. Isolation and characterization of cDNA clones for the 35 kDa pulmonary surfactant-associated protein. *J. Biol. Chem.* 261:9029–33

42. White R, Damm D, Miller J, Spratt K, Schilling J, et al. 1985. Isolation and characterization of the human pulmonary surfactant apoprotein gene. *Nature* 317:361–63

43. Katyal SL, Singh G, Locker J. 1992. Characterization of a second human pulmonary surfactant-associated protein SP-A gene. *Am. J. Respir. Cell Mol. Biol.* 6:446–52

44. Floros J, DiAngelo S, Koptides M, Karinch AM, Rogan P, et al. 1996. Human SP-A locus: allele frequencies and linkage disequilibrium between the two surfactant protein A genes. *Am. J. Respir. Cell Mol. Biol.* 15:489–98

45. Floros J, Karinch AM. 1995. Genetics of neonatal disease as they relate to the surfactant protein genes in surfactant therapy for lung disease. In *Surfactant Therapy for Lung Disease*, ed. C Lenfant, pp. 95–106. New York: Dekker

46. Krizkova L, Sakthivel R, Olowe SA, Rogan P, Floros J. 1994. Human SP-A: genotype and single strand conformation polymorphism analysis. *Am. J. Physiol.* 266(10):L519–27

47. McCormick SM, Mendelson CR. 1994. Human SP-A1 and SP-A2 genes are differentially regulated during development and by cAMP and glucocorticoids. *Am. J. Physiol.* 266(10):L367–74

48. Karinch AM, Deiter G, Ballard P, Floros J. 1997. Regulation of expression of human SP-A1 and SP-A2 genes in explant culture. *Pediatr. Res.* 41:A269 (Abstr.)

49. Phelps DS, Floros J, Taeusch HW. 1986. Post-translational modification of the major human surfactant-associated proteins. *Biochem. J.* 237:373–77

50. Phelps DS, Floros J. 1988. Proline hydroxylation alters the electrophoretic mobility of pulmonary surfactant-associated protein A. *Electrophoresis* 9:231–33

51. Voss T, Eistetter H, Schafer KP, Engel J. 1988. Macromolecular organization of natural and recombinant lung surfactant protein SP 28–36. Structural homology with complement factor Clq. *J. Mol. Biol.* 20:219–27

52. Voss T, Melchers K, Scheirle G, Schafer KP. 1991. Structural comparison of recombinant pulmonary surfactant protein SP-A derived from two human coding sequences: implications for the chain composition of natural human SP-A. *Am. J. Respir. Cell Mol. Biol.* 4:88–94

53. Vamvakopoulos NC, Modi WS, Floros J. 1995. Mapping the human pulmonary surfactant-associated protein B gene (SFTP3) to chromosome 2p12→p11.2. *Cytogenet. Cell Genet.* 68:8–10

54. Pilot-Matias TJ, Kister SE, Fox JF, Kropp K, Glasser SW, Whitsett JA. 1989. Structure and organization of the gene encoding human pulmonary surfactant proteolipid SP-B. *DNA* 8:75–86

55. Floros J, Phelps DS. 1997. Pulmonary surfactant. In *Anesthesia: Biologic Foundations*, ed. JF Biebuyck, C Lynch III, M Maze, WM Zapol, pp. 1257–79. New York: Raven

56. Veletza SV, Rogan PK, TenHave T, Olowe SA, Floros J. 1996. Racial differences in allelic distribution at the human pulmonary surfactant protein B gene locus (SP-B). *Exp. Lung Res.* 22:489–94

57. Floros J, Veletza SV, Kotikalapudi P, Krizkova L, Karinch AM, et al. 1995. Dinucleotide repeats in the human surfactant protein-B gene and respiratory-distress syndrome. *Biochem. J.* 305:583–90

58. Jacobs KA, Phelps DS, Steinbrink R, Fisch J, Kriz R, et al. 1987. Isolation of a cDNA clone encoding a high molecular weight precursor to a 6-kDa pulmonary surfactant-associated protein. *J. Biol. Chem.* 262:9808–11

59. Voorhout WF, Veenendaal T, Haagsman HP, Weaver TE, Whitsett JA, et al. 1992. Intracellular processing of pulmonary surfactant protein B in an endosomal/lysosomal compartment. *Am. J. Physiol.* 263(7):L479–86

60. Lin S, Akinbi HT, Breslin JS, Weaver TE. 1996. Structural requirements for targeting of surfactant protein B (SP-B) to secretory granules in vitro and in vivo. *J. Biol. Chem.* 271(33):19689–95

61. Korfhagen TR, Bruno MD, Ross GF, Huelsman KM, Ikegami M, et al. 1996. Altered surfactant function and structure in SP-A gene targeted mice. *Proc. Natl. Acad. Sci. USA* 93:9594–99

62. Ikegami M, Korfhagen TR, Bruno MD, Whitsett JA, Jobe AH. 1997. Surfactant metabolism in surfactant protein A-deficient mice. *Am. J. Physiol.* 272(16):L479–85

63. Suzuki Y, Fujita Y, Kogishi K. 1989. Reconstitution of tubular myelin from synthetic lipids and proteins associated with pig pulmonary surfactant. *Am. Rev. Respir. Dis.* 140:75–81

64. Williams MC, Hawgood S, Hamilton RL. 1991. Changes in lipid structure produced by surfactant proteins SP-A, SP-B, and SP-C. *Am. J. Respir. Cell Mol. Biol.* 5:41–50

65. Schürch S, Possmayer F, Cheng S, Cockshutt AM. 1992. Pulmonary SP-A enhances adsorption and appears to induce surface sorting of lipid extract surfactant. *Am. J. Physiol.* 263(7):L210–18

66. Pison U, Max M, Neuendank A, Weissbach S, Pietschmann S. 1994. Host defense capacities of pulmonary surfactant: evidence for 'non-surfactant' functions of the surfactant system. *Eur. J. Clin. Invest.* 24:586–99

67. Blau H, Riklis S, Kravtsov V, Kalina M. 1994. Secretion of cytokines by rat alveolar epithelial cells: possible regulatory role for SP-A. *Am. J. Physiol.* 266(10):L148–55

68. Wintergerst E, Manz-Keinke H, Plattner H, Schlepper-Schafer J. 1989. The interaction of a lung surfactant protein (SP-A) with macrophages is mannose dependent. *Eur. J. Cell Biol.* 50:291–98

69. Malhotra R, Haurum J, Thiel S, Sim RB. 1992. Interaction of Clq receptor with lung surfactant protein-A. *Eur. J. Immunol.* 22:1437–45

70. Phelps DS. 1995. Pulmonary surfactant modulation of host-defense function. *Appl. Cardiopulm. Pathophysiol.* 5:221–29

71. Wilsher ML, Hughes DA, Haslam PL. 1988. Immunoregulatory properties of pulmonary surfactant: influence of variations in the phospholipid profile. *Clin. Exp. Immunol.* 73:117–22

72. Mancini NM, Bene MC, Gerard H, Chabot F, Faure G, et al. 1993. Early effects of short-time cigarette smoking on the human lung—a study of bronchoalveolar lavage fluids. *Lung* 171:277–91

73. Wright JR, Youmans DC. 1993. Pulmonary surfactant protein A simulates chemotaxis of alveolar macrophage. *Am. J. Physiol.* 264(8):L338–44

74. Van Iwaarden JF, Van Strijp JAG, Ebskamp MJM, Welmers AC, Verhoef J, Van Golde LMG. 1991. Surfactant protein A is opsonin in phagocytosis of herpes simplex virus type 1 by rat alveolar macrophages. *Am. J. Physiol.* 261(5):L204–9

75. Van Iwaarden F, Welmers B, Verhoef J, Haagsman HP, Van Golde LMG. 1990. Pulmonary surfactant protein A enhances the host-defense mechanism of rat alveolar macrophages. *Am. J. Respir. Cell Mol. Biol.* 2:91–98

76. Kremlev SG, Umstead TM, Phelps DS. 1994. Effects of surfactant protein A and surfactant lipids on lymphocyte proliferation in vitro. *Am. J. Physiol.* 267(11):L357–64

77. Kremlev SG, Phelps DS. 1994. Surfactant protein A stimulation of inflammatory cytokine and immunoglobulin production. *Am. J. Physiol.* 267(11):L712–19

78. Kremlev SG, Umstead TM, Phelps DS. 1997. Surfactant protein A (SP-A) regulates cytokine production in the monocytic cell line THP-1. *Am. J. Physiol.* 272(16):L996–1004

79. Longo ML, Bisagno AM, Zasadzinski JAN, Bruni R, Waring AJ. 1993. A function of lung surfactant protein SP-B. *Science* 261:453–55

80. Rider ED, Ikegami M, Whitsett JA, Hull W, Absolom D, Jobe AH. 1993. Treatment responses to surfactants containing natural surfactant proteins in preterm rabbits. *Am. Rev. Respir. Dis.* 147:669–76

81. deMello DE, Chi EY, Doo E, Lagunoff D. 1987. Absence of tubular myelin in lungs of infants dying with hyaline membrane disease. *Am. J. Pathol.* 127:131–39

82. Robertson R, Kobayashi T, Ganzuka M, Grossmann G, Li WZ, Suzuki Y. 1991. Experimental neonatal respiratory failure induced by a monoclonal antibody to the hydrophobic surfactant-associated protein SP-B. *Pediatr. Res.* 30:239–43

83. Kobayashi T, Nitta K, Takahashi R, Kurashima K, Robertson B, Suzuki Y. 1991. Activity of pulmonary surfactant after blocking the associated proteins SP-A and SP-B. *J. Appl. Physiol.* 71(2):530–36

84. Nogee LM, deMello DE, Dehner LP, Colten HR. 1993. Brief report: deficiency of pulmonary surfactant protein B in congenital alveolar proteinosis. *N. Engl. J. Med.* 328:406–10

85. Clark JC, Wert SE, Bachurski CJ, Stahlman MT, Stripp BR, et al. 1995. Targeted disruption of the surfactant protein B gene disrupts surfactant homeostasis, causing respiratory failure in newborn mice. *Proc. Natl. Acad. Sci. USA* 92:7794–98

86. Clark JC, Weaver TE, Iwamoto HS, Ikegami M, Jobe AH, et al. 1997. Decreased lung compliance and air trapping in heterozygous SP-B-deficient mice. *Am. J. Respir. Cell Mol. Biol.* 16:46–52

87. Usher RH, Allen AC, McLean FH. 1971. Risk of respiratory distress syndrome related to gestational age, route of delivery and maternal diabetes. *Am. J. Obstet.*

Gynecol. 111:826–32

88. Miller HC, Futrakul P. 1968. Birth weight, gestational age, and sex as determining factors in the incidence of respiratory distress syndrome of prematurely born infants. *J. Pediar.* 72(5):628–35

89. Field DJ, Milner AD, Hopkin IE, Madeley RJ. 1987. Changing patterns in neonatal respiratory distress. *Pediatr. Pulmonol.* 3:231–35

90. Fujikura T, Fröehlich LA. 1966. The influence of race and other factors on pulmonary hyaline membranes. *Am. J. Obstet. Gynecol.* 95:572–78

91. Hulsey TC, Alexander GR, Robillard PY, Annibale DJ, Keenan A. 1993. Hyaline membrane disease: the role of ethnicity and maternal risk characteristics. *Am. J. Obstet. Gynecol.* 168:572–76

92. Farrell PM, Wood RE. 1976. Epidemiology of hyaline membrane disease in the United States: analysis of national mortality statistics. *Pediatrics* 58:167–76

93. Richardson DC, Torday JS. 1994. Racial differences in predictive value of the lecithin/sphingomyelin ratio. *Am. J. Obstet. Gynecol.* 5:1273–74

94. Olowe SA, Akinkugbe A. 1978. Amniotic fluid lecithin/sphingomyelin ratio: comparison between an African and a North American community. *Pediatrics* 62:38–41

95. Perelman RH, Palta M, Kirby R, Farrell PM. 1986. Discordance between male and female deaths due to the respiratory distress syndrome. *Pediatrics* 78(2):238–44

96. Berman S, Tanasijevic MJ, Alvarez JF, Ludmir J, Lieberman E, Richardson DK. 1996. Racial differences in the predictive value of the TDx fetal lung maturity assay. *Am. J. Obstet. Gynecol.* 175:73–77

97. Shanklin DR. 1963. The sex of premature infants with hyaline membrane disease. *South. Med. J.* 56:1018–22

98. Farrell PM, Avery ME. 1975. Hyaline membrane disease. In *American Review of Respiratory Disease*, III:657–88. US Dep. Health, Educ. Welf. Bethesda, MD: NIH

99. Khoury MJ, Marks JS, McCarthy BJ, Zaro SM. 1985. Factors affecting the sex differential in neonatal mortality: the role of respiratory distress syndrome. *Am. J. Obstet. Gynecol.* 151(6):777–82

100. Graven SN, Mesenheimer HR. 1965. Respiratory distress syndrome and the high risk mother. *Am. J. Child. Dis.* 109:489–94

101. Graven SN, Opitz JM, Harrison M. 1966. The respiratory distress syndrome: risk related to maternal factors. *Am. J. Obstet. Gynecol.* 96:969–76

102. Lankenau HM. 1976. A genetic and statistical study of the respiratory distress syndrome. *Eur. J. Pediatr.* 123:167–77

103. Myrianthopoulos NC, Churchill JA, Baszynski AJ. 1971. Respiratory distress syndrome in twins. *Acta Genet. Med. Gemellol.* 20:199–204

104. Khoury MJ, Calle EE, Joesoef RM. 1989. Recurrence of low birth weight in siblings. *J. Clin. Epidemiol.* 42(12): 1171–78

105. Klebanoff MA, Meirik O, Berendes HW. 1989. Second-generation consequences of small-for-dates birth. *Pediatrics* 84 (2):343–47

106. deMello DE, Phelps DS, Patel G, Floros J, Lagunoff D. 1989. Expression of the 35 kDa and low molecular weight surfactant-associated proteins in the lungs of infants dying with respiratory distress syndrome. *Am. J. Pathol.* 134:1285–93

107. deMello DE, Hayman S, Phelps D, Floros J. 1993. Immunogold of SP-A in lungs of infants dying from respiratory distress syndrome. *Am. J. Pathol.* 142:1631–40

108. Kala P, TenHave T, Nielsen H, Dunn M, Floros J. 1998. Association of pulmonary surfactant protein A (SP-A) gene and RDS: interaction with SP-B. *Pediatr. Res.* In press

109. Gluck L, Kulovich MV. 1973. Lecithin/sphingomyelin ratios in amniotic fluid in normal and abnormal pregnancy. *Am. J. Obstet. Gynecol.* 115(4):539–46

110. Torday J, Carson L, Lawson EE. 1979. Saturated phosphatidylcholine in amniotic fluid and prediction of the respiratory distress syndrome. *N. Engl. J. Med.* 301:1013–18

111. Hallman M, Merritt TA, Akino T, Bry K. 1991. Surfactant protein A, phosphatidylcholine, and surfactant inhibitors in epithelial lining fluid. *Am. Rev. Resp. Dis.* 144:1376–84

112. Pryhuber GS, Hull WM, Fink I, McMahan MJ, Whitsett JA. 1991. Ontogeny of surfactant proteins A and B in human amniotic fluid as indices of fetal lung maturity. *Pediatr. Res.* 30(6):597–605

113. Possmayer F. 1988. Pulmonary perspective: a proposed nomenclature for pulmonary surfactant-associated proteins. *Am. Rev. Respir. Dis.* 138:990–98

114. Teja K, Cooper PH, Squires JE, Schnatterly PT. 1981. Pulmonary alveolar pro-

teinosis in four siblings. *N. Engl. J. Med.* 305:1390–92

115. Nogee LM, Garnier G, Dietz HC, Singer L, Murphy AM, et al. 1994. A mutation in the surfactant protein B gene responsible for fatal neonatal respiratory disease in multiple kindreds. *J. Clin. Invest.* 93:1860–83

116. deMello DE, Nogee LM, Hayman S, Krous JF, Hussain M, et al. 1994. Molecular and phenotypic variability in the congenital alveolar proteinosis syndrome associated with inherited surfactant protein B deficiency. *J. Pediatr.* 125:43–50

117. Ballard PL, Nogee LM, Beers MF, Ballard RA, Planer BC, et al. 1995. Partial deficiency of surfactant protein B in an infant with chronic lung disease. *Pediatrics* 96:1046–52

118. deMello DE, Heyman S, Phelps DS, Hamvas S, Nogee L, et al. 1994. Ultrastructure of lung in surfactant protein B deficiency. *Am. J. Resp. Cell Mol. Biol.* 11:230–39

119. Hamvas A, Cole FS, deMello DE, Moxley M, Whitsett JA, et al. 1994. Surfactant protein B deficiency: antenatal diagnosis and prospective treatment with surfactant replacement. *J. Pediatr.* 125:356–61

120. Hamvas A, Nogee LM, Mallory GB, Spray TL, Huddleston CB, et al. 1997. Lung transplantation for treatment of infants with surfactant protein B deficiency. *J. Pediatr.* 130(2):231–39

121. Doyle IR, Nicholas TE, Bersten AD. 1995. Serum surfactant protein-A levels in patients with acute cardiogenic pulmonary edema and adult respiratory distress syndrome. *Am. J. Respir. Crit. Care Med.* 152:307–17

122. McCormack FX, King TE Jr, Voelker DR, Robinson PC, Mason RJ. 1991. Idiopathic pulmonary fibrosis. *Am. Rev. Respir. Dis.* 144:160–66

123. McCormack FX, King TE Jr, Bucher BL, Nielsen L, Mason RJ. 1995. Surfactant protein A predicts survival in idiopathic pulmonary fibrosis. *Am. J. Respir. Crit. Care Med.* 152:751–59

124. Masuda T, Shimura S, Sasaki H, Takishima T. 1991. Surfactant apoprotein-A concentration in sputum for diagnosis of pulmonary alveolar proteinosis. *Lancet* 337:580–82

125. Phelps DS, Rose RM. 1991. Increased recovery of surfactant protein-A in AIDS-related pneumonia. *Am. Rev. Respir. Dis.* 143:1072–75

126. Hamm H, Fabel H, Bartsch W. 1992. The surfactant system of the adult lung: physiology and clinical perspectives. *Clin. Invest.* 70:637–57

126a. Max M, Pison U, Floros J. 1996. Frequency of SP-B and SP-A1 gene polymorphisms in the acute respiratory distress syndrome (ARDS). *Appl. Cardiopulm. Pathophysiol.* 6:111–18

126b. Petty TL. 1994. Th acute respiratory distress syndrome. *Chest* 105:44S–47S (Suppl.)

126c. Bernard GR, Artigas A, Brigham KL, Carlet J, Falke K, et al, Consensus Committee. 1994. The American-European consensus conference on ARDS. Definitions, mechanisms, relevant outcomes, and clinical trial coordination. *Am. J. Respir. Crit. Care Med.* 149:818–24

127. Nagourney BA, Usher RH, Kramer MS. 1990. Is there a familial tendency in the etiology of respiratory distress syndrome? *Pediatr. Res.* 27(4):217A (Abstr.)

128. Spielman RS, McGinnis RE, Ewens WJ. 1993. Transmission test for linkage disequilibrium: the insulin gene region and insulin-dependent diabetes mellitus (IDDM). *Am. J. Hum. Genet.* 52:506–16

129. Greenberg DA. 1993. Linkage analysis of "necessary" disease loci versus "susceptibility" loci. *Am. J. Hum. Genet.* 52:135–43

130. Moya FR, Montes HF, Thomas VL, Mouzinho AM, Smith JF, Rosenfeld CR. 1994. Surfactant protein A and saturated phosphatidylcholine in respiratory distress syndrome. *Am. J. Respir. Crit. Care Med.* 150:1672–77

131. Crowley P, Chalmers I, Keirse MJNC. 1990. The effects of corticosteroid administration before preterm delivery: an overview of the evidence from controlled trials. *Brit. J. Obstet. Gynecol.* 97:11–25

132. Collaborative Group on Antenatal Steroid Therapy. 1981. Effect of antenatal dexamethasone administration on the prevention of respiratory distress syndrome. *Am. J. Obstet. Gynecol.* 141:276–87

133. NIH Consensus Conference. 1995. Effect of corticosteroids for fetal maturation on perinatal outcomes. *J. Am. Med. Assoc.* 273:413–18

134. Corder EH, Saunders AM, Strittmatter WJ, Schmechel DE, Goskel PC, et al. 1993. Gene dose of apolipoprotein-E type 4 allele and the risk of Alzheimer's disease in late onset families. *Science* 261:921–23

135. Tang MX, Maestre G, Tsai WY, Liu

XH, Feng L, et al. 1996. Relative risk of Alzheimer's disease and age-at-onset distributions, based on APOE genotypes among elderly African Americans, Caucasians, and Hispanics in New York City. *Am. J. Hum. Genet.* 58:574–84

136. Weiss KM. 1993. Segregation analysis: discrete traits in families. In *Genetic Variation and Human Disease*, ed. KM Weiss, pp. 69–91. Cambridge: Cambridge Univ. Press

137. Risch N, Merikangas K. 1996. The future of genetic studies of complex human diseases. *Science* 273:1516–17

138. Sham PC, Curtis D. 1995. An extended transmission/disequilibrium test (TDT) for multi-allele marker loci. *Ann. Med. Genet.* 59:323–36

Annu. Rev. Physiol. 1998. 60:385–405

PREBÖTZINGER COMPLEX AND PACEMAKER NEURONS: Hypothesized Site and Kernel for Respiratory Rhythm Generation

Jens C. Rekling and Jack L. Feldman
Systems Neurobiology Laboratory, Departments of Neurobiology and Physiological
Science, University of California Los Angeles, Los Angeles, California 90095-1527;
e-mail: feldman@ucla.edu

KEY WORDS: respiration, breathing, brainstem, ventral respiratory group, endogenous bursting

ABSTRACT

Identification of the sites and mechanisms underlying the generation of respiratory rhythm is of longstanding interest to physiologists and neurobiologists. Recently, with the development of novel experimental preparations, especially in vitro en bloc and slice preparations of rodent brainstem, progress has been made. In particular, a site in the ventrolateral medulla, the preBötzinger Complex, is hypothesized to contain neuronal circuits generating respiratory rhythm. Lesions or disruption of synaptic transmission within the preBötzinger Complex, either in vivo or in vitro, can abolish respiratory activity. Furthermore, the persistence of respiratory rhythm following interference with postsynaptic inhibition and the subsequent discovery of neurons with endogenous bursting properties within the preBötzinger Complex have led to the hypothesis that rhythmogenesis results from synchronized activity of pacemaker or group-pacemaker neurons.

INTRODUCTION

Breathing is a fundamental physiological process produced by movements generated and controlled by efferent signals from the nervous system. Of particular interest is understanding its underlying mechanisms in humans, and a substantial and insightful literature exists describing the phenomenology of the neural control of breathing in human subjects. Unfortunately, such experiments rarely

385

illuminate the actions of the brain at molecular, synaptic, cellular, and network levels. Until activity at the level of single neurons is routinely and noninvasively measured in humans, animal models, which permit the application of a broad range of neurobiological techniques, must serve as surrogates. For studies of neural control of breathing, anesthetized or decerebrate cats were the model of choice from 1920 to about 1985; more recently, rodents have become increasingly favored. By 1986, the location of neuronal populations that contain the basic circuits generating respiratory rhythm and pattern in the brainstem and spinal cord were well understood from in vivo experiments (Figure 1), as were interconnections, projections, firing patterns, and basic pharmacology of respiratory neurons found in these regions (see 1–6). However, in vivo preparations are poorly suited for thorough investigations of the synaptic and cellular physiology of neurons, and preparations allowing more detailed studies were needed to advance the understanding of control of respiration at the cellular and network levels. Here we review recent progress identifying critical sites and possible cellular mechanisms involved in the generation of the respiratory rhythm that have relied on novel preparations developed over the past decade, i.e. the in vitro en bloc brainstem/spinal cord preparation (7, 8) and the medullary slice isolated from neonatal rodents (9). These novel preparations generate a respiratory-related rhythm in vitro, and their exploitation has led to useful observations of the cellular and synaptic physiology of brainstem and spinal cord respiratory neurons and has suggested two hypotheses that we discuss: (*a*) Site hypothesis—the preBötzinger Complex is the site for respiratory rhythm generation; (*b*) rhythmogenesis hypothesis—pacemaker or group-pacemaker neurons are the cellular kernel for respiratory rhythm.

RESPIRATORY RHYTHMOGENESIS: LESSONS FROM IN VIVO STUDIES

Neuronal mechanisms cannot be fully studied unless the relevant sites are known. In order to understand how the respiratory rhythm is generated, the site(s) responsible for rhythm generation must be identified with precision sufficient to allow targeted cellular studies. For two millennia, there has been reasonable evidence that respiratory rhythm is generated within the brainstem. Our contemporary view is based on the observations in mammals, including traumatically injured humans, that respiratory movements of the chest and upper airways persist following transection of the neuraxis rostral to the brainstem, but that only upper airway respiratory movements persist following spinomedullary transection (1).

The brainstem contains several anatomically distinct groups of neurons (Figure 1) involved in various aspects of the neural control of breathing, such

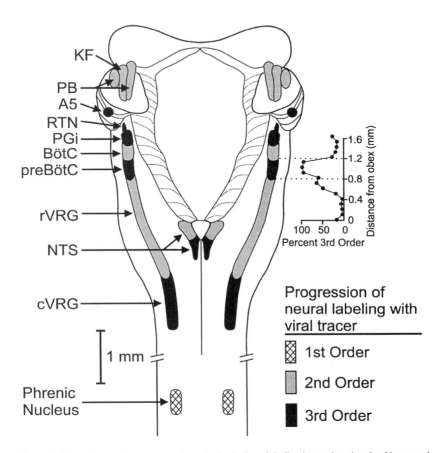

Figure 1 Dorsal view of brainstem and cervical spinal cord, indicating regions involved in control of breathing and progression of labeling with a viral tracer injected into the phrenic nerve. The percentage of labeled 3rd Order neurons (propiobulbar neurons) in the preBötzinger Complex and adjacent regions is plotted in the inset at right. Note that the preBötzinger Complex contains almost 100% 3rd Order neurons, whereas adjacent regions, rVRG, and Bötzinger Complex contain 0–20%. BötC, Bötzinger Complex; cVRG, caudal ventral respiratory group; KF, Kölliker-Fuse nucleus; NTS, nucleus tractus solitarius; PB, parabrachial nuclei; PGi, paragigantocellular reticular nucleus; preBötC, preBötzinger Complex; RTN, retrotrapezoid nucleus; rVRG, rostral ventral respiratory group (modified from 21).

as central chemoreception, afferent signal processing, rhythm generation, and motor pattern formation. Studies both in vivo and in vitro suggest a single site in the rostral medulla as critical in rhythmogenesis. The site, named the preBötzinger Complex (9, 10), is ventral to the compact division of the nucleus ambiguus, midway between the facial nucleus and the obex, caudal to the Bötzinger Complex (containing predominantly expiratory neurons) and rostral to the rostral ventral respiratory group (VRG), which contains predominantly inspiratory bulbospinal neurons (Figure 1).

Although the specific hypothesis concerning the preBötzinger Complex came from in vitro experiments and was widely disseminated in 1991 (9; see below), a retrospective analysis of earlier work in vivo points to a site in the rostral ventrolateral medulla with a central role in rhythmogenesis. Below are some observations from in vivo experiments (cat, rat, or rabbit) consistent with the preBötzinger Complex hypothesis.

1. Correlation analysis of interactions between inspiratory neurons in the ventrolateral medulla reveals that in most coupled pairs, there is an excitatory projection from a rostral neuron to a more caudal neuron (11); Segers et al (11) suggest a rostrocaudal polarization in the VRG column, with more rostral neurons driving more caudal neurons. The firing pattern of neurons located in the most rostral VRG, i.e. the preBötzinger Complex, differs from the firing pattern of neurons in the immediately rostral Bötzinger and immediately caudal VRG regions (12–14). The preBötzinger Complex contains pre-I neurons that fire before the onset of inspiratory activity, early inspiratory neurons, and postinspiratory neurons, all classes of cells proposed to be involved in respiratory phase transitions (1, 15–17). Prior to these studies, most recordings of ventrolateral respiratory neurons were much more caudal (e.g. 18, 19), skewing our view of the types, numbers, and distributions of respiratory neurons.

2. The preBötzinger Complex contains very few bulbospinal neurons and a high percentage of propriobulbar neurons (neurons with axonal arborizations in the medulla), as demonstrated by retrograde transport of fluorescent markers and trans-synaptic transport of pseudorabies virus (9, 20, 21). Thus a region 800 to 1200 μm rostral to the obex in rat, i.e. the preBötzinger Complex, contains almost 100% propriobulbar neurons, whereas the adjacent Bötzinger Complex contain $\approx$20% and the adjacent rostral ventral respiratory group (rVRG) close to 0% (21; Figure 1). These data suggest the ventrolateral respiratory cell column is heterogeneous and that most of the column, with the exception of the preBötzinger Complex, serves as a premotor nucleus controlling respiratory motoneurons.

3. Local cooling or injection of procaine (a reversible Na^+ channel blocker) into the medial area of the nucleus retrofacialis, located proximal to the preBötzinger Complex at its rostral boundary, abolishes respiration in rabbits (22, 23). Bilateral lesion of the retrofacial nucleus by radiofrequency lesions or injections of kainic acid result in cessation of all phasic phrenic discharges in cats (24).

4. Blocking excitatory synaptic transmission in vivo by microinjection of excitatory amino acid antagonists in the retrofacial area of cat (25) or rat (26) brainstem leads to perturbed rhythmogenesis and occasionally apnea. Injection of muscimol (a $GABA_A$ agonist) into the preBötzinger Complex of rats in vivo eliminates respiratory activity (27). Blockade of synaptic transmission by unilateral injection of ω-conotoxin GVIA into the adult cat preBötzinger Complex induces central apnea (28).

5. Respiratory activity persists in rostral cranial nerves after transections of the cat medulla near the obex or after destruction of neurons in the dorsal respiratory group (DRG) by kainic acid or electrocoagulation (29–31). This demonstrates that more caudal parts of the ventrolateral medulla (caudal ventral respiratory group; cVRG) and the dorsal respiratory group (DRG) are not principal sites for rhythmogenesis.

Thus the picture emerging from in vivo studies is that the rostral ventrolateral medulla may indeed have an obligatory role in rhythmogenesis, whereas more caudal and dorsal medullary structures may not.

NEURAL CONTROL OF RESPIRATION: IN VITRO MODELS

In 1984, Suzue reported that an in vitro en bloc preparation of the newborn rat brainstem and spinal cord maintained in vitro generates a spontaneous rhythmic motor output (7). Short rhythmic bursts of activity representing respiratory motor outflow are present in spinal ventral roots and cranial nerves and are in synchrony with upward movements of the (still attached) thorax (see also 8, 32). This in vitro approach was extended with the development of the transverse brainstem slice preparation, where the rhythm-generating circuits remain intact, and an endogenous respiratory-related motor output is present in rootlets of the hypoglossal (XII) nerve (9). These preparations have attracted the interest of increasing numbers of investigators who exploit them to address basic questions regarding the neural control of breathing. Six classes of problems are presently being addressed: (a) Where and how is respiratory rhythm generated? (b) What are the cellular mechanisms underlying modulation of respiratory rhythm?

(*c*) How is respiratory motoneuronal excitability controlled? (*d*) What are the sites and mechanisms of central chemoreception? (*e*) How are pulmonary afferent signals processed? and (*f*) What are the developmental sequelae underlying the fetal ontogenesis and postnatal maturation of respiratory control mechanisms?

Rhythmogenesis and the preBötzinger Complex

The idea that a compact region in the rostral ventrolateral medulla is essential for rhythmogenesis originated from in vitro studies. A series of transection studies in the newborn rat en bloc in vitro preparation (otherwise impossible in the intact animal) suggested a critical site in the rostral medulla (9). With the en bloc brainstem and spinal cord placed in a Vibratome^{TM}, respiratory rhythm persists following serial microsectioning of thin ($\approx$50–75 μm) transverse sections starting at the pontomedullary border and proceeding caudally until the caudal part of the retrofacial nucleus (rostral nucleus ambiguus; rNA) is reached. Further sectioning perturbs and then abolishes the rhythm. Similarly, caudal to rostral microsectioning, starting at the spinomedullary border, does not perturb the respiratory-related rhythm (recorded in the facial nerve) until at a level 200 μm caudal to the caudal part of the rNA. Horizontal sectioning of the medulla, dorsal to nucleus ambiguus, does not abolish the rhythm in the remaining ventral half (9, 33). These lesion experiments place a site critical for rhythm generation ventral to the rNA (RFN), midway between the facial nucleus and the obex, sandwiched between Bötzinger Complex and rVRG. In the newborn rat, this corresponds to a region between $\approx$400 and $\approx$600 μm rostral to the obex (Figure 2). A brainstem slice framed by these sections (350 μm) can generate a respiratory-related rhythmic motor output on

---→

Figure 2 Sagittal and transversal view of the location of the preBötzinger Complex. *A* Sagittal view of the ventral medulla showing the preBötzinger Complex and neighboring regions in the newborn rat. Note that the preBötzinger Complex is ventral to the nucleus ambiguus approximately midway between the facial nucleus and the obex. cNA, caudal nucleus ambiguus; LRN, lateral reticular nucleus; rNA, rostral nucleus ambiguus; rVRG, rostral ventral respiratory group; VII, facial nucleus (modified from 4). *B* Transverse section of rat brainstem at the level of the preBötzinger Complex (see *A*). Data from three types of experiments give overlapping localization of the preBötzinger Complex to the region ventral to NA. + symbols are locations of respiratory-modulated neurons in neonatal rat en bloc brainstem (modified from 32). 0 symbols are sites where injection of AMPA receptor antagonist slows then stops respiratory motor outflow in neonatal rat brainstem slice (modified from 34). X symbols represent 3rd order neurons in adult rats labeled after pseudorabies virus injections into diaphragm or phrenic nerve (modified from 21). These sites have been mapped by scaling the larger adult brainstem to the size of the neonatal brainstem and aligning with the NA as the reference point. *Inset* Triangles indicate sites where lesions affect gasping but not eupnea in adult rats. *Circles* indicate sites affecting eupnea but not gasping in adult rats. (Sites redrawn from 105.)

A

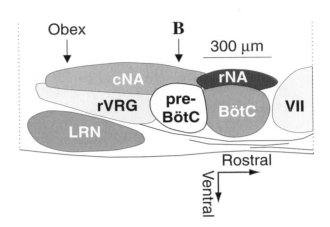

B

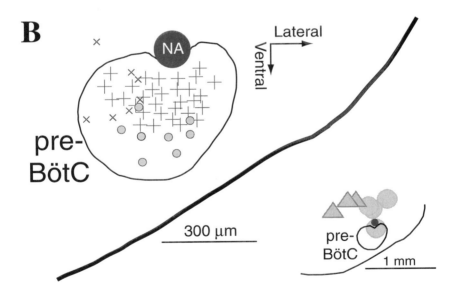

hypoglossal nerves (9). The critical site was named the preBötzinger Complex. [Given conventional neuroanatomical terminology, this region, caudal to the Bötzinger Complex, should be called the postBötzinger Complex. However, this region was identified and named by physiologists (10) who put primacy in this site as the (putative) kernel of respiratory rhythm, preceding all other sites in the timing of activity.] The importance of this region for rhythmogenesis is confirmed by injection of CNQX (a non-NMDA receptor antagonist) into the preBötzinger Complex in the slice, which completely abolishes the respiratory rhythm recorded from the hypoglossal roots (9, 34; Figure 2). These observations also establish that synaptic interactions between propriobulbar respiratory neurons in the preBötzinger Complex involve excitatory amino acids acting on AMPA channels, whose normal function is essential for rhythm generation. Conversely, synaptic inhibition mediated by the inhibitory amino acid neurotransmitters GABA or glycine is not essential for rhythm generation in the neonatal rodent, because GABA/glycine antagonists or changes in extracellular $[Cl^-]$ do not abolish respiratory rhythm (26, 35, 36).

To understand the cellular basis of rhythmogenesis, the electrophysiological, biochemical, and synaptic properties of neurons within the preBötzinger Complex need to be delineated; this work is still in its early stages. The firing pattern of neurons in the rostral ventrolateral medulla, including the VRG and the preBötzinger Complex, has been analyzed in relation to respiratory cycle phase. Several distinct respiratory-related neuron types are observed, including neurons with endogenous bursting properties (32, 33, 37–40). The intrinsic properties of inspiratory neurons found in the VRG and preBötzinger Complex reveals that different types of inspiratory neurons have A-like, I_h-like, high- and low-voltage activated Ca^{2+}, and persistent Na^+ currents (41–45). Finally, the synaptic connections between certain subtypes of respiratory neurons in the VRG within the brainstem in vitro are beginning to be elucidated (46–48). The functional phenotype (rhythm-generating, pattern-forming, premotor) of those neurons with these various properties is still unknown. Nonetheless, many models for respiratory rhythm generation have been proposed for which such properties are stipulated to be present in neurons with particular functional roles (e.g. 4, 15, 49).

Neuromodulators Affecting Rhythm

In in vitro preparations, a large number of neuromodulators, including 5-HT, histamine, acetylcholine, glutamate, substance P, thyrotropin-releasing hormone (TRH), noradrenaline, GABA, glycine, and [Met5] and [Leu5] enkephalin affect the frequency and/or amplitude of the respiratory rhythm (50–64). Several of these neuromodulators (GABA, catecholamines, TRH, substance P, μ-opioids) modulate respiratory frequency by acting on neurons within the preBötzinger Complex, activating $G_{i/o}$-protein-dependent mechanisms (59, 60,

64). For example, TRH increases respiratory frequency (50, 59, 64, 65), and putative group-pacemaker neurons (see below) are depolarized postsynaptically by this small neuropeptide. Thus postsynaptic depolarization of neurons intimately involved in rhythm generation may be a general cellular mechanism for increasing frequency (57, 59).

Synaptic Drive to Respiratory Motoneurons

Whole-cell patch recordings from respiratory-modulated spinal and cranial motoneurons have provided insights into the pharmacology and modulation of endogenous respiratory synaptic drive. The inspiratory synaptic drive to hypoglossal and phrenic motoneurons is mediated by an excitatory amino acid mainly acting on AMPA receptors. This excitatory synaptic drive is under pre- and postsynaptic modulatory control through activation of 5-HT, TRH, noradrenaline, adenosine, and metabotropic glutamate receptors (34, 66–75). Premotor neurons projecting to spinal and cranial respiratory motoneurons are located in the VRG and DRG (21, 76). The electrophysiological properties of the neurons located in the DRG have been investigated by combining retrograde labeling of premotor neurons in the ventral nucleus tractus solitarius (vNTS) (the anatomical location of the DRG) and intracellular recordings. These neurons are under modulatory control by $GABA_B$ receptors, which may control repetitive firing activity and participate in presynaptic inhibition (77–80).

Central Chemoreception and Pulmonary Reflexes

Central chemosensitivity remains functional, although blunted, in vitro, and a significant number of ventral medullary neurons in en bloc preparations are intrinsically chemosensitive (81–87). A decrease in pH (induced by increasing $[CO_2]$ in the superfusate) can depolarize or hyperpolarize respiratory neurons via postsynaptic actions (87). These responses are seen only in neurons with dendrites extending to the surface of the medulla, suggesting that the channels mediating chemosensitivity are located in distal dendrites.

When the lungs are left attached to the brainstem-spinal cord in vitro preparation, the classical Breuer-Hering expiratory prolongation (88, 89) and inspiratory shortening (N Mellen & JL Feldman, personal communication) reflexes in response to lung inflation can be elicited. The expiratory prolongation requires activation of $GABA_A$ receptors (88, 90).

Maturation of Respiratory Control Mechanisms

The use of in vitro preparations from animals of different pre- and postnatal ages reveals developmental changes in such properties as hypoxia tolerance, network connections, and neuromodulation (73, 91–99). Respiratory motor activity emerges early in the third trimester ($\approx$E17–E18 in rat) (91, 94), preceded by widespread rhythmic motor patterns that may represent activity in generalized primordial rhythm-generating networks (100). Rhythmic activity in these perinatal animals under in vitro conditions can be maintained by anaerobic metabolism and depends on high levels of glucose in the bathing solution, whereas aerobic metabolism dominates in the adult animals (92, 101).

The role of glycinergic inhibition in rhythmogenesis at different developmental stages is controversial. Slices from mice up to the age of P21 display rhythmogenesis (73, 99), and a study using a tilted-sagittal slice from rats of various postnatal ages suggests that glycinergic synaptic inhibition is essential for rhythmogenesis in animals older than 15 days (97). However, block of glycinergic transmission does not abolish respiratory rhythm in mice between P0 and P22 in the transverse slice in vitro (99). The major difference between these two studies is the amount of respiratory-related structures contained in the preparation; the blockage of rhythm in the tilted-sagittal slice in older animals may be due to an effect of glycinergic antagonist on neuronal structures upstream to the preBötzinger Complex.

CRITIQUE OF IN VITRO MODELS

The respiratory-related motor rhythm in in vitro preparations differs from that in intact animals. Under typical experimental conditions, the rhythm in vitro is slower than the resting frequency in vivo in the newborn rat: 9 cycles/min in vitro versus 46 cycles/min in vivo (32). This marked change in frequency is partly explained by removal of afferents (vagotomy in particular, which removes afferent signals from the lungs) and the low temperature under which the in vitro preparations are kept ($\approx28°C$; at body temperature, respiratory rhythm is present at higher frequency but persists for less than one hour) (32). Thus bilateral vagotomy in newborn rats in vivo decreases respiratory frequency to a level comparable to the frequency in vitro at the same temperature, and decreasing the temperature from 35 to 27°C in vitro decreases the frequency by $\approx40\%$ (32, 102).

The pattern of discharge on the phrenic and cranial nerves during inspiration changes from an incrementing pattern in vivo to a decrementing pattern in vitro. Since the discharge pattern of motor nerves during gasping is also decrementing and at a low frequency, the rhythm in vitro could represent gasping (103). However, a careful analysis suggests otherwise.

1. Lesion studies demonstrate that the preBötzinger Complex is essential for eupnea, not gasping. Respiratory-related activity in the slice disappears following complete bilateral removal of the preBötzinger Complex (104). Subsequent exposure of the slice to anoxic conditions elicits a different, more gasp-like pattern of motor output. These discharges differ from the normal rhythm in the slice by having a steeper onset and a larger amplitude. In rats, electrolytic lesions of the lateral tegmental field dorsomedial to the

nucleus ambiguus (gasping center; 103), quite distant from the preBötzinger Complex (which is ventral and ventromedial to nucleus ambiguus), abolish gasping but not eupnea (103, 105; Figure 2). Although we consider this evidence against the idea that rhythm in the slice is gasping, St John and colleagues reach a different conclusion (103); because the preBötzinger Complex is the source of rhythm in the slice and because they surmise that their gasping center is synonymous with the preBötzinger Complex, the rhythm must be gasping. We believe that their conclusions are not warranted by their data: St John and colleagues (103, 105) do not recognize the obvious distinction between the lateral tegmental field dorsomedial to the nucleus ambiguus (gasping center) and the preBötzinger Complex, which is ventral and ventromedial to the nucleus ambiguus (Figure 2). This is particularly curious because in their own experiments, lesions closer to the preBötzinger Complex abolish eupnea (see figure 4 in Reference 105). So even if there is a gasping center, it is not the preBötzinger Complex.

2. Removal of afferent inputs, such as vagotomy, have significant effects in vivo; thus a transformed pattern in vitro in the absence of all afferent input should be expected. The decrementing phrenic nerve motor discharge envelope in vitro may be induced by the loss of afferent input from the lungs, because vagotomy in vivo in young animals (<4 days) transforms respiratory motor discharge from an augmenting to a decrementing pattern (32; for example, see 106). In addition, arterially perfused in vitro preparations of adult mice or guinea pigs show either incrementing discharge envelopes or change from incrementing to decrementing envelopes throughout the recording period while the periodicity remains stable (107, 108). These observations suggest that the decrementing discharge envelope is a result of a transformed eupneic pattern and does not reflect a radical shift towards an independently generated gasp-like pattern.

3. Severe hypoxia or anoxia in the preBötzinger Complex could underlie gasping, which follows severe hypoxia in vivo, but this is not the case under standard in vitro conditions either in en bloc or in slice preparations. Careful measurements of O_2 partial pressure and pH in en bloc preparations show that the neurons located more superficial than 700 μm (including the preBötzinger Complex) are functioning under aerobic conditions (109). In slices, the diffusion distances for O_2 to deeper structures is greatly reduced due to the large rostral and caudal surfaces, and the rhythm in slices as thin as 350 μm is similar to that observed in en bloc preparations.

In conclusion, in vitro preparations have become valuable models for studies of respiratory rhythmogenesis and cellular physiology of respiratory neurons.

We believe that detailed data at the cellular and molecular level obtained in these in vitro preparations will set the stage for understanding respiration in more intact animals, provided that care is taken in extrapolating data obtained from such reduced systems.

CELLULAR BASIS OF RESPIRATORY RHYTHM GENERATION: THE PACEMAKER HYPOTHESIS

Oscillations of neural activity ranging from 500/s to 1/day are a basic feature of brain function. In brain regions where neural oscillations are fairly well understood, a detailed description of intrinsic neuronal properties, synaptic physiology, and connections have been crucial in forming constrained models that reproduce experimental data. One example is the synchronized oscillations in the thalamus, which result from interactions between intrinsic conductances and network interactions among thalamocortical and perigeniculate neurons (110, 111). The same kind of detailed information about the respiratory neurons and their interconnections is lacking, and the mechanisms underlying respiratory rhythmicity are therefore unknown. However, each investigator has a favorite hypothesis and many models have been proposed (4, 15–17, 26, 44, 49, 59, 112–114). Universally these models are based on incomplete cellular data and assumptions about connectivity and remain highly speculative, but they have been useful in focusing efforts to design experiments relevant to their elaboration and testing.

Pacemaker Neurons

The notion that neurons with pacemaker properties (relatively slow oscillations of membrane potential by cyclic activation and inactivation of intrinsic conductances or intracellular messengers, e.g. I_{Ca}, cAMP) may be involved in respiratory rhythmogenesis, initially speculative (e.g. 115), became a serious hypothesis following the observation that attenuation of Cl^--mediated synaptic inhibition does not block the respiratory-related rhythm in the en bloc in vitro preparation (26, 35, 36). Thus when the extracellular $[Cl^-]$ is reduced (36) or set at nominally zero (26), the burst discharge pattern of respiratory neurons is augmented, but the underlying rhythm in respiratory motor nerve output persists. With separate or subsequent antagonism of inhibitory amino acid receptors, i.e. $GABA_A$, $GABA_B$, and/or glycine, the rhythm remains. Other types of postsynaptic inhibition or even presynaptic inhibition could be involved, but these observations suggest that conventional reciprocal postsynaptic inhibition between groups of respiratory neurons is not the cellular basis for rhythm, making neurons intrinsically capable of generating cyclic discharges, i.e. pacemaker neurons, reasonable candidates. With the subsequent identification of the preBötzinger Complex as a putative site for rhythmogenesis, an obvious test was to determine if pacemaker neurons were present there, and they were (9). When respiratory-related rhythm in the slice is suppressed, a subclass of inspiratory-modulated neurons within the preBötzinger Complex displays oscillatory discharges in a membrane voltage window between -45 and -55 mV. The expression in these neurons of properties consistent with voltage-dependent channels with a region of negative slope in the current-voltage relationship is a characteristic signature of endogenously oscillating pacemakers (4, 5). At more hyperpolarized membrane potentials (-60 mV) these neurons show no spike activity, and when recorded from in rhythmic slices, exhibit trains of low amplitude EPSPs in phase with the inspiratory discharges on the XII nerve. The existence of neurons capable of endogenous bursting has been further substantiated by experiments showing that neurons in the preBötzinger Complex produce regular rhythmic bursts when synaptically isolated by a low-Ca^{2+}/high-Mg^{2+} solution (40). The conductances that give rise to the bursting and, more importantly, the synaptic connections among the pacemaker neurons and with the rest of the respiratory network are yet to be determined. Critical tests of the obligatory role of pacemaker neurons in respiratory rhythmogenesis will probably require such information.

The discovery of pacemaker neurons in the preBötzinger Complex led to the hypothesis that a hybrid network of pacemaker and more mundane neurons were responsible for rhythmogenesis (4, 26; Figure 3A). Thus pacemaker neurons receive tonic excitatory inputs necessary to bring the membrane potential into the voltage window where bursting occurs; the characteristic current-voltage profile (negative slope conductance) provides a means to control the bursting frequency by tonic depolarizing or hyperpolarizing inputs. Because permissive inputs may be necessary to maintain bursting, these neurons are classified as conditional bursting pacemakers. Synchronization of their oscillatory activity is proposed to be a consequence of recurrent excitatory synaptic coupling. Because of the variability of intrinsic and afferent properties, there may be a dispersion in the membrane potential and consequently the functional state (quiescent, oscillatory, beating) of different pacemaker neurons. As a wave of excitation at the onset of inspiration spreads through the network of coupled pacemaker neurons, the differences in state may lead to a spatial and temporal dispersion of onset times of spiking within the population, with some neurons bursting early and some later. In this scheme rhythmogenesis is a direct result of endogenous pacemaker properties of a certain class of neurons, but tonic excitatory input to and interconnections among pacemaker neurons is a prerequisite for synchronization of the rhythm, with inhibitory inputs regulating the shape, duration, and interval between bursts.

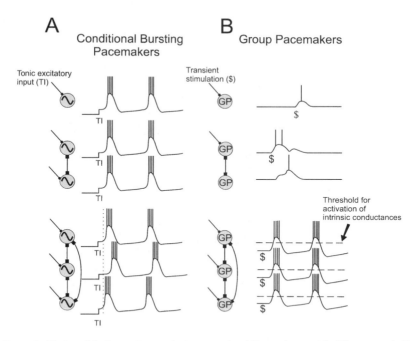

Figure 3 Two models for respiratory rhythmogenesis: *A* Pacemaker model. When synaptically isolated, single conditional bursting pacemaker neurons are capable of bursting by virtue of non-linear intrinsic properties. Tonic excitatory input may be necessary to depolarize the neurons to a level where bursting occurs, as indicated. The oscillation of two coupled pacemaker neurons would synchronize through mutual excitatory connections. The oscillation of many coupled pacemaker neurons would synchronize, although there could be a temporal and amplitude dispersion of the on- and offset of individual bursting because the strength of the tonic inputs might vary. *B* Group-pacemaker model. Single group-pacemaker neurons are incapable of intrinsic bursting, either when stimulated ($) by transient (or tonic) excitatory input or intracellular current. Two coupled group-pacemaker would excite each other through recurrent synaptic connections, but the associated depolarization would be too small for activation of burst firing and subsequent long-lasting hyperpolarization. Transient (or tonic) stimulation of several coupled group-pacemaker neurons would lead to self-sustained burst firing, as phasic synaptic input would recruit depolarizing and hyperpolarizing intrinsic conductances.

Onimaru and coworkers have described a group of neurons (Pre-I neurons) with endogenous bursting properties that fire preceding and succeeding cervical root (C4) inspiratory activity but are silent during inspiration (38). These neurons are proposed to be the primary respiratory rhythm-generating neurons by virtue of their endogenous bursting properties (39, 114). However, this class of cells is generally found more rostral in the medulla than the preBötzinger Complex in the en bloc preparation and has yet to be observed (or reported) in the oscillating slice preparation (40, 44), raising doubts about their obligatory role in rhythmogenesis.

Group-Pacemaker Neurons

A different class of neurons with special voltage-dependent conductances in the preBötzinger Complex may underlie respiratory rhythmogenesis (44, 59). Three different types of inspiratory neurons (types 1–3), located rostral to and within the preBötzinger Complex, can be identified based on their characteristic response to current injection and membrane potential trajectory throughout the respiratory cycle (44). Approximately 50% of the type-1 neurons have endogenous bursting properties and an A-like current. Type-2 neurons have an I_h-like current, and type-3 a low-voltage-activated Ca^{2+}-like current. All three types receive excitatory synaptic input before the onset of the XII nerve inspiratory burst, but with very different latencies (type-1: ≈400 ms; type-2: ≈170 ms; type-3: ≈100 ms). Of interest are the type-1 neurons, with the earliest onset prior to inspiration, because they exhibit a prolonged postinspiratory hyperpolarization that lasts throughout expiration. This long-lasting hyperpolarization does not reverse at hyperpolarized potentials (JC Rekling, unpublished data) and therefore appears to result from activation of an intrinsic conductance by the phasic depolarization produced by the inspiratory synaptic drive. Interestingly, long-lasting hyperpolarizations in type-1 neurons are not elicited by transient somatic current injection, i.e. with the same duration as an inspiratory burst, suggesting that the currents flowing or transmitters released during inspiration recruit a different set of intrinsic conductances than current injection at the soma. Thus the oscillation of membrane potential in these neurons is driven by depolarization at the onset of inspiration triggered by excitatory input, and hyperpolarization between inspirations due to an intrinsic conductance activated by the inspiratory depolarization (Figure 3B). Given these properties, such neurons could form a group-pacemaker driving respiratory rhythm (59). In the group-pacemaker hypothesis, type-1 neurons, mutually interconnected by excitatory connections, initiate inspiration by generating a population burst of activity from positive, i.e. recurrent, feedback. Endogenous membrane properties would then amplify the depolarizing action of recurrent synaptic input before and at the onset of inspiration. During inspiration, various conductances would be activated in these neurons (e.g. I_{Ca^{2+},K^+}, or electrogenic pumps) that terminate the inspiratory burst and produce an obligatory and prolonged hyperpolarization. During the initial part of the long-lasting hyperpolarization, type-1 neurons remain below threshold for firing; as these neurons slowly depolarize during expiration, the most excitable type-1 neurons start to spike, leading to another positive feedback cycle initiating the next inspiration. Respiratory frequency would be regulated by tonic excitatory and inhibitory inputs to type-1 neurons by affecting the time it takes for their membrane potential to reach threshold for spikes and for activating conductances that terminate their bursts. The fact that TRH depolarizes type-1 neurons postsynaptically and increases the frequency of the rhythm (59) is consistent with this latter proposal. An important distinction of the group-pacemaker hypothesis is that individual neurons need not generate cyclic burst discharges when synaptically isolated or in response to tonic (or transient) input and that rhythm generation is a property that emerges from the recurrent interactions among these neurons. The intrinsic conductances serve to phase-lock mutually interconnected type-1 neurons during inspiration and expiration, and phasic recurrent synaptic input may be necessary for full activation of these properties.

CONCLUSION

In vivo and in vitro experiments point to a single site in the rostral ventrolateral medulla, the preBötzinger Complex, as critical for respiratory rhythmogenesis. The development of preparations that continue to generate a respiratory-related rhythm in vitro has been instrumental in forming and testing this hypothesis. The persistence of rhythmogenesis after removal of Cl^--mediated inhibition and the presence of conditional bursting pacemakers and putative group-pacemakers in the preBötzinger Complex have led to the hypotheses that respiratory rhythm may be generated by interconnected pacemaker cells or group-pacemaker cells. In the long run, the impetus that these hypotheses have given investigators to exploit in vitro preparations and to tackle fundamental problems of neural control of breathing may be as important as whether these hypotheses are correct.

ACKNOWLEDGMENTS

This work was supported in part by grants from the National Institutes of Health: NS 24742, HL 37941, and HL 40959.

Visit the *Annual Reviews home page* at
http://www.AnnualReviews.org.

Literature Cited

1. Feldman J. 1986. Neurophysiology of breathing in mammals. In *Handbook of Physiology. The Nervous System. Intrinsic Regulatory System in the Brain*, ed. FE Bloom, pp. 463–524. Washington, DC: Am. Physiol. Soc.
2. Bianchi A, Denavit-Saubie M, Champagnat J. 1995. Central control of breathing in mammals: neuronal circuitry, membrane properties, and neurotransmitters. *Physiol. Rev.* 75:1–45
3. Duffin J, Ezure K, Lipski J. 1995. Breathing rhythm generation: focus on the rostral ventrolateral medulla. *News Physiol. Sci.* 10:133–40
4. Smith J, Funk G, Johnson S, Feldman J. 1995. Cellular and synaptic mechanisms generating respiratory rhythms: insights

from in vitro and computational studies. In *Ventral Brainstem Mechanisms and Control of Respiration and Blood Pressure*, ed. C Trouth, R Millis, H Kiwull-Schone, M Schlafke, pp. 463–96. New York: Dekker

5. Feldman J, Smith J. 1995. Neural control of respiratory pattern in mammals: an overview. In *Regulation of Breathing*, ed. J Dempsey, A Pack, pp. 39–69. New York: Dekker

6. Richter D, Ballanyi K, Ramirez J. 1996. Respiratory rhythm generation. In *Neural Control of Respiratory Muscles*, ed. A Miller, A Bianchi, B Bishop, pp. 119–31. Boca Raton: CRC Press

7. Suzue T. 1984. Respiratory rhythm generation in the in vitro brain stem-spinal cord preparation of the neonatal rat. *J. Physiol.* 354:173–83

8. Smith J, Feldman J. 1987. In vitro brainstem-spinal cord preparations for study of motor systems for mammalian respiration and locomotion. *J. Neurosci. Methods* 21:321–33

9. Smith J, Ellenberger H, Ballanyi K, Richter D, Feldman J. 1991. Pre-Bötzinger complex: a brainstem region that may generate respiratory rhythm in mammals. *Science* 254:726–29

10. Feldman J, Connelly C, Ellenberger H, Smith J. 1990. The cardiorespiratory circuitry within the brainstem. *Eur. J. Neurosci. Suppl.* 3:171

11. Segers L, Shannon R, Saporta S, Lindsey B. 1987. Functional associations among simultaneously monitored lateral medullary respiratory neurons in the cat. I. Evidence for excitatory and inhibitory actions of inspiratory neurons. *J. Neurophysiol.* 57:1078–100

12. Ezure K. 1990. Synaptic connections between medullary respiratory neurons and considerations on the genesis of respiratory rhythm. *Prog. Neurobiol.* 35:429–50

13. Schwarzacher S, Smith J, Richter D. 1995. Pre-Bötzinger complex in the cat. *J. Neurophysiol.* 73:1452–61

14. Connelly C, Dobbins E, Feldman J. 1992. Pre-Bötzinger complex in cats: respiratory neuronal discharge patterns. *Brain Res.* 590:337–40

15. Rybak I, Paton J, Schwaber J. 1997. Modeling neural mechanisms for genesis of respiratory rhythm and pattern. I. Models of respiratory neurons. *J. Neurophysiol.* 77:1994–2006

16. Rybak I, Paton J, Schwaber J. 1997. Modeling neural mechanisms for genesis of respiratory rhythm and pattern. II. Network models of the central respiratory pattern generator. *J. Neurophysiol.* 77:2007–26

17. Rybak I, Paton J, Schwaber J. 1997. Modeling neural mechanisms for genesis of respiratory rhythm and pattern. III. Comparison of model performances during afferent nerve stimulation. *J. Neurophysiol.* 77:2027–39

18. Ballantyne D, Richter D. 1986. The non-uniform character of expiratory synaptic activity in expiratory bulbospinal neurones of the cat. *J. Physiol.* 370:433–56

19. Richter D, Heyde F, Gabriel M. 1975. Intracellular recordings from different types of medullary respiratory neurons of the cat. *J. Neurophysiol.* 38:1162–71

20. Ellenberger H, Feldman J. 1990. Subnuclear organization of the lateral tegmental field of the rat. I: nucleus ambiguus and ventral respiratory group. *J. Comp. Neurol.* 294:202–11

21. Dobbins E, Feldman J. 1994. Brainstem network controlling descending drive to phrenic motoneurons in rat. *J. Comp. Neurol.* 347:64–86

22. Budzinska K, von Eulen EC, Kao F, Pantaleo T, Yamamoto Y. 1985. Effects of graded focal cold block in rostral areas of the medulla. *Acta Physiol. Scand.* 124:329–40

23. Zhang F, Wu Z, Li Y. 1991. Effect of blocking medial area of nucleus retrofacialis on respiratory rhythm. *Respir. Physiol.* 85:73–81

24. St. John W, Hwang Q, Nattie E, Zhou D. 1989. Functions of the retrofacial nucleus in chemosensitivity and ventilatory neurogenesis. *Respir. Physiol.* 76:159–71

25. Abrahams T, Hornby P, Walton D, Taveira DA, Gillis R. 1991. An excitatory amino acid(s) in the ventrolateral medulla is (are) required for breathing to occur in the anesthetized cat. *J. Pharmacol. Exp. Ther.* 259:1388–95

26. Feldman J, Smith J. 1989. Cellular mechanisms underlying modulation of breathing pattern in mammals. *Ann. NY Acad. Sci.* 563:114–30

27. Koshiya N, Guyenet P. 1996. Tonic sympathetic chemoreflex after blockade of respiratory rhythmogenesis in the rat. *J. Physiol.* 491:859–69

28. Ramirez J, Pierrefiche O, Schwarzacher S, Filloux F, McIntosh J, et al. 1994. The influence of N-type calcium channel blockers on the respiratory network of adult cats. *Soc. Neurosci. Abstr.* 20:1755

29. Speck D, Feldman J. 1982. The effects of microstimulation and microlesions in the ventral and dorsal respiratory groups in medulla of cat. *J. Neurosci.* 2:744–57

30. Huang Q, St. John W. 1988. Respiratory neural activities after caudal-to-rostral ablation of medullary regions. *J. Appl. Physiol.* 64:1405–11

31. Hilaire G, Monteau R, Gauthier P, Rega P, Morin D. 1990. Functional significance of the dorsal respiratory group in adult and newborn rats: in vivo and in vitro studies. *Neurosci. Lett.* 111:133–38

32. Smith J, Greer J, Liu G, Feldman J. 1990. Neural mechanisms generating respiratory pattern in mammalian brain stem-spinal cord in vitro. I. Spatiotemporal patterns of motor and medullary neuron activity. *J. Neurophysiol.* 64:1149–69

33. Arata A, Onimaru H, Homma I. 1990. Respiration-related neurons in the ventral medulla of newborn rats in vitro. *Brain Res. Bull.* 24:599–604

34. Funk G, Smith J, Feldman J. 1993. Generation and transmission of respiratory oscillations in medullary slices: role of excitatory amino acids. *J. Neurophysiol.* 70:1497–515

35. Smith J, Feldman J. 1987. Central respiratory pattern generation studied in an in vitro mammalian brainstem-spinal cord preparation. In *Respiratory Muscles and Their Neural Control,* ed. G Sieck, W Cameron, S Gandivia, pp. 27–36. New York: Liss

36. Onimaru H, Arata A, Homma I. 1990. Inhibitory synaptic inputs to the respiratory rhythm generator in the medulla isolated from newborn rats. *Pflügers Arch.* 417:425–32

37. Onimaru H, Homma I. 1987. Respiratory rhythm generator neurons in medulla of brainstem-spinal cord preparation from newborn rat. *Brain Res.* 403:380–84

38. Onimaru H, Arata A, Homma I. 1987. Localization of respiratory rhythm-generating neurons in the medulla of brainstem-spinal cord preparations from newborn rats. *Neurosci. Lett.* 78:151–55

39. Onimaru H, Arata A, Homma I. 1989. Firing properties of respiratory rhythm generating neurons in the absence of synaptic transmission in rat medulla in vitro. *Exp. Brain Res.* 76:530–36

40. Johnson S, Smith J, Funk G, Feldman J. 1994. Pacemaker behavior of respiratory neurons in medullary slices from neonatal rat. *J. Neurophysiol.* 72:2598–608

41. Smith J, Ballanyi K, Richter D. 1992. Whole-cell patch-clamp recordings from respiratory neurons in neonatal rat brainstem in vitro. *Neurosci. Lett.* 134:153–56

42. Onimaru H, Homma I. 1992. Whole cell recordings from respiratory neurons in the medulla of brainstem-spinal cord prepara-

tions isolated from newborn rats. *Pflügers Arch.* 420:399–406

43. Onimaru H, Arata A, Homma I. 1995. Intrinsic burst generation of preinspiratory neurons in the medulla of brainstem-spinal cord preparations isolated from newborn rats. *Exp. Brain Res.* 106:57–68

44. Rekling J, Champagnat J, Denavit-Saubie M. 1996. Electroresponsive properties and membrane potential trajectories of three types of inspiratory neurons in the newborn mouse brain stem in vitro. *J. Neurophysiol.* 75:795–810

45. Onimaru H, Ballanyi K, Richter D. 1996. Calcium-dependent responses in neurons of the isolated respiratory network of newborn rats. *J. Physiol.* 491:677–95

46. Onimaru H, Homma I, Iwatsuki K. 1992. Excitation of inspiratory neurons by preinspiratory neurons in rat medulla in vitro. *Brain Res. Bull.* 29:879–82

47. Onimaru H, Kashiwagi M, Arata A, Homma I. 1993. Possible mutual excitatory couplings between inspiratory neurons in caudal ventrolateral medulla of brainstem-spinal cord preparation isolated from newborn rat. *Neurosci. Lett.* 150:203–6

48. Kashiwagi M, Onimaru H, Homma I. 1993. Correlation analysis of respiratory neuron activity in ventrolateral medulla of brainstem-spinal cord preparation isolated from newborn rat. *Exp. Brain Res.* 95:277–90

49. Ramirez J, Richter D. 1996. The neuronal mechanisms of respiratory rhythm generation. *Curr. Opin. Neurobiol.* 6:817–25

50. Murakoshi T, Suzue T, Tamai S. 1985. A pharmacological study on respiratory rhythm in the isolated brainstem-spinal cord preparation of the newborn rat. *Br. J. Pharmacol.* 86:95–104

51. Hilaire G, Monteau R, Errchidi S. 1989. Possible modulation of the medullary respiratory rhythm generator by the noradrenergic A5 area: an in vitro study in the newborn rat. *Brain Res.* 485:325–32

52. Errchidi S, Hilaire G, Monteau R. 1990. Permanent release of noradrenaline modulates respiratory frequency in the newborn rat: an in vitro study. *J. Physiol.* 429:497–510

53. Morin D, Hennequin S, Monteau R, Hilaire G. 1990. Serotonergic influences on central respiratory activity: an in vitro study in the newborn rat. *Brain Res.* 535:281–87

54. Morin D, Monteau R, Hilaire G. 1991. 5-Hydroxytryptamine modulates central respiratory activity in the newborn rat: an

in vitro study. *Eur. J. Pharmacol.* 192:89–95

55. Errchidi S, Monteau R, Hilaire G. 1991. Noradrenergic modulation of the medullary respiratory rhythm generator in the newborn rat: an in vitro study. *J. Physiol.* 443:477–98

56. Di Pasquale E, Morin D, Monteau R, Hilaire G. 1992. Serotonergic modulation of the respiratory rhythm generator at birth: an in vitro study in the rat. *Neurosci. Lett.* 143:91–95

57. Yamamoto Y, Onimaru H, Homma I. 1992. Effect of substance P on respiratory rhythm and pre-inspiratory neurons in the ventrolateral structure of rostral medulla oblongata: an in vitro study. *Brain Res.* 599:272–76

58. Arata A, Onimaru H, Homma I. 1993. Effects of cAMP on respiratory rhythm generation in brainstem-spinal cord preparation from newborn rat. *Brain Res.* 605:193–99

59. Rekling J, Champagnat J, Denavit-Saubie M. 1996. Thyrotropin-releasing hormone (TRH) depolarizes a subset of inspiratory neurons in the newborn mouse brain stem in vitro. *J. Neurophysiol.* 75:811–19

60. Johnson S, Smith J, Feldman J. 1996. Modulation of respiratory rhythm in vitro: role of Gi/o protein-mediated mechanisms. *J. Appl. Physiol.* 80:2120–33

61. Bonham A. 1995. Neurotransmitters in the CNS control of breathing. *Respir. Physiol.* 101:219–30

62. Greer J, Carter J, Al-Zubaidy Z. 1995. Opioid depression of respiration in neonatal rats. *J. Physiol.* 485:845–55

63. Al-Zubaidy Z, Erickson R, Greer J. 1996. Serotonergic and noradrenergic effects on respiratory neural discharge in the medullary slice preparation of neonatal rats. *Pflügers Arch.* 431:942–49

64. Greer J, Al-Zubaidy Z, Carter J. 1996. Thyrotropin-releasing hormone stimulates perinatal rat respiration in vitro. *Am. J. Physiol.* 271:R1160–41

65. Hedner J, Hedner T, Jonason J, Lundberg D. 1981. Central respiratory stimulant effect by thyrotropin in releasing hormone in the rat. *Neurosci. Lett.* 25:317–20

66. McCrimmon D, Smith J, Feldman J. 1989. Involvement of excitatory amino acids in neurotransmission of inspiratory drive to spinal respiratory motoneurons. *J. Neurosci.* 9:1910–21

67. Liu G, Feldman J, Smith J. 1990. Excitatory amino acid-mediated transmission of inspiratory drive to phrenic motoneurons. *J. Neurophysiol.* 64:423–36

68. Greer J, Smith J, Feldman J. 1991. Role of excitatory amino acids in the generation and transmission of respiratory drive in neonatal rat. *J. Physiol.* 437:727–49

69. Greer J, Smith J, Feldman J. 1992. Glutamate release and presynaptic action of AP4 during inspiratory drive to phrenic motoneurons. *Brain Res.* 576:355–57

70. Monteau R, Morin D, Hennequin S, Hilaire G. 1990. Differential effects of serotonin on respiratory activity of hypoglossal and cervical motoneurons: an in vitro study on the newborn rat. *Neurosci. Lett.* 111:127–32

71. Morin D, Monteau R, Hilaire G. 1992. Compared effects of serotonin on cervical and hypoglossal inspiratory activities: an in vitro study in the newborn rat. *J. Physiol.* 451:605–29

72. Lindsay A, Feldman J. 1993. Modulation of respiratory activity of neonatal rat phrenic motoneurones by serotonin. *J. Physiol.* 461:213–33

73. Funk G, Smith J, Feldman J. 1994. Development of thyrotropin-releasing hormone and norepinephrine potentiation of inspiratory-related hypoglossal motoneuron discharge in neonatal and juvenile mice in vitro. *J. Neurophysiol.* 72:2538–41

74. Dong X, Feldman J. 1995. Modulation of inspiratory drive to phrenic motoneurons by presynaptic adenosine A1 receptors. *J. Neurosci.* 15:3458–67

75. Dong X, Morin D, Feldman J. 1996. Multiple actions of 1S,3R-ACPD in modulating endogenous synaptic transmission to spinal respiratory motoneurons. *J. Neurosci.* 16:4971–82

76. Ono T, Ishiwata Y, Inaba N, Kuroda T, Nakamura Y. 1994. Hypoglossal premotor neurons with rhythmical inspiratory-related activity in the cat: localization and projection to the phrenic nucleus. *Exp. Brain Res.* 98:1–12

77. Dekin M, Getting P, Johnson S. 1987. In vitro characterization of neurons in the ventral part of the nucleus tractus solitarius. I. Identification of neuronal types and repetitive firing properties. *J. Neurophysiol.* 58:195–214

78. Dekin M, Getting P. 1987. In vitro characterization of neurons in the ventral part of the nucleus tractus solitarius. II. Ionic basis for repetitive firing patterns. *J. Neurophysiol.* 58:215–29

79. Wagner P, Dekin M. 1993. GABA$_b$ receptors are coupled to a barium-insensitive outward rectifying potassium conductance in premotor respiratory neurons. *J. Neurophysiol.* 69:286–89

80. Dekin M. 1993. Inward rectification and its effects on the repetitive firing properties of bulbospinal neurons located in the ventral part of the nucleus tractus solitarius. *J. Neurophysiol.* 70:590–601

81. Harada Y, Kuno M, Wang Y. 1985. Differential effects of carbon dioxide and pH on central chemoreceptors in the rat in vitro. *J. Physiol.* 368:679–93

82. Monteau R, Morin D, Hilaire G. 1990. Acetylcholine and central chemosensitivity: in vitro study in the newborn rat. *Respir. Physiol.* 81:241–53

83. Issa F, Remmers J. 1992. Identification of a subsurface area in the ventral medulla sensitive to local changes in PCO_2. *J. Appl. Physiol.* 72:439–46

84. Okada Y, Muckenhoff K, Scheid P. 1993. Hypercapnia and medullary neurons in the isolated brain stem-spinal cord of the rat. *Respir. Physiol.* 93:327–36

85. Morin-Surun M, Boudinot E, Schafer T, Denavit-Saubie M. 1995. Localization of chemosensitive structures in the isolated brainstem of adult guinea-pig. *J. Physiol.* a 485:203–12

86. Volker A, Ballanyi K, Richter D. 1995. Anoxic disturbance of the isolated respiratory network of neonatal rats. *Exp. Brain Res.* 103:9–19

87. Kawai A, Ballantyne D, Muckenhoff K, Scheid P. 1996. Chemosensitive medullary neurones in the brainstem-spinal cord preparation of the neonatal rat. *J. Physiol.* 492:277–92

88. Murakoshi T, Otsuka M. 1985. Respiratory reflexes in an isolated brainstem-lung preparation of the newborn rat: possible involvement of gamma-aminobutyric acid and glycine. *Neurosci. Lett.* 62:63–68

89. Mellen N, McCrimmon D, Feldman J. 1996. Expiratory (E-)neurons mediate expiratory lengthening in a lung attached in vitro brainstem-spinal cord preparation. *Soc. Neurosci. Abstr.* 22:1596

90. McCrimmon D, Mellen N, Feldman J. 1996. Lung inflation-induced expiratory lengthening requires $GABA_A$ receptor activation in a lung attached in vitro brainstem-spinal cord preparation. *Soc. Neurosci. Abstr.* 22:1596

91. Greer J, Smith J, Feldman J. 1992. Respiratory and locomotor patterns generated in the fetal rat brain stem-spinal cord in vitro. *J. Neurophysiol.* 67:996–99

92. Ballanyi K, Kuwana S, Volker A, Morawietz G, Richter D. 1992. Developmental changes in the hypoxia tolerance of the in vitro respiratory network of rats. *Neu-*

rosci. Lett. 148:141–44

93. Di Pasquale E, Monteau R, Hilaire G. 1994. Endogenous serotonin modulates the fetal respiratory rhythm: an in vitro study in the rat. *Brain Res. Dev. Brain Res.* 80:222–32

94. Di Pasquale E, Monteau R, Hilaire G. 1994. Involvement of the rostral ventrolateral medulla in respiratory rhythm genesis during the peri-natal period: an in vitro study in newborn and fetal rats. *Brain Res. Dev. Brain Res.* 78:243–52

95. Paton J, Ramirez J, Richter D. 1994. Mechanisms of respiratory rhythm generation change profoundly during early life in mice and rats. *Neurosci. Lett.* 170:167–70

96. Paton J, Ramirez J, Richter D. 1994. Functionally intact in vitro preparation generating respiratory activity in neonatal and mature mammals. *Pflügers Arch.* 428:250–60

97. Paton J, Richter D. 1995. Role of fast inhibitory synaptic mechanisms in respiratory rhythm generation in the maturing mouse. *J. Physiol.* 484:505–21

98. Paton J, Richter D. 1995. Maturational changes in the respiratory rhythm generator of the mouse. *Pflügers Arch.* 430:115–24

99. Ramirez J, Quellmalz U, Richter D. 1996. Postnatal changes in the mammalian respiratory network as revealed by the transverse brainstem slice of mice. *J. Physiol.* 491:799–812

100. Champagnat J, Fortin G. 1997. Primordial respiratory-like rhythm generation in the vertebrate embryo. *Trends Neurosci.* 20:119–24

101. Ballanyi K, Volker A, Richter D. 1996. Functional relevance of anaerobic metabolism in the isolated respiratory network of newborn rats. *Pflügers Arch.* 432:741–48

102. Fedorko L, Kelly E, England S. 1988. Importance of vagal afferents in determining ventilation in newborn rats. *J. Appl. Physiol.* 65:1033–39

103. St John W. 1996. Medullary regions for neurogenesis of gasping: noeud vital or noeuds vitals *J. Appl. Physiol.* 81:1865–77

104. Ramirez J, Telgkamp P, Elsen F, Richter D. 1996. Gasp-like activity in the transverse rhythmic slice preparation of mice. *Soc. Neurosci. Abstr.* 22:1373

105. Fung M, Wang W, St John W. 1994. Medullary loci critical for expression of gasping in adult rats. *J. Physiol.* 480:597–611

106. Wang W, Fung M, Darnall R, St. John W. 1996. Characterizations and comparisons of eupnoea and gasping in neonatal rats. *J. Physiol.* 490:277–92

107. Paton J. 1996. The ventral medullary respiratory network of the mature mouse studied in a working heart-brainstem preparation. *J. Physiol.* 493:819–31

108. Morin-Surun M, Boudinot E, Sarraseca H, Fortin G, Denavit-Saubie M. 1992. Respiratory network remains functional in a mature guinea pig brainstem isolated in vitro. *Exp. Brain Res.* 90:375–83

109. Brockhaus J, Ballanyi K, Smith J, Richter D. 1993. Microenvironment of respiratory neurons in the in vitro brainstem-spinal cord of neonatal rats. *J. Physiol.* 462:421–45

110. Bal T, von Krosigk M, McCormick D. 1995. Synaptic and membrane mechanisms underlying synchronized oscillations in the ferret lateral geniculate nucleus in vitro. *J. Physiol.* 483:641–63

111. McCormick D, Bal T. 1997. Sleep and arousal: thalamocortical mechanisms. *Annu. Rev. Neurosci.* 20:185–215

112. Richter D, Ballanyi K, Schwarzacher S. 1992. Mechanisms of respiratory rhythm generation. *Curr. Opin. Neurobiol.* 2:788–93

113. Ogilvie M, Gottschalk A, Anders K, Richter D, Pack A. 1992. A network model of respiratory rhythmogenesis. *Am. J. Physiol.* 263:R962–75

114. Onimaru H. 1995. Studies of the respiratory center using isolated brainstem-spinal cord preparations. *Neurosci. Res.* 21:183–90

115. Feldman J, Cleland C. 1982. Possible roles of pacemaker neurons in mammalian respiratory rhythmogenesis. In *Cellular Pacemakers,* ed. D Carpenter, pp. 104–28. New York: Wiley

Annu. Rev. Physiol. 1998. 60:407–29

SEXUAL DIFFERENTIATION OF AVIAN BRAIN AND BEHAVIOR: Current Views on Gonadal Hormone-Dependent and Independent Mechanisms

Barney A. Schlinger

Department of Physiological Science, and Laboratory of Neuroendocrinology, Brain Research Institute, University of California, Los Angeles, California 90095-1927; e-mail: Schlinge@lifesci.ucla.edu

KEY WORDS: steroids, song system, estrogens, songbirds, quail

ABSTRACT

Gonadal hormones are known to act during development to establish permanent sex differences in the anatomy and function of the vertebrate brain. They also act on the adult brain to activate reproductive behaviors. However, there are wide gaps in our understanding of how sexually dimorphic neural circuits translate into sex differences in behavior and other CNS functions. Moreover, not all sexually dimorphic properties of the adult brain can be attributed to known effects of gonadal hormones during development or adulthood, and factors other than gonadal steroids may contribute to these sex differences. This paper reviews sexual differentiation and the role of gonadal steroids and non-gonadal factors on sexually dimorphic development of the avian brain.

INTRODUCTION

The evolutionary forces that lead to speciation create individual organisms with great genotypic and phenotypic similarity. An enormous number of common molecular events must occur to sculpt individuals of a species. Yet, within the common genetic boundaries that define a species, there is wide diversity of individual phenotypes. The most striking differences in phenotypes are between males and females of the same species.

407

0066-4278/98/0315-0407$08.00

Elucidation of the processes underlying sex determination, sexual differentiation, and sexual behavior has been a major preoccupation of biologists for decades. The pioneering work of Jost and others established that many sex differences in anatomy, physiology, and behavior can be controlled by hormones and that manipulation of the internal environment during development can lead to permanent differences in the expression of sex-specific behaviors and reproductive physiology (1–4). Efforts then concentrated on identification of the discrete properties of the brain (anatomical, physiological, chemical) that determine sexually dimorphic behaviors.

These undertakings have provided insight into many steroid-dependent, sexually differentiated traits, beginning with the expression of sex-specific gene products in the gonadal primordium, the formation of the gonads, and the secretion of different hormones by the gonads during embryogenesis. Thus the exposure of males and females to different hormonal milieus during development cause many of the sex differences in the brain and in behavior. For example, the secretion of testosterone by the testes of fetal rats induces the differentiation of a spinal neural circuit that controls muscles involved in erection of the penis (5, 6). The target muscles of these motoneurons are well established, and the actions of hormones developmentally to promote survival of the penile muscles and their motoneurons are well characterized. The chain of events linking the development of the testes and the development of this neuromuscular system is logical in the sense that testicular gametogenesis would be useless in the absence of physical machinery necessary to achieve insemination of the female. Thus it is a logical evolutionary step to allow the testes to direct subsequent physical attributes required to allow proper testicular function, including actions on the neuromuscular system that control penile erection.

However, some sexually dimorphic behaviors are not so clearly tied to gonadal function—for example, certain dimorphic cognitive functions in humans (7). Indeed, some aspects of sex-specific brain development may be hormone independent. For example, cells cultured from brains of male and female rodent embryos before the onset of gonadal hormone secretion develop some sex-specific neurochemical properties (8). Thus the dogma that gonadal hormones control all aspects of brain sexual differentiation may not be true.

The study of avian species has contributed to our understanding of sex differences in the brain (9–13). Sexual selection is a powerful force in shaping the behavior and the morphology of birds, and many behaviors in birds are visually and/or acoustically conspicuous, so that sex differences in their behavior are easily observed and documented. Studies of the control of singing behavior in birds were the first to identify anatomical sex differences in the brains of any vertebrate (14). Birds have also been useful for investigating the developmental control of sex differences in brain and behavior. The facts that each bird embryo develops independently in an external egg and that some birds hatch in a relatively immature state make it possible to manipulate the external or internal environments independently of the mother or other embryos. Furthermore, birds demonstrate a remarkable diversity of patterns of reproductive behaviors that may involve hormone-dependent as well as hormone-independent events.

In this paper, I briefly summarize some of what we have learned about sexual differentiation of brain and behavior in birds, a subject that has also been covered in other reviews (9–13). A special focus is on avian copulatory and singing behaviors; most is known about the neural and hormonal bases for their sexually dimorphic expression.

REPRODUCTIVE BEHAVIOR IN BIRDS

The fact that birds use a variety of mating systems has proven useful for identification of the neural and hormonal mechanisms governing behavior. Some examples of this diversity in behavior and physiology are described in this review, but the principal focus is on the typical patterns exhibited by many seasonal breeding birds, especially those whose reproduction is governed by changes in photoperiod.

Many birds are sexually dimorphic in some physical characteristics, usually in the color and/or structure of the body feathers. At the onset of the reproductive cycle, males undergo a molt to acquire a breeding or nuptial plumage. They then set out to identify and defend a territory that will used for copulation and/or for nesting. Territorial boundaries are defined by their defense against conspecific males. In defense of territories, males call or sing at or near the territorial boundary (15–17); they may fight with one another, or they may use ritualized displays to limit actual physical encounters. Females appear to choose males based on the quality of their territory and the quality or complexity of their songs, plumage, or physical ornaments. In some species, males engage in physical displays that seem to serve no other function than to stimulate the female visually, exposing plumage, physical ornaments, or physical prowess. In response to stimuli from the male, reproductively competent females will crouch into a receptive posture and allow or even solicit males to copulate. Copulation is accomplished by males of different species in different ways. The male Japanese quail (*Coturnix japonica*) (10, 18) approaches the female with a characteristic strutting display, grabs neck feathers of the female, and positions his body over hers to achieve a mount. The male inseminates the female by maneuvering his pelvis beneath hers to achieve a cloacal contact. Female birds can be inseminated before or during the period that they are ovulating and depositing eggs in the nest. Males often participate in a mate-guarding behavior, which is aggressive in nature but is distinguishable from territorial aggression because the focus of the attention is on the mobile female and not on the fixed territorial boundary. Once the eggs are laid, the male, the female, or both participate in incubation.

In seasonal breeding species, especially those in temperate climates, the breeding season is defined by activation of the hypothalamic-pituitary-gonadal (H-P-G) axis by photoperiodic cues (19) and social interactions (20, 21). Changes in H-P-G function in bird species include changes in the levels of circulating gonadal steroids: progesterone (P) in females, estradiol (E_2) in females and in some males, testosterone (T) in males and females, and dihydrotestosterone (DHT) in males (22). However, little is known about other secretions of the gonads in adult birds, such as inhibin, activin, or Mullerian-inhibiting hormone (MIH) (23). Nevertheless, in most birds, estradiol circulates at relatively high levels in females during all phases of the ovulatory cycle, and testosterone is the dominant circulating gonadal steroid in males.

In adult birds high levels of gonadal steroids in blood generally correspond with the appearance of sex-specific reproductive behaviors. When estrogen levels rise in the blood, female songbirds respond to stimuli from the male and solicit copulations. Similarly, when testosterone levels are high in males, they proceed through the full sequence of reproductive behaviors, including calls and songs, defense of breeding territories and of females, and copulatory behavior (18, 21, 22, 24–28). Thus these behaviors of males and females are under the activational control of gonadal steroids. However, although these data seem to imply that female-typical behaviors are under estrogenic control and that male behaviors are under androgenic control, T in males functions largely as a prohormone in that T can undergo conversion into estrogen in the brain of males, and brain estrogen may be critical for the activation of male behavior (18, 26–28). The fact that both masculine and feminine behaviors can be activated by the same hormone implies that differences must exist in the local mechanisms by which estrogen is made available to neural sites or in the neural substrates upon which estrogen acts.

Although this general neuroendocrine paradigm for the activation and expression of adult reproductive behavior holds true for many species, other bird species depart from this general pattern for some or many characteristics. For example, in some species, only reproductively active males sing, whereas in other species, both males and females sing, and in some cases, members of one or both sexes sing outside of the breeding season (15, 29). Thus the development of the neural substrate controlling song may be subject to complex regulation. In other species, territorial aggression also occurs in the autumn when birds establish feeding territories, and some birds sing in defense of these territories. Because plasma gonadal steroid levels are often basal at this time (30, 31), factors other than gonadal steroids may activate these behaviors.

Hormonal Activation of Avian Copulatory and Singing Behaviors

In some cases, differences in sexually dimorphic behaviors result purely from differences in the secretion of hormones (i.e. activational sex differences). However, these types of behavioral differences can also be the result of sex differences in the responses of male and female brains to the actions of gonadal steroids, and physical differences between males and females may constrain behaviors. For example, in the neotropical golden-collared manakin (*Manacus vitellinus*), reproductively active males make sounds by flipping their wings to communicate acoustically. The wing musculature and the structure of some wing feathers are sexually dimorphic and may limit expression of this behavior to males (32). Of the various sexually dimorphic behaviors, the reproductive behaviors of male Japanese quail and song in the male zebra finch (*Taenopygia guttata*) have been studied most extensively, and a number of the neural and hormonal mechanisms that underlie these differences have been elucidated.

COPULATORY BEHAVIOR IN JAPANESE QUAIL   If adult male Japanese quail are castrated, or exposed to short-day photoperiods to induce gonadal regression, reproductive behaviors are eliminated (33, 34), and treatment with testosterone restores the behaviors. In contrast, adult females do not express these behaviors, even if they are ovariectomized and given testosterone in supra-physiological amounts (18, 34). The findings in females suggest that regions of the brain involved in the control of masculine reproductive behaviors by testosterone are different in adult males and females. Other reproductive behaviors in quail are controlled by hormones during adulthood. For example, female Japanese quail crow when given testosterone (18). This suggests that inherent sex differences control some but not all neural circuits affecting reproductive behaviors in the adult quail brain.

SINGING BEHAVIOR IN THE OSCINE PASSERINES   Song is a complex vocal behavior of the oscine songbirds. In the zebra finch, the expression of song resembles that of copulatory behaviors in quail. Adult male zebra finches sing a song learned during a critical developmental period from conspecific males, usually from the fathers (35, 36). Adult song expression is dependent on steroid hormones. Castrated males sing less than reproductively intact adult males, and the administration of testosterone restores song expression in castrated males (24). Adult female zebra finches do not sing, even after treatment with testosterone. Despite this strict sexually dimorphic expression of adult song in the zebra finch, in many other species, females sing naturally as adults or can be induced to sing with testosterone treatment (24, 37, 38). Furthermore, in many species, song can be expressed in nonreproductive contexts (see 39).

To reiterate, the two best-studied behaviors, masculine copulatory behavior of quail and song of passerine species, share some developmental properties in common and some differences. Both behaviors are sexually dimorphic and reproductive. However, unlike copulatory behavior, song is not limited to sexually dimorphic expression in reproductive contexts. Other behaviors beyond the scope of this review, such as partner preference (mate choice) and aggressive behaviors, can also be sexually dimorphic in adult birds (e.g. 40, 41). Much less is known about the hormonal and neural bases of these latter behaviors, but the neural and hormonal mechanisms controlling the development and expression of these behaviors will likely show some overlap and possible interdependence.

HORMONAL EFFECTS ON THE DEVELOPMENT OF SEX DIFFERENCES IN BEHAVIOR

Masculine Copulatory Behavior

Copulatory behavior in galliformes is organized by gonadal secretions. When male quail are exposed to estrogen during a discrete critical period of embryonic development, they are unable to express masculine copulatory behaviors when reproductive maturity is reached, even in the presence of high adult levels of circulating androgens (9, 42). Moreover, when female quail are exposed as embryos to drugs that block estrogen synthesis or the function of estrogen, they respond to testosterone in adulthood and display masculine copulatory behavior (43, 44). The period in development when the quail brain is sensitive to the demasculinizing effects of estradiol is well characterized. The injection of estradiol into quail eggs on day 12 of embryonic development demasculinizes developing males (42), although the quail brain may still be sensitive to some gonadal steroid effects after this time (45). For instance, steroid effects after hatching may modify the reproductive behavior of males (see below). In contrast, the female behavioral phenotype appears to be fully established before hatching.

The effects of gonadal steroids on the development of masculine copulatory behavior have also been investigated in the zebra finch. Males exposed to estrogen after hatching copulate less than untreated males (40, 46). This suggests that the neural circuits controlling copulation in songbirds and galliformes are similarly demasculinized by endogenous estrogen. However, the sensitive period for the effects of estrogen may differ across species (i.e. predominantly prehatching in quail; posthatching in the zebra finch). It would be useful to define precisely the critical period for development of copulatory behavior in songbirds because estrogens probably influence other behaviors as well (see below).

In summary, the secretion of estradiol during development demasculinizes/feminizes copulatory behaviors and plays a prominent role in development of other sex-specific phenotypic characters as well. Moreover, estrogens are synthesized in larger amounts in developing ovaries than in developing testes.

Sex Determination in Birds

As in mammals, in birds sex is determined by the chromosome composition (47). Birds with two Z chromosomes are male, and birds with one Z chromosome and one W chromosome are female. During early embryogenesis in the heterogametic females (approximately day 6 of the 18-day incubation period in chickens), the gonadal primordia differentiate, ultimately becoming a single left ovary. In the homogametic male, the gonadal primordia develop into bilateral testes. Estrogen synthesis is probably one of the earliest events in ovarian differentiation in birds. Treatment of female chickens or zebra finches on or about day 5 of incubation with a potent inhibitor of aromatase (estrogen synthase; CYP19) leads to the growth of paired testes or ovotestes with little ovarian tissue (48–50). Likewise, treatment of male embryos with estradiol feminizes the testes (9, 48, 51). Thus testicular differentiation in birds proceeds in the absence of an estrogenic signal.

Non-Neural Sexual Differentiation in Birds

Estradiol is also a critical signal for the differentiation of other female-specific characteristics. For example, in ducks, accessory sex organs such as the syrinx and the genital tubercle develop into male-specific structures in the absence of any hormonal signal (reviewed by 9, 51, 52), whereas exposure of these tissues to estrogen causes development in a feminine fashion (51). Thus androgens appear to have no masculinizing influence on these structures.

Estradiol is not the only factor contributing to a non-neural, sexually dimorphic phenotype in birds. For example, plumage color is a dimorphic trait in many bird species. There is evidence that plumage color in some birds is not dependent on gonadal steroids, but rather is determined genetically. Some evidence comes from the striking case reports of gynandromorphs (lateral sex chimeras) (47, 51). In these birds, the left half of the body expresses one phenotype (usually female), whereas the right half expresses the opposite phenotype (usually male). Such strict laterality would be impossible if the sexual phenotype were determined fully by hormones, which have access to all tissues. Such a condition would be possible if the sex phenotype, or at least some attributes of that phenotype, were determined genetically in a cell-autonomous, hormone-independent manner (47).

Halverson & Dvorak (47) described a mutant gynandromorphic Eclectus parrot (*Eclectus*) in which males are green and females are red. The gynandromorph had male plumage on the left and female plumage on the right, with a distinct sharp lateral line separating the two. Despite this plumage mosaic, the bird had left and right testes. Presumably, plumage development was under direct genetic control, as is thought to be the case in other bird species (for review, see 52). By contrast, testicular development is dependent on the hormonal environment. The fact that the plumage of this gynandromorph gradually became more male-like with age suggests that genetic and hormonal determinants of this sexual phenotype interact. In summary, birds have a mixture of chromosomal sex-determining and hormonal sex-determining mechanisms. Both types of mechanisms may influence sexual differentiation of the neural circuits controlling song as well (see below).

Gonadal Steroid Synthesis in Developing Birds

Studies of hormonal levels in avian embryos and of the steroidogenic capabilities of the developing gonads agree on two points: (*a*) Estradiol is present in larger amounts in developing females than in developing males. (*b*) The ovary is the principal site of estrogen synthesis (53–57). Figure 1 illustrates the primary steroidogenic enzymes and their principal substrates and products in gonadal tissues. In developing quail, chickens, and ducks, ovaries produce more estrogen than do testes because of higher CYP19 activity in ovaries than in testes (54, 57–59). Moreover, the time course of expression of aromatase in developing hens correlates with the timing of early estrogen-dependent events. Yoshida et al (57) examined the expression of two of the

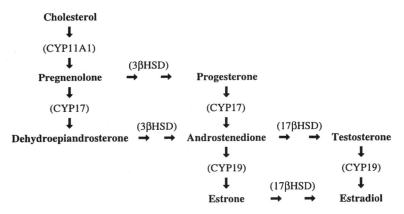

Figure 1 The principal enzymes (*parentheses*) that catalyze the conversion of cholesterol to the gonadal steroids. CYP11A1 = cytochrome P450 side-chain cleavage; CYP17 = cytochrome P450 17α-hydroxylase/C17-20 lyase; 3βHSD = 3β-hydroxysteroid dehydrogenase/isomerase; 17βHSD = 17β-hydroxysteroid dehydrogenase.

four essential steroidogenic enzymes (see Figure 1), CYP19 and cytochrome P45017α-hydroxylase/lyase (CYP17), in the gonads of male and female chicken embryos. CYP19 converts androgens to estrogens (testosterone to estradiol; androstenedione to estrone), and CYP17 is involved in the formation of androgens by catalyzing the conversion of progesterone to androstenedione or pregnenolone to dehydroepiandrosterone. Thus both enzymes are required for estrogens to be synthesized, and androgens will predominate if aromatase is absent.

Expression of these genes was examined in gonads from chicken embryos and hatchlings using RNA probes derived from chicken CYP17 and quail CYP19 cDNAs (57). In addition, estradiol was extracted from gonads and measured by radioimmunoassay. CYP17 was expressed at relatively similar levels in gonads of both sexes beginning on day 5. CYP19 was first detected in ovaries beginning on day 6.5 of incubation and was undetectable in testes until embryonic day 16 and later, when it was present in low levels. More estradiol was extracted from ovaries than from testes at all ages examined, especially on embryonic day 10, but some estradiol was present in testes at each age. The presence of estradiol itself establishes that the three remaining enzymes required for gonadal steroid synthesis from cholesterol [P450scc (CYP11A1), 3β-HSD, and 17β-HSD] are active in the gonads of these birds (Figure 1). In summary, these data support the view that the developing chicken ovary is capable of substantial estrogen production, whereas the testes produce androgen and only small amounts of estrogen. These data are compatible with the view that the developing ovary of birds is an active site for the formation of estrogens, which feminize/demasculinize the developing embryo. The role of testicular androgen synthesis is not known, but if aromatase is active elsewhere in the embryo, then testosterone secretion by the testes might partially feminize/demasculinize the male phenotype (60; see below). Obviously, any estradiol produced directly by the testes could produce the same effect.

SEX DIFFERENCES IN THE BRAIN

Sex differences in neuroanatomical and neurochemical properties of the adult avian brain include differences in the medial preoptic nucleus (POM) of the Japanese quail, an area known to be involved in the control of masculine copulatory behavior (18), and several nuclei (HVC, RA, Area X) involved in the control of song learning and song expression in oscine songbirds (61).

The Medial Preoptic Nucleus of Quail

The POM is larger in adult males than in adult females (62, 63); in addition, several dimorphic properties of the POM include the size of neurons and number of CYP19-expressing neurons in the dorsolateral POM, and the overall rate of dopamine turnover in the POM (18). The POM is involved in the induction of masculine copulatory behaviors in these birds, as evidenced by the fact that electrolytic lesions targeted to the POM eliminate the ability of testosterone-treated males to copulate (18).

Local conversion of androgen to estrogen in the brains of male quail is a critical event in the activation of masculine reproductive behaviors. For example, testosterone fails to induce masculine copulatory behavior in castrated male quail when an aromatase inhibitor is administered simultaneously (18). CYP19 is more active in the preoptic area of adult male quail than in adult females (64) due in part to the presence of more aromatase-expressing neurons in males (18). Testosterone can increase aromatase activity and expression in adult male quail depleted of endogenous testosterone (18, 27). The induction of aromatase in the POM by testosterone may also be sexually dimorphic because CYP19 activity in the POM of females is often less than is seen in males (18). This is important because the local activity of aromatase controls the extent to which nearby estrogen receptors are occupied by estrogen and the magnitude of the expression of masculine reproductive behaviors (27).

Song-Control Nuclei of Oscine Passerines

The neural circuitry underlying the expression of song and song learning in oscine passerines (65, 66) is regulated by steroid hormones both during neural development and in the adult CNS (61). This system includes discrete nuclei found largely in the telencephalon (65). Two circuits are generally recognized: a motor circuit that controls song expression and a circuit that controls learning. The motor circuit includes the higher vocal center (HVC), located in the dorsal neostriatum, which innervates the robust nucleus of the archistriatum (RA), which, in turn, innervates motoneurons that originate in the tracheosyringeal hypoglossal nucleus (nXIIts) of the medulla and innervate the syrinx or vocal organ. The learning circuit includes a projection from HVC to Area X of the lobus paraolfactorius. Area X projects to the medial nucleus of the lateral dorsal thalamus (DLM), which projects in turn to the magnocellular nucleus of the neostriatum (MAN). The lateral MAN (lMAN) receives projections from DLM and projects to nucleus RA.

In the zebra finch, a species in which adult song expression is rigidly sexually dimorphic (adult males sing, whereas females do not), the neural song system is sexually dimorphic (14). Several of the song nuclei are larger in adult males than in adult females. For example, Area X is not visible in the female brain but is prominent in the male brain. Two other nuclei, HVC and RA, are approximately fivefold larger in males than in females (Figure 2). Sexually dimorphic attributes of the song system include not only the volumes of nuclei

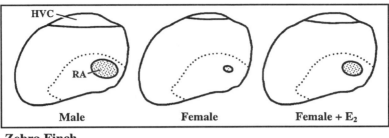

Zebra Finch

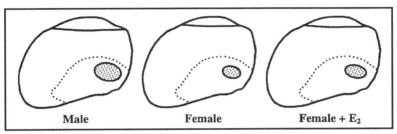

Starling

Figure 2   Highly schematic diagram illustrating the left telencephalic hemisphere of the songbird brain in coronal section with the approximate sizes and positions of two nuclei of the song control system: HVC, the *clear nucleus* in the dorsal telencephalon; and RA, the *stippled nucleus* in the archistriatum. Diagrams illustrate relative sizes of these nuclei in normal adult males and females and in adult females that had been treated developmentally with estradiol E_2. Data for the zebra finch were taken from Gurney (72, 73); data for the European starling were taken from Casto et al (69). (Note: Zebra finch brain is smaller overall than that of the starling.)

but also the numbers and sizes of neurons in these nuclei, their capacity to bind androgen in adulthood, and their connectivity (61).

There is substantial variability in vocal performance between sexes, among species, and even among individuals of the same sex. This is true also for properties of the neural circuitry controlling song (29, 67, 68). In species like the zebra finch, the highly sexually dimorphic song circuitry reflects the dimorphism in song behavior (14). In other species, such as the tropical duetting bay wren (*Thryothorus nigricapilla*), a species in which both males and females sing songs of equal complexity, no sex differences have been detected in the song circuit (29). In intermediate cases, such as the European starling (*Sturnus vulgaris*), females sing but to a lesser degree than males. Females have a clearly identifiable song system, and the song nuclei are about half the size of those in adult males (69; Figure 2).

HORMONAL BASIS OF SEX DIFFERENCES IN THE BRAIN

The POM of Japanese Quail

As described above, steroids activate the expression of adult copulatory behaviors by acting on a sexually dimorphic neural substrate that is organized early in development. Although the demasculinizing effects of embryonic estrogens on copulatory behavior are clearest, there is little evidence for permanent effects of estrogen on the brain structures that control copulatory behavior. Indeed, the prominent sex differences observed in the gross structure of the quail POM are solely the result of differences in adult gonadal steroid levels (18). Castration reduces the volume of the adult male POM, and testosterone fully restores its volume. Moreover, treatment of ovariectomized females with testosterone induces a POM as large as is seen in males (70). Thus the volume of the POM itself is regulated by activational effects of testosterone. Treatment of male embryos with estradiol does not affect the overall volume of the POM despite the fact that male sexual behavior is fully demasculinized (18).

To determine if there are permanent organizational effects of estrogen on less conspicuous cellular properties of the POM, Balthazart and colleagues analyzed neuron size and aromatase immunoreactivity in the POM of adults after treatment with estrogen or an aromatase inhibitor during embryogenesis (18). They found only limited evidence for any organizational actions of estrogen on neuroanatomical or neurochemical properties of the brain and were unable to establish the neuroanatomical basis for masculine behavior (18).

The Neural Song System of the Zebra Finch

A ROLE FOR ESTROGEN   Treatment of hatchling songbirds with gonadal steroids produces profound changes in the structure and chemistry of the brain. Treatment of female zebra finches shortly after hatching with estradiol causes the development of a functionally masculine neural song system, including the capacity to sing as adults and masculinized anatomical and cellular properties of the song system (40, 71–77). Such masculinization alters the number and size of neurons in song system nuclei (HVC, RA, lMAN, Area X), the connectivity between nuclei, and the capacity of cells in some nuclei to accumulate androgens (for review, see 61).

In addition to the numerous effects of estrogen, androgen may have a direct minor role in masculinizing the zebra finch song system. In early studies, testosterone was shown to have effects similar to estradiol (72), but estradiol is more potent than testosterone in this regard (78). Treatment of hatchling females with 5α-dihydrotestosterone (DHT) can increase the number of neurons in nucleus RA of adults (72, 73, 79). However, treatment of developing males with an inhibitor of 5α-reductase, the enzyme that converts testosterone into the potent androgen DHT, can demasculinize RA neuron number (80), but females treated with DHT after hatching do not sing as adults (71); estradiol itself can also increase neuron number in RA (78), and treatments of hatching females with DHT in combination with estradiol produce no greater masculinization (81). Thus it seems likely that endogenous androgen has little or no direct role (i.e. by acting through androgen receptors) in masculinizing the zebra finch song system, but rather acts via conversion to estradiol in extraglandular tissues including brain.

There is no question that posthatching estrogen treatment of females produces dramatic effects in the zebra finch brain, but exogenous estrogens do not fully masculinize the female song system. Although females treated after hatching with estrogen can sing, the sizes of various parts of the song system remain about half that seen in normal males (Figure 2). The organizing actions of estrogens have been studied in only one other songbird, the European starling (69). In this species, treatment with exogenous estrogen has only minor effects, so that the song system is only minimally masculinized (Figure 2). This result is hard to interpret given the fact that the song system of adult female starlings is already reasonably well developed, especially when compared with that of a female zebra finch. It is possible that the morphology of the song system in adult females already reflects that of an estrogen-stimulated animal and that exogenous estrogen treatments have little or no further effect. Presumably, some other factor is required to achieve the full masculine song system morphology, such as might also be required to fully masculinize the circuit in the zebra finch.

The masculinizing effects of estradiol on the zebra finch song system are paradoxical. We have said that estrogens are fundamental for feminine development in birds because estrogens are critical in guiding differentiation of ovarian but not testicular tissue. Moreover, estrogens then continue to feminize and demasculinize other secondary structures, including those found in the brain. However, in the case of song, estradiol is a masculinizing hormone. Presumably, as in quail, estrogens act in some fashion at the level of the preoptic area to demasculinize/feminize reproductive behavior. Yet they act on the telencephalic song system to masculinize song. How estrogens exert different regional effects on brain sexual differentiation has been investigated in a number of laboratories.

The most important single piece of evidence supporting a masculinizing role for estrogen is that treatment of developing females with estradiol produces a masculine neural song system. No other hormone or drug has replicated this effect. If estrogen is the endogenous masculinizing signal, then we would expect to find higher estrogen levels in the blood and tissues of developing males.

In one experiment in hatchling male zebra finches, estradiol was reported to circulate at high levels (82). However, in two subsequent experiments, the levels of estradiol in blood of hatchling zebra finches were low, and there were no differences between males and females (83, 84). However, estrone was present at fairly high levels (84), and the levels of estrone in males varied by age in a pattern similar to that reported earlier for estradiol (82). These results suggest that estrogens are synthesized in male zebra finches after hatching, but it remains unclear if they circulate at higher levels in males than in females. CYP19 activity in gonads of hatchling zebra finches (84) is similar to that in galliformes: Namely, CYP19 activity is abundant in the ovary and low in testes (84). This result does not support a mechanism for secretion of greater amounts of estrogen into the blood of males.

However, evidence supporting a role for estrogen in brain development comes from studies examining CYP19 activity in the songbird brain. The enzyme is present in zebra finch males during early development (84) in or near regions known to have estrogen receptors (85) and thought to be important for estrogen actions (86). This finding is compatible with the concept that under physiological conditions, locally formed estrogen masculinizes the brain of the songbird. The pattern of CYP19 expression in brain appears to be unique to songbirds and is not seen in non-songbird species (27). Because expression of CYP19 in the brain is not sexually dimorphic (84, 87), local aromatization could only produce a sexually dimorphic estrogenic signal to developing neural circuits if substrate availability was rate limiting in estrogen formation. We cannot fully exclude a role for the testes in providing estrogen to the developing brain. CYP19 does appear to be present at only very low levels in testes (see above), but it is expressed by testicular tissue after treatment of testes with db-cAMP (88; B Schlinger, manuscript submitted). Perhaps the presence of some non-testicular signal, i.e. a pituitary gonadotropin, is required to allow detection of CYP19 in testes with current methods. Even low levels of aromatase might be sufficient to produce a biologically active amount of estrogen if other steroidogenic enzymes are expressed at high levels.

DOUBTS ABOUT A ROLE FOR ESTROGEN   Despite strong evidence for estrogen effects, there is also considerable doubt that estradiol is the endogenous masculinizing hormone in developing males. As discussed above, there is no conclusive evidence for sex differences in circulating estrogens during the critical period for song masculinization. Also, estrogen has demasculinizing effects on neural and non-neural characteristics of developing birds, and it would be unusual for the same developmental signal to have opposite developmental effects (11, 12, 13). Furthermore, additional evidence suggests that estrogen (from any tissue source) may not be the endogenous hormone involved in masculinizing the neural song system of developing male zebra finches.

Doubts were first raised when treatment of male zebra finches with estrogen receptor antagonists to block estrogen action failed to demasculinize the song system (89, 90). However, the antagonists used may not have blocked estrogen receptors in the brain (91). In another series of studies, the administration to male zebra finches (during early development) of fadrozole, which inhibits CYP19 in zebra finch brain and ovary, did not prevent masculinization of the song system (49, 50). Similar results were then obtained by another laboratory with a similar aromatase inhibitor (93). However, testosterone levels are elevated in adult male zebra finches after treatment with fadrozole (94), possibly because of interference with negative feedback regulation of pituitary and gonadal function, and elevated testosterone levels could provide sufficient substrate to circumvent the competitive inhibition of CYP19.

Questions have also been raised about the role of the testes in masculine song development, as estrogen is required for ovarian differentiation in developing birds. Treatments of embryos with CYP19 inhibitors prior to the start of ovarian differentiation can lead to masculine gonadal development in female birds. This experimental model has been used to evaluate the role of the gonads in the development of the neural song system (49, 50). Treatment of female zebra finches with fadrozole on embryonic day 5 or 8 causes development of gonads with a mixture of ovarian and testicular tissue (a full right testis and a left ovotestis). Seminiferous tubules are well formed and may contain well-developed spermatozoa, and circulating androgen levels are higher in these females compared with that in control females (49, 50). Nevertheless, these females have a virtually fully feminine neural song system. These data provide quite convincing evidence that such testes are not wholly capable of inducing masculine development of the neural song system.

ALTERNATIVE MECHANISMS FOR MASCULINIZATION OF THE SONG SYSTEM

Direct Genetic Control of Brain Sexual Differentiation

If testicular secretions and/or estradiol itself do not act alone to direct masculine development of the avian song system, what other factors might contribute to the development of this system? One possibility is that some aspects of the sex-specific song system depend on hormones, whereas other aspects are determined genetically, independently of hormones. As discussed above, sex-specific plumage in some birds may develop in a hormone-independent, cell-autonomous manner, and the same mechanism may be operative for sexually dimorphic aspects of brain function as well (39, 52). For example, Arnold (52) argues that if sex-specific gonadal development is mediated by the expression of one or more discrete gene products, then it is not unreasonable to expect that the process of sex-specific neural development might be susceptible to capture by specific gene products as well. Furthermore, Arnold points out that there is already evidence in mammals for hormone-independent, sex-specific neural development and for the expression in brain of a putative gene product, the mammalian testis-determining gene *SRY*, that could direct sex-specific neural development. Given the evidence that estrogens or the testes themselves may not be involved in masculine development of the neural song system in zebra finches, it is reasonable to invoke other factors in sex-specific neural development in songbirds, including direct genetic control (52).

We have argued that the development of the neural song system in songbirds is not organized developmentally by gonadal secretions because song is not simply a sex-specific reproductive behavior; it is a behavior that can be expressed both by males and females, sometimes in nonreproductive contexts (39). For example, it is intriguing that the expression of song and some aggressive behaviors are correlated and that there is often a relationship between these behaviors and bird plumage. Because sex-specific plumages may develop independently of gonadal hormones, it may well be that the neural control of behaviors associated with plumage type may also develop independently of gonadal hormones.

One example where plumage, behavior, and neural circuitry are related is in a North American songbird, the white-throated sparrow (*Zonotrichia albicollis*). This species displays two distinct types of plumage morphs called white-striped and tan-striped. The white-striped morph has a white and black crown-stripe; the tan-striped morph has a more tan and brown crown-stripe (95, 96). There are also two principal karyotypes observed in these birds. Two autosomes, chromosomes 2 and 3, are polymorphic. Chromosome 2 can exist in the presumed ancestral form (2) or a newly derived form (2m). Birds possessing the 2m chromosome always express the white-striped morph, while birds lacking 2m express the tan-striped morph (96). Because the plumage morph is designated by an autosome, both males and females can be white- or tan-striped. This genetic polymorphism is maintained by an assortative mating system in which birds of opposite morph form breeding pairs (97). Thus white-striped males mate with tan-striped females, and tan-striped males mate with white-striped females (95, 97).

In this species, aggressive and singing behaviors are associated with morph type. On the breeding grounds, white-striped birds are more aggressive than tan-striped birds, and white-striped birds sing more than tan-striped birds. This distinction is seen in both males and females (95, 97, 98). Thus white-throated sparrows have morphs that display traditional sex roles during the breeding season: White-striped males are brightly colored and aggressive; tan-striped females have a duller breeding plumage, behave less aggressively, and rarely sing in defense of territory. White-throated sparrows also have morphs that display a form of sex reversal: White-striped females are brightly colored, are aggressive and sing; tan-striped males are less aggressive and sing less than white-striped males. Thus there is evidence for sex-dependent and morph-dependent expression of singing and aggressive behavior in this species.

The fact that both males and females of this species sing indicates that the song system is probably organized differently than a sex-specific neural circuit like the one that controls male copulatory behavior. DeVoogd and colleagues investigated the anatomy of the song system in breeding white-throated sparrows (68) and found that sex differences are maintained in all the song-control nuclei. Males have a larger song system than females, despite the fact that white-striped females sing like tan-striped males in quality and in quantity. Nevertheless, like starlings (see above), all female white-throated sparrows have a substantial song system, unlike the zebra finch, a species in which the song system is undeveloped in females (14). The two morphs of the white-throated sparrow also show differences in the song system that reflect differences in singing behavior. Several nuclei (Area X, lMAN, and NXII-ts) are larger in white-striped males than in tan-striped males, and they are larger in white-striped females than in tan-striped females. It is unlikely that the differences across morphs are under activational control, because morphs of the same sex show no difference in circulating gonadal steroids. By contrast, differences between the sexes might be influenced by circulating steroids because breeding males have higher levels of plasma testosterone than do breeding females (68).

Thus in this one species, there is evidence for gonadal hormone-dependent and hormone-independent features of song expression and of anatomical properties of the neural song system. Unless we invoke morph-specific differences in gonadal hormone secretion, it is unlikely that gonadal steroids are solely responsible for behavioral differences across morphs. Since a genetic polymorphism accounts for the plumage variation in these birds, it is possible that the morph-specific expression of song and aggressive behaviors are also regulated by the same polymorphism. Synergy might exist between gonadal function and genotype in the regulation of sexual phenotypes in this species.

Individual Variability in the Expression of a Sexually Dimorphic Behavior

The inherent nature of the sexual differentiation paradigm frequently leads to the view that one pattern of male behavior and one pattern of female behavior exist. Females exposed to ovarian estrogens are fully female, males are fully male. However, there is substantial variability in the expression of sex-specific behaviors across individuals of a species. The white-throated sparrow illustrates this phenomenon across the two discrete morphs, irrespective of sex. Furthermore, variable behavioral expression is also a feature of some sex-specific behaviors of birds with traditional masculine and feminine phenotypes. For example, reproductively active, adult male Japanese quail exhibit individual variability in response to the visual stimulus of conspecifics (99). When tested in an arena where experimental birds are separated from stimulus birds by a clear glass plate, adult males, but not females or reproductively inactive males, respond by running to the glass plate, pacing vigorously back and forth in front of the glass and pecking at the glass itself. This behavior was originally referred to as aggressiveness, but this designation has been disputed (100). Nevertheless, when pecking or pacing behavior was quantified in groups of 18 males that were raised under identical conditions, the intensity of the pecking activity varied some 14-fold; the behavior of some males resembled that of females, while others showed a robust behavioral response. The variability in behavior appeared to reflect an intrinsic behavioral potential specific to each individual male. First, the intensity of each bird's response was remarkably constant across repeated daily tests (99). Second, the intensity of each bird's behavior was associated with the levels of brain aromatase activity (activity in the hypothalamus/preoptic area was higher in males showing the more vigorous behavioral response), and not with differences in levels of circulating gonadal steroids (101). The variable response of individual males could be independent of the activational actions of gonadal steroids (i.e. differences in basal metabolic rate). Indeed, the sex difference in the expression of the behavior suggests that the variability in the male behavior was established developmentally, when the circuit initially became sexually dimorphic. Thus during the process of sexually dimorphic brain development, individual differences are also established. The creation of these individual differences may be a critical property of brain sexual differentiation.

The behavior of male quail may be modified developmentally by endogenous gonadal steroids. Adkins-Regan (60) found that males treated as embryos with an aromatase inhibitor actually showed increased levels of copulatory behavior. One possibility is that developing males are exposed naturally to some estrogen that slightly demasculinizes their brains and that the effect of hormones on the expression of the behavior is not all-or-none, but can be titrated. Slight differences in estrogen availability to the brain (from differences in testicular androgen secretion or in brain aromatase) could lead to individual reproductive behaviors in males with different levels of intensity.

This variability in behavior can also be influenced by estrogens derived from other sources, including steroids synthesized in the mother. For example, as they lay their eggs, female quail deposit estradiol into egg yolks (102). Similarly, female canaries (*Serinus canarius*) deposit testosterone into egg yolks (103). In the case of canaries, there appears to be a relationship between the amount of testosterone deposited in each egg and the ultimate behavioral phenotype of the embryo in the egg (103). Testosterone levels in the yolk are correlated with birds' dominance status later in life. Those birds exposed to more testosterone in yolk are dominant over birds with less testosterone in yolk. Because the last egg laid in a clutch contains higher testosterone levels than the first egg, androgen concentrations increase with successively laid eggs. Thus the birds who were born last in a clutch tend to be the most aggressive. These results suggest that maternal aromatizable androgen or estrogen is available to organize aggressive circuits during development, independently of any steroids secreted by the gonads of the embryo.

CONCLUSIONS

Studies by ethologists, neurobiologists, and endocrinologists have taught us a great deal about the organizational effects of gonadal steroids on masculine behavior. The two behaviors that have been studied the most intensely are the copulatory behavior of quail and song behavior in songbirds. Yet, in both cases, the cascade of genetic, biochemical, and anatomical events that lead to the observed sex differences in adult behavior are not fully understood. In the case of quail, we have not identified the discrete structures in the brain that are differentially organized and that allow adult males to perform their full sequence of masculine copulatory behaviors in response to testosterone. There may also be specific gonadal hormone-dependent or independent mechanisms that act developmentally to induce differences in the individual male quail in the expression of steroid-dependent behaviors in adulthood. In the case of songbirds, we do not know where or when estrogens are produced developmentally; nor do we know how these estrogens are made available to the brain to masculinize neural circuits controlling song without demasculinizing those circuits controlling other reproductive behaviors. In addition, some studies of songbirds suggest that sex-specific gene expression intrinsic to the developing brain itself may contribute to sexually dimorphic brain development. Birds probably employ multiple, interacting mechanisms to produce the diversity of behavioral phenotypes associated with reproduction that are expressed across different species and across individuals within a single species. Gonadal hormones, hormones derived from non-gonadal sources, and cell-autonomous (genetic) factors probably all contribute to the development of sexually dimorphic neural circuits. Undoubtedly, future studies will shed much light on the nature of these developmental signals and on their capacity to sculpt features of the developing brain.

ACKNOWLEDGMENTS

I am grateful to Alison Kendrick and Drs. Colin Saldanha and Jean Wilson for their careful reviewing of this manuscript. I am also grateful to the many colleagues and collaborators with whom I have had the privilege of discussing the issues presented in this paper. This work was supported by National Science Foundation grant IBN-9602139.

Visit the *Annual Reviews home page* at
http://www.AnnualReviews.org.

Literature Cited

1. Phoenix CH, Goy RW, Gerall AA, Young WC. 1959. Organizing action of prenatally administered testosterone propionate on the tissues mediating mating behavior in the female guinea pig. *Endocrinology* 65:369–82
2. Jost A, Vigier B, Prepin J, Perchellet JP. 1973. Studies on sex differentiation in mammals. *Rec. Prog. Horm. Res.* 29:1–41
3. Goy RW, McEwen BS. 1980. *Sexual Differentiation of the Brain*. Cambridge, MA: MIT Press
4. Wilson JD, George FW, Renfree MB. 1995. The endocrine role in mammalian sexual differentiation. *Rec. Prog. Horm. Res.* 50:349–64
5. Arnold AP, Gorski RA. 1984. Gonadal steroid induction of structural sex differences in the central nervous system. *Annu. Rev. Neurosci.* 7:413–42
6. Breedlove SM. 1992. Sexual dimorphism in the vertebrate central nervous system. *J. Neurosci.* 12:4133–42
7. Collaer ML, Hines M. 1995. Human behavioral sex differences: a role for gonadal hormones during early development? *Psychol. Bull.* 118:55–107
8. Pilgrim C, Hutchison JB. 1994. Developmental regulation of sex differences in the brain: Can the role of gonadal hormones be redefined? *Neuroscience* 60:843–55
9. Adkins EK. 1981. Early organizational effects of hormones. In *Neuroendocrinology of Reproduction: Physiology and Behavior*, ed. NT Adler, pp. 159–228. New York: Plenum
10. Adkins-Regan E. 1987. Sexual differentiation in birds. *Trends Neurosci.* 10:517–22
11. Arnold AP, Schlinger BA. 1993. Sexual differentiation of brain and behavior: The zebra finch is not just a flying rat. *Brain Behav. Evol.* 42:231–41
12. Balthazart J, Ball GF. 1995. Sexual differentiation of brain and behavior in birds. *Trends Endocrinol. Metab.* 6:21–29
13. Arnold AP, Wade J, Grisham W, Jacobs EC, Campagnoni AT. 1996. Sexual differentiation of the brain in songbirds. *Dev. Neurosci.* 18:124–36
14. Nottebohm F, Arnold AP. 1976. Sexual dimorphism in vocal control areas of the song bird brain. *Science* 194:211–13
15. Lack D. 1943. *The Life of the Robin*. London: Witherby
16. Krebs JR. 1977. Bird song and territory defense. *New Scient.* 70:534–36
17. Catchpole CK. 1982. The evolution of bird sounds in relation to mating and spacing behavior. In *Acoustic Communication in Birds*, ed. DE Kroodsma, EH Miller, H Ouellet, pp. 297–319. New York: Academic
18. Balthazart J, Tlemcani O, Ball GF. 1996. Do sex differences in the brain explain sex differences in the hormonal induction of reproductive behavior? What 25 years of research on the Japanese Quail tells us. *Horm. Behav.* 30:627–61
19. Wingfield JC, Farner DS. 1980. Control of seasonal reproduction in temperate-zone birds. *Prog. Repr. Biol.* 5:62–101
20. Kroodsma DE. 1976. Reproductive development in a female songbird: differential stimulation by quality of male song. *Science* 192:574–75
21. Wingfield JC, Marler P. 1988. Endocrine basis of communication in reproduction and aggression. In *The Physiology of Reproduction*, ed. E Knobel, J Neill, pp. 1647–77. New York: Raven
22. Wingfield JC, Ball GF, Dufty AM Jr, Hegner RE, Ramenofsky M. 1987. Testosterone and aggression in birds. *Am. Sci.* 75:602–8
23. Hidalgo A, Barami, K, Iverson K, Goldman SA. 1995. Estrogens and nonestrenic ovarian influences combine to promote the recruitment and decrease the turnover of new neurons in the adult female canary brain. *J. Neurobiol.* 27:470–87
24. Arnold AP. 1975. The effects of castration and androgen replacement on song, courtship, and aggression in zebra finches

(*Poephila guttata*). *J. Exp. Zool.* 191:309–26

25. Harding CF, Sheridan K, Walters MJ. 1983. Hormonal specificity and activation of sexual behavior in male zebra finches. *Horm. Behav.* 17:111–33

26. Hutchison JB, Steimer Th. 1984. Androgen metabolism in the brain: behavioral correlates. *Prog. Brain. Res.* 61:23–51

27. Schlinger BA, Callard GV. 1991. Brain-steroid interactions and the control of aggressiveness in birds. In *Neuroendocrine Perspectives,* ed. EE Muller, RM MacLeod, 9:1–43. New York: Springer-Verlag

28. Schlinger BA, Arnold AP. 1995. Estrogen synthesis and secretion by the songbird brain. In *Neurobiological Effects of Sex Steroid Hormones,* ed. PE Micevych, RP Hammer, Jr, pp. 297–323. Cambridge: Cambridge Univ. Press

29. Brenowitz EA, Arnold AP, Levin RN. 1985. Neural correlates of female song in tropical duetting birds. *Brain Res.* 343:104–12

30. Logan CA, Wingfield JC. 1990. Autumnal territorial aggression is independent of plasma testosterone in mockingbirds. *Horm. Behav.* 24:568–81

31. Schwabl H. 1992. Winter and breeding territorial behavior and levels of reproductive hormones of migratory European robins. *Ornis Scand.* 23:271–76

32. Lowe PR. 1942. The anatomy of Gould's manakin (*Manacus vitellinus*) in relation to its display. *Ibis* 6(14):50–83

33. Beach F, Inman NG. 1965. Effects of castration and androgen replacement on mating in male quail. *Proc. Natl. Acad. Sci. USA* 54:1426–31

34. Adkins EK, Adler NT. 1972. Hormonal control of behavior in the Japanese quail. *J. Comp. Physiol. Psychol.* 81:27–36

35. Immelman K. 1969. Song development in the zebra finch and other estrildid finches. In *Bird Vocalizations,* ed. RE Hinde, pp. 61–74. Cambridge: Cambridge Univ. Press

36. Zann R. 1990. Song and call learning in wild zebra finches in south-east Australia. *Anim. Behav.* 40:811–28

37. Kern MD, King JR. 1972. Testosterone-induced singing in female white-crowned sparrows. *Condor* 74:204–9

38. Nottebohm F. 1980. Testosterone triggers growth of brain vocal control nuclei in adult female canaries. *Brain Res.* 189:429–36

39. Kendrick AM, Schlinger BA. 1996. Independent differentiation of sexual and social traits. *Horm. Behav.* 30:600–10

40. Adkins-Regan E, Ascenzi M. 1987. Social and sexual behaviour of male and female zebra finches treated with oestradiol during the nestling period. *Anim. Behav.* 35:1100–12

41. Mansukhani V, Adkins-Regan E, Yang S. 1996. Sexual partner preference in female zebra finches: the role of early hormones and social environment. *Horm. Behav.* 30:506–13

42. Adkins EK. 1979. Effect of embryonic treatment with estradiol or testosterone on sexual differentiation of the quail brain. *Neuroendocrinology* 29:178–85

43. Adkins EK. 1976. Embryonic exposure to an antiestrogen masculinizes behavior of female quail. *Physiol. Behav.* 17:357–59

44. Balthazart J, De Clerck A, Foidart A. 1992. Behavioral demasculinization of female quail is induced by estrogens: studies with the new aromatase inhibitor, R76713. *Horm. Behav.* 26:179–203

45. Schumacher M, Balthazart J. 1984. The postnatal demasculinization of sexual behavior in the Japanese quail (*Coturnix coturnix japonica*). *Horm. Behav.* 18:298–312

46. Adkins-Regan E, Mansukhani V, Seiwert C, Thompson R. 1994. Sexual differentiation of brain and behavior in the zebra finch: critical periods for effects of early estrogen treatment. *J. Neurobiol.* 25:865–77

47. Halverson JL, Dvorak J. 1993. Genetic control of sex determination in birds and the potential for its manipulation. *Poultry Sci.* 72:890–96

48. Elbrecht A, Smith RG. 1992. Aromatase enzyme activity and sex determination in chickens. *Science* 255:467–70

49. Wade J, Arnold AP. 1996. Functional testicular tissue does not masculinize development of the zebra finch song system. *Proc. Natl. Acad. Sci. USA* 93:5264–68

50. Wade J, Springer ML, Wingfield JC, Arnold AP. 1996. Neither testicular androgens nor embryonic aromatase activity alter morphology of the neural song system in zebra finches. *Biol. Reprod.* 55:1126–32

51. Witschi E. 1961. Sex and secondary sexual characters. In *Biology and Comparative Physiology of Birds,* ed. AJ Marshall, 2:115–68. New York: Academic

52. Arnold AP. 1996. Genetically triggered sexual differentiation of brain and behavior. *Horm. Behav.* 30:495–505

53. Tanabe Y, Yano T, Nakamura T. 1983. Steroid hormone synthesis and secretion by testes, ovary, and adrenals of

embryonic and postembryonic ducks. *Gen. Comp. Endocrinol.* 49:144–53

54. Scheib D, Guichard A, Mignot THM, Reyss-Brion M. 1985. Early sex-differences in hormonal potentialities of gonads from quail embryos with a sex-linked pigmentation marker: an in vitro radioimmunoassay study. *Gen. Comp. Endocrinol.* 60:266–72

55. Tanabe Y, Saito N, Nakamura T. 1986. Ontogenetic steroidogenesis by testes, ovary and adrenals of embryonic and postembryonic chickens (*Gallus domesticus*). *Gen. Comp. Endocrinol.* 63:456–63

56. Schumacher M, Sulon J, Balthazart J. 1988. Changes in serum concentrations of steroids during embryonic and posthatching development of male and female Japanese quail (*Coturnix japonica*). *J. Endocrinol.* 118:127–34

57. Yoshida K, Shimada K, Saito N. 1996. Expression of P450$_{17\alpha}$ hydroxylase and P450 aromatase genes in the chicken gonad before and after sexual differentiation. *Gen. Comp. Endocrinol.* 102:233–40

58. Imatake H, Suzuki K, Inao H, Kohmoto K, Tamaoki BI. 1988. Sexual differences in steroidogenic enzymes in embryonic gonads of the chicken (*Gallus domesticus*). *Gen. Comp. Endocrinol.* 69:153–62

59. Imatake H, Suzuki K, Inao H, Kohmoto K, Tamaoki BI. 1989. Biosynthetic pathways of testosterone and estradiol-17β in slices of the embryonic ovary and testis of the chicken (*Gallus domesticus*). *Gen. Comp. Endocrinol.* 73:69–79

60. Adkins-Regan E. 1985. Exposure of embryos to an aromatization inhibitor increases copulatory behavior in male quail. *Behav. Proc.* 11:153–58

61. Arnold AP. 1992. Developmental plasticity in neural circuits controlling birdsong: sexual differentiation and the neural basis of learning. *J. Neurobiol.* 23:1506–28

62. Viglietti-Panzica C, Panzica GC, Fiori MG, Calcagni M, Anselmetti GC, Balthazart J. 1986. A sexually dimophic nucleus in the quail preoptic area. *Neurosci. Lett.* 64:129–34

63. Adkins-Regan E, Watson JT. 1990. Sexual dimorphism in the avian brain is not limited to the song system of songbirds: a morphometric analysis of the brain of the quail (*Coturnix japonica*). *Brain Res.* 514:320–26

64. Schlinger BA, Callard GV. 1987. A comparison of aromatase, 5α- and 5β-reductase activities in the brain and pituitary of male and female quail (*C.c. japonica*). *J. Exp. Zool.* 242:171–80

65. Nottebohm F, Stokes TM, Leonard CM.

1976. Central control of song in the canary (*Serinus canarius*). *J. Comp. Neurol.* 165:457–86

66. Margoliash D, Fortune ES, Sutter ML, Yu AC, Wren-Hardin BD, Dave A. 1994. Distributed representation in the song system of oscines: evolutionary implications and functional consequences. *Brain Behav. Evol.* 44:247–64

67. Canady R, Kroodsma D, Nottebohm F. 1984. Population differences in complexity of a learned skill are correlates with the brain space involved. *Proc. Natl. Acad. Sci. USA* 81:6232–34

68. DeVoogd TJ, Houtman AM, Falls JB. 1995. White-throated sparrow morphs that differ in song production rate also differ in the anatomy of some song-related brain areas. *Neurobiology* 28:202–13

69. Casto JM, Ball GF. 1996. Early administration of 17β-estradiol partially masculinizes song control regions and α2-adrenergic receptor distribution in European starlings (*Sturnus vulgaris*). *Horm. Behav.* 30:387–406

70. Panzica GC, Viglietta-Panzica C, Calcagni M, Ansellmetti GC, Schumacher M, Balthazart J. 1987. Sexual differentiation and hormonal control of the sexually dimorphic preoptic nucleus in quail. *Brain Res.* 416:59–68

71. Gurney M, Konishi M. 1980. Hormone induced sexual differentiation of brain and behavior in zebra finches. *Science* 208:1380–82

72. Gurney M. 1981. Hormonal control of cell form and number in the zebra finch song system. *J. Neurosci.* 1:658–73

73. Gurney M. 1982. Behavioral correlates of sexual differentiation in the zebra finch song system. *Brain Res.* 231:153–72

74. Pohl-Apel G. 1985. The correlation between the degree of brain masculinization and song quality in estradiol-treated female zebra finches. *Brain Res.* 336:381–83

75. Pohl-Apel G, Sosinka G, Sossinka R. 1984. Hormonal determination of song capacity in females of the zebra finch: critical phase of treatment. *Z. Tierpsychol.* 64:330–36

76. Simpson HB, Vicario DS. 1991. Early estrogen treatment alone causes female zebra finches to produce male-like vocalizations. *J. Neurobiol.* 22:755–76

77. Simpson HB, Vicario DS. 1991. Early estrogen treatment of female zebra finches masculinizes the brain pathway for learned vocalization. *J. Neurobiol.* 22:777–93

78. Grisham W, Arnold AP. 1995. A direct comparison of the masculinizing effects of testosterone, androstenedione, estrogen, and progesterone on the development of the zebra finch song system. *J. Neurobiol.* 26:163–70

79. Schlinger BA, Arnold AP. 1991 Androgen effects on development of the zebra finch song system. *Brain Res.* 561:99–105

80. Grisham W, Tam, A, Greco C, Schlinger BA, and Arnold, AP. 1997. A putative 5α-reductase inhibitor demasculinizes portions of the zebra finch song system. *Brain Res.* 750:122–28

81. Jacobs EC, Grisham W, Arnold AP. 1995. Lack of a synergistic effect between estradiol and dihydrotestosterone in the masculinization of the zebra finch song system. *J. Neurobiol.* 27:513–19

82. Hutchison JB, Wingfield JC, Hutchison RE. 1984. Sex differences in plasma concentrations of steroids during the sensitive period for brain differentiation in the zebra finch. *J. Endocrinol.* 103:363–69

83. Adkins-Regan E, Abdelnabi M, Mobarak M, Ottinger MA. 1990. Sex steroid levels in developing and adult male and female zebra finches. *Gen. Comp. Endocrinol.* 78:93–109

84. Schlinger BA, Arnold AP. 1992. Plasma sex steroids and tissue aromatization in hatchling zebra finches: implications for the sexual differentiation of singing behavior. *Endocrinology* 130:289–99

85. Gahr M. 1996. Developmental changes in the distribution of oestrogen receptor mRNA expressing cells in the forebrain of female, male and masculinized female zebra finches. *NeuroReport* 7:2469–73

86. Grisham W, Mathews GA, Arnold AP. 1994. Local intracerebral implants of estrogen masculinize some aspects of the zebra finch song system. *J. Neurobiol.* 25:185–96

87. Wade J, Schlinger BA, Arnold AP. 1995. Aromatase and 5β-reductase activity in cultures of developing zebra finch brain: an investigation of sex and regional differences. *J. Neurobiol.* 27:240–51

88. Schlinger BA, Cam VT, Arnold AP. 1994. Dibutyryl cAMP effects on neural and non-neural aromatase in developing zebra finches. *Soc. Neurosci. Abstr.* 20:460

89. Mathews GA, Brenowitz EA, Arnold AP. 1988. Paradoxical hypermasculinization of the zebra finch song system by an antiestrogen. *Horm. Behav.* 22:540–51

90. Mathews GA, Arnold AP. 1990. Antiestrogens fail to prevent the masculine ontogeny of the zebra finch song system. *Gen. Comp. Endocrinol.* 80:48–58

91. Mathews GA, Arnold AP. 1991. Tamoxifen fails to block estradiol accumulation, yet is weakly accumulated by the juvenile zebra finch anterior hypothalamus: an autoradiographic study. *J. Neurobiol.* 22:970–75

92. Wade J, Schlinger BA, Hodges L, Arnold AP. 1994. Fadrozole: a potent and specific inhibitor of aromatase in the zebra finch brain. *Gen. Comp. Endocrinol.* 94:53–61

93. Balthazart J, Absil P, Fiasse V, Ball GF. 1994. Effects of the aromatase inhibitor R76713 on sexual differentiation of brain and behavior in the zebra finch. *Behavior* 131:225–60

94. Lane N, Grisham W, Brown S, Thompson L, Arnold A, Schlinger B. 1996. Plasma testosterone and tissue 17α-hydroxylase activity in castrated and fadrozole treated male zebra finches. *Soc. Neurosci. Abstr.* 22:156

95. Lowther JK. 1961. Polymorphism in the white-throated sparrow, *Zonotrichia albicollis* (Gmelin). *Can. J. Zool.* 39:281–92

96. Thorneycroft HB. 1975. A cytogenetic study of the white-throated sparrow, *Zonotrichia albicollis. Evolution* 29:611–21

97. Houtman AM, Falls JB. 1994. Negative assortative mating in the white-throated sparrow, *Zonotrichia albicollis*: the role of mate choice and intra-sexual competition. *Anim. Behav.* 48:377–83

98. Kopachena JG, Falls JB. 1993. Aggressive performance as a behavioral correlate of plumage polymorphism in the white-throated sparrow (*Zonotrichia albicollis*). *Behaviour* 124:249–66

99. Schlinger BA, Palter B, Callard GV. 1987. A method to quantify aggressiveness in Japanese quail (*Coturnix c. japonica*). *Physiol. Behav.* 40:343–48

100. Balthazart J, Castagna C, Ball GF. 1997. Aromatization inhibition blocks the activation and sexual differentiation of appetitive male sexual behavior in Japanese quail. *Behav. Neurosci.* 111:381–97

101. Schlinger BA, Callard GV.1989. Aromatase in quail brain: correlations with aggressiveness. *Endocrinology* 124:437–43

102. Adkins-Regan, E, Ottinger MA, Park J. 1995. Maternal transfer of estradiol to egg yolks alters sexual differentiation of avian offspring. *J. Exp. Zool.* 271:466–70

103. Schwabl H. 1993. Yolk is a source of maternal testosterone for developing birds. *Proc. Natl. Acad. Sci. USA* 90:11446–50

Annu. Rev. Physiol. 1998. 60:431–60

THE PHYSIOLOGY OF PARATHYROID HORMONE-RELATED PROTEIN:
An Emerging Role as a Developmental Factor

J. J. Wysolmerski[1] and A. F. Stewart[2]
[1]Division of Endocrinology, Yale University School of Medicine, New Haven, Connecticut 06520; [2]Division of Endocrinology, University of Pittsburgh Medical Center, Pittsburgh, Pennsylvania 15213

KEY WORDS: vascular smooth muscle, pancreatic islet, skeleton, mammary gland, protein processing, nuclear targeting

ABSTRACT

Parathyroid hormone-related protein (PTHrP) is the agent responsible for humoral hypercalcemia of malignancy. Its pathogenic role in this syndrome is well established, and attention has focused in recent years on the elucidation of the roles played by PTHrP in normal developmental and adult physiology. This review focuses on studies of the past two years: (*a*) elucidation of the posttranslational processing pattern of PTHrP, the mechanisms of action of the various secretory forms of PTHrP, the role of PTHrP as an intracrine regulator of cell growth and cell death; (*b*) the emergence of PTHrP as a critical developmental factor in the mammary gland, epidermis, and the skeleton; and (*c*) the advances in understanding of the roles of PTHrP in the regulation of pancreatic islet mass, vascular smooth muscle tone and proliferation, and materno-fetal calcium transfer across the placenta.

INTRODUCTION

Parathyroid hormone-related protein (PTHrP) was isolated and partially sequenced in 1987 (1, 2). The role of PTHrP in the humoral hypercalcemia of malignancy (HHM) syndrome (1, 2), the structure of the PTHrP gene (3–5), the regulation of PTHrP gene expression (3–6), the posttranslational processing of

431

PTHrP (3–7), the receptors employed by PTHrP (6–8), and the normal physiological roles of PTHrP (9, 10) have been the subject of detailed reviews. An introduction describing each these areas follows, but this review focuses on recent progress in the PTHrP story.

The discovery of PTHrP was the culmination of a search by several laboratories for the humoral agent responsible for the common paraneoplastic syndrome HHM (1, 2). The term parathyroid hormone-related protein derives from the

A. The Three Initial PTHrP Translation Products

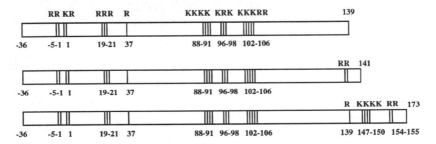

B. PTHrP Functional Domains

SP	P	PTH	- LIKE	CONSERVED	UNIQUE
-36		1	14	36	111	173

C. Posttranslational Processing

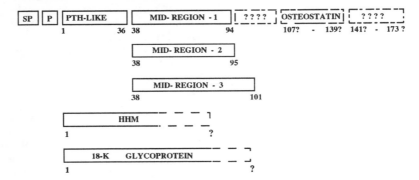

facts that the first 13 amino acids of PTHrP are highly homologous with those in the same position in parathyroid hormone (PTH) and that both peptides act via a single PTH/PTHrP receptor (3–8). However, this structure-derived terminology is prohibitively narrow: PTH is produced by only two tissues, the parathyroid gland and the central nervous system (CNS), and it functions primarily to regulate systemic calcium homeostasis through its skeletal and renal actions. In contrast, PTHrP is produced by virtually every cell and tissue within the body and has a broad range of functions, most of which have little to do with calcium homeostasis. These functions will be enumerated below, but it is important to recognize that PTHrP has less in common functionally with PTH than with epidermal growth factor (EGF), transforming growth factor beta (TGF-β), insulin-like growth factor I (IGF-I), or any of a number of developmental factors. A more appropriate name might be TGF-γ or a name that reflects its developmental and physiological roles.

PTHrP is the product of a single gene, a gene that is highly similar in organization and sequence to the PTH gene. The structure and ancestry of the gene and its relationship to the PTH gene have been reviewed in detail (3–5). Through alternative splicing, the multi-exonic PTHrP gene gives rise to three initial translation products: PTHrP(1–139), PTHrP(1–141), and PTHrP(1–173) (6, 7). These three peptides are identical in positions 1–139 and differ only in their carboxy termini (Figure 1). The PTHrP sequence is extraordinarily highly conserved among species, with the rodent and human sequences differing in only three amino acids in the 1–111 region (3–7).

The three initial PTHrP translation products undergo extensive posttranslational processing (Figure 1) and give rise to a family of mature secretory forms of the peptide, each with its own physiological function(s) and each with

←——————————————————————————

Figure 1 Diagram of the three PTHrP initial translation products and of the mature PTHrP secretory forms that result from posttranslational processing. *Panel A* indicates the three initial translation products that arise from alternative splicing. The three species are identical except for their carboxy termini. Note the abundance of basic residues (R, arginine; K, lysine), particularly in the 88–106 region. *Panel B* indicates the functional domains of the PTHrP precursors. *Panel C* demonstrates the peptides generated by posttranslational processing. SP, signal peptide; P, propeptide; PTH-like, region with homology to parathyroid hormone; osteostatin, the region with osteoclast-inhibiting activity; conserved, region intensely conserved, together with the 1–36 region, in human, mouse, rat, dog, baboon, and chicken PTHrP; unique, indicates a region two ways: not as highly conserved as the 1–111 region, and the 141–173 region encoded only in the primate genome; HHM, indicates a peptide associated with humoral hypercalcemia of malignancy; 18-K glycoprotein, identified as a secretory peptide produced by epidermal keratinocytes. See text for further details. The *boxes* that are formed by *solid lines* indicate that the peptide structure is fully known. Those with *dotted lines* are presumed to exist but have not been formally defined. (Adapted with permission from Reference 15.)

its own receptor or receptors. For example, the amino-terminal PTHrP secretory form, PTHrP(1–36), acts through the classical PTH/PTHrP receptor (7, 8) and through a structurally undefined amino-terminal PTHrP receptor (7, 11), thereby initiating multiple events (e.g. vasorelaxation, bone resorption, cellular proliferation). Mid-region PTHrP appears to have its own cognate receptor (12) and to have different effects, for example, on placental calcium transport (discussed below) that neither PTH nor amino-terminal PTHrP possesses. The carboxy-terminal PTHrP peptide, PTHrP(107–139), appears to act through a still different receptor and to have other effects such as inhibition of osteoclastic bone resorption (13).

PTHrP is expressed in almost every tissue in the body (6, 7, 9, 10). Its functions or physiological roles can be broadly divided into four categories. First, PTHrP appears to stimulate transepithelial calcium transport in a variety of tissues, including the renal tubule, the placenta, the mammary gland, and possibly the shell gland of the egg-laying hen. Second, PTHrP is a smooth muscle relaxant in a broad range of tissues, including uterus, urinary bladder, stomach, small intestine, colon, and the arterial wall. In each of these tissues, PTHrP is upregulated by mechanical stretch. Third, PTHrP is a regulator of cellular proliferation, differentiation, and apoptosis in many cell types. Finally, disruption of the PTHrP gene or its receptor is lethal in fetal or immediate postpartum life, indicating that PTHrP is an important, sometimes necessary developmental factor.

POSTTRANSLATIONAL PROCESSING AND INTRACELLULAR TARGETING OF PTHrP

The steps in PTHrP processing, as understood in 1995, are summarized in recent reviews (3–7). Recently, four additional features of posttranslational processing of PTHrP have been identified.

The Three Mid-Region Secretory Forms of PTHrP

Work by Soifer et al (14) reported in 1992 and reviewed subsequently (3–7) demonstrated that a mid-region secretory form of PTHrP begins, as demonstrated by N-terminal sequencing, at alanine in position 38 (Figure 1), indicating that Arg37 is a monobasic-processing site in the PTHrP precursor [an observation supported by the demonstration that site-directed mutagenesis of this arginine to other amino acids prevents processing at this site (15)]. More importantly, these findings demonstrated that a discrete mid-region form of PTHrP is secreted and defined the amino terminus of this mid-region secretory form of PTHrP as Ala38. With the purification of mid-region PTHrP in quantities sufficient for mass spectroscopic analysis and tryptic digestion, the carboxy terminus of this peptide was defined (15). Indeed, not one but three mid-region secretory forms of PTHrP were defined, all beginning at Ala38 and each terminating at a different amino acid: 94, 95, and 101. Thus the authentic mid-region secretory forms of PTHrP are PTHrP(38–94), PTHrP(38–95), and PTHrP(38–101). These observations are important for several reasons. First, the multibasic region spanning amino acids 87–106 in the PTHrP precursor (Figure 1) is a cleavage site for prohormone convertases, as had been suspected (3–7). Second, the initial PTHrP translation product is a prohormone capable of generating a family of mature daughter peptides. Third, because these mid-region peptides are derived from the 38–111 region of the precursor, a highly conserved domain among the many species from which it has been sequenced (mouse, rat, human, dog, chicken, baboon), these mid-region peptides probably have important physiological functions. Finally, because one of the mid-region species terminates at position 101, because the prohormone convertase site employed appears to be the lysine/arginine cluster at PTHrP(102–106), and because one of the most abundant PTHrP mRNA species encodes PTHrP(1–139), it seems highly likely that PTHrP(107–139) is an additional secretory form of PTHrP, as suggested by Fenton et al (13). One unsettled issue is whether the mid-region PTHrP(38–94) peptide is amidated at the carboxy terminus. The terminal proline in position 94 is followed in the PTHrP precursor sequence by the Gly-dibasic consensus sequence for carboxy-terminal amidation, and the amidating enzyme, peptidyl α-amidating monooxygenase (PAM) is present in the same cells that produce PTHrP (3–7, 15); thus carboxy-terminal amidation probably occurs, but has not been documented.

Identification of a Receptor for Mid-Region PTHrP

The facts that the mid-region of PTHrP is highly conserved among species (3–7), that a mid-region PTHrP species is secreted by PTHrP-producing cells into the medium (14), and that mid-region PTHrP is present in the circulation of patients with HHM syndrome (reviewed in References 16 and 17), suggest that mid-region PTHrP(s) have biological functions probably mediated by specific receptors that recognize mid-region PTHrP sequences. The biological effects of mid-region PTHrP are discussed below. Using this logic, and working with a mid-region PTHrP peptide, PTHrP(67–86), Orloff and collaborators have characterized a receptor for the mid-region form of PTHrP (12). The mid-region PTHrP agonist employed, PTHrP(67–86), previously was shown by others to be biologically active in several systems (see below) and is included in the PTHrP(38–94) sequence (15). Orloff and collaborators have reported that PTHrP(67–86) stimulates cytosolic calcium responses in squamous carcinoma cells in doses as low as 10^{-12} M, that this response cannot be inhibited by PTH(7–34) (an antagonist of the classical amino-terminal PTHrP receptor), that these responses are additive with cytosolic calcium responses induced by amino-terminal PTHrP, and that they are accompanied by increases in phosphatidyli-nositols (12). Thus a protein kinase C-coupled response in squamous carcinoma cells appears to be separate from the PKC-induced response to amino-terminal PTHrP mediated by the classical PTH/PTHrP receptor. This response is not accompanied by an adenylyl cyclase response (12). Studies aimed at demon-strating a cell surface receptor using standard radioligand approaches were unsuccessful, suggesting either that the mid-region PTHrP receptor is a low-abundance receptor or that the ligand employed, PTHrP(67–86)amide, is not the optimal ligand. Interestingly, the ability to recognize PTHrP(67–86) could be conferred upon *Xenopus laevis* oocytes by injection of polyA+ RNA derived from the squamous cells (12). This finding is important because it demonstrates that the cytosolic calcium increment is present in another cell type and suggests a means for the molecular cloning of the mid-region PTHrP receptor cDNA.

Physiological Functions of Mid-Region PTHrP

Work of several types suggests that mid-region PTHrP will have important physiological functions. First, as noted above, this region of PTHrP is highly conserved. The rodent and human PTHrPs differ in the 38–101 region by only two amino acids (3–7). Second, the mid-region peptide is secreted by a variety of cell types (14), both via the regulated secretory pathway and the constitutive pathway (18), and it is present in the circulation of patients with HHM syndrome in concentrations higher that those of any other PTHrP secretory form (16, 17).

Rodda and collaborators showed that mid-region PTHrP displays biological activity in a perfused sheep placental system (see below and Reference 19). Luparello and collaborators reported that PTHrP(67–86) inhibits the growth of the breast carcinoma line 8701-BC (20). As noted above, PTHrP(67–86)amide increases cytosolic calcium levels in human squamous carcinoma lines (12). Subsequently, Wu et al (15) demonstrated that a mid-region PTHrP, PTHrP(38–94)amide, also increases cytosolic calcium levels in a pancreatic β cell line (RIN 1046–38), a human squamous carcinoma line (YCC-SQ-1), and a vas-cular smooth muscle cell line (A-10). These responses occurred with doses of PTHrP(38–94)amide in the 10^{-12} to 10^{-10} M range, as was reported for PTHrP(67–86) (12). These cytosolic calcium responses were not accompanied by increases in cAMP levels, suggesting that the mid-region PTHrP receptor is coupled to the PKC but not to the PKA pathway (12, 15). These responses indicate that mid-region PTHrP is biologically active, but, except for the effect on placental calcium transport and effect on the mammary carcinoma growth, the nature of these effects remains to be fully explored. It is assumed that physiological effects of mid-region PTHrP will be observed in many tissues, because the mid-region peptide appears to be produced by most cell types.

Carboxy-Terminal Multibasic Sites in the PTHrP Precursor May Serve as Intracellular Targeting Signals that Direct PTHrP into a Degradative Pathway

Ditmer and collaborators observed that the (87–106) multibasic region of PTHrP, in addition to serving as a prohormone convertase substrate site, may also target the PTHrP precursor to an unknown intracellular site for degradation (21). To study the importance of these multibasic sites, they prepared cDNAs encoding the truncated PTHrP species—PTHrP(1–18), PTHrP(1–36), PTHrP(1–87), PTHrP(1–95), PTHrP(1–101), PTHrP(1–146), PTHrP(1–152), and PTHrP(1–173)—and transfected these cDNAs into COS cells (representing the constitutive secretory pathway) and into BE neuroblastoma cells (representing the regulated secretory pathway). As expected, because peptides containing fewer than 60–80 amino acids fail to traverse the secretory pathway, the PTHrP(1–18) and PTHrP(1–36) constructs did not yield intracellular or secreted PTHrP(1–18) or PTHrP(1–36). Also as expected, the PTHrP(1–173) construct (the wild-type or native construct) led to the synthesis and secretion of PTHrP from both cell types. The surprising finding was that the PTHrP(1–87), (1–95), and (1–101) mutant constructs generated more PTHrP production, as measured by appearance in the culture medium and in cell extracts (as much as 60-fold more), than the full-length cDNA, and PTHrP accumulated in conditioned medium more rapidly with the shorter constructs. Further, the percentage of PTHrP remaining within cell extracts was lower with the shorter constructs. Collectively, these findings suggest that sequences within the carboxy-terminal region direct or target the full-length precursor into an as yet undefined degradative pathway. As yet there is no direct evidence that PTHrP is actually targeted for degradation, and the site of this putative degradation and the amino acids in the carboxy terminus responsible for this targeting remain to be defined. In this vein, Meerovich et al in a preliminary report have suggested, using a rabbit reticulocyte lysate in vitro translation system, that PTHrP binds to ubiquitin moieties, and incubation with the proteasome inhibitor MG132 prevents degradation of PTHrP translated in vitro (22). These in vitro events may reflect events in intact cells.

DUAL MECHANISMS OF ACTION: CELL SURFACE RECEPTORS AND NUCLEAR TARGETING

PTHrP enters the classical secretory pathway, beginning with signal peptide-mediated entry into the endoplasmic reticulum, traverses the Golgi stacks and the *trans*-Golgi network, then enters the transport vesicles of the constitutive secretory pathway or the secretory granules of the regulated secretory pathway, depending upon the cell in question, and finally undergoes posttranslational glycosylation and cleavage by prohormone convertases, as described above (3–7, 18, 23). Through the work of Kaiser, Henderson, Karaplis, and their colleagues (24–26), it now appears that PTHrP also exerts some effects through intracrine mechanisms via nuclear or nucleolar targeting. Although exogenously added PTHrP(1–34) stimulates the proliferation of squamous epithelial cells, introduction of PTHrP anti-sense mRNA by stable transfection paradoxically also enhances proliferation (24, 25), an effect that could not be prevented by the addition of anti-PTHrP antisera. Thus it is possible that PTHrP mediates some effects via intracellular actions. The PTHrP sequence contains three clusters of basic residues in the (87–106) region (Figure 1) that are similar in sequence and configuration to the single and bipartite nuclear and nucleolar localization sequences in viral transcription factors and in certain growth factors, such as basic fibroblast growth factor (bFGF) and fibroblast growth factor-3 (FGF-3) (24, 25). PTHrP can be identified immunocytochemically in the nucleus, particularly the nucleolus, in normal bone cells, and in COS-7 cells transfected with PTHrP (26). Moreover, deletion of the multibasic (87–106) region prevents this nucleolar localization, and deletion of the PTHrP signal peptide, which would divert PTHrP away from the secretory pathway, enhances nucleolar localization (26). Further, expression of the multibasic region of PTHrP as a fusion protein with β-galactosidase targets β-galactosidase to the nucleolus. (26). Thus PTHrP appears in the nucleolus under normal circumstances and is targeted to the nucleolus by sequences in the (87–106) multibasic region. This sequence can direct other chimeric proteins to the nucleolus. In addition, Henderson et al have demonstrated that this nucleolar targeting may have functional consequences: When the basic sequences are deleted from PTHrP constructs transfected into chondrocytes, the chondrocytes are protected from apoptotic cell death induced by serum deprivation (26).

One unresolved issue relates to the question of how PTHrP can, under some circumstances, enter the secretory pathway and, at the same time, avoid entry into the endoplasmic reticulum but remain in the cytoplasm and enter the nucleus. This phenomenon has been described for a variety of viral proteins, as well as for bFGF and for FGF-3 (24–28). In this case, the peptide enters the secretory pathway when it is translated with a signal peptide. On the other hand, the use of an alternative translation initiation site may result in a peptide without a signal peptide, which can escape the endoplasmic reticulum and instead be released into the cytoplasm and enter the nucleus. Burtis has suggested that this phenomenon may occur in the case of PTHrP through the use of an in-frame alternative translation initiation (CUG) site in codon five in the PTHrP precursor (WJ Burtis, personal communication). The importance of this putative alternative translational start site in the PTHrP mRNA has not been documented.

An alternate mechanism through which PTHrP sequences might find their way to the nucleus would be through secretion via the classical secretory pathway followed by receptor-mediated endocytosis/internalization and release of ligand within the cell. This sequence has been reported for acidic and bFGF and for angiogenin (24–30). In these cases, nuclear localization after entry into the cell via endocytosis is mediated by nuclear or nucleolar targeting signals.

PTHrP AS A DEVELOPMENTAL REGULATORY MOLECULE

PTHrP is produced during fetal development, as evidenced both by immuno-histochemistry and in situ hybridization histochemistry (6, 10). Furthermore, the PTH/PTHrP receptor is also widely expressed during fetal life (31). In fact, PTHrP and the PTH/PTHrP receptor are believed to be one of the earliest peptide hormone/receptor systems operative in mouse development and can be detected in late morulas (32). We do not consider further the fetal sites of PTHrP and/or PTH/PTHrP receptor expression in this review (see References 6 and 10 for a complete review), but rather highlight two points. First, as mentioned above, PTHrP and the PTH/PTHrP receptor are expressed in tissues derived from all three germ layers and extraembryonic sites such as the amnion and trophoblast (33, 34). Second, in most sites, PTHrP and the PTH/PTHrP receptor are coordinately expressed in adjacent cells, implying that amino-terminal PTHrP and the PTH/PTHrP receptor may be involved in paracrine signaling pathways in such sites (31). For example, PTHrP appears to be produced by the perichondrium, whereas the PTH/PTHrP receptor is present on a subset of maturing chondrocytes (31, 35–37). In extraskeletal sites, PTHrP is predominantly expressed in the surface epithelium of developing organs, and the PTH/PTHrP receptor resides on the mesenchymal cells adjacent to and sometimes enveloping the epithelial structures (31).

The widespread expression of PTHrP during fetal life implies functional roles during development, and studies in transgenic mice that overexpress or underexpress PTHrP have begun to shed some light on what those functions might be. Two principal concepts have emerged; namely, PTHrP plays a role in the regulation of chondrocyte growth and differentiation during fetal bone development and in epithelial-mesenchymal interactions during the development of epithelial organs. We discuss these areas in some detail below but first describe the potential role of PTHrP in early development.

PTHrP in Early Development

Acting through the PTH/PTHrP receptor, PTHrP participates in the differentiation of parietal endoderm from primitive endoderm. In 1981, Evain et al demonstrated that PTH induces a cAMP response in F9 teratocarcinoma cells treated with retinoic acid and dibutyrl cAMP (38). Chan et al subsequently showed that PTHrP mRNA expression is upregulated during the differentiation of F9 cells into parietal endoderm-like cells and that PTHrP facilitates the differentiation (39). These findings were extended by van de Stolpe et al who found that PTHrP is produced by differentiating trophoectoderm in murine pre-implantation embryos and that the PTH/PTHrP receptor is expressed on both primitive endoderm cells and differentiating parietal endoderm cells but is not expressed by the visceral endoderm (32). They demonstrated that the acquisition of PTH/PTHrP receptor expression is a hallmark of primitive endoderm differentiation and that PTHrP can induce the differentiation of these cells to a parietal endoderm phenotype, further enhancing PTH/PTHrP receptor expression (32). They proposed a model by which PTHrP, produced by the trophoectoderm, participates in the recruitment and/or differentiation of parietal endodermal cells from the inner cell mass as they migrate along the basement membrane established by the trophoblastic cells. Behrendtsen and colleagues have shown that PTHrP is critical to the outgrowth of parietal endoderm from inner cell masses cultured from mouse blastocysts (40). In these studies, PTHrP appears to modulate the matrix requirements for the outgrowth of parietal endoderm, suggesting that there may be cross-talk between PTH/PTHrP receptor second messenger systems and integrin signaling in the endoderm cells (40). In summary, PTHrP may play a critical role in the formation of the extraembryonic tissues in early mammalian development. If this is concept is correct, PTHrP must be a component of a redundant system because PTHrP-knockout embryos survive to birth (41). It is possible that maternal PTHrP may complement the lack of fetal PTHrP in the knockout embryos, allowing them to form normal extraembryonic structures (40). However, this possibility is unlikely because PTH/PTHrP receptor knockout embryos also form normal early extraembryonic membranes (42). These mice frequently die at mid-gestation for reasons that remain unclear, but they develop normal-appearing parietal endoderm and Reichert's membrane (42). Hence, the exact role of PTHrP during early development is unclear, but PTHrP probably contributes in some fashion to the formation of the extraembryonic tissues.

The Role of PTHrP During Skeletal Development

Chondrocytes express the PTH receptor in vitro and treatment of chondrocytes in culture with PTH delays their differentiation, suggesting that signaling through the receptor affects cartilage growth and/or differentiation (43, 44). Studies in transgenic animals have confirmed and extended these observations by demonstrating that PTHrP and the PTH/PTHrP receptor are critical for the proper sequence of chondrocyte proliferation and differentiation during development of fetal bone (Figure 2) (36, 41, 42, 45). The initial evidence of this role came from the studies of Karaplis and colleagues in which the PTHrP gene in mice was disrupted by homologous recombination (41). These PTHrP-knockout mice have a lethal form of chondrodysplasia that causes short-limbed dwarfism characterized by premature and inappropriate ossification of the developing skeleton. The mice die shortly after birth, presumably because the ossified shield chest interferes with breathing. Histologically, the abnormal growth plate is characterized by decreased numbers of resting and proliferative chondrocytes and premature endochondral and perichondral ossification (Figure 2A,B) (37, 41, 46). These findings suggest that the absence of PTHrP causes accelerated chondrocyte differentiation and premature ossification, leading to disruption of the growth plate and failure of bone elongation.

This interpretation was corroborated by Weir et al who overexpressed PTHrP in transgenic mice using the procollagen II promoter, which targets proliferating and prehypertrophic chondrocytes (45). These col II-PTHrP mice also had short-limbed dwarfism, in this case due to delay in chondrocyte differentiation, so that the more severely affected mice were born with a completely cartilaginous endochondral skeleton. At birth the long bones in these mice consist of a mass of hypertrophic cartilage that slowly calcifies and ossifies in a circumferential ring around a central mass of retained cartilage (Figure 2C,D) (45). This curious pattern of chondrocyte differentiation may result from a pattern of transgene expression that led to a gradient of PTHrP highest in the center of the cartilaginous bone mold and diminishing in a centripetal fashion. Taken together, these reports establish that PTHrP acts as a brake on the program of chondrocyte differentiation during bone development. The fact that both acceleration and slowing of chondrocyte differentiation lead to growth failure underscores the precise temporal regulation of chondrocyte proliferation, differentiation, and ossification that must occur for the proper elongation of endochondral bones.

These effects of PTHrP on chondrocyte differentiation are due to amino-terminal species of PTHrP acting via the PTH/PTHrP receptor. Lanske et al recently demonstrated that disruption of the PTH/PTHrP receptor gene by homologous recombination causes an almost identical skeletal phenotype to that in the PTHrP-null mouse (41, 42). Additionally, activating mutations of the PTH/PTHrP receptor cause Jansen's metaphyseal chondrodysplasia (47, 48), a rare human form of chondrodysplasia characterized by short-limbed dwarfism, dumbbell-like deformities of the foreshortened long bones, and hypercalcemia and hypophosphatemia. The biochemical abnormalities appear to result from a mutation that constitutively activates the PTH/PTHrP receptor in the classical PTH target organs—bone and kidney—whereas the developmental abnormalities are most likely due to constitutively activated PTH/PTHrP receptors on

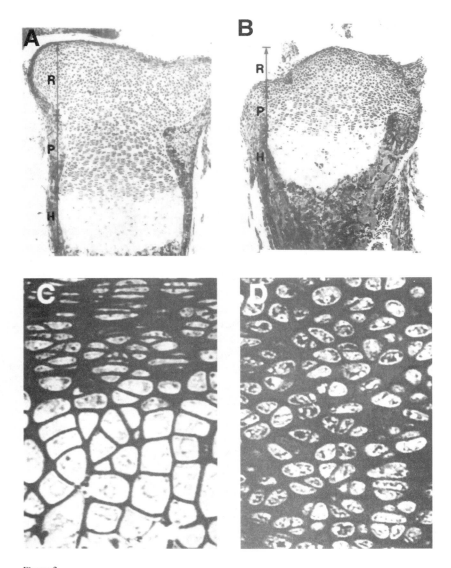

Figure 2

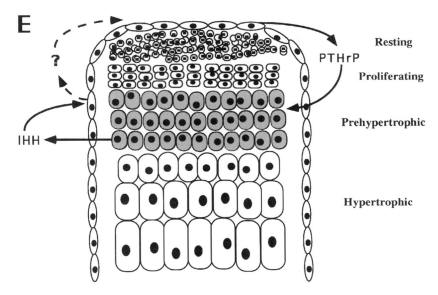

Figure 2   The role of PTHrP in chondrocyte differentiation in the growth plate.   (*Panels A,B*) Low-power views of the proximal tibia of a PTHrP-knockout fetus (*B*) compared with that of a normal control (*A*). The zones of resting, proliferating, and of prehypertrophic and hypertrophic chondrocytes are noted in diagram (*E*). The absence of PTHrP accelerates chondrocyte differentiation, which results in an overall shortened epiphysis, markedly diminished numbers of resting and proliferative chondrocytes, and premature calcification in the knockout mice. (Reproduced from Reference 37 with permission).

(*Panels C,D*) Sections taken from equivalent portions of a metatarsal growth plate of a 6-day-old transgenic mouse overexpressing PTHrP in chondrocytes (*D*) as compared with that taken from a 6-day-old normal littermate (*C*). In the normal growth plate, the expected progression of resting to prehypertrophic to hypertrophic chondrocytes is seen (*C*). In contrast, in PTHrP overexpression, there is a profound delay in chondrocyte differentiation, resulting in an accumulation of prehypertrophic chondrocytes and the complete absence of bone formation. (Reproduced from Reference 51 with permission).

(*Panel E*) Schematic representation of the proposed interactions of PTHrP and Indian Hedgehog (IHH) during chondrocyte differentiation in the growth plate.   IHH appears to be produced by cells in the lower zone of prehypertrophic chondrocytes and to act on the adjacent perichondrium (elongated cells at the periphery). IHH somehow causes these perichondrial cells to communicate (*dotted arrows*) with the perichondrium at the ends of the bone to induce the production of PTHrP. PTHrP, in turn, acts via PTH/PTHrP receptors located on prehypertrophic chondrocytes (*shaded cells*) to impair their further differentiation by upregulating Bcl-2 expression.

chondrocytes (47, 48). Endochondral bone formation in this disorder is associated with the retention of cartilage in the metaphyses that slowly resolves by the second decade of life, leaving a misshapen adult skeleton (49). These findings resemble the findings in the col II-PTHrP transgenic mice, in which overexpression of PTHrP is associated with a slow resolution of a similar pseudo-growth plate (45). Thus both underexpression and overactivity of the PTH/PTHrP receptor cause abnormalities in chondrocyte differentiation that are similar to the abnormalities caused by underexpression or overexpression of PTHrP.

It is apparent from these studies that PTHrP acts through the PTH/PTHrP receptor to retard chondrocyte differentiation during endochondral bone formation. Attempts are being made to identify the signaling networks upstream and downstream of PTHrP during bone formation and to identify the mechanisms by which PTHrP affects chondrocyte differentiation. There is general agreement on several points. First, as evidenced by immunohistochemistry and in situ hybridization, PTHrP is expressed in the perichondrium, perhaps most intensely at the distal ends of forming long bones, and at the site of the initial bone-collar in the mid-shafts of these bones (31, 36, 37). Second, the PTH/PTHrP receptor appears to be expressed in the lower zone of proliferating and maturing prehypertrophic chondrocytes within the growth plate and in mature osteoblasts within the primary spongiosum, near the growth plate (31, 35, 37). There is uncertainty, however, as to the extent and location of PTHrP expression within the chondrocytes of the growth plate itself. Immunohistochemical studies suggest that PTHrP is expressed in resting chondrocytes and in the zone of transition between proliferative and hypertrophic chondrocytes (37). In situ hybridization studies suggest that PTHrP mRNA is expressed in the terminal hypertrophic chondrocytes (31). These differences may be related to the differences in technique and/or to differences in the developmental stages examined, because PTHrP gene expression appear to depend on the developmental stages of the bones examined (31).

Despite the lack of a consensus about PTHrP expression in the growth plate, some of the upstream and downstream signaling partners for PTHrP in bone development have been defined (Figure 2E). First, Vortkamp et al demonstrated that Indian hedgehog (IHH), one of the mammalian homologues of the Drosophila segment polarity gene known as hedgehog, appears to act upstream of PTHrP to regulate chondrocyte differentiation (36). IHH is expressed in prehypertrophic chondrocytes and acts on the perichondrium to upregulate PTHrP expression. Furthermore, overexpression of IHH in developing chick limbs blocks chondrocyte differentiation similar to that seen with overexpression of PTHrP in chondrocytes. This response was not seen in organ cultures of long bones from PTHrP-null mice, indicating that PTHrP functions downstream of IHH and mediates the effect of IHH on chondrocyte differentiation. These data suggest a paracrine signaling loop in which IHH, synthesized by the prehypertrophic chondrocytes, acts in the perichondrium to increase secretion of PTHrP, which acts on PTH/PTHrP receptors on prehypertrophic cells to stimulate their differentiation into hypertrophic chondrocytes (36). This is an appealing model of IHH and PTHrP interaction, but several aspects have not been defined. First, it is unclear if IHH acts directly upstream of PTHrP or if there are intermediate steps between the two signaling molecules. Second, the perichondrium at the distal portion of the developing long bones (the site of most intense IHH-induced PTHrP production) is separated from the PTH/PTHrP receptor pool in the prehypertrophic chondrocytes, so it is not clear how the ligand would gain access to the responsive cells, given the distance involved and the propensity for PTHrP to be degraded rapidly in the extracellular milieu (17, 50, 52).

Finally, a possible downstream effector pathway might retard the enhancement of chondrocyte differentiation by PTHrP and delay primary ossification of developing bones. The ultimate fate of hypertrophic chondrocytes may be to undergo apoptosis prior to calcification of the cartilaginous matrix (53), and PTHrP may prevent apoptotic death by increasing the levels of Bcl-2 in differentiating chondrocytes (51). PTHrP, acting through an intracrine pathway, may regulate chondrocyte apoptosis in vitro (26). It is not clear whether the higher level of Bcl-2 seen in chondrocytes upon PTHrP-treatment (51) is a direct consequence of PTHrP-signaling or secondary to the expected delay in chondrocyte differentiation, but PTHrP overexpression appears to cause retention of large numbers of prehypertrophic and hypertrophic chondrocytes within the developing bones of the col II-PTHrP transgenic mice (45, 51).

In summary, progress has been made in defining the role of PTHrP in fetal bone development. The role of PTHrP in mature bone, perhaps in modulating osteoblast formation and/or function, has not been defined.

The Role of PTHrP in Regulating Epithelial-Mesenchymal Interactions During Organogenesis

Another developmental action of PTHrP may be to modulate the ability of mesenchymal cells to support the proper morphogenesis of epithelial organs. This role was suggested by studies of transgenic mice with overexpression of PTHrP in the developing epidermis and mammary gland utilizing the human keratin-14 promoter (52, 53), implying that PTHrP regulates epithelial-mesenchymal cross-talk during development of hair follicles and mammary glands. However, as discussed below, PTHrP may play a more general role in these processes during organogenesis.

Normal human keratinocytes were the first nonmalignant cells shown to produce PTHrP (54), and PTHrP and the PTH/PTHrP receptor are both expressed during skin development (31). To investigate the function of PTHrP in skin, Wysolmerski et al utilized the human keratin-14 (K14) promoter to target

PTHrP overexpression to basal keratinocytes and to the outer root sheath cells of hair follicles, sites that normally produce PTHrP (52). These mice have a striking phenotype, namely an almost complete failure of ventral hair follicle initiation, and a severe delay in hair follicle initiation on the dorsal surface. Furthermore, there was a shift in the distribution and pattern of the hair types that ultimately developed. Hair follicle initiation is critically dependent on the proper exchange of signals between fetal keratinocytes and dermal mesenchymal cells (55). PTHrP mRNA is detectable in the epidermis as early as 14 days of gestation in the rat and appears to be expressed preferentially in hair follicles in both rat and mouse fetuses (31; JJ Wysolmerski, unpublished observations). The PTH/PTHrP receptor is expressed in the mesenchymal cells of the developing dermis adjacent to the epidermis and enveloping the developing hair follicles (31). In addition, PTHrP stimulates adenylyl cyclase activity in dermal fibroblasts, and dermal fibroblasts produce a soluble factor that stimulates PTHrP production in squamous carcinoma cells (56, 57). Thus on the basis of localization and functional data, there appears to be a paracrine loop in skin in which PTHrP derived from epidermis modulates the ability of the fetal dermal cells to support hair follicle development. In turn, dermal cells appear to regulate production of PTHrP by the epidermis.

The mammary gland consists of a series of branching tubes that form through a process known as branching morphogenesis (Figure 3) (58). This process of branching growth is similar to that in other epithelial organs such as lung and salivary glands and requires communication between epithelial cells and mesenchymal cells (58). Hence, it is significant that both overexpression and underexpression of PTHrP have been shown to disrupt branching morphogenesis during mammary gland development (53; JJ Wysolmerski et al, submitted). Overexpression of PTHrP in the myoepithelial cells of transgenic mice impairs ductular proliferation and elongation as well as side-branching during the phase of mammary development that occurs at the time of sexual maturation (Figure 4) (53), and overexpression of PTHrP impairs the formation of terminal ductules during early pregnancy or in response to treatment with exogenous estrogen and progesterone (53). These effects are the result of the amino-terminal PTHrP acting through the PTH/PTHrP receptor, because overexpression of PTH itself in myoepithelial cells has the same consequences as overexpression of PTHrP, and delivery of amino-terminal PTHrP(1–36) in pellet form into the mammary glands of normal mice also impairs estrogen- and progesterone-induced ductular proliferation. In normal mice, PTHrP appears to be expressed by both luminal and myoepithelial cells of the mammary gland (60, 61), and myoepithelial cells and mammary stromal cells express the PTH/PTHrP receptor (60, 62, 63). Both stromal and myoepithelial cells are important in the branching growth of the mammary gland during sexual maturation and early pregnancy (64), and ligand and receptor are appropriately positioned to participate in this process.

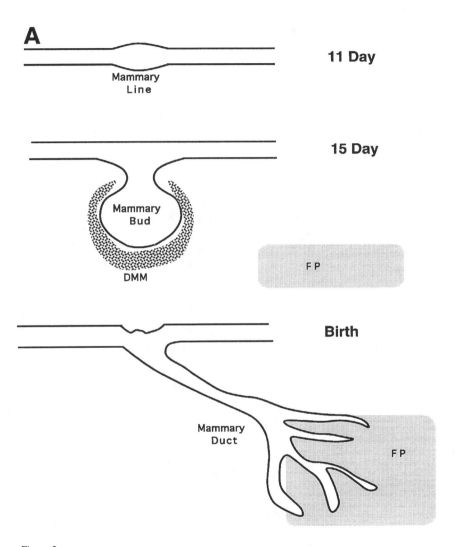

Figure 3

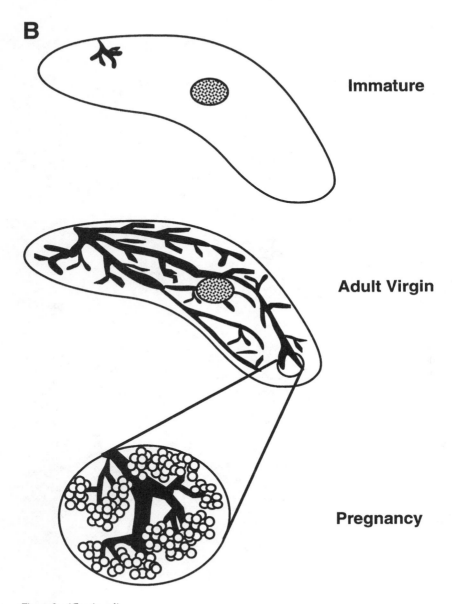

Figure 3   (*Continued*)

Studies of mammary development in PTHrP-null mice indicate that PTHrP is essential for branching morphogenesis. First, Philbrick et al reported that PTHrP-null mice rescued from neonatal death by insertion of a PTHrP transgene fail to develop mammary glands (65). These rescued-null mice survive to maturity but have no mammary epithelial duct system. In PTHrP-null and PTH/PTHrP receptor knockout animals, the first step in the development of the embryonic mammary gland, the formation of the mammary bud, occurs normally, but the mammary bud subsequently fails to undergo the initial round of branching morphogenesis. Instead, in the absence of PTHrP or its receptor, the mammary epithelial ducts degenerate and disappear by birth (JJ Wysolmerski et al, submitted). Because PTHrP is produced by the mammary epithelial cells and because the PTH/PTHrP receptor is found only on mammary stromal cells during embryonic development, this phenotype most likely is due to a failure of epithelial-to-mesenchymal signaling (Figure 3A) (JJ Wysolmerski et al, submitted). Therefore, both underexpression and overexpression of PTHrP support

---

Figure 3   Development of the murine mammary gland. (*Panel A*) Schematic representation of embryonic mammary development. The murine mammary glands first form on embryonic days 10–11, as ridge-like epidermal thickenings on the ventral surface of the embryo extending from the anterior limb buds to the posterior limb buds bilaterally. These ridges are referred to as the mammary lines or nipple lines. On embryonic day 12, under the inductive influence of the condensed dense mammary mesenchyme (DMM), cells within the mammary line migrate into the dermis to form the five pairs of mammary buds. In female embryos, the mammary buds, once formed, remain quiescent until embryonic day 16 when they initiate a phase of branching morphogenesis resulting in the formation of a rudimentary mammary duct system that penetrates into a specialized stromal compartment known as the mammary fat pad (FP). At birth, the mammary gland consists of a rudimentary duct system with about 10–15 branches that just enter into the mammary fat pad; this pattern changes little until sexual maturation occurs. The formation of the mammary bud and the initial round of branching morphogenesis are dependent on a series of reciprocal interactions between mammary epithelial cells and the dense mammary mesenchyme. (*Panel B*) Schematic representation of postnatal mammary development of the fourth inguinal mammary gland. In immature mice, the mammary gland maintains its neonatal architecture. At about 3–4 weeks of age, when the mouse begins to mature sexually, the mammary duct system expands into the mammary fat pad through a second round of branching morphogenesis. This process is dependent on ovarian hormones and at the end of sexual maturity results in an extensively branched duct system that fills the entire mammary fat pad (*middle figure*). The final phase of mammary development occurs during pregnancy. Again, guided by the hormonal milieu, the duct system undergoes a third round of branching growth to produce a series of terminal ductules. In addition, the mammary epithelial cells, which remain relatively undifferentiated until pregnancy, now undergo terminal differentiation to form the acini that are responsible for milk production (*bottom figure*). The *stippled oval* in the two top figures represents a lymph node that is a characteristic landmark of the fourth inguinal mammary gland in mice. As noted in the text, both underexpression and overexpression of PTHrP have profound effects on branching morphogenesis during embryogenesis and sexual maturation, respectively.

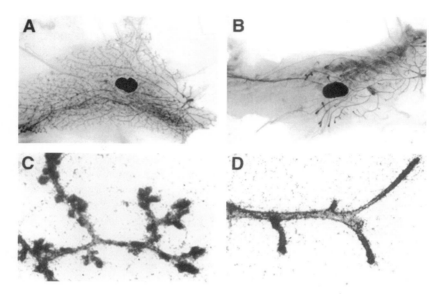

Figure 4 Overexpression of PTHrP impairs branching morphogenesis during mammary gland development. The fourth inguinal mammary glands from 6-week-old transgenic mice overexpressing PTHrP in mammary myoepithelial cells (*Panels B,D*) were compared with mammary glands from 6-week-old littermates (*Panels A,C*). Specimens were prepared as whole mounts and stained with carmine aluminum, which stains the mammary ducts but not the fatty stroma (53). *Panels C,D* represent higher power views of panels *A,B*. Overexpression of PTHrP results in an inhibition of ductular elongation (compare *A,B*) and a much simpler ductal architecture, with many fewer side branches than in control glands (compare *C,D*). The *dark oval* in the center of the fat pad is a lymph node characteristically found in the fourth inguinal mammary gland. (Modified and reproduced from Reference 53 with permission.)

a critical role for PTHrP in modulating mammary stromal function in branching morphogenesis.

PTHrP AND THE PANCREATIC ISLET

PTHrP is produced in the normal pancreatic islet (66, 67), by the α β, δ, and PP cells, which produce glucagon, insulin, somatostatin, and pancreatic polypeptide, respectively (66, 67). The most common cells in the islet and therefore most PTHrP-producing cells in the islet are the insulin-producing β cells, where PTHrP is processed into multiple secretory forms, co-packaged in secretory granules with insulin, and secreted in a regulated fashion in response to insulin secretagogues (14, 15, 18).

The β cell, or at least the rat insulinoma β cell line RIN 1046–38, also responds to levels of PTHrP(1–36) as low as 10^{-12} M, with an increment in cytosolic calcium (67). This response is dose related and is unaccompanied by an increase in cAMP production (67). Although the presence of PTH/PTHrP receptor mRNA on β cells has not been documented, the cytosolic calcium findings suggest that β cells secrete PTHrP and respond to the peptide and that PTHrP plays an autocrine or paracrine role within the islet.

To define what this role might be, we have prepared transgenic mice in which PTHrP is targeted to and overexpressed some 10- to 30-fold in the β cells (68). These mice are hypoglycemic (blood glucose values in the 40–50 mg/dl range in the fasting state) and are hyperinsulinemic. Perfusion of islets isolated from RIP-PTHrP mice and from normal littermates with low, normal, and high glucose concentrations leads to equivalent increases in insulin secretion, suggesting that individual islets in these mice sense and respond to ambient glucose concentrations normally. However, islet mass is increased in these animals: Islet mass appears to be normal at birth, is twice normal at 8–12 weeks of age, and is four times normal by 1 year of age (68, 69). Thus hyperinsulinemia and hypoglycemia appear to be due to an increase in islet mass. In theory, the increase in islet mass could result from an enhancement in β cell proliferation in existing islets, prolongation in β cell survival in existing islets, increase in the rate of development of new islets from ductal or other precursor cells, or some combination of the above.

Regardless of the mechanism underlying the effects on β cell mass, the potential application of these findings to the therapy of diabetes mellitus is exciting. Diabetes mellitus results from either a reduction in islet mass in Type I (insulin-dependent) diabetes mellitus or an inadequate islet insulin secretory response to insulin resistance in Type II (non-insulin-dependent) diabetes. Introduction of factors that regulate normal islet mass by gene transfer techniques into animal or human cadaver, or into living donor-derived islets that can be transplanted into diabetic hosts, might provide an advance in treatment.

PTHrP AND PLACENTAL CALCIUM TRANSPORT

Production of PTHrP by the fetal parathyroid glands appears to play a critical role in maintaining the normal uphill maternal-to-fetal calcium gradient. Parathyroidectomy in fetal lambs causes a loss of this gradient and fetal hypocalcemia. The infusion of PTH peptides or PTHrP(1–34) into the fetal circulation does not restore the gradient or correct the fetal hypocalcemia. In contrast, infusion of PTHrP(1–86), (1–108), or (1–141) corrects the placental calcium gradient, suggesting that the mid-region of PTHrP, specifically the (35–86) region, must establish and maintain the calcium gradient. The infusion of PTHrP(67–86)amide and, to a lesser extent, PTHrP(75–86)amide directly into the fetal circulation can also drive the placental calcium pump. These findings have been summarized extensively in recent reviews (3–7, 19) and are not discussed here in detail. In the past year, however, three important advances have been made in understanding PTHrP-placental calcium transport. First, Kovacs and collaborators reported that placental calcium transport in impaired and serum calcium levels are low in PTHrP-null mice as compared with their heterozygous or normal littermates (70). Intraperitoneal injection of the fetal mice in utero with PTH peptides or PTHrP(1–34) had no effect on the calcium gradient, whereas infusion of PTHrP(1–86) or PTHrP(67–86) stimulated trans-placental calcium transport. These findings confirm the importance of PTHrP in fetal calcium homeostasis and in placental calcium transport and confirm the importance of mid-region PTHrP in driving the placental calcium pump. To study the latter issue further, they then studied the placental calcium gradient in mothers and fetuses deficient for the PTH/PTHrP receptor (70), the receptor that recognizes the PTH(1–34) region. Again, as was predicted, the receptor-null fetuses were hypocalcemic (they lacked the skeletal and renal responses to PTH and amino-terminal PTHrP) but, interestingly, placental calcium trans-port was more efficient than normal, as though the placentae and the factors that regulate the placental calcium pump were enhanced in the presence of fetal hypocalcemia. These findings underscore the importance of the mid-region of PTHrP in placental calcium transport and provide additional evidence for the existence of a receptor that recognizes the mid-region of PTHrP. As has been suggested by Abbas et al using a fetal pig model (71), these findings indicate that fetal serum calcium regulates the circulating level of PTHrP in the fetus. Although a logical place for this regulation to occur is the fetal parathyroid gland where PTHrP is known to be produced (3–7, 19), placental PTHrP (or PTHrP produced in other unidentified sites) may also be regulated by the fetal serum calcium concentration, and locally acting placental PTHrP may participate in the regulation of placental calcium transport (72).

Although synthetic PTHrP(67–86)amide is capable of driving the placental calcium pump, it remains to be demonstrated that this peptide is actually formed in nature. Pursuing this question, Wu et al (see above) reported that there are at least three authentic mid-region secretory forms of PTHrP: PTHrP(38–94), PTHrP(38–95), and PTHrP(38–101) (15) (Figure 1). They speculated that the PTHrP(38–94) form must be amidated, given its carboxy-terminal amidation signal, and therefore synthesized PTHrP(38–94)amide. This was shown to be active in a number of systems in vitro and to be effective in vivo in driving the placental calcium pump (15). These effects are presumed to be mediated via the same mid-region PTHrP receptor deduced by Orloff et al (12).

Future studies need to be directed to characterizing the mid-region receptor in molecular terms, to understanding the signaling events that couple binding by this receptor to activation of placental calcium transport, and to defining, in quantitative terms, the relative contributions of the parathyroid glands, the placenta, and other fetal tissues to placental calcium transport.

PTHrP AND THE CARDIOVASCULAR SYSTEM

PTHrP also appears to play several roles is the cardiovascular system. There are at least three chapters to this story: PTHrP as a cardiac hormone, PTHrP as a vasodilatory substance, and PTHrP as a regulator of smooth muscle proliferation. The first two of these chapters have been reviewed recently (72–76) and are discussed only cursorily here. The third role has not been reviewed in detail previously and therefore is discussed below.

PTHrP and the Heart

PTHrP can be viewed has a cardiac hormone that is produced in both adult and fetal human and animal atrial and ventricular cardiomyocytes (for recent reviews, see References 23 and 72). At the electron microscopic level of immunohistology, PTHrP can be visualized within dense core secretory granules in the cardiomyocyte. PTHrP mRNA expression in the heart is increased by physiological maneuvers that increase ventricular or atrial workload or distention. Whether PTHrP is actually secreted in response to such maneuvers remains to be demonstrated, but secretion might occur given the presence of PTHrP in dense core secretory granules. Whether the target of secreted PTHrP is autocrine or paracrine, such as the cardiomyocyte, or systemic, such as the arterial wall smooth muscle cell, is unknown.

PTHrP has effects on the intact heart, the isolated perfused heart, and the coronary artery (72–74). PTHrP accelerates heart rate in vivo and in the isolated perfused heart, an effect that may be mediated by direct action of PTHrP on the sinus node and conducting system (75). PTHrP also exerts inotropic effects in vivo and in the isolated perfused heart, possibly as a consequence of increased coronary blood flow due to the vasodilatory action of PTHrP on the coronary circulation (discussed below) (74).

PTHrP as a Peripheral Vascular Vasodilator

PTHrP is produced in the vascular smooth muscle cell and the endothelial cell (72, 76). PTHrP levels appear to be upregulated in vascular smooth muscle in response to mechanical distention of the arterial wall, to increases in arterial pressure, and to vasoconstrictors such as angiotensin II (72). PTHrP is also a potent vasodilator (73, 77). Indeed, PTH or PTHrP can cause vasodilation in numerous arterial beds, including the renal arterial system, the coronary circulation, the pulmonary vasculature, the mesenteric vessels, and the CNS arteries

(72, 73). The vasodilatory effects of PTHrP on smooth muscle are mediated, at least in part, by activation of adenylyl cyclase in the vascular smooth muscle cell and by the production of nitric oxide (78, 79). The vasodilatory effect appears to be independent of the endothelium, because removal of the endothelium has no effect on the response (78). The vasodilatory effects are thought to be the result of interaction of PTHrP with the classical PTH/PTHrP receptor, which is expressed in vascular smooth muscle cells (79). Interestingly, the receptor, which is coupled to the PKC/phosphoinositol/cytosolic calcium pathway and the adenylyl cyclase/PKA pathway in bone and renal cells, signals only through the adenylyl cyclase system and not the PKC/phosphoinositol/cytosolic calcium pathway in vascular smooth muscle cells. The inability to activate the latter pathway appears to be due to a lack of the proper Gq or Go nucleotide-binding proteins in vascular smooth muscle cells (79). Collectively, these studies suggest that production of PTHrP by the vascular smooth muscle cell and by the endothelial cell relaxes arterial smooth muscle, counteracts or balances vasoconstrictor effects, and may act as a local modulator (paracrine or autocrine) of vascular tone and regional blood flow.

PTHrP as a Regulator of Vascular Smooth Muscle Proliferation

In contrast to the known cardiac and vasodilatory actions of PTHrP, PTHrP also appears to play a role in vascular smooth muscle cell proliferation and may therefore exert important roles in arterial modeling and remodeling in response to injury. PTHrP is upregulated in the vascular tree in response to mechanical stretch and vasoconstrictors (noted above) and in response to vascular injury induced by balloon distention (80, 81) or endothelial scraping (82). Ozeki et al, using immunohistochemical and in situ hybridization, demonstrated that PTHrP expression and production in the neointima of rat carotid arteries are activated within 2 days of vascular injury and continue to increase for 14 days (82). Human coronary arteries removed at autopsy or at the time of bypass grafting also exhibit increased PTHrP expression (83). Thus PTHrP may participate in the vascular response to injury and in pathological processes such as atherosclerosis and arterial restenosis following arterial bypass grafting and angioplasty.

It is not known whether PTHrP activates or inhibits proliferation of vascular smooth muscle or the neointima, or whether the role of PTHrP in the vascular modeling/remodeling/restenosis process is quantitatively significant in comparison with other peptide growth factors already implicated in this process, such as platelet-derived growth factor and bFGF (for a review, see 84, 85). It is clear that PTHrP is not essential for cardiovascular development, because PTHrP-knockout mice develop normal cardiovascular systems (41). However, because the animals die at birth of skeletal and, perhaps, other defects, the role of PTHrP in vascular remodeling, local regulation of vascular flow, and the vascular response to injury in adult animals is undefined. With these cautionary notes, Pirola and coworkers (79, 81) and Massfelder et al (86) demonstrated that PTHrP(1–36) and PTHrP(1–141) inhibit the proliferation of cultured primary rat aortic vascular smooth muscle cells; the clonal fetal rat aortic smooth muscle cell line, A-10; and cultured bovine aortic cells. These observations suggest that PTHrP upregulation in the arterial wall following vascular injury serves to downregulate or counter-regulate inappropriate, overexuberant vascular proliferation and implies that therapeutic delivery of PTHrP to the injured vascular wall might inhibit restenosis following angioplasty of coronary arteries.

However, Massfelder et al (86) reported that introduction of PTHrP into vascular smooth muscle cells by gene transfer paradoxically stimulates proliferation. Proliferation in the same cells is inhibited when PTHrP is added to the culture medium. The diametrically opposite growth responses to PTHrP when it is added to the culture medium, compared with the effects when it is introduced by gene transfer to the inside of the cell, are compatible with the possibility that in the latter circumstance, as described below, PTHrP mediates its effects by transport into the nucleus. If this hypothesis proves to be correct, then the interpretation of the upregulation of PTHrP in the vascular wall following injury would most properly be construed as one in which PTHrP enhances intimal hyperplasia and restenosis, and the therapeutic implications would change from exciting to worrisome. Clearly this area requires further investigation.

SUMMARY

The decade since the purification and structural identification of PTHrP has seen the cloning of cDNAs and genes encoding PTHrP in multiple species, characterization of the posttranslational processing pattern of the PTHrP precursors, development of PTHrP immunoassays, and development of animal and human models of the HHM syndrome. These studies explained pathogenesis of the humoral syndrome that in many ways resembled hyperparathyroidism but was not due to PTH.

These events were exciting and, at least to some extent, predictable. What was unexpected was the finding that PTHrP and its multiple receptors are present in many normal tissues, that absence of PTHrP or its receptor causes fetal or perinatal death, and that PTHrP has a diverse array of developmental and physiological roles.

Studies in the next decade address at least three areas. The first is the further characterization of the developmental roles of PTHrP, particularly in regard to the developmental signals that activate and deactivate PTHrP expression; the receptors and the signaling molecules, intracellular and intercellular, that mediate its effects; the cellular/biochemical basis of the nuclear targeting of PTHrP; and how nuclear targeting influences cell cycle events and apoptosis. A second area of research will address the postnatal roles of PTHrP in normal physiology including the regulation of smooth muscle tone; interaction with other systemic and local smooth muscle regulatory systems such as the renin-angiotensin system; its role in transplacental, transmammary, and renal epithelial calcium transport; and its effects on cell growth, differentiation, and death in adults. The third area of study just beginning to unfold concerns the therapeutic possibilities intrinsic in the PTHrP molecule such as its effects on vascular restenosis in atherosclerotic disease; its effects on islet mass in patients with diabetes mellitus; its anabolic effects in osteoporosis; and possible use in checking the growth of squamous carcinomas or other tumors that produce it and express its receptors. Study of PHTrP began at the bedside, fermented in the basic laboratory for a decade, and now returns to the bedside with clinical application. One such cycle has already been completed: the development of sensitive, specific, and reliable PTHrP immunoassays for the diagnosis of the HHM syndrome. Other examples will surely follow.

ACKNOWLEDGMENTS

The authors thank Drs. Arthur Broadus, Rupangi Vasavada, William J Burtis, John Orloff, William Philbrick, Thierry Massfelder, Maureen Dunbar, Jean-Jacques Helwig, Terence Wu, Barbara Dryer, and Pamela Dann for their many helpful discussions in considering the information included in this chapter. This work was supported by a grant from the Department of Veterans Affairs; National Institutes of Health grants DK 47168, DK 51081, DK 45735, CA 09331; and Department of Defense grant DAMD 17–96–1–6198.

Visit the *Annual Reviews home page* at
http://www.AnnualReviews.org.

Literature Cited

1. Stewart AF, Insogna KL, Broadus AE. 1995. Malignancy-associated hypercalcemia. In *Endocrinology*, ed. L DeGroot, 3:1061–74. Philadelphia: Saunders
2. Stewart AF. 1996. Humoral hypercalcemia of malignancy. In *The American Society for Bone and Mineral Research Primer on Metabolic Bone Diseases and Disorders of Mineral Metabolism*, ed. M Favus, 3:198–203. New York: Raven
3. Yang KH, Stewart AF. 1996. The PTH-related protein gene and protein products. In *Principles of Bone Biology*, ed. JP Bilezikian, L Raisz, G Rodan, pp. 347–76. San Diego: Academic
4. Martin TJ, Moseley TJ. 1995. Parathyroid hormone-related protein. In *Endocrinology*, ed. LJ DeGroot, 3:967–77. Philadelphia: Saunders
5. Strewler GJ, Nissenson RA. 1996. Parathyroid hormone-related protein. In *The American Society for Bone and Mineral*

Research Primer on Metabolic Bone Diseases and Disorders of Mineral Metabolism, ed. M Favus, 3:71–73. New York: Raven

6. Broadus AE, Stewart AF. 1994. Parathyroid hormone-related protein: structure, processing and physiological actions. In *The Parathyroids, Basic and Clinical Concepts*, ed. JP Bilezikian, MA Levine, R Marcus, pp. 259–94. New York: Raven

7. Orloff JJ, Stewart AF. 1995. Parathyroid hormone-related protein as a prohormone: posttranslational processing and receptor interactions. In *Endocrine Reviews Monograph Series*, ed. A Negro-Villar, A4:207–10. Bethesda, MD: Endocrine Soc.

8. Segre GV. 1994. Receptors for parathyroid hormone and parathyroid hormone-related protein. In *The Parathyroids*, ed. JP Bilezikian, MA Levine, R Marcus, pp. 213–29. New York: Raven

9. Nissenson RA, Halloran B, eds. 1992. *Parathyroid Hormone-related Protein.* Boca Raton, FL: CRC Press

10. Philbrick WM, Wysolmerski JJ, Galbraith S, Holt E, Orloff JJ, et al. 1996. Defining the physiologic roles of parathyroid ormone-related protein in normal physiology. *Physiol. Rev.* 76:127–73

11. Orloff JJ, Kats Y, Urena P, Schipani E, Vasavada RC, et al. 1995. Further evidence for a novel receptor for amino-terminal parathyroid hormone-related protein on keratinocytes and squamous carcinoma cell lines. *Endocrinology* 136:3016–23

12. Orloff JJ, Kats Y, Nathanson MH, Moyer SM, Mitnick MA, et al. 1996. A mid-region parathyroid hormone-related peptide mobilizes cytosolic calcium and stimulates formation of inositol trisphosphate in a squamous carcinoma cell line. *Endocrinology* 137:5376–85

13. Fenton AJ, Kemp BE, Hammonds RG, Mitchelhill K, Moseley JM, et al. 1991. A potent inhibitor of osteoclastic bone resorption within a highly conserved pentapeptide region of PTHrP(107–111). *Endocrinology* 129:3424–26

14. Soifer NE, Dee KE, Insogna KL, Burtis WJ, Matovcik LM, et al. 1992. Parathyroid hormone-related protein: evidence for secretion of a novel mid-region fragment by three different cell types. *J. Biol. Chem.* 267:18236–43

15. Wu T, Vasavada R, Yang K, Massfelder T, Ganz M, et al. 1996. Structural and physiologic characterization of the mid-region secretory form of PTHrP. *J. Biol. Chem.* 271:24371–81

16. Burtis WJ, Dann P, Gaich GA, Soifer NE. 1994. A high abundance midregion species

of parathyroid hormone-related protein: immunological and chromatographic characterization in plasma. *J. Clin. Endocrinol. Metab.* 78:317–22

17. Bucht E, Eklund A, Toss G, Lewensohn R, Granberg B, et al. 1992. Parathyroid hormone-related peptide, measured by a midmolecule radioimmunoassay, in various hypercalcaemic and normocalcaemic conditions. *Acta Endocrinol.* 127:294–300

18. Plawner LL, Philbrick WM, Burtis WJ, Broadus AE, Stewart AF. 1995. Secretion of parathyroid hormone-related protein: cell-specific secretion via the regulated vs. the constitutive secretory pathway. *J. Biol. Chem.* 270:14078–84

19. Rodda CP, Kubota M, Heath JA, Ebeling PR, Moseley JM, et al. 1988. Evidence for a novel parathyroid hormone-related protein in fetal lamb parathyroid glands and sheep placenta: comparisons with a similar protein implicated in humoral hypercalcaemia of malignancy. *J. Endocrinol.* 117:261–71

20. Luparello C, Burtis WJ, Raue F, Birch MA, Gallagher JA. 1995. Parathyroid hormone-related peptide and 8701-BC breast cancer cell growth and invasion in vitro: evidence for growth-inhibiting and invasion-promoting effects. *Mol. Cell Endocrinol.* 111:225–32

21. Ditmer LS, Burton DW, Deftos LJ. 1996. Elimination of the carboxy-terminal sequences of parathyroid hormone-related protein 1-173 increases production and secretion of the truncated forms. *Endocrinology* 137:1608–17

22. Meerovich K, Wing S, Goltzman D. 1996. Preproparathyroid hormone-related protein, a secreted peptide, is degraded by the ubiquitin proteolytic system. *J. Bone Min. Res.* 11(Suppl):S200 (Abstr.)

23. Deftos LJ, Burton DW, Brandt DW. 1993. PTH-like protein is a secretory product of atrial myocytes. *J. Clin. Invest.* 92:727–35

24. Kaiser SM, Laneuville P, Bernier SM, Rhim JS, Kremer R, et al. 1992. Enhanced growth of a human keratinocyte line by antisense RNA for PTHrP. *J. Biol. Chem.* 267:13623–28

25. Kaiser SM, Sebag M, Rhim JS, Kremer R, Goltzman D. 1994. Antisense-mediated inhibition of parathyroid hormone-related peptide production in a keratinocyte cell line impedes differentiation. *Mol. Endocrinol.* 8:139–47

26. Henderson JE, Amizuka N, Warshawsky H, Diasotto D, Lanske BMK, et al. Nucleolar localization of parathyroid hormone-related peptide enhances survival of chondrocytes under conditions that promote

apoptotic cell death. *Mol. Cell Biol.* 15:4064–75

27. Kiefer P, Dickson C. 1995. Nucleolar association of fibroblast growth factor 3 via specific sequence motifs has inhibitory effects on cell growth. *Mol. Cell Biol.* 15:4364–74

28. Baldin V, Roman A-M, Bosc-Bierne I, Amalric F, Bouche G. 1990. Translocation of bFGF to the nucleus is G1 phase cell cycle specific in bovine aortic endothelial cells. *EMBO J.* 9:1511–17

29. Moroianu J, Riordan JF. 1994. Nuclear translocation of angiogenin in proliferating endothelial cells is essential to its angiogenic activity. *Proc. Natl. Acad. Sci. USA* 91:1677–81

30. Kiefer P, Peters G, Dickson C. 1993. Retention of fibroblast growth factor 3 in the Golgi complex may regulate its export cells. *Mol. Cell. Biol.* 13:5781–93

31. Lee K, Deeds JD, Segre GV. 1995. Expression of parathyroid hormone-related peptide and its receptor messenger ribonucleic acids during fetal development of rats. *Endocrinology* 136:453–63

32. van de Stolpe A, Karperian M, Lowik CWGM, Juppner H, Segre GV, et al. 1993. Parathyroid hormone-related peptide as an endogenous inducer of parietal endoderm differentiation. *J. Cell Biol.* 120:235–43

33. Beck F, Tucci J, Senior PV. 1993. Expression of parathyroid hormone-related protein mRNA by uterine tissues and extraembrypnic membranes during gestation in rats. *J. Reprod. Fertil.* 99:343–52

34. Karperian M, Lanser P, DeLaat SW, Boonstra J, DeFize LHK. 1996. Parathyroid hormone-related peptide mRNA expression during murine postimplantation development: evidence for involvement in multiple differentiation processes. *Int. J. Dev. Biol.* 40:599–608

35. Lee K, Deeds JD, Bond AT, Juppner H, Abou-Samra AB, Segre GV. 1993. In situ localization of PTH/PTHrP receptor mRNA in the bone of fetal and young rats. *Bone* 14:341–45

36. Vortkamp A, Lee K, Lanske B, Segre GV, Kronenberg HM, Tabin CJ. 1996. Regulation of rate of cartilage differentiation by indian hedgehog and PTH-related protein. *Science* 273:613–22

37. Amizuka N, Warshawsky H, Henderson JE, Goltzman D, Karaplis A. 1994. Parathyroid hormone-related peptide-depleted mice show abnormal epiphyseal cartilage development and altered endochondral bone formation. *J. Cell Biol.* 126:1611–23

38. Evain DE, Binet E, Anderson WB. 1981. Alterations in calcitonin and parathyroid

hormone responsiveness of adenylate cyclase in F9 embryonal carcinoma cells treated with retinoic acid and dibutyryl cyclic AMP. *J. Cell Physiol.* 109:453–59

39. Chan SDH, Strewler GJ, King KL, Nissenson RA. 1990. Expression of a parathyroid hormone-like protein and its receptor during differentiation of embryonal carcinoma cells. *Mol. Endocrinol.* 4:639–46

40. Behrendtsen O, Alexander CM, Werb Z. 1995. Cooperative interactions between extracellular matrix, integrins and parathyroid hormone-related peptide regulate parietal endoderm differentiation in mouse embryos. *Development* 121:4137–48

41. Karaplis AC, Luz A, Glowacki J, Bronson RJ, Tybolewicz VLJ, et al. 1994. Lethal skeletal dysplasia from targeted disruption of the parathyroid hormone-related peptide gene. *Genes Dev.* 8:277–89

42. Lanske B, Karaplis AC, Lee K, Luz A, Vortkamp A, et al. 1996. PTH/PTHrP receptor in early development and indian hedgehog-regulated bone growth. *Science* 273:663–66

43. Iwamoto M, Akitoshi J, Murakami H, Shimazu A, Nakashima K, et al. 1994. Changes in parathyroid hormone receptors during chondrocyte cytodifferentiation. *J. Biol. Chem.* 269:17245–51

44. Kato Y, Shimazu A, Nakashima K, Suzuki F, Jikko A, Iwamoto M. 1990. Effects of parathyroid hormone and calcitonin on alkaline phosphatase activity and matrix calcification in rabbit growth plate chondrocyte cultures. *Endocrinology* 127:114–18

45. Weir EC, Philbrick WM, Amling M, Neff LA, Baron RE, Broadus AE. 1996. Targeted overexpression of parathyroid hormone-related peptide in chondrocytes causes chondrodysplasia and delayed endochondral bone formation. *Proc. Natl. Acad. Sci. USA* 93:10240–45

46. Amizuka N, Karaplis AC, Henderson JE, Warshawsky H, Lipman ML, et al. 1996. Haploinsufficiency of parathyroid hormone-related peptide (PTHrP) results in abnormal postnatal bone development. *J. Cell Biol.* 175:166–76

47. Schipani E, Kruse K, Juppner H. 1995. A constitutively active mutant PTH-PTHrP receptor in Jansen-type metaphyseal chondrodysplasia. *Science* 268:98–100

48. Schipani E, Langman CB, Parfitt AM, Jensen BA, Kikuchi S, et al. 1996. Constitutively activated receptors for parathyroid hormone and parathyroid hormone-related peptide in Jansen's metaphyseal chondrodysplasia. *N. Engl. J. Med.* 335:708–14

49. Jaffe HL. 1972. Metaphysial dysostosis. In *Metabolic, Degenerative, and Inflamma-*

tory Diseases of Bones and Joints, pp. 222–26. Philadelphia: Lea & Febiger

50. Kukreja SC, Danza JJ, Wimbiscus SA, Fishe JE, McKee RL, et al. 1994. Inactivation by plasma may be responsible for lack of efficacy of parathyroid hormone antagonists in hypercalcemia of malignancy. *Endocrinology* 134:2184–88

51. Amling M, Neff L, Tanaka S, Inoue D, Kuida K, et al. 1997. Bcl-2 lies downstream of parathyroid hormone-related peptide in a signalling pathway that regulates chondrocyte maturation during skeletal development. *J. Cell Biol.* 136:205–13

52. Wysolmerski JJ, Broadus AE, Zhou J, Fuchs E, Milstone LM, Philbrick WM. 1994. Overexpression of parathyroid hormone-related protein in the skin of transgenic mice interferes with hair follicle development. *Proc. Natl. Acad. Sci. USA* 91:1133–37

53. Wysolmerski JJ, McCaughern-Carucci JF, Daifotis AG, Broadus AE, Philbrick WM. 1995. Overexpression of parathyroid hormone-related protein or parathyroid hormone in transgenic mice impairs branching morphogenesis during mammary gland development. *Development* 121:3539–47

54. Merendino JJ, Insogna KL, Milstone LM, Broadus AE, Stewart AF. 1986. Cultured human keratinocytes produce a parathyroid hormone-like protein. *Science* 231:388–90

55. Hardy MH. 1992. The secret life of the hair follicle. *Trends Genet.* 8:55–60

56. Wu TL, Insogna KI, Hough LM, Milstone L, Stewart AF. 1987. Skin-derived fibroblasts respond to human parathyroid hormone-like adenylate cyclase-stimulating proteins. *J. Clin. Endocrinol. Metab.* 65:105–9

57. Lowik CWGM, Hoekman K, Offringa R. 1992. Regulation of parathyroid hormone-like protein production in cultured normal and malignant keratinocytes. *J. Invest. Dermatol.* 98:198–203

58. Daniel CW, Silberstein GB. 1987. Postnatal development of the rodent mammary gland. In *The Mammary Gland, Development, Regulation and Function*, MC Neville, CW Daniel, pp. 3–36. New York: Plenum

59. Deleted in proof

60. Ferrari SL, Rizzoli R, Bonjour JP. 1992. Parathyroid hormone-related protein production by primary cultures of mammary epithelial cells. *J. Cell Physiol.* 150:304–11

61. Seitz PK, Cooper KM, Ives KL, Ishizuka J, Townsend CM, et al. 1993. Parathyroid hormone-related peptide production and action in a myoepithelial cell line derived from normal human breast. *Endocrinology* 133:1116–24

62. Ferrari SL, Rizzoli R, Chaponnier C, Gubbiani G, Bonjour JP. 1993. Parathyroid hormone-related protein increases cAMP production in mammary epithelial cells. *Am. J. Physiol.* 264:E471–75

63. Dunbar ME, Philbrick WM, Broadus AE, Wysolmerski JJ. 1996. PTHrP modulates branching morphogenesis of mammary epithelial cells in vitro. *J. Bone Min. Res.* 11(Suppl. 1):S200 (Abstr.)

64. Niranjan B, Buluwela L, Yant J, Perushinghe N, Atherton A, et al. 1995. HGF/SF: a potent cytokine for mammary growth, morphogenesis and development. *Development* 121:2897–908

65. Philbrick WM, Weir EC, Karaplis AC, Dreyer BE, Broadus AE. 1996. Rescue of the PTHrP-null mouse reveals multiple developmental defects. *J. Bone Min. Res.* 11(Suppl.):S157

66. Drucker DJ, Asa SL, Henderson J, Goltzman D. 1989. The PTHrP gene is expressed in the normal and neoplastic human endocrine pancreas. *Mol. Endocrinol.* 3:1589–95

67. Gaich G, Orloff JJ, Atillasoy EJ, Burtis WJ, Ganz MB, Stewart AF. 1993. Amino-terminal parathyroid hormone-related protein: specific binding and cytosolic calcium responses in rat insulinoma cells. *Endocrinology* 132:1402–9

68. Vasavada R, Cavaliere C, D'Ercole AJ, Dann P, Burtis WJ, et al. 1996. Overexpression of PTHrP in the pancreatic islets of transgenic mice causes hypoglycemia, hyperinsulinemia and islet hyperplasia. *J. Biol. Chem.* 271:1200–8

69. Vasavada RC, Dann P, Stewart AF. 1996. Persistent islet hyperplasia and hypoglycemia in the rat insulin promoter-targeted PTHrP overexpressing transgenic mouse. *Diabetes* 45(Suppl. 2):9A

70. Kovacs CS, Lanske B, Hunzelman JL, Guo J, Karaplis AC, Kronenberg HM. 1996. Parathyroid hormone-related peptide (PTHrP) regulates fetal-placental calcium transport through a receptor distinct from the PTH/PTHrP receptor. *Proc. Natl. Acad. Sci. USA* 93:15233–38

71. Abbas S, Ratcliffe WA, Moniz C, Dixit M, Caple IW, et al. 1994. The role of parathyroid hormone-related protein in calcium homeostasis in the fetal pig. *Exp. Physiol.* 79:527–36

72. Massfelder T, Helwig J-J, Stewart AF. 1996. PTHrP as a cardiovascular regulatory peptide. *Endocrinology* 137:3151–53

73. Mok LLS, Nickols GA, Thompson JC, Cooper CW. 1989. Parathyroid hormone as a smooth muscle relaxant. *Endocri. Rev.* 10:420–36

74. Ogino K, Burkhoff D, Bilezikian JP. 1995. The hemodynamic basis for the cardiac effects of parathyroid hormone (PTH) and PTH-related protein. *Endocrinology* 136:3024–30

75. Hara M, Ogino K, Burkhoff D, Rosen MR, Bilezikian JP. 1995. Cardiac actions of parathyroid hormone-related protein: electrophysiological properties. *J. Bone Min. Res.* 10(Suppl. 1):S491

76. Kramer S, Reynolds FH Jr, Castillo M, Valenzuela DM, Thorikay M, Sorvillo JM. 1991. Immunlogical identification and distribution of parathyroid hormone-like protein polypeptides in normal and malignant tissues. *Endocrinology* 128:1927–37

77. Winquist RJ, Baskin EP, Vlasuk GP. 1987. Synthetic tumor-derived human hypercalcemia factor exhibits parathyroid hormone-like vasorelaxation in renal arteries. *Biochem. Biophys. Res. Commun.* 149:227–32

78. Massfelder T, Stewart AF, Endlich K, Soifer N, Clement T, et al. 1996. Immunohistologic detection of parathyroid hormone-related protein in human renal vasculature and endothelium: independent linkage of its renodilatory actions with nitric oxide and cyclic AMP. *Kidney Int.* 50:1591–603

79. Maeda S, Wu S, Juppner H, Green J, Aragay AM, et al. 1996. Cell-specific signal transduction of PTH-related protein through stably expressed recombinant PTH/PTHrP in vascular smooth muscle cells. *Endocrinology* 137:3154–62

80. Takahashi K, Inoue D, Ando K, Matsumoto T, Ikeda K, Fujita T. 1995. Parathyroid hormone-related peptide as a locally produced vasorelaxant: regulation of its mRNA by hypertension in rats. *Biochem. Biophys. Res. Commun.* 208:447–55

81. Pirola CJ, Wang H-M, Kamyar A, Wu S, Enomoto H, et al. 1993. Angiotensin II regulates parathyroid hormone-related protein expression in cultured rat aortic smooth muscle cells through transcriptional and post-transcriptional mechanisms. *J. Biol. Chem.* 286:1987–94

82. Ozeki S, Ohtsuru A, Seto S, Takeshita S, Yano H, et al. 1996. Evidence that implicates the PTH-related protein in vascular restenosis. *Arterioscler. Thromb. Vasc. Biol.* 16:565–75

83. Nakayama T, Ohtsuru A, Enomoto H, Namba H, Ozeki S, et al. 1994. Coronary atherosclertotic smooth muscle cells overexpress human parathyroid hormone-related peptides. *Biochem. Biophys. Res. Commun.* 200:1028–35

84. Ross R. 1993. The pathogenesis of atherosclerosis: a perspective for the 1990s. *Nature* 362:801–9

85. Schwartz SM, deBlois D, O'Brien ERM. 1995. The intima. Soil for atherosclerosis and restenosis. *Circ. Res.* 77:445–65

86. Massfelder T, Khosravi S, Wu T, Helwig J-J, Stewart AF. 1997. Parathyroid hormone-related protein regulates proliferation in vascular smooth muscle cells in a bi-directional fashion. *FASEB J.* 11:A197 (Abstr.)

Annu. Rev. Physiol. 1998. 60:461–96

THE LUTEINIZING HORMONE RECEPTOR[1]

Maria L. Dufau

Molecular Endocrinology Section, Endocrinology and Reproduction Research Branch, National Institute of Child Health and Human Development, National Institutes of Health, Bethesda, Maryland 20892; e-mail: dufau@helix.nih.gov

KEY WORDS: hormone binding, signal transduction, gene structure, gene regulation, disease states

ABSTRACT

The luteinizing hormone receptor (LHR) is a member of the subfamily of glycoprotein hormone receptors within the superfamily of G protein–coupled receptor (GPCR)/seven-transmembrane domain receptors. Over the past eight years, major advances have been made in determining the structure and function of the LHR and its gene. The hormone-binding domain has been localized to exons 1–7 in the extracellular (EC) domain/region of the receptor, which contains several leucine-rich repeats. High-affinity binding of LH and human chorionic gonadotropin (hCG) causes secondary hormone or receptor contacts to be established with regions of the EC loop/transmembrane module that initiate signal transduction.

Models of hormone-receptor interaction have been derived from the crystal structures of hCG and of the ribonuclease inhibitor, which also contains leucine-rich repeats. Such models provide a framework for the interpretation of mutational studies and for further experiments. The extracellular domain of the receptor has been overexpressed in vitro, which will facilitate crystallographic resolution of the structure of the receptor-binding site. The transmembrane domain/loop/cytoplasmic module transduces the signal for coupling to G proteins.

Several constitutive, activating mutations that cause human disease have been found in helix VI and adjacent structures. These mutations have provided valuable information about mechanisms of signal transfer and G protein coupling. The structure of the LHR gene has been elucidated, and the regulation of its transcription is beginning to be understood. Valuable insights into receptor evolution have been derived from analysis of sequence homologies, the gene structure of

---

glycoprotein hormone receptors and other members of the GPCR family, and the glycoprotein hormone receptor–like precursors identified in several invertebrate species.

INTRODUCTION

Reproduction in mammals is dependent on the pulsatile release of pituitary gonadotropic hormones—luteinizing hormone (LH) and follicle-stimulating hormone (FSH)—which act together to regulate gonadal function. Biological actions of LH and FSH include stimulation of the maturation and function of the testis and ovary and regulation of gametogenesis and steroidogenesis (10).

In the testis, LH acts through plasma membrane receptors on the Leydig cells to maintain general metabolic processes and steroidogenic enzymes, and to regulate the production and secretion of androgens (22). Testicular LH receptors (LHR) are expressed during fetal life, postnatally, at puberty, and throughout adult life.

In the ovary, LH promotes the maturation of follicular cells. After the initial inductive effect of FSH on LHR expression in the small and medium follicles, LH enhances the subsequent stages of follicular development and steroidogenesis in granulosa and luteal cells (97). The LH surge triggers ovulation by promoting the rupture of the preovulatory follicle and the release of the ovum. hCG, which is synthesized and secreted by syncytiotrophoblastic cells of the placenta from the time of implantation, maintains the secretions of estrogen and progesterone by the corpus luteum during pregnancy (10). During fetal development, LHR is not detectable in the fetal ovary but is expressed in early neonatal life.

hCG is structurally similar to LH and binds with high affinity to LHR on the surface of target tissue cells. Because of its abundance and stability, hCG is often used as the radioligand in LHR-binding studies. hCG is also less prone to degradation following iodination (10, 32, 82, 126, 127). The resolution of the crystal structure of hCG (72, 133) also makes it the ligand of choice for structural studies on hormone-receptor interactions.

The pituitary and placental glycoprotein hormones [LH, hCG, FSH, and thyrotropin (TSH)] are heterodimers that contain a common α-subunit and dissimilar β-subunits that confer biological specificity on the individual hormones. The two subunits are linked by noncovalent interactions stabilized by a β cysteine loop that forms a "seatbelt"encircling loop 2 of the α-subunit (72, 133).

Structurally, the glycoprotein hormones are members of the superfamily of cysteine-knot growth factors that include nerve growth factor and transforming growth factor β. In contrast to other members of this class, the glycoprotein hormones associate with their receptors only as heterodimers. Gonadotropin receptors bind the intact heterodimeric hormone, but the individual hormone subunits are devoid of binding activity (12).

The LHR belongs to a GPRC subclass that includes receptors for pituitary and placental glycoprotein hormones LH, FSH, TSH, and hCG. Expression of the LHR is induced by FSH and primarily by LH itself (10, 22, 106). However, growth hormone, either alone or with prolactin, supports receptor expression and prevents receptor loss following hypophysectomy (13, 144).

Although the steroidogenic actions of LH are exerted primarily through cAMP-mediated events in the gonads (13, 26), the phosphoinositide (PI) signaling pathway also functions in the ovary (21). Pulsatile endogenous LH secretion or exogenous pulsatile or single low-dose treatment with LH or hCG maintains LHR levels and steroidogenic enzymes in the adult Leydig cell. However, experimental or endogenous elevations of hCG secretion (e.g. as in patients with choriocarcinoma), major increases in LH levels, or administration of a single pharmacological dose of LH or hCG can cause down-regulation of the LHR and desensitization to the hormonal signal (13, 22).

Unlike the adult testis, the fetal and immature testes are refractory to desensitization, and treatment with LH or hCG causes up-regulation (22). In addition to such actions in the gonads, secretion of high levels of hCG from trophoblastic and nontrophoblastic tumors sometimes causes stimulation of thyroid function. A thyrotropic action of hCG also occurs in normal pregnancy and in hyperemesis gravidarum (137). Although homology between the hCG and TSH molecules and their receptors may be the basis for such cross-reactivity (137), hCG may also act through the low level of LHR in the human thyroid gland (31).

LHR is expressed primarily in gonadal tissues and has been studied extensively in Leydig and ovarian cells and in cell membrane preparations from several species, including rat, mouse, and pig, and in stable murine cell lines (22, 97, 106). LH/hCG receptors have been identified in rat prostate gland and in several human tissues that are not recognized as target tissues, including the nonpregnant uterus, placenta, fallopian tubes, uterine vessels, umbilical cord, brain, and lymphocytes (76, 93, 96, 116, 120). In addition, LH and hCG also bind to *Candida albicans* blastopores, and chorionic gonadotropin-like proteins present in yeast induce transition of the yeast from blastopores to hyphal forms. This system may control the pathogenicity of these organisms (11).

The presence of LHR has been detected by immunocytochemistry in epithelial cells of the normal mammary gland, in benign breast lesions, malignant breast tumors, and in several cancer cell lines (T47D, MCF7, and ZR75). In addition, the presence of LHR mRNA was demonstrated by reverse transcription using primers covering exons 2–11 (79b). This information is relevant to the interpretation of published data about the protective action of early pregnancy on breast cancer (79a, 56a) and the antiproliferative influence of hCG in cultured mammary epithelial and breast cancer cells (1a).

The LHR cDNA was cloned from pig testis and rat, mouse, and human ovarian libraries (36, 77, 79, 81), and the gene structure has been defined in rat, human, and mouse (2, 48, 64, 121, 122). The receptor is a sialoglycoprotein that belongs to the GPRC/seven-transmembrane domain superfamily. The size of the mature receptor is 80–90 kDa, of which about 15 kDa are contributed by carbohydrate chains (23). This review describes our current understanding of receptor structure and coupling functions and of gene structure and regulation. The identification of familial and sporadic mutations that cause human diseases and the evolutionary considerations of receptor structure and function are also reviewed.

STRUCTURE OF THE RECEPTOR

The cDNA for the LHR encodes a 75-kDa glycoprotein that contains 674 amino acids (77, 79) (Figure 1). The receptor is composed of two functional units— the extracellular hormone-binding domain (121, 135) and the seven-membrane transmembrane/cytoplasmic module, which is the anchoring unit that transduces the signal initiated in the extracellular domain and couples to G proteins.

---→

Figure 1   Left: The deduced amino acid sequence of the extracellular (EC), transmembrane (TM), and cytoplasmic (CT) domains of the rat LHR (79). Exon divisions are indicated by *vertical lines*, and exons are numbered 1–11 (122). Signal peptide amino acids are within *hexagons*, and those for the mature peptide are within *circles*. According to mutations, amino acids relevant for hormone binding are within *triangles*, and those relevant to signal transduction are within *squares*. The cysteine residues relevant to binding are within *shaded circles* in exons 1, 5, and 6. The corresponding amino acids in the rat for constitutive activating mutations found in the human (see Figure 5) are shown within *stars*. The form B truncated variant of LHR diverges from holoreceptor (form A) at 294 (I) (121). *Closed arrows* indicate functional glycosylation sites with N-linked glycosyl chains at amino acids 152 and 173; *open arrows* indicate other consensus glycosylation sites. Phosphorylation sites are indicated in the CT-tail. The ERW sequence in the LHR, which corresponds to the DRY signature sequence in GPCRs, is *underlined*. Cys[621] and Cys[622] are palmitoylated.

Right: The LHR gene (122) [to be compared with FSHR (39) and TSHR (35) genes] introns are indicated by *arrows*. The LHR promoter domain, −1 to −173 bp, transcription initiation sites are indicated by *small arrows*. Within 6.3 kb of the 3′ untranslated region (UTR) from TAG (termination codon) reside two core polyadenylation sites, pA$_1$ and pA$_2$ (43). Also indicated is a comparison of the LHR 3′ UTR with FSH and TSH and β-adrenergic receptors 3′ UTRs, as well as the insertion of a line R domain only in LHR. The nucleotide similarities between the regions of the glycoprotein sequences are shown.

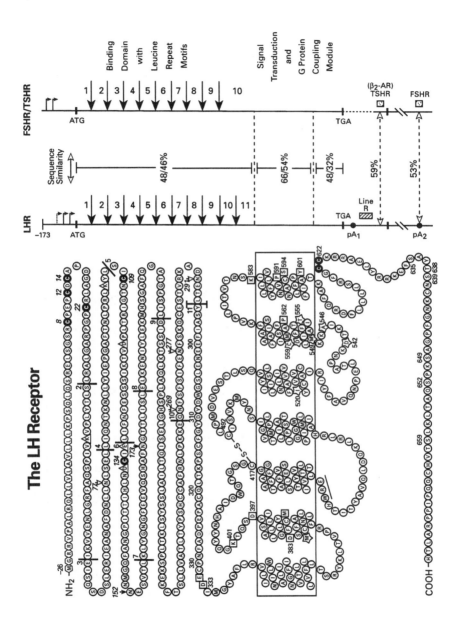

The large extracellular domain of 341 amino acids binds LH and hCG with high affinity (125, 131). At the N terminus, the LHR contains a cleavable signal sequence of 26 amino acids in the rat and 22 amino acids in the human that directs insertion of the LHR into the endoplasmic reticulum processing pathway.

The extracellular domain of the LHR has six potential glycosylation sites (AsnXxxSer/Thr) and seven transmembrane helices connected by three extracellular and three intracellular loops. The receptor contains cysteine residues in the first and second extracellular loops, as do other members of the superfamily. In rhodopsin these residues form an intramolecular disulfide bridge that stabilizes the helical seven-transmembrane structure.

The intracellular C-terminal portion of the receptor of 69 amino acids contains one consensus site in the rat and two in the pig for protein kinase C phosphorylation, and one potential site for tyrosine kinase phosphorylation. The C-terminal sequence also contains several serines and threonines that are amenable to phosphorylation by protein kinase A. In addition, two adjacent cysteines $(Cys^{621, 622})$ are palmitoylated (56, 143) and provide additional membrane anchorage sites and a fourth intracellular loop that may be relevant for coupling functions and/or regulation.

Mutations of Cys^{621} or Cys^{622} in the LHR to Ser or Gly residues causes an increase in hormone-induced receptor down-regulation (56). In addition, a C-terminal truncation that deletes these cysteine residues impairs receptor processing, leading to its intracellular accumulation (36, 143). Unlike the β-adrenergic receptor, palmitoylated cysteine is not required for efficient coupling of the LHR to the G protein Gs (6).

The N-terminal extracellular domain is characterized primarily by its sequence similarity to the polypeptide-binding leucine-rich repeat (LRR) protein carboxypeptidase N (113b) and to insulin-like growth factor–binding proteins (3). These proteins are similar in primary sequence to the LH, FSH, and TSH receptors in that they contain the N-terminal cysteine domain followed by the repeat motif PxxαFxxLxxLxxLxL (α = aliphatic). The LRR domains of the LH, FSH, and TSH receptors share sequence similarities of about 43% within exons 2–8. However, the similarity diminishes at the N- and C-terminal domains of the extracellular region with the presence of amino acid inserts in the FSH and TSH receptors, suggesting that these regions may be important for denoting hormone specificity.

Among the glycoprotein hormone receptors considerable similarity also exists within the transmembrane modules (80%) and among the extra- and intracellular loops and intracellular C-terminal tails. The overall similarity between the seven-transmembrane module of the LHR and other GPRCs is low, for example, 26% to the β-adrenergic receptor and less to other members of the rhodopsin-type family. However, within the transmembrane (TM), EL1–3, IL1–3, and C-terminal domains many of the amino acids and motifs conserved within the family of GPRCs are also present in the LHR (6, 108a, 114a).

THE LIGAND-BINDING DOMAIN

The extracellular domain of the LHR binds with high affinity and high specificity to LH and hCG (121, 135), as demonstrated by studies of an alternatively spliced variant derived from the extracellular domain (form B) and of a truncated (exon 1–10) cDNA in COS1 cells. The hormone-binding properties of the LHR external domain in transfected cells were similar to those of the holoreceptor (form A) (121). The variant form B containing 294 (rat) or 297 (pig) amino acids of the external domain of the receptor and 22 unique amino acids at the C terminus was secreted into the medium, while the holoreceptor was expressed as a membrane-associated protein (121, 128a).

This soluble variant of the LHR could affect the availability of LH to the membrane receptor in gonadal cells during development and in the ovary at certain stages of the reproductive cycle. To date, there have been no reports of the expression of this form of the receptor in vivo, either in the circulation or in biological fluids. However, use of this LHR variant as an experimental tool has provided insight into the domains that are important for hormone binding.

The extracellular region of the LHR has been overexpressed in baculovirus-infected insect cells (85, 87, 140) and in *Escherichia coli* (15). Overexpression of the LHR in insect cells yields a 38-kDa high-mannose protein that is located intracellularly and is membrane bound (140). Baculovirus expression of the extracellular binding domain with a His tag at the C terminus permits one-step purification of the protein in a nickel column (128). This procedure can be scaled-up for the production of sufficient quantities of receptors for crystallization and makes possible elucidation of the structure of the binding site.

The extracellular binding domain of the human LH/hCG receptor has been expressed fused to the surface of the cpIII filamentous phage coat protein and bound hCG attached to a solid phase surface (76a). This immobilized LHR preparation displayed on the surface of the phage is potentially useful for rapid evaluation of mutant LHR LH/hCG during structure function studies, and for screening of peptide libraries. It should also permit the preparation of hormone-receptor complexes released from the phage by cleavage of an enterokinase site introduced at the junction of LHR and the coat protein (76a).

The hydrophobic leucine repeat region that constitutes much of the binding domain is intercalated between cysteine-rich domains in exons 1 and 9. The LHR contains only three cysteine residues (Cys[109, 134, 282]) that are not conserved in the extracellular domain of the FSHR or TSHR. Cys^{109} and Cys^{134} are in domains that have been implicated in LH/hCG binding in chimeric and mutational studies of the glycoprotein hormones (8, 140). Thus, these cysteine residues contribute to hormone-binding activity and perhaps form a disulfide bond (139). Furthermore, individual mutations of all the cysteine residues in exon 1 ($Cys^{8, 12, 14, 22}$) to serine showed that they are essential for hormone binding (139). Mutation of the analogous residues in the TSHR did not affect TSH binding (64a), suggesting that these residues have a unique essential function in LH/hCG binding. These findings demonstrate that the functional binding domain utilizes all cysteines N-terminal to exon 7 and localize the binding site to this N-terminal region of the extracellular domain.

Another class of extracellular cysteine residues is specifically important for surface expression of the receptors because its mutations of these residues cause intracellular retention of the LHR but do not affect hormone binding. These residues include Cys^{257} and Cys^{258} (exon 9); Cys^{321}, Cys^{331}, Cys^{417} (EL1); and Cys^{492} (EL2) (exon 11) (139). Mutations of several non-cysteine residues in the transmembrane/cytoplasmic module also impair membrane insertion (131, 91, 42a). It is evident that a wide range of extracellular and transmembrane/cytoplasmic amino acids in exons 7–11 of the LHR are required for membrane insertion. In general, for those mutations that affect receptor processing, it is difficult to assess the possible causal relationship with membrane insertion or signal transfer. For this reason, the interpretation of the mutant effect is questionable.

The extracellular and transmembrane domains in the TSHR are linked by disulfide bonds (77a). Disulfide bonding has been implicated in LHR complex formation and in the surface expression of a functional LHR holoreceptor after cotransfection of extracellular and transmembrane/cytoplasmic module cDNA constructs in SF9 cells (94). The mutation studies also suggest that the LHR extracellular/transmembrane interactions may require disulfide bonds (139). Upon hormone binding, release of a half-cysteine from a disulfide bond could lead to signal transfer to G protein response elements. A specific domain in the β-subunit of LH that is conserved in thioredoxin (C-G-P-C) catalyzes disulfide rearrangement in ribonuclease, and a similar mode of disulfide rearrangement leading to signal transfer may be applicable for LHR (7).

LHR contains N-linked glycosyl residues of the complex type, with terminal sialic acid on its extracellular domain (24, 80). The functional importance of carbohydrates in receptor binding is suggested by the fact that there is a major-loss (>95%) in ^{125}I-hCG binding to the deglycosylated purified receptor electroblotted to nitrocellulose membranes (53). Tunicamycin-treated transfected SF9 cells express carbohydrate-free LHR that lacks hormone-binding activity (140). Similar findings were observed after tunicamycin treatment of Leydig cell tumor cells (MLTC), a murine cell line that expresses LHRs (53a). However, tunicamycin treatment of 293 cells stably transfected with LHR has no effect on hormone binding. In this case, the molecular weight of the putative deglycosylated receptor under denatured/reducing conditions is higher than that observed with the receptor that had mutations of all glycosylation sites. This observation suggests that tunicamycin treatment was ineffective, prossibly because a mixture of tunicamycins was used (20), whereas tunicamycin B2 (a specific inhibitor of N-glycosylation that doess not inhibit protein synthesis) was used in other studies (53a, 140).

A functional glycosyl chain at Asn^{173} is essential, and another at Asn^{152} is of major importance for hormone binding by the receptor (140, 141). In addition, a nonfunctional chain is present at Asn^{269}, Asn^{277}, or Asn^{291}. Although the potential glycosylation site at residue 77 does not carry a carbohydrate chain when the LHR is expressed in insect cells, its mutation to Gln causes decreased hormone binding (141). This decrease also occurs when Asn^{77}Gln is expressed in COS1 cells (140). Recently, all putative glycosylation sites have been reported to have carbohydrate chains when the receptor is stably expressed in HEK 293 cells (20). However, this conclusion was based on minor reductions of molecular weight in SDS gels with individual mutations of consensus glycosylation sequences. Also, the mutant Asn^{173} to Gln receptor could not be expressed (20). However, a construct with mutations at all six glycosylation sites was found to be expressed (20), as were Gln mutants analyzed in previous reports when using transiently expressed COS and SF1 cells (141, 140).

LH receptors overexpressed in insect cells contain only high-mannose carbohydrate chains, and the chains linked at Asn^{173} and Asn^{152} are sufficient for high-affinity hormone binding. This suggests that processing of high-mannose chains to complex forms is not required for ligand binding (140). Similarly, treatment of HEK293 cells that stably express LHR with 1-deoxymanojirimycin (which inhibits the maturation of the high-mannose chains) does not reduce hormone binding (92b). Selective enzymatic cleavage of glycosyl chains has shown that only the proximal N-acetylglucosamine residue, which is common to both high-mannose and complex carbohydrate chains, is necessary for conformation of the receptor for high-affinity binding of hormone (140).

The carbohydrate chains of the LHR appear to be involved in refolding and conformational stability of the mature receptor and in intramolecular folding of the nascent receptor, rather than in hormone binding. Reduction and boiling of the form B receptor (extracellular domain) before electrophoretic separation and transfer to nitrocellulose does not reduce the ability of the glycoprotein to renature to the active binding conformation. Renaturation occurs as long as the receptor bears the proximal N-acetylglucosamine residues on Asn^{152} and Asn^{173} and on the four cysteines in exon 1.

In the FSHR, the glycosyl chain corresponding to that located at Asn^{173} in the LHR is essential for binding activity (19). However, mutation of the same site in the TSHR had no effect on ligand binding (64a). The fact that the extracellular receptor domain of the receptor expressed in bacteria or in phage (15, 76a) can bind hormone does not preclude the relevance of the glycosyl residues for folding or stability of the receptor conformation in the mammalian or insect cell (140). Hormone binding in bacteria is achieved after refolding that yielded receptor aggregates, whereas monomeric binding was observed in the phage. In both instances, a form of direct or indirect solid-phase binding was used rather than conventional binding assays in solution. The reported lack of effects of enzymatic deglycosylation on ovarian cell receptors (53a, 90) may be due either to incomplete deglycosylation or to provision of conformational stability by the membrane constraints. In contrast, soluble purified receptors are more susceptible to destabilization of their binding conformation (80).

Several reports of mutagenesis within the extracellular binding domain, as well as chimeric and deletion studies, have further localized the binding regions of the receptor. These studies indicate that multiple binding domains are present between amino acids 1 and 184 (8, 43, 91a, 95, 118a, 139) Chimeric studies using regions of the LHR and FSHR have shown that the domain from amino acids 58 to 93 (within exons 3–4) of the LHR blocked FSH binding, whereas the amino acid 95–171 domain of the LHR is required for hCG binding (43).

In addition to the conformation induced by intrinsic restrictive or facilitatory structures, conserved sequences must also provide an integral part of the structure. It is likely that the hormone-binding domain encompasses most of the region spanning exons 1–8 (8), that significant tertiary structures contribute by folding, and that disulfide loops are involved in the configuration of the receptor.

HORMONE-RECEPTOR INTERACTION

Resolution of the crystal structure of hCG (73, 133) has clarified early findings concerning hormone-receptor interactions and facilitated investigations on the localization of the receptor-binding domains within the hCG molecule. The unique β-subunit of hCG has a seatbelt structure formed by an intramolecular disulfide bridge (Cys^{26}-Cys^{110}) that embraces the α long loop 2 of the hormone (L2). Although there is no consensus as to the location of the receptor-binding domains, those of relevance are present in the same region of the hCG molecule (Figure 2). These domains include highly conserved residues within the helical region (α 40–50) of the α–subunit long loop, adjacent to the Asn^{52}/carbohydrate chain, and the α C terminus (α 88–92), as well as residues from the β determinant loop (β 94–99) (an integral part of the seatbelt formed by Cys^{93}-Cys^{100}) and the β long loop (β 38–57).

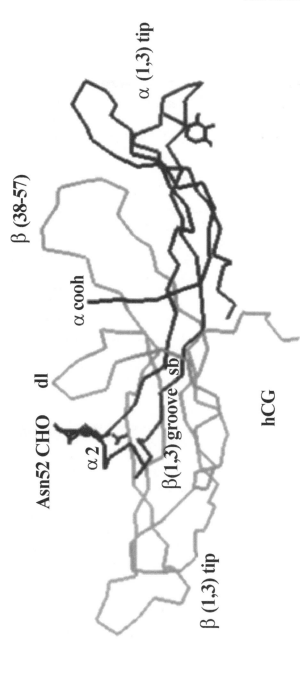

Figure 2 Crystal structure of hCG [protein data bank (PDB):1hcn] (133). α-subunit (*black*); β-subunit (*gray*); loop structure of the α- and β-subunits are shown. Also shown are the hairpin loops of the subunits [$\alpha(1,3)$ tip and $\beta(1,3)$ tip]. The α long loop contains the Asn^{52} carbohydrate (CHO) and is wrapped by the β-subunit seatbelt (sb). This region is important for receptor binding (see text). The determinant loop (dl), carboxyl terminal of the α-subunit (α COOH), and the long loop β 38–57 are on the same face of the hormone.

Within the α-subunit, Lys[44] in the long loop (134), Phe[18] in loop 1 (111), and residues α 90–92 at the C-terminal end (91, 105a) are important for hormone binding. The N-linked carbohydrate residue at Asn[52] of the α-subunit is essential for signal transduction (107).

Two domains of the β-subunit [(β 38–57) and the β determinant loop (β 94–99)] may be important in receptor binding, but the data are inconsistent (4, 9, 14, 57, 83, 111). Comparison of the amino acid sequences of hCG and FSH suggests that these domains may be important for binding specificity. The determinant loop of hCG and LH contains positively charged hydrophilic residues (Lys and Arg) but that of FSH contains negatively charged residues (Asp and Glu). Within the β long loop (β 38–57), hCG contains largely hydrophobic amino acids, but those in FSH are highly charged.

Studies using synthetic peptides have demonstrated the importance of the β 38–57 domain in hormone binding (57, 58). Moreover, mutation of Arg[43] to leucine reduced receptor-binding activity (14). However, substitution of the β 38–57 loop with FSH amino acids did not affect hCG-binding activity (83, 111). Residues of the β determinant loop (Arg[94], Arg[95], Ser[96], and Asp[99]) have been implicated in hCG binding and stimulation of steroidogenesis (14, 47, 57). The finding that a chimeric hCG/FSH β-subunit containing hCG residues 1–93 and FSH residues 94–114 (including the β determinant loop) exhibited major FSH-binding activity and only minor hCG binding (9) indicated the importance of this loop in binding specificity. However, in a related study using tethered α- and β-subunits, mutagenesis of the cysteine residues that form the determinant loop (93–100) did not affect hormone-binding activity (4).

Additional mutations of residues within β-loops 1, 2, and 3 do not affect binding (111). Two independent reports have concluded that a receptor-binding domain is located at the α/β-subunit interface between the α long loop and the β seatbelt (95), or in the $\beta(1, 3)$ major groove of hCG (17). Thus, interacting regions between the subunits are likely to be involved in the formation of receptor-binding domains. Although the data are not consistent, these studies have indicated that the α-subunit has more influence on binding than does the β-subunit.

Previous observations derived from cross-linking studies using hCG radiolabeled either in the α- or β-subunit likewise demonstrated that direct interaction with the receptor involves the α-subunit rather than the β-subunit. This finding that receptor binding occurred largely through the α-subunit led to the proposal that the β-subunit confers hormone specificity mainly by inducing conformational changes in the α-subunit (70).

Mechanistic models of hCG binding and subsequent signal transduction by the receptor have been based on the assumptions that hormone binding leads to either secondary hormone interaction with the TM (tether) or to a conformational change of the extracellular domain that initiates signal transfer (84). The two modes of action can be differentiated by the identification of contact points on the TM for either hormone (tether) or the extracellular domain of the receptor.

Several studies have supported the tether mode of activation, based on expression of a hormone-binding LHR/TM module (95), peptide competition experiments indicating hormonal interaction with EL3 (115), and reverse mutagenesis of Lys[91] of the α-subunit of hCG and Asp[397] of EL1, suggesting a counterion interaction between hormone and TM module (54). Other studies using epitope mapping with monoclonal antibodies have supported an interaction between the extracellular domain of the receptor and its TM module (17).

Competitive binding studies with peptide sequences have localized specific domains on the LHR to amino acids 25–40 in exons 1 and 2, and amino acids 107–121 in exons 4 and 5 (95). Independent studies have shown that mutation of Cys[109] and Cys[134] (exons 5 and 6) each resulted in a 75% decrease in binding activity (140). Also, the finding that mutation of Glu[132] or Asp[135] flanking Cys[134] caused complete loss of binding activity confirmed the importance of the exon 6 domain (91a).

The α tip of the hCG [$\alpha(1, 3)$ hairpin loops] is masked in the holoreceptor but is accessible in the soluble extracellular receptor, indicating that it lies near the TM domain, and immunoradiometric assays have placed the $\alpha(1, 3)$ tip of the hormone near the EL2 of the holoreceptor (55, 133). In contrast, the hCG $\beta(1, 3)$ tip was not masked by either the receptor-binding domain or the membrane module of the receptor. Thus, a working model of hormone binding/signal transfer is that hCG binds via the seatbelt region, with the $\alpha(1, 3)$ tip exposed outside the extracellular domain and free to interact with EL2 to initiate signal transfer (Figure 3).

The crystal structure of the porcine ribonuclease inhibitor, another class of LRR proteins, and its binding to ribonuclease A have been resolved to 2.5 Å (60). This inhibitor consists of a semicircular repeated series of β sheets connected by α helices, with repeat domains containing the LxxLxL motif located immediately prior to the β turn. This motif is common to the LHR and the carboxyl end of the carboxypeptidase N/insulin-like growth factor leucine-rich repeats. The ligand contacts occur primarily via the β loops at the N- and C-terminal domains of the protein (61).

The structure of ribonuclease inhibitor shares common features with that of the glycoprotein hormone receptors on several levels. These include the LRR framework between exons 2 and 8 and the relatively limited ligand-binding contacts proposed to be mainly at the N terminus for hCG/LH and the N- and C-termini for FSH. Molecular homology models of interaction between hCG and the extracellular hormone-binding domain of the LHR have been performed by several groups, based on the crystal structure of hCG and a homology model of the LRR porcine ribonuclease inhibitor. The major difficulty with these

β **(1,3) tip**

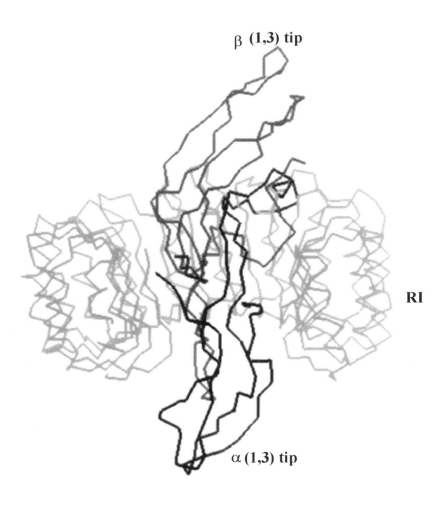

RI

α **(1,3) tip**

hCG

Figure 3 Proposed model of hCG (PDB:1hcn) (133) (*black*), binding to ribonuclease inhibitor
(RI) (PDB:1bnh) (*gray*), according to Jiang et al (55). The $\alpha(1,3)$ tip is proximal to the TM/loop
module within the TM domain. Signal transfer is initiated by hormone contact.

models is the alignment of the imperfect LHR leucine-rich repeats and the ribonuclease strand-helix repeats, and the observation that the N-terminal binding domain is located largely outside the LRR motif.

Jiang et al's model (55) has focused on the putative LHR-binding domain in exons 5 and 6 within the leucine-rich repeats. The secondary structural alignment (PHD program) predicts eight repeats of an α helical domain in the middle of each exon (exons 2–8), the β sheet at the end and beginning of the next exon (LxxLxL), and the loop structure (most likely the binding region) following the β sheet (Figure 4). The central region of the receptor contains a strong negative electrostatic potential. Modeling hCG by its surface potential

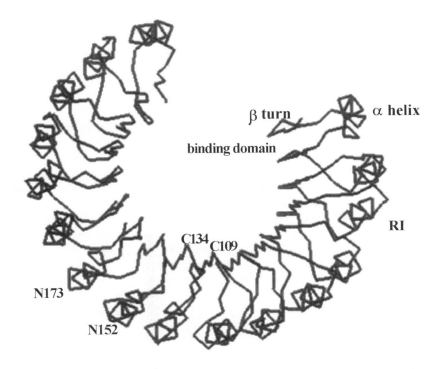

Ribonuclease Inhibitor

Figure 4 Crystal structure of porcine ribonuclease inhibitor (PDB:1bnh) (60). Horseshoe conformation is formed from regular repeat units of β sheets and α helical domains. Ribonuclease A–binding sites are at the β turns (61). LHR C109 and C134 and glycosylation sites N173 and N152 are shown according to the LRR alignment of Remy et al (95). With this orientation, the Cys[109] and Cys[134] may contact hormone, whereas the glycosylation sites are outside the hormone-binding domain in the convex surface.

yields a structure with the $\beta(1, 3)$ tip perpendicular to the plane of the receptor, and the $\alpha(1, 3)$ tip adjacent to the TM domain (95).

The positions of the Asn[152] and Asn[173] carbohydrate chains of the LHR are on the outer surface of the α helical domain, not within the binding domain. This observation is consistent with findings that the receptor's carbohydrate chain is important in processing, folding, and structural stability but not in hormone binding (140). In this model, the Cys[109] and Cys[134] residues are adjacent to each other on consecutive β loops within the proposed binding domain, allowing for disulfide formation (139). Similar models have been proposed by other investigators (91, 95).

Moyle's model (84) utilizes a different orientation and alignment of the LRR strand/helix repeats. It predicts that the center of the LRR fits into the central groove of hCG and that this conformational change induces interactions with the TM directly under the extracellular domain. Elements of both models may be found to be correct upon ultimate elucidation of the structure of the LHR:hCG complex by NMR and X-ray crystallography.

SIGNAL TRANSDUCTION/G COUPLING

The signal transduction pathways of the gonadotropin receptors include activation of both the adenylate cyclase/cyclic AMP (cAMP) and phospholipase C/InsP$_3$ systems. Like certain other members of the GPCR family, LHR interacts primarily with G$_s$ and to a variable degree with G$_q$/11 and G$_i$. In several GPCRs, receptor activation involves changes in the hydrophobic transmembrane helices, with or without the participation of the extracellular loops (6, 108a, 114a). The intracellular loops appear to form contact sites for interaction with G proteins, in some cases in conjunction with the carboxy-terminal cytoplasmic domain.

The specificity of receptor/G protein interaction depends on the appropriate configuration of the intracellular surface of the receptor. In most members of the GPCR family, coupling of the G protein with the activated receptor is accompanied by significant changes in agonist-binding affinity (114a). However, the affinity of the LHR for LH and hCG is not affected by GTP or its nonhydrolyzable analogues.

In several receptors the importance of the cytoplasmic loop(s) in G protein activation has been demonstrated by mutational analysis and by competition studies using synthetic peptides containing the amino acid sequences of domains within the loops (127a). The N-terminal and C-terminal domains of the third intracellular loop and regions of the cytoplasmic tail are often involved in G protein coupling (108a, 114a). The coupling of G$_s$ to the LHR appears to depend largely on the formation of an amphipathic, cationic helical conformation of the C-terminal region of the third loop that contributes to protein-protein interaction.

Much of the current information about receptor domains that participate in G protein coupling and signal transduction has come from functional and biochemical studies of cells and membrane preparations and from structure-function studies of mutated receptors and naturally occurring LHR mutations that cause disordered gonadal function. High-affinity interactions occur between the hormone and the extracellular domain of LHR (121, 135). These interactions are probably followed by low-affinity contacts (51), such as ionic interactions, between the hormone and/or the extracellular regions of the receptor, with possible sites within the EC loop(s) and/or transmembrane region. Mutation of the conserved Asp^{383} to Asn in the second TM helix reduces high-affinity hormone binding by 300-fold, with an equivalent increase in the EC_{50} for stimulation of cAMP formation (50). This residue may serve as a site for interaction with the hormone or the extracellular domain of the receptor. This mutation also abolishes the Na^+-sensitivity of the binding affinity of LHR for LH (92).

Several amino acids in the LHR participate in signal transduction. Substitution of the acidic Asp residue within the conserved Asp-Arg-Tyr (DRY) triplet (located at the N terminus of ILII) markedly reduces or abolishes signal transduction in several GPCRs (15a). However, mutation of the equivalent amino acid ($Glu^{441}Gln$) of the corresponding triplet (Glu-Arg-Trp) does not affect hormone binding or signal transduction but interfers with insertion of the receptor into the membrane (131).

Substitution of Asp^{397} in EL1 is important in signal transduction and does not influence the hormone-binding affinity of the receptor. However, reciprocal charge substitution between Lys^{91} in the C terminus of the hCG α-subunit and Asp^{397} in EL1 suggests that an interaction between these residues that initiates signal transfer (52, 54). The participation of EL3 in primary or secondary hormone interactions has also been suggested by peptide competition studies and alanine mutational scans (30, 91, 105, 105a).

In addition, immunological studies suggest that interactions occur between the $\alpha(1, 3)$ tips of the hormone and EL2 (95). There is also evidence for an essential involvement of Lys^{583} in the generation of cAMP and $InsP_3$ at the junction of ELIII with TMVII (33a, 104). Ion pairing may occur between Lys^{583} and Asp^{397}, which are adjacent, owing to the arrangement of the transmembrane helices (105) (Figure 1). However, according to a recent model, Lys^{583} is not exposed on the surface of the receptor but is oriented inward to the central cleft on the same face as Asp^{578} in TMVI (117) [a relevant residue in signal transduction and receptor activation (112, 113)—see Figure 5. Note that because the human LHR amino acid numbering in this figure includes the signal peptide, Asp^{578} corresponds to Asp^{556} in the mature rat peptide shown in Figure 1]. Thus ELIII may provide the conduit for propagation of the signal to

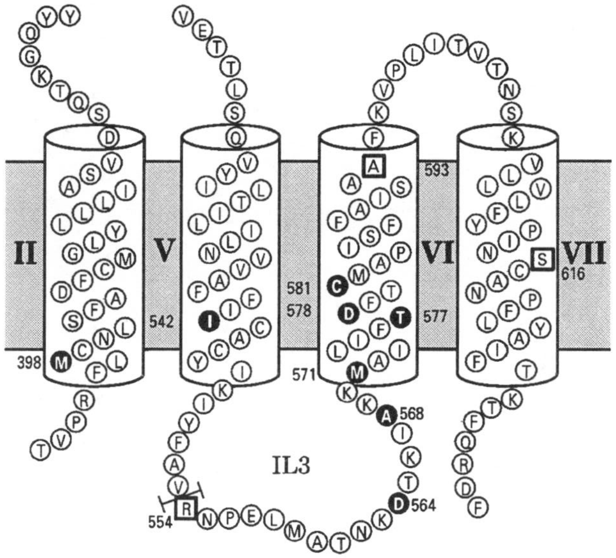

	Mutation Site		
Location	Amino Acid	Nucleotide
TMII	Met³⁹⁸→Tyr	¹¹⁹³T→C (67)
TMV	Ile⁵⁴²→Leu*	¹⁶²⁴A→C (75)
IL3	Asp⁵⁶⁴→Gly#	¹⁶⁹¹A→G (75)
IL3	Ala⁵⁶⁸→Val	¹⁷⁰³C→A (74)
IL3	Arg⁵⁵⁴→Stop†	¹⁶⁶⁰CGA→TGA (73)
TM VI	Met⁵⁷¹→Ile	¹⁷¹³G→A (66,69)
TM VI	Thr⁵⁷⁷→Ile	¹⁷³⁰C→T (69)
TM VI	Asp⁵⁷⁸→Gly or Tyr*	¹⁷³³A→G (113,69,136) ¹⁷³²G→T
TM VI	Cy⁵⁸¹→Arg	¹⁷⁴¹T→C (75)
TM VI	Ala⁵⁹³→Pro†	¹⁷⁷⁷G→C (68)
TM VII	Ser⁶¹⁶→Tyr†	¹⁸⁴⁷C→A (73)

†These mutations cause Leydig cell hypoplasia/aplasia and all others, gonadotropin independent precocious puberty. Equivalent mutation site in the TSH* and FSH# receptor. IL-intracellular loop TM-transmembrane domain.

Figure 5   Constitutive activating (*dark circles*) and inactivating (*squares*) mutations of the human LHR that cause disease. The region relevant in coupling functions coincides with the highest abundance of naturally occurring mutations. Amino acid numbers include the signal sequence of 22 amino acids. For conversion to the rat sequence amino acid of mature peptide in Figure 1 subtract 22.

TMVI or TMVII through hormone-induced conformational changes involving electrostatic or hydrogen bonding.

Mutational studies indicate that the generation of independent cAMP and InsP$_3$ signals involves Lys[583] (104) (Figure 1). In addition, Tyr[601] in TMVII [within the highly conserved NPxxY motif, where Y is implicated in internalization of β-adrenergic and TSH receptors (113a, 114a)] is essential for hormone-induced signal transduction. Pro[562] and Pro[591], in TMVI and TMVII, respectively, are also important for efficient signaling (108a, 114a). Studies with LH and FSH chimeras indicate that the C-terminal one-third of LHR is important for PLC activation and that TMV-TMVII and the cytoplasmic tail are required for maximal efficiency (42). These findings demonstrate involvement of ILIII (and/or the putative ILIV) in receptor activation. This observation differs from findings in dopamine/muscarinic receptor chimeric constructs, in which both ILII and ILIII are important for inositol phosphate signaling (132).

In the testis and ovary, agonist-activated LHR is coupled primarily to G$_s$, leading to stimulation of adenylate cyclase and phosphorylation of intracellular proteins through activation of protein kinase A (10, 22). In addition, agonist activation of LH/hCG receptors promotes PI hydrolysis and calcium signaling in the ovaries (21, 65) and in several cell lines transiently or stably expressing the LHR (36). PI hydrolysis probably results from stimulation of phospholipase C by $\beta\gamma$-subunits released from G$_s$ or G$_i$, rather than to the release of α-subunits from G$_{q/11}$ (40, 92a).

In contrast, there is no convincing evidence for activation of the phospholipase C/calcium signaling pathway by LH in the Leydig cells, where androgen production is increased solely by cAMP (13, 22, 119). However, LHR in the Leydig cells couples to G$_i$ (58a), and LHR interacts with G$_{i\alpha}$ and G$_{s\alpha}$ in bovine corpus luteum, transfected HEK293 cells, and porcine ovarian follicular membranes (40, 92a).

The extent to which GPRCs activate both adenylate cyclase and phospholipase C varies among cell types. This variation may depend on differences in receptor density and in the G protein subunits present in individual tissues and at specific stages of differentiation. In the Leydig cell, lack of stimulation of the PI pathway could be due to the presence of specific inhibitors, deficient receptor coupling or $\beta\gamma$ activation, or competition for overlapping effector sites of an unidentified G protein.

The wide differences in gonadotropin concentrations (ED$_{50}$ 50–100 pM versus 2500 pM hCG, respectively) needed for stimulation of adenylate cyclase and PI hydrolysis in Leydig cells expressing LHR (36) confirm the predominance of the G$_s$ adenylate cyclase pathway for signaling by the LHR. The PI pathway may operate at certain stages during the ovarian cycle, when maximal levels of $\beta\gamma$ could be generated by increased hormonal stimulation.

Several naturally occurring mutations of the human LHR cause constitutive activation or inactivation of effector signaling (Figure 5). Valuable insights into signal transduction and receptor coupling have been derived from studies of these naturally occurring mutations of the human LHR that impair gonadal function. The inherited disorder testotoxicosis (familial male-limited precocious puberty) results from activating mutations in LHR principally in TMVI (66, 69, 113, 136, 75), in IL3 (73–75), TMII (67), and TMV (75) (Figure 5). This disorder is characterized by Leydig cell hyperplasia with premature puberty and early onset of spermatogenesis in boys as early as three years of age. These patients have blood testosterone levels in the pubertal range, with low or undetectable LH levels.

Mutation of Asp^{578} to glycine in TMVI is the most common cause of this disorder, which can either be inherited as an autosomal domain defect (112, 113) or be present in sporadic sexual precocity (68, 112, 136). Cells transfected with the mutant LHR cDNAs have increased cAMP production, which in most cases is stimulated by LH or hCG. The nature of the mutation is important, because replacement of Asp^{578} with the Asn residue that is comparable in size and charge (51) instead of Gly, Glu, Ser, Leu, Phe, or Tyr, caused no change in the activity of the receptor (65). Substitution of Asp^{578} with Tyr caused the highest constitutive activity, probably because of destabilization of the helices by the aromatic side chain. Moreover, Tyr, Phe, and Leu replacement showed constitutive activation of the PI pathway in addition to the primary activation of adenylate cyclase (65).

Asp^{578} and other residues in TM6 are believed to maintain the receptor in an inactive state, probably through electrostatic or hydrogen bonding with residues in closely adjacent TM helices (65, 112, 113). Residues in other transmembrane domains may also have a stabilizing role. Hormonal stimulation or mutations that disrupt the structural constraint in the receptor can cause conformational changes that lead to interaction with the cognate G protein(s) and initiation of intracellular signaling. The C-terminal portion of a loop of IL3 appears to be critically involved in G protein coupling (73–75). Changes in structure of the loop, whether by mutations in this region or by perturbations of mutated transmembrane helices, could lead to G protein coupling.

Similar mutations in the TSHR cause activation and disordered thyroid function [e.g. familial hyperthyroidism, toxic hyperplasia-germline, or neomutation (28)]. Likewise, somatic mutations in TSHR play a role in the development and autonomous growth of certain toxic thyroid adenomas (27). In the FSHR, a single constitutive activating mutation has been reported and is located in IL3 ($Asp^{567}Gly$), corresponding to a known activating mutation in the LHR. COS-7 cells transfected with the mutant FSHR cDNA showed a 50% increase in basal cAMP production. This mutation was discovered in a hypophysectomized patient on androgen replacement therapy, who was fertile despite the lack of LH and FSH. It is presumed that the retention of fertility is the consequence of the activating mutation in the FSHR (34).

However, a recent study found that mutations of several conserved amino acid in TMVI and IL3 of the FSHR, known to cause constitutive activation of the LH and TSH receptors [including Asp^{567} to Gly (IL3)], did not increase the basal activity of the FSH receptor expressed in HEK293 cells (human embryonic kidney fibroblast) (69a). The reason for this discrepancy is not clear. However, the need for normalization of the cAMP production data in the original study and the lack of evaluation of receptor expression were noted. In addition, the increases in basal cAMP were considered minor compared with those found in equivalent mutations of the LH receptor or chimeric constructs of the FSHR with TMVI and TMVII of the LHR (0.5 versus 6-10-fold) (69a). The fact that transmembrane regions of V and VI of the LHR are required for constitutive activation by an Asp^{567}Gly mutation in the FSHR IL3, while such activation does not occur when the homologous FSHR TMV and TMVI are present, suggests these interactions constrain the receptor. In contrast, the interactions of TMV and TMVI of the LHR are amenable for destabilization by constitutively activating mutations of the IL3 of the LHR (wild-type LHR) or FSR/LHR-TMV/TMVI (chimera) (69a).

Conversely, homozygous missense or nonsense inactivating mutations of the LHR have been detected in TMVI, TMVII, and ILIII (68, 73) that are responsible for the rare autosomal recessive form of male psuedohermaphroditism due to Leydig cell hypoplasia or aplasia (18). Such mutations reduce or abolish the function of LHR (68, 73). The inactivating mutations of TMVI and TMVII presumably distort the α helices and cause permanent uncoupling of the receptor, whereas the Arg^{554}Stop mutation causes deletion of the key structures required for signal transduction and G protein coupling (C-terminal IL3, TMVI, and TMVII) (Figure 5). The sisters of patients with this condition had normal pubertal development but primary amenorrhea (73). A female (46XX) who was homozygous for for the Arg^{554}Stop mutation had a small uterus and cystic ovaries that contained normal-sized follicles and no evidence of luteinization. These ovarian findings are consistent with the predominant role of FSH and growth factors in follicular development and an absent or suboptimal LH stimulus for follicular maturation, ovulation, and luteinization.

In males, mutations of Ala^{593}Pro and Arg^{554}Stop cause the most extreme form of the condition (68, 73). Afflicted subjects (XY) have female external genitalia, urethral and vaginal orifices, and undescended or abdominal testes. Blood testosterone levels are very low and are not increased by hCG treatment. The Ser^{616}Tyr causes a less severe loss of function, and the single subject reported with this mutation had a male phenotype with descended testes at birth (73). The presence of a micropenis indicates adequate androgen production in early fetal life during the development of the male external genitalia, but submaximal production thereafter. It is not known if the reduced or absent binding of LH by the mutant receptors is due to reduced cell-surface expression of receptors, impaired transcription, or formation of nonfunctional receptors.

PHOSPHORYLATION, DESENSITIZATION

The cytoplasmic C-terminal domain and intracellular loops of the LHR contain several serines and threonines and a single tyrosine residue that are amenable to phosphorylation and could participate in agonist-induced desensitization. Affinity-purified ovarian and testicular receptors are rapidly phosphorylated (within 10 min) at serine and threonine residues by the catalytic subunit of protein kinase A (80). Gonadotropin binding initially increases, and decreases LHR phosphorylation, suggesting that agonist occupancy of the receptor causes a series of conformational changes that influence its susceptibility to phosphorylation (80).

In other studies, cAMP and protein kinase C–induced phosphorylation of LHR in a stably transfected cell line was mapped to Ser^{635}, Ser^{639}, Ser^{649}, and Ser^{652} in the C-terminal cytoplasmic tail (Figure 1). This study also indicated that protein kinase A–induced phosphorylation cannot fully account for hCG-induced uncoupling of LHR (41). Another report concluded that LH/hCG-induced desensitization of murine LHR is not caused by phosphorylation by protein kinase A or C but may involve a β-adrenergic receptor kinase–like enzyme (37). Uncoupling of the LHR from adenylyl cyclase was not accompanied by internalization of the receptor (37).

Furthermore, cells stably transfected with LHR constructs truncated at amino acid 628 (ct628), resulting in a 43-residue deletion that eliminates all serine, threonine, and tyrosine residues from the C-terminal tail, desensitized to the same degree as the wild-type receptor (142). These findings indicate that phosphorylation of this region of the receptor is not involved in desensitization, but that other phosphorylation sites in LHR (e.g. IL1–4) may participate in this process.

Other studies conclude that phosphorylation and desensitization are impaired and receptor internalization is enhanced by truncation at amino acid 631 (98, 131). The discrepancy in the studies of the two types of truncated LHR has been attributed to the presence of the tyrosinyl-arginine carboxyl terminus in the ct631 but not the ct628 truncation (142), which through its positive charge density could interfere with the desensitization process. A follow-up study reported that simultaneous mutations of $Ser^{235, 239, 649, 652}Ala$ markedly impaired phosphorylation of the mutated receptor stably transfected in human embryonic kidney cells , but that hCG-induced desensitization was preserved and showed only a minor delay in its onset (130). Also, phorbol ester treatment reduced subsequent responses to low hCG concentrations (0.2–0.5 ng/ml) in cells expressing the wild-type receptor, but this impairment was not evident at higher hCG levels (130). This effect was not found in cells expressing the serine mutant receptors. Despite the disparate findings of these reports, the removal of phosphorylation sites from the C-terminal tail of LHR, whether by truncation or mutation, does not produce the expected changes. Consequently, phosphorylation of residues within this domain does not appear to be essential for desensitization. Further studies of the loops and evaluation of the participation of other kinases in desensitization will be necessary to unravel the mechanisms responsible for agonist-induced uncoupling of the LHR.

GENE STRUCTURE AND REGULATION

Organization of the LHR Gene

The LHR gene has been analyzed most extensively in the rat (63, 121, 122) and to a lesser extent in human and mouse (2, 48). The LHR gene spans over 70 kb and consists of 11 exons separated by 10 introns, all of which are located in the extracellular domain (Figure 1, *right*). Exons 1–10 encode the 5' untranslated region and most of the extracellular domain. Exon 11 encodes the rest of the receptor, including a 47-residue segment of the extracellular domain adjacent to the plasma membrane, the transmembrane domains and their connecting loops, the cytoplasmic tail, and the 3' flanking region. Exon 1 contains the 5' flanking region; signal peptide in the human, rat, and pig; and four cysteines that are conserved in TSH and FSH. The leucine-rich repeat motif is represented genomically by the insertion of introns at 70-bp intervals between exons 2 and 8 (see above).

Truncated forms of the receptor that lack either the transmembrane/cytoplasmic module or the transmembrane domain have been identified in pig (77) and rat testes (121, 122) and in human ovarian libraries (5, 81). These forms result from splicing at various alternative acceptor splice sites in exon 11, with or without elimination of exon 9. The existence of these alternately spliced forms in target tissues can be inferred from the presence of truncated mRNAs that presumably generate the receptor variants and from expression studies in mammalian cells with identification of soluble product in the culture medium or entrapped in membranes within the cells. The soluble rat (121) and pig truncated variant (form B) (77), which results from splicing at an alternate acceptor site in exon 11 and lacks the transmembrane/cytoplasmic module, is the major spliced variant of the receptor in luteinized ovaries and in Leydig cells (121, 128a).

The exon-intron junction structure and location are conserved between the rat and human LHR genes, and the organization of the LHR is generally similar among species. This organization corresponds to phase 2 configuration, with interruption at the second nucleotide of the codon. The genes encoding the other glycoprotein hormone receptors (35, 39) are organized as 10 exons, of which exons 1–9 are homologous to LHR exons 1–10, and exon 10 of the other glycoprotein receptors corresponds to exon 11 of LHR and encodes the transmembrane/cytoplasmic module. The LHR gene is located in the human on chromosome 2p21, proximal to the location of the FSHR gene at 2p21-p16. The human TSHR gene is located on chromosome 14q31 (100–102).

The 5′ Flanking Region: Promoter Domain, Upstream Regulatory Elements and Transacting Binding Proteins

The structure of the 5′ flanking region of the LHR gene differs in the rat (122, 125), mouse (48), and human (2). In the rat, a TATA-less promoter (Figure 6, *top*) region within the 5′ 173 bp contains three initiator-like elements ($Inr_{1,2,3}$) that encompass two major transcriptional start sites (TSS) at −14 (122) or −13 (53, 129) and −19, and a minor start site at −33 within the Inr_3

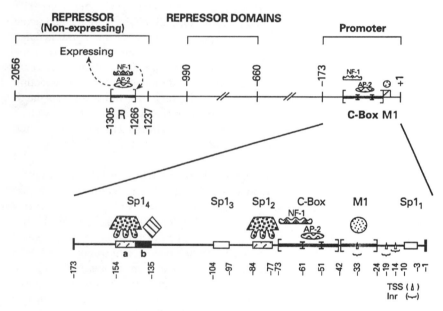

Figure 6   The promoter domain and 5′ flanking region of the rat LHR. *Top:* The LHR promoter is constitutively repressed by two inhibitory domains within amino acids −173 to −1237 bp. A third inhibitory domain at −1266 to −1266 includes the R domain. AP-2-induced repression is present only in nonexpressing cells. In expressing cells, the NF-1 neutral factor binds this site. *Bottom:* Regulatory elements and transfactor binding within the promoter domain. TSS, transcriptional start sites; Inr, initiator element. $Sp1_2$ (consensus Sp1 element) and $Sp1_4$ (nonconsensus) bind the Sp1 protein. The C-box binds AP-2 (inhibitory) only in expressing cells and NF-1 (neutral) only in nonexpressing cells. M1 binds a protein that is important for tissue-specific activation. Competition of AP-2 factor with NF-1 for overlapping elements at the promoter and upstream domain contributes to activation and silencing of gene transcription.

initiator element. Transcription of the rat gene is dependent on binding of the Sp1 protein to two of four Sp1 domains (Sp1$_2$, Sp1$_4$), each of which contributes 50% of the activity (123–125). GC-rich Sp1 DNA-binding domains and initiator elements may act cooperatively to direct gene transcription and operate as an Sp1/Inr-directed transcriptional complex in the LHR (114, 123–125).

Promoter activity is regulated by at least three additional DNA domains [R (−1266 to −1377 bp), C-box (−42 to −73 bp), and M1 (−24 to −42)], which bind multiple transcription regulators in a tissue-specific manner. The M1 protein has different properties in mouse Leydig tumor cells (MLTC) and Chinese hamster ovary cells (CHO). This protein acts as an activator in MLTC but not in CHO cells, where its lack of function may be due to the absence of LHR gene transcription in nonexpressing cells (25, 123–125). C-box binding factors either inhibit the LHR promoter activity (AP-2) or block inhibition (NF-1) through overlapping nonidentical DNA-binding elements. The LHR promoter is constitutively repressed by at least two domains located 5′ to the promoter at −173 to −626 and −626 to −990. A third repressor region is located between nucleotides −2056 and −1237, includes the R domain (−1207 to −1266), and is present only in nonexpressing cells (Figure 6, *bottom*). The protein-binding domain in this sequence is localized to a 20-bp subdomain (−1266 to −1275). Deletion of sequences between −173 and −1237 reverses constitutive inhibition in MLTC cells but not in CHO cells (124, 125).

In MLTC, a promoter-based AP-2 element may compete with an NF-1-like protein for overlapping elements to turn transcript initiation off and on from the promoter domain. Removal of the AP-2 element from the C-box results in MLTC-specific activation that presumably involves an M1-C box interaction. Thus the expressing cell has a functional target for hormonal induction within the C-box that is not present in the nonexpressing CHO cells. The upstream R domain is inhibitory only in nonexpressing cells. C-box binding factors compete for this upstream element in a tissue-specific manner, and binding of either AP-2 or NF-1 transfactor to the R domain is mutually exclusive. The AP-2 repressor binds preferentially to this upstream domain in nonexpressing cells, and this selectivity may be critical for tissue-specific LHR gene expression (25, 123–125).

Promoter studies have been undertaken in the mouse and human genes. The 5′ flanking region of the mouse LHR gene has sequence similarities to the rat gene (48). This TATA-less gene contains initiator elements adjacent to the initiation codon, and one of the two Sp1 elements is functional. In contrast to the rat, the mouse gene is not repressed by upstream domains, and several transcription initiation sites are located in the −310 region, 5′ to the promoter domain at −1 to −173 from the initiation codon (29, 48).

The human gene has been isolated from a lymphocyte genomic library (2). It contains many of the same transcription factor binding elements that are required for rat LHR promoter activity and its regulation. These include Sp1, AP-2, and NF-1 elements located within the −1 to −176 domain (from ATG), although not in the same aligned positions. The transcriptional start site (TSS) of this gene is located upstream of the (−176 to −1) domain at position −1085 (from ATG), and TATA-like sequences upstream of this TSS were proposed to be the promoter region. It is unknown whether the putative upstream promoter (5′ to −1085 bp) directs the transcription of this gene. It is also not known if the functional elements within the (−1 to −176) domain contribute to the overall basal promoter activity, operate as a separate downstream promoter or serve as the sole promoter of this gene.

The recent isolation of a 6-kb LHR gene fragment containing exon 1 from the human placenta revealed the presence of a second LHR gene (32a) (Genbank Accession No. AF024642). This clone (gene II) (32a) differs from that of a lymphocyte library gene (gene I) (2) in the sequence of the coding region and the proposed location of the promoter (5′ to transcriptional start site −1085). The sequence differences in gene II include several base changes in the 5′-flanking region and deletion of six nucleotides in the coding region (exon 1) (32a), which conforms to the sequence of the human ovarian cDNA (54a, 81). Both LHR genes are present in the human genome. Gene II promoter activity is localized exclusively to the 176-bp domain 5′ flanking the initiation codon, and initiation sites in this domain were identified in human testis, ovary, and in human choriocarcinoma cells (JAR cells). Two Sp1 domains are of central importance to transcriptional activity, and inhibitory sites were identified in the promoter domain at an AP-2 element and 5′ ERE half site. Significant LHR promoter activity is attributed to the lack of substantial inhibition by upstream domains in the rat 5′ UTR (123–125) and is increased by the addition of cAMP. The human LHR 176-bp gene is regulated by basal inhibitory activity of the AP-2 and ERE elements and by cAMP-mediated activation. These recent findings suggest that differential promoter activity and expression of LHR cDNAs is linked to gene diversity (32a).

The 3′ Flanking Region: Functional Polyadenylation Domains

Within the 6.3 kb of the 3′ noncoding region of the LHR gene, two functional polyadenylation (pA) domains (pA_1 = H1, nt 2368–2491 and pA_2 55679−5768), each containing two core pA signals (AAUAUA in H1 and AAUAAA in H2) (Figure 1, right), are responsible for the formation of two major sets of mRNAs [2.3 or 2.6 kb (corresponding to alternatively spliced form B-extracellular and holoreceptor, respectively)] and 5.8 kb (holoreceptor + form B not resolved). Either pA domain is sufficient to direct 3′-end processing (43, 44). The differences between the major mRNA species are attributable to the extension of the 3′ noncoding region. The functional efficiency of each pA domain is related to the specific poly A signal, distal downstream elements, and tissue-specific factors (43, 45). In addition to 3′ flanking pA, utilization of pA sites within introns 3, 4, and 10 results in formation of alternate mRNAs that have been expressed in 293 cells to produce peptides of 81, 116, and 294 amino acids that are able to bind hormone (64).

The diversity of the LHR mRNA transcripts in target and nontarget tissues results from alternative splicing of introns and from the use of two pA domains within the 3′-flanking region. (43, 63, 64, 77, 121, 122). Multiple LHR and LHR mRNA species are present in the ovaries and testes of different species (16, 44, 71, 109, 110, 138). In the rat ovary, LHR mRNA species of 5.8 kb (predominant), 2.3 and 2.6 kb (abundant), and 4.4 kb (minor) are present at most stages of ovarian maturation. Three additional minor species (8.0, 1.9, and 1.4 kb) are present at specific developmental stages (110). In the rat testis, similar mRNA species were present but in lower abundance. The human testis and thyroid contain 4.5 and 2.6 kb LHR mRNA species (31). The LHR mRNA levels in adult rat Leydig cells were only twofold higher than those of the progenitor cells and about one-third as high as levels in the immature Leydig cells. In contrast, the binding capacity in adult Leydig cells was 15- to 19-fold higher than in progenitor immature cells (110).

These studies demonstrate the importance of translational efficiency and protein stability in determining the receptor level in adult Leydig cells. Homologous down-regulation of the LHR in vivo during follicular and luteal desensitization correlates with the steady state receptor mRNA level (43, 71). In the luteinizing rat ovary and cultured porcine luteal cells, homologous down-regulation of the receptor also correlates with a decrease in mRNA stability (16, 78), whereas in MA10 cells, down-regulation is associated with decreased LHR transcription (85).

LHR mRNAs messages and their translated products are present in some nontarget human tissues (76, 93, 96, 116, 120). Multiple LHR mRNAs and translation products are present in the epithelial cells of the rat prostate (93, 116). The stimulation of cAMP production in these cells by hCG demonstrates that the receptors in the prostate cells are functional (93). LHRs are also present in the testicular luminal side of the endothelial testicular microvasculature, where they participate in the transcytosis of the cognate hormone into the interstitial space. Following LH binding to the LHR, the complex undergoes internalization via coated pits (33).

EVOLUTIONARY ASPECTS

Current concepts about the evolutionary relationships among the glycoprotein hormones and their GPCRs assume the existence of an intronless prokaryote precursor gene that lacked a signal peptide and encoded a plasma membrane receptor and subsequently diverged into at least two families. The precursor

GPCR has been retained in evolution in members of the adrenergic/small pep-tide family of receptors (Family 1), which is characterized by a set of common motifs in the TM and loop domains (108a, 114a). A second family of GPCRs, including parathyroid hormone (1), corticotropin-releasing hormone (89), and glucagon receptor (49), is defined by the presence of conserved domains in the first intracellular loop and TM VII and an extracellular domain that is interme-diate in size between those of the small peptide–binding receptors and the gly-coprotein hormone receptors (62). A potential precursor GPCR with sequence characteristics from both families has been isolated from slime mold (59).

The glycoprotein hormone receptors may have arisen as a result of recom-binant events early in evolution between the Family 1 GPCR and a member of the leucine-rich repeat family (7, 121, 122, 99). The obvious functional and sequence division of the LHR into an extracellular leucine-rich repeat hormone-binding module and the TM/loop domain, which contains the signal transduc-tion apparatus, supports a fusion of two separate modules. Identification of LHR-like proteins in the coelenterate sea anenome (86), the mollusc *Lymmea stagnalis* (118), and the arthropod *Drosophila* (9) suggests that the LRR/GPCR recombinant event took place prior to vertebrate evolution. The deduced amino acid sequences of these GPCRs (86, 118, 9) show remarkable similarity to the mammalian LHR, FSHR, and TSHR, in particular between LHR exons 2 and 8 within the leucine-rich repeat region, and in the TM/loop module.

Intronic positions within the LHR extracellular domain are conserved in the *Drosophila* GPCR (38), and the intronic sites appear to be conserved at the same position within the leucine-rich repeat (LXXL/XL) in other leucine-rich repeat proteins (Accession gene bank number Z81130). Thus the initial recombina-tion event may have involved an intron-containing leucine-rich repeat module. The origin of the TM/loop module is unclear. Although the mammalian LHR is derived from Family 1 in terms of its conserved motifs and intronless TM/loop domain, the presence of introns in the invertebrate LHR-like *Drosophila* gly-coprotein hormone precursor is a paradox (38).

The existence of several common intronic positions between the corticotro-pin-releasing hormone receptor (120a), the *Drosophila* GPCR (38), and alter-native splice sites B, C, and D in the LHR (77) indicates that hot spots may exist on the gene of this module that have become cleavage splice sites and/or potential intron insertion sites across families and species. The modular con-figuration of the vertebrate and invertebrate receptors supports the proposal for genetic recombination of a gene that expresses both the heptahelical membrane module and an external ligand-binding domain (121).

Within the glycoprotein family, the LHR could have followed the other mem-bers in evolution. Its two pA domains (Figure 1) are separated by a known trans-poson, a repetitive DNA line R domain that might represent an insertion that carries the proximal pA domain pA_1 and downstream sequences (Figure 1). This conclusion is based on the homology of the limited 3' untranslated sequences available for other GPCRs such as the TSH, FSH, and β-adrenergic receptors (43), in which the repetitive line R domain does not appear to be present (43) (Figure 1).

Visit the *Annual Reviews home page* at
http://www.AnnualReviews.org.

Literature Cited

1. Abou-Samra AB, Juppner H, Force T, Freeman MW, Kong XF, et al. 1992. Expression cloning of a common receptor for parathyroid hormone and parathyroid hormone-related peptide from rat osteoblast-like cells: A single receptor stimulates intracellular accumulation of both cAMP and inositol trisphosphates and increases intracellular free calcium. *Proc. Natl. Acad. Sci. USA* 89:2732–36

1a. Alvarado MV, Alvarado NE, Russo J, Russo IH. 1994. Human chorionic gonadotropin inhibits proliferation and induces expression of inhibin in human breast epithelial cells in vitro. *In Vitro Cell. Dev. Biol. A* 30:4–8

2. Atger M, Misrahi M, Sar S, Le Flem L, Dessen P, Milgrom E. 1995. Structure of the human luteinizing hormone-choriogonadotropin receptor gene: usual promoter and 5' non-coding regions. *Mol. Cell. Endocrinol.* 111:113–23

3. Baxter RC, Martin JL, Beniac VA. 1989. High molecular weight insulin-like growth factor binding protein complex. Purification and properties of the acid-labile subunit from human serum. *J. Biol. Chem.* 264:11843–48

4. Ben-Menahem D, Kudi M, Pixley MR, Sato A, Suganuma N, et al. 1997. The biological action of single-chain choriogonadotropin is not dependent on the individual disulfide bonds of the β subunit. *J. Biol. Chem.* 272:6827–30

5. Bernard MP, Myers RV, Moyle WR. 1990. Cloning of rat lutropin receptor analogs lacking the soybean lectin domain. *Mol. Cell. Endocrinol.* 71:R19–R23

5a. Berthezine F, Forest MG, Girmand JA, Claustrat B, Mornex R. 1976. Leydig cell agenesis: a cause of male pseudohermaphroditism. *N. Engl. J. Med.* 295:969–72

6. Birnbaumer M. 1995. Mutations and diseases of G proteins coupled receptors. *J. Recept. Signal Transd. Res.* 15:133–60

7. Boniface JM, Reichert LE Jr. 1990. Evidence for a novel thioredoxin-like catalytic property of gonadotropin hormones. *Science* 247:61–64

8. Braun T, Schofield PR, Sprengel R. 1991. Amino-terminal leucine-rich repeats in gonadotropin receptors determine hormone selectivity. *EMBO J.* 10:1885–90

9. Campbell RK, Dean-Emig DM, Moyle WR. 1991. Conversion of hCG into a follitropin by protein engineering. *Proc. Natl. Acad. Sci. USA* 88:760–64

10. Catt K, Dufau ML. 1991. Gonadotropic hormones: biosynthesis secretion, receptors and actions. In *Reproductive Endocrinology*, ed. SSC Yen, RB Jaffe, pp. 105–55, Philadelphia: Saunders

11. Caticha O, Odell WD. 1994. Characterization and purification of hCG like protein binding site in *Candida albicans*. *Endocrinol. Res.* 20:1–19

12. Catt KJ, Dufau ML, Tsuruhara T. 1973. Absence of intrinsic biological activity in LH and hCG subunits. *J. Clin. Endocrinol.* 36:73–78

13. Catt KJ, Harwood JP, Clayton RN, Davies TF, Chan V, Dufau ML. 1980. Regulation of peptide hormone receptors and gonadal steroidogenesis. *Recent Prog. Horm. Res.* 36:557–622

14. Chen F, Puett D. 1991. Contributions of arginines-43 and 94 of human choriogonadotropin beta to receptor binding and activation as determined by oligonucleotide-based mutagenesis. *Biochemistry* 30:10171–75

15. Chen W, Bahl OP. 1993. High expression of the hormone binding active extracellular domain (1294) of rat lutropin receptor in *Escherichia coli*. *Mol. Cell. Endocrinol.* 91:35–41

15a. Chung FZ, Wang CD, Potter SPC, Venter

JC, Frazer CM. 1988. Site directed mutagenesis and continuous expression of human β-adrenergic receptors. *J. Biol. Chem.* 263:4052–55

16. Chuzel F, Schteingart H, Vigier M, Avalet O Saez JM. 1995. Transcriptional and post-transcriptional regulation of luteotropin/chorionic gonadotropin receptor by the agonist in Leydig cells. *Eur. J. BioChem.* 229:516–25

17. Cosowsky L, Rao SNV, MacDonald GJ, Papkoff H, Campbell RK, Moyle WR. 1995. The grove between the α- and β-subunits of hormones with LH activity appears to contact the LH receptor and its conformation is changed during hormone binding. *J. Biol. Chem.* 270:20011–19

18. David R, Yoom DJ, Landin L. 1984. A syndrome of gonadotropin resistance possibly due to a luteinizing hormone receptor defect. *J. Clin. Endocrinol. Metab.* 59:156–60

19. Davis DP, Liu X, Segaloff DL. 1995. Identification of sites of N-linked glycosylation on the follicle-stimulating hormone (FSH) receptor and assessment of their role in FSH receptor function. *Mol. Endocrinol.* 9:159–69

20. Davis DP, Rozell TG, Liu X, Segaloff DL. 1997. The six N-linked carbohydrates of the lutropin/choriogonadotropin receptor are not absolutely required for correct folding, cell surface expression, hormone binding, or signal transduction. *Mol. Endocrinol.* 97:550–62

21. Davis JS, West LA, Farese RV. 1984. Effects of LH on phosphoinositide metabolism in rat granulosa cells. *J. Biol. Chem.* 259:32768–74

22. Dufau ML. 1988. Endocrine regulation and communicating function of the Leydig cell. *Annu. Rev. Physiol.* 50:483–508

23. Dufau ML. 1990. The luteinizing hormone/human chorionic gonadotrophin receptor of testis and ovary. In *Receptor Purification*, ed. G Litwack, pp. 147–71. Clifton, NJ: Humana

24. Dufau ML. 1990. Ovarian and testicular LH/hCG receptors. In *Glycoprotein Hormones*, ed. WW Chin, I Boime, p. 367. Norwell, Ma: Serono Symp.

25. Dufau ML, Tsai Morris CH, Zhang H, Buczko E. 1995. Structure and regulation of the LH receptor gene. *J. Steroid Biochem. Mol. Biol.* 53:286–91

26. Dufau ML, Tsuruhara T, Horner KA, Podesta E, Catt KJ. 1977. Evidence for an intermediate role of cAMP and protein kinase during gonadotropin action on steroidogenesis in testicular interstitial cells. *Proc. Natl. Acad. Sci. USA* 74:3419–23

27. Duprez L, Parma J, Dumont J. 1996. Diversity and prevalence of ionic mutations in the TSH receptor gene as a cause of toxic adenoma. *J. Endocrinol. Invest.* 19(Suppl.):69–72

28. Duprez L, Parma J, Van Sande J, Allgeier A, Leclere J, et al. 1994. Germline mutations in the thyrotropin receptor gene cause non-autoimmune autosomal dominant hyperthyroidism. *Nat. Genet.* 7:396–401

29. El-Hefnawy T, Krawczky Z, Nikula H, Viherä, Huhtaniemi I. 1996. Regulation of function of the murine luteinizing hormone receptor promoter by *cis*- and *trans*-acting elements in mouse Leydig tumor cells. *Mol. Cell. Endocrinol.* 119:207–17

30. Fernandez LM, Puett D. 1996. Lys583 in the third extracellular loop of the lutropin/choriogonadotropin receptor is critical for signaling. *J. Biol. Chem.* 271:925–30

31. Frazier AL, Robbins LS, Stork PJ, Sprengel R, Segaloff DL, Cone RD. 1990. Isolation of TSH and LH/CG Receptor cDNAs from human thyroid: regulation by tissue specific splicing. *Mol. Endocrinol.* 90:1264–76

32. Furuhashi M, Shikone T, Fuad AF, Tadashi S, Hsueh AJW, et al. 1995. Fusing the carboxy-terminal peptide of the chorionic gonadotropin (CG) β-subunit to the common α-subunit: retention of O-linked glycosylation and enhanced in vivo bioactivity of chimeric human CG. *Mol. Endocrinol.* 9:54–62

32a. Geng Y, Tsai Morris CH, Buzcko E, Dufau ML. 1997. Expression of the human luteinizing hormone receptor gene: evidence for multiple promoter activity and gene diversity. *FASEB J.* 11:497 (Abstr.)

33. Ghinea N, Mai TV, Groyer-Picard MT, Milgrom E. 1994. How protein hormones reach their target cells. Receptor mediated transcytosis of hCG through endothelial cells. *J. Cell Biol.* 125:87–97

33a. Gilchrist RL, Ryu KS, Ji I, Ji TH. 1996. The luteinizing hormone/chorionic gonadotropin receptor has distinct transmembrane conductors for cAMP and inositol phosphate signals. *J. Biol. Chem.* 271:19283–87

34. Gromoll J, Timoni M, Nieschlag E. 1996. An activating mutation of the follicle-stimulating hormone receptor

autonomously sustains spermatogenesis in a hypophysectomized man. *J. Clin. Endocrinol. Metab.* 81:1367–70

35. Gross B, Misrahi M, Sar S, Milgrom E. 1991. Composite structure of the human throtropin receptor gene. *Biochem. Biophys. Acta* 177:679–87

36. Guderman T, Birnbaumer M, Birnbaumer L. 1992. Evidence for dual coupling of the murine luteinizing hormone receptor to adenylate cyclase and phosphoinositide breakdown and Ca^{2+} mobilization. *J. Biol. Chem.* 267:4479–88

37. Gudermann T, Birnbaumer L, Birnbaumer L. 1995. Homologous desensitization of the murine luteinizing hormone receptor expressed in L cells. *Mol. Cell. Endocrinol.* 110:125–35

38. Hauser F, Nothacker HP, Grimmelikhuijzen CJP. 1997. Molecular cloning and developmental regulation of a novel receptor from *Drosophilia melanogaster* structurally related to members of the thyroid-stimulating hormone, follicle-stimulating hormone, luteinizing hormone/choriogonadotropic receptor family from mammals. *J. Biol. Chem.* 272:1002–9

39. Heckert LL, Daley I, Griswold MD. 1992. Structural organization of the follicle-stimulating hormone receptor gene. *Mol. Endocrinol.* 6:70–80

40. Herrlich A, Kühn B, Grosse R, Schmid A, Schultz G, Gudermann T. 1995. Involvement of Gs and Gi proteins in dual coupling of the luteinizing hormone receptor to adenylate cyclase and phospholipase C. *J. Biol. Chem.* 271:16764–72

41. Hipkin WR, Sanchez-Yague J, Ascoli M. 1993. Agonist-induced phosphorylation of the luteinizing hormone/chorionic gonadotropin receptor expressed in a stably transfected cell line. *Mol. Endocrinol.* 7:823–32

42. Hirsch B, Kudo M, Naro F, Conti M, Hsueh AJW. 1996. The C-terminal third of the human luteinizing hormone receptor is important for inositol phosphate release: analysis using chimeric human LH/follicle-stimulating hormone receptors. *Mol. Endocrinol.* 10:1127–37

42a. Hong S, Ryu KS, Oh MS, Ji I, Ji TH. 1997. Roles of transmembrane prolines and proline-induced kinks of the lutropin/choriogonadotropin receptor. *J Biol. Chem.* 272:4166–71.

43. Hu ZZ, Buczko E, Zhuang L, Dufau ML. 1994. Sequence of the 3' noncoding region of the luteinizing hormone receptor gene and identification of two

polyadenylation domains that generate the major mRNA forms. *Biochem. Biophys. Acta* 1220:330–37

44. Hu ZZ, Tsai Morris CH, Buczko E, Dufau ML. 1990. Hormonal regulation of LH receptor mRNA and expression in the rat ovary. *FEBS Lett.* 274:181–84

45. Hu ZZ, Zhuang L, Buczko M, Dufau ML. 1995. Role of the 3'-noncoding region in posttranscriptional processes of the rat LH receptor gene expression. *FASEB J. Abstr.*

46. Deleted in proof

47. Huang J, Ujihara M, Xia H, Chen F, Yoshida H, et al. 1993. Mutagenesis of the determinant loop region of human choriogonadotropin beta. *Mol. Cell. Endocrinol.* 20:211–18

48. Huhtaniemi IT, Eskola V, Pakarinen P, Matikainen T, Sprengel R. 1992. The murine luteinizing hormone and follicle-stimulating hormone receptor genes: transcription initiation sites, putative promoter sequences and promoter activity. *Mol. Cell. Endocrinol.* 88:55–66

49. Jelinek LJ, Lok S, Rosenberg GB, Smith RA, Grant FJ, et al. 1993. Expression cloning and signaling properties of the rat glucagon receptor. *Science* 259:1614–16

50. Ji I, Ji TH. 1991. Asp383 in the second transmembrane domain of the lutropin receptor is important for high affinity hormone binding and cAMP production. *J. Biol. Chem.* 266:14953–57

51. Ji I, Ji TH. 1991. Human choriogonadotropin binds a lutropin receptor with essentially no terminal extension and stimulates cAMP synthesis. *J. Biol. Chem.* 266:13076–79

52. Ji I, Zeng H, Ji TH. 1993. Receptor activation and signal generation by the lutropin/choriogonadotropin receptors Asp^{397} is important for receptor activation. *J. Biol. Chem.* 268:20851–54

53. Ji I, Koo YB, JI TH. 1994. Characterization of the rat LH/CG receptor gene: dominant suppressors, proximal regulators and transcription start sites. *Endocrinol. J.* 2:279–87

53a. Ji I, Slaughter RG, Ji TH. 1990. N-linked oligosaccharides are not required for hormone binding of the lutropin receptor in a Leydig tumor cell line and rat granulosa cell. *Endocrinology* 127:494–96

54. Ji I, Zeng H, Ji TH. 1993. Receptor activation and signal generation by the lutropin/choriogonadotropin receptor. Cooperation between Asp^{397} of the

492   DUFAU

receptor and a-Lys91 of the hormone. *J. Biol. Chem.* 268:22971–74

54a. Jia XC, Oikawa M, Bo M, Tanaka T, Ny T, et al. 1991. Expression of human luteinizing hormone (LH) receptor: interaction with LH and chorionic gonadotropin from human but not equine, rat and bovine species. *Mol. Endocrinol.* 5:759–68

55. Jiang X, Dreano M, Buckler DR, Cheng S, Ythier A, et al. 1995. Structural predictions for the ligand-binding region of glycoprotein hormone receptors and the nature of hormone-receptor interactions. *Structure* 3:1341–53

56. Kawate N, Menon KMJ. 1994. Palmitoylation of luteinizing hormone/human choriogonadotropin receptors in transfected cells. *J. Biol. Chem.* 269:30651–58

56a. Kelsey JL, Gammon MD, John EM. 1993. Reproductive factors and breast cancer. *Epidemiol. Rev.* 15:36–47

57. Keutmann HT, Charlesworth MC, Kitzmann K, Mason KA, Johnson L, Ryan RJ. 1988. Primary and secondary structural determinants in the receptor binding sequence β(38–57) from human luteinizing hormone. *Biochemistry* 21:8939–44

58. Keutmann HT, Charlesworth MC, Mason KA, Ostrea T. 1987. Receptor-binding region in human choriogonadotropin/lutropin beta subunit. *Proc. Natl. Acad. Sci. USA* 84:2038–42

58a. Khanum A, Dufau ML. 1986. Inhibitory action of forskolin on adenylate cyclase activity and cAMP generation. *J. Biol. Chem.* 261:11456–59

59. Klein PS, Sun TJ, Saxe CL, Kimmel AR, Johnson RL, Devreotes PN. 1988. A chemoattractant receptor controls development in *Dictyostelium discoideum. Science* 241:1467–72

60. Kobe B, Deisenhofer J. 1993. Crystal structure of porcine ribonuclease inhibitor, a protein with leucine-rich repeats. *Nature* 366:751–56

61. Kobe B, Deisenhofer JA. 1995. Structural basis of the interactions between leucine-rich repeats and protein ligands. *Nature* 374:183–86

62. Kong XF, Schipani E, Lanske B, Joun H, Karperien M, et al. 1994. The rat, mouse and human genes encoding the receptor for parathyroid hormone and parathyroid hormone-related peptide are highly homologous. *Biochem. Biophys. Res. Commun.* 200:1290–99

63. Koo YB, Ji I, Slaughter RG, Ji TH. 1991. Structure of the LH receptor gene and multiple exons of the coding sequences. *Endocrinology* 128:2297–308

64. Koo YB, Li IJ, Ji TH. 1994. Characterization of different sizes of rat luteinizing hormone/chorionic gonadotropin receptor messenger ribonucleic acids. *Endocrinology* 134:19–26

64a. Kosugi S, Ban T, Akamizu T, Kohn LD. 1992. Role of cysteine residues in the extracellular domain and exoplasmic loops of the transmembrane domain of the TSH receptor: effect of mutation to serine on TSH receptor activity and response to thyroid stimulating autoantibodies. *Biochem. Biophys. Res. Commun.* 189:1754–62

65. Kosugi S, Mori T, Shenker A. 1996. The role of Asp^{578} in maintaining the inactive conformation of the human lutropin/chorionic gonadotropin receptor. *J. Biol. Chem.* 271:31813–17

66. Kosugi S, Van Dop C, Geffner ME, Rabl W, Carel C, et al. 1995. Characterization of heterozygous mutations causing constitutive activation of the luteinizing hormone receptor in familial male precocious puberty. *Hum. Mol. Genet.* 4:183–88

67. Kraaij R, Post M, Kremer H, Milgrom E. 1995. A missense mutation in the second transmembrane segment of the luteinizing hormone receptor causes familial male-limited precocious puberty. *J. Clin. Endocrinol. Metab.* 80:3168–72

68. Kremer H, Kraaj R, Toledo SPA, Post M, Fridman JB, et al. 1995. Male pseudohermaphroditism due to a homozygous missense mutation of the luteinizing hormone receptor gene. *Nat. Genet.* 9:160–64

69. Kremer H, Mariman E, Otten BJ, Moll GW, Stoelinga BA, et al. 1993. Cosegregation of missense mutations of the luteinizing hormone receptor gene with familial male-limited precocious puberty. *Hum. Mol. Genet.* 2:1779–83

70. Kusuda S, Dufau ML. 1986. Purification and characterization of the rat ovarian receptor for luteinizing hormone: structural studies and subunit interaction. *J. Biol. Chem.* 261:16161–66

71. LaPolt PS, Oikawa M, Jia XC, Dargan AJW, Hsueh AJW. 1990. Gonadotropin induced up- and down-regulation of rat ovarian LH receptor message levels during follicular growth, ovulation, and luteinization. *Endocrinology* 1126:3277–79

72. Lapthorn AJ, Harris DC, Littlejohn A, Lustbader JW, Canfield RE, et al. 1994.

Crystal structure of human chorionic gonadotropin. *Nature* 369:455–61

73. Latronico AC, Anasti J, Arnhold IVP, Rapaport R, Mendoca BB, et al. 1996. Brief report: testicular and ovarian resistance to luteinizing hormone caused by inactivating mutations of the luteinizing hormone receptor gene. *N. Engl. J. Med.* 334:507–12

74. Latronico AC, Anasta J, Mendonca BB, Arnhold I, Domenice S, et al. 1995. A novel mutation of the luteinizing hormone receptor gene causing male gonadotropin-independent precocious puberty. *J. Clin. Endocrinol. Metab.* 80:2490–94

75. Laue L, Chan WY, Hsueh AJW, Kudo M, Hsu SY, et al. 1995. Genetic heterogeneity of activating mutations of the luteinizing hormone receptor gene in familial male-limited precocious puberty. *Proc. Natl. Acad. Sci. USA* 92:1906–10

76. Lei ZM, Rao CV, Pridham D. 1993. Novel coexpression of human chorionic gonadotropin/luteinizing hormone receptors and their ligand hCG in human fallopian tubes. *J. Clin. Endocrinol. Metab.* 132:2262–70

76a. Lobel LI, Rausch P, Trakht I, Pollak S, Lustbader JW. 1997. Filamentous phage displaying the extracellular domain of the LH/hCG receptor bind hCG specifically. *Endocrinology* 138:1232–39

77. Loosfelt H, Misrahi M, Atger M, Salesse R, VuHai-Luu Thi MT, et al. 1989. Cloning and sequencing of porcine LH-hCG receptor cDNA; variants lacking the transmembrane domain. *Science* 245:525–28

77a. Loosfelt H, Pichon C, Jolivet A, Misrahi M, Caillon B, et al. 1992. Two-subunit structure of the human thyrotropin receptor. *Proc. Natl. Acad. Sci. USA* 89:3765–69

78. Lu LD, Peegel H, Mosier SM, Menon KMJ. 1993. Loss of lutropin/human choriogonadotropin receptor messenger ribonucleic acid during ligand-induced down-regulation occurs post-transcriptionally. *Endocrinology* 132:235–40

79. McFarland KC, Sprengel R, Phillips HS, Kilher M, Rosemblit N, et al. 1989. Lutropin-choriogonodotropin receptor: an unusual member of the G-coupled receptor family. *Science* 245:494–99

79a. Mac-Mahon B, Cole P, Liu M, Lowe CR, Mirra AP, et al. 1970. Age at birth and breast cancer risk. *Bull. WHO* 43:209–221

79b. Meduri G, Charnaux H, Loosfelt H, Jolivet A, Spyratos F, et al. 1997. Luteinizing hormone/human chorionic gonadotropin receptors in breast cancer. *Cancer Res.* 57:857–64

80. Minegishi T, Delgado C, Dufau ML. 1989. Phosphorylation and glycosylation of the luteinizing hormone receptor. *Proc. Natl. Acad. Sci. USA.* 86:1470–74

81. Minegishi T, Nakamura K, Takakura Y, Miyamoto Y, Ibuki Y, et al. 1990. Cloning and sequencing of human LH/hCG receptor cDNA. *Biophys. Res. Commun.* 172:1049–54

82. Morell AG, Gregoriadis IH, Scheinber J, Hickman, Ashwell G. 1971. The roles of sialic acid in determining the survival of glycoproteins in the circulation. *J. Biol. Chem.* 246:1461–66

83. Moyle WR, Campbell RK, Myers RV, Bernard MP, Han Y, Wang X. 1994. Co-evolution of ligand-receptor pairs. *Nature* 368:251–55

84. Moyle WR, Campbell RK, Venkateswara R, Ayad NG, Bernard MP, et al. 1995. Model of human chorionic gonadotropin and lutropin receptor interaction that explains signal transduction of glycoprotein hormones. *J. Biol. Chem.* 270:20020–31

85. Nelson S, Ascoli M. 1992. Epidermal growth factor, phorbol ester and 3′, 5′-cyclic adenosine monophosphate decrease the transcription of the luteinizing hormone/chorionic gonadotropin receptor gene in MA-10 Leydig tumor. *Endocrinology* 131:615–20

86. Nothacker HP, Grimmelikhuigen JP. 1993. Molecular cloning of a novel putative G protein-coupled receptor from sea anemones structurally related to members of the FSH, TSH, LH/hCG receptor family from mammals. *Biochem. Biophys. Res. Commun.* 197:1062–69

87. Pajot-Augy E, Couture L, Bozon V, Remy JJ, Biache G, et al. 1995. High level expression of recombinant porcine LH receptor in baculovirus-infected insect cells or caterpillars. *J. Mol. Endocrinol.* 14:51–66

88. Deleted in proof

89. Perrin MH, Donaldson CJ, Chen R, Lewis KA, Vale WW. 1993. Cloning and functional expression of a rat brain corticotropin releasing factor (CRF) receptor. *Endocrinology* 133:3058–61

90. Petaja-Repo UE, Merz WE, Rajaniemi HJ. 1991. Significance of the glycan moiety of the rat ovarian luteinizing hormone/chorionic gonadotropin (CG) receptor and human CG for receptor-hormone interaction. *Endocrinology* 128:1209–17

91. Puett D, Bhowmick N, Fernandez LM, Huang J, Wu C, Narayan P. 1996. HCG-receptor binding and transmembrane signaling. *Mol. Cell. Endocrinol.* 125:55–64

92. Quintana J, Wang H, Ascoli M. 1993. The regulation of the binding affinity of the luteinizing hormone choriogonadotropin receptor by sodium ions is mediated by a highly conserved aspartate located in the second transmembrane domain of G protein-coupled receptors. *Mol. Endocrinol.* 7:767–75

92a. Rajagopalan-Gupta RM, Rasenick MM, Hunzicker-Dunn M. 1997. Luteinizing hormone/choriogonadotropin-dependent cholera toxin-catalyzed adenosine 5′-diphosphate (ADP)-ribosylation of the long and short forms of Gsa and pertussis toxin-centralized ADP-ribosylation of $G_{i\alpha}$. *Mol. Endocrinol.* 11:538–49

92b. Rajaniemi HJ, Petaja-Repo VE, Piefola EM. 1996. Structure and functional significance of the carbohydrates of the LH/hCG receptor. *Mol. Cell. Endocrinol.* 125:101–5

93. Reiter E, McNamara M, Closset J, Hennen G. 1995. Expression and functionality of luteinizing hormone/chorionic gonadotropin receptor in the rat prostate. *Endocrinology* 136:917–23

94. Remy JJ, Bozon V, Couture L, Goxe B, Salesse R, et al. 1993. Reconstitution of a high-affinity functional lutropin receptor by coexpression of its extracellular and membrane domains. *Biochem. Biophys. Res. Commun.* 193:1023–30

95. Remy JJ, Couture L, Pantel J, Haertle T, Rabesona H, et al. 1996. Mapping of hCG-receptor complexes. *Mol. Cell. Endocrinol.* 125:79–91

96. Reshef E, Lei ZM, Rao CV, Pridham DD, Chegini N, Luborsky JL. 1990. The presence of gonadotropin receptors in nonpregnant uterus, human placenta, fetal membranes and decidua. *J. Clin. Endocrinol. Metab.* 70:421–30

97. Richards JS, Hedin L. 1988. Molecular aspects of hormone action in ovarian follicular development, ovulation and luteinization. *Annu. Rev. Physiol.* 50:441–63

98. Rodriguez MC, Xie YB, Haiyun W, Colllison K, Segaloff DL. 1992. Effects of truncations of the cytoplasmic tail of the luteinizing hormone/chorionic gonadotropin receptor on receptor-mediated hormone internalization. *Mol. Endocrinol.* 6:327–37

99. Rothberg JM, Jacobs JR, Goodman CS, Artavanis-Tsakonas S. 1990. Slit: an extracellular protein necessary for development of midline glia and commissural axon pathways contains both EGF and LRR domains. *Genes Dev.* 4:2169–87

100. Rousseau-Merck MF, Atger M, Loosfelt H, Milgrom E, Berger R. 1993. Chromosomal localization of the human follicle-stimulating hormone receptor gene on 2p21-p16 is similar to that of the luteinizing hormone receptor gene. *Genomics.* 15:222–24

101. Rousseau-Merck MF, Misrahi M, Atger M, Loosfelt H, Milgrom E, Berger R. 1990. Localization of the human luteinizing hormone/choriogonadotropin receptor gene to chromosome 2p21. *Cytogenet. Cell Genet.* 54:77–79

102. Rousseau-Merck MF, Misrahi M, Loosfelt H, Atger M, Milgrom E, Berger R. 1990. Assignment of the human thyroid stimulating hormone receptor (TSHR) gene to chromosome 14aq31. *Genomics.* 8:233–36

103. Russo D, Ghazenbalk GD, Nagayama Y, Wadsworth HL, Rapoport B. 1991. Site-directed mutagenesis of the human thyrotropin receptor; role of Asn linked oligosaccharides in the expression of a functional receptor. *Mol. Endocrinol.* 5:29–33

104. Deleted in proof

105. Ryu KS, Gilcrist RL, Ji I, Kim SJ, Ji TH. 1996. Exoloop 3 of the luteinizing hormone receptor. Lys 583 is essential and irreplaceable for human choriogonadotropin (hCG) dependent receptor activation but not for high affinity hCG binding. *J. Biol. Chem.* 271:7301–4

105a. Ryu KS, Ji I, Chang L, Ji TH. 1996. Molecular mechanism of LH/hCG receptor activation. *Mol. Cell. Endocinol.* 125:93–100

106. Saez JM. 1994. Leydig cells: endocrine, paracrine and autocrine regulation. *Endocr. Rev.* 15:574–626

107. Sairam MR, Bargavi GM. 1988. A role for glycosylation of the α-subunit in transduction of biological signal in glyco-protein hormones. *Science* 263:3046–49

108. Sanchez-Yague J, Rodriguez MC, Segaloff DL, Ascoli M. 1992. Truncation of the cytoplasmic tail of lutropin choriogonadotropin receptor prevents agonist-induced uncoupling. *J. Biol. Chem.* 267:7217–20

108a. Schwartz TW. 1996. Molecular structure of G-protein-coupled receptors. In *Receptor Pharmacology*, ed. JC Foreman,

T Johansen, pp. 65–84. New York: CRC. 300 pp.

109. Segaloff D, Wang H, Richards JS. 1990. Hormone regulation of luteinizing hormone/chorionic gonadotropin receptor mRNA in rat ovarian cells during follicular development and luteinization. *Mol. Endocrinol.* 4:1856–65

110. Shan LX, Hardy MP. 1992. Developmental changes in levels of luteinizing hormone receptor and androgen in rat Leydig cells. *Endocrinology* 131:1107–14

111. Shao K, Bahl OP. 1997. Effect of modification of the β hairpin and long loops simultaneously. *Mol. Cell. Endocrinol.* 127:179–87

112. Shenker A. 1995. G protein-coupled receptors structure and function: the impact of disease-causing mutations. In *Genetic and Molecular Biological Aspects of Endocrine Disease*, ed. RV Thakker, pp. 427–45. London: Bailliere Tindall

113. Shenker A, Laue L, Kosugi S, Meredino JJ, Minegishi T, Cutler GB. 1993. A constitutively activating mutation of the luteinizing hormone receptor in familial male precocious puberty. *Nature* 365:652–54

113a. Shi Y, Zhou M. 1995. Thyrotropin internalization is directed by a highly conserved motif in the seventh transmembrane region of its receptor. *Endocr. J.* 3:409–14

113b. Skidgel RA, Bennett CD, Schiling JW, Fan FL, Weerasinghe DK, Erdos EG. 1988. Amino acid sequence of the N-terminus and selected tryptic peptides of the active subunit of human plasma carboxypeptidase N: comparison with other carboxypeptidases. *Biochem. Biophys. Res. Commun.* 154:1323–29

114. Smale TS. 1994. Core promoter architecture for eukaryotic protein-coding genes. In *Transcription Mechanism and Regulation*, ed. RC Conaway, JW Conaway, pp. 63–81. New York: Raven

114a. Strader CD, Fong TM, Tota MR, Underwood D. 1994. Structure and function of G-protein coupled receptors. *Annu. Rev. Biochem.* 63:101–32

115. Sugahara T, Pixley MR, Minami S, Perlas E, Ben-Menahem D, et al. 1995. Biosynthesis of a biologically active single peptide chain containing the human common α and β subunits in tandem. *Proc. Natl. Acad. Sci. USA* 92:2041–45

116. Tao YX, Lei ZM, Rao CV, Woodworth SH. 1995. Novel expression of luteiniz-ing hormone/chorionic gonadotropin receptor gene in rat prostates. *Mol. Cell. Endocrinol.* 111:R9–R12

117. Tayar EN. 1996. Advances in the molecular understanding of gonadotropin receptor interaction. *Mol. Cell. Endocrinol.* 125:65–70

118. Tensen CP, van Kesteren ER, Planta RJ, Cox KJA, Burke JF, et al. 1994. A G protein-coupled receptor with low density lipoprotein-binding motifs suggests a role for lipoproteins in G-linked signal transduction. *Proc. Natl. Acad. Sci. USA* 91:4816–20

118a. Thomas D, Rozell TG, Liu X, Segaloff DL. 1996. Mutational analyses of the extracellular domain of the full-length choriogonadotropin receptor suggest leucine-rich repeats 1–6 are involved in hormone binding. *Mol. Endocrinol.* 10:760–68

119. Tomic M, Dufau ML, Catt K, Stojilkovic S. 1995. Calcium signaling in single rat Leydig cells. *Endocrinology* 136:3422–29

120. Toth P, Li X, Rao CV, Lincoln-Sanfilippo JA, Spinato I, Yusman MA. 1994. Expression of functional human chorionic gonadotropin/human luteinizing hormone receptor gene in human uterine arteries. *J. Clin. Endocrinol. Metab.* 79:307–15

120a. Tsai-Morris CH, Buczko E, Geng Y, Gamboa-Pinto A, Dufau ML. 1996. The genomic structure of the corticortropin releasing factor receptor. *J. Biol. Chem.* 271:14519–25

121. Tsai-Morris CH, Buczko E, Wang W, Dufau ML. 1990. Intronic nature of the rat luteininzing hormone receptor gene defines a soluble receptor subspecies with hormone binding activity. *J. Biol. Chem.* 265:19385–88

122. Tsai-Morris CH, Buczko E, Wang W, Xie XZ, Dufau ML. 1991. Structural organization of the rat luteinizing hormone (LH) receptor gene. *J. Biol. Chem.* 266:11355–59

123. Tsai-Morris CH, Geng Y, Buczko E, Dufau ML. 1995. Characterization of diverse functional elements in the upstream Sp1 domain of the rat luteinizing hormone receptor gene promoter. *J. Biol. Chem.* 270:7487–94

124. Tsai-Morris CH, Geng Y, Xie XZ, Buczko E, Dufau ML. 1994. Transcriptional protein binding domains governing basal expression of the rat luteinizing hormone receptor gene. *J. Biol. Chem.* 269:15868–75

125. Tsai-Morris CH, Wei W, Buczko E.

1993. Promoter and regulatory regions of the rat luteinizing hormone receptor gene. *J. Biol. Chem.* 268:18267–71

126. Tsuruhara T, Dufau ML, Hichman J, Catt KJ. 1972. Biological properties of hCG after removal of terminal sialic acid and galactose residues. *Endocrinology* 91:296–302

127. Tsuruhara T, Van Hall E, Dufau ML, Catt KJ. 1972. Ovarian binding of intact and desialylated hCG in vivo and in vitro. *Endocrinology* 91:463–69

127a. Varrault A, Nguyen DL, McClue S, Harris B, Jouin P, et al. 1994. 5-Hydroxytryptamine 1A receptor synthetic peptides J. *Biol. Chem.* 269: 16720–25

128. Vlase H, Matsuoka N, Graves PN, Magmulsson RP, Davies TF. 1997. Folding-dependent binding of thyrotropin (TSH) and TSH receptor autoantibodies to the murine TSH receptor ectodomain. *Endocrinology* 138:1658–66

128a. VuHai-Luu Thi MT, Misrahi M, Houllier A, Jolivet A, Milgrom E. 1992. Variant forms of the pig lutropin/choriogonadotropin receptor. *Biochemistry* 31: 8377–83

129. Wang H, Nelson S, Ascoli M, Segaloff DL. 1992 The 5′ flanking region of the rat lutropin/choriogonadotropin receptor gene confers Leydig cell expression and negative regulation of gene transcription by cAMP. *Mol. Endocrinol.* 6:320–26

130. Wang Z, Liu X, Ascoli M. 1997. Phosphorylation of the lutropin choriogonadotropin receptor facilitates uncoupling of the receptor from adenylate cyclase and endocytosis of bound hormone. *Mol. Endocrinol.* 11:183–92

131. Wang Z, Wang H, Ascoli M. 1993. Mutation of highly conserved acidic residue present in the second intracellular loop of G-protein-coupled receptors does not impair hormone binding or signal transduction of the luteinizing hormone chorionic gonadotropin receptor. *Mol. Endocrinol.* 7:85–93

132. Wong SKF, Slaughter C, Ruoho AE, Ross EM. 1990. Chimeric muscarinic cholinergic: β-adrenergic receptor that activate G_s in response to muscarinic agonists. *J. Biol. Chem.* 265:6219–24

133. Wu H, Lustbader JW, Liu Y, Canfield RE, Hendrickson WA. 1994. Structure of human chorionic gonadotropin at 2.6 Å resolution from MAD analysis of the selenomethionyl protein. *Structure* 2:545–58

134. Xia H, Chen F, Puett D. 1994. A region in the human glycoprotein hormone alpha-subunit important in holoprotein formation and receptor binding. *Endocrinology* 134:1768–70

135. Xie YB, Wang H, Segaloff DL. 1990. Extracellular domain of lutropin/choriogonadotropin receptor expressed in transfected cells binds choriogonadotropin with high affinity. *J. Biol. Chem.* 265:21411–14

136. Yano K, Hidaka A, Saji M, Polymeropoulos MH, Okuno A, et al. 1994. A sporadic case of male limited precocious puberty has the same constitutively activating point mutation in luteinizing hormone/choriogonadotropin receptor gene as familial cases. *J. Clin. Endocrinol. Metab.* 79:1818–23

137. Yoshimura M, Hershman M. 1995. Thyrotropic action of human chorionic gonadotropin. *Thyroid* 5:425–34

138. Zhang FP, Hamalainen T, Kaipia A, Pakarinen P, Huhtaniemi I. 1994. Ontogeny of luteinizing hormone receptor gene expression in the rat testis. *Endocrinology* 134:2206–13

139. Zhang R, Buczko E, Dufau ML. 1996. Requirement of cysteine residues in exons 1 to 6 of the extracellular domain of the luteinizing hormone receptor for gonadotropin binding. *J. Biol. Chem.* 271:5755–60

140. Zhang R, Cai H, Fatima N, Buczko E, Dufau ML. 1995. Functional glycosylation sites for the rat luteinizing hormone receptor required for ligand binding. *J. Biol. Chem.* 270:21722–28

141. Zhang R, Tsai-Morris CH, Kitamura M, Buczko E, Dufau ML. 1991. Changes in binding activity of luteinizing hormone receptors by site directed mutagenesis of potential glycosylation sites. *Biochem. Biophys. Res. Commun.* 181:804–8

142. Zhu X, Guderman T, Birnbaumer M, Birnbaumer LH. 1993. A luteinizing hormone receptor with a severely truncated cytoplasmic tail (LHR-ct628) desensitizes to the same degree as the full length receptor. *J. Biol. Chem.* 268: 1723–28

143. Zhu Z, Wang H, Ascoli A. 1995. The lutropin/choriogonadotropin receptor is palmitoylated at intracellular cysteine residues. *Mol. Endocrinol.* 9:141–50

144. Zipf WB, Wukie JJ. 1983. Role of prolactin and growth hormone in the maintenance of normal Leydig cell function. In *Male Reproduction and Fertility*, ed. A Negro-Vilar, pp. 65–73. New York: Raven

Annu. Rev. Physiol. 1998. 60:497–523

SEX IN THE 90s: *SRY* and the Switch to the Male Pathway

Blanche Capel

Department of Cell Biology, Duke University Medical Center, Durham, North Carolina 27710; e-mail: B.Capel@cellbio.duke.edu

KEY WORDS: mammalian sex determination, testis organogenesis, HMG proteins, *SOX9*, *DAX1*

ABSTRACT

In mammals the male sex determination switch is controlled by a single gene on the Y chromosome, *SRY*. *SRY* encodes a protein with an HMG-like DNA-binding domain, which probably acts as a local organizer of chromatin structure. It is believed to regulate downstream genes in the sex determination cascade, although no direct targets of SRY are clearly known. More genes in the pathway have been isolated through mutation approaches in mouse and human. At least three genes, *SRY* itself, *SOX9*, and *DAX1*, are dosage sensitive, providing molecular evidence that the sex determination step operates at a critical threshold. *SRY* initiates development of a testis from the bipotential cells of the early gonad. The dimorphic male and female pathways present a rare opportunity to link a pivotal gene in development with morphogenetic mechanisms that operate to pattern an organ and the differentiation of its cells. Mechanisms of testis organogenesis triggered downstream of *SRY* include pathways of cell signaling controlling cell reorganization, cell proliferation, cell migration, and vascularization.

INTRODUCTION

Sex determination in different species can occur by a number of different mechanisms (reviewed by 12). Some species have an identical genetic makeup between the sexes and depend on external signals to control their sexual phenotypes, i.e. environmental sex determination (ESD). For example, in some fish sexual phenotype can be labile in adult life and is controlled by group dynamics that include hormonal and/or visual signals (40). In many reptiles (alligators and turtles), the sexual phenotype depends on the incubation temperature of the

497

embryo (116). In other species, chromosomal differences between the sexes provide an internal means of regulating sex determination. In this latter group, sex determination can be controlled by dosage-dependent mechanisms (DSD) or by the presence of a dominant gene (GSD), often on a heterogametic chromosome. Both *Drosophila* and *Caenorhabditis elegans* depend on a DSD system. In both cases the sex determination switch is controlled by the ratio of X chromosomes to autosomes. Although *Drosophila* has a Y chromosome, it is irrelevant for sex determination because XO individuals are male and XXY individuals are female.

Eutherian mammals belong to the GSD group: Females carry two X chromosomes, and males carry a single X chromosome and one Y chromosome that encodes a dominant gene that triggers male sex determination. Sexual development in mammals has been described as a three-step process: At the first step the genetic sex of the embryo is decided when the oocyte is fertilized by an X- or a Y-bearing sperm. In the second step, sex determination occurs when the fate of the bipotential gonad is determined by the expression of the Y-linked genic switch in the XY embryos. In the third step, male or female differentiation results from the hormonal secretions of the developing testis or ovary (108).

For most developmental processes, molecular information gained from work in non-vertebrate systems has been extremely valuable in rapidly advancing the field. Sex determination pathways in *Drosophila* and *Caenorhabditis elegans* have been worked out in molecular detail (23, 67, 113). In both organisms, the sex determination and dosage compensation pathways are linked, and many of the genes and proteins are known. However, no homology exists between these two systems or with any elements defined in vertebrate pathways, suggesting that the mechanisms for sex determination have evolved independently many times. This finding stands in sharp contrast to most other developmental pathways; for example, the homeobox gene control of body axis formation, where the proteins involved bear a high degree of homology from flies to mammals (48, 98). For this reason, work on *Drosophila* and *C. elegans* thus far has not shed much light on the mammalian sex determination system.

The existence of common primordia for alternative pathways of sexual development is an ancient and widespread phenomena in the animal kingdom (94). Furthermore, basic testis and ovary structure and function are similar in many vertebrates, suggesting that the basic pathways involved in building a testis or an ovary are conserved. It may be the proximal switch mechanisms that have evolved independently, giving rise to systems controlled primarily by temperature, hormones, dosage, or dominant genes, depending on differing developmental circumstances of the animals. Fish and other animals that live in water can rely on diffusion of chemical cues and presumably benefit from the ability to switch sex in adult life, depending on the optimal survival requirements of the group. Among lizards and turtles, instances of temperature-dependent and genotypic sex determination have been documented (26). Some evolutionary biologists suggest that the genic switch on the mammalian Y chromosome has been superimposed on older systems of sex determination that were primarily temperature or hormone based (26, 147). Mammals, after all, cannot rely on environmental cues for dimorphic development, either hormone or temperature based, because they develop within a temperature-controlled uterine environment, bathed in maternal hormones.

This maternal hormone environment may explain why the fundamental developmental pathway in mammals is female. Jost showed that surgical removal of the gonads during embryonic development of the rabbit resulted in development of female sexual characteristics no matter what the chromosomal sex of the embryo (79). Mainly because of this experiment, the female developmental pathway has often been referred to as the default pathway, although this terminology may be misleading because it suggests that the female pathway is not an active, genetically controlled process. Jost's experiments demonstrated that male secondary sexual differentiation depends on the presence of a testis in eutherian mammals. Hormones produced and exported by the developing testis are responsible for differentiation of the male urogenital tract and all male secondary sex characteristics. In the absence of the dominant gene on the Y chromosome, the basic cascade of gene expression in the embryo leads to the development of an ovary from the bipotential gonad and consequent development of female secondary sex characteristics. So far, no ovary-determining genes have been clearly identified in this pathway, although they must exist. Indeed, some investigators argue that the male sex-determining gene may function to repress the female pathway (53, 78, 95).

In 1959, the Y chromosome in mammals was shown to carry a dominant genetic determinant, such that 48:XXXY individuals are male and XO individuals are female (37, 74, 143). Through the work of cytogeneticists, who linked the presence or absence of a testis to Y chromosome translocations, rearrangements, or deletions, the minimal portion of the Y chromosome required to specify maleness was successively narrowed down (reviewed in 46, 57). In 1990, the gene from the sex-determining region of the Y chromosome was isolated in human (SRY)[1] and mouse (Sry) and shown to be conserved on the Y chromosome of all mammals so far tested (52, 126). Sry is both necessary and sufficient to trigger male development. Mutations of this gene in humans, or deletion of this single gene from the Y chromosome in mice (Y^{Tdym1}) (54, 89), lead to female development. Conversely, the presence of this gene in

---

[1] In accordance with convention, throughout this review SRY will be used to refer to the gene from humans and other animals whereas Sry will be used to refer to the gene from mouse. SRY will refer to the protein in all species.

Sry transgenic mice on an XX background leads to the initiation of testis development and complete sex reversal (33, 83). It is believed that the expression of *Sry* in XY embryos interrupts development along the ovarian pathway and initiates a pattern of testis development in the bipotential gonad (87, 88, 100).

As in flies and worms, chromosomal differences between the sexes in mammals require gene dosage regulation. Dosage inequalities that result from the heterogametic system in mammals are resolved by the process of X-inactivation, which silences expression of most genes from one of the X chromosomes in XX individuals (4). It has been widely, but not universally, believed that X-inactivation and sex determination are independent processes in mammals (20). However, there is evidence in marsupials that the dosage of the X chromosome controls the differentiation of some dimorphic secondary sex characteristics (123), and there is also good evidence that dosage of a gene on the X chromosome is linked to sex determination in eutherian mammals (for review, see 111).

This review focuses on mammalian sex determination in mouse and human. Although *Sry* is often referred to as the mammalian sex determination gene, this is true only in the sense that *Sry* is the single Y-linked gene both necessary and sufficient to initiate male development. *Sry* operates as a molecular switch; however, it is clear that there are many critical genes required in both the male and female sex-determining pathways. Much of the recent progress in the field has related to *Sry* partly because it provides a unique and valuable access point for dissection of the sex determination pathway. Below, I summarize what is currently understood about the *Sry* gene, its transcript, and its protein. Other genes in the gonadogenesis/sex determination pathway discovered through expression and mutation approaches are described. Cell biology of the testis and the mechanisms operating downstream of *Sry* that trigger the testis developmental pathway in the bipotential gonad are also discussed.

SRY EXPRESSION

Linear Versus Circular Transcripts

Sry is expressed in the mouse gonad, in a narrow window of time between 10.5 and 12.0 days post-coital (dpc), immediately before the divergence of ovarian and testicular development is apparent, as the cells of the XY gonad organize into testis cords. Expression of *Sry* is limited to the gonadal portion of the urogenital ridge (ugr) from 10.5 to 12.0 dpc, as shown by in situ hybridization (84; A Swain & R Lovell-Badge, unpublished observations), polymerase chain reaction (76), and RNase protection techniques (55). Because of the low level of *Sry* expression, the gonadal transcript is undetectable on Northern blots. *Sry* expression has been analyzed only in the mouse during the critical period of gonadogenesis. RNase protection assays reveal that the mouse ugr *Sry* transcript is distinct. It initiates at a promoter specific to the ugr, and it includes

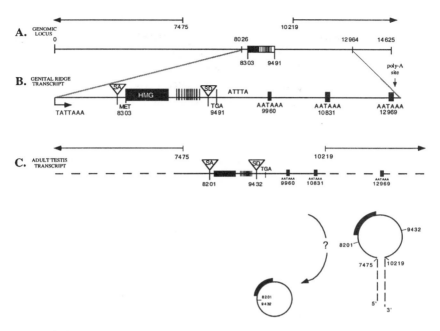

Figure 1   Structure of the mouse *Sry* transcript. *A.* Diagram of the Sry locus. The *Sry* gene sequence lies within a large inverted repeat that extends more than 15 kb on either side. *B.* The specific ugr transcript. The ugr transcript initiates at a gonad-specific promoter located inside the 5′ arm of the inverted repeat. RNAase protection mapping shows that it extends as a single 5 kb exon, passing two potential poly-A sites, and terminating at the third. This transcript includes ≈1.2 kb of coding region plus 3.5 kb of 3′ UTR. *C.* Primary and circular testis transcripts. The prominent adult testis transcript is a 1.2 kb circular RNA. RNAase protection analysis reveals a large minor transcript extending into the inverted repeat sequence at the 5′ and 3′ ends of the mouse *Sry* locus (*dashed lines*). The mechanism by which the circular transcript forms is not well understood, although it might arise as the result of an attack of a 3′ splice donor (SD) against a 5′ splice acceptor (SA). This event could be mediated by pairing between the homologous tails of the transcript.

3.5 kilobases of 3′ untranslated sequence not present in transcripts reported in other tissues (Figure 1) (55).

In the adult mouse testis (and in some other heterologous sites), the *Sry* transcript is circular and probably results from cleavage of a larger primary transcript present at very low levels. The primary transcript is initiated at an unidentified promoter >1 kb 5′ of the specific ugr promoter and continues beyond the ugr polyadenylation site (55) (Figure 1). The mouse *Sry* gene lies within a large inverted repeat extending more than 15 kb on either side of the unique coding region (54). The long primary transcript found in adult testis encodes homologous arms of this inverted repeat that could give rise to a secondary structure capable of splicing to generate a circular transcript (18). In mouse, the circular transcript may be a consequence of the chromosomal situation of the gene. Experiments have shown that as few as 400 base pairs of the inverted repeats are sufficient for circularization of the *Sry* transcript in transfected COS cells (29). The circular RNA is thought not to be translated because it is not associated with polysomes (18). No inverted repeat surrounds the human *SRY* gene, and the circular transcript has not been found in humans or other mammals so far. If circularization is one means of disabling the *Sry* transcript when necessary, other species must disable the *Sry* transcript by other means.

No function has been assigned to the circular transcript through genetic analysis. It is expressed primarily in germ cells in the adult testis; however, no cell-autonomous effect on sperm development has been observed in mutants. The original XY-XY^{Tdym1} mosaic male transmitted its Y^{Tdym1} chromosome deleted for the *Sry* locus normally (54, 89). Similarly in humans, a mosaic father transmitted a mutant *SRY* allele containing a premature termination codon to two XY daughters (1, 62). In both cases, the mutant sperm developed normally in the absence of a functional *SRY* gene. However, it is possible that neighboring sperm with a normal *SRY* gene, developing in the same mosaic testis, compensated for the loss of a functional SRY protein in some cells.

The specific ugr transcription initiation site eliminates the 5' end of the inverted repeat present in transcripts in adult testes and other heterologous cell types (55). This may account for the absence of the circular transcript in the fetal gonad. The 3' region of the ugr transcript may also contain regulatory information. Detailed RNAase protection studies have defined a 3.5 kb untranslated region (UTR), 3' of the open reading frame (ORF) in the mouse ugr transcript (55). It seems likely that the UTR is involved in mediating post-transcriptional control: stability of the transcript, splicing, and/or translation. Regulation of *Sry* at the post-transcriptional, translational, and post-translational levels probably requires other interactive proteins. Cell lines derived from the genital ridge (where *Sry* is normally expressed and functional) have been established for in vitro studies of the regulation of *Sry* and of its interactions with other proteins normally expressed at the same time and in the same cell type (16).

Because human fetal tissue is not easily available, detailed analysis of the *SRY* transcript in humans is based largely on the testis transcript and transcripts generated in heterologous cell types in culture. Whether the human ugr transcript is different outside the ORF is unknown. The ORF of both mouse and human transcripts is encoded within a single exon common to the testis and ugr transcripts, and there is evidence that splicing does not occur within this ORF (22). *SRY* mRNA expression in humans (22) and in some other mammals occurs over a longer time period than the ≈40 h window of expression during mouse gonadogenesis (55). This gene is expressed in tissues other than those of the gonad and testis in marsupial, human, and mouse (22, 59, 151), but no role has been ascribed to expression of *Sry/SRY* in other tissues. For example, in humans with mutations in *SRY*, no defects other than sex reversal have been described (121). In the absence of detailed antibody studies, it is not known whether expression of the protein parallels expression of the transcript in any species. Controls of translation and nuclear localization may exist.

Regulation of the Level of the Sry Transcript

The transcriptional regulation of *Sry* is still uncharacterized, although efforts to define the limits of the 5' regulatory region are under way in transgenic animals. Several problems have impeded progress of these experiments. For instance, efforts to devise a transcriptional reporter construct [e.g. with varying amounts of Sry 5' sequence driving β-galactosidase (β-gal)] have not been successful (V Navarez & R Lovell-Badge, personal communication); thus the efficacy of the transgene has relied on assays of sex reversal in transgenic animals. An in vitro assay for *Sry* expression would be valuable for defining the regulatory elements of the gene. *Sry* has been expressed from exogenous promoters in cell lines but has not yet been expressed from its own promoter sequences.

From transgenic studies where *Sry* is activated normally in a genetic female, it is assumed that all upstream genes required for activation are present on an XX genetic background. Several genes have been identified that appear to act upstream of gonad formation in both sexes, but none has been directly linked to activation of *Sry*. Based on the loss of gonads in null mutant mice, steroidogenic factor 1 (*Sf1*), the Wilms' tumor gene (*Wt1*), and two homeobox genes, *Lim1* (also known as *Lmx1*) and *Emx2*, all appear to be required for genital ridge development. In *Sf1*$^{-/-}$ mutant mice, initial steps in gonad formation occur, but between 11.5 and 12.5 dpc the gonadal primordium regresses by apoptosis (90). *Sry* is still expressed in *Sf1*$^{-/-}$ mutants (B Capel, unpublished results), showing that SF1 is not required for the transcriptional activation of *Sry*. In *Wt1*$^{-/-}$ mutants, the genital ridge also forms initially, but thickening of the coelomic epithelium does not occur; by 14.5 dpc, no remnant of the gonad remains (85). At present, *Wt1* is not a likely candidate for an activation factor for *Sry* (P Koopman, personal communication). Most *Lim1*$^{-/-}$ embryos die before gonad development begins (124). In the few *Lim1*$^{-/-}$ mice that survive to birth, both gonads and kidneys are missing, but it is not known whether they never formed or regressed as in *Sf1*$^{-/-}$ and *Wt1*$^{-/-}$ mutants (R Behringer, personal communication). In *Emx2*$^{-/-}$ mutant mice, development of the gonad becomes aberrant after 11.5 dpc. Regression of the gonad may be a result of defects in proliferation, differentiation, and/or survival of mesonephric or gonadal cells (104).

Many experiments suggest that the level of *Sry* expression is at a critical threshold for sex determination and thus is highly sensitive to dosage effects.

For example, in mutants in which regions of the Y chromosome between *Sry* and the centromere are deleted (*Sry*[del]), the expression of *Sry* is depressed, resulting in mice that are sex reversed (17). In *Sry* transgenics, the level of *Sry* expression correlates with the frequency of sex reversal in different strains (A Hacker, N Vivian & R Lovell-Badge, unpublished results). Recent results in other sex-reversed mice also support this view (see below; C Nagamine, unpublished results). In humans, 10 to 20% of all 46 XY females harbor a mutation in *SRY* (15). De novo mutations in *SRY* almost always result in a complete failure of testicular differentiation and unambiguous female development, but in some families the unaffected father harbors the same mutation as the XY daughters. Several explanations for this finding include gonadal mosaicism in the father and variable penetrance of the mutation. Because the timing and expression level of *Sry* is critical in mouse, it is possible that these conditional sex reversal cases result from variable genetic backgrounds affecting the level of *SRY* expression in humans (15). A case of partial sex reversal has been found associated with deletion of sequences 3′ of the *SRY* ORF. This deletion has been postulated also to affect the level of *SRY* expression (96).

THE SRY PROTEIN

Sry Encodes a Protein with a Conserved High Mobility Group (HMG) Box DNA-Binding Domain

Sry encodes a protein with an HMG box DNA-binding domain that is believed to regulate transcription of downstream genes (58, 88, 126). The HMG box region of *Sry* is highly conserved across all mammalian species sequenced. Mutations found within the DNA-binding domain of the human *SRY*, in cases of XY sex reversal, provide strong evidence that *SRY* is the sex-determining gene (58, 62–65). Many mutations have now been described in sex-reversed males within the HMG box of human *SRY* (Figure 2) (15, 63) and one located 5′ of the ORF (97). No polymorphisms have been found in the HMG domain of normal males (15).

SRY sequences outside the HMG-binding domain bear little homology between species, either at the nucleotide or amino acid levels. For example, the glutamine-rich repeat region located 3′ of the HMG box in the mouse protein is absent in human *SRY*. Activation of a target reporter gene in assays performed in heterologous cell types was shown to depend on the presence of the glutamine repeat sequence. The human protein did not activate the target in this assay (30). One possibility is that additional proteins associate with the human protein and serve as activator or repressor domains at binding sites. *SRY* may act as a repressor, an activator, or both in vivo, and its activity could be determined by a combinatorial complex at the binding site (82, 88).

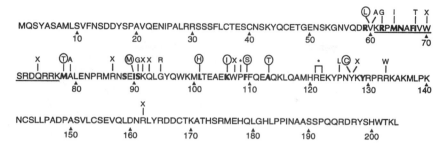

Figure 2   Amino acid sequence of the human SRY protein. Known mutations leading to amino acid changes causing 46:XY male to female sex reversal are indicated. *Asterisks* represent 1 or 4 bp deletions resulting in frameshifts. Mutations expected to destabilize the protein structure are *circled*; amino acids that contact the DNA appear in **bold**. The nuclear localization signal is underlined.

The regions of *Sry* outside the DNA-binding domain evolved rapidly (136, 137, 146), a process that might tune SRY for interactions with other proteins. This finding has led to the hypothesis that the rapid evolution of *Sry* may contribute to speciation (146). However, recent data reveal little variation between species in marsupial *Sry* sequences outside the HMG box DNA-binding region, indicating that speciation is not necessarily associated with divergence of *Sry* sequences (50). The rapid evolution of these sequences could also reflect few sequence-specific restraints on these regions, coupled with the location of *Sry* on the Y chromosome, which, lacking a pairing partner, is known to evolve rapidly.

A screen of an 8.5 dpc embryonic mouse cDNA library, using the *Sry* HMG domain as a probe, produced a number of *Sry*-related HMG box–containing *SOX* genes, members of a large family of genes all related through >60% homology in the HMG DNA-binding domain (25). So far, they all recognize and bind to the same DNA target sequence in site-selection assays in vitro, albeit with some differences in affinity (28). These proteins probably play highly specific roles in development. Their specificity likely depends on limited expression in specific cell types, nuclear localization, and interaction with different protein partners required for their activities as regulators. Efforts are under way to produce chimeric proteins between different SOX proteins and between SOX proteins and *Sry* to determine which regions of *SOX* genes regulate the specificity of transcriptional activation (V Harley, E Eicher & R Lovell-Badge, personal communications).

SRY Is Thought to Be Localized in the Nucleus, Where It Binds and Bends DNA

An antibody that detects nuclear localization of the human SRY protein has been reported. Nuclear localization is dependent on the presence of a nuclear localization signal in the HMG domain (118). Efforts to obtain antibodies against mouse SRY have been unsuccessful; therefore, it has not been possible to study SRY protein localization during development. Entry into the nucleus may be a further level of regulation of SRY activity: Nuclear localization signals might be masked by regulatory proteins, limiting the access of HMG proteins to the nucleus under some conditions. Other SOX proteins also contain nuclear localization sequences (131). SOX9 is expressed in both male and female gonadal cells; however, soon after Sry expression begins in the male, SOX9 is transported to the nucleus of pre-Sertoli cells as their differentiation process initiates (27).

The HMG proteins, originally isolated as a heterogeneous group of non-histone components of the nucleosome complex (47), all contained a DNA-binding domain that became known as the HMG box. SRY and the SOX proteins contain the HMG-binding domain; however, they belong to a subset of the HMG proteins that display site-specific DNA-binding properties. Like other site-specific HMG proteins, they bind the minor groove of the DNA helix. They recognize bent or pre-structured DNA, and they bind linear DNA and induce a bend when they bind (36). Most data suggest that the SOX proteins and SRY function as local organizers of chromatin structure, rather than as classic activators or repressors (117). It is thought that HMG proteins play an architectural role in facilitating the assembly of nucleoprotein complexes at the target site (51). Studies of another HMG family member, LEF1, suggest that the bend induced in DNA may juxtapose other transcription factors bound at distant sites, resulting in the activation or repression of transcription of a target gene (43).

Comparisons of normal SRY and mutant SRY proteins from humans with 46 XY sex reversal in in vitro binding assays have distinguished mutations that affect DNA binding or bending properties (58). Molecular modeling of the interaction of SRY with chromatin has identified amino acids important to the structural stability of the protein and those involved in critical contact points with DNA (144) (Figures 2 and 3). Many of the mutations identified in XY sex-reversed individuals fall into one of these categories.

The HMG family member LEF1 interacts with β-catenin, a protein with a well-defined role linking the cytoskeleton with adhesion junctions. Interaction between β-catenin and LEF1 results in the nuclear localization of the complex and the activation of downstream targets of LEF1 (6, 68). Expression patterns and deficiencies in $Lef1^{-/-}$ mice both suggest a functional role for LEF1 in tissues undergoing mesenchymal/epithelial inductions (140). It is often the case that cells embarking on a new transcriptional differentiation program also change cell shape and associations with other cells. The interaction of β-catenin, a cell structural protein, with an HMG protein known to regulate

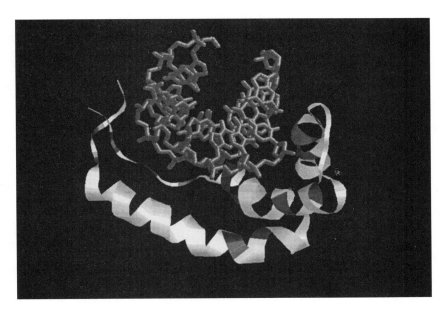

Figure 3   The HMG box of SRY bound to the DNA sequence 5′ dGTTTGTGC. *Light areas* indicate three α helices of the SRY HMG box. Studies of human sex reversal (XY females) have implicated mutations affecting the residues highlighted in *gray*. Most of these mutations affect residues that contact the DNA (144). The image was rendered by C Mitchell & V Harley using RasMol2.6 (120). Molecular coordinates are from the Brookhaven Protein Data Base.

transcription provides a molecular link between cell shape changes and control of transcription. Given its role in cytoskeletal structure, β-catenin could be recruited to the nucleus to play some role in establishing and stabilizing chromatin domain structure induced by HMG proteins. It is not yet known whether this paradigm can be extended from LEF1 to other HMG proteins. Association between SRY (or any other SOX protein) and β-catenin has not been reported.

Specific Downstream Targets of SRY Have Been Difficult to Identify

One problem in identifying downstream targets of SRY is that no in vitro cell culture system has been available for conducting the assays. The battery of interacting proteins involved in regulating SRY and downstream targets may be present only in the cells in which *Sry* is natively expressed. Although this missing co-factor hypothesis seems likely, and has precedents in related pathways (125), it is also possible that SRY action is more global than gene specific. For example, if SRY establishes expression domains in chromatin, it may not activate a classical promoter construct in transfection assays. It is also possible that the right pathway has not been tested.

An approach to finding genes downstream of *Sry* is to identify early differences in expression between male and female gonads using differential screens. This approach has revealed differences, but genes isolated from these screens are frequently abundantly expressed [e.g. α-globin and 3-β-hydrosteroid dehydrogenase (3-β-HSD)] (109; B Capel, unpublished data) and not particularly informative. Apart from differences in the expression of enzymatic steroid pathways, several early differences in expression between male and female gonads have been characterized downstream of *Sry* in the genes *Amh* (55, 105), *Sf1* (70), *Desert hedgehog* (*Dhh*) (10), and *Bmp8* (150).

Anti-Müllerian Hormone (AMH), otherwise known as Müllerian-inhibiting substance (MIS), is expressed by Sertoli cells and is an important factor in male differentiation; however, it is not required for testis formation. In the $Amh^{-/-}$ mouse, Müllerian ducts persist, which leads to infertility due to ductal defects; however, testis development occurs normally (7, 8). SRY induces expression of *AMH*, but *AMH* is unlikely to be a direct binding target of SRY because mutation of the SRY-binding site 5′ of *AMH* does not affect activation (56). However, this result could be explained if SRY promoted assembly of an activation complex at the *AMH* promoter, even if binding affinity were reduced by the mutation (145).

Differences in the expression of *Sf1* have been reported between male and female gonads after 12.5 dpc (70, 91). In addition to its role in the early formation of the gonad, SF1 acts at later stages of testis development to control androgen synthesis pathways in Leydig cells and to activate *AMH* in Sertoli cells (125). It may also have other roles in Sertoli cell differentiation that are critical to testis formation. A conditional $Sf1^{-/-}$ mouse would be required to address this point since the early loss of the gonad in the null mutant precludes examination of later steps in testis development. This is also true for *Wt1*, which may also have a second role in testis development based on human mutations that lead to gonadal abnormalities (see below).

Desert hedgehog (*Dhh*) and *Patched* (*Ptc*) expression are involved in signaling pathways between Sertoli and germ cells (10), and *Bmp8* is also required within the testis for proper regulation of spermatogenesis (150). Although all three genes show expression differences between male and female gonads, neither *Dhh* nor *Bmp8* is required for testis morphogenesis because the testis develops normally in both deletion mutants. SRY also activates *Fra1* in vitro (24), but *Fra1* is not expressed at the appropriate developmental time in the mouse gonad, thus excluding a role for *Fra1* in sex determination (77) and illustrating the hazards of relying on data obtained in heterologous cell types.

MUTATIONS AFFECTING SEX DETERMINATION

Another approach to identify genes in the sex determination cascade is to study naturally occurring mutations known to affect sex determination in mouse and humans (see Table 1).

Mutations That Affect Sex Determination in Mouse

This analysis in mouse has centered on the Y^{POS} effect. The Y^{POS} chromosome functions normally within the *Mus musculus Poschiavinus* strain, but when crossed onto other genetic backgrounds (in particular, C57BL6), this Y chromosome leads to a high incidence of ovotestes or complete sex reversal and has been used as a classic genetic hypomorph to reveal other genes in the pathway

Table 1   Sex-reversal syndromes associated with gonadal dysgenesis

	Chromosome	Gene
Mouse		
Y^{POS}	Y	Sry
T^{Orl} (deletion)/Y^{AKR}	17/Y	Brachyury (+/−)
T^{hp} (deletion)/Y^{AKR}	17/Y	Brachyury (+/−)
W^{19H}, W^e	5	c-Kit
Sl^d	10	Mgf^{Sl-d}
Tda1	2 ctr	?
Tda2	4 dist	?
Tda3	5 ctr	?
XY^{Tdym1}	Y	Sry
XY^{del}	Y	?
Human		
XY gonadal dysgenesis	Y (+?)	~15% SRY
DSS, duplication	Xp21	DAX1
Campomelic dysplasia	17q	SOX9
Denys-Drash	11p	WT1
Frasier	11p	WT1
Deletions	9pter	?
Deletions	10qter	?
Short-rib polydactyly type IV	?	?
X-linked alpha thallasemia/ mental retardation (ATR-X)	Xq13	XH2
Smith-Lemli-Opitz	7q32.1 (?)	?

Most entries are self-explanatory. T^{Orl} and T^{hp} are both deletions in the *Brachury* region of chromosome 17 (more than one gene may be deleted). Effects are revealed in association with a Y chromosome from the AKR strain. XY^{del} are a set of deletions of repeat sequences between *Sry* and the centromere that affect *Sry* expression. XY gonadal dysgenesis is a complex set of syndromes of which ~15% are associated with mutations in the HMG domain of *SRY*.

(34). These data implicate testis-determining autosomal (*Tda*) loci, termed *Tda1, Tda2, Tda3*, etc, that affect sex determination. Backcross mapping has shown a high correlation of sex reversal with chromosomes 2, 4, and perhaps 5 (35).

Levels of *Sry* expression have been examined in a variant of this allele: The Y^{TIR} allele: The level of *Sry* expression is depressed in sex-reversed mice carrying this allele and appears to recover near normal in crosses that relieve the effect. This finding suggests that at least part of the Y^{POS} effect is due to a genetic interaction that affects the level of *Sry* expression (C Nagamine, personal communication). One of the interactive loci appears to be a protein involved in the transcriptional regulation or stability of *Sry* RNA. A combined transgenic and comparative sequence approach indicates that this effect does not map to the 5' regulatory region, the coding region of the Y^{POS} *Sry* gene, or the proximal 3' region. By process of elimination, this maps the Y^{POS} effect to the distal 3' region of the gene (K Albrecht & E Eicher, personal communication).

Several other mouse mutations give a high incidence of male-to-female sex reversal revealed by a cross in which the Y chromosome from the AKR/J inbred strain is placed on a C57BL/6J background carrying either of two alleles at the T locus on mouse chromosome 17 (T^{Orl} and T^{hp}) (32, 142), or alleles at the dominant white spotting locus *W(cKit)*, or its ligand *Steel* (13, 19, 107). These cases usually result in ovotestes; however, the basis for sex reversal is not known.

Mutations That Affect Sex Determination in Humans

One gene involved in sex determination identified through a human mutation approach is *SOX9*, which encodes a *SRY*-related HMG box–containing protein. *SOX9* was identified by cloning the chromosomal breakpoints of translocations in patients with campomelic dysplasia, a disabling bone disease associated with a high incidence of male-to-female sex reversal (38, 141). In addition to its role in bone morphogenesis, *Sox9* is closely associated with testis development in mouse, and it may be essential for Sertoli cell differentiation. Expression of the gene is upregulated in the XY gonad soon after expression of *Sry* begins, and expression of *Sox9* is conserved in testis formation in other mammals and in chick (27, 81, 122). Genetic evidence suggests that *SOX9* and *SRY* operate in the same pathway to specify male development because female development is not affected in patients with campomelic dysplasia. Evidence from human mutational analysis indicates that *SOX9* is haplo insufficient. Sequenced mutations are present in a single allele and are predicted to result in loss of function rather than to act as dominant-negative proteins (38). These data suggest that the dosage level of SOX9, SRY, and other proteins in the sex determination pathway is critical for normal male development.

A region of the short arm of the X chromosome, Xp21, can cause male-to-female sex reversal when duplicated or translocated to an autosome. It is postulated that a dosage-sensitive gene, *DSS* (dosage-sensitive sex reversal), encoded in Xp21 can cause female development, even in the presence of a functional copy of *SRY* on the Y chromosome (5, 110).

This finding suggested that the dosage of the X chromosome is important for sex determination in mammals, even though the process normally depends on the dominant action of *SRY*. Because XXY individuals are male, it is assumed that levels of DSS are usually regulated by X chromosome inactivation mechanisms ensuring that XX cells produce a single allele dose. This dosage control is bypassed by duplication within the active X chromosome or translocation of the DSS to an autosome. The usual inactivation of all but one X chromosome in mammalian cells would normally mask any effects resulting from X chromosome dosage differences between males and females.

In eutherian mammals, all secondary sex characteristics are downstream of the development of a testis or ovary and probably depend on hormonal secretions of the developing gonad; however, in marsupials, some sex-specific secondary characteristics develop prior to the development of a testis. An *SRY* gene has been isolated in marsupials that is likely the pivotal testis determination signal (39); however, the initial development of a pouch or a scrotum is believed to be controlled by the ratio of X chromosomes to autosomes (123). This finding implies that several mechanisms of sex determination may be superimposed in mammals. Eutherian mammals and marsupials have evolved a mode of sex determination dependent on a dominant genic determinant present on the Y chromosome. However, marsupials appear to have retained a partial dependence on the X:autosome ratio. It could be that a dosage mechanism underlies genic sex determination in eutherian mammals as well but is normally masked by X inactivation that controls the dosage of the X-linked determinant. In males, the single X chromosome was originally thought not to be inactivated, but a recent report indicates that some somatic cells of the testis do inactivate their X chromosome during critical stages of testis determination (75). These data suggest a different model in which inactivation of the single X chromosome in Sertoli cell precursors permits the testis-determining gene *SRY* to initiate the male pathway.

An X-linked gene, *DAX1* (DSS-AHC critical region on the *X* gene *1*), has been isolated from the interval Xp21. Although several other genes are present in this interval, *DAX1* is the leading candidate for the gene responsible for dosage-sensitive sex reversal syndrome (106, 148, 149). Mutations in *DAX1* lead to adrenal hypoplasia. Expression of *Dax1* in the mouse gonad is also consistent with a role in sex determination: Expression is coincident with *Sry* expression at 11.5 dpc, it continues in the ovary, but turns off in testis after the initiation of cord development about 12.0 dpc (132). *Dax1* and *Sf1*, both of which encode orphan nuclear receptors, might act in a common pathway of endocrine development since their expression co-localizes in multiple cell lineages (71, 73). Similar to *Sf1*, *Dax1* may act at more than one stage of development. At the bifurcation of the developmental pathways of ovary and testis, *DSS* probably acts either as a dosage-sensitive competitor of the male pathway or as an initiator of the female pathway. One might have predicted that *DSS* would be conserved on the X chromosome of all mammals, although this is not a requisite for dosage control. In marsupials and monotremes, the entire syntenic cluster in Xp21, including *DAX1*, is located on an autosome and is probably not part of the ancient X chromosome (50). Efforts to overexpress *Dax1* in transgenic mice to determine whether an increased dose of the gene can trigger female development of an XY embryo are under way (A Swain & R Lovell-Badge, personal communication).

Sox3, the SOX gene most closely related to *Sry* itself, maps to a region of the X chromosome believed to be part of the original X chromosome shared by all mammals. It has been suggested that the SOX3 gene was originally present on the X and Y chromosomes, but the Y-linked allele *SRY*, once isolated from recombination, evolved rapidly (25, 50). Because all the *Sry*-related SOX genes recognize the same DNA-binding target sequence in vitro, it has been speculated that SRY could compete with SOX3. If *SRY* gradually evolved away from SOX3, it could acquire a function as a male-determining gene by competing for a binding site and interfering with an ancient X-linked function of SOX3 to initiate the female pathway (49, 69). There is no evidence for this hypothesis.

Sox3 is expressed in early neural tissue and in somatic cells of the developing gonad of both sexes (25). Human mutations in this gene are associated with an X-linked mental retardation syndrome but show no defect in primary testis development. Larger deletions of this region of the X chromosome (Xq26-27) are associated with premature ovarian failure, but there is no reason to believe that *SOX3* is responsible, nor is there any association of *SOX3* with primary ovarian developmental defects (129). Because *Sox3* likely plays a critical role early in embryonic development (M Parsons & R Lovell-Badge, personal communication), a conditional null mutant mouse and/or a mouse overexpressing this gene may be required to resolve this issue.

Two human disorders, Denys-Drash syndrome (DDS) and Frasier syndrome, are associated with genitourinary defects. DDS is due to mutations in the *WT1* gene that include an amino acid substitution affecting a protein-DNA contact point, premature termination of protein translation, or the elimination of a splicing isoform. In each case, the DDS patient is heterozygous for the mutation, suggesting that there is also a critical dosage or dominant-negative effect of this protein in the sex determination pathway (60). For any one of these mutations, there is a wide range of phenotypic variation among DDS patients (21, 60, 114). Frasier syndrome similarly includes a range of genitourinary abnormalities, including chronic renal failure, gonadal dysgenesis, and a high incidence of gonadoblastoma. In five patients diagnosed with Frasier syndrome, mutations were found in the WT1 splice donor site in intron 9; these mutations are predicted to remove the KTS motif between the last two zinc fingers (K McElreavey, personal communication).

Other disorders associated with sex reversal include X-linked alpha thal-lasemia/mental retardation (ATR-X) and Smith-Lemli-Opitz (SLO). ATR-X has been mapped to the *XH2* gene on Xq13 (42, 72, 128). *XH2* is a homologue of a *Drosophila* gene implicated in general transcriptional domain activation (134). SLO has been mapped to 7q32.1, although no candidate gene has been identified (2). This disorder impairs cholesterol biosynthesis (80), perhaps leading to deficiencies in steroid hormone production. The genes responsible for several other human syndromes associated with gonadal dysgenesis are still unknown. Table 1 presents a summary of these findings.

CELL BIOLOGY OF THE DEVELOPING TESTIS

The gonad arises as an identical primordium in male and female embryos. If *Sry* is not expressed, ovarian development is initiated. If a Y chromosome is present, *Sry* is expressed at a critical time in development and acts as a genetic switch to divert development of the undifferentiated gonad from the female to the male pathway. After *Sry* is expressed, the gonad grows in size and the cells reorganize into cord-like structures. In the absence of *Sry* expression, little change in size or cellular organization is apparent. Thus *Sry* apparently triggers mechanisms that lead to the divergence of organ architecture. Based on genetic analysis of XX-XY chimeras, the gene is required only in the supporting cell lineage, which gives rise to the Sertoli cells in the testis (14, 112).

Sry is thought to act as a cell fate determinant in pre-Sertoli cells, which probably recruit other cell types in the developing testis to the male pathway by cell-cell interactions (87, 92). In addition, *Sry* acts as a morphogenetic switch, initiating cell-cell reorganization processes such as extracellular matrix remodeling, cell associations, cell movements, and vascularization. These changes are apparent 12–24 h after *Sry* expression reaches its peak. It is not clear to what extent these two functions of *Sry* are separable, because the full differentiation of Sertoli cells may depend on the structural reorganization of the gonad (31, 66, 135). Differentiation of mammary epithelial cells, for example, requires contact with a laminin subunit normally present in the basal lamina (3, 130).

At least three somatic cell lineages participate in gonadal differentiation in addition to germ cells: the supporting cell lineage (Sertoli cells in the male; follicle (granulosa) cells in the female); the steroid-producing lineage (Leydig cells in the male; theca cells in the female); and connective tissue cells. The primordial germ cells are the only lineage whose origin is clearly established (44, 45); however, they are believed to play no role in determining the structure of the testis (i.e. in organizing the somatic cell lineages). In mutants lacking germ cells, the testis forms normally (99, 103). In females, however, germ cells are required to maintain the follicular structure of the ovary (101, 133).

The supporting and steroidogenic cells are thought to be present in the undifferentiated gonad by 11.5 dpc (102). It is not know whether they are distinct from the earliest stages of gonadogenesis. The expression of SF1 in a population of cells that segregate to the adrenal gland and the gonad during development of the adreno-genital primordium suggests that steroid lineage cells of these two organs originate together (61), but it does not address the issue of whether these cells are precursors of Leydig and Sertoli cells. Sertoli and Leydig cells may arise as a homogeneous population that takes on distinct differentiation characteristics through signaling processes similar to those that occur in other embryonic systems, for example by lateral inhibition signaling (86) or by mesenchymal/epithelial inductive interactions (9). They are distinguished clearly only after cord formation, when Sertoli cells aggregate inside cords and Leydig cells are partitioned to the interstitium. The third somatic cell group is a collection of cell types that comprise the connective tissue cells, about which little is known. These cells include endothelial cells and fibroblasts in both testis and ovary. The peritubular myoid cell, however, is specific to the male gonad, where it directly abuts Sertoli cells, surrounds the testis cords, and separates the Sertoli cells from the steroid-secreting Leydig cells in the interstitial tissue. In contrast, ovarian follicle cells are directly apposed to the steroid-secreting theca cells.

Organ culture experiments suggest that the myoid cells arise from a population of cells that migrate into the genital ridge from the mesonephros after 11.5 dpc. These experiments showed that the placement of a filter membrane between the mesonephros and gonad blocked cord formation (11, 102). The organ culture system has been refined by the use of a transgenic mouse that ubiquitously expresses β-gal (ROSA26) (41). When a mesonephros from a "blue" mouse is placed alongside a gonad from a "white" mouse (wild-type CD1) and cultured in vitro, blue cells move from the mesonephros to the gonad (93). Cell migration from the mesonephros to the gonad is a male-specific mechanism dependent on downstream responses to *Sry* activity within the genital ridge (Figure 4A). Cells can be induced to migrate into a female gonad by placing a small piece of a male gonad against the outside surface of the female gonad, demonstrating that the signal is an active rather than permissive chemoattractant signal. When cells are induced to migrate into a female gonad, cord organization is also induced in the female tissue. The identity of the migrating cell types has been hampered by the absence of markers specific to the early cell lineages of the gonad; however, three migrating cell types have been distinguished.

Many cells that migrate from the mesonephros into the male gonad are associated with the vasculature. Some of these cells can be identified with a marker for endothelial cells, PECAM. Others are closely associated with the endothelial cells and are thought to be a myoepithelial cell type. The physiological

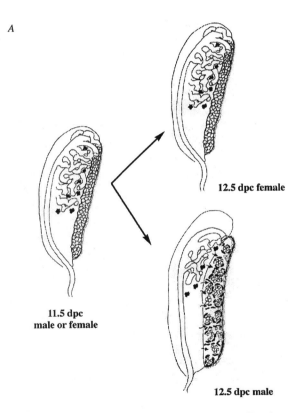

A

12.5 dpc female

**11.5 dpc
male or female**

12.5 dpc male

Figure 4   A. Migrating cells partition the cells in the gonadal primordium into testis cords. At 11.5 dpc, cells competent to respond to a migratory signal exist in the mesonephros of male and female gonads. Between 11.5 and 12.5 dpc, in response to a signal from the XY gonad, cells migrate into a male but not a female gonad. *B*. Models of cellular interactions critical for cord formation. Migrating cells may contribute structural components to the development of the basal lamina surrounding Sertoli cell cords. Alternatively, or additionally, migrating cells may provide lateral signals leading to the differentiation of Sertoli and peritubular myoid cells.

B

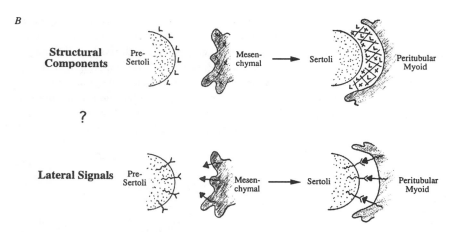

Figure 4   *(Continued)*

significance of this finding is not clear; however, it may be that the vasculature must be fully functional at an earlier stage in the testis than in the ovary. The male gonad is growing more rapidly at this stage, so that oxygen requirements are higher. Alternatively, the testicular vasculature may be required to export testosterone and AMH to masculinize the embryo, whereas the female embryo has no pressing requirement for the export of embryonic estrogens. Whether growth of the vasculature plays an architectural role in the floor plan of the organ is not known. There are no markers for peritubular myoid cells; however, some of the cells migrating into the gonad are located in direct apposition to Sertoli cells, bind the testis cords, and do not label with endothelial-specific markers. Based on work on cells of the adult testis (127, 138), peritubular myoid cells are believed to associate with Sertoli cells and participate in the formation of the testis cords. One possibility is that the arrival of this cell type triggers the polarization of the pre-Sertoli cell, possibly by bringing into the gonad a particular component required for the deposition of the basal lamina (115, 119, 139). Alternatively, or in addition, these cells may provide lateral signals that promote further differentiation of the Sertoli cell and other cell types already present in the gonad (see Figure 4*B*).

SUMMARY

The decision to enter the male developmental pathway in mammals is controlled by *Sry*, the dominant genetic switch on the Y chromosome. Much remains to be learned about the regulation of the *Sry* gene. SRY acts as a DNA-binding protein that probably plays a role in establishing higher-order chromatin structure.

While the direct targets of SRY have not been identified, SRY controls Sertoli cell differentiation and testis morphogenesis in the supporting cells of the gonad. Its activity may involve both activation and repression of downstream targets to divert development from the female pathway. Thus far, at least three genes in the pathway—*SRY, SOX9*, and *DAX1*—have been shown to be dosage sensitive, suggesting that this system is operating at a finely balanced threshold between male and female development. Studies of induced mouse mutations that impair sex determination and identification of human mutations associated with sex reversal have provided insight into the sex determination pathway. Because of the dimorphic nature of the male and female pathways, this system provides a rare opportunity to identify molecular and cellular mechanisms that link the expression of a pivotal gene in development with morphogenetic mechanisms that operate to pattern the development of an organ and the differentiation of its cells. In addition to the intrinsic interest in how mammalian sexual differentiation is controlled, the study will have broad relevance to our understanding of how the formation of organs is genetically controlled.

ACKNOWLEDGMENTS

I gratefully acknowledge support for my research from the March of Dimes grant #FY97-0436, the Tobacco Research Foundation grant #4203R1, and the American Cancer Society grant #DB-78952. I thank many colleagues cited throughout this review for generous permission to report unpublished results. The three-dimensional view of SRY protein interacting with DNA was contributed by Claire Mitchell and Vince Harley. I also thank Andrew Sinclair, Claude Nagamine, Robin Lovell-Badge, and members of my laboratory for critical reading of this manuscript and many helpful suggestions. I am indebted to Jean Wilson for his lucid editorial suggestions.

> Visit the *Annual Reviews home page* at
> http://www.AnnualReviews.org.

Literature Cited

1. Affara NA, Chalmers IJ, Ferguson-Smith MA. 1993. Analysis of the *SRY* gene in 22 sex-reversed XY females identifies four new point mutations in the conserved DNA binding domain. *Hum. Mol. Genet.* 2:785–89
2. Alley T, Scherer S, Huizenga J, Tsui L-C, Wallace M. 1997. Physical mapping of the chromosome 7 breakpoint region in an SLOS patient with t(7;20)(q32.1;q13.2). *Am. J. Med. Genet.* 68:279–81
3. Ashkenas J, Muschler J, Bissell MJ.

1996. The extracellular matrix in epithelial biology: shared molecules and common themes in distant phyla. *Dev. Biol.* 180:433–44
4. Ballabio A, Willard H. 1992. Mammalian X-chromosome inactivation and the *XIST* gene. *Curr. Opin. Genet. Dev.* 2:439–47
5. Bardoni B, Zanaria E, Guioli S, Floridia G, Worley K, et al. 1994. A dosage sensitive locus at chromosome Xp21 is involved in male to female sex reversal. *Nat. Genet.* 7:497–501

6. Behrens J, von Kries J, Kühl M, Bruhn L, Wedlich D, et al. 1996. Functional interaction of β-catenin with the transcription factor LEF-1. *Nature* 382:638–42

7. Behringer RR. 1995. The Müllerian inhibitor and mammalian sexual development. *Philos. Trans. R. Soc. B.* 350:285–89

8. Behringer RR, Finegold MJ, Cate RL. 1994. Müllerian inhibiting substance function during mammalian sexual development. *Cell* 79:415–25

9. Birchmeier W, Birchmeier C. 1994. Mesenchymal-epithelial transitions. *BioEssays* 16:305–7

10. Bitgood MJ, Shen L, McMahon AP. 1996. Sertoli cell signaling by Desert hedgehog regulates the male germline. *Curr. Biol.* 6:298–304

11. Buehr M, Gu S, McLaren A. 1992. Mesonephric contribution to testis differentiation in the fetal mouse. *Development* 117:273–81

12. Bull JJ. 1983. *Evolution of Sex Determining Mechanisms.* Menlo Park, CA: Benjamin/Cummings. 316 pp.

13. Burgoyne PS, Palmer SJ. 1991. The genetics of XY sex reversal in the mouse and other animals. *Semin. Dev. Biol.* 2:277–84

14. Burgoyne P, Palmer S. 1993. Cellular basis of sex determination and sex reversal in mammals. In *Gonadal Development and Function*, ed. SG Hillier, pp. 17–29. New York: Raven

15. Cameron F, Sinclair A. 1997. Mutations in *SRY* and *SOX9*: testis-determining genes. *Hum. Mutat.* 9:388–95

16. Capel B, Hawkins R, Hirst E, Kioussis D, Lovell-Badge R. 1996. Establishment and characterization of conditionally immortalized cells from the mouse urogenital ridge. *J. Cell. Sci.* 109:899–909

17. Capel B, Raspberry C, Dyson J, Bishop C, Simpson E, et al. 1993. Deletion of Y chromosomal sequences located outside the testis determining region can influence *Sry* expression and cause XY female sex reversal. *Nat. Genet.* 5:301–7

18. Capel B, Swain A, Nicolis S, Hacker A, Walter M, et al. 1993. Circular transcripts of the testis-determining gene *Sry* in adult mouse testis. *Cell* 73:1019–30

19. Cattanach BE, Rasberry C, Beechey CV. 1995. XY sex reversal associated with autosomal deletions. *Mouse Genome* 93:421–26

20. Chandra HS. 1985. Is human X chromosome inactivation a sex-determining device? *Proc. Natl. Acad. Sci. USA* 82:6947–49

21. Clarkson PA, Davies HR, Williams DM, Chaudhary R, Hughes IA, Patterson MN. 1993. Mutational screening of the Wilms' tumour gene, *WT1*, in males with genital abnormalities. *J. Med. Genet.* 30:767–72

22. Clepet C, Schafer AJ, Sinclair AH, Palmer MS, Lovell-Badge R, Goodfellow PN. 1993. The human *SRY* transcript. *Hum. Mol. Genet.* 2:2007–12

23. Cline TW, Meyer BJ. Vive la difference: males vs females in flies vs worms. 1996. *Annu. Rev. Genet.* 30:637–702

24. Cohen D, Sinclair A, McGovern J. 1994. SRY protein enhances transcription of *Fos*-related antigen 1 promoter constructs. *Proc. Natl. Acad. Sci. USA* 91:4372–76

25. Collignon J, Sockanathan S, Hacker A, Cohen-Tannoudji M, Norris D, et al. 1996. A comparison of the properties of *Sox-3* with *Sry* and two related genes, *Sox-1* and *Sox-2*. *Development* 122:509–20

26. Crews D. 1994. Temperature, steroids, and sex determination. *J. Endocrinol.* 142:1–8

27. da Silva SM, Hacker A, Harley V, Goodfellow P, Swain A, Lovell-Badge R. 1996. *Sox9* expression during gonadal development implies a conserved role for the gene in testis differentiation in mammals and birds. *Nat. Genet.* 14:62–68

28. Denny P, Swift S, Connor F, Ashworth A. 1992. A testis specific gene related to *SRY* encodes a sequence-specific DNA binding protein. *EMBO J.* 10:3705–12

29. Dubin RA, Kazmi MA, Ostrer H. 1995. Inverted repeats are necessary for circularization of the mouse testis *Sry* transcript. *Gene* 167:245–48

30. Dubin R, Ostrer H. 1994. *Sry* is a transcriptional activator. *Mol. Endocrinol.* 8:1182–92

31. Dym M, Lamsam CS, Jia MC, Kleinman HK, Papadopoulos V. 1991. Basement membrane increases G-protein levels and follicle stimulating hormone responsiveness of Sertoli cell adenylyl cyclase activity. *Endocrinology* 128:1167–76

32. Eicher EM. 1988. Autosomal genes involved in mammalian primary sex determination. *Philos. Trans. R. Soc. London Ser. B* 322:109–18

33. Eicher EM, Shown EP, Washburn LL. 1995. Sex reversal in C57BL/6J-Y^POS mice corrected by a *Sry* transgene. *Philos. Trans. R. Soc. Ser. B* 350:263–69

34. Eicher EM, Washburn LL. 1986. Genetic control of primary sex determination in mice. *Annu. Rev. Genet.* 20:327–60

35. Eicher E, Washburn L, Schork N, Lee B,

Shown E, et al. 1996. Sex-determining genes on mouse autosomes identified by linkage analysis of C57BL/6J-Y^{POS}. *Nat. Genet.* 14:206–9

36. Ferrari S, Harley VR, Pontiggia A, Goodfellow PN, Lovell-Badge R, Bianchi ME. 1992. SRY, like HMG1, recognizes sharp angles in DNA. *EMBO J.* 11:4497–506

37. Ford CE, Jones KW, Polani PE, de Almeida JC, Briggs JH. 1959. A sex-chromosome anomaly in a case of gonadal dysgenesis (Turner's syndrome). *Lancet* i:711–13

38. Foster J, Dominguez-Steglich M, Guioli S, Kwok C, Weller P, et al. 1994. Campomelic dysplasia and autosomal sex reversal caused by mutations in an *SRY*-related gene. *Nature* 372:525–29

39. Foster JW, Graves JA. 1994. An SRY-related sequence on the marsupial X chromosome: implications for the evolution of the mammalian testis-determining gene. *Proc. Natl. Acad. Sci. USA* 91:1927–31

40. Francis RC, Soma K, Fernald RD. 1993. Social regulation of the brain-pituitary-gonadal axis. *Proc. Natl. Acad. Sci. USA* 90:7791–98

41. Friedrich G, Soriano P. 1991. Promoter trap in embryonic stem cells: a genetic screen to identify and mutate developmental genes in mice. *Genes Dev.* 75:1513–23

42. Gibbons R, Picketts D, Villard L, Higgs D. 1995. Mutations in a putative global transcriptional regulator cause X-linked mental retardation with α-thalassemia (ATR-X syndrome). *Cell* 80:837–45

43. Giese K, Cox J, Grosschedl R. 1992. The HMG domain of lymphoid enhancer factor 1 bends DNA and facilitates assembly of functional nucleoprotein structures. *Cell* 69:1–20

44. Ginsburg M, Snow M, McLaren A. 1990. Primordial germ cells in the mouse embryo during gastrulation. *Development* 110:521–28

45. Gomperts M, Wylie C, Heasman J. 1994. Primordial germ cell migration. *Ciba Found. Symp.* 182:121–34

46. Goodfellow PN, Darling SM. 1988. Genetics of sex determination in man and mouse. *Development* 102:251–58

47. Goodwin G, Sanders C, Johns E. 1973. A new group of chromatin-associated proteins with a high content of acidic and basic amino acids. *Eur. J. Biochem.* 38:14–19

48. Graham A, Papalopulu N, Krumlauf R. 1989. The murine and Drosophila homeobox gene complexes have common features of organization and expression. *Cell* 57:367–78

49. Graves J. 1995. The origin and function of the mamalian Y chromosome and Y-borne genes—an evolving understanding. *BioEssays* 17:311–20

50. Graves J. 1996. Mammals that break the rules: genetics of marsupials and monotremes. *Annu. Rev. Genet.* 30:233–60

51. Grosschedl R, Giese K, Pagel J. 1994. HMG domain proteins: architectural elements in the assembly of nucleoprotein structures. *Trends Genet.* 10:94–100

52. Gubbay J, Collignon J, Koopman P, Capel B, Economou A, et al. 1990. A gene mapping to the sex-determining region of the mouse Y chromosome is a member of a novel family of embryonically expressed genes. *Nature* 346:245–50

53. Gubbay J, Lovell-Badge R. 1994. The mouse Y chromosome. In *Molecular Genetics of Sex Determination,* ed. S Wachtel, pp. 43–67. London: Academic

54. Gubbay J, Vivian N, Economou A, Jackson D, Goodfellow P, Lovell-Badge R. 1992. Inverted repeat structure of the *Sry* locus in mice. *Proc. Natl. Acad. Sci. USA* 89:7953–57

55. Hacker A, Capel B, Goodfellow P, Lovell-Badge R. 1995. Expression of *Sry,* the mouse sex determining gene. *Development* 121:1603–14

56. Haqq C, King C-Y, Ukiyama E, Falsafi S, Haqq T, et al. 1994. Molecular basis of mammalian sexual determination: activation of Müllerian inhibiting substance gene expression by SRY. *Science* 266:1494–500

57. Haqq CM, Donahoe PK. 1997. Regulation of sexual dimorphism in mammals. *Physiol. Rev.* In press

58. Harley VR, Jackson DI, Hextal PJ, Hawkins JR, Berkovitz GD, et al. 1992. DNA binding activity of recombinant *SRY* from normal males and XY females. *Science* 225:453–56

59. Harry JL, Koopman P, Brennan FE, Graves JAM, Renfree MB. 1995. Widespread expression of the testis-determining gene *SRY* in marsupials. *Nat. Genet.* 11:347–49

60. Hastie ND. 1992. Dominant negative mutations in the Wilms tumour (*WT1*) gene causes Denys-Drash syndrome—proof that a tumour-suppressor gene plays a crucial role in normal genitourinary development. *Hum. Mol. Genet.* 1:293–95

61. Hatano O, Takakusu A, Nomura M, Morohashi K. 1996. Identical origin of

adrenal cortex and gonad revealed by expression profiles of Ad4BP/SF1. *Genes Cells* 1:663–71

62. Hawkins J. 1994. Sex determination. *Hum. Mol. Genet.* 3:1463–67

63. Hawkins J. 1995. Genetics of XY sex reversal. *J. Endocrinol.* 147:183–87

64. Hawkins JR, Taylor A, Berta P, Levilliers J, Van der Auwera B, Goodfellow PN. 1992. Mutational analysis of *SRY*: nonsense and missense mutations in XY sex reversal. *Hum. Genet.* 88:471–74

65. Hawkins JR, Taylor A, Goodfellow PN, Migeon CJ, Smith KD, Berkovitz GD. 1992. Evidence for increased prevalence of *SRY* mutations in XY females with complete rather than partial gonadal dysgenesis. *Am. J. Hum. Genet.* 51:979–84

66. Hay ED. 1993. Extracellular matrix alters epithelial differentiation. *Curr. Opin. Cell Biol.* 5:1029–35

67. Hodgkin J. 1992. Genetic sex determination, mechanisms and evolution. *BioEssays* 14:253–61

68. Huber O, Korn R, McLaughlin J, Ohsugi M, Hermann B, Kemler R. 1996. Nuclear localization of β-catenin by interaction with transcription factor LEF-1. *Mech. Dev.* 59:3–10

69. Hughes RL, Pearse AM, Cooper DW, Joss JMP, Johnston PG, Jones MK. 1993. The genetic basis of marsupial gonadogenesis and sexual phenotype. In *Sex Chromosomes and Sex Determining Genes,* ed. KC Reed, JAM Graves, pp. 17–48. Chur, Switz.: Harwood

70. Ikeda Y, Shen W-H, Ingraham H, Parker K. 1994. Developmental expression of mouse steroidogenic factor 1, an essential regulator of the steroid hydroxylases. *Mol. Endocrinol.* 8:654–62

71. Ikeda Y, Swain A, Weber TJ, Hentges KE, Zanaria E, et al. 1996. Steroidogenic factor 1 and *Dax-1* colocalize in multiple cell lineages: potential links in endocrine development. *Mol. Endocrinol.* 10:1261–72

72. Ion A, Telvi L, Chaussain J, Galacteros F, Valayer J, et al. 1996. A novel mutation in the putative DNA helicase *SH2* is responsible for male-to-female sex reversal associated with an atypica form of the ATR-X syndrome. *Am. J. Hum. Genet.* 58:1185–91

73. Ito M, Yu R, Jameson J. 1997. *DAX1* inhibits *SF-1* mediated transactivation via a carboxy-terminal domain that is deleted in adrenal hypoplasia congenita. *Mol. Cell. Biol.* 17:1476–83

74. Jacobs PA, Strong JA. 1959. A case of human intersexuality having a possible XXY sex-determining mechanism. *Nature* 183:302–3

75. Jamieson RV, Zhou SX, Tan S-S, Tam PPL. 1997. X-chromosome inactivation during the development of the male urogenital ridge of the mouse. *Int. J. Dev. Biol.* 41:49–55

76. Jeske YWA, Bowles J, Greenfield A, Koopman P. 1995. Expression of a linear *Sry* transcript in the mouse genital ridge. *Nat. Genet.* 10:480–82

77. Jeske YWA, Mishina Y, Cohen D, Behringer R, Koopman P. 1996. Analysis of the role of *Amh* and *Fra1* in the *Sry* regulatory pathway. *Mol. Reprod. Dev.* 44:153–58

78. Jimenez R, Sanchez A, Burgos M, De La Guardia RD. 1996. Puzzling out the genetics of mammalian sex determination. *Trends Genet.* 12:164–66

79. Jost A. 1947. Recherches sur la différenciation sexuelle de l'embryon de lapin. *Arch Anat. Microsc. Morph. Exp.* 36:271–315

80. Kelley R. 1997. A new face for an old syndrome. *Am. J. Med. Genet.* 65:251–56

81. Kent J, Wheatley SC, Andrews JE, Sinclair AH, Koopman P. 1996. A male-specific role for *SOX9* in vertebrate sex determination. *Development* 122:2813–22

82. Koopman P. 1995. The molecular biology of *SRY* and its role in sex determination in mammals. *Reprod. Fertil. Dev.* 7:713–22

83. Koopman P, Gubbay J, Vivian N, Goodfellow P, Lovell-Badge R. 1991. Male development of chromosomally female mice transgenic for *Sry. Nature* 351:117–21

84. Koopman P, Münsterberg A, Capel B, Vivian N, Lovell-Badge R. 1990. Expression of a candidate sex-determining gene during mouse testis differentiation. *Nature* 348:450–52

85. Kriedberg JA, Sariola H, Loring JM, Maeda M, Pelletier J, et al. 1993. *Wt-1* is required for early kidney development. *Cell* 74:679–91

86. Lardelli M, Williams R, Lendahl U. 1995. *Notch-related* genes in animal development. *Int. J. Dev. Biol.* 39:769–80

87. Lovell-Badge R. 1992. The role of *Sry* in mammalian sex determination. In *Postimplantation Development in the Mouse. Ciba Found. Symp.* 165:162–82

88. Lovell-Badge R. 1992. Sex determining gene expression during embryogenesis. *Philos. Trans. R. Soc. London Ser. B* 335:159–64

89. Lovell-Badge R, Robertson E. 1990. XY female mice resulting from a heritable mutation in the murine primary

testis determining gene, *Tdy. Development* 109:635–46

90. Luo X, Ikeda Y, Parker K. 1994. A cell-specific nuclear receptor is essential for adrenal and gonadal development and sexual differentiation. *Cell* 77:481–90

91. Luo X, Ikeda Y, Parker KL. 1995. The cell-specific nuclear receptor steroidogenic factor 1 plays multiple roles in reproductive function. *Philos. Trans. R. Soc. London Ser. B* 350:279–83

92. Magre S, Jost A. 1991. Sertoli cells and testicular differentiation in the rat fetus. *J. Electron Microsc. Tech.* 19:172–88

93. Martineau J, Nordqvist K, Tilmann C, Lovell-Badge R, Capel B. 1997. Male specific cell migration into the developing gonad. *Curr. Biol.* Submitted

94. McCarrey JR, Abbott UK. 1979. Mechanisms of genetic sex determination, gonadal sex determination and germ-cell development in animals. *Adv. Genet.* 20:217–90

95. McElreavey K, Vilain E, Abbas N, Herskowitz I, Fellous M. 1993. A regulatory cascade hypothesis for mammalian sex determination: SRY represses a negative regulator of male development. *Proc. Natl. Acad. Sci. USA* 90:3368–72

96. McElreavey K, Vilain E, Barbaux S, Fuqua J, Fechner P et al. 1996. Loss of sequences 3′ to the testis-determining gene, *SRY*, including the Y pseudoautosomal boundary associated with partial testicular determination. *Proc. Natl. Acad. Sci. USA* 93:8590–94

97. McElreavey K, Vilain E, Boucekkine C, Vidaud M, Jaubert F, et al. 1992. XY sex reversal associated with a deletion 5′ to the *SRY* HMG box in the testis-determining region. *Proc. Natl. Acad. Sci. USA* 89:11016–20

98. McGinnis W, Krumlauf R. 1992. Homeobox genes and axial patterning. *Cell* 68:283–302

99. McLaren A. 1985. Relation of germ cell sex to gonadal differentiation. In *The Origin and Evolution of Sex*, ed. HO Halvorson, A Monroy, pp. 289–300. New York: Liss

100. McLaren A. 1988. Sex determination in mammals. *Trends Genet.* 4:153–57

101. McLaren A. 1990. Of MIS and the mouse. *Nature* 345:111

102. Merchant-Larios H, Moreno-Mendoza N, Buehr M. 1993. The role of the mesonephros in cell differentiation and morphogenesis of the mouse fetal testis. *Int. J. Dev. Biol.* 37:407–15

103. Mintz B, Russell ES. 1957. Gene-induced embryological modifications of primordial germ cells in the mouse. *J. Exp. Zool.* 134:207–37

104. Miyamoto N, Yoshida M, Kuratani S, Matsuo I, Aizawa S. 1997. Defects of urogenital development in mice lacking *Emx2. Development* 124:1653–64

105. Münsterberg A, Lovell-Badge R. 1991. Expression of the mouse anti-Müllerian hormone gene suggests a role in both male and female sexual differentiation. *Development* 113:613–24

106. Muscatelli F, Strom T, Walker A, Zanaria E, Recan D, et al. 1994. Mutations in the *DAX-1* gene give rise to both X-linked adrenal hypoplasia congenita and hypogonadotropic hypogonadism. *Nature* 372:672–76

107. Nagamine CM, Carlisle C. 1996. The dominant white spotting oncogene allele Kit^{W-42J} exacerbates XY^{DOM} sex reversal. *Development* 122:3597–605

108. Nordqvist K, Lovell-Badge R. 1994. Setbacks on the road to sexual fulfillment. *Nat. Genet.* 7:7–9

109. Nordqvist K, Töhönen V. 1997. An mRNA differential display strategy for cloning genes expressed during mouse gonad development. *Int. J. Dev. Biol.* 41:627–36

110. Ogata T, Hawkins J, Taylor A, Matsuo N, Hata J-I, Goodfellow P. 1992. Sex reversal in a child with a 46,X,Yp+ karytype: support for the existence of a gene(s), located in distal Xp, involved in testis formation. *J. Med. Genet.* 29:226–30

111. Ogata T, Matsuo N. 1996. Sex determining gene on the X chromosome short arm: dosage sensitive sex reversal. *Acta Paed. Jpn.* 38:390–98

112. Palmer SJ, Burgoyne PS. 1991. In situ analysis of fetal, prepuberal and adult XX-XY chimaeric mouse testes: Sertoli cells are predominantly, but not exclusively, XY. *Development* 112:265–68

113. Parkhurst S, Meneely P. 1994. Sex determination and dosage compensation: lessons from flies and worms. *Science* 264:924–32

114. Pelletier J, Bruening W, Klashtan C, Mauer S, Manivel J, et al. 1991. Germline mutations in the Wilms' tumor suppressor gene are associated with abnormal urogenital development in Denys-Drash syndrome. *Cell* 67:437–47

115. Pelliniemi LJ, Frojdman K, Paranko J. 1993. Cell biology of testicular development. In *Molecular Biology of the Male Reproductive System*, ed. DD Kretser. Orlando, FL: Academic

116. Pieau C. 1996. Temperature variation and

sex determination in reptiles. *BioEssays* 18:19–26

117. Pontiggia A, Rimini R, Harley V, Goodfellow P, Lovell-Badge R, Bianchi M. 1994. Sex-reversing mutations affect the architecture of SRY-DNA complexes. *EMBO J.* 13:6115–24

118. Poulat F, Girard F, Chevron M-P, Goze C, Rebillard X, et al. 1995. Nuclear localization of the testis determining gene product SRY. *J. Cell Biol.* 128:737–48

119. Richardson LL, Kleinman HK, Dym M. 1995. Basement membrane gene expression by Sertoli and peritubular myoid cells in vitro in the rat. *Biol. Reprod.* 52:320–30

120. Sayle R, Milner-White E. 1995. RAS-MOL: biomolecular graphics for all. *Trends Biochem. Sci.* 20:374

121. Schafer A, Goodfellow P. 1996. Sex determination in humans. *BioEssays* 18:955–63

122. Schafer AJ, Dominguez-Steglich MA, Guioli S, Kwok C, Weller PA, et al. 1995. The role of *SOX9* in autosomal sex reversal and campomelic dysplasia. *Philos. Trans. R. Soc. London Ser. B* 350:271–78

123. Sharman G, Hughes R, Cooper D. 1990. The chromosomal basis of sex differentiation in marsupials. In *Mammals from Pouches and Eggs: Genetics, Breeding and Evolution of Marsupials and Monotremes*, ed. J Graves, R Hope, D Cooper, pp. 309–24. Melbourne: CSIRO

124. Shawlot W, Behringer R. 1995. Requirement for *Lim1* in head-organizer function. *Nature* 374:425–30

125. Shen W-H, Moore C, Ikeda Y, Parker K, Ingraham H. 1994. Nuclear receptor steroidogenic factor 1 regulates the Müllerian inhibiting substance gene: a link to the sex determination cascade. *Cell* 77:651–61

126. Sinclair AH, Berta P, Palmer MS, Hawkins JR, Griffiths BL, et al. 1990. A gene from the human sex-determining region encodes a protein with homology to a conserved DNA-binding motif. *Nature* 346:240–44

127. Skinner MK, Tung PS, Fritz IB. 1985. Cooperativity between Sertoli cells and testicular peritubular cells in the production and deposition of extracellular matrix components. *J. Cell Biol.* 100:1941–47

128. Stayton C, Dabovic B, Gulisano M, Gecz J, Broccoli V, et al. 1994. Cloning and characterization of a new human Xq13 gene, encoding a putative helicase. *Hum. Mol. Genet.* 3:1957–64

129. Stevanovic M, Lovell-Badge R, Collignon J, Goodfellow PN. 1993. *SOX3* is an X-linked gene related to *SRY*. *Hum.*

Mol. Genet. 2:2013–18

130. Streuli CH, Bissell MJ. 1991. Mammary epithelial cells, extracellular matrix, and gene expression. *Cancer Treat Res.* 53:365–81

131. Sudbeck P, Scherer G. 1997. Two independent nuclear localization signals are present in the DNA-binding high-mobility group domains of SRY and Sox9. *J. Biol. Chem.* In press

132. Swain A, Zanaria E, Hacker A, Lovell-Badge R, Camerino G. 1996. Mouse *Dax1* expression is consistent with a role in sex determination as well as in adrenal and hypothalamus function. *Nat. Genet.* 12:404–9

133. Taketo-Hosotani T, Merchant-Larios H, Thau RB, Koide SS. 1985. Testicular cell differentiation in fetal mouse ovaries following transplantation into adult male mice. *J. Exp. Zool.* 236:229–37

134. Tamkun J, Deuring R, Scott M, Kissinger M, Pattatucci A, et al. 1992. *brahma*: A regulator of Drosophila homeotic genes structurally related to the yeast transcriptional activator SNF2/SW12. *Cell* 68:561–72

135. Thompson EW. 1995. Secreted products and extracellular matrix from testicular peritubular myoid cells influence androgen-binding protein secretion by Sertoli cells in culture. *J. Androl.* 16:28–35

136. Tucker P, Lundrigan B. 1993. Rapid evolution of the sex determining locus in Old World mice and rats. *Nature* 364:715–17

137. Tucker PK, Lundrigan BL. 1995. The nature of gene evolution on the mammalian Y chromosome; lessons from *Sry*. *Philos. Trans. R. Soc. London Ser. B* 350:221–27

138. Tung PS, Fritz IB. 1987. Morphogenetic restructuring and formation of basement membranes by Sertoli cells and testis peritubular cells in co-culture: inhibition of the morphogenetic cascade by cyclic AMP derivatives and by blocking direct cell contact. *Dev. Biol.* 120:139–53

139. Tung PS, Skinner MK, Fritz IB. 1987. Cooperativity between Sertoli cells and peritubular myoid cells in the formation of the basal lamina in the seminiferous tubule. *Ann. NY Acad. Sci.* 438:435–46

140. Van Genderen C, Okamura RM, Fariñas I, Quo R-G, Parslow TG, et al. 1994. Development of several organs that require inductive epithelial-mesenchymal interactions is impaired in *LEF-1*-deficient mice. *Genes Dev.* 8:2691–703

141. Wagner T, Wirth J, Meyer J, Zabel B, Held M, et al. 1994. Autosomal sex reversal and campomelic dysplasia are caused by

mutations in and around the *SRY*-related gene *SOX-9. Cell* 79:1111–20

142. Washburn L, Eicher E. 1989. Normal testis determination in the mouse depends on genetic interaction of a locus on chromosome 17 and the Y chromosome. *Genetics* 123:173–79

143. Welshons WJ, Russell LB. 1959. The Y chromosome as the bearer of male determining factors in the mouse. *Proc. Natl. Acad. Sci. USA* 45:560–66

144. Werner MH, Huth JR, Gronenborn AM, Clore GM. 1995. Molecular basis of human 46,XY sex reversal revealed from the three dimensional solution structure of the human SRY DNA complex. *Cell* 81:705–14

145. Werner M, Huth J, Gronenborn A, Clore G. 1996. Molecular determinants of mammalian sex. *Trends Biochem. Sci.* 21:302–8

146. Whitfield S, Lovell-Badge R, Goodfellow PN. 1993. Rapid sequence evolution of the sex determining gene *SRY. Nature* 364:713–15

147. Wilkins AS. 1995. Moving up the hierarchy: A hypothesis on the evolution of a genetic sex determination pathway. *BioEssays* 17:71–77

148. Zanaria E, Bardoni B, Dabovic B, Calvari V, Fraccaro M, et al. 1995. Xp duplications and sex reversal. *Philos. Trans. R. Soc. London Ser. B* 350:291–96

149. Zanaria E, Muscatelli F, Bardoni B, Strom T, Guioli S, et al. 1994. An unusual member of the nuclear hormone receptor superfamily responsible for X-linked adrenal hypoplasia congenita. *Nature* 372:635–41

150. Zhao GQ, Dend K, Labosky PA, Liaw L, Hogan BL. 1996. The gene encoding bone morphogenic protein 8B is required for the initiation and maintenance of spermatogenesis in the mouse. *Genes Dev.* 10:1657–69

151. Zwingman T, Erickson R, Boyer T, Ao A. 1993. Transcription of the sex-determining region genes *Sry* and *Zfy* in the mouse preimplantation embryo. *Proc. Natl. Acad. Sci. USA* 90:814–17

SPECIAL TOPIC: APOPOTOSIS

Introduction, E. Brad Thompson, *Special Topic Editor*

The Model

In the 25 years since the term apoptosis was coined (1), a vast quantity of work has been done in search of the cause of the phenomena it originally described. Several discoveries of fundamental importance have been made as a result of the energy the concept has imparted to our thinking about cell death. The basic reasoning that has driven this research is a combination of definite facts and more speculative intuitions: It is certain that some cells are genetically destined for death during the normal development of multi-cell organisms. When these fated cells die, there is little or no gross inflammatory response. This entire process is probably controlled universally by intercellular signal molecules; certainly this is true in several well-studied instances. In lower organisms (nematodes, flies) several specific intracellular genes have been identified for particular sets of cells. Thus the general model is one of intercellular signaling molecules playing on intracellular effector systems that balance the individual cell's progress to life or death. By extrapolation, it is widely held that all apoptosis, and not only these programmed cell deaths during ontogeny, is regulated by the same mechanisms. Apoptosis [first called shrinkage necrosis (2)] was originally observed in mature human/vertebrate tissues as stochastic loss of cells that showed distinctive histopathic morphology and caused little inflammatory response. It was known, and has been widely confirmed since, that death morphologies closely resembling these spontaneous deaths can be evoked in various cells by several natural ligands, as in the classic example of thymic lymphoid cell death following administration of glucocorticoids. Because these ligands are known regulators of gene expression, it has been reasoned that altered expression of certain genes must cause apoptotic cell death. Then by a leap of faith, or inspired intuition, it is argued that these genes are the same as those involved with the genetic pathways of programmed cell death, now turned on after ontogeny in the post-developmental cell by physiological, pathological or pharmacological agents. The key tenets of this model state that there is a universal genetic program for cell death, that a variety of stimuli can activate this program, and that even though many transduction mechanisms are involved, eventually all apoptosis requires activation of a Final Common Pathway. In support of this argument are the discoveries that the products of *ced3, ced4* (2a–d), and *ced9*, the three genes known to regulate developmental death of a specific set of cells in the nematode *Caenorhabditis elegans*, have analogous genes that also regulate death in vertebrates. (These genes have been found to code for the caspases, a class of cysteine proteases, and for the Bcl2 family of proteins.) It should be remembered, however, that this is still a model. As yet no precise biochemical pathway has been shown to be identical in an ontologically programmed or spontaneous random cell death and in a ligand-induced cell death.

The Morphology of Death: Apoptosis, Necrosis,... and Much, Much More?

Before discussing the wealth of papers on apoptosis, the strengths and weaknesses of the reasoning that led to the basic model should be briefly examined. First, is all cell death divisible, as is often asserted (3), into the simple dichotomy, apoptosis or necrosis? In apoptosis, cells shrink and dissociate from surrounding cells, their organelles retain definition for a long time, and the nucleus displays a distinctive pattern of heterochromatization and eventual fragmentation. These and other defining morphologic features have been reviewed often (3–6). On the other hand, necrotic cells swell, their mitochondria dilate, other organelles dissolve, and plasma membranes rupture, whereas the nuclear changes are relatively unremarkable (3). The classic causes of necrosis include hyperthermia; inhibition of oxidative phosphorylation, glycolysis or the Krebs cycle; autolysis; hypoxia; complement; and a variety of toxins (3). With the original meaning of apoptosis based on the histology of the dying cells, and with the morphologic criteria used to define the apoptotic cell, it is not apparent that all cell death can be readily fitted into either category. In a scholarly review of the historical categorization of cell death, Majno & Joris point out that several forms of dying cells fail to fit neatly into the specific morphology supposed to be seen in necrotic or apoptotic cells (7). Noting that all apoptotic cells shrink, and that non-apoptotic cells swell, these authors suggest that oncosis (for swelling) be substituted for necrosis, which they maintain is only a subset of oncotic cell deaths. Ellis et al (8), Columbano (9), and Clarke (10) point out other perplexing examples of cell death, in which neither the apoptotic nor the necrotic/oncotic criteria are fairly met by the changes in observed cell morphology. All these concerns may be swept aside by declaring that the morphologic details may vary from one cell type to another, but the fundamental biochemistry must be the same (the Final Common Pathway). Perhaps—but the original definition of apoptosis was morphologic, and it is wise to keep an open mind as to whether differing morphologic appearances reflect fundamentally differing biochemical mechanisms. If not, then why need any morphologic criterion be valid? In the extreme, why must a cell that looks apoptotic differ in fundamental mechanism even from one that looks necrotic/oncotic? If we think that necrosis and classic apoptosis must be driven by different mechanisms, then so may the other morphologies. In some papers, the distinctions between even necrosis and apoptosis begin to blur (11). Although little has been written about it, the morphology of death in the developmental deletion of cells in the nematode, which involves the interplay of the *ced3, 4,* and *9* genes, may not be identical to that of classic vertebrate apoptosis (12). Other invertebrate cell deaths also may be non-canonical (3). In at least two papers, DNA ladders indicative of internucleosomal endonucleolysis were reported in necrotic cells (13, 14). Agents supposed to be classic causes of necrosis (hypoxia, Na azide, KCN) have now been shown to cause apoptosis as well (15–19), and Bcl2, the vertebrate homologue of *ced9* and the pre-eminent inhibitor of programmed cell death and/or apoptosis, also ameliorates necrosis (15, 20). Oxidized low-density lipoproteins have been reported to cause necrosis and apoptosis (11). Is there only a dichotomy? Are the morphologic boundaries drawn by entirely different biochemistries? The reason this is important is that models shape our experimental thinking. A dichotomous model calls for one to think in terms of one pathway or another and encourages a tendency to discard or ignore patterns that do not fit. For example, how does the model explain instances in which cell death measured, e.g. by clonogenicity, exceeds the number of apoptotic cells (21, 22)? If apoptosis is the mode of death caused by a given agent, how can this be? A more flexible model may take into account the same basic set of regulatory and effector systems by maintaining that their kinetic and quantitative contributions result in a spectrum of morphologies. As these manifest themselves on differing basic cellular structures and tissues, some feature of classic apoptosis, or even necrosis, may predominate. The human mind prefers dichotomies because they simplify the world; but nature often displays continua in its processes.

The Biochemistry of Cell Deaths

Once such agnostic thoughts occur, they force open the door to concerns over other basic elements in the model. If there is no simple dichotomy in modes of cell death, perhaps there is more than one basic genetic program for death and more than one final pathway (Figure 1). Perhaps some ligand-induced cell death could result from confused or inappropriate regulation of gene expression rather than from turning on pre-set genetic programs. Complete faith in the Final Common Pathway has led to some wasted effort in the field. For example, it was once widely believed that induction of specific apoptotic endonucleases caused apoptosis (23). Subsequently, many papers appeared that relied solely on the evidence of internucleosomal DNA lysis as definitive proof of apoptosis. Later

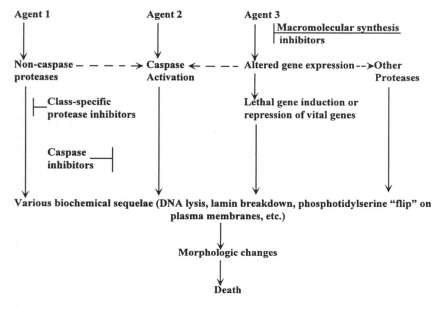

Figure 1   Potential pathways to apoptosis.

it was shown that cells could be killed even when such lysis was blocked and, further, that some of the cytoplasmic and membrane changes seen in apoptosis could be brought about without any nuclei present. This leaves the question whether the internucleosomal DNA lysis is only a frequently associated but nonessential event, i.e. not part of the Final Common Pathway. If so, it seems unsafe to use it as the sole defining test in cases otherwise not defined as apoptotic. If internucleosomal DNA lysis does form part of the inescapable set of ultimate lethal collapse in certain cells but not others, then there is more than one final pathway.

   Although the point of this essay is not to discredit or overturn the basic model under which many in the field operate, it is intended to suggest that it contains several testable weaknesses. Its strengths speak for themselves; it is a great, unifying concept that continues to drive important new discoveries. Models, however, are meant to be tested, not to be invoked as dogma. By noting some aspects of the model that are open to question and by testing their limits, it should be possible to design new experiments that will improve our understanding of the important fundamental processes involved in cell death.

   In considering the question of uniformity of the final biochemical mechanisms of cell death, one problem lies in the issues involving gene regulation as an essential element. Part of the early thinking on the subject, as noted above, was that gene regulation must be involved. In agreement with this model were numerous experiments showing that blocking either RNA and/or protein synthesis blocked the apoptosis caused by a variety of ligands in a number of cell systems. Actually, a surrogate biochemical test for apoptosis was normally used, because a total block in either RNA or protein synthesis must itself eventually be lethal. (The process usually is not stated, although a few papers claim that such blocks themselves can cause apoptosis of certain cell types.) Then, with the discovery of caspases, constitutive cysteine proteases that when activated cause cell death in many cells and systems, the necessity of gene induction was called into question. Many systems have been shown to activate caspase cascades, and caspases are capable of producing some of the biochemical markers of apoptosis. For example, cell extracts containing activated caspases, when applied to isolated nuclei, have been shown to cause DNA lysis into internucleosomal ladders (24). Those in favor of a uniform, caspase-driven Final Common Pathway would argue that this negates the need for an induced, specific endonuclease. On the other hand, the nucleases in isolated nuclei are poised to act, and they can be set off by numerous agents. The cell-free experiment does not prove that in intact cells an identical mechanism is employed. One simple ad hoc reconciliation of the two sets of results has been to hypothesize that in cases where macromolecular synthesis is required, some induction of a caspase or other factor necessary for caspase action is needed before the proteases are set into action. This could prove to be so; yet reports already are being made of systems in which addition of caspase inhibitors fails to block apoptosis (25, 26). The caspase faithful might argue that the inhibitors used were somehow ineffective. An alternative possibility is that there really are cell death pathways that require macromolecular synthesis leading to lethal consequences that do not require caspase activation or in which their activation is a secondary event, whereas in others, caspases are the central agents of death (Figure 1). This clearly is a point that needs experimental attention in testing the Final Common Pathway model.

To reiterate, the defining morphologic appearance of cells undergoing apoptosis was provided in several early papers. Since then, other cell deaths called apoptosis have been seen that do not show all these changes. Many studies provide only perfunctory examination of the dying cells to see whether they satisfy the defining morphologic criteria. If all these types of cell death are really apoptotic while satisfying only some of the morphologic criteria, then perhaps some criteria should be dropped from the definition, leaving a core of basic changes to be explained by a Final Common Pathway. One morphologic sine qua non may be cell shrinkage; there may be others. Alternatively, if the variety of death morphologies are not simply the reflection of varied cell make-up, but actually represent a basic part of the process in that cell type, then we are led to the conclusion that there may be more than one path to cell death, or at the least, that the Final Common Pathway can have variants. Another way of putting this is to say that if the final path involves general breakdown of key biochemical structures, this may be achieved by several kinds of enzymes, e.g. proteases. Experimental evidence supporting this comes from work showing that admission of various proteases into cells can cause what appears to be apoptosis (27), and that calpain (28) or certain granzymes (29, 30) can produce cell death. It has been argued that these proteases simply activate caspases, which are the ultimate killers, but the point deserves further attention, because recent data suggest that this is not always the case (25, 26, 29–31). In this light, a careful comparison of the detailed morphology alongside the biochemistry of a particular cell type subjected to several apoptosis-inducing forces of differing physical or biochemical nature, e.g. chemotherapy agents, radiation, and TNF, would be helpful.

This special section is not an attempt to cover every current topic in the field of apoptosis. Instead, we have selected certain highly topical and fast moving areas to discuss in detail. In these chapters, the reviewers present critical ideas and the evidence for and against them. I review the role of the proto-oncogene c-*myc* in apoptosis. In a system-specific manner, this gene has a role to play in the process both when inappropriately expressed and when deeply down-regulated. The hypotheses currently proposed to explain these phenomena and their consequences are discussed. In the chapter by Kidd, a thorough analysis of the role of proteases in apoptosis is presented. He discusses the caspases, which have provoked much interest in the past few years. He also discusses other proteases and their effects in apoptotic systems. This chapter also considers the question of protease substrates and of the possible role of kinases linked to protease action. Kroemer, Dallaporta & Resche-Rigon present the case for the functions of mitochondria in the spectrum of deaths ranging from apoptosis to necrosis. In particular, these authors call attention to the role of mitochondrial permeability transition and present the data for its relevance to a variety of cell deaths. They discuss how this ties into both caspase-mediated cell death and cell deaths mediated by alternative pathways. King & Cidlowski discuss the roles of proteins important to regulation of the cell cycle and how points in the cell cycle appear to be monitored biochemically as the cell replicates its DNA and divides. The effects and contributions of cell cycle-specific proteins and other relevant proteins, including c-myc, p53, E2F, and the cyclin/CKD system, are discussed in their review. In the review by Kolesnick & Krönke, the case for ceramide as an important signaling molecule in apoptotic systems is presented. These authors also discuss the interrelationships between the protease pathways and ceramide. They argue that there may be differing pathways driven by ceramide signaling, some of which use the caspase system, while others do not.

The reader will note that several of these reviews present the notion that there is more than a simple dichotomy between necrosis and apoptosis. All the authors hope that this conceptualization and the discussions around specific systems will provide readers with a thought-provoking overview of the field.

Visit the *Annual Reviews* home page at
http://www.AnnualReviews.org.

Literature Cited

1. Kerr JFR, Wyllie AH, Currie AR. 1972. Apoptosis: a basic biological phenomenon with wide-ranging implications in tissue kinetics. *Br. J. Cancer* 26:239–57
2. Kerr JFR. 1971. Shrinkage necrosis: a distinct mode of cellular death. *J. Pathol.* 105:13–20
2a. Vaux DL. 1997. CED-4—the third horseman of apoptosis. *Cell* 90:389–90
2b. Zou H, Henzel WJ, Liu X, Lutschg A, Wang X. 1997. Apaf-1, a human protein homologous to C. elegans CED-4, participates in cytochrome *c*-dependent activation of caspase-3. *Cell* 90:405–13
2c. Hengartner MO. 1997. CED-4 is a stranger no more. *Nature* 388:714–15
2d. Chinnaiyan AM, Chaudhary D, O'Rourke K, Koonin EV, Dixit VM. 1997. Role of CED-4 in the activation of CED-3. *Nature* 388:728–29
3. Wyllie AH. 1981. Cell death: a new classification separating apoptosis from necrosis. In *Cell Death in Biology and Pathology,* ed. ID Bowen, RA Lockshin, pp. 9–34. London: Chapman & Hall
4. Wyllie AH, Duvall E, Blow JJ. 1984. Intracellular mechanisms in cell death in normal and pathological tissues. In *Cell Aging and Cell Death,* ed. I Davies, DC Sigee, pp. 269–94. London: Cambridge Univ. Press
5. Wyllie AH, Kerr JKR, Currie, AR. 1980. Cell death: the significance of apoptosis. *Int. Rev. Cytol.* 68:251–306
6. Wyllie AH. 1987. Apoptosis: cell death in tissue regulation. *J. Pathol.* 153:313–16
7. Majno G, Joris I. 1995. Apoptosis, oncosis, and necrosis. An overview of cell death. *Am. J. Pathol.* 146:3–15
8. Ellis RE, Yuan J, Horvitz HR. 1991. Mechanisms and functions of cell death. *Annu. Rev. Cell Biol.* 7:663–98
9. Columbano A. 1995. Cell death: current difficulties in discriminating apoptosis from necrosis in the context of pathological processes in vivo. *J. Cell. Biochem.* 58:181–90
10. Clarke PGH. 1990. Developmental cell death: morphological diversity and multiple mechanisms. *Anat. Embryol.* 81:195–213
11. Escargueil-Blanc I, Salvayre R, Négre-Salvayre A. 1994. Necrosis and apoptosis induced by oxidized low density lipoproteins occur through two calcium-dependent pathways in lymphoblastoid cells. *FASEB J.* 8:1075–80
12. Robertson AMG, Thomson JN. 1982. Morphology of programmed cell death in the ventral nerve cord of *Caenorhabditis elegans* larvae. *J. Embryol. Exp. Morph.* 67:89–100
13. Fukuda K, Kojiro M, Chiu JF. 1993. Demonstration of extensive chromatin cleavage in transplanted Morris hepatoma 777 tissue: apoptosis or necrosis? *Am. J. Pathol.* 142:935–46
14. Shen W, Kamendulis LM, Ray SD, Corcoran GB. 1992. Acetaminophen-induced cytotoxicity in cultured mouse hepatocytes: effects of Ca(2+)-endonuclease, DNA repair, and glutathione depletion inhibitors on DNA fragmentation and cell death. *Toxicol. Appl. Pharmacol.* 112:32–40
15. Shimizu S, Eguchi Y, Kamiike W, Itoh Y, Hasegawa J, et al. 1996. Induction of apoptosis as well as necrosis by hypoxia and predominant prevention of apoptosis by Bcl-2 and Bcl-X_L. *Cancer Res.* 56:2161–66
16. Mills EM, Gunasekar PG, Pavlakovic G, Isom GE. 1996. Cyanide-induced apoptosis and oxidative stress in differentiated PC12 cells. *J. Neurochem.* 67:1039–46

17. Beeri R, Symon Z, Brezis M, Ben-Sasson SA, Baehr PH, et al. 1995. Rapid DNA fragmentation from hypoxia along the thick ascending limb of rat kidneys. *Kidney Int.* 47:1806–10

18. Tanaka M, Ito H, Adachi S, Akimoto H, Nishikawa T, et al. 1994. Hypoxia induces apoptosis with enhanced expression of Fas antigen messenger RNA in cultured neonatal rat cardiomyocytes. *Circ. Res.* 75:426–33

19. Vaux DL, Whitney D, Weissman IL. 1996. Activation of physiological cell death mechanisms by a necrosis-causing agent. *Microsc. Res. Tech.* 34:259–66

20. Shimizu S, Eguchi Y, Kamiike W, Waguri S, Uchiyama Y, et al. 1996. Retardation of chemical hypoxia-induced necrotic cell death by Bcl-2 and ICE inhibitors: possible involvement of common mediators in apoptotic and necrotic signal transductions. *Oncogene* 12:2045–50

21. Hopcia KL, McCarey YL, Sylvester FC, Held KD. 1996. Radiation-induced apoptosis in HL60 cells: oxygen effect, relationship between apoptosis and loss of clonogenicity, and dependence of time to apoptosis on radiation dose. *Radiat. Res.* 145:315–23

22. Yin DX, Schimke RT. 1995. BCL-2 expression delays drug-induced apoptosis but does not increase clonogenic survival after drug treatment in HeLa cells. *Cancer Res.* 55:4922–28

23. Wyllie AH, Arends MJ, Morris RG, Walker SW, Evan G. 1992. The apoptosis endonuclease and its regulation. *Semin. Immunol.* 4:389–97

24. Martin SJ, Newmeyer DD, Mathias S, Farschon DM, Wang HC, et al. 1995. Cell-free reconstitution of Fas-, UV radiation- and ceramide-induced apoptosis. *EMBO J.* 14:5191–200

25. McConkey DJ. 1996. Calcium-dependent, interleukin 1-converting enzyme inhibitor-insensitive degradation of lamin B1 and DNA fragmentation in isolated thymocyte nuclei. *J. Biol. Chem.* 271: 22398–406

26. McCarthy NJ, Whyte MKB, Gilbert CS, Evan GI. 1997. Inhibition of Ced-3/ICE-related proteases does not prevent cell death induced by oncogenes, DNA damage, or the Bcl-2 homologue Bak. *J. Cell Biol.* 136:215–27

27. Williams MS, Henkart PA. 1994. Apoptotic cell death induced by intracellular proteolysis. *J. Immunol.* 153:4247–55

28. Squier MKT, Miller ACK, Malkinson AM, Cohen JJ. 1994. Calpain activation in apoptosis. *J. Cell. Physiol.* 159:229–37

29. Sarin A, Williams MS, Alexander-Miller MA, Berzofsky JA, Zacharchuk CM, Henkart PA. 1997. Target cell lysis by CTL granule exocytosis is independent of ICE/Ced-3 family proteases. *Immunity* 6:209–15

30. Anel A, Gamen S, Alava MA, Schmitt-Verhulst AM, Pineiro A, Naval J. 1997. Inhibition of CPP32-like proteases prevents granzyme B- and Fas-, but not granzyme A-based cytotoxicity exerted by CTL clones. *J. Immunol.* 158:1999–2006

31. Lotem J, Sachs L. 1996. Differential suppression by protease inhibitors and cytokines of apoptosis induced by wildtype p53 and cytotoxic agents. *Proc. Natl. Acad. Sci. USA* 93:12507–12

Annu. Rev. Physiol. 1998. 60:533–73

PROTEOLYTIC ACTIVITIES THAT MEDIATE APOPTOSIS

Vincent J. Kidd

Department of Tumor Cell Biology, St. Jude Children's Research Hospital, 332 N. Lauderdale, Memphis, Tennessee 38101; e-mail: vincent.kidd@stjude.org

KEY WORDS: cell death, proteolysis, TNF receptors, Fas, Wsl-1/DR-3/TRAMP, DR-4/TRAIL, ICE, CPP32, caspase, signaling, DISC, IAP

ABSTRACT

Since the discovery that cells can activate their own suicide program, investigators have attempted to determine whether the events that are associated with this form of cell death are genetically determined. The discovery that the *ced-3* gene of *Caenorhabditis elegans* encodes a cysteine protease essential for developmentally regulated apoptosis ignited interest in this area of research. As a result, we now know that cell death is specified by a number of genes and that this biologic process contributes significantly to development, tumorigenesis, and autoimmune disease. In this review I summarize what is currently known about signaling pathways involved in apoptosis, with particular emphasis on the function of the cysteine proteases known as caspases. However, there is also evidence that protease-independent cell death pathways exist. Is there a relationship between these two distinct mechanisms? If so, how do they communicate? Finally, even though the involvement of tumor necrosis factor/nerve growth factor family of receptors and cysteine proteases has been elegantly established as a component of many apoptotic signaling pathways, what happens downstream of these initial events? Why are only a selected group of cellular proteins—many nuclear—the targets of these proteases? Are nuclear events essential for apoptosis in vivo? Are the cellular genes that encode products involved in apoptotic signaling frequent targets of mutation/alteration during tumorigenesis? These are only a few questions that may be answered in the next ten years.

HISTORICAL INTRODUCTION

The death of individual cells from a larger population was first recognized during vertebrate development studies more than 40 years ago (1, 2). In the early 1970s, Kerr, Wyllie & Currie found that cells undergo at least two distinct forms of death: the well-characterized, and usually rapid, necrotic tissue damage induced by trauma, and a more protracted and morphologically distinct form of cell death that they termed apoptosis (3, 4). Necrotic cell death is violent, characterized by cytoplasmic swelling, the rupturing of cellular membranes, and the disintegration of subcellular and nuclear components. Conversely, apoptosis is characterized by an ordered series of events that take place over a longer period of time. The length of time required for cells to undergo cell death is usually specified by the stimuli that trigger apoptosis (e.g. glucocorticoid, Fas ligand, growth factor withdrawal) (5–23), as well as the cell type. Although necrosis may be more analogous to random acts of violence that characterize murder, apoptosis is more appropriately referred to as cellular suicide. Apoptotic death is initiated by the cell when it senses that its environment or physical state has been compromised; this is, indeed, the ultimate self-sacrifice.

The criteria for determining whether a cell is undergoing apoptosis versus necrosis include distinct morphological changes in the appearance of the cell, as well as alterations in biochemical and molecular markers (3, 24, 25). For example, apoptotic cells often shrink and undergo cytoplasmic membrane blebbing, their chromosomes rapidly condense and aggregate around the nuclear periphery, and small apoptotic bodies are formed. In many, but not all, apoptotic cells, the condensed chromosomes are acted upon by specific nucleases that cleave the DNA to produce a characteristic ladder (5, 10). Conversely, necrotic cells swell and burst following physical trauma. The resulting cellular debris is quickly cleared by macrophages. Another distinction between necrotic and apoptotic cells is the requirement for new mRNA and protein expression during the early stages of some forms of apoptosis (restricted to specific cell types and stimuli). Apoptotic responses that help regulate immune defenses are most often associated with mRNA and protein synthesis (14, 16, 17, 26, 27). The nature of the stimuli that triggers cell death, e.g. T-cell receptor activation (14, 15, 28, 29), may be another important determinant of a requirement for de novo mRNA/protein synthesis during apoptosis. Such attributes of cell death remain controversial, particularly among those who strongly support the notion that the inherent apoptotic machinery (in the form of inactive precursors) is present in all living cells (30–35). This latter view of apoptosis is consistent with the process of neuronal cell death, as well as death mediated by some members of the tumor necrosis factor (TNF) receptor family, e.g. TNFR1 (36). In support of this view, it has been shown that a TNFR1-mediated proliferative response can be suppressed by the addition of protein synthesis inhibitors (37). Conversely, TNFR1-mediated apoptosis is not affected by the same agents. Thus the proper balance of intra- and/or extracellular signals (e.g. cellular response to withdrawal of a necessary growth factor, γ-irradiation, or chemical mutagens of DNA) can determine whether a cell survives or is executed. Although there is evidence for rescue of certain forms of cell death (e.g. apoptosis induced by growth-factor withdrawal), once the death program passes a certain point (usually disruption of nuclear organization) there can be no reprieve.

Many of the early mechanistic studies of apoptosis were performed by biochemical and molecular analysis of cultured mammalian cells following their exposure to numerous physical, chemical, and biochemical agents that trigger cell death (38–40). These studies offered further proof that each cell had the inherent capacity to trigger its own death, given an appropriate signal. This early work also provided the first hints that the ability of tumor cells to undergo apoptosis, as compared with normal cells, was compromised. Inhibition of apoptosis might be fundamental for tumor progression. Independently, developmental biologists were identifying the genes responsible for determining cell fate (38, 41–46). In organisms such as the nematode *Caenorhabditis elegans* and the fruit fly *Drosophila melanogaster*, large numbers of cells are eliminated by programmed cell death during development. Such cells can be readily identified by nuclear and cytoplasmic changes similar to those that accompany cell death in higher vertebrates. These organisms are more easily manipulated genetically than vertebrates, allowing the generation of mutants that disrupt the death of specific cells. These mutants can then be used to isolate the genes involved in these biologic processes. In the developing fly and nematode, there are many points where determination of cell fate is dependent on the action of cellular death genes. Therefore, the identification of mutant phenotypes that failed to eliminate specific cells by programmed cell death (PCD) during development facilitated the identification and characterization of the genes that regulate apoptotic pathways.

Studies of *C. elegans* development carried out by Horvitz and colleagues during the past decade have contributed significantly to our understanding of cell death (38, 41). Their genetic analyses resulted in the identification of three cellular genes required for PCD during development of *C. elegans*. A loss-of-function mutation in any of these genes prevents the death of specific cells during development; accordingly, all three genes were designated *C. elegans death* (*ced*) genes (47–49). The isolation and molecular characterization of these genes demonstrated that the *ced-3* gene was homologous to the mammalian interleukin-1β-converting enzyme (ICE) (47). ICE was originally isolated from mammalian cells as an enzyme essential for the proper processing and biologic activation of pro-interleukin-1β, a cytokine involved in mediating cellular inflammatory response (50). Furthermore, when the *C. elegans ced-3* gene was expressed in mammalian fibroblasts, apoptosis was rapidly induced (51). Independently, Steller and colleagues (44, 52) used genetic screens of *Drosophila* to identify the genes essential for apoptosis during fly development. These discoveries have provided a solid foundation for the study of apoptosis, as well as demonstrating that defects in cell death contribute significantly to disease.

Strong parallels can be seen when the mechanisms that regulate apoptosis are compared with those that regulate the cell cycle. Explosive growth in our understanding of the mechanisms regulating the cell cycle has taken place as a result of the realization that the mammalian cell cycle is governed by complex layers of control that respond to both external and internal factors, e.g. involving CDC2-related protein kinases, cyclins, and cyclin-dependent kinase inhibitors (CKIs) (53, 54). Such tight control of the cell cycle provides constant monitoring of progression through cell division, with important checks and balances to help ensure that genetic catastrophes occur infrequently. In a similar manner, the demonstration that the *ced-3* gene encodes a cysteine protease essential for programmed cell death has acted as a catalyst for the recent rapid growth in this field.

PROTEASE SIGNALING OF CELL DEATH

The first clues suggesting that apoptosis often requires specific proteases came from studies of drug-induced death of tumor cells (22, 23, 42, 55). These early studies focused on the relationship between the action of protease inhibitors and chemotherapeutic drugs, as well as on their relationship to events that occur during specific intervals of the cell cycle. Even though these experiments were limited by the availability of reagents, they revealed the diverse nature of apoptotic signaling (e.g. selective inhibition of RNA synthesis, transcription, and/or translation). The serine protease inhibitors N-tosyl-L-phenyl-alanylchloromethyl ketone (TPCK) and N-tosyl-L-lysylchloromethyl ketone (TLCK) were particularly effective in preventing certain forms of cell death, thereby establishing an important link between cellular proteases and apoptotic signaling.

The Death Receptors

The activation of the caspase proteases has been linked to the aggregation of cell surface receptors related to the TNF and nerve growth factor (NGF) families (including TNFR1, TNFR2, CD95/APO-1/FasR, DR-2/APO-2/TRAIL, DR-3/Wsl-1/TRAMP/APO-3, CAR1, CD30, and CD40) (20, 36, 56–80). Caspase activation occurs when receptor-sensitive target cells are exposed to the appropriate ligand, or when the receptors self-aggregate in response to their high cell–surface density (62, 63, 72). These receptors are type-I membrane proteins, each containing an extracellular ligand-binding domain of two to six cysteine-rich repeated subdomains, a transmembrane (TM) domain, and a cytoplasmic domain that is essential for mediating either a proliferative or an apoptotic response (Figure 1) (62, 63, 71, 72). The ligand-binding domains of these TNF

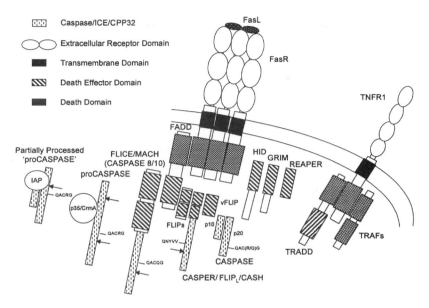

Figure 1   Schematic representation of the prototype TNF receptors Fas and TNFR1 and their interactions with cytoplasmic proteins with death domains (DD) and/or death effector domains (DED). The *Drosophila reaper, hid,* and *grim* genes, which act in much the same way as vertebrate TNFRs are shown. The effects of the p35, crmA, XIAP, and FLIP inhibitors with a cellular caspase are shown.

receptors have structurally similar motifs, but they do not share significant sequence identity. Similarly, the intracellular domains of these receptors all contain an ≈80 amino acid region termed a death domain (DD) that is involved in transducing proliferative and/or apoptotic signals through its interaction with cytoplasmic proteins containing similar DD motifs (5, 10, 64, 67, 69, 71, 72, 78, 81–85). Although it has been suggested that these DD motifs are involved in generating a death signal, molecular analysis of the *Drosophila reaper* gene has demonstrated that this motif is essential for protein-protein interactions and is not responsible for a death signal per se (82). The same DD motif is required for TNFR1-mediated NF-κB activation and suppression of apoptosis, which is consistent with its proposed role in mediating protein-protein interactions (36, 58, 86–88). Many of these receptors are expressed at constitutive low levels in a broad range of tissues and cell types, but the expression of some receptors (e.g. TNFR2) can be induced in response to different stimuli.

Ligands for many of the TNF receptors have also been identified (20, 60, 62, 63, 72, 76, 79, 80, 89, 90). They are synthesized as type-II membrane proteins that require proteolysis to generate a soluble cytokine. Unlike mitogenic receptors that undergo dimerization, followed by the activation of either their own intrinsic tyrosine kinase or the recruitment of a cytoplasmic tyrosine protein kinase, TNFRs appear to function during cell death by recruiting novel proteins without intrinsic protein kinase activity. Ligand binding to the death receptor helps to facilitate oligomerization of these proteins, which is essential for a physiologic response (62, 63; see R Kolesnick & M Kronke, this volume, for a more detailed discussion). The various TNF receptors can also self-aggregate in the absence of ligand, mimicking what occurs when ligand is bound. The ability to self-aggregate appears to be dependent on the presence of a suitable DD and on the density of these receptors on the cell surface (62, 63, 72). This self-aggregation has been exploited to demonstrate the cytotoxic nature of newly isolated receptors because usually neither the ligand nor an appropriate bivalent receptor antibody is available (7, 73–75, 79).

Once the receptor oligomerizes, specific cytoplasmic proteins containing a similar DD are recruited to the aggregated receptor complex (e.g. TRADD, TRAF2, RIP, FADD/MORT1, RAIDD, CRADD, caspase 8/FLICE/MACH/Mch5, and caspase 10/FLICE2/Mch4) (36, 67, 71, 81, 83, 86, 91–98). Many of these cytoplasmic DD proteins function as adapters, linking the receptor to either a downstream protein kinase (e.g. the JNK protein kinase) or a caspase protease (Figure 2). The activation of the JNK protein kinase has been linked to the proliferative response of TNFR1, whereas the caspase proteases are the downstream targets of activation when cell death is specified by FasR, TNFRs, Wsl-1/DR-3/TRAMP, CAR1, or DR-4/TRAIL. It should be noted that a controversy regarding the activation of the JNK protein kinase during TNF-mediated apoptosis has arisen in the literature. Verheij et al (99) have suggested that JNK activation and c-jun phosphorylation occur following TNF- and ceramide-mediated apoptosis. Others have shown that the death effector functions of TNFR1 are not associated with these phenomena (100). Data from other laboratories demonstrating that JNK activity is associated with NF-κB activation and a proliferative response is most consistent with the conclusions of Liu et al (100). Furthermore, the FasR appears to mediate a much stronger apoptotic response than TNFR1 (7, 95, 101). Nevertheless, two separate studies have been published suggesting that NF-κB can be activated by stimulation of the FasR in certain cell types and with selected stimuli (95, 101). The associated factors (TRAFs) are responsible for mediating JNK protein kinase activity, NF-κB activation, and suppressing cell death (36, 100). Conversely, the Fas-associated protein with death domain (FADD/MORT1), FADD-like ICE (FLICE/MACH1), TNFR1-associated death domain protein (TRADD), and RIP-associated Ich-1/CED-3 homologous protein with death domain (RAIDD) are required for apoptotic signaling (66, 68, 97, 102).

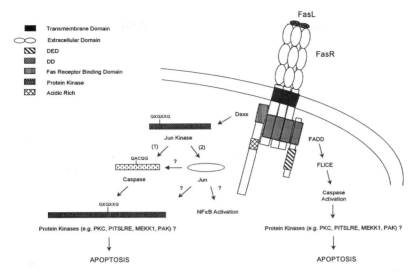

Figure 2 A model depicting the differences between Daxx- and FADD-mediated responses to FasR activation is shown. The details of FADD-mediated apoptosis have been presented in numerous publications (62, 64, 66, 67, 69, 70, 72). The participation of protein kinases is still speculative, but a number of publications report that specific protein kinases are activated by caspase processing (102a–d, 119, 99, 141, 142). Shown in more detail is the activation of JNK by Daxx, the subsequent activation of (1) caspases and (2) the transcription factor c-Jun, the activation of additional protein kinases by caspase processing, and subsequent apoptosis. The target of c-Jun is not known but several possibilities include the caspases, protein kinases, and NF-κB.

In a recent study, Baltimore and coworkers isolated a novel FasR-binding protein by two-hybrid interactive cloning (102a) (Figure 2). This protein, denoted Daxx for Fas death domain-associated protein, interacts with the DD of the FasR even though it does not have a DD sequence of its own. The FasR-binding domain was mapped to the carboxy-terminal region of this $\approx$120 kDa protein. This is the only region with significant homology to other proteins, but a 62 amino acid segment contains >70% glutamic acid and aspartic acid. Daxx co-expression can potentiate a FasR-mediated cell death signal, but its overexpression alone is not capable of inducing apoptosis. The most novel aspect of this study was the demonstration of JNK/SAPK pathway activation following transient transfection of Daxx. Intriguingly, a caxboxyl-terminal deletion mutant of Daxx (removing the protein region important for FasR-binding) acted as a dominant-negative inhibitor of Fas-mediated cell death and JNK activation, providing further evidence for its involvement. Additionally, the authors demonstrated that Daxx and FADD define two distinct FasR-mediated apoptotic signaling pathways (Figure 2). This might explain the conflicting results regarding JNK activation in response to FasR stimulation (99, 100). These results may also explain the FasR-mediated proliferative response observed in other studies (95, 101). It is possible, depending on cell type and possibly other factors, that stimulation of the FasR and recruitment of Daxx can lead to either apoptosis or proliferation, whereas the recruitment of FADD results exclusively in cell death (Figure 2). The activation of JNK in response to FasR stimulation might also be linked to the activation of several other protein kinases observed during FasR-mediated apoptosis (Figure 2) (102b–e, 139, 141, 142).

The TRAFs, TRADD, FADD, and possibly Daxx appear to function solely as adaptor proteins, whereas FLICE/MACH1 (recently renamed caspase 8) and FLICE2/Mch4 (recently renamed caspase 10) also have an associated protease function. These proteins contain a death effector domain (DED) that is highly related to a similar sequence found in the ICE/CPP32/caspase proteins (66, 68–70, 72). Caspase 8, caspase 10, and Daxx are unique because of their ability to directly interact with the FasR. Once these proteins associate with the oligomerized receptor, the resulting activation of its DED, or in the case of Daxx an undefined region, potentiates the death signal through the activation of caspases or JNK. Many of these adaptor proteins were isolated by two-hybrid interactive screening, using the DD from either FasR or TNFR1 as bait. In addition, when FADD or TRADD were used as the bait in a two-hybrid screen, they were re-isolated due to the strong affinity for protein-protein interactions in this motif. This is further evidence that both DDs and DEDs are essential for the protein-protein interactions required for receptor function.

Several new members of the TNF receptor family have recently been isolated by two-hybrid interactive cloning using the same DD bait, as well as by homology searches of the human EST database (73–75, 78, 79). Wsl-1/DR-3/TRAMP/APO-3, DR-4/TRAIL, and CAR1 are all capable of inducing apoptosis when overexpressed in mammalian or avian cells. In addition, Wsl-1/DR-3/TRAMP/APO-3 mediates NF-κB activation, suggesting that its function is more similar to TNFR1 than to FasR. Unlike some of the other TNF family receptors, the Wsl-1/DR-3/TRAMP/APO-3 receptor is preferentially expressed on thymocytes, lymphocytes, and some neuronal cells. When the Wsl-1/DR-3/TRAMP/APO-3 receptor signals apoptosis, FADD is recruited to the oligomerized receptor complex. This apoptotic response can be effectively inhibited by zVAD-fmk, a broad-spectrum polypeptide inhibitor of ICE-like proteases, as well as specific viral gene products (see section on Inhibitors of Caspases). However, expression of the apoptosis inhibitor gene *bcl-2* does not affect the apoptotic response elicited by this receptor. These data suggest that a proteolytic cascade, similar to those associated with FasR and TNFR1, is linked to other receptors in this family and that these protease cascades are an essential component of many apoptotic pathways.

The Caspase Proteases

In the past two years, ten cysteine proteases related to the interleukin-1β-converting enzyme (ICE) have been identified as essential components of many apoptotic signaling pathways (Figure 3, Table 1) (66, 102–112). The *C. elegans ced-3* gene was isolated, and its predicted protein sequence was found to be very similar to the mammalian ICE protein (47). Prior to the identification of *ced-3* as a homologue of mammalian ICE, protease involvement in apoptotic signaling was demonstrated by the use of nonspecific protease inhibitors (113–117). These studies were often inconsistent because of the broad, nonspecific nature of the protease inhibitors used. Even so, these studies suggest that proteases are essential elements of apoptotic signaling pathways. Specific serine protease

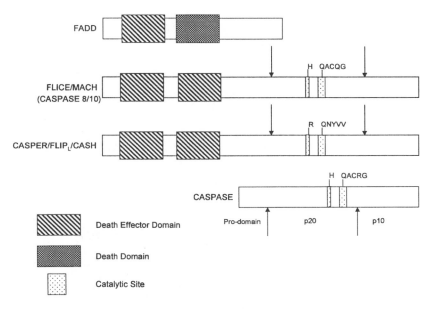

Figure 3 Schematic representation of a caspase. Shown are the locations of the pro-domain, the active site, and the cleavage sites involved in autocatalytic activation or used by another caspase for activation. For comparison a schematic is shown of the structures of caspases 8 and 10 (FLICE/MACH) and FLIP$_L$/Casper/CASH, which are much like other caspases except for the DED found in the amino-terminal portion of these proteins. In the case of the FLIP$_L$/Casper/CASH protein, the active site of the caspase has been extensively modified (as shown). The DED is lost once caspase 8 or 10 is activated (see 62, 66, 67, 70 for details). Also shown is the related structure of the adapter protein FADD.

Table 1 Caspase protease family

Protease name	Other names for enzyme	Recognition site	Peptide, chemical inhibitors	Viral inhibitors	Substrates
caspase 1	ICE, CED-3	YVAD ↓ G YVPD ↓ S	zVAD, YVAD, DEVD, NO	p35, CrmA, E8-FLIP	pIL-1β, pYama, PARP, pNEDD2, pICE, actin, PITSLRE
caspase 2	ICH-1, NEDD-2		zVAD	p35	pNEDD2, PARP
caspase 3	CPP32, Yama, apopain	DEVD ↓ G DMQD ↓ N YVPD ↓ S	DEVD-CHO, zVAD, TPCK, NO	p35, CrmA	pCPP32, PARP, PKCδ, PITSLRE, DNA-PK, SREBP, pRb, rho-GDI, fodrin?
caspase 4	ICErel-II, TX, ICH-2		zVAD, YVAD, DEVD	p35	pICE, pTX, PARP
caspase 5	ICErel-III, TY, ICH-3			CrmA	
caspase 6	Mch2	VEID ↓ NG	zVAD, TLCK	p35, CrmA	PARP, lamins
caspase 7	Mch3, ICE-LAP3, CMH-1		EVD, DEVD-CHO	CrmA	PARP, pcaspase 6
caspase 8	FLICE1, MACH1, Mch5		zVAD, DEVD, IETD	CrmA, E8-FLIP	pICE-like, pCPP32-like
caspase 9	ICE-LAP6, Mch6			CrmA	PARP
caspase 10	FLICE2, Mch4		DEVD	p35	PARP, pICE-like, pCPP32-like

A listing of many of the currently known mammalian caspases. Pertinent characteristics, such as their other names, cleavage sites (if known), inhibitors, and substrates, are shown. Details can be found in the text and references therein.

inhibitors can block the apoptotic activity of numerous ICE-related cysteine proteases (e.g. the ability of TPCK to block drug-induced and Fas-mediated cell death) (118, 119), which suggests that these enzymes represent a separate, and possibly distinct, subgroup of proteases that functions as mediators of death signals, much like the protein kinase cascades that are responsible for mitogenic signaling.

Many of the ICE-like proteases, referred to as caspases 1–10 (120), were isolated by molecular cloning using PCR-based methodologies (Table 1) (111, 112). The term caspase is based on a common nomenclature system adopted by investigators in the field; c reflects a cysteine protease mechanism, and aspase refers to the ability of these proteases to cleave a protein following an aspartic acid residue (50, 121). These caspases can induce apoptosis when they are ectopically expressed in mammalian cells. However, it should be pointed out that ectopic expression of several serine proteases with no known apoptotic function, including trypsin, chymotrypsin, and proteinase K (113), can also induce cell death. The caspases have been divided into three groups based on similarities in their structure: ICE-like, CPP32-like, and Ich1-like (39, 111, 112, 121). Many of the caspase enzymes contain a conserved sequence, QAC(R/Q)G, required for the catalytic activity of these enzymes (Figures 1 and 3) (50, 122, 123). However, both FLICE1/MACH1 (caspase 8) and FLICE2/Mch4 (caspase 10) contain the sequence QACQG at their active sites (66, 69), whereas a novel FADD- and caspase-related inducer of apoptosis (Casper) (123a–d) contains a sequence QNYVW (see Figures 1 and 3). All the caspases cleave their substrates following an aspartic acid (D) residue. The mechanism responsible for Casper-induced apoptosis in not known. The preferred recognition sequences for three of the caspases have been identified: Caspase 1 recognizes the sequence YVAD, caspase 3 recognizes the sequence DEVD, and caspase 6 recognizes the sequence VEID (121, 124, 125). One caveat to the assignment of recognition sequences to individual caspases is the very strong possibility that their specificity is flexible (see Cellular Protease Targets for further discussion).

A mammalian caspase polypeptide consists of a variable amino-terminal pro-domain and two enzyme subunits (Figure 3) (50, 108, 121). These functional subunits include an ≈17–20-kDa protein species (Figures 1 and 3; p20), which contain the active site of the enzyme, and a ≈10-kDa subunit (Figure 3, p10). In a site-directed mutational analysis of murine caspase 2, amino acid residues necessary for activation and function were identified (122). Residues involved in generating the p20 subunit by autocatalysis were necessary for biologic activity. In addition, the specificity of aspartate residues involved in intramolecular cleavages was confirmed. Interestingly, mutations at these various sites had differential effects on the overall cleavage pattern of the protein. Once these subunits are generated by cleavage of the proenzyme, they often heterodimerize.

The activation of these caspases is directly linked to the aggregation of the TNF receptors (see above). In some cases (e.g. FLICE/MACH1/caspase 8), two DEDs occupy the carboxy-terminal domain of the protein, whereas the amino-terminal region contains a caspase-related domain (36, 67, 97, 128). A functional caspase enzyme can be generated following receptor oligomerization by autocatalysis, by the action of another caspase, or by granzyme B cleavage of the caspase precursor (zymogen) (116, 127–130). Thus a proteolytic cascade linked to these receptors is an integral part of the cellular apoptotic signaling apparatus associated with diverse stimuli. The activation of caspases can occur sequentially, as well as in parallel pathways, and some cellular targets are processed by multiple caspases/proteases (39, 68, 110, 111, 131). It should be noted that examples of caspase-independent apoptotic signaling have also been observed (132) (described in more detail below).

Where are these caspases located within a viable cell, and what happens once apoptosis is triggered? This is an important question, particularly because the morphologic changes of apoptosis can occur in the cytoplasm independently of nuclear events (30, 31, 133). One approach used to address this question involves the enucleation of cells prior to apoptotic stimuli (30, 31). Somewhat surprisingly, the enucleated cells exhibit many of the physical and biochemical characteristics, e.g. membrane blebbing, of cells containing a nucleus. Additional studies of cell death in neuronal cells has demonstrated that de novo synthesis of RNAs and/or proteins is not required for the induction or execution of cell death (134, 135). Such experiments are the basis of a popular model, which suggests that much of the cellular apoptotic machinery exists in a pro-form in viable cells and that apoptosis occurs independently of nuclear factors (35, 136). Although this is an appealing model with experimental evidence supporting this interpretation, it may not be indicative of all cells undergoing apoptosis. Furthermore, many of the known caspase substrates are nuclear proteins (e.g. PARP, lamins; protein kinases PKCδ, PCKθ, PITSLRE, MDM2, and MEKK1; topoisomerase U1–70K; and the retinoblastoma protein) (102b–e, 137–144, 144a). Considering the limited number of cellular proteins that are cleaved by caspases during apoptosis, the selection of predominantly nuclear targets as substrates suggests that the nucleus is an active participant in death. In addition, some stimuli (such as the negative selection of autoreactive T cells) that trigger apoptosis are dependent on active gene transcription and translation (16, 17). Finally, in a study of etoposide-induced apoptosis in HL-60 human acute myelomonocytic leukemia cells, multiple caspase homologues were found in both the cytoplasm and nucleus (145). The mechanism responsible for the appearance of active nuclear caspases has not been definitively established; however, the data suggest (a) that there is transport of the active caspase into the nucleus and (b) that specific, inactive caspases are already in the nucleus awaiting activation promoted by a factor or another caspase.

The identification of caspase substrates has contributed significantly to determining the sites of cleavage. Many of the caspases cleave at highly related, possibly even identical, sites in vitro and in vivo (68, 121, 110, 131, 137, 141, 142, 145–154). Thus it is not clear whether each caspase has a specific recognition site that directs its cleavage or if the caspases are functionally redundant. Possibly both assumptions are true. These observations are quite similar to the developments that have taken place in cell cycle research, where a number of cellular proteins were mis-identified as substrates of the cyclin-dependent p34^{cdc2} protein kinase (CDK1) (156–158), prior to the identification of additional CDK family members. During the past six years, many of these substrates have been identified as bona fide targets of other cyclin/CDK complexes, or even multiple cyclin/CDK complexes (159). Furthermore, only one caspase (Ced-3) has been isolated from the nematode *C. elegans* thus far, whereas at least ten distinct caspases have been found in mammals. This discrepancy could reflect signal and/or cell-type specificity in mammals that is not required in *C. elegans*. The apparent functional redundancy of these proteases may be necessary to prevent the catastrophic effects that might occur if all caspase function were lost. The large family of mammalian caspase proteases may have evolved to protect cells from the potentially lethal effects of environmental stress. Such stress could result in mutations and/or loss of normal proliferative controls. In fact, there is experimental evidence to support this hypothesis. Disruption of the caspase 1 gene in mice is not lethal and, in fact, may have no significant effect on the development or viability of the mouse (160, 161). However, thymocytes from these caspase 1$^{-/-}$ mice no longer respond properly to UV-irradiation or glucocorticoid. In contrast, elimination of the caspase 3 gene from mice primarily affects the development of certain neuronal cells (see Regulation of Development by Caspases) (162).

Although the identification of caspase targets will undoubtedly provide important new information regarding caspase function, and ultimately the mechanism(s) responsible for apoptosis, it may be just as important to understand why many cellular proteins are not targeted for cleavage by these proteases. Of particular interest is the mechanism(s) responsible for the selection of specific cellular proteins for caspase cleavage. Is caspase processing linked to phosphorylation and/or dephosphorylation of these cleavage sites? More importantly, do caspase activities regulate additional cellular processes such as progression through the cell cycle? The answers could have significant impact on how the process of cell death is viewed, as well as the possible relationship(s) between death and other cell functions.

Granzymes and Cathepsin D

There is substantial evidence supporting the role of additional proteases, other than the caspases, in various forms of apoptosis (128–130, 163–166). These proteases include the granzymes and cathepsin D. Granzyme B is a serine esterase that can activate several members of the caspase family (see 167 for a detailed review). Studies of granzyme B are extremely relevant to any discussion of programmed cell death because cytotoxic T lymphocytes (CTL) induce apoptosis by releasing granzyme B and perforin. Perforin is essential for this process because its activity is required to form pores in the membrane of the cell under attack. These pores then allow granzyme B to enter the cell and initiate apoptosis. The in vivo targets of granzyme B remain obscure. Recently, granzyme B was shown to activate caspase 3 and caspase 9 directly in vitro (128–130, 165, 168, 169). Treatment of mouse embryonic fibroblasts deficient in caspase 1 (the caspase 1 gene has been knocked out) with perforin and granzyme B does not result in apoptosis (130), which suggests that caspase 1 is downstream of caspase 3. However, if thymocytes from the same caspase $1^{-/-}$ mouse are used in the same experiment, caspase 3 is processed and activated, and the nuclear enzyme poly(ADP-ribose) polymerase (PARP; a nuclear marker for apoptosis in many cell types) is processed appropriately. Granzyme B is also capable of cleaving and activating caspase 3, and although caspase 1 is also cleaved by granzyme B, it is not activated (165, 168, 170). One interpretation of these results is that a caspase 1-dependent pathway is necessary for caspase 3 activation in fibroblasts, whereas a caspase 1-independent pathway is intrinsic to the thymic cells from the same mouse. Even though this may be correct, it is important to consider the possibility that multiple, parallel apoptotic signaling pathways could coordinately regulate cell death in a number of different cell types. Such parallel signaling pathways could provide functional redundancy, or they could represent another level of cellular control in response to different stimuli.

Granzyme B may help activate the nuclear events associated with CTL-induced apoptosis, consistent with the observations indicating that it can be passively transported into the nucleus (164). Once the granzyme is inside the nucleus, it apparently binds to nuclear/nucleolar proteins. The translocation of granzyme B into the nucleus, however, is not accompanied by alterations in either the active or passive nuclear transport properties of the cell. It will be of interest to determine whether granzyme B targets nuclear proteins or components of the nuclear envelope. If granzyme B does affect nuclear proteins, it might suggest that the nucleus is required for the proper execution of cell death in certain cell types. Although enucleated cells have been found to be fully competent to execute certain aspects of a cell death program, this situation is rarely encountered in vivo. The apoptotic machinery required for certain death signals may be contained entirely within the cytoplasm; however, both nuclear and cytoplasmic factors may be necessary for a response to other death signals.

Besides the caspases and granzymes, the aspartic protease cathepsin D and the serine protease AP24 (apoptosis protease 24) may also be involved in interferon-γ (IFN-γ)-, TNF-, and Fas-mediated cell death (40, 42, 166, 171). Cathepsin D is best known for its proteolysis of endocytosed proteins in the lysosome, proteolytic activation of secreted proteins, and an extracellular activity associated with the migration of metastatic cells (166). Its function during cytokine-mediated programmed cell death was revealed by its isolation in a genetic screen for positive mediators of IFN-γ-induced apoptosis of HeLa cells. Expression of cathepsin D antisense constructs effectively inhibited IFN-γ-, TNF-, and Fas-mediated apoptosis. In addition, when these cells were treated with pepstatin A, a specific inhibitor of aspartic proteases, a significant reduction in the level of apoptotic cells was observed. Thus cathepsin D and AP24 may have previously unrecognized roles in certain forms of apoptosis.

Receptor/Protease Complexes

How do death receptors activate an intracellular death program? What prevents the inadvertent activation of this apoptotic signaling pathway? Two of the most-studied receptor complexes are TNFR1 and FasR (7, 36, 56–60, 64, 65, 69, 71). TNFR1 presents its own particular challenge because it can mediate both proliferative and death responses (60, 63, 88, 100). The FasR complex, denoted as the death-inducing signaling complex (DISC) by Krammer and colleagues, has provided an excellent model for determining how these complexes assemble once the ligand is bound, as well as the subsequent intracellular changes that follow (60, 62, 64, 67, 70, 172, 173). As mentioned above, the DD has been implicated in the recruitment of specific proteins that interact with the TNF-related receptors and, depending on which cytoplasmic DD-containing proteins are recruited, potentiate either a proliferative or death signal (36, 67, 81, 83, 86, 91, 93–98). For example, once the TNF and Fas receptors are activated by binding their respective ligands, cytoplasmic proteins containing similar DDs (e.g. TRADD and FADD) are recruited to interact with the DD of these receptors, as well as with each other (Figure 1). FADD, but not TRADD, also contains a motif at its amino terminus, the DED, which is responsible for signaling downstream apoptotic targets (66, 67, 92, 174). Thus although the DD is associated with a number of TNF receptors and adaptor proteins, the DED is found only in FADD, caspase 8, and caspase 10 (Figure 3). Most of these proteins are involved in signaling cell death, but the related TRAFs are not. This appears to be an important distinction, with the presence or absence of these DED domains determining whether these receptor complexes stimulate cell proliferation or trigger cell death. For example, the TNF-related receptors (particularly TNFR1) can function in an anti-apoptotic capacity by recruiting cytoplasmic proteins (e.g. TRAF) that contain DDs but not DEDs. Conversely, the FasR is primarily associated with apoptotic signals, which is consistent with its interactions with FADD, caspase 8, and caspase 10, all of which have DEDs.

The dynamics of receptor/complex interactions and their effect on caspase activity have been best defined for the FasR and its corresponding DISC (60, 62, 64, 67, 70, 172, 173). Molecular analysis of the DISC following persistent activation by agonistic FasR antibodies has revealed that several novel peptides generated for the DISC correspond to cleavage products of the caspase 8 prodomain (70). Furthermore, the release of the active subunits of caspase 8, namely p20 and p10, into the cytoplasm is associated with the activation of a protease cascade in these cells. All the cytosolic caspase 8 appears to be recruited to the DISC and converted to the active p10 and p20 subunits, which eventually depletes all of the caspase 8 precursor from the cytoplasm. DISC-associated caspase 8 activation was blocked by several peptide inhibitors (e.g. zVAD-fmk, zDEVD-fmk, and zIETD-fmk), but not by the peptide inhibitor Ac-YVAD-CHO or CrmA overexpression. CrmA is well known for its ability to inhibit Fas-mediated apoptosis (see Inhibitors of Caspases), so its inability to block caspase 8 processing and activation suggests that a CrmA-inhibitable caspase is blocked downstream of caspase 8. When fluorescent substrates were used to monitor the caspase activities following FasR activation, a caspase 1-like activity was rapidly and transiently activated, whereas a caspase 3-like activity gradually increased with time (64, 68, 125, 175). Similar sequential activation of caspases was also seen when cell-free systems were used to examine lysates from Fas-activated and nonactivated cells (32). It will be of interest to determine whether the activation of additional FasR (DISC)-associated caspases (e.g. caspase 10) results in the same sequential activation of downstream caspases and substrate proteolysis.

Many important questions regarding the changes that occur in these receptor/protease complexes once ligand binds have not been answered. Obviously, these complexes are dynamic entities, assembled and physically altered during apoptotic signaling. Are there other proteins involved in this signaling process? In all likelihood there are important downstream effectors that are not part of the DISC. Of particular interest are the PKCδ, PKCθ, MEKK1, and PITSLRE protein kinases, all of which are activated by caspase processing during apoptosis (119, 139, 141, 142). Are these protein kinases linked to the caspase cleavage of other substrates? Such crosstalk between the caspases and protein kinases during cell death would suggest yet another level of cellular control. Perhaps the most important and exciting questions concerning the regulation of cell death involve the elucidation of a link between receptor/caspase activation and the many physical changes (e.g. changes in cellular organelles, nuclear morphology, chromatin condensation, and DNA cleavage) that occur as a result of apoptosis.

Cellular Protease Targets

Clearly, the early apoptotic events associated with the TNF- and Fas-related receptors (e.g. receptor interaction with TRADD, FADD, and caspases 8 and 10) have been characterized more extensively than the events occurring in the later stages of cell death (e.g. dissolution of the nuclear envelope, disruption of the transcription, processing and translation of RNAs, chromatin condensation and DNA cleavage by nucleases). Our understanding of how specific TNF receptor/caspase complexes are formed and activated can now be exploited to identify the relevant cellular target(s) of these proteases, as well as their downstream targets (71). What are the downstream effectors? A downstream effector of a receptor-caspase complex should be a protein whose function is altered in a meaningful manner by the action of the caspases (e.g. the activation of additional caspase proteases) (112, 112, 154, 176). It should be emphasized, however, that a number of important components in apoptotic pathways may not be linked directly to caspases.

As mentioned above, all the known caspases cleave their substrates after an aspartic acid residue. Relatively few of these substrates have been identified. Those that have been fall into three categories: (*a*) other caspase proteases, (*b*) cellular proteins that need to be inactivated for cell death to occur, and (*c*) cellular proteins whose activation is required for execution of cell death. Examples of proteins in the first group include many of the pro-enzyme forms of the caspases: pro-caspase 1, pro-caspase 3, pro-caspase 8, and pro-caspase 10 (66, 68–70, 110, 111, 129, 175, 177). This list will undoubtedly grow as new caspases are identified and as the nature of receptor-caspase complexes associated with various apoptotic stimuli is elucidated.

The second group of substrates includes poly(ADP-ribose) polymerase (PARP), the 70-kDa protein component of the U1-ribonucleoprotein (U1–70K), the catalytic subunit of the DNA-dependent protein kinase (DNA-PK), the GDP dissociation inhibitor for the Rho family GTPases (D4-GDI), the retinoblastoma protein (pRb), fodrin, actin, and lamins (137–139, 143, 144, 146, 148, 154, 178, 179). Cleavage of these proteins by caspases results in their functional inactivation, which may be critical for progression of cell death. PARP, U1–70K, and DNA-PK function in the splicing of mRNA and the repair of double-strand DNA breaks, whereas D4-GD1 is required for Rho GTPase signaling and cytoskeletal events; their functional inactivation would be useful in the context of cell death (137, 138, 146, 148, 154, 179). The pRb protein participates in the regulation of the cell cycle, and it exhibits an anti-apoptotic effect (143, 144). Obviously, neither this effect nor a vigorous cell cycle is desirable during apoptosis (143, 144). Finally, fodrin, actin, and the lamins are important structural components necessary to maintain cell shape and integrity. The disruption of the cytoskeleton and nuclear envelope are events that have been associated with most forms of apoptosis (110, 150–153).

The third group of proteins, all of which could serve as downstream effectors of caspase-mediated apoptosis, include the protein kinases PKCδ, PKCθ, MEKK1, and PITSLRE; the sterol regulatory element-binding proteins 1 and 2 (SREBP-1 and SREBP-2); and the DNA fragmentation factor (DFF) (102b–e, 119, 139, 141, 142, 180, 181). Activation or alteration of specific protein kinase activities by caspase processing raises the intriguing possibility that crosstalk between these proteases and protein kinases contributes to cell death. Overexpression of PKCδ, PKCθ < MEKK1, and PITSLRE cDNAs that mimic their apoptotic cleavage products results in cell death (119, 141). If caspase processing of these protein kinases alters their substrate specificity significantly, it would suggest that they are active participants, and not merely by-standers, in apoptotic signaling. It is possible that these protein kinases regulate caspase activity by phosphorylating important cleavage sites or nearby residues in substrates; considering the number of cellular proteins that have likely caspase cleavage sites and the actual number of proteins cleaved, this hypothesis is attractive. The cleavage of the SREBP-1 and SREBP-2 proteins releases an amino-terminal fragment that can activate transcription of specific genes (180). Activation of a transcription factor could facilitate the expression of specific genes during apoptosis, quite similar to the induction of the steroid orphan receptor Nurr-77 that occurs during T-cell receptor-mediated apoptosis (16, 17).

Protease-Independent Signaling

Many of the recent studies of apoptotic signaling pathways have focused on the role of the caspase proteases and their cellular targets. However, caspase-independent pathways that contribute significantly to cell death may also exist. Evidence for this comes from a study of the Bcl-2 antagonists Bax and Bak, as well as the *C. elegans ced-4* gene (132, 182–185). Bax is a member of the Bcl-2 protein family whose expression can induce cell death, presumably by forming heterodimers with Bcl-2 (188). The ratio of Bcl-2 antagonists to Bcl-2 agonists in these heterodimers helps to determine the sensitivity of a cell to death signals (184, 187–191). Bax overexpression results in cell death, as determined by characteristic morphological changes, nuclear condensation, and DNA fragmentation (132, 183, 186, 187, 192). A concomitant increase in the proteolytic cleavage of DEVD-AFC, a specific fluorogenic peptide substrate of caspase 1, was also observed, but caspase 3 activity was not increased when measured in a similar manner. Suppression of caspase activity in these cells by zVAD-fmk, an effective inhibitor of caspase 1 and all other tested caspases, prevented chromatin condensation and DNA fragmentation (132). On the other hand, changes in membrane permeability, cell membrane blebbing, and cytoplasmic vacuolation were not inhibited. Similarly, apoptosis induced by specific oncogenes, radiation-induced DNA damage, or overexpression of Bak did not require caspase activity (182, 193, 194). Ectopic expression of the *C. elegans ced-4* gene in the yeast *Schizosaccharomyces pombe* induced rapid chromatin condensation and cell death, which was inhibited by expression of the *ced-9* gene (185). The possibility that either an undefined caspase activity or another protease participates in Bax- and Bak-mediated death cannot be ruled out. However, these results suggest that Bax activates two separate apoptotic pathways, one of which is caspase-dependent and the other caspase-independent. Whether a similar situation exists for other mediators of cell death is not known.

INHIBITORS OF CASPASES

Normal, nontransformed cells have an inherent capacity to initiate and block apoptotic signals. In the proper context, these functions allow a cell to defend itself against viral invasion or potentially deleterious alterations in its genome. As an example of the former, virally infected cells can undergo apoptosis mediated by activated cytotoxic T cells to defend themselves against viral infection (195). Cell-autonomous mechanisms of apoptosis, which do not rely on the delivery of apoptotic-inducing proteins from another cell, can also contribute to cell death. However, many of these cellular suicide programs are subverted by oncogenes and viruses to promote their own survival. As we have learned more about the mechanisms involved in signaling cell death, it has become apparent that these agents recruit cellular inhibitors of apoptosis to promote their own survival in an otherwise unhealthy cell.

The Bcl-2 Family of Genes

The *bcl-2* gene was first isolated as the proto-oncogene involved in a t(14;18) translocation found in human follicular lymphomas (196–198). Numerous studies have shown that Bcl-2 can protect cells from (or at least delay) apoptosis induced by a number of stimuli, including growth factor withdrawal (e.g. from IL-3-dependent 32D myeloid cells) (199, 200); trophic factor withdrawal (e.g. neurons) (201); *c-myc* overexpression (9, 202–204); p53-regulated (205); and Fas- (125, 206, 207) and glucocorticoid-induced cell death (208). The Bcl-2 family of proteins have been localized to cytoplasmic and nuclear membranes, where they may function to generate membrane pores (209–215). X-ray and NMR analysis of Bcl-x$_L$ indicates that its tertiary structure is very similar to pore-forming bacterial toxins, suggesting that it too may function by forming similar pores (215). Thus far the *C. elegans ced-9* gene is the only bcl-2 homologue in the nematode, and it effectively prevents programmed cell death in this organism (49, 216–218); however, a single amino acid substitution in Ced-9 protein transforms it into a death agonist (192). This ability of Bcl-2 to protect cells from apoptosis suggests that its normal function is to negatively regulate essential apoptotic gene products. Of course, other interpretations of these observations are compatible. Additional evidence supporting Bcl-2 function as a pore-forming agent has come from studies using cell-free apoptotic systems (211–213). The release of cytochrome c from mitochondria, which is essential for apoptosis to occur (219), can be prevented by Bcl-2. This effect is circumvented when sufficient cytochrome c is added back into the system. Thus Bcl-2 appears to inhibit cytochrome c translocation from mitochondria, which is consistent with its possible role in forming membrane pores.

At least 11 distinct bcl-2-related genes have been identified in mammals; they include *bcl-2, bcl-x_L, bcl-w, bfl-1, BRAG-1*, and *mcl-1* (antagonists of apoptosis); and *bax, bik, bad, bax*, and *bcl-xs* (agonists of apoptosis) (184, 186, 187, 189, 220–222a, 231c). All these family members can either homo- or heterodimerize with one another, depending on their abundance in a particular cell (187, 222). In fact, the ratio of Bcl-2 agonists to antagonists may help determine cellular sensitivity to various apoptotic stimuli. Bax-induced cell death in mammalian cells is caspase independent (132). Intriguingly, expression of mammalian *bax* or *bak* in yeast is lethal, but this cell death is not accompanied by the activation of caspase-like activities or internucleosomal DNA fragmentation, and it cannot be rescued by the baculovirus p35 protein (182, 183, 193). Further studies are certainly warranted to determine whether this response defines a conserved, caspase-independent apoptotic signaling pathway in eukaryotes.

The phosphorylation status of several Bcl-2 family members, including Bcl-2 and Bad, may also influence their ability to bind to other Bcl-2 family members (223–225). Furthermore, Bcl-2 may target protein kinases and phosphatases to cytoplasmic membranes (223, 224, 226–228). The Raf-1 protein kinase is targeted to mitochondria by Bcl-2, whereas a constitutively active form of Raf-1 enhances Bcl-2-mediated resistance to apoptosis and hyperphosphorylation of Bad, a death agonist (224, 225). In separate studies, Bcl-2 was found in association with the calcium-regulated phosphatase calcineurin on cytoplasmic membranes, suggesting that it might affect gene expression in these cells (227, 228). Calcineurin associated with Bcl-2 was active, but it was incapable of facilitating the nuclear translocation of NF-AT, one of calcineurin's proposed functions. NF-AT is a transcription factor essential for activation-induced T-cell death. When Bax, a Bcl-2 family agonist, was co-expressed in these same cells, the interaction between Bcl-2 and calcineurin was disrupted, and NF-AT was translocated into the nucleus.

Overexpression of *bcl-2* or other related death antagonists will effectively block apoptosis caused by a variety of stimuli in vitro and in vivo (125, 207, 229–231). Normally, Fas-mediated cell death is accompanied by mitochondrial damage. This Fas-induced damage can be effectively blocked by either overexpression of *bcl-2* or caspase inhibitors, suggesting that Bcl-2 functions upstream of the caspases (207). Genetic studies in *C. elegans* are also consistent with this interpretation, with the *Bcl-2* gene homologue *ced-9* functioning upstream of the caspase gene homologue *ced-3* (49, 216–217). Thus the endogenous levels of these proteins in a given cell should influence the cell's sensitivity to apoptotic signals. In support of this hypothesis, the *C. elegans* CED-9 protein was recently found in association with CED-4, a death agonist (218). This association inhibited the ability of CED-4 to induce apoptosis, presumably by blocking the ability of CED-4 to activate the CED-3 caspase-like protein.

In the process of biochemically defining mammalian cytosolic proteins that activate caspase 3, Wang and colleagues identified three distinct apoptosis activating factors (Apaf-1–3) (231a,b). Apaf-2 was shown to be the electron transfer protein cytochrome *c*, which when added to an in vitro apoptotic system facilitates apoptosis (231a). Bcl-2 may protect cells from death, in part, by preventing cytochrome *c* release from mitochondria and/or binding to and inhibiting CED-4. Recently, Apaf-1 was isolated and shown to be a mammalian CED-4 homologue that can bind to cytochrome *c*, possibly resulting in the activation of caspase 3 (CED-3 in *C. elegans*) (231b). Activation of caspase 3 also requires a third factor, Apaf-3, a 45-kDa protein not yet identified. Thus, as suggested by genetic studies in *C. elegans*, CED-4/Apaf-1 may function as an adaptor protein to facilitate the interaction of CED-9/Bcl-2 and CED-3/caspase 3. Clearly, mammalian and nematode death pathways are highly conserved. Finally, an intriguing question concerns the possibility that one or more of the Bcl antagonists are cleaved by caspases to generate Bcl agonists. Examination of the human Bcl-2 and Bcl-x$_L$ protein sequences reveals that both contain a possible caspase recognition sequence, LFRD↓G, at a location that almost mimics the region removed from Bcl-x$_S$ (231c). Thus caspase activation could lead to the subsequent cleavage of Bcl-2 and/or Bcl-x$_L$, inactivating their antagonist function(s) and/or creating agonists. If this occurs, it could further define the nature of CED-3/CED-4/CEd-9 (caspase/Apaf-1/Bcl-2 in humans) interactions and their consequences.

CrmA, p35, and the Cellular IAPs

The identification of the caspase proteases as downstream effectors of TNF receptor-related apoptotic pathways has facilitated the identification of cellular, viral, and synthetic inhibitors of cell death. The caspase inhibitors initially identified in these experiments correspond to viral genes whose function is to prevent host cell death (137, 138, 232–240). Viruses inhibit host cell death by blocking caspase activity, by activating a Bcl-2 antagonist, or by influencing cellular transcription factors that regulate apoptotic or anti-apoptotic gene functions. One novel class of viral genes whose product effectively inhibits apoptosis corresponds to the *crmA* gene from the cowpox virus and to the p35-kDa inhibitor of apoptosis (IAP) from baculovirus (137, 138, 232–237). The cowpox virus-encoded cytokine response modifier A (crmA) is a 38-kDa serine protease inhibitor (serpin) that can effectively block both TNF- and Fas-mediated apoptosis, apparently by forming a stable complex with the caspase (232, 234, 241). CrmA preferentially inhibits caspase 1-like proteases versus caspase 3-like proteases, as well as granzyme B (233, 234).

The p35 protein from baculovirus is another viral protein inhibitor of cell death, which was discovered as a viral gene mutation that causes premature death of the host (242). The substrate specificity of p35 is much broader than that of crmA because it can inhibit both caspase 1-like proteases and caspase 3-like proteases with similar effectiveness (236, 237, 243). Another baculovirus gene product that can inhibit apoptosis is the IAP protein, which has no apparent sequence identity with p35, even though both proteins function equally well to block apoptosis in insect cells (193, 235, 244–247). Mammalian *iap* gene homologues, *c-iap1* and *c-iap2*, have been found to interact with TNFR2 via the TRAF1 and TRAF2 adaptor proteins and effectively suppress apoptosis in selected cell lines (245, 248). The baculovirus IAP protein has also been shown to inhibit *reaper*-mediated apoptosis in *Drosophila,* possibly via its interaction with the DCP-1/drICE protease (244). In an effort to identify additional cellular targets of the IAPs, two-hybrid screens have been performed using a *Drosophila* embryonic cDNA library (247). An alternatively spliced product of the *Drosophila mod* gene, *mdg4* (whose product has been named doom), was identified by its interaction with IAP. This alternatively spliced *mdg4* gene transcript does not contain a leucine-zipper motif (BTB) found in normal *mod* gene transcripts. The *mod* gene encodes a protein that regulates chromatin structure and gene expression. The *mdg4* gene transcript contains a unique sequence, designated DSD in place of the BTB, and its ectopic expression in insect SF-21 cells causes apoptosis. Deletion/mutation analysis of the *mdg4* gene transcript demonstrated that the DSD motif was necessary and sufficient to induce apoptosis. The mechanism of the DSD-induced apoptosis is not clear, but it may involve sequestering and/or altering the normal cellular localization of the *iap* gene products (247).

Recent studies of the human X-chromosome-linked *iap* gene product (XIAP) have shown that it functions by directly inhibiting at least two members of the caspase family of proteases (247a). XIAP was found to effectively inhibit many cell death signals, including cytochrome *c*-mediated nuclear destruction that is not affected by exogenously added bcl-2. Further examination of this inhibitory activity demonstrated that XIAP functions by directly binding to the partially processed products of the caspase 3 and 7 zymogens; in the presence of XIAP, the caspase 3 zymogen precursor was cleaved at a site between the large and small subunits without the subsequent removal of the pro-domain (Figure 1). Thus while caspase 8 can be activated in the presence of XIAP, the subsequent activation of caspase 3 is inhibited, as are the morphologic changes (e.g. nuclear envelope destruction, chromatin condensation) normally associated with caspase 8-mediated apoptosis. In addition to the ability of XIAP to inhibit caspase-mediated death in vivo, XIAP was shown to efficiently bind and inhibit caspase 3 and 7 in vitro (247a). Interestingly, although XIAP could bind and inhibit a partially processed caspase in vitro, it could not bind the unprocessed pro-zymogen form of the caspase, suggesting that XIAP directly binds active caspase 3 and caspase 7 but not their inactive zymogen precursors. Clearly, further elucidation of IAP function may provide significant insights into the apoptotic process. In addition, it would be of interest to determine whether the processing and/or activity of caspases is affected by phosphorylation/dephosphorylation. Such post-translational modifications could greatly enhance the control of cell death processes.

Viral and Cellular FLICE-Inhibitory Proteins (FLIPs)

The isolation and characterization of cellular genes responsible for mediating apoptotic signals (e.g. the caspase-mediated death pathways involving receptors, adaptors, and proteases) has resulted in the identification of numerous viral genes that encode death inhibitors (238–240). Many of the protein-protein interactive domains, such as the DD and DED, are excellent potential targets of these viral inhibitors. When death receptors or adaptors containing mutations in their DD and/or DED are expressed in cells, they function in a dominant-negative fashion to inhibit cell death (67, 249). Based on these observations, genomic databases were screened in an attempt to identify novel genes with homology to the DED (238–240). Several viral genes encoding proteins with DED-related motifs were identified: the equine herpesvirus type 2 E8 protein, bovine herpesvirus-4, herpesvirus saimiri (HVS), human herpesvirus-8 (HHV-8), and the human molluscipox virus (molluscum contagiosum virus, MCV). These viral proteins interact with FADD and/or the caspase 8 (FLICE1) pro-domain when they are cotransfected into mammalian cells and have been termed FLIPs (FLICE-inhibitory proteins). Based on the similarities between the caspase 8 and caspase 10 sequences, including the pro-domain, it is likely that these viral FLIPs will also effectively inhibit apoptotic signals mediated by caspase 10.

In addition, various TNFRs are able to act as in vivo partners of numerous FLIPs, resulting in inhibition of their receptors' death activity, although not to the same extent observed when they are associated with FADD (238, 240). The expression of viral transcripts corresponding to the FLIPs during the viral replication cycle appear well before cellular lysis, suggesting that they may protect the virally infected cells from premature apoptosis by viral overload (240). Others have observed that loss-of-function mutations in the *p35, iap,* and *E1B19K* viral genes lead to a decrease in viral productivity following infection (242, 244, 250). This suggests that a general mechanism for inhibition of cell death may be utilized by a large number of viruses and that there are potentially many more of these viral death-inhibitory proteins. By blocking the DD or DED in the caspase system of proteins, these viral proteins can effectively inhibit apoptosis mediated by caspases (195, 242, 244).

As anticipated, cellular FLIPs have now been identified (123a–d). FLIP$_S$, one form of the human cellular FLIPs, is short and contains two DEDS, much like the viral FLIPs. FLIPs can also effectively block cellular death induced by all known death receptors. However, in contrast to the viral FLIPs, a much longer human protein, FLIP$_L$, has been identified. Three groups have also identified this protein: Casper (for caspase-eight-related protein) (123b); I-FLICE (for an inhibitor of FLICE) (123c); and CASH (for caspase homologue) (123d). FLIP$_L$/Casper/CASH/I-FLICE is apparently generated by alternative splicing and contains the same two DEDs found in FLIP$_S$ and a caspase-like domain in which a tyrosine has been substituted for the cysteine normally found in the active site (Figures 1 and 3). The exact function of FLIP$_L$ is controversial, with two groups (123b, 123c) reporting that FLIP$_L$ overexpression induces or potentiates apoptosis, whereas other groups (123a,d) report that it effectively inhibits apoptosis. These differences are unlikely to be due to cell-type specificity because it was shown that FLIP$_L$/Casper/CASH/I-FLICE induced apoptosis in HeLa cells (123b), and others reported that it did not have cytocidal effects when expressed in the same cells (123c). A more likely explanation is that the discrepancy reflects differences in the level of expression of the protein. Tschopp and colleagues reported that while a very high, nonphysiological level of FLIP$_L$ was capable of inducing apoptosis in 293T cells, a lower, more physiological level was not (123a).

Synthetic Peptide Inhibitors and Substrates of Caspases

In an attempt to understand the mechanisms underlying various apoptotic signaling pathways, synthetic peptide inhibitors that mimic cleavage sites of the caspases (usually at an Asp-X bond) have been chemically derived and used for in vitro and in vivo analysis of enzyme activity (32, 124, 172, 251). These peptides are generally very small, 3 to 4 amino acids in length, and include zVAD-fmk (benzyloxycarbonyl-Val-Ala-Asp-fluoromethylketone), DEVD-fmk (acetyl-Asp-Glu-Val-Asp-fluoromethylketone), YVAD-fmk (acetyl-Tyr-Val-Ala-Asp-fluoromethylketone), and VEID-fmk (acetyl-Val-Glu-Ile-Asp-fluoromethyl-ketone). The sequences of these various peptides are based on the caspase recognition sites of substrates. YVAD-fmk is based on the caspase 1 recognition site in pro-interleukin-1 , DEVD-fmk is based on the caspase 3 recognition site found in PARP, and VEID-fmk is based on the caspase 6 recognition site in lamin. These inhibitors are not highly specific, but they do appear to effect caspases identified within a particular group (e.g. caspase 3-like). Even though these peptides are related to one another, their subtle sequence differences can dramatically influence the specificity of their substrate inhibition. The zVAD-fmk and YVAD-fmk peptides are capable of effectively blocking most caspase-mediated apoptosis (e.g. caspase 1 and 3), whereas DEVD-fmk effectively blocks only caspase 3 (CPP32-like) protease activity, and VEID-fmk primarily blocks caspase 6 activity (32, 125, 172). These peptide inhibitors are soluble, relatively stable (a half-life of 2–4 h), and show dose-dependent inhibition of cell death after several different stimuli (e.g. Fas-induced death is inhibited best by 10 μM zVAD-fmk) (32, 172). In fact, the rate of enzyme inactivation by these peptide inhibitors can be determined by addition of excess inhibitor to the enzyme reactions and observing the nature of the time-dependent inhibition of substrate hydrolysis (125).

Peptide substrates for these caspases are also available [e.g. YVAD-AMC (acetyl-Tyr-Val-Ala-Asp-aminomethylcoumarin) and DEVD-AMC (acetyl-Asp-Glu-Val-Asp-aminomethylcoumarin)]. The hydrolysis of these substrates by caspase activities associated with cytosolic or nuclear proteins can be measured by determining the amount of fluorescent AMC product formation (125, 145). In addition, the molecular weight of a caspase or caspases responsible for a particular biologic response can be determined by affinity labeling with N-(N-benzyloxycarbonylglutamyl-$N\epsilon$-biotinyllysyl)-aspartic acid [(2, 6-dimethylbenzoyl)oxy]methyl ketone followed by one- or two-dimensional gel analysis of the proteins. This approach was used effectively by Kaufmann and colleagues (145) to demonstrate that multiple caspase isoforms (i.e. two species that comigrated with active caspase 6 and three species that comigrated with active caspase 3) were associated with ectoposide-induced apoptosis in HL-60 cells. This affinity labeling of caspases also helped these investigators to demonstrate that a unique set of nuclear pro-caspases (i.e. pro-caspase 2) exists in these cells. Considerable effort is currently being focused on the development of caspase-specific inhibitors, which would have potentially important clinical and pharmacological uses, as well as important research applications. Caspase-specific inhibitors could be used to target selected apoptotic pathways, such as the Fas-mediated pathways recently associated with several autoimmune disorders (252). These inhibitors could also be used to block individual caspase proteases, allowing the definitive identification of each protease involved in the processing of specific substrates, as well as helping to order the upstream and downstream events within a particular apoptotic signaling pathway.

REGULATION OF DEVELOPMENT BY CASPASES

Much of the early work demonstrating that PCD was mediated by a specific set of genes came from developmental studies of *C. elegans* and *Drosophila* (44, 47, 216). Loss-of-function mutations in genes such as *reaper* (*rpr*) in *Drosophila* and *ced-3* in *C. elegans* prevent the normal death of specific cells during development (44, 47). Thus much like the conserved cyclin/CDK regulatory pathway in eukaryotes, which facilitated the isolation of the human CDK1 homologue by complementation of a yeast *ts* mutant (253), the conserved nature of apoptotic signaling in *Drosophila* and *C. elegans* has resulted in the identification of the important genes.

Drosophila and Reaper

In contrast to the vertebrate TNF-related receptors described above, *Drosophila* expresses a group of unique DED-containing proteins corresponding to the *rpr*, *head involution defective* (*hid*), and *grim* genes (43–46) (Figure 1). These proteins act as apoptotic activators that mediate their function through one or more caspases, and all are essential for triggering PCD (157). Apoptotic signals generated by activation of reaper, hid, and grim can be effectively blocked by the baculovirus p35 protein (244), suggesting that the general mechanism of PCD in *Drosophila* is similar to that of vertebrates.

Much like the FADD, TRADD, and FLICE/MACH1 (caspase 8) and FLICE2/Mch4 (caspase 10) proteins in vertebrates, these proteins contain death domains. However, none of these proteins contains the pro-caspase-like domains associated with caspase 8 and 10, and in the case of the 65-amino acid *rpr* gene product, encode little more than a DED. DED function in these proteins may be linked to promoting protein-protein interactions involving these activators and their corresponding caspases. In a recent study of *rpr*, it was shown that mutations in its DED, mimicking mutations in the DEDs of TRADD, FADD, and FLICE1/MACH1 known to affect their binding to the TNF and Fas receptors, did not influence the ability of reaper to induce cell death per se (82). When all the relevant *Drosophila* caspases, as well as other possible death effectors, are identified, the similarities and differences between PCD pathways and apoptotic signaling in vertebrates should be clear.

C. elegans and the ced Genes

Horvitz and colleagues were the first to use genetic analysis of *C. elegans* to determine whether genes are responsible for the PCD that occurs during development (38, 47, 49, 216). They identified three genes essential for cell death to occur: *ced-3*, *ced-4*, and *ced-9*. The *ced-3* gene encoded a pro-apoptotic product that could be directly inhibited by the product encoded by the *ced-9* gene (47, 256). Similarities between the *ced-3* gene product and the interleukin-1β-converting enzyme (ICE) suggest that a cellular protease is responsible for these PCDs, and its deletion or inactivation in *C. elegans* completely prevents the death of cells that normally occur during development (38). Furthermore, the *ced-3* gene product can induce apoptosis in transfected mammalian cells (51). Conversely, the *ced-9* gene product can inhibit the pro-apoptotic function of the *ced-3* gene, and it was shown that this gene is a *C. elegans* homologue of the mammalian bcl-2 gene (38, 49, 216). The exact function of the final *ced* gene, *ced-4*, was not elucidated until recently when it was demonstrated that CED-4 acts as an adaptor that allows interaction between CED-3 and CED-9 (48, 217, 218). In addition, ectopic expression of the *ced-4* gene in *S. pombe* leads to rapid chromatin condensation and cell death (185).

The CED-9 protein was isolated as a binding-partner of CED-4 in an interactive genetic screen (218). Loss-of-function mutants in the *ced-9* gene prevented the corresponding protein from associating with CED-4. Normally, CED-4 is localized in the cytosol, but when CED-9 is expressed in mammalian cells, it targets CED-4 from the cytosol to intracellular membranes, suggesting that CED-9 plays an important role in the subcellular localization of CED-4 (218). It will be of interest to determine whether the relationship between CED-4 and CED-9 is associated with the phenotype of CED-4 overexpression in *S. pombe* (185, 218). The rather striking ability of ectopic *ced-4* gene expression to induce chromatin condensation and death in yeast may indicate that this interaction is, indeed, one of the functions of CED-9 and that its sequestering of CED-4 inhibits apoptosis. In a separate study, the product of the *ced-4* gene was shown to facilitate the interaction of CED-3 with CED-9 (217). Furthermore, CED-4 also facilitated physical interactions between the mammalian ICE and FLICE proteins. The exact relationship between these three proteins is not clear but will undoubtedly be the focus of intense research.

Effects of Caspase Gene Elimination on Mouse Development

In mammals, the elimination of either the ICE (caspase 1) or CPP32 (caspase 3) genes in mice by homologous recombination produces two very distinctive phenotypes (160–162). Deletion of ICE did not affect the normal development of the caspase $1^{-/-}$ mice or the ability of their thymocytes to respond to exposure to glucocorticoid or UV. However, the thymic cells from these caspase $1^{-/-}$ mice were insensitive to apoptosis mediated by the Fas receptor (161). Conversely, deletion of the CPP32 (caspase 3) gene in mice resulted in developmental defects primarily affecting neuronal cells and the brain, which resulted in premature embryonic lethality (162). This phenotype is of some interest because the developmental defects exhibited by these caspase $3^{-/-}$ mice are very similar to the neuronal hyperplasia that occurs in loss-of-function *ced-3* gene mutants in *C. elegans* (41, 48). It will be of interest to determine whether there are phenotypes associated with other caspase gene knockouts, or if their functions are conserved well enough to act in a redundant fashion.

CASPASE INVOLVEMENT IN DISEASE

The relationship between Fas/TNF receptor function and the targeting of certain immune cells for elimination by apoptosis has been of interest for some time. Clearly, defects in the ability of these cells to be eliminated from their host could contribute significantly to the pathogenesis of many autoimmune-type disorders (25, 255). In addition, many tumors, particularly those that have become refractory to chemotherapeutic drugs, have circumvented the apoptotic signaling pathways that would normally lead to their elimination (22, 256). By doing so, they enhance their chances for survival, as well as increase the frequency of genetic mutations within that particular cell's genome (255, 257). The identification of specific genes required for normal apoptotic signaling should facilitate this analysis and possibly demonstrate that the normal function of these genes is required to avoid these diseases (see below).

Cancer

As mentioned above, several early cell death experiments were based on the ability of certain tumor cells to become insensitive to the chemotherapeutic drugs being used for treatment (22, 173, 256). A number of studies have shown that the in vivo effects of these drugs are to induce tumor cell apoptosis, which suggests that the acquired insensitivity of these cells to cytotoxic drugs and radiation-treatment is the result of inactivation of one or more genes involved in apoptotic signaling (258, 259). In several studies it was elegantly demonstrated that the ability of tumor cells to undergo apoptosis was linked to the tumor suppressor p53. Even so, there is little proof of a direct relationship between the function of pro-apoptotic proteins and the elimination of tumor cells.

The isolation of the *bcl-2* gene, which is responsible for certain follicular lymphomas, was a milestone for investigators studying tumorigenesis and programmed cell death (196–198). This was the first example of an oncogene whose function was linked to the regulation of apoptosis, demonstrating that alterations in apoptotic signaling pathways and mitogenic pathways could contribute to tumorigenesis (255, 257, 260, 261). The *bcl-2* gene was isolated almost 12 years ago, and yet its exact function is not known. But the pioneering studies of many laboratories have demonstrated that defects in pro- and/or anti-apoptotic genes are as significantly linked to tumorigenesis, as are the defects that occur in the well-studied mitogenic and cell cycle pathways involved in normal cell proliferation. In fact, recent experiments have suggested that significant crosstalk between Bcl-2 and the regulators of cell cycle occurs and that Bcl-2 likely contributes to life and death decisions made at cell cycle checkpoints (222, 227, 228, 262). Further evidence of the involvement of Bcl-2 family members in cancer came from a recent study that identified frameshift mutations in the *bax* gene in a subset of colon tumors (263). This particular subset of colon cancers, the microsatellite mutator phenotype (MMP), exhibits exaggerated genomic instability at simple nucleotide repeat sequences scattered throughout the genome as a result of dysfunctional DNA mismatch-repair enzymes. In this study, more than 50% of the MMP colon tumors examined contained frameshift mutations in a tract of eight deoxyguanosines [$(G)_8$] within their *bax* genes. By eliminating Bax, a Bcl-2 antagonist, these cells can promote their own survival in much the same way as do tumors that overexpress Bcl-2, e.g. follicular lymphomas described above. This is further, direct evidence that the ability to properly signal cell death may be just as crucial as the control of the cell cycle in tumor cells.

Recently, several studies have linked a heterozygous loss-of-function allele of the *FasR* gene to increased frequency of Hodgkin's lymphoma (264). One interpretation of this data is that the enhanced survival capabilities of the $FasR^{+/-}$ cells allow them to accumulate genetic insults that can ultimately result in malignancy. In this sense, these genes function as tumor suppressors. However, unlike other traditional tumor suppressors, activating mutations in these genes result in the complete destruction of tissues and organs, leading to death.

Autoimmune Disease

The dysfunction of many cellular immune responses contributes significantly to the development of autoimmune disorders (72, 252). The resulting inflammatory response and cellular damage that occur can result in the loss of organ function or even death. The nature of these diseases suggests that many are linked to defects in apoptotic signaling. In fact, mutations in both the Fas receptor and Fas ligand have been associated with autoimmune-type disorders (252). Targeted mutations in the *FasR* gene of mice result in cellular hyperplasia in the peripheral lymphatic organs and liver (265). Another possible interpretation of how Fas-mediated cell death could contribute to autoimmune disease has been recently suggested by two groups (89, 266) who suggest that the Fas ligand may normally function to eliminate activated T cells as soon as they enter sites of "immune privilege." This might explain why the inflammatory response in many organs associated with immune privilege, such as the endothelium, eye, and Sertoli cells of the testis, is so dramatic in *gld* mice, which harbor a defective *FasL* gene (252).

The Fas/TNF receptors are clearly important participants in immune surveillance because even partial loss-of-function within one of the signaling components of these apoptotic pathways could significantly alter the course of life. If this surveillance mechanism is altered even minimally, there are obvious consequences as a result. Furthermore, the fact that altering these pathways either up or down can result in autoimmune disorders or cancer demonstrates that their influence and importance persist long after development and birth.

Visit the *Annual Reviews home page* at
http://www.AnnualReviews.org.

Literature Cited

1. Glucksman A. 1951. Cell deaths in normal vertebrate ontogeny. *Biol. Rev.* 26:59–86
2. Saunders JW Jr. 1966. Death in embryonic systems. *Science* 154:604–12
3. Kerr JFR, Wyllie AH, Currie AR. 1972. Apoptosis: a basic biological phenomenon with wide-ranging implications in tissue kinetics. *Br. J. Cancer* 26:239–57
4. Wyllie AH, Kerr JFR, Currie AR. 1981. Cell death: the significance of apoptosis. *Int. Rev. Cytol.* 68:251–305
5. Wyllie AH. 1980. Glucocorticoid-induced thymocyte apoptosis is associated with endogenous endo-nuclease activation. *Nature* 284:555–56
6. Cohen JJ. 1992. Glucocorticoid-induced apoptosis in the thymus. *Semin. Immunol.* 4:363–69
7. Trauth BC, Klas C, Peters AM, Matzku S, Moller P, et al. 1989. Monoclonal antibody-mediated tumor regression by induction of apoptosis. *Science* 245: 301–5
8. Evan GI, Wyllie AH, Gilbert CS, Littlewood TD, Land H, et al. 1992. Induction of apoptosis in fibroblasts by c-myc protein. *Cell* 69:119–28
9. Askew DS, Ashmun RA, Simmons BC, Cleveland JL. 1991. Constitutive *c-myc* expression in an IL-3-dependent myeloid cell line suppresses cell cycle arrest and accelerates apoptosis. *Oncogene* 6:1915–22
10. Williams GT, Smith CA, Spooncer E, Dexter TM, Taylor DR. 1990. Haemopoietic colony stimulating factors promote cell survival by suppressing apoptosis. *Nature* 343:76–79
11. Ucker DS, Wilson JD, Hebshi LD. 1994. Target cell death triggered by cytotoxic T lymphocytes: A target cell mutant distinguishes passive pore formation and active cell suicide mechanisms. *Mol. Cell. Biol.* 14:427–36
12. Sarma V, Wolf FW, Marks RM, Shows TB, Dixit VM. 1992. Cloning of a novel tumor necrosis factor-α-inducible primary response gene that is differentially expressed in development and tube-like formation in vitro. *J. Immunol.* 148:3302–12
13. Kelley LL, Green WF, Hicks GG, Bondurant MC, Koury MJ, Ruley HE. 1994. Apoptosis in erythroid progenitors deprived of erythropoietin occurs during the G1 and S phases of the cell cyle without growth arrest or stabilization of wild-type p53. *Mol. Cell Biol.* 14:4183–92
14. Owens GP, Hahn WE, Cohen JJ. 1991. Identification of mRNAs associated with programmed cell death in immature thymocytes. *Mol. Cell. Biol.* 11:4177–88
15. McConkey DJ, Hartzell P, Orrenius S. 1990. Rapid turnover of endogenous endonuclease activity in thymocytes: effects of inhibitors of macromolecular synthesis. *Arch. Biochem. Biophys.* 278:284–87
16. Liu Z-G, Smith SW, McLaughlin KA, Schwartz LM, Osborne BA. 1994. Apoptotic signals delivered through the T-cell receptor of a T-cell hybrid require the immediate-early gene nur77. *Nature* 367:281–84
17. Woronicz JD, Calnan B, Ngo V, Winoto A. 1994. Requirement for the orphan steroid receptor Nur77 in apoptosis of T-cell hybridomas. *Nature* 367:277–81
18. Harrington EA, Bennett MR, Fanidi A, Evan GI. 1994. c-Myc-induced apoptosis in fibroblasts is inhibited by specific cytokines. *EMBO J.* 13:3286–95

19. Hamburger V, Oppenheim RW. 1982. Naturally occurring neuronal death in vertebrates. *Neurosci. Commun.* 1:39–55

20. Rabizadeh S, Oh J, Zhong LT, Yang J, Bitler CM, et al. 1993. Induction of apoptosis by the low-affinity NGF receptor. *Science* 261:345–48

21. Oppenheim RW. 1991. Cell death during development of the nervous system. *Annu. Rev. Neurosci.* 14:453–501

22. Hickman JA. 1992. Apoptosis induced by anticancer drugs. *Cancer Metastasis Rev.* 11:121–39

23. Fisher DE. 1994. Apoptosis in cancer therapy: crossing the threshold. *Cell* 78:539–42

24. Gerschenson LE, Rotello RJ. 1992. Apoptosis: a different type of cell death. *FASEB J.* 6:2450–55

25. Oberhammer FA, Hochegger K, Froschl G, Tiefenbacher R, Pavelka M. 1994. Chromatin condensation during apoptosis is accompanied by degradation of lamin A+B, without enhanced activation of cdc2 kinase. *J. Cell Biol.* 126:827–37

26. Vaux DL, Weissman IL. 1993. Neither macromolecular synthesis nor Myc is required for cell death via the mechanism that can be controlled by bcl-2. *Mol. Cell. Biol.* 13:7000–5

27. Martin SJ, Bonham AM, Cotter TG. 1990. The involvement of RNA and protein synthesis in programmed cell death (apoptosis) in human leukaemia HL-60 cells. *Biochem. Soc. Trans.* 18:634–36

28. Krammer PH, Behrmann I, Daniel P, Dhein J, Debatin K. 1994. Regulation of apoptosis in the immune system. *Curr. Biol.* 6:279–89

29. Wang J, Stohlman SA, Dennert G. 1994. TCR cross-linking induces CTL death via internal action of TNF. *J. Immunol.* 151:3824–32

30. Jacobson MD, Burne JF, Raff MC. 1994. Programmed cell death and Bcl-2 protection in the absence of a nucleus. *EMBO J.* 13:1899–910

31. Schulze-Ostoff K, Walczak H, Droge W, Krammer PH. 1994. Cell nucleus and DNA fragmentation are not required for apoptosis. *J. Cell Biol.* 127:15–20

32. Enari M, Hase A, Nagata S. 1995. Apoptosis by a cytosolic extract from Fas-activated cells. *EMBO J.* 14:5201–8

33. Martin SJ, Finucane DM, Amarante-Mendes GP, O'Brien GA, Green DR. 1996. Phosphatidylserine externalization during CD95-induced apoptosis of cells and cytoplasts requires ICE/CED-3 protease activity. *J. Biol. Chem.* 271:28753–56

34. Nakajima H, Golstein P, Henkart PA. 1995. The target cell nucleus is not required for cell-mediated granzyme-or Fas-based cytoxicity. *J. Exp. Med.* 181:1905–9

35. Weil M, Jacobson MD, Coles HSR, Davies TJ, Gardner RL, et al. 1996. Constitutive expression of the machinery for programmed cell death. *J. Cell Biol.* 133:1053–59

36. Hsu H, Shu H, Pan M, Goeddel DV. 1996. TRADD-TRAF2 and TRADD-FADD interactions define two distinct TNF receptor 1 signal transduction pathways. *Cell* 84:299–308

37. Fiers W, Beyaert R, Boone E, Cornelis S, Declercq W, et al. 1996. TNF-induced intracellular signaling leading to gene induction or to cytotoxicity by necrosis or by apoptosis. *J. Inflamm.* 47:67–75

38. Ellis RE, Yuan J, Horvitz HR. 1991. Mechanisms and functions of cell death. *Annu. Rev. Cell Biol.* 4:663–98

39. Fraser A, Evan G. 1996. A license to kill. *Cell* 85:781–84

40. Martin SJ, Lennon SV, Bonham AM, Cotter TG. 1990. Induction of apoptosis (programmed cell death) in human leukemic HL-60 cells by inhibition of RNA or protein synthesis. *J. Immunol.* 145:1859–67

41. Sulston JE, Horvitz HR. 1977. Postembryonic cell lineages of the nematode *Caenorhabditis elegans*. *Dev. Biol.* 82:110–56

42. Bruno S, Del Bino G, Lassota P, Giaretti W, Darzynkiewicz Z. 1992. Inhibitors of proteases prevent endonucleolysis accompanying apoptotic death of HL-60 leukemic cells and normal thymocytes. *Leukemia* 6:1113–20

43. White K, Grether ME, Abrams JM, Young L, Farrell K, Steller H. 1994. Genetic control of programmed cell death in *Drosophila*. *Science* 264:677–83

44. White K, Tahaoglu E, Steller H. 1996. Cell killing by the *Drosophila* gene *reaper*. *Science* 271:805–9

45. Grether ME, Abrams JM, Agapite J, White K, Steller H. 1995. The *head involution defective* gene of *Drosophila melanogaster* functions in programmed cell death. *Genes Dev.* 9:1694–708

46. Chen P, Nordstrom W, Gish B, Abrams JM. 1996. *grim,* a novel cell death gene in *Drosophila*. *Genes Dev.* 10:1773–82

47. Yuan J, Shaham S, Ledoux S, Ellis HM, Horvitz HR. 1993. The *C. elegans* cell death gene *ced-3* encodes a protein

similar to mammalian interleukin-1 β-converting enzyme. *Cell* 75:641–52

48. Shaham S, Horvitz HR. 1996. An alternatively spliced C. elegans ced-4 RNA encodes a novel cell death inhibitor. *Cell* 86:201–8

49. Hengartner MO, Ellis RE, Horvitz HR. 1992. *Caenorhabditis elegans* gene *ced-9* protects cells from programmed cell death. *Nature* 356:494–99

50. Wilson KP, Black JF, Thomson JA, Kim EE, Griffith JP, et al. 1994. Structure and mechanism of interleukin-1-β-converting enzyme. *Nature* 370:270–75

51. Miura M, Zhu H, Rotello R, Hartwieg EA, Yuan J. 1993. Induction of apoptosis in fibroblasts by IL-1 β-converting enzyme, a mammalian homolog of the C. elegans cell death gene *ced-3*. *Cell* 75:653–60

52. Nordstrom W, Chen P, Steller H, Abrams JM. 1996. Activation of the *reaper* gene during ectopic cell killing in *Drosophila*. *Dev. Biol.* 180:213–26

53. Sherr CJ, Roberts JM. 1995. Inhibitors of mammalian G_1 cyclin-dependent kinases. *Genes Dev.* 9:1149–63

54. Sherr CJ. 1994. G1 phase progression: cycling on cue. *Cell* 79:551–55

55. McConkey DJ, Jondal M, Orrenius S. 1992. Cellular signaling in thymocyte apoptosis. *Semin. Immunol.* 4:371–77

56. Schall TJ, Lewis M, Koller KJ, Lee A, Rice GC, et al. 1990. Molecular cloning and expression of a receptor for human tumor necrosis factor. *Cell* 61:361–70

57. Loetscher H, Pan Y-CE, Lahm H-W, Gentz R, Brockhaus M, et al. 1990. Molecular cloning and expression of the human 55 kd tumor necrosis factor receptor. *Cell* 61:351–59

58. Shu HB, Takeuchi M, Goeddel DV. 1996. The tumor necrosis factor receptor 2 signal transducers TRAF2 and c-IAP1 are components of the tumor necrosis factor receptor 1 signaling complex. *Proc. Natl. Acad. Sci. USA* 93:13973–78

59. Zheng L, Fisher G, Miller RE, Peschon J, Lynch DH, Lenardo MJ. 1995. Induction of apoptosis in mature T cells by tumor necrosis factor. *Nature* 377:348–51

60. Schulze-Ostoff K, Krammer PH, Droge W. 1994. Divergent signalling via APO-1/Fas and the TNF receptor, two homologous molecules involved in physiological cell death. *EMBO J.* 13:4587–96

61. Frade JM, Rogriquez-Tebar A, Barde Y-A. 1996. Induction of cell death by endogenous nerve growth factor through its p75 receptor. *Nature* 383:166–68

62. Peter ME, Kischkel FC, Hellbardt S, Chinnaiyan AM, Krammer PH, Dixit VM. 1996. CD95 (APO-1/-Fas)-associating signalling proteins. *Cell Death Differ.* 3:161–70

63. Vandenabeele P, Declercq W, Beyaert R, Fiers W. 1995. Two tumour necrosis factor receptors: structure and function. *Trends Cell Biol.* 5:392–99

64. Kischkel FC, Hellbardt S, Behrmann I, Germer M, Pawlita M, et al. 1995. Cytotoxicity-dependent APO-1 (Fas/CD95)-associated proteins form a death-inducing signaling complex (DISC) with the receptor. *Proc. Natl. Acad. Sci. USA* 14:5579–88

65. Ju S, Panks DJ, Cui H, Ettinger R, El-Khatib M, et al. 1995. Fas(CD95)/FasL interactions required for programmed cell death after T-cell activation. *Nature* 373:444–48

66. Muzio M, Chinnaiyan AM, Kischkel FC, O'Rourke K, Shevchenko A, et al. 1996. FLICE, a novel FADD-homologous ICE/CED-3-like protease, is recruited to the CD95 (Fas/Apo-1) death-inducing signaling complex. *Cell* 85:817–27

67. Boldin MP, Goncharov TM, Goltsev YV, Wallach D. 1996. Involvement of MACH a novel MORT1/-FADD-interacting protease, in Fas/Apo-1 and TNF receptor-induced cell death. *Cell* 85:803–15

68. Srinivasula SM, Ahmad M, Fernandes-Alnemri T, Litwack G, Alnemri ES. 1996. Molecular ordering of the Fas-apoptotic pathways: The Fas/Apo-1 protease Mch5 is a CrmA-inhibitable protease that activates multiple Ced3/ICE-like cysteine proteases. *Proc. Natl. Acad. Sci. USA* 93:14486–91

69. Vincenz C, Dixit VM. 1997. Fas-associated death domain protein interleukin-1β-converting enzyme 2 (FLICE2), and ICE/CED-3 homologue, is proximally involved in CD95- and p55-mediated death signaling. *J. Biol. Chem.* 272:6578–83

70. Medema JP, Scaffidi C, Kischkel FC, Shevchenko A, Mann M, et al. 1997. FLICE is activated by association with the CD95 death-inducing signaling complex (DISC). *EMBO J.* 16:794–804

71. Cleveland JL, Ihle JN. 1995. Contenders in FasL/TNF death signaling. *Cell* 81:479–82

72. Nagata S. 1997. Apoptosis by death factor. *Cell* 88:355–65

73. Brojatsch J, Naughton J, Rolls MM, Zingler K, Young JAT. 1996. CAR1, a TNFR-related protein, is a cellular

receptor for cytopathic avian leukosis-sarcoma viruses and mediates apoptosis. *Cell* 87:845–55

74. Chinnaiyan AM, O'Rourke K, Yu G, Lyons RH, Garg M, et al. 1996. Signal transduction by DR3, a death domain-containing receptor related to TNFR-1 and CD95. *Science* 274:990–92

75. Kitson J, Raven T, Jiang Y, Goeddel DV, Giles KM, et al. 1996. A death-domain-containing receptor that mediates apoptosis. *Nature* 384:372–75

76. Wiley SR, Schooley K, Smolak PJ, Din WS, Huang C, et al. 1995. Identification and characterization of a new member of the TNF family that induces apoptosis. *Immunity* 3:673–82

77. Bodmer J, Burns K, Schneider P, Hofmann K, Steiner V, et al. 1997. TRAMP, a novel apoptosis-mediating receptor with sequence homology to tumor necrosis factor receptor 1 and Fas (APO-1/CD95). *Immunity* 6:79–88

78. Marsters SA, Sheridan JP, Donahue CJ, Pitti RM, Gray CL, et al. 1996. Apo-3, a new member of the tumor necrosis factor receptor family, contains a death domain and activates apoptosis and NF-κB. *Curr. Biol.* 6:1669–76

79. Pitti RM, Marsters SA, Ruppert S, Donahue CJ, Moore A, Ashkenazi A. 1996. Induction of apoptosis by Apo-2 ligand, a new member of the tumor necrosis factor cytokine family. *J. Biol. Chem.* 271:12687–90

80. Pan G, O'Rourke K, Chinnaiyan AM, Gentz R, Ebner R, et al. 1997. The receptor for the cytotoxic ligand TRAIL. *Science* 276:111–13

81. Hofmann K, Tschopp J. 1995. The death domain motif found in Fas(APO-1) and TNF receptor is present in proteins involved in apoptosis and axonal guidance. *FEBS Lett.* 371:321–23

82. Chen P, Lee P, Otto L, Abrams J. 1996. Apoptotic activity of REAPER is distinct from signaling by the tumor necrosis factor receptor 1 death domain. *J. Biol. Chem.* 271:25735–37

83. Golstein P, Marguet D, Depraetere V. 1995. Homology between Reaper and the cell death domains of Fas and TNFR1. *Cell* 81:185–86

84. Huang BH, Eberstadt M, Olejniczak ET, Meadows RP, Fesik SW. 1996. NMR structure and mutagenesis of the Fas(APO-1/CD95) death domain. *Nature* 384:638–41

85. Duan H, Dixit VM. 1997. RAIDD is a new "death" adaptor molecule. *Nature* 385:86–89

86. Uren AG, Vaux DL. 1996. TRAF proteins and meprins share a conserved domain. *Trends Biochem. Sci.* 21:244–45

87. Lee SY, Choi Y. 1997. TRAF-interacting protein (TRIP): a novel component of the tumor necrosis factor receptor (TNFR)- and CD30-TRAF signaling complexes that inhibits TRAF2-mediated NF-κB activation. *J. Exp. Med.* 185:1275–85

88. Hsu H, Huang J, Shu H, Baichwal V, Goeddel DV. 1996. TNF-dependent recruitment of the protein kinase RIP to the TNF receptor-1 signaling complex. *Immunity* 4:387–96

89. Griffith TS, Brunner T, Fletcher SM, Green DR, Ferguson TA. 1995. Fas ligand-induced apoptosis as a mechanism of immune privilege. *Science* 270:1189–92

90. Hunter T. 1993. Braking the cycle. *Cell* 75:839–41

91. Stanger BZ, Leder P, Lee T, Kim E, Seed B. 1995. RIP: A novel protein containing a death domain that interacts with Fas/APO-1 (CD95) in yeast and causes cell death. *Cell* 81:513–23

92. Chinnaiyan AM, O'Rourke K, Tewari M, Dixit VM. 1995. FADD, a novel death domain-containing protein, interacts with the death domain of Fas and initiates apoptosis. *Cell* 81:505–12

93. Chu K, Niu X, Williams LT. 1995. A Fas-associated protein factor, FAF1, potentiates Fas-mediated apoptosis. *Proc. Natl. Acad. Sci. USA* 92:11894–98

94. Zhang J, Winoto A. 1996. A mouse Fas-associated protein with homology to the human MORT1/FADD protein is essential for Fas-induced apoptosis. *Mol. Cell. Biol.* 16:2756–63

95. Packham G, Lahti JM, Fee BE, Gawn JM, Coustan-Smith E, et al. 1997. Fas activates NF-κB and induces apoptosis in T-cell lines by signaling pathways distinct from those induced by TNF-α. *Cell Death Differ.* 4:130–39

96. Ting AT, Pimentel-Muinos FX, Seed B. 1996. RIP mediates tumor necrosis factor receptor 1 activation of NF-κB but not Fas/APO-1-initiated apoptosis. *EMBO J.* 15:6189–96

97. Hsu HL, Xiong J, Goeddel DV. 1995. The TNF receptor 1-associated protein TRADD signals cell death and NF-κB activation. *Cell* 81:495–504

98. Uren AG, Pakusch M, Hawkins CJ, Puls KL, Vaux DL. 1996. Cloning and expression of apoptosis inhibitory protein homologs that function to inhibit apoptosis and/or bind tumor necrosis factor

receptor-associated factors. *Proc. Natl. Acad. Sci. USA* 93:4974–78

99. Verheij M, Bose R, Lin XH, Yao B, Jarvis WD, et al. 1996. Requirement for ceramide-initiated SAPK/JNK signalling in stress-induced apoptosis. *Nature* 380:75–79

100. Liu Z-G, Hsu H, Goeddel DV, Karin M. 1996. Dissection of TNF receptor 1 effector functions: JNK activation is not linked to apoptosis while NF-κB activation prevents cell death. *Cell* 87:565–76

101. Ponton A, Clement M, Stamenkovic I. 1996. The CD95 (APO-1/Fas) receptor activates NF-κB independently of its cytotoxic function. *J. Biol. Chem.* 271:8991–95

102. Wang L, Miura M, Bergeron L, Zhu H, Yuan JY. 1994. *Ich-1,* an *Ice/ced-3*-related gene, encodes both positive and negative regulators of programmed cell death. *Cell* 78:739–50

102a. Yang X, Khosravi-Far R, Chang HY, Baltimore D. 1997. Daxx, a novel Fas-binding protein that activates JNK and apoptosis. *Cell* 89:1067–76

102b. Datta R, Kojima H, Yoshida K, Kufe D. 1997. Caspase-3-mediated cleavage of protein kinase C θ in induction of apoptosis. *J. Biol. Chem.* 272:20317–20

102c. Cardone MH, Salveson GS, Widmann C, Johnson G, Frisch SM. 1997. The regulation of aniokis: MEKK-1 activation requires cleavage by caspases. *Cell* 90:315–23

102d. Lassignal-Johnson N, Garder AM, Diener KM, Lange-Carter CA, Gleavy J, et al. 1996. Signal transduction pathways regulated by mitogen-activated/extracellular response kinase kinase induced cell death. *J. Biol. Chem.* 271:3229–37

102e. Rudel T, Bokoch GM. 1997. Membrane and morphological changes in apoptotic cells regulated by caspase-mediated activation of PAK2. *Science* 276:1571–74

103. Alnemri ES, Fernandes-Alnemri T, Litwack G. 1995. Cloning and expression of four novel isoforms of human interleukin-1β converting enzyme with different apoptotic activities. *J. Biol. Chem.* 270:4312–17

104. Fernandes-Alnemri T, Litwack G, Alnemri ES. 1995. Mch2, a new member of the apoptotic *Ced-3/Ice* cysteine protease gene family. *Cancer Res.* 55:2737–42

105. Kamens J, Paskind M, Hugunin M, Talanian RV, Allen H, et al. 1995. Identification and characterization of ICH-2, a novel member of the interleukin-1

β-converting enzyme family of cysteine proteases. *J. Biol. Chem.* 270:15250–56

106. Munday NA, Vaillancourt JP, Ali A, Casano FJ, Miller DK, et al. 1995. Molecular cloning and pro-apoptotic activity of ICE$_{rel}$II and ICE$_{rel}$III, members of the ICE/CED-3 family of cysteine proteases. *J. Biol. Chem.* 270:15870–76

107. Fernandes-Alnemri T, Litwack G, Alnemri ES. 1994. CPP32, a novel human apoptotic protein with homology to *Caenorhabditis elegans* cell death protein Ced-3 and mammalian interleukin-1-β-converting enzyme. *J. Biol. Chem.* 269:30761–64

108. Nicholson DW, Ali A, Thornberry NA, Vailancourt JP, Ding CK, et al. 1995. Identification and inhibition of the ICE/CED-3 protease necessary for mammalian apoptosis. *Nature* 376:37–43

109. Srinivasula SM, Fernandes-Alnemri T, Zangrilli J, Robertson N, Armstrong RC, et al. 1996. The Ced-3/interleukin 1β converting enzyme-like homolog Mch6 and the lamin-cleaving enzyme Mch2α are substrates for the apoptotic mediator CPP32. *J. Biol. Chem.* 271:27099–106

110. Wang S, Miura M, Jung Y, Zhu H, Gagliardini V, et al. 1996. Identification and characterization of Ich-3, a member of the interleukin 1β converting enzyme (ICE)/Ced-3 family and an upstream regulator of ICE. *J. Biol. Chem.* 271:20580–87

111. Yuan J. 1995. Molecular control of life and death. *Curr. Opin. Cell Biol.* 7:211–14

112. Whyte M. 1996. ICE/CED-3 proteases in apoptosis. *Trends Cell Biol.* 6:245–48

113. Henkart PA. 1996. ICE family proteases: mediators of all apoptotic cell death? *Immunity* 4:195–201

114. Shiver JW, Su L, Henkart PA. 1992. Cytotoxicity with target DNA breakdown by rat basophilic leukemia cells expressing both cytolysin and granzyme A. *Cell* 71:315–22

115. Collins MKL, Rivas AL. 1993. The control of apoptosis in mammalian cells. *Trends Biochem. Sci.* 18:307–9

116. Heusel JW, Wesselschmidt RL, Shresta S, Russell JH, Ley TJ. 1994. Cytotoxic lymphocytes require granzyme B for the rapid induction of DNA fragmentation and apoptosis in allogeneic target cells. *Cell* 76:977–87

117. Rukenstein A, Rydel RE, Greene LA. 1991. Multiple agents rescue PC12 cells from serum-free cell death by transla-

tion- and transcription-independent mechanisms. *J. Neurosci.* 11:2552–63

118. Shaw E, Mares-Guia M, Cohen W. 1965. Evidence for an active-center histidine in trypsin through use of a specific reagent, 1-chloro-3-tosylamido-7-amino-2-heptanone, the chloromethyl ketone derived from *N-α*-tosyl-L-lysine. *Biochemistry* 4:2219–24

119. Lahti JM, Xiang J, Heath LS, Campana D, Kidd VJ. 1995. PITSLRE protein kinase activity is associated with apoptosis. *Mol. Cell. Biol.* 15:1–11

120. Alnemri ES, Livingston DJ, Nicholson DW, Salvesen G, Thornberry NA, et al. 1996. Human ICE/CED-3 protease nomenclature. *Cell* 87:171

121. Margolin N, Raybuck SA, Wilson KP, Chen W, Fox T, et al. 1997. Substrate and inhibitor specificity of interleukin-1β-converting enzyme and related caspases. *J. Biol. Chem.* 272:7223–28

122. Allet B, Hochmann A, Martinou I, Berger A, Missotten M, et al. 1996. Dissecting processing and apoptotic activity of a cysteine protease by mutant analysis. *J. Cell Biol.* 135:479–86

123. Yamin T-T, Ayala JM, Miller DK. 1996. Activation of the native 45-kDa precursor form of interleukin-1-converting enzyme. *J. Biol. Chem.* 271:13273–82

123a. Irmier M, Thome M, Hahne M, Schneider P, Hofmann K, et al. 1997. Inhibition of death receptor signals by cellular FLIP. *Nature* 388:190–95

123b. Shu H-B, Halpin DR, Goeddel DV. 1997. Casper is a FADD- and caspase-related inducer of apoptosis. *Immunity* 6:715–63

123c. Goltsev YV, Kovalenko AV, Arnold E, Varfolomeev EE, Brodianskii VM, Wallach D. 1997. CASH, a novel caspase homologue with death effector domains. *J. Biol. Chem.* 272:19641–44

123d. Hu S, Vincenz C, Ni J, Gentz R, Dixit VM. 1997. I-FLICE, a novel inhibitor of tumor necrosis factor receptor 1- and CD95-induced apoptosis. *J. Biol. Chem.* 272:17255–58

124. Milligan CE, Prevette D, Yaginuma H, Homma S, Cardwell C, et al. 1995. Specific peptide inhibitors of the ICE/CPP32-like proteases block apoptosis. *Neuron* 15:385–93

125. Armstrong RC, Aja T, Xiang J, Gaur S, Krebs JF, et al. 1996. Fas-induced activation of the cell death-related protease CPP32 is inhibited by Bcl-2 and by ICE family protease inhibitors. *J. Biol. Chem.* 271:16850–55

126. Deleted in proof

127. Doherty PC. 1993. Cell-mediated cytotoxicity. *Cell* 75:607–12

128. Darmon AJ, Nicholson DW, Bleackley RC. 1995. Activation of the apoptotic protease CPP32 by cytotoxic T-cell-derived granzyme B. *Nature* 377:446–48

129. Martin SJ, Amarante-Mendes GP, Shi L, Chuang T, Casiano CA, et al. 1996. The cytotoxic cell protease granzyme B initiates apoptosis in a cell-free system by proteolytic processing and activation of the ICE/CED-3 family protease, CPP32, via a novel two-step mechanism. *EMBO J.* 15:2407–16

130. Shi L, Chen G, MacDonald G, Bergeron L, Li H, et al. 1996. Activation of an interleukin 1 converting enzyme-dependent apoptosis pathway by granzyme B. *Proc. Natl. Acad. Sci. USA* 93:11002–7

131. Sarin A, Wu M, Henkart PA. 1996. Different interleukin-1β converting enzyme (ICE) family protease requirements for the apoptotic death of T lymphocytes triggered by diverse stimuli. *J. Exp. Med.* 184:2445–50

132. Xiang J, Chao DT, Korsmeyer SJ. 1996. BAX-induced cell death may not require interleukin 1β-converting enzyme-like proteases. *Proc. Natl. Acad. Sci. USA* 93:14559–63

133. Lazebnik YA, Cole S, Cooke CA, Nelson WG, Earnshaw WC. 1993. Nuclear events of apoptosis in vitro in cell-free extracts: a model system for analysis of the active phase of apoptosis. *J. Cell Biol.* 123:7–22

134. Batistatou A, Greene LA. 1993. Internucleosomal DNA cleavage and neuronal cell survival/death. *J. Cell Biol.* 122:523–32

135. Troy CM, Stefanis L, Prochiantz A, Greene LA, Shelanski ML. 1996. The contrasting roles of ICE family proteases and interleukin-1β in apoptosis induced by tropic factor withdrawal and by copper/zinc superoxide dismutase downregulation. *Proc. Natl. Acad. Sci. USA* 93:5635–40

136. Jacobson MD, Weil M, Raff MC. 1996. Role of Ced3/ICE-family proteases in staurosporine-induced programmed cell death. *J. Cell Biol.* 133:1041–51

137. Lazebnik YA, Kaufmann SH, Desnoyers S, Poirier GG, Earnshaw WC. 1994. Cleavage of poly(ADP-ribose) polymerase by a proteinase with properties like ICE. *Nature* 371:347–48

138. Tewari M, Beidler DR, Dixit VM. 1995. CrmA-inhibitable cleavage of the

70-kDa protein component of the U1 small nuclear ribonucleoprotein during Fas- and tumor necrosis factor-induced apoptosis. *J. Biol. Chem.* 270:18738–41

139. Emoto Y, Manome Y, Meinhardt G, Kisaki H, Kharbanda S, et al. 1995. Proteolytic activation of protein kinase C-δ by an ICE-like protease in apoptotic cells. *EMBO J.* 14:6148–56

140. Takahashi A, Alnemri ES, Lazebnik YA, Fernandes-Alnemri T, Litwack G, et al. 1996. Cleavage of lamin A by Mch2α but not CPP32: Multiple interleukin 1β-converting enzyme-related proteases with distinct substrate recognition properties are active in apoptosis. *Proc. Natl. Acad. Sci. USA* 93:8395–400

141. Ghayur T, Hugunin M, Talanian RV, Ratnofsky S, Quinlan C, et al. 1996. Proteolytic activation of protein kinase C-δ by and ICE/CED 3-like protease induces characteristics of apoptosis. *J. Exp. Med.* 184:2399–404

142. Beyaert R, Kidd VJ, Cornelis S, Van de Craen M, Denecker G, et al. 1997. Cleavage of PITSLRE kinases by ICE/CASP-1 and CPP32/CASP-3 during apoptosis induced by tumor necrosis factor. *J. Biol. Chem.* 272:11694–97

143. Janicke RU, Walker CL, Lin XY, Porter AG. 1996. Specific cleavage of the retinoblastoma protein by an ICE-like protease in apoptosis. *EMBO J.* 15:6969–78

144. Tan X, Martin SJ, Green DR, Wang JYJ. 1997. Degradation of retinoblastoma protein in tumor necrosis factor- and CD95-induced cell death. *J. Biol. Chem.* 272:9613–16

144a. Erhardt P, Tomaselli KJ, Cooper GM. 1997. Identification of the MDM2 oncoprotein as a substrate for CPP32-like apoptotic proteases. *J. Biol. Chem.* 272:15049–52

145. Martins LM, Kottke T, Mesner PW, Basi GS, Sinha S, et al. 1997. Activation of multiple interleukin-1β converting enzyme homologues in cytosol and nuclei of HL-60 cells during etoposide-induced apoptosis. *J. Biol. Chem.* 272:7421–30

146. Gu Y, Sarnecki C, Aldape RA, Livingston DJ, Su MS. 1995. Cleavage of poly(ADP-ribose) polymerase by interleukin-1β converting enzyme and its homologs TX and Nedd-2. *J. Biol. Chem.* 270:18715–18

147. Dubrez L, Savoy I, Hamman A, Solary E. 1996. Pivotal role of a DEVD-sensitive step in etoposide-induced and Fas-mediated apoptotic pathways. *EMBO J.* 15:5504–12

148. Cryns VL, Bergeron L, Zhu H, Li H, Yuan J. 1996. Specific cleavage of α-fodrin during Fas- and tumor necrosis factor-induced apoptosis is mediated by an interleukin-1β-converting enzyme/Ced-3 protease distinct from the poly(ADP-ribose) polymerase protease. *J. Biol. Chem.* 271:31277–82

149. Takahashi A, Musy P, Martins LM, Poirier GG, Moyer RW, Earnshaw WC. 1996. CrmA/SPI-2 inhibition of an endogenous ICE-related protease responsible for lamin A cleavage and apoptotic nuclear fragmentation. *J. Biol. Chem.* 271:32487–90

150. Martin SJ, O'Brien GA, Nishioka WK, McGahon AJ, Mahboubi A, et al. 1995. Proteolysis of fodrin (non-erythroid spectrin) during apoptosis. *J. Biol. Chem.* 270:6425–28

151. Rao L, Perez D, White E. 1996. Lamin proteolysis facilitates nuclear events during apoptosis. *J. Cell Biol.* 135:1441–55

152. Mashima T, Naito M, Noguchi K, Miller DK, Nicholson DW, Tsuruo T. 1997. Actin cleavage by CPP-32/apopain during the development of apoptosis. *Oncogene* 14:1007–12

153. Orth K, Chinnaiyan AM, Garg M, Froelich CJ, Dixit VM. 1996. The CED-3/ICE-like protease Mch2 is activated during apoptosis and cleaves the death substrate lamin A. *J. Biol. Chem.* 271:16443–46

154. Song Q, Burrows SR, Smith G, Lees-Miller SP, Kumar S, et al. 1996. Interleukin-1β-converting enzyme-like protease cleaves DNA-dependent protein kinase in cytotoxic T cell killing. *J. Exp. Med.* 184:619–26

155. Pronk GJ, Ramer K, Amiri P, Williams LT. 1996. Requirement of an ICE-like protease for induction of apoptosis and ceramide generation by REAPER. *Science* 271:808–10

156. Moreno S, Nurse P. 1990. Substrates for p34^{cdc2}: in vivo veritas? *Cell* 61:549–51

157. Nigg EA. 1991. The substrates of the cdc2 kinase. *Semin. Cell Biol.* 2:261–70

158. Nigg EA. 1993. Cellular substrates of p34^{cdc2} and its companion cyclin-dependent kinases. *Trends Cell Biol.* 3:296–301

159. Morgan DO. 1995. Principles of CDK regulation. *Nature* 374:131–34

160. Li P, Allen H, Banerjee S, Franklin S, Herzog L, et al. 1995. Mice deficient in IL-1β-converting enzyme are defective in production of mature IL-1β and resis-

tant to endotoxic shock. *Cell* 80:401–11

161. Kuida K, Lippke JA, Ku G, Harding MW, Livingston DJ, et al. 1995. Altered cytokine export and apoptosis in mice deficient in interleukin-1β converting enzyme. *Science* 267:2000–3

162. Kuida K, Zheng TS, Na S, Kuan C, Yang D, et al. 1996. Decreased apoptosis in the brain and premature lethality in CPP32-deficient mice. *Nature* 384:368–72

163. Shimizu T, Pommier Y. 1996. DNA fragmentation induced by protease activation in p53-null human leukemia HL60 cells undergoing apoptosis following treatment with the topoisomerase I inhibitor camptothecin: cell-free system studies. *Exp. Cell Res.* 226:292–301

164. Jans DA, Jans P, Briggs LJ, Sutton V, Trapan JA. 1996. Nuclear transport of granzyme B(Fragmentin-2). *J. Biol. Chem.* 271:30781–89

165. Quan LT, Tewari M, O'Rourke K, Dixit VM, Snipas SJ, et al. 1996. Proteolytic activation of the cell death protease Yama/CPP32 by granzyme B. *Proc. Natl. Acad. Sci. USA* 93:1972–76

166. Deiss LP, Galinka H, Berissi H, Cohen O, Kimchi A. 1996. Cathepsin D protease mediates programmed cell death induced by interferon-, Fas/APO-1 and TNF-α. *EMBO J.* 15:3861–70

167. Greenberg AH. 1996. Activation of apoptosis pathways by granzyme B. *Cell Death Differ.* 3:269–74

168. Duan DR, Orth K, Chinnaiyan AM, Poirier GG, Froelich CJ, et al. 1996. ICE-LAP6, a novel member of the ICE/Ced-3 gene family, is activated by the cytotoxic T cell protease granzyme B. *J. Biol. Chem.* 271:16720–24

169. Anel A, Gamen S, Alava MA, Schmitt-Verhulst A, Pineiro A, Naval J. 1997. Inhibition of CPP32-like proteases prevents granzyme B- and Fas-, but not granzyme A-based cytotoxicity exerted by CTL clones. *J. Immunol.* 158:1999–2006

170. Darmon AJ, Ehrman N, Caputo A, Fujinaga J, Bleackley RC. 1994. The cytotoxic T cell proteinase granzyme B does not activate interleukin-1β-converting enzyme. *J. Biol. Chem.* 269:32043–46

171. Gorczyca W, Gong J, Ardelt B, Traganos F, Darzynkiewicz Z. 1993. The cell cycle related differences in susceptibility of HL-60 cells to apoptosis induced by various antitumor agents. *Cancer Res.* 53:3186–92

172. Los M, Van de Craen M, Penning LC, Schenk H, Westendrop M, et al. 1995. Requirement of an ICE/-CED-3 protease

for Fas/APO-1-mediated apoptosis. *Nature* 375:81–83

173. Chu K, Niu X, Williams LT. 1995. A Fas-associated protein factor, FAF1, potentiates Fas-mediated apoptosis. *Proc. Natl. Acad. Sci. USA* 92:11894–98

174. Grimm S, Stanger BZ, Leder P. 1996. RIP and FADD: Two "death domain"-containing proteins can induce apoptosis by convergent, but dissociable, pathways. *Proc. Natl. Acad. Sci. USA* 93:10923–27

175. Enari E, Talanian RV, Wong WW, Nagata S. 1996. Sequential activation of ICE-like and CPP32-like proteases during Fas-mediated apoptosis. *Nature* 380:723–26

176. Kumar S, Lavin MF. 1996. The ICE family of cysteine proteases as effectors of cell death. *Cell Death Differ.* 3:255–67

177. MacFarlane M, Cain K, Sun X, Alnemri ES, Cohen DR. 1997. Processing/activation of at least four interleukin-1β converting enzyme-like proteases occurs during the execution phase of apoptosis in human monocytic tumor cells. *J. Cell Biol.* 137:469–79

178. Lindahl T, Satoh MS, Poirier GG, Klungland A. 1995. Post-translational modification of poly(ADP-ribose) polymerase induced by DNA strand breaks. *Trends Biochem. Sci.* 20:405–11

179. Na S, Chuang T, Cunningham A, Turi TG, Hanke JH, et al. 1996. D4-GDI, a substrate of CPP32, is proteolyzed during Fas-induced apoptosis. *J. Biol. Chem.* 271:11209–13

180. Wang X, Pai J, Wiedenfeld EA, Medina JC, Slaughter C, et al. 1995. Purification of an interleukin-1 converting enzyme-related cysteine protease that cleaves sterol regulatory element-binding proteins between the leucine zipper and transmembrane domains. *J. Biol. Chem.* 270:18044–50

181. Liu X, Zou H, Slaughter C, Wang X. 1997. DFF, a heterodimeric protein that functions downstream of caspase 3 to trigger DNA fragmentation during apoptosis. *Cell* 89:175–84

182. Ink B, Zornig M, Baum B, Hajibagheri N, James C, et al. 1997. Human bak induces cell death in *Schizosaccharomyces pombe* with morphological changes similar to those with apoptosis in mammalian cells. *Mol. Cell. Biol.* 17:2468–74

183. Jurgensmeier JM, Krajewski S, Armstrong RC, Wilson GM, Oltersdorf T, et al. 1997. Bax- and bak-induced cell death in the fission yeast *Schizosaccha-*

romyces pombe. Mol. Biol. Cell 8:325–39

184. Chittenden T, Harrington EA, O'Connor R, Flemington C, Lutz RJ, et al. 1995. Induction of apoptosis by the Bcl-2 homologue Bak. *Nature* 374:733–36

185. James C, Gschmeissner S, Fraser A, Evan GI. 1997. CED-4 induces chromatin condensation in *Schizosaccharomyces pombe* and is inhibited by direct physical association with CED-9. *Curr. Biol.* 7:246–52

186. Oltvai ZN, Milliman CL, Korsmeyer SJ. 1993. Bcl-2 heterodimerizes in vivo with a conserved homolog, Bax, that accelerates programed cell death. *Cell* 74:609–19

187. Sedlak TW, Oltvai ZN, Yang E, Wang K, Boise LH, et al. 1995. Multiple Bcl-2 family members demonstrate selective dimerizations with Bax. *Proc. Natl. Acad. Sci. USA* 92:7834–38

188. Yin X-M, Oltvai ZN, Korsmeyer SJ. 1994. BH1 and BH2 domains of Bcl-2 are required for inhibition of apoptosis and heterodimerization with Bax. *Nature* 369:321–23

189. Kiefer MC, Brauer MJ, Powers VC, Wu JJ, Umansky SR, et al. 1995. Modulation of apoptosis by the widely distributed Bcl-2 homologue Bak. *Nature* 374:736–39

190. Gottschalk AR, Boise LH, Oltvai ZN, Accavitti MA, Korsmeyer SJ, et al. 1996. The ability of Bcl-x_L and Bcl-2 to prevent apoptosis can be differentially regulated. *Cell Death Differ.* 3:113–18

191. Zha H, Sime-Sempe C, Sato T, Reed JC. 1996. Proapoptotic protein Bax heterodimerizes with Bcl-2 and homodimerizes with Bax via a novel domain (BH3) distinct from BH1 and BH2. *J. Biol. Chem.* 271:7440–44

192. Hunter JJ, Parslow TG. 1996. A peptide sequence from Bax that converts Bcl-2 into an activator of apoptosis. *J. Biol. Chem.* 271:8521–24

193. Orth K, Dixit VM. 1997. Bik and bak induce apoptosis downstream of CrmA but upstream of inhibitor of apoptosis. *J. Biol. Chem.* 272:8841–44

194. McCarthy NJ, Whyte M, Gilbert CS, Evan G. 1997. Inhibition of Ced-3/ICE-related proteases does not prevent cell death induced by oncogenes, DNA damage, or the bcl-2 homologue bak. *J. Cell Biol.* 136:215–27

195. Gillet G, Brun G. 1996. Viral inhibition of apoptosis. *Trends Cell Biol.* 4:312–17

196. Bakhshi A, Jensen JP, Goldman P, Wright JJ, McBride OW, et al. 1985.

Cloning the chromosomal breakpoint of t(14:18) human lymphomas: clustering around J_H on chromosome 14 and near a transcriptional unit on 18. *Cell* 41:899–906

197. Cleary ML, Sklar J. 1985. Nucleotide sequence of a t(14:18) chromosomal breakpoint in follicular lymphoma and demonstration of a breakpoint-cluster region near a transcriptionally active locus on chromosome 18. *Proc. Natl. Acad. Sci. USA* 82:7439–43

198. Tsujimoto Y, Gorham J, Cossman J, Jaffe E, Croce CM. 1985. The t(14:18) chromosome translocations involved in B-cell neoplasms result from mistakes in VDJ joining. *Science* 229:1390–93

199. Vaux DL, Aguila HL, Weissman IL. 1992. Bcl-2 prevents death of factor-deprived cells but fails to prevent apoptosis in targets of cell mediated killing. *Int. Immunol.* 4:821–24

200. Vaux DL, Cory S, Adams JM. 1988. Bcl-2 gene promotes haemopoietic cell survival and cooperates with c-myc to immortalize pre-B cells. *Nature* 335:440–42

201. Garcia I, Martinou I, Tsujimoto Y, Martinou JC. 1992. Prevention of programmed cell death of sympathetic neurons by the Bcl-2 proto-oncogene. *Science* 258:302–4

202. Fanidi A, Harrington EA, Evan GI. 1992. Cooperative interaction between c-myc and bcl-2 proto-oncogene. *Nature* 359:554–56

203. Bissonnette RP, Echeverri F, Mahboubi A, Green DR. 1992. Apoptotic cell death induced by c-myc is inhibited by bcl-2. *Nature* 359:552–54

204. Wagner AJ, Small MB, Hay N. 1993. Myc-mediated apoptosis is blocked by ectopic expression of Bcl-2. *Mol. Cell Biol.* 13:2432–40

205. Chiou SK, Rao L, White E. 1994. Bcl-2 blocks p53-dependent apoptosis. *Mol. Cell. Biol.* 14:2556–63

206. Chinnaiyan AM, Dixit VM. 1996. The cell-death machine. *Curr. Biol.* 6:555–62

207. Boise LH, Thompson CB. 1997. Bcl-x_l can inhibit apoptosis in cells that have undergone Fas-induced protease activation. *Proc. Natl. Acad. Sci. USA* 94:3759–64

208. Vaux DL, Weissman IL, Kim SK. 1992. Prevention of programmed cell death in *Caenorhabditis elegans* by human bcl-2. *Science* 258:1955–57

209. Hockenbery DM, Oltvai ZN, Yin XM, Milliman CL, Korsmeyer SJ. 1993.

Bcl-2 functions in an antioxidant pathway to prevent apoptosis. *Cell* 75:241–51

210. Hockenbery D, Nunez G, Milliman C, Schreiber RD, Korsmeyer SJ. 1990. Bcl-2 is an inner mitochondrial membrane protein that blocks programmed cell death. *Nature* 348:334–36

211. Newmeyer DD, Farschon DM, Reed JC. 1994. Cell-free apoptosis in Xenopus egg extracts: inhibition by bcl-2 and requirement for an organelle fraction enriched in mitochondria. *Cell* 79:353–64

212. Kluck RM, Bossy-Wetzel E, Green DR, Newmeyer DD. 1997. The release of cytochrome *c* from mitochondria: a primary site for bcl-2 regulation of apoptosis. *Science* 275:1132–36

213. Yang J, Liu X, Bhalla K, Kim CN, Ibrado AM, et al. 1997. Prevention of apoptosis by bcl-2: release of cytochrome *c* from mitochondria blocked. *Science* 275:1129–32

214. Susin SA, Zamzami N, Castedo M, Hirsch T, Marchetti P, et al. 1996. Bcl-2 inhibits the mitochondrial release of an apoptogenic protease. *J. Exp. Med.* 184:1331–41

215. Muchmore SW, Sattler M, Liang H, Meadows RP, Harlan JE, et al. 1996. X-ray and NMR structure of human Bcl-x_L, an inhibitor of programmed cell death. *Nature* 381:335–41

216. Hengartner MO, Horvitz HR. 1994. C. elegans cell survival gene *ced-9* encodes a functional homolog of the mammalian proto-oncogene *bcl-2*. *Cell* 76:665–76

217. Chinnaiyan AM, O'Rourke K, Lane BR, Dixit VM. 1997. Interaction of CED-4 with CED-3 and CED-9: a molecular framework for cell death. *Science* 275:1122–26

218. Wu D, Wallen HD, Nunez G. 1997. Interaction and regulation of subcellular localization of CED-4 by CED-9. *Science* 275:1126–29

219. Liu X, Kim CN, Yang J, Jemmerson R, Wang X. 1996. Induction of apoptotic program in cell-free extracts: requirement for dATP and cytochrome *c*. *Cell* 86:147–57

220. Boise LH, Gonzalez-Garcia M, Postema CE, Ding L, Lindsten T, et al. 1993. *bcl-x,* a *bcl-2*-related gene that functions as a dominant regulator of apoptotic cell death. *Cell* 74:597–608

221. Farrow SN, White JHM, Martinou I, Raven T, Pun K-T, et al. 1995. Cloning of a *bcl-2* homologue by interaction with adenovirus E1B 19K. *Nature* 374:731–33

222. Oltvai ZN, Korsmeyer SJ. 1994. Checkpoints of dueling dimers foil death wishes. *Cell* 79:189–92

222a. Reed JC. 1997. Double identity for proteins of the Bcl-2 family. *Nature* 387:773–76

223. Chen C, Faller DV. 1996. Phosphorylation of Bcl-2 protein and association with p21^{Ras} in Ras-induced apoptosis. *J. Biol. Chem.* 271:2376–79

224. Wang H, Rapp U, Reed JC. 1996. Bcl-2 targets the protein kinase Raf-1 to mitochondria. *Cell* 87:629–38

225. Zha J, Harada H, Yang E, Jockel J, Korsmeyer SJ. 1996. Serine phosphorylation of death agonist BAD in response to survival factor results in binding to 14–3–3 not bcl-x_l. *Cell* 87:619–28

226. Wang H-G, Takayama S, Rapp UR, Reed JC. 1996. Bcl-2 interacting protein, BAG-1, binds to and activates the kinase Raf-1. *Proc. Natl. Acad. Sci. USA* 93:7063–68

227. Linette GP, Li Y, Roth K, Korsmeyer SJ. 1996. Cross talk between cell death and cell cycle progression: Bcl-2 regulates NFAT-mediated activation. *Proc. Natl. Acad. Sci. USA* 93:9545–52

228. Shibasaki F, Kondo E, Akagi T, McKeon F. 1997. Suppression of signaling through transcription factor NF-AT by interactions between calcineurin and bcl-2. *Nature* 386:728–31

229. Martin SJ, Takayama S, McGahon AJ, Miyashita T, Corbeil J, et al. 1995. Inhibition of ceramide-induced apoptosis by Bcl-2. *Cell Death Differ.* 2:253–57

230. Zhang J, Alter N, Reed JC, Borner C, Obeid LM. 1996. Bcl-2 interrupts the ceramide-mediated pathway of cell death. *Proc. Natl. Acad. Sci. USA* 93:5325–28

231. Mandal M, Maggirwar SB, Sharma N, Kaufmann SH, Sun S, Kumar R. 1996. Bcl-2 prevents CD95 (Fas/APO-1)-induced degradation of lamin B and poly(ADP-ribose) polymerase and restores the NF-κB signaling pathway. *J. Biol. Chem.* 271:30354–59

231a. Liu X, Kim CN, Yang J, Jemmerson R, Wang X. 1996. Induction of apoptotic program in cell-free extracts: requirement for dATO and cytochrome *c*. *Cell* 86:147–57

231b. Zou H, Henzel WJ, Liu X, Lutschg A, Wang X. 1997. Apaf-1, a human protein homologous to C. elegans CED-4, participates in cytochrome *c*-dependent activation of caspase-3. *Cell* 90:405–13

231c. Boise LH, Gonzalez-Garcia M, Postema CE, Ding L, Lindsten T, et al. 1993.

bcl-x, a bcl-2-related gene that functions as a dominant regulator of apoptotic death. *Cell* 74:597–608

232. Gagliardini V, Fernandez P, Lee RKK, Drexler HCA, Rotello RJ, et al. 1994. Prevention of vertebrate neuronal death by the *crmA* gene. *Science* 263:826–28

233. Komiyama T, Ray CA, Pickup DJ, Howard AD, Thornberry NA, et al. 1994. Inhibition of interleukin-1β converting enzyme by the Cowpox virus serpin CrmA. *J. Biol. Chem.* 269:19331–37

234. Ray CA, Black RA, Kronheim SR, Greenstreet TA, Sleath PR, et al. 1992. Viral inhibition of inflammation: cowpox virus encodes an inhibitor of the interleukin-1β converting enzyme. *Cell* 69:597–604

235. Clem RJ, Hardwick JM, Miller LK. 1996. Anti-apoptotic genes of baculoviruses. *Cell Death Differ.* 3:9–16

236. Xue D, Horvitz HR. 1995. Inhibition of the *Caenorhabditis elegans* cell-death protease CED-3 by a CED-3 cleavage site in baculovirus p35 protein. *Nature* 377:248–51

237. Bump NJ, Hackett M, Hugunin M, Seshagiri S, Brady K, et al. 1995. Inhibition of ICE family proteases by baculovirus antiapoptotic protein p35. *Science* 269:1885–88

238. Bertin J, Armstrong RC, Ottilie S, Martin DA, Wang Y, et al. 1997. Death effector domain-containing herpesvirus and poxvirus proteins inhibit both Fas- and TNFR1-induced apoptosis. *Proc. Natl. Acad. Sci. USA* 94:1172–76

239. Hu S, Vincenz C, Buller M, Dixit VM. 1997. A novel family of viral death effector domain-containing molecules that inhibit both CD95 and tumor necrosis factor receptor-1-induced apoptosis. *J. Biol. Chem.* 272:9621–24

240. Thome M, Schneider P, Hofmann K, Fickenscher H, Meini E, et al. 1997. Viral FLICE-inhibitory proteins (FLIPs) prevent apoptosis induced by death receptors. *Nature* 386:517–21

241. Tewari M, Telford WG, Miller RA, Dixit VM. 1995. CrmA, a poxvirus-encoded serpin, inhibits cytotoxic T-lymphocyte-mediated apoptosis. *J. Biol. Chem.* 270:22705–8

242. Clem RJ, Fechheimer M, Miller LK. 1991. Prevention of apoptosis by a baculovirus gene during infection of insect cells. *Science* 254:1388–90

243. Robertson NM, Zangrilli J, Fernandes-Alnemri T, Friesen PD, Litwack G, Alnemri ES. 1997. Baculovirus p35 inhibits the glucocorticoid-mediated pathways of cell death. *Cancer Res.* 57:43–47

244. Hay BA, Wassarman DA, Rubin GM. 1995. Drosophila homologs of baculovirus inhibitor of apoptosis proteins function to block cell death. *Cell* 83:1253–62

245. Liston P, Roy N, Tamai K, Lefebvre C, Baird S, et al. 1996. Suppression of apoptosis in mammalian cells by NAIP and a related family of IAP genes. *Nature* 379:349–53

246. Hampton MB, Vanags DM, Porn-Ares MI, Orrenius S. 1996. Involvement of extracellular calcium during phosphatidylserine exposure during apoptosis. *FEBS Lett.* 399:277–82

247. Harvey AJ, Bidwai AP, Miller LK. 1997. Doom, a product of the *Drosophila mod(mdg4)* gene, induces apoptosis and binds to baculovirus inhibitor-of-apoptosis proteins. *Mol. Cell. Biol.* 17:2835–43

247a. Deveraux QL, Takahashi R, Salvesen GS, Reed JC. 1997. X-linked IAP is a direct inhibitor of cell-death proteases. *Nature* 388:300–4

248. Duckett C, Nava VE, Gedrich RW, Clem RJ, Van Dongen JL, et al. 1996. A conserved family of cellular genes related to the baculovirus *iap* gene and encoding apoptosis inhibitors. *EMBO J.* 15:2685–94

249. Chinnaiyan AM, Tepper CG, Seldin MF, O'Rourke K, Kischkel FC, et al. 1996. FADD/MORT1 is a common mediator of CD95 (Fas/APO-1) and tumor necrosis factor receptor-induced apoptosis. *J. Biol. Chem.* 271:4961–65

250. White E, Sabbatini P, Debbas M, Wold WSM, Kusher DI, Gooding LR. 1992. The 19-kiloDalton adenovirus E1B transforming protein inhibits programmed cell death and prevents cytolysis by tumor-necrosis-factor-α. *Mol. Cell. Biol.* 12:2570–80

251. Boudreau N, Sympson CJ, Werb Z, Bissell MJ. 1995. Suppression of ICE and apoptosis in mammary epithelial cells by extracellular matrix. *Science* 267:891–93

252. Cohen P, Eisenberg RA. 1991. *Lpr* and *gld:* single gene models of systemic autoimmunity and lymphoproliferative disease. *Annu. Rev. Immunol.* 9:243–69

253. Lee MG, Nurse P. 1987. Complementation used to clone a human homologue of the fission yeast cell cycle control gene *cdc2*. *Nature* 327:31–35

254. Deleted in proof

255. Green DR, Martin SJ. 1995. The killer and the executioner: how apoptosis controls malignancy. *Curr. Opin. Immunol.* 7:694–703

256. Hickman JA, Beere HM, Wood AC, Waters CM, Parmar R. 1992. Mechanisms of cytotoxicity caused by antitumour drugs. *Toxicol. Lett.* 64–65 (Suppl.1):553–61

257. Ashwell JD, Berger NA, Cidlowski JA, Lane DP, Korsmeyer SJ. 1994. Coming to terms with death: apoptosis in cancer and immune development. *Curr. Biol.* 15:147–51

258. Strasser A, Harris AW, Cory S. 1991. bcl-2 transgene inhibits T cell death and perturbs thymic self-censorship. *Cell* 67:889–99

259. Lowe SW, Schmitt EM, Smith SW, Osborne BA, Jacks T. 1993. p53 is required for radiation-induced apoptosis in mouse thymocytes. *Nature* 362:847–49

260. Korsmeyer SJ. 1992. Bcl-2 initiates a new category of oncogenes: regulators of cell death. *Blood* 80:879–86

261. Reed JC. 1994. Bcl-2 and the regulation of programmed cell death. *J. Cell Biol.* 124:1–6

262. Shibasaki F, McKeon F. 1995. Calcineurin functions in Ca^{2+}-activated cell death in mammalian cells. *J. Cell Biol.* 131:735–43

263. Rampino N, Yamamoto H, Ionov Y, Li Y, Sawai H, Reed JC, Perucho M. 1997. Somatic frameshift mutations in the *bax* gene in colon cancers of the microsatellite mutator phenotype. *Science* 275:967–69

264. Fisher GH, Rosenberg FJ, Strauss SE, Dale JK, Middelton LA, et al. 1995. Dominant interfering Fas gene mutations impair apoptosis in a human autoimmune proliferative syndrome. *Cell* 81:935–46

265. Adachi M, Suematsu S, Kondo T, Ogasawara J, Tanaka T, et al. 1995. Targeted mutation in the Fas gene causes hyperplasia in the peripheral lymphoid organs and liver. *Nat. Genet.* 11:294–300

266. Bellgrau D, Gold D, Selawry H, Moore P, Franzusoff A, Duke RC. 1995. A role for CD95 ligand in preventing graft rejection. *Nature* 377:630–32

Annu. Rev. Physiol. 1998. 60:575–600

THE MANY ROLES OF c-Myc IN APOPTOSIS

E. Brad Thompson
Department of Human Biological Chemistry and Genetics, The University of Texas Medical Branch, 301 University Boulevard, Galveston, Texas 77555-0645; e-mail: bthompso@utmb.edu

KEY WORDS: apoptosis, c-*myc*, cell death, induction, repression

ABSTRACT

The proto-oncogene c-*myc* encodes a transcription factor c-Myc, which is of great importance in controlling cell growth and vitality. The quantity of c-Myc is carefully controlled by many mechanisms, and its actions to induce and repress genes are modulated by interactions with other regulatory proteins. Understanding the kinetic and quantitative relationships that determine how and what genes c-Myc regulates is essential to understanding how Myc is involved in apoptosis. Reduction of c-*myc* expression and its inappropriate expression can be associated with cellular apoptosis. This review outlines the nature and regulation of the c-*myc* gene and of c-Myc and presents the systems and conditions in which Myc-related apoptotic events occur. Hypotheses of the mechanisms by which expression and repression of c-*myc* lead to apoptosis are discussed.

INTRODUCTION

Many proto-oncogenes have been shown to participate in the regulation of apoptosis. Closely intertwined with their actions are various growth factors and other genes that participate in the control of cellular growth. Rather than giving a compilation of the numerous published experiments on all these proto-oncogenes, here I evaluate the duality of action of one gene, c-*myc*. This gene has been identified as an important component of normal cell growth and as a major human oncogene when inappropriately expressed. Recently, both unregulated expression and regulated repression of c-*myc* have been found to be involved in the regulation of apoptotic cell death.

575

0066-4278/98/0315-0575$08.00

The basic facts concerning c-*myc* are simple. It is a gene whose protein product c-Myc is expressed continually in cycling cells. In quiescent Go cells, it is expressed at very low levels. Mutations that cause structurally normal or certain mutant forms of c-Myc to be expressed continually at levels even higher than those in normal, cycling cells are found in a number of human malignancies. This inappropriate overexpression is part of the multistep oncogenic process and is often found together with oncogenic mutations of other proto-oncogenes, e.g. *ras*. In spontaneous human malignancies, elevated c-*myc* often occurs in conjunction with such other oncogenic mutations.

A role for c-*myc* in apoptosis has been documented in several systems of cultured cells. Treatments that cause apoptotic death of several cell types have been shown to first greatly lower c-*myc* expression. In some of these systems, replacement of c-*myc* expression alone, or in conjunction with a second critical gene, has prevented apoptosis and relieved cells—at least partially— from growth factor dependence. In other cases, paradoxically, overexpression of c-*myc* while essential growth factors were withheld accelerated cell death. This result led to the proposal that overexpression, or even normal expression, of c-*myc* is a signal for cell cycle progression and for apoptosis and that the cell must prevent the latter by countervailing gene expression.

THE c-*myc* GENE, ITS PRODUCTS AND PARTNERS

Detailed reviews of the overall properties of c-*myc* are available (1–7); thus only an outline sufficient for the present topic is given here. The c-*myc* gene is found with conserved topology in organisms from *Xenopus* to human. It consists of three exons: Exon 1 is noncoding, whereas exons 2 and 3 contain the coding information for the major Myc proteins. Several promoters are scattered about the 5' end of the gene, but promoters P_1 and P_2, located at or near the beginning of exon 1, account for 90–95% of the transcripts and yield mRNAs of about 2.2 and 2.4 kb. From these mRNAs, Myc proteins of ≈64 and 67 kDa are translated. Translational control mechanisms result in proteins differing in primary sequence by 14 amino acids. Other translation start sites occasionally can produce additional peptides, e.g. one from exon 1, but the physiological or pathological significance of these minor proteins remains moot. Regulation of c-*myc* expression and cellular c-Myc content due to variations in transcription start site use, however, are significant in some cases (2, 8). Some transcription from the antisense strand of the c-*myc* gene DNA has also been noted; its significance remains unclear.

Several functional domains of the resulting major Myc 64–67 kDa protein have been mapped. These domains include regions carrying signals for nuclear localization, nonspecific and site-specific DNA binding, and oligomerization.

The latter site contains an amphipathic helix or leucine zipper, such as is conserved in many oligomerizing regulatory proteins, e.g. Jun and Fos. A basic region associated with a helix-loop-helix sequence is encoded next to the amphipathic helix. Other regions of note are a proline/glutamine-rich sequence near the c-*myc* N terminus and an acidic domain abutting the nonspecific DNA-binding sector. Specific serines and threonines in Myc in a region near the middle of the primary sequence may be phosphorylated. Several studies suggest that this phosphorylation affects Myc functions. Thus Myc may be a phosphoprotein transcription factor that acts as a heteromeric dimer. Its primary dimer partner is the smaller but related protein Max.

Max is a 160 amino acid protein similar in sequence to the C-terminal portion of c-Myc but encoded in an independent gene. The mouse homologue of the human gene *max* is termed *myn*. Max contains both the basic region/helix-loop-helix and amphipathic helix domains. Heterodimers of Myc and Max tightly bind a specific DNA sequence to regulate gene transcription. Myc contains a transactivation domain located toward its N terminus, whereas the shorter Max lacks this domain. The canonical core of the sequence-specific DNA-binding site for Myc is CACGTG; this sequence appears capable of regulating reporter genes when placed in a promoter construct and stimulated with Myc/Max. Myc sites have been found in the promoters of several genes, notably that of ornithine decarboxylase (see below).

Myc is a short-lived protein; both the protein and its mRNA have half-lives of about 30 min (10–60 min in various systems). Max, on the other hand, is relatively stable and appears to be in molecular excess to Myc in many cells. Myc/Max heterodimers are formed preferentially when both are present. Max/Max homodimers form more readily than do Myc/Myc, and the (Max)$_2$ dimers can bind the CACGTG sequence specifically with fair avidity, but Max homodimers have less sequence specificity than the heterodimers. In any case, (Max)$_2$ is usually phosphorylated and as such does not bind DNA. (Myc)$_2$ homodimers are rare and also do not bind DNA. As with many transcription factors, multiple reversible binding reactions with a complex set of binding partners give precision to Myc/Max actions. First, the DNA binding site itself is important. Sequences flanking the simple CACGTG hexamer affect Myc/Max binding and give greater specificity to sites for the heterodimer. Max/Max homodimers appear to be less fastidious in choice of DNA site, whereas Myc/Myc homodimers do not appear to exist. The heterodimer can also bind certain noncognate sequences. Myc can also bind single- and double-stranded DNA nonspecifically, presumably with lower affinity, as with many transcription factors, e.g. the steroid hormone family of receptors.

Myc and Max have several other known protein binding partners. Max can associate with the Mad family of proteins and with Mxil, whereas c-Myc can bind TBP of the basal TATA-box recognition group of proteins. As part of the Myc/Max heterodimer, Myc also can associate with the transcription factor AP-2 and with the Rb-like protein p107. Similar to c-Myc, Mad proteins have short half-lifes, while Max is highly stable. Thus cells have multiple ways to vary the transcriptional regulatory functions of c-Myc through the balance of interactions with these proteins, which in turn are regulated by varying half-lives and other DNA and protein associations. Reviews of these effects are available (3–6, 9); however, most studies to date are at best only semi-quantitative, and the important and complex studies relating quantitative determinations of binding kinetics with the functional dynamics of these factors are still to come.

REGULATION OF c-*myc*

Levels of c-*myc* mRNA are delicately controlled by a combination of mechanisms. The regulation of transcription initiation from the various start sites has been analyzed by most of the current methods. Regulatory region/promoter analysis has mostly been carried out by reference to initiation from the major start sites P_1 and P_2. The data reveal a complex promoter that contains potential and/or actual binding sites for several transcription factors, such as Jun/Fos (AP-1), Oct, PuF, E2F, TBF, NF-κB, SREBP, GR, OBP, CF-1, PDGF, MF1a, MF2, p55, MBP-1, and several ribonucleoproteins. There is also a site with potential for forming triple-helical DNA. The use of these sites when they are packed into chromatin in vivo is unknown, although a good start has been made in understanding promoter occupancy by in vivo footprinting (10). Nevertheless, it is clear that quantitatively much of both positive and negative regulation of c-*myc* is at the level of primary transcript formation.

However, several other levels of regulation occur. Some regulation of c-*myc* occurs by a mechanism analogous to the bacterial phenomenon of attenuation. The transcription of c-*myc* can be interrupted by retention of RNA polymerase at the promoter-proximal end of exon 1, which results in failure to produce mRNA containing the coding sequences in exons 2 and 3 (11, 12). This device is operative in a number of well-studied examples such as HL-60 cells induced to differentiate. The concomitant ≈10-fold reduction in Myc protein and mRNA is caused largely by such a failure of transcription elongation.

There are also post-transcriptional controls on Myc levels, through regulation of RNA and protein stability. Both c-*myc* mRNA and c-Myc protein have naturally short half-lives, around 30 min. Thus they are poised for dramatic regulation in cellular pool size as a consequence of variations in half-life. The half-life of c-*myc* mRNA can vary considerably through polyadenylation-related mechanisms and others. Usually c-*myc* mRNA and protein levels vary in parallel, but several examples are known in which the half-life of c-Myc is controlled independently from that of its mRNA.

TRANSCRIPTIONAL ACTIVITY OF c-Myc

Acting with its various partner proteins, c-Myc is able to regulate the transcription of genes. Specific induction of several genes by c-Myc include ornithine decarboxylase, cyclins A and E, and α-prothymosin. Recently lactate dehydrogenase-A and rcl have been added to this list, along with several still unidentified genes (13, 14). Ornithine decarboxylase contains two CACGTG motifs in its regulatory region, which confer Myc-dependent regulation to reporter genes in artificial constructs. Induction of cyclin D1 has also been observed, although studies using a hybrid protein in which c-Myc fused to the ligand-binding domain of the estrogen receptor (to provide estrogen-activated c-Myc) need re-evaluation. A potent, ligand-dependent transactivation domain has been found in the estrogen receptor ligand-binding domain; therefore, its effect on any experiment where the chimeric c-Myc-estrogen receptor fragment is used must be taken into consideration. (This also applies to several studies using the same chimeric protein to study c-Myc-induced apoptosis.) Several other genes have been shown to contain the CACGTC sequence in their regulatory regions and are potential targets for regulation by c-Myc. Noteworthy is the gene for the tumor suppressor protein p53, itself a transcription factor. Myc and p53 levels tend to correlate, and certain actions of c-Myc appear to require p53 (see below).

Myc can also repress transcription of certain genes, at least in part through their Inr sequence. This regulation utilizes portions of the c-Myc N-terminal domain and causes repression of cyclin D1 and inhibition at the adenovirus late promoter. Myc, independently of Max, can also interact with the transcription factor YY-1 to vary expression of genes dependent on the latter. This can result in repression or activation of such genes. If c-Myc sometimes represses genes while acting independently of Max, it is obvious that under proper circumstances, elevating the Max/Myc ratio could draw the Myc engaged in such repression into Max/Myc dimers. Unless one were aware that the mechanism was relief of gene repression by c-Myc, the result could be incorrectly interpreted as a Max-specific induction. Conversely, a decrease in the Max/Myc ratio would be seen as repression of such genes. But the association of cause would appear to differ, depending on how the shift in ratio occurred. For instance, a simple increase in Myc would point to Myc as the (co)repressor. On the other hand, if Mad were increased, drawing off Max into the Mad/Max dimer, while Myc remained constant, it would not be immediately apparent that Myc was acting in its repressor capacity. This hypothetical instance shows the difficulty of ascribing specific mechanisms to complex biological phenomena after changing a single member of this interactive network of factors. Such considerations are rarely included in studies involving Myc's roles in apoptosis.

The details of the above mechanisms have been reviewed extensively elsewhere, but this outline should suffice to remind us that Myc is a cellular protein of great power and importance, attested to by the multiple levels of control exerted over its expression and function. The timing of expression of c-*myc* and the level of its c-Myc product proteins, together with the levels of all the regulatory proteins with which c-Myc interacts, results in varied levels of regulation of many genes.

MYC AND CELL GROWTH

The idea that c-*myc* plays an important role in cell growth and differentiation is well established. Many questions remain, however, as to exactly what that role is. In cultured cells, it is generally true that c-*myc* mRNA and protein levels are elevated early after stimuli to growth are given. Myc levels rise and remain elevated as long as the cells continue to replicate. The fact that c-Myc, such a short-lived and highly regulated protein, remains elevated throughout the cell cycle suggests that it must function frequently if not continually, or that its function is controlled by some post-translational mechanism. What these continuing functions are has not been defined in detail, although evidence indicates that c-Myc functions to move cells from G1 into S phase and that it functions in G2 (15). In normally growing adult tissues, c-*myc* expression correlates with growth, and when quiescent tissues are stimulated to grow, as in regenerating liver, c-*myc* expression is increased (3).

Myc expression does not always correlate with growth, however. The ES cell lines used to create the null *myc* mice appear to have grown steadily and well; thus at least some cells can survive with reduced c-Myc. During embryonic development, vigorous growth of several systems is seen without high c-*myc* expression. Knockout of the c-*myc* gene in mice still allows embryonic growth for 9–10 days, albeit with abnormal development (3). Thus c-*myc* expression is not always required for cell growth, but it is required for normal development.

Cessation of cell growth often is preceded and accompanied by greatly lowered c-*myc* expression, and use of antisense oligonucleotides to lower c-Myc levels usually results in growth inhibition, if not death. Forced overexpression of c-*myc* provokes and sustains prolonged growth and also can cause cell death under certain conditions. In conjunction with other oncogenic alterations, simple c-Myc overexpression causes cancers to develop. Malignant cells in vivo and in vitro often express c-*myc* at elevated levels throughout the cell cycle.

MYC AND APOPTOSIS

How does Myc, this potent transcription factor and regulator of cell growth, enter into apoptosis and cell death? Two lines of evidence indicate that, in appropriate circumstances, both under and overexpression of c-Myc can lead to cell death.

Systems in Which Reduction of c-myc Leads to Apoptosis

DOWN-REGULATION OF c-*myc* BY GLUCOCORTICOIDS   In 1986, Eastman-Reks and Vedeckis noted that in addition to c-*myb* and c-Ki-*ras*, c-*myc* mRNA was down-regulated in mouse S49 lymphoid cells when they were treated with a lethal concentration of the glucocorticoid dexamethasone (16). Subsequently, we observed the same effect in the human leukemic clonal cell line CEM-C7 (17, 18), which was later confirmed by Wood et al (19). The protein c-Myc also was down-regulated, and this occurred in a glucocorticoid receptor-dependent manner because the phenomenon did not occur in cells deficient in functional GR and was reversed by displacing the agonist dexamethasone with the GR-binding antagonist RU486 (20). Clones of CEM cells resistant to glucocorticoid-induced apoptosis failed to show c-*myc* down-regulation, including a clone that was resistant to apoptosis despite containing an active GR. Thus the c-*myc* response correlates with absence of glucocorticoid-evoked apoptosis and not just to glucocorticoid receptor status. Unlike several other down-regulated genes, which fell more or less in parallel with overt morphologic apoptosis, the fall in c-Myc preceded overt cell death by many hours, suggesting that Myc was at or near the begining of a sequence that led to cell death. Subsequent apoptosis was blocked by cycloheximide (19), suggesting that protein synthesis was required for the final events.

Jurkat cells are insensitive to glucocorticoids unless supplied with GR. When this was done, c-*myc* was down-regulated following administration of dexamethasone, and the cells underwent apoptosis (21). In the mouse lymphoid cell line P1798, growth is blocked by glucocorticoids. In serum-supplemented medium, these cells die only many days later. These cells also display rapid, glucocorticoid-evoked loss of c-*myc* transcripts (22, 23). When P1798 cells are grown in serum-free medium, they are killed by application of glucocorticoids (24). It appears that serum exerts an effect that protects these cells from the lethal but not growth-inhibitory consequences of glucocorticoidal repression of c-Myc.

In some of these in vitro systems of transformed lymphoid cells, sustaining c-Myc levels protects against apoptosis. Transient transfection of plasmids expressing c-*myc* under control of promoters that could not be down-regulated by glucocorticoids provided significant anti-apoptotic effects in the CEM cell system (18). In the P1798 cell system, overexpression of c-*myc* or cyclin D3 alone did not protect, but when c-*myc* and cyclin D3 (which glucocorticoids also down-regulate in these cells) were co-expressed, the cells showed inhibition of apoptosis in the presence of glucocorticoid (23).

DOWN-REGULATION OF c-*myc* VIA ACTIVATION OF SURFACE RECEPTORS   In B-cell systems, down-regulation of c-*myc* has been closely correlated with the actions of several agents that cause apoptosis. In B-lymphoid cell lines used as models for tolerance via clonal deletion, growth arrest and apoptosis follow exposure to antisera against their surface IgM. These cells show a biphasic response in c-*myc* after such treatment, with a sharp, brief up-swing followed by a prolonged reduction. The two effects can be dissociated by various treatments, and it appears that it is the loss of c-*myc* expression that matters. If c-*myc* expression is maintained, growth arrest and apoptosis are prevented (25–28). WEHI 231 cell mutants resistant to the anti-Ig apoptotic effect still displayed a transient increase in c-*myc* mRNA after addition of the antibody, but they failed to show the subsequent sharp drop; thus it is the reduction and not the elevation in c-Myc that correlates with apoptosis. In B-lymphoma cells, TGF-β causes both a decrease in c-*myc* expression and apoptosis. Steps that prevent the loss of c-*myc* products due to TGF-β treatment also prevent apoptosis (27). Conversely, treatments that increase c-*myc* expression do not cause apoptosis. Myc levels in WEHI 231 cells appear to be under the control of NF-κB/Rel. Treatments that reduce functional levels of NF-κB/Rel lead to lowered c-*myc* expression and to apoptosis. Furthermore, such apoptosis is inhibited by expression of exogenous c-*myc*. In another experiment in this system, elevation of Mad, which presumably reduces functional Myc/Max complexes by sequestering Max, caused WEHI 231 cell apoptosis (29).

Burkitt's lymphoma (Ramos) cells treated with anti-IgM undergo apoptosis subsequent to a reduction of about fourfold in c-*myc* mRNA. (This appears to be due to a reduction in mRNA half-life, with no change in transcription rate.) Antisense oligonucleotides to c-*myc* cause its repression, and this treatment also induces apoptosis (30).

Therefore, a key factor in apoptosis in transformed T lymphocytes (caused by glucocorticoids) and in B-lymphoid cell lines (caused by TGF-β, anti-Ig antibodies or elevated Mad) is down-regulation of c-*myc* or inhibition of c-Myc function. Agents that cause such regulation cause apoptosis, whereas prevention of reduced c-*myc* expression prevents or significantly diminishes the apoptosis caused by those agents.

Other Correlations Between Lowered c-myc Expression and Apoptosis

With less extensive tests of causality, correlations between reductions in c-Myc and apoptosis have been noted in other circumstances. The CEM-C1 lymphoid cell clone is resistant to glucocorticoids and to forskolin. However, when these agents are combined, apoptosis ensues, and this is preceded by a sharp reduction in c-Myc (31). The apoptosis of CEM cells caused by the oxysterol 25-hydroxycholesterol (32) is preceded by a $\geq 90\%$ reduction in c-Myc levels; clones selected for resistance to the sterol do not show the c-Myc response (33). In the human erythroleukemia line K562, antisense oligonucleotides to the homeobox gene DLX-7 reduce c-*myc* and GATA-1 expression, and cause apoptosis (34). Treatment of the K562 cells with protein phosphatase inhibitors okadaic acid or calyculin A caused down-regulation of c-*myc* and *max* expression, and led to apoptosis (35). The lethal effect was not reversed by removal of the drug, although expression of the proto-oncogenes returned to normal. In various IL-3-dependent myeloid cell lines, withdrawal of the interleukin leads to growth cessation and apoptosis. This correlates closely with antecedent down-regulation of c-*myc* expression. Introduction of the c-*myc* gene in order to force its unregulated expression led in several cases to partial or complete independence from IL-3 (36, 37) and not to cell death. However, in the case of 32D cells, the overexpression of c-*myc* coupled with IL-3 withdrawal actually accelerated apoptosis (28, 38; see below). In several experiments, HL-60 myeloid blasts were pushed to apoptosis by treatments that reduce *myc* expression and, in one instance, either reduction or elevation of c-*myc* expression led to the lethal consequence. The authors suggest that the rate of change in Myc levels may be relevant (39). Sphingosine elevation in HL-60 cells causes a high percentage of HL-60 cells to undergo apoptosis, associated with reduction in c-*myc* mRNA (40). HL-60 cells treated with the cyclophosphamide prodrug Mafosfamide also showed a dose- and time-dependent correlation between c-*myc* mRNA level reduction and apoptosis (41). However, treatment of HL-60 cells with sodium phenylacetate lowered c-*myc* expression and produced differentiation with growth arrest without cytotoxicity (42). Reductions of c-*myc* expression correlating with apoptosis are not limited to hematopoietic cell systems and have occasionally been reported in other cell types. For example, when treated with sodium nitroprusside to release nitric oxide, the epithelial cancer cell line NA undergoes apoptosis. Expression of c-*myc* mRNA was rapidly reduced, as was that of c-*myb*; cell death with features of apoptosis ensued (43). Use of antisense oligonucleotides to c-*myc*, creating rapid down-regulation of c-Myc, led to apoptosis of a human esophageal cancer cell line. Such cells showed reduced tumorigenicity in nude mice (44). Treatment of MCF-7 breast adenocarcinoma cells with doxorubicin caused a prolonged reduction of c-*myc* mRNA, paralleling DNA fragmentation and growth arrest, followed by loss of cells (45). In sum, there are frequent examples of cell systems in which down-regulation of c-*myc* expression, resulting in lowered c-Myc content, is closely correlated with cellular apoptosis.

Effects of Direct Reduction of c-myc mRNA
By Use of Antisense Oligonucleotides

It has long been known that c-*myc* mRNA levels can be reduced by use of short antisense oligonucleotides (ASODs) made to hybridize with at least the first five translated codons in the c-*myc* gene. Many groups have made use of this to study the effect of lowering c-*myc* mRNA levels with or without simultaneous use of other pharmacologic agents. The results show that in a variety of transformed cell types, e.g. lymphoid, erythroblastic, epithelial, myeloid, melanoid, in vitro administration of ASODs lowers c-*myc* mRNA and c-Myc protein and reduces or stops growth. In some cases, this is associated with initiation of apoptosis, in others only with growth inhibition (Table 1). In vivo use of ASODs to c-*myc* resulted in growth inhibition of implanted CML blasts or melanomas in test animals (Table 1). Special evaluation for apoptosis was not carried out in the case of the CML tumors, but the melanomas were evaluated for and showed signs of apoptosis. These results, taken with the reservation that use of ASODs produces a variety of side effects that can confuse interpretation of causal mechanisms (50, 60), support the view that in many transformed cells lowering c-Myc levels per se leads to growth inhibition, and apoptosis often ensues.

Some instructive examples illustrate important principles about the Myc question. When various independently derived lines of Burkitt's lymphoma (transformed B) cells were treated in vitro with anti-*myc* ASODs, or with anti-IgM, c-*myc* was down-regulated in all (30). Two of three EBV-negative lines showed apoptosis after anti-IgM, and in one line tested with ASOD to c-*myc*, the cells were also killed, showing an apoptotic phenotype. All three of the EBV-positive lines responded to anti-IgM with slowed growth, but not apoptosis. One cell line, Daudi, treated with ASOD to c-*myc* showed growth inhibition and loss of viability but without the morphological features of apoptosis. Treatment with anti CD-40 could prevent the apoptosis of Ramos cells that followed exposure to ASOD to c-*myc* without blocking the reduction in c-Myc. Thus these results illustrate the point that varied backgrounds of gene expression and cellular activities, such as these caused by EBV infection or treatment with anti-CD40, can result in a cell state that avoids death due to loss of sufficient c-Myc. At least two possibilities are consistent with such a situation: (a) c-Myc directly or indirectly represses one or more lethal genes. When Myc levels fall sufficiently, these genes are derepressed unless some other agent, e.g. anti CD-40, that blocks their expression or action is supplied. (b) Conversely, c-Myc is essential for induction and continued expression of essential vitality genes. When Myc levels get too low, the gene products cannot be maintained at concentrations adequate to support cell viability. Note that neither model requires that the expression of the identical lethality or vitality genes changes

Table 1 Growth inhibition and apoptosis following treatment with antisense oligonucleotides to c-*myc*

Cell or Tumor	Growth inhibition		Apoptosis		Reference
	in vivo	in vitro	in vivo	in vitro	
Human acute lymphoblastic leukemia (CEM-C7)		+		+	18
Burkitt's lymphoma lines					30
Ramos (EBV−)		+		+	
Daudi (EBV+)		+		−	
Small cell lung cancer lines GLC4, GLC4-cDDP[a], GLC4-Adr		+		−	46
Human erythroblasts		+		−	47
Human CML blasts[b]	+	+	?	?	48
Melanoma lines[c]	+	+	+	+	49, 50
Thyroid cancer lines		+		?	51
Orbital fibroblasts		+		−	52
Monomyeloid cells (HL-60)		+		+	36
Burkitt's lymphoma (Daudi, ST486)		+		?	53
Ovarian cancer lines		+		+[e]	54[d]
Lymphoma U937				+	55[e]
Breast Cancer MCF-7				+	55
Ewing's sarcoma CHP-100				+	55
Burkitt's lymphoma ST-486				+	55
Breast cancer (MCF-7, MDA-MB-231)		+		?	56
Human T lymphocytes +IL-2 or PHA		+		−	57
Burkitt lymphomas (ST486, JD38)		+		?	58
Hematopoietic cells		+		?	59
Esophageal cancer cells		+		+	44

[a]In the *cis*-platinum-resistant line, treatment with antisense c-*myc* enhanced drug sensitivity.
[b]Synergism observed between antisense c-*myc* and atisense *bcr-abl*.
[c]For cautions regarding the mechanism of these effects, see 50, 60.
[d]Various patterns of cell viability response were seen with antisense c-*myc* ± antisense p53.
[e]Cell viability assayed without specific diagnostic tests for apoptosis.
Symbols: +, effect tested for and seen; −, effect tested for and not seen; ?, not tested (or not reported).

in each specific cell line, i.e. only one or more critical gene needs to be altered. The particular connections of such genes with all the potential machinery for apoptosis could then account for cell death. If one excludes the necessity for a Final Common Pathway, suggesting instead that the particular biochemical and morphological accompaniments of the specific death may be defined by any of several subsets of lethal machinery, one can reconcile the result seen with the Ramos and Daudi cells, where treatment with ASOD to c-*myc* killed both, one with, the other without, classic apoptotic morphology.

Two other examples highlight a potentially important feature of c-Myc expression and cell death. HL-60 cells were treated with ASODs to c-*myc*, resulting in a population of cells with a significantly lower content of nuclear c-Myc. This treatment was also associated with a significant fraction of the cells exhibiting apoptosis. Upon withdrawal of the ASOD, c-Myc levels returned to normal in all but a small pool of the cells, and an even greater portion of the cells underwent apoptosis (34). Thus either inappropriate up- or down-regulation of c-Myc can cause apoptosis in this system. The authors suggest that the rate of change in c-Myc, as well as the absolute level, can be important in evoking apoptosis. As with all such observations, cell context is important. CEM-C7 cells treated with dexamethasone showed deep down-regulation of c-Myc. Rescue by addition of the antiglucocorticoid RU486 results in rapid restoration of c-Myc levels, without apoptosis (20). As mentioned above, removal of IL-3, their essential growth factor, from 32D cells leads to deep reduction in c-*myc* expression and to apoptosis. Overexpression of c-*myc* in this B-cell line under such circumstances accelerates the apoptotic response (28, 38).

Systems in Which c-myc Up-Regulation Leads to or Sensitizes to Apoptosis

In other circumstances, elevated c-*myc* expression appears causal or sensitizing in generating apoptosis (see 7, 28, 61–72 for reviews). The clearest examples of this phenomenon occur in vitro, in cell systems dependent on defined or undefined growth factors. In such systems, withdrawal of the factor(s), coupled with deliberate, forced expression of c-*myc*, can lead to apoptosis. An early experiment of this effect by Askew et al showed that withdrawal of IL-3 from IL-3 dependent 32D.3 myeloid cells led to down-regulation of c-*myc* and cell death. When continued c-*myc* expression was ensured in such cultures by introducing appropriate expression plasmids, apoptosis was accelerated, not reversed (38). Subsequently, it was shown that IL-3 treatment per se was not sufficient to block the cell death brought about by forced expression of exogenous c-*myc*. Cells were kept in IL-3 medium and allowed to reach confluence. Under these conditions these cells down-regulate c-*myc* and stop growing. Forced overexpression of a transfected c-*myc* gene caused the quiescent cells to die although IL-3 was present (73). Shortly after the earlier study on 32D.3 cells, similar experimental manipulations were found to lead to apoptotic death of Rat-1 fibroblasts (74). When the serum in the medium was reduced to a level that allowed survival with little growth, and comparisons were made between various control cells and cells infected with a retrovirus that carried a constitutively expressed c-*myc* gene, the latter cells became apoptotic. This experiment was repeated later, using a MycER^{TM} construct that expressed a fusion protein of Myc coupled to a mutant ligand-binding domain of the estrogen receptor. The effect of the mutation was twofold: It made the ligand-binding domain insensitive to the normal estrogen agonists but sensitive to the partial agonist/partial antagonist 4-hydroxytamoxifen. Second, the mutation inactivated the transactivation domain that lies within the estrogen receptor ligand-binding domain, thus minimizing the danger that the results observed could be due to the estrogen receptor part of the hybrid molecule. When Rat-1 cells were deprived of serum, they gradually died; however, tamoxifen induction of the MycER protein accelerated this apoptotic death (75). The basic experimental design used in these two studies continues to be employed in other cultured cell systems to show that forced overexpression of c-*myc* in cells that are unable to cycle for a variety of reasons frequently leads to a high rate of apoptosis (76, 77). It is interesting that in F9 teratocarcinoma cells caused to differentiate by treatment with retinoic acid plus cyclic AMP (77), only 70% of the cells were killed under such circumstances, and only when c-*myc* overexpression by induction with cadmium was forced before or just after blocking growth. Later expression of c-*myc* caused no mortality. The 30% of cells that survived differentiated without apoptosis despite the c-*myc* expression. In other circumstances, deliberate expression of c-*myc* during differentiation did not appear to kill (78). In chicken, overexpression of v-*myc* sensitizes the primitive B cells in the bursa of Fabricius to the apoptosis that ensues after γ-radiation or mechanical dispersion, and such cells are protected by co-expressing v-*rel* (79, 80). Clearly, inappropriate overexpression of c-*myc* can cause or raise the susceptibility to apoptosis in several types of cells when the cells are unable to grow. However, these effects may be closely related to specific sets of circumstances. In Chinese hamster ovary (CHO) cells overexpressing c-*myc*, some methods of blocking cell growth resulted in apoptosis, while others did not (81). What is the case in naturally growing cells? Can overexpressed c-Myc kill them? Apparently, if enough is expressed.

Gross overexpression of c-*myc* in heat-shocked CHO cells carrying multiple copies of the oncogene led to cell death, but this result required a high level of c-Myc, at least 40 times normal. Lesser degrees of overexpression had no effect on DNA synthesis or cell viability (82, 83). When exogenous Eμ-*myc* was placed in transgenic mice, the overriding effect observed was lymphadenopathy, an expanded population of B cells, and eventual lymphoid tumorigenesis (84). Later analysis, intentionally examing for it, disclosed increased apoptosis in the lymphoid cells of such mice (85). When cultured in vitro, the nonmalignant pre-B cells from these animals grew to only slightly higher densities than cells from normal animals. After months in culture, the cells constitutively expressing c-*myc* from the transgenic mice underwent transformation, growing to much higher densities. Splenocytes from transgenic c-*myc*-expressing mice showed increased apoptosis in culture (86), and hepatocytes expressing transgenic c-*myc* also showed increased apoptosis (87). A recent study specifically directed at apoptosis in the lymphoid tumors arising in Eμ-*myc* transgenic mice found that in the majority of such mice, the tumors contain foci of apoptotic cells expressing extremely high levels of p53 and c-*myc* (88). Mammary and other tumors from c-*myc* transgenic mice also showed apoptosis in vivo (89–91).

A clear example of c-Myc-dependent apoptosis is seen in some T-cell hybridoma cell lines (somatic cell hybrids between T cells and permanently transformed cell lines) (61, 92, 93), in which ligation of the surface antigen receptor results in apoptosis. This is associated with expression of c-Myc, and when this expression is blocked by antisense oligonucleotides or addition of TGF-β, apoptosis is inhibited. Expression of a dominant-negative form of Max inhibits as well. Although activation of certain growth factor transduction pathways or expression of V-*abl* ameliorates apoptosis, Bcl-2 does not. Interestingly, it appears that B-cell lymphomas do not show association between Myc elevation and apoptosis and, in fact, are protected by c-Myc (25, 27, 92). The differences that account for the responses of the Myc-sensitive and the Myc-dependent lymphoid cells are not known.

Mechanisms of c-Myc-Mediated Apoptosis and Its Modulation

The mechanisms responsible for apoptosis associated with inappropriate c-Myc expression are not specifically known. In some systems, p53 seems to be important or essential for Myc-evoked apoptosis. Expression of p53 appears to be associated with several, but not all, instances of apoptosis occurring after inappropriate c-*myc* overexpression (88, 94–96). Indeed, p53 overexpression by itself can cause apoptosis (97, 98), but the known regulation of the cell cycle by p53—that which involves regulation of the cyclin inhibitor p21—does not appear to explain p53-driven apoptosis (98–100). But there does not appear to be a universal requirement for p53 in apoptosis following elevated c-Myc. Experiments in several cell systems show that elevated c-Myc can bring about apoptosis in the absence of p53 (101, 102). The molecular relationships are obviously complex, and even in a single cell type, e.g. thymocytes, p53 may be involved in some apoptotic signals and not others (103). The role of p53 in apoptosis is discussed further by KL King and JL Cidlowski (this volume).

Max does seem to be necessary for apoptosis following inappropriate c-Myc expression in both the T-cell hybridoma and Rat-1 fibroblast systems (104, 105). Thus it is likely that one or more of the known repressive or inductive functions of Myc/Max are involved in the apoptotic events that follow (61).

Bcl-2 can ameliorate the apoptosis associated with inappropriate c-Myc expression in some (101) but not all (61) cell systems. In the hepatoma cell line HuH-7, removal of serum, together with enforced c-*myc* expression and zinc added to the medium, leads to apoptosis. Although addition of various growth factors did not alter this outcome, overexpression of Bcl-2 did (106). One group found that Mcl-1, a Bcl-2 family gene, gave partial protection against Myc-related apoptosis in CHO cells (107). On the other hand, Bcl-2 did not protect against activation-induced cell death in the T-cell hybridoma system in which Myc/Max are involved (61 and references therein). Bax, a family member that antagonizes the action of Bcl-2, is sometimes found elevated in c-Myc hyperexpression states (101).

Ornithine decarboxylase is one of the proven targets for transcriptional stimulation by c-Myc (108). In the 32D.3 cell system, where removal of IL-3 coupled with forced c-*myc* expression leads to rapid apoptosis, ornithine decarboxylase is induced. Forced expression of the enzyme itself also causes apoptosis, and in both cases the ornithine decarboxylase inhibitor DFMO inhibits apoptosis (109). The role of ornithine decarboxylase in other Myc-related systems has not been examined extensively.

Reactive oxygen has also been suggested as a frequent though not invariant cause of cell catastrophe (106, 110). In the HuH-7 hepatoma cell culture system (106), it was found that serum withdrawal caused apoptosis that could be ameliorated by addition of glutamine, which in turn was associated with increased intracellular glutathione. Other treatments aimed at blocking reactive oxygen were also protective. As mentioned above, growth factors had no protective effect. Whether the apparent generation of reactive oxygen species was c-Myc specific or was due to the culture conditions in the absence of serum was not determined (111). On the other hand, in the Rat-1A cell system, the antioxidant N-acetyl-L-cysteine did not protect against apoptosis following serum withdrawal coupled with overexpression of the MycER hybrid and activation by estradiol (112). However, it should be recalled that this MycER hybrid contains estrogen receptor transactivation domains; therefore, these results cannot be ascribed with certainty only to the effects of Myc overexpression. Present evidence is inconclusive as to whether generation of reactive oxygen species is the universal mechanism of c-Myc-induced cell death.

Several components of the cyclin/cdk complex have been implicated in some apoptotic systems associated with elevated c-Myc. In the classic Rat-1A fibroblast system, cyclin A mRNA was elevated in those cells overexpressing c-Myc and undergoing apoptosis. Forced overexpression of cyclin A itself led to apoptosis. The blocking of c-Myc-evoked apoptosis by Bcl-2 expression led to a more balanced expression of several cyclins, possibly speaking to the complex balance between expressed genes required to maintain cell viability while avoiding apoptosis (113). Cyclin D3 expression, as well as c-Myc, was found to correlate with tumor necrosis factor (TNF) sensitivity of HeLa cells (114). Manipulations that affected cyclin D3 levels were effective in altering susceptibility of cells to TNF, with cellular cyclin D3 content inversely related to the ability of TNF to kill. Co-expression of c-*myc* and cyclin D3 protected P1798 cells from glucocorticoid-evoked apoptosis (23).

Another gene important for cell cycle progression, recently proposed as important in c-Myc's apoptotic effects is *cdc25A* (115). This protein phosphatase, whose transcription is under the control of c-Myc, is required at certain phases of the cell cycle. As with most such proteins, the exact list of its substrates has yet to be completed; thus how it connects with other regulatory molecules to participate in apoptosis remains to be elucidated fully.

Other genes implicated in the apoptotic actions of c-Myc include the general translation factor eIF4E, whose expression inhibits apoptosis imposed by inappropriate Myc expression in fibroblasts after serum was removed (116). Why a general translation factor should have such an action awaits further experiments. Induction of cyclin D1 may be involved. The protease calpain is also involved in apoptosis of muscle satellite cells, which follows serum withdrawal. Among the genes subsequently activated is c-*myc*. When activation of calpain was prevented, subsequent apoptosis was inhibited (117). In the T-cell hybridoma system, interfering with Max action is protective against c-Myc-driven apoptosis (61, 104). In C562 (a chronic myelogenous leukemic cell line), *bcr-abl* expression appears to protect against a variety of apoptotic agents, and it has been suggested that a link between ABL, which may be involved in c-*myc* regulation, and c-Myc is somehow involved, i.e. Bcl-2 blocks the apoptotic process set off by Myc (118, 119).

In sum, c-Myc expression results in or enhances apoptosis in several systems that include (*a*) cell lines that stop growing because of high density, removal of specific growth factors, or reduction of serum in their medium; (*b*) cells in which c-Myc is greatly overexpressed; (*c*) cells exposed to a variety of toxic agents; (*d*) T-cell hybridoma lines activated by surface antigens; and (*e*) forced in vivo expression. The in vivo case is complicated; obviously classic c-*myc* overexpression experiments were not embryonic lethal, which would be expected if overexpression always caused apoptosis. Instead, they led to relatively normal animals with higher incidence of cancers in certain organs. When examined carefully and with hindsight gained from the tissue culture systems, the c-Myc transgenic animals appear to have a higher rate of apoptosis than normal, at least in certain tissues. Whether the microenvironment of some cells in vivo makes them equivalent to cycle-restrictive in vitro conditions (*a–d*) is a difficult but important issue.

Hypotheses for Mechanism of Apoptosis Associated with Inappropriate c-Myc Expression

Great stress has been laid on the apoptotic effects of inappropriate c-Myc expression (7, 28, 61–72). Two hypotheses have been proposed: (*a*) Apoptosis results from a mismatch in signals for advancing through the cell replicative cycle and in signals that call for or come from stopping the cycle. (*b*) c-Myc itself is responsible for specific signals that both advance the cell cycle and initiate apoptotic death. The latter must be countered by specific anti-apoptotic gene expression to avoid cell death. In its most advanced version, this specific opposing signals model proposes that every time c-*myc* is expressed, both sets of signals are set off, plus the third set of anti-apoptotic signals if the cell is not to die. The anti-apoptotic signals could be entirely part of the genes of the cell cycle, independent genes, or a combination of the two. A full extension of the second hypothesis states that even in the normal replicative growth of cells, when c-Myc is expressed, these events must take place. These anti-apoptotic signals might come from products of the normally cycling cells or from a cascade of events that emanate more specifically from c-*myc* expression itself (for presentations and discussions of these hypotheses, see the reviews indicated above). At the moment, no definitive evidence proves either theory correct.

Evidence that favors the first idea, that simultaneous grow and stop signals in cells whose normal cycling has been interfered with while c-*myc* is continually expressed, comes from several sides. First, c-*myc* is not unique as a growth gene whose overexpression is associated with apoptosis. Many other genes involved in growth signaling are associated with or causative of apoptosis: e.g. overexpression of cJun and/or cFos (120–136), cyclin A (137), PU-1 (138), p53 (cited above), E2F (139, 140), papilloma virus E2 gene (141), *ras* (136) in various combinations with other agents (142–146, 90), *rho* (147, 148), and *mos* (149). Similar to *myc*, expression of *ras* has also been reported to protect against apoptosis (see References 150–154). Some of the above genes may be linked directly to c-Myc mechanism of action, but it is doubtful that all are part of a singular Myc-initiated apoptotic pathway. If not, does each initiate independent and specific grow/die signals that require specific anti-die signals? This would seem metabolically burdensome and an unlikely evolutionary strategy. Under some circumstances, expression of several of these genes, similar to Myc, protects against apoptosis. The extensive interlocking pathways and ambivalent actions of these genes suggest that among the many mechanisms that trigger apoptosis are those that somehow misregulate the cell cycle in a less specific manner than the alternative hypothesis proposes. IL-3-dependent cells allowed to grow to confluence, and therefore stopped by contact inhibition, die despite the continued presence of IL-3 if c-Myc expression continues. It could be argued that the signals for anti-apoptosis are inherently expressed during the cell cycle. As discussed in the Introduction to this special section, it may be that various imbalances in the signaling network initiate apoptosis. The complex sets of binding, phosphorylation, and activation kinetics involved in maintaining cellular integrity and function may be open to a variety of maladjustments that trigger various functions capable of initiating lethal events. The initial function and its interactions and connections with the complex of molecules that at various times are involved in cell death could define the particular sequence of events and could thus account for some of the subtle but distinct differences described in the morphology and biochemistry of non-necrotic dying cells. Another suggestion has been that cells have the capacity to sense some molecule indicative of a general imbalance, and this sets off apoptosis (155). A specific example of this notion is one proposing that the treatments with apoptotic agents ultimately lead to some disastrous metabolic consequence, e.g. excess production of reactive oxygen.

Whatever its mechanism(s), the imbalanced-signal hypothesis can explain many, if not all the categories by which c-Myc causes apoptosis. In most, the coincident exposure to apoptotic agents for which c-Myc sensitizes the cell probably interferes with natural cell cycling. For example, treatment with various anticancer drugs, ionizing radiation, or exposure to calcium ionophores often causes apoptosis. Each of these agents, along with most of the other known causes whose effect is heightened by c-Myc, disturbs the natural flow of the cell cycle. What about c-*myc* expression in vivo? Much of the data describe heightened rates of apoptosis in tumors resulting from forced *myc* expression. Because regions of tumors vary widely in their access to nutrients and oxygen, it may be that they are recapitulating the very kind of tissue culture conditions originally described: high levels of c-Myc while a critical nutrient is removed. The original description of c-*myc* constitutive expression in B cells specifically does not note greatly heightened apoptosis (84). When these cells were placed in tissue culture, this effect became obvious. The tissue culture conditions could be limiting in an undefined way. In later experiments, apoptosis was specifically looked for in vivo and found in bone marrow and in tumors. The points raised above concerning foci of limiting factors could therefore apply. Gross overexpression of c-Myc, as seen in some apoptotic regions of tumors, could be acting by special mechanisms because the abundance of c-Myc (and p53) would greatly upset the association kinetics between these and other critical regulatory proteins.

Evidence in support of the dual signal theory, that specific genes for cycle progression, apoptosis, and anti-apoptosis all must be activated every time c-*myc* is expressed, comes from experiments showing that cells caught in the situation of Myc expression and growth factor/serum removal can be rescued by addition of growth factors that have little or no ability to restart the cell cycle (156). Bcl-2 can also act in nongrowing cells to suppress apoptosis despite elevated c-Myc (28). In other words, various experiments show that it is possible to separate protection against inappropriate c-Myc expression from activation of the cell cycle. Clearly, the entire apparatus of the cell cycle is not necessary to protect against c-Myc. Why this is so is not clear. One interpretation is that these experiments demonstrate protective effects that normally occur as part of the cell cycle, but do not alone cause the entire cycle to proceed. Alternatively, the treatments used may produce general anti-apoptotic responses, for example by reducing the level of reactive oxygen species or some other effector of apoptosis. Such general protection does not provide compelling evidence of dual specific signals that are obligate consequences of c-*myc* expression. Finally, of course, the ability to dissociate protection against c-Myc and the expression of the entire cell cycle may indeed be an indication that there are specific dual signals. Further evidence lies in the findings that cdc25A and ornithine decarboxylase, both products of genes controlled by c-Myc, are themselves apoptotic when overexpressed (28, 108, 109, 115). Currently, these results give only a glimmering that there might be a specific set of genes, as proposed. If true, a further issue will be whether they are general or cell/system specific.

Scientific hypotheses and models are most valuable when phrased so that meaningful tests can be done. The challenge now is to refine these two hypotheses so that they can be more definitively tested. For the specific model, the task seems clear: Find the proposed specific genes. Techniques exist that in theory allow screening for them. For the confused grow/no grow signals model, it may be necessary to work out in detail what takes place in several specific systems; then compare results. If there are multiple central biochemical signals or consequences of such confusion, they must be identified and proven to be the events to which the cell responds. The importance of the problem certainly justifies the effort that will be required.

SUMMARY

The potent and important transcription factor c-Myc is involved in apoptosis in several ways. Clear examples exist of c-Myc reduction leading to apoptosis and in which maintaining c-Myc prevents apoptosis. These relationships occur in a variety of cell types but have been most thoroughly explored in B- and T-lymphoid cell lines. Testable hypotheses accounting for the fact that c-Myc reduction is an apoptotic signal state that the transcription factor is required to repress lethal genes or to maintain expression of vital genes. Such genes are being sought. In other systems, inappropriate expression of c-*myc* appears to cause apoptosis. This is most obvious when cells are not allowed to grow while there is simultaneous forced expression of c-*myc*. Gross overexpression of the gene also is apoptotic. Cells also may be sensitized to a variety of apoptotic agents by expression of c-*myc*. Two hypotheses have been advanced to explain these results. One idea suggests that cells respond to confusion of signals resulting from forced c-*myc* expression with apoptosis. The other proposes that a natural consequence of c-*myc* expression is dual signals, those for growth and those for death. It is also possible that no single theory will suffice to explain all instances of c-*myc*-enforced expression. Data are available that support each theory, and further experiments will be necessary to sustain or refute them.

ACKNOWLEDGMENTS

Thanks to Drs. LM Boxer, Stanford University Medical Center, and EA Thompson, Jr, University of Texas Medical Branch, for their valuable comments and advice regarding this chapter.

Visit the *Annual Reviews home page* at
http://www.AnnualReviews.org.

Literature Cited

1. Marcu KB, Bossone SA, Patel AJ. 1992. *myc* function and regulation. *Annu. Rev. Biochem.* 61:809–60
2. Spencer CA, Groudine M. 1991. Control of c-*myc* regulation in normal and neoplastic cells. *Adv. Cancer Res.* 56:1–48
3. Lemaitre JM, Buckle RS, Méchali M. 1996. c-Myc in the control of cell proliferation and embryonic development. *Adv. Cancer Res.* 70:96–144
4. Ryan KM, Birnie GD. 1996. Myc oncogenes: the enigmatic family. *Biochem. J.* 314:713–21
5. Henriksson M, Luscher B. 1996. Proteins of the Myc network: essential regulators of cell growth and differentiation. *Adv. Cancer Res.* 68:109–82
6. Shrivastava A, Calame K. 1995. Association with c-Myc: an alternated mechanism for c-Myc function. *Curr. Top. Microbiol. Immunol.* 194:273–82
7. Vastrik I, Makela TP, Koskinen PJ, Klefstrom J, Alitalo K. 1994. Myc protein: partners and antagonists. *Crit. Rev. Oncog.* 5(1):59–68
8. Ma T, Mahajan PB, Thompson EA Jr. 1992. Glucocorticoid regulation of c-*myc* promoter utilization in P1798 T-lymphoma cells. *Mol. Endocrinol.* 6:960–68
9. Hurlin PJ, Ayer DE, Grandori C, Eisenman RN. 1994. The Max transcription factor network: involvement of Mad in differentiation and an approach to identification of target genes. *Cold Spring Harb. Symp. Quant. Biol.* 59:109–16
10. Plet A, Tourkine N, Mechti N, Jeanteur

P, Blanchard JM. 1992. In vivo footprints between the murine c-*myc* P1 and P2 promoters. *Oncogene* 7:1847–51
11. Strobl LJ, Eick D. 1992. Hold back of RNA polymerase II at the transcription start site mediates down-regulation of c-*myc* in vivo. *EMBO J.* 11(9):3307–14
12. Krumm A, Meulia T, Brunvand M, Groudine M. 1992. The block to transcriptional elongation within the human c-*myc* gene is determined in the promoter-proximal region. *Genes Dev.* 6:2201–13
13. Lewis BC, Shim H, Li Q, Wu CS, Lee LA, et al. 1997. Identification of putative c-Myc-responsivie genes: characterization of *rcl*, a novel growth-related gene. *Mol. Cell Biol.* 17(9)4967–78
14. Shim H, Dolde C, Lewis BC, Wu CS, Dang G, et al. 1997. c-Myc transactivation of LDH-A: implications for tumor metabolism and growth. *Proc. Natl. Acad. Sci. USA* 94(13)6658–63
15. Seth A, Gupta S, Davis RJ. 1993. Cell cycle regulation of the c-Myc transcriptional activation domain. *Mol. Cell. Biol.* 13(7):4125–36
16. Eastman-Reks SB, Vedeckis WV. 1986. Glucocorticoid inhibition of c-*myc*, c-*myb*, and c-Ki-ras expression in a mouse lymphoma cell line. *Cancer Res.* 46(5):2457–62
17. Yuh YS, Thompson EB. 1989. Glucocorticoid effect on oncogene/growth gene expression in human T lymphoblastic leukemic cell line CCRF-CEM: specific c-*myc* mRNA suppression by dexamethasone. *J. Biol. Chem.* 264:10904–10

18. Thulasi R, Harbour DV, Thompson EB. 1993. Suppression of c-*myc* is a critical step in glucocorticoid-induced human leukemic cell lysis. *J. Biol. Chem.* 268:18306–12

19. Wood AC, Waters CM, Garner A, Hickman JA. 1994. Changes in c-*myc* expression and the kinetics of dexamethasone-induced programmed cell death (apoptosis) in human lymphoid leukaemia cells. *Br. J. Cancer* 69:663–69

20. Thompson EB, Thulasi R, Saeed MF, Johnson BH. 1995. Glucocorticoid antagonist RU486 reverses agonist-induced apoptosis and c-*myc* repression in human leukemic CEM-C7 cells. *Ann. NY Acad. Sci.* 761:261–77

21. Helmberg A, Auphan N, Caelles C, Karin M. 1995. Glucocorticoid-induced apoptosis of human leukemic cells is caused by the repressive function of the glucocorticoid receptor. *EMBO J.* 14:452–60

22. Forsthoefel AM, Thompson EA Jr. 1987. Glucocorticoid regulation of transcription of the c-*myc* cellular protooncogene in P1798 cells. *Mol. Endocrinol.* 1:899–907

23. Rhee K, Bresnahan W, Hirai A, Hirai M, Thompson EA. 1995. c-Myc and cyclin D3 (CcnD3) genes are independent targets for glucocorticoid inhibition of lymphoid cell proliferation. *Cancer Res.* 55(18):4188–95

24. Thompson EA Jr. 1991. Glucocorticoid insensitivity of P1798 lymphoma cells is associated with production of a factor that attenuates the lytic response. *Cancer Res.* 51:5551–56

25. McCormack JE, Pepe VH, Kent RB, Dean M, Marshak-Rothstein A, Sonenshein GE. 1984. Specific regulation of c-*myc* oncogene expression in a murine B-cell lymphoma. *Proc. Natl. Acad. Sci. USA* 81:5546–50

26. Sonenshein GE. 1997. Down-modulation of c-Myc expression induces apoptosis of B lymphocyte models of tolerance via clonal deletion. *J. Immunol.* 158:1994–97

27. Fischer G, Kent SC, Joseph L, Green DR, Scott DW. 1994. Lymphoma models for B cell activation and tolerance. X. Anti-μ-mediated growth arrest and apoptosis of murine B cell lymphomas are prevented by the stabilization of myc. *J. Exp. Med.* 179:221–28

28. Packham G, Cleveland JL. 1995. c-Myc and apoptosis. *Biochim. Biophys. Acta* 1242:11–28

29. Wu M, Arsura M, Bellas RE, Fitzgerald MJ, Lee H, et al. 1996. Inhibition of c-*myc* expression induces apoptosis of WEHI 231 murine B cells. *Mol. Cell. Biol.* 16(9):5015–25

30. Kaptein JS, Lin CKE, Wang CL, Nguyen TT, Kalunta CI, et al. 1996. Anti-IgM-mediated regulation of c-*myc* and its possible relationship to apoptosis. *J. Biol. Chem.* 271(3):18875–84

31. Medh RD, Saeed MF, Johnson BH, Thompson EB. 1997. Synergism between glucocorticoid and protein kinase A pathways evokes death of resistant human leukemic CEM-C1 cells: correlation with c-Myc down-regulation. *Cancer Res.* Submitted

32. Ayala-Torres S, Moller PC, Johnson BH, Thompson EB. 1997. Characteristics of 25-hydroxycholesterol-induced apoptosis in the human leukemic cell line CEM. *Exp. Cell Res.* 235:35–47

33. Ayala-Torres S, Zhou F, Thompson EB. 1997. Apoptosis induced by oxysterol in CEM cells is associated with negative regulation of c-*myc*. *Mol. Cell. Biol.* Submitted

34. Shimamoto T, Nakamura S, Bollekens J, Ruddle FH, Takeshita K. 1997. Inhibition of DLX-7 homeobox gene causes decreased expression of GATA-1 and c-*myc* genes and apoptosis. *Proc. Natl. Acad. Sci. USA* 94(7):3245–49

35. Lerga A, Belandia B, Delgado MD, Cuadrado MA, Richard C, et al. 1995. Down-regulation of c-Myc and Max genes is associated with inhibition of protein phosphatase 2A in K562 human leukemia cells. *Biochem. Biophys. Res. Commun.* 215(3):889–95

36. Dean M, Cleveland J, Kim HY, Campisi J, Levine RA, et al. 1988. Deregulation of the c-*myc* and N-myc genes in transformed cells. *Curr. Top. Microbiol. Immunol.* 141:216–22

37. Cory S, Bernard O, Bowtell D, Schrader S, Schrader JW. 1987. Murine c-*myc* retroviruses alter the growth requirements of myeloid cell lines. *Oncogene Res.* 1(1):61–76

38. Askew DS, Ashmun RA, Simmons BC, Cleveland JL. 1991. Constitutive c-*myc* expression in an IL-3-dependent myeloid cell line suppresses cell cycle arrest and accelerates apoptosis. *Oncogene* 6:1915–22

39. Kimura S, Maekawa T, Hirakawa K, Murakami A, Abe T. 1995. Alteration of c-*myc* expression by antisense oligodeoxynucleotides enhances the induction of apoptosis in HL-60 cells. *Cancer Res.* 55:1379–84

40. Ohta H, Sweeney EA, Masamune A, Yatomi Y, Hakomori S, Igarashi Y. 1995. Induction of apoptosis by sphingosine in

human leukemic HL-60 cells: a possible endogenous modulator of apoptotic DNA fragmentation occurring during phorbol ester-induced differentiation. *Cancer Res.* 55(3):691–97

41. Davidoff AN, Mendelow BV. 1993. c-*myc* expression is down-regulated in mafosfamide-treated HL-60 cells undergoing apoptosis. *Anticancer Res.* 13(4):1167–70

42. Samid D, Shack S, Sherman LT. 1992. Phenylacetate: a novel nontoxic inducer of tumor cell differentiation. *Cancer Res.* 52(7):1988–92

43. Sumitani K, Kamijo R, Nagumo M. 1997. Cytotoxic effect of sodium nitroprusside on cancer cells: involvement of apoptosis and suppression of c-*myc* and c-*myb* proto-oncogene expression. *Anticancer Res.* 17(2A):865–71

44. Zhao X, Wang X, Zhou C, Peng R, Yan S, Wu M. 1995. Abrupt reduction of c-*myc* expression by antisense RNA inducing terminal differentiation and apoptosis of a human esophageal cancer cell line. *Sci. China-Ser. B* 38(5):580–90

45. Fornari FA Jr, Jarvis WD, Grant S, Orr MS, Randolph JK, et al. 1994. Induction of differentiation and growth arrest associated with nascent (nonoligosomal) DNA fragmentation and reduced c-*myc* expression in MCF-7 human breast tumor cells after continuous exposure to a sublethal concentration of doxorubicin. *Cell Growth Differ.* 5(7):723–33

46. Van Waardenburg RC, Prins J, Meijer C, Uges DR, De Vries EG, Mulder NH. 1996. Effects of c-*myc* oncogene modulation of drug resistance in human small cell lung carcinoma cell lines. *Anticancer Res.* 16(4A):1963–70

47. Bondurant MC, Yamashita T, Muta K. Krantz SB, Koury MJ. 1996. c-myc expression affects proliferation but not terminal differentiation or survival of explanted erythroid progenitor cells. *J. Cell. Physiol.* 168(2):255–63

48. Skorski T, Nieborowska-Skorska M, Wlodarski P, Zon G, Iozzo RV, Calabretta B. 1996. Antisense oligodeoxynucleotide combination therapy of primary chronic myelogenous leukemia blasts crisis in SCID mice. *Blood* 88(3):1005–12

49. Leonetti C, D'Agnano I, Lozupone F, Valentini A, Geiser T, et al. 1996. Antitumor effect of c-*myc* antisense phosphorothioate oligodeoxynucleotides on human melanoma cells in vitro and in mice. *J. Natl. Cancer Inst.* 88(7):419–29

50. Stein CA. 1996. Antitumor effects of antisense phosphorothioate c-*myc* oligo-

deoxynucleotides: a question of mechanism. *J. Natl. Cancer Inst.* 88(7):391–93

51. Cerutti J, Trapasso F, Battaglia C, Zhang L, Martelli ML, et al. 1996. Block of c-*myc* expression by antisense oligonucleotides inhibits proliferation of human thyroid carcinoma cell lines. *Clin. Cancer Res.* 2:119–26

52. Heufelder AE, Bahn RS. 1995. Modulation of cellular functions in retroorbital fibroblasts using antisense oligonucleotides targeting the c-*myc* protooncogene. *Invest. Ophthalmol. Visual Sci.* 36(7): 1420–32

53. Williams SA, Chang L, Buzby JS, Suen Y, Cairo MS. 1996. Cationic lipids reduce time and dose of c-*myc* antisense oligodeoxynucleotides required to specifically inhibit Burkitt's lymphoma cell growth. *Leukemia* 10(12):1980–89

54. Janicek MF, Sevin BU, Nguyen HN, Averette HE. 1995. Combination antigene therapy targeting c-*myc* and p53 in ovarian cancer cell lines. *Gynecol. Oncol.* 59(1):87–92

55. Bergan R, Hakim F, Schwartz GN, Kyle E, Cepada R, et al. 1996. Electroporation of synthetic oligodeoxynucleotides: a novel technique for ex vivo bone marrow purging. *Blood* 88(2):731–41

56. Watson PH, Pon RT, Shiu RPC. 1991. Inhibition of c-*myc* expression by phosphorothioate antisense oligonucleotide identifies a critical role for c-*myc* in the growth of human breast cancer. *Cancer Res.* 51:3996–4000

57. Harel-Bellan A, Ferris DK, Vinocour M, Holt JT, Farrar WL. 1988. Specific inhibition of c-*myc* protein biosynthesis using an antisense synthetic deoxyoligonucleotide in human T lymphocytes. *J. Immunol.* 140:2431–35

58. McManaway ME, Neckers LM, Loke SL, Al-Nasser AA, Redner R, et al. 1990. Tumour-specific inhibition of lymphoma growth by an antisense oligodeoxynucleotide. *Lancet* 335:808–11

59. Loke SL, Stein C, Zhang X, Avigan M, Cohen J, Neckers LM. 1988. Delivery of c-*myc* antisense phosphorothioate oligodeoxynucleotides to hematopoietic cells in culture by liposome fusion: specific reduction in c-*myc* protein expression correlates with inhibition of cell growth and DNA synthesis. *Curr. Topics Microbiol. Immunol.* 141:282–89

60. Wagner RW. 1994. Gene inhibition using antisense oligodeoxynucleotides. *Nature* 372:333–35

61. Green DR, Mahboubi A, Nishioka W, Oja S, Echeverri F, et al. 1994. Promotion and

inhibition of activation-induced apoptosis in T-cell hybridomas by oncogenes and related signals. *Immunol. Rev.* 142:321–42

62. Evan GI, Brown L, Whyte M, Harrington E. 1995. Apoptosis and the cell cycle. *Curr. Opin. Cell Biol.* 7:285–34

63. Kuchino Y, Asai A, Kitanaka C. 1996. Myc-mediated apoptosis. *Prog. Mol. Subcell. Biol.* 16:104–29

64. Desbarats L, Schneider A, Muller D, Burgin A, Eilers M. 1996. Myc: a single gene controls both proliferation and apoptosis in mammalian cells. *Experientia* 52(12):1123–29

65. Chiarugi V, Ruggiero M. 1996. Role of three cancer "master genes" p53, bcl1 and c-*myc* on the apoptotic process. *Tumori* 82(3):205–9

66. Lotem J, Sachs L. 1996. Control of apoptosis in hematopoiesis and leukemia by cytokines, tumor suppressor and oncogenes. *Leukemia* 10(6):925–31

67. Henriksson M, Luscher B. 1996. Proteins of the Myc network: essential regulators of cell growth and differentiation. *Adv. Cancer Res.* 68:109–82

68. Evan G, Harrington E, Fanidi A, Land H, Amati B, Bennett M. 1994. Integrated control of cell proliferation and cell death by the c-*myc* oncogene. *Philos. Trans. R. Soc. London Ser. B* 345:(1313):269–75

69. Harrington EA, Fanidi A, Evan GI. 1994. Oncogenes and cell death. *Curr. Opin. Genet. Dev.* 4(1):120–29

70. Sachs L, Lotem J. 1993. Control of programmed cell death in normal and leukemic cells: new implications for therapy. *Blood* 82(1):15–21

71. Evan GI, Littlewood TD. 1993. The role of c-*myc* in cell growth. *Curr. Opin. Genet. Dev.* 3(1):44–49

72. Koskinen PJ, Alitalo K. 1993. Role of myc amplification and overexpression in cell growth, differentiation and death. *Semin. Cancer Biol.* 4(1):3–12

73. Askew DS, Ihle JN, Cleveland JL. 1993. Activation of apoptosis associated with enforced myc expression in myeloid progenitor cells is dominant to the suppression of apoptosis by interleukin-3 or erythropoietin. *Blood* 82(7):2079–87

74. Evan GI, Wyllie AH, Gilbert CS, Littlewood TD, Land H, et al. 1992. Induction of apoptosis in fibroblasts by c-*myc* protein. *Cell* 69:119–28

75. Littlewood TD, Hancock DC, Danielian PS, Parker MG, Evan GI. 1995. A modified oestrogen receptor ligand-binding domain as an improved switch for the regulation of heterologous proteins. *Nucleic Acids Res.* 23(10):1686–90

76. Roussel MF, Cleveland JL, Shurtleff SA, Sherr CJ. 1991. Myc rescue of a mutant CSF-1 receptor impaired in mitogenic signalling. *Nature* 353:361–63

77. Onclercq R, Babinet C, Cremisi C. 1989. Exogenous c-*myc* gene overexpression interferes with early events in F9 cell differentiation. *Oncogene Res.* 4(4):293–302

78. Nishikura K, Kim U, Murray JM. 1990. Differentiation of F9 cells is independent of c-*myc* expression. *Oncogene* 5(7):981–88

79. Neiman PE, Thomas SJ, Loring G. 1991. Induction of apoptosis during normal and neoplastic B-cell development in the bursa of Fabricius. *Proc. Natl. Acad. Sci. USA* 88(13):5857–61

80. Nieman PE, Summers J, Thomas SJ, Xuereb S, Loring G. 1994. Genetic instability and apoptotic cell death during neoplastic progression of v-myc-initiated B-cell lymphomas in the bursa of Fabricius. *Cold Spring Harb. Symp. Quant. Biol.* 59:509–15

81. Gibson AW, Cheng T, Johnston RN. 1995. Apoptosis induced by c-Myc overexpression is dependent on growth conditions. *Exp. Cell Res.* 218:351–58

82. Wurm FM, Gwinn KA, Kingston RE. 1986. Inducible overproduction of the mouse c-*myc* protein in mammalian cells. *Proc. Natl. Acad. Sci. USA* 83(15):5414–18

83. Pallavicini MG, Rosette C, Reitsma M, Deteresa PS, Gray JW. 1990. Relationship of c-*myc* gene copy number and gene expression: cellular effects of elevated c-*myc* protein. *J. Cell. Physiol.* 143(2):372–80

84. Harris AW, Pinkert CA, Crawford M, Langdon WY, Brinster RL, Adams JM. 1988. The Eμ-*myc* transgenic mouse: a model for high-incidence spontaneous lymphoma and leukemia of early B cells. *J. Exp. Med.* 167:353–71

85. Jacobsen KA, Prasad VS, Sidman CL, Osmond DG. 1994. Apoptosis and macrophage-mediated deletion of precursor B cells in the bone marrow of Eμ-*myc* transgenic mice. *Blood* 84(8):2784–94

86. Scott DW, Lamers M, Kohler G, Sidman CL, Maddox B, Carsetti R. 1996. Role of c-*myc* and CD45 in spontaneous and anti-receptor-induced apoptosis in adult murine B cells. *Int. Immunol.* 8(9):1375–85

87. Shiota G, Kawasaki H, Nakamura T, Schmidt EV. 1995. Characterization of double transgenic mice expressing hepatocyte growth factor and transforming

growth factor alpha. *Res. Commun. Mol. Pathol. Pharmacol.* 90(1):17–24

88. Prasad VS, LaFond RE, Zhou M, Jacobsen KA, Osmond DG, Sidman CL. 1997. Upregulation of endogenous p53 and induction of in vivo apoptosis in B-lineage lymphomas of *Eμ-myc* transgenic mice by deregulated c-*myc* transgene. *Mol. Carcinogenesis* 18:66–77

89. Amundadottir LT, Nass SJ, Berchem GJ, Johnson MD, Dickson RB. 1996. Cooperation of TGFα and c-Myc in mouse mammary tumorigenesis: coordinated stimulation of growth and suppression of apoptosis. *Oncogene* 13(4):757–65

90. Hundley JE, Koester SK, Troyer DA, Hilsenbeck SG, Barrington RE, Windle JJ. 1997. Differential regulation of cell cycle characteristics and apoptosis in MMTV-*myc* and MMTV-*ras* mouse mammary tumors. *Cancer Res.* 57(4):600–3

91. Morgenbesser SD, DePinho RA. 1994. Use of transgenic mice to study myc family gene function in normal mammalian development and in cancer. *Semin. Cancer Biol.* 5(1):21–36

92. Shi Y, Bissonnette RP, Glynn JM, Guilbert LJ, Cotter TG, Green DR. 1992. Role for c-*myc* in activation-induced apoptotic cell death in T cell hybridomas. *Science* 257:212–14

93. Green DR, Bissonnette RP, Glynn JM, Shi Y. 1992. Activation-induced apoptosis in lymphoid systems. *Semin. Immunol.* 4(6):379–88

94. Wang Y, Ramqvist T, Szekely L, Axelson H, Klein G, Wiman KG. 1993. Reconstitution of wild-type p53 expression triggers apoptosis in a p53-negative v-*myc* retrovirus-induced T-cell lymphoma line. *Cell Growth Differ.* 4:467–73

95. Hermeking H, Eick D. 1994. Mediation of c-*myc*-induced apoptosis by p53. *Science* 265:2091–93

96. Wagner AJ, Kokontis JM, Hay N. 1994. Myc-mediated apoptosis requires wild-type p53 in a manner independent of cell cycle arrest and the ability of p53 to induce p21 wafl/cip1. *Genes Dev.* 8:2817–30

97. Yonish-Rouach E, Resnitzky D, Lotem J, Sachs L, Kimchi A, Oren M. 1991. Wild-type p53 induces apoptosis of myeloid leukaemic cells that is inhibited by interleukin-6. *Nature* 353:345–47

98. Kastan MB, Canman CE, Leonard CJ. 1995. p53, cell cycle control and apoptosis: implications for cancer. *Cancer Metastasis Rev.* 14(1):3–15

99. Marx J. 1993. How p53 suppresses cell growth. *Science* 262:1644–45

100. Harris CC. 1996. p53 tumor suppressor gene: at the crossroads of molecular carcinogenesis, molecular epidemiology, and cancer risk assessment. *Environ. Health Perspect.* 104(3):435–39

101. Sakamuro D, Eviner V, Elliott KJ, Showe L, White E, Prendergast GC. 1995. C-Myc induces apoptosis in epithelial cells by both p53-dependent and p53-independent mechanisms. *Oncogene* 11(11):2411–18

102. Hsu B, Martin MC, El-Naggar AK, Stephens LC, Brisbay S, McDonnell TJ. 1995. Evidence that c-myc mediated apoptosis does not require wild-type p53 during lymphomagenesis. *Oncogene* 11:175–79

103. Clarke AR, Purdie CA, Harrison DJ, Morris RG, Bird CC, et al. 1993. Thymocyte apoptosis induced by p53-dependent and independent pathways. *Nature* 362:849–52

104. Bissonnette RP, McGahon A, Mahboubi A, Green DR. 1994. Functional Myc-Max heterodimer is required for activation-induced apoptosis in T cell hybridomas. *J. Exp. Med.* 180(6):2413–18

105. Amati B, Littlewood TD, Evan GI, Land H. 1993. The c-Myc protein induces cell cycle progression and apoptosis through dimerization with Max. *EMBO J.* 12(13):5083–87

106. Czaja MJ. 1996. Induction of hepatoma cell apoptosis by c-*myc* requires zinc and occurs in the absence of DNA fragmentation. *Am. J. Physiol.* 270:G60–70

107. Reynolds JE, Yang T, Qian L, Jenkinson JD, Zhou P, et al. 1994. Mcl-1, a member of the Bcl-2 family, delays apoptosis induced by c-Myc overexpression in Chinese hamster ovary cells. *Cancer Res.* 54(24):6348–52

108. Packham G, Cleveland JL. 1995. The role of ornithine decarboxylase in c-Myc-induced apoptosis. *Curr. Topics Microbiol. Immunol.* 194:283–90

109. Packham G, Cleveland JL. 1994. Ornithine decarboxylase is a mediator of c-Myc-induced apoptosis. *Mol. Cell. Biol.* 14(9):41–47

110. Jacobson MD. 1996. Reactive oxygen species and programmed cell death. *Trends Biochem. Sci.* 21(3):83–86

111. Xu Y, Nguyen Q, Lo DC, Czaja MJ. 1997. c-*myc*-dependent hepatoma cell apoptosis results from oxidative stress and not a deficiency of growth factors. *J. Cell. Physiol.* 170:192–99

112. Yildiz D, Ercal N, Frank RL, Matthews RH. 1996. Effects of 4-hydroxynonenal

and *N*-acetyl-L-cysteine on Myc-induced apoptosis. *Toxicol. Lett.* 89(3):215–21

113. Hoang AT, Cohen KJ, Barrett JF, Bergstrom DA, Dang CV. 1994. Participation of cyclin A in Myc-induced apoptosis. *Proc. Natl. Acad. Sci. USA* 91(15):6875–79

114. Janicke RU, Lin XY, Lee FH, Porter AG. 1996. Cyclin D3 sensitizes tumor cells to tumor necrosis factor-induced, c-Myc-dependent apoptosis. *Mol. Cell. Biol.* 16(10):5245–53

115. Zornig M, Evan GI. 1996. Cell cycle: on target with Myc. *Curr. Biol.* 6(12):1553–56

116. Polunovsky VA, Rosenwald IB, Tan AT, White J, Chiang L, et al. 1996. Translational control of programmed cell death: eukaryotic translation initiation factor 4E blocks apoptosis in growth-factor-restricted fibroblasts with physiologically expressed or deregulated Myc. *Mol. Cell. Biol.* 16(11):6573–81

117. Mampuru LJ, Chen SJ, Kalenik JL, Bradley ME, Lee TC. 1996. Analysis of events associated with serum deprivation-induced apoptosis in C3H/So18 muscle satellite cells. *Exp. Cell Res.* 226(2):372–80

118. McGahon A, Bissonnette R, Schmitt M, Cotter KM, Green DR, Cotter TG. 1994. BCR-ABL maintains resistance of chronic myelogenous leukemia cells to apoptotic cell death. *Blood* 83(5):1179–87

119. Hsu B, Marin MC, McDonnell TJ. 1995. Cell death regulation during multistep lymphomagenesis. *Cancer Lett.* 94:17–23

120. Zhou F, Thompson EB. 1996. Role of c-*jun* induction in the glucocorticoid-evoked apoptotic pathway in human leukemic lymphoblasts. *Mol. Endocrinol.* 10(3):306–16

121. Bossy-Wetzel E, Bakiri L, Yaniv M. 1997. Induction of apoptosis by the transcription factor c-Jun. *EMBO J.* 16(7):1695–709

122. Kondo T, Sharp FR, Honkaniemi J, Mikawa S, Epstein CJ, Chan PH. 1997. DNA fragmentation and prolonged expression of c-*fos*, c-*jun*, and hsp70 in kainic acid-induced neuronal cell death in transgenic mice overexpressing human CuZn-superoxide dismutase. *J. Cereb. Blood Flow Metab.* 17(3):241–56

123. Ferrer I, Olive M, Blanco R, Cinos C, Planas AM. 1996. Selective c-Jun overexpression is associated with ionizing radiation-induced apoptosis in the developing cerebellum of the rat. *Brain Res.*

Mol. Brain Res. 38(1):91–100

124. Singh N, Sun Y, Nakamura K, Smith MR, Colburn NH. 1995. c-Jun/AP-1 as possible mediators of tumor necrosis factor-alpha-induced apoptotic response in mouse JB6 tumor cells. *Oncol. Res.* 7(7-8):353–62

125. Messina A, Jaworowski A, Bell C. 1996. Detection of jun but not fos protein during developmental cell death in sympathetic neurons. *J. Comp. Neurol.* 372(4):544–50

126. Ferrer I, Segui J, Olive M. 1996. Strong c-Jun immunoreactivity is associated with apoptotic cell death in human tumors of the central nervous system. *Neurosci. Lett.* 214(1):49–52

127. Ferrer I, Olive M, Ribera J, Planas AM. 1996. Naturally occurring (programmed) and radiation-induced apoptosis are associated with selective c-Jun expression in the developing rat brain. *Eur. J. Neurosci.* 8(60):1286–98

128. Soriano MA, Ferrer I, Rodriguez-Farre E, Planas AM. 1996. Apoptosis and c-Jun in the thalamus of the rat following cortical infarction. *NeuroReport* 7(2):425–28

129. Freemerman AJ, Turner AJ, Birrer MJ, Szabo E, Valerie K, Grant S. 1996. Role of c-*jun* in human myeloid leukemia cell apoptosis induced by pharmacological inhibitors of protein kinase C. *Mol. Pharmacol.* 49(5):788–95

130. Zhao R, Rabo YB, Egyhazi S, Andersson A, Edgren MR, et al. 1995. Apoptosis and c-*jun* induction by cisplatin in a human melanoma cell line and a drug-resistant daughter cell line. *Anticancer Drugs* 6(5):657–58

131. Gillardon F, Baurle J, Grusser-Cornehls U, Zimmermann M. 1995. DNA fragmentation and activation of c-Jun in the cerebellum of mutant mice (weaver, Purkinje cell degeneration). *NeuroReport* 6(13):1766–68

132. Sawai H, Okazaki T, Yamamoto H, Okano H, Takeda Y, et al. 1995. Requirement of AP-1 for ceramide-induced apoptosis in human leukemia HL-60 cells. *J. Biol. Chem.* 270(45):27326–31

133. Ham J, Babij C, Whitfield J, Pfarr CM, Lallemand D, et al. 1995. A c-Jun dominant negative mutant protects sympathetic neurons against programmed cell death. *Neuron* 14(5):927–39

134. Piechaczyk M, Blanchard JM. 1994. c-*fos* proto-oncogene regulation and function. *Crit. Rev. Oncol. Hematol.* 17(2):93–131

135. Testolin L, Carson C, Wang Y, Walker PR, Armato U, Sikorska M. 1997. Jun and JNK kinase are activated in thymocytes in response to VM26 and radiation

but not glucocorticoids. *Exp. Cell Res.* 230(2):220–32

136. Hu L, Hatano M, Ruther U, Tokuhisa T. 1996. Overexpression of c-Fos induces apoptosis of CD43+ pro-B cells. *J. Immunol.* 157(9):3804–11

137. Bortner DM, Rosenberg MP. 1995. Overexpression of cyclin A in the mammary glands of transgenic mice results in the induction of nuclear abnormalities and increased apoptosis. *Cell Growth Differ.* 6(12):1579–89

138. Yamada T, Kondoh N, Matsumoto M, Yoshida M, Maekawa A, Oikawa T. 1997. Overexpression of PU.1 induces growth and differentiation inhibition and apoptotic cell death in murine erythroleukemia cells. *Blood* 89(4):1383–93

139. Adams PD, Kaelin WG Jr. 1996. The cellular effects of E2F overexpression. *Curr. Top. Microbiol. Immunol.* 208:79–93

140. Shan B, Lee WH. 1994. Deregulated expression of E2F-1 induces S-phase entry and leads to apoptosis. *Mol. Cell. Biol.* 14(12):8166–73

141. Desaintes C, Demeret C, Goyat S, Yaniv M, Thierry F. 1997. Expression of the papillomavirus E2 protein in HeLa cells leads to apoptosis. *EMBO J.* 16(3):504–14

142. Troppmair J, Rapp UR. 1994. Apoptosis regulation by Raf, Bcl-2, and R-Ras. In *Raf Kinases in Development and Tumors*, pp. 245–49

143. Green DR, McGahon A, Martin SJ. 1996. Regulation of apoptosis by oncogenes. *J. Cell. Biochem.* 60:33–38

144. Lebowitz PF, Sakamuro D, Prendergast GC. 1997. Farnesyl transferase inhibitors induce apoptosis of Ras-transformed cells denied substratum attachment. *Cancer Res.* 57(4):708–13

145. Hundley JE, Koester SK, Troyer DA, Hilsenbeck SG, Subler MA, Windle JJ. 1997. Increased tumor proliferation and genomic instability without decreased apoptosis in MMTV-*ras* mice deficient in p53. *Mol. Cell. Biol.* 17(2):723–31

146. di Jeso B, Ulianich L, Racioppi L, D'Armiento F, Feliciello A, et al. 1995. Serum withdrawal induces apoptotic cell death in Ki-ras transformed but not in normal differentiated thyroid cells. *Biochem. Biophys. Res. Commun.* 214(3):819–24

147. Esteve P, del Peso L, Lacal JC. 1995. Induction of apoptosis by *rho* in NIH 3T3 cells requires two complementary signals. Ceramides function as a progression factor for apoptosis. *Oncogene* 11(12):2657–65

148. Jimenez B, Arends M, Esteve P, Perona R, Sanchez R, et al. 1995. Induction of apoptosis in NIH 3T3 cells after serum deprivation by overexpression of rho-p21, a GTPase protein of the ras superfamily. *Oncogene* 10(5):811–16

149. Fukasawa K, Rulong S, Resau J, Pinto da Silva P, Woude GF. 1995. Overexpression of mos oncogene product in Swiss 3T3 cells induces apoptosis preferentially during S-phase. *Oncogene* 10(1):1–8

150. Fan J, Banerjee D, Stambrook PJ, Bertino JR. 1997. Modulation of cytotoxicity of chemotherapeutic drugs by activated H-ras. *Biochem. Pharmacol.* 53(8):1203–9

151. Chou CC, Yung BY. 1997. Antiapoptotic effect of ras in the apoptosis induced by serum deprivation and exposure to actinomycin D. *Naunyn Schmiedebergs Arch. Pharmacol.* 355(2):177–82

152. Ward RL, Todd AV, Santiago F, O'Connor T, Hawkins NJ. 1997. Activation of the K-ras oncogene in colorectal neoplasms is associated with decreased apoptosis. *Cancer* 79(6):1106–13

153. Jansen B, Schlagbauer-Wadl H, Eichler HG, Wolff K, van Elsas A, et al. 1997. Activated N-ras contributes to the chemoresistance of human melanoma in severe combined immunodeficiency (SCID) mice by blocking apoptosis. *Cancer Res.* 57(3):362–65

154. Fernandes RS, McGowan AJ, Cotter TG. 1996. Mutant H-ras overexpression inhibits drug and U.V. induced apoptosis. *Anticancer Res.* 16(4A):1691–705

155. Thompson EB. 1994. Apoptosis and steroid hormones. *Mol. Endocrinol.* 8:665–73

156. Harrington EA, Bennett MR, Fanidi A, Evan GI. 1994. c-Myc-induced apoptosis in fibroblasts is inhibited by specific cytokines. *EMBO J.* 13(14):3286–95

Annu. Rev. Physiol. 1998. 60:601–17

CELL CYCLE REGULATION AND APOPTOSIS[1]

K. L. King and J. A. Cidlowski#*

*Department of Molecular and Cellular Physiology, University of Cincinnati Medical Center, P. O. Box 670576, Cincinnati, Ohio 45267-0576; #National Institutes of Health, National Institute of Environmental Health Sciences, P.O. Box 12233 MD E2-02, Research Triangle Park, North Carolina 27709; e-mail: cidlowski@niehs.nih.gov

KEY WORDS: p53, pRb, E2F, cell death, cell cycle, lymphocytes

ABSTRACT

Tissue homeostasis requires a balance between cell proliferation and death. Apoptosis and proliferation are linked by cell cycle regulators, and apoptotic stimuli affect both cell proliferation and death. Glucocorticoids induce G1 arrest and apoptosis in transformed lymphoid cells. Decreased expression of the cell cycle components c-*myc* and cyclin D3 is essential for glucocorticoid-induced growth arrest and death in dividing cells. Other G1 regulators, such as p53, pRb, and E2F, have also been implicated in apoptosis. Mice lacking either p53 or E2F display aberrant cell proliferation and tumor formation, suggesting that these proteins are involved in the elimination of abnormal cells through apoptosis. In contrast, pRb induces G1 arrest and suppresses apoptosis in cultured cells. Mice that lack pRb are nonviable and show ectopic mitosis and massive cell death, suggesting that pRb is an apoptotic suppressor. Further analysis of common components of apoptotic and cell cycle machinery may provide insight into the coordinated regulation of these antagonistic processes.

INTRODUCTION

Tissue homeostasis is dependent on the proper relationships among cell proliferation, differentiation, and cell death. As somatic cells proliferate, the cell

---

[1] The US Government has the right to retain a nonexclusive, royalty-free license in and to any copyright covering this paper.

mitotic cycle progression is tightly regulated by an intricate network of positive and negative signals, and much is known about the molecules involved in cell cycle control. Programmed cell death, or apoptosis, is also a highly regulated process by which an organism eliminates unwanted cells without eliciting an inflammatory response. Apoptosis is involved in many physiological processes including tissue homeostasis, embryonic development, and the immune response (1). Mitosis and apoptosis display several similar morphological features. Both mitotic and apoptotic cells lose substrate attachment and become rounded. During both processes, cells shrink, condense their chromatin, and display rapid membrane blebbing. Although a number of similarities exist between mitotic and apoptotic cells, several distinct differences are also apparent. For example, only apoptotic cells display fragmentation of their DNA into approximately 200 base-pair fragments. At the end of apoptosis, the cell is broken into multiple apoptotic bodies that are phagocytosed by neighboring cells. Because cellular contents are not released, this occurs with little inflammation. During mitosis, DNA is segregated and the nucleus is divided into two distinct but equal parts. The mitotic process ends with cytokinesis and the production of a new daughter cell. Furthermore, cell cycle components such as p53, pRb, and E2F, have been shown to participate in both cell cycle progression and apoptosis. Hence, comparison of apoptosis and cell proliferation may provide insight into the regulation and molecular mechanisms of these two antagonistic processes.

Multiple inducers of apoptosis have been identified. These signals are often cell-type specific, and a partial list includes growth factor withdrawal, ionizing radiation, Ca^{2+} influx, tumor necrosis factor, viral infection, and glucocorticoids. In response to these signals, the cell induces a programmed cascade of events that results in the destruction of the cell. A number of catalytic pathways are induced during apoptosis, including protease activation, which leads to the destruction of cellular proteins, and nuclease activation, which results in DNA fragmentation and RNA degradation. Caspases, also called ICE proteases, are a family of cysteine proteases that act as effectors of the mammalian cell death pathway (2). Their activation leads to morphological changes characteristic of the apoptotic process.

CELL PROLIFERATION AND APOPTOSIS

The balance between proliferation and apoptosis must be strictly maintained to sustain tissue homeostasis. An imbalance between these two processes can result in either unwanted tissue atrophy or tissue growth. For example, when adrenalectomized rats are treated with the synthetic glucocorticoid dexamethasone, a steroid that induces thymocyte apoptosis, the wet weight of the rat thymus decreases by 50% within 24 h owing to an increase in the rate of apoptosis of cortical thymocytes that is not offset by an increase in mitosis (3). Tumor formation can result from a decrease in cell death, as well as an increase in cell proliferation. For example, when bcl-2, an anti-apoptotic gene, is overexpressed, neoplasia results because of a reduction of apoptosis that is not offset by a decrease in cell proliferation (4, 4a,b).

Cell Cycle Checkpoints

Because it is essential to identify and eliminate cells proliferating inappropriately, apoptosis and proliferation are tightly coupled, and cell cycle regulators can influence both cell division and cell death (5, 6). The timing and order of cell cycle events are monitored during cell cycle checkpoints that occur at the G1/S phase boundary, in S phase, and during the G2/M phases (7). These checkpoints ensure that critical events in a particular phase of the cell cycle are completed before a new phase is initiated, thereby preventing the formation of genetically abnormal cells. Cell cycle progression can be blocked at these checkpoints in response to the status of both the intracellular and extracellular environment. For example, the expression of certain genes required for DNA synthesis occurs only in the presence of growth factors, thus linking the extracellular environment to cell proliferation. Additionally, growth arrest can be induced when DNA damage is detected or when chromosomes are misaligned on the mitotic spindle (8). Upon repair of the damage, progression through the cell cycle resumes. An alternative to repairing damaged cells is simply to eliminate them through the process of apoptosis. Thus as a cell progresses through the cell cycle, it must determine whether to complete cell division, arrest growth to repair cellular damage, or undergo apoptosis if the damage is too severe to be repaired or if the cell is incapable of repairing the DNA. It is at the checkpoints that the cell determines which of these options is suitable.

The cell cycle control system is based on two protein families: the cyclin-dependent protein kinases (Cdks) and the cyclins. Cdks allow progression through the different phases of the cell cycle by phosphorylating substrates. Their kinase activity is dependent on the presence of activating subunits known as cyclins. The abundance of specific cyclins increases during the phase of the cell cycle wherein they are required and decreases during phases in which they are not needed. For example, in most circumstances cyclin D associates with Cdk4 and Cdk6 during early G1, whereas cyclin E activates Cdk2 during G1 to S phase transition. Cyclin A binds to Cdk2 or Cdc2 during S phase and the G2 to M phase transition, and the cyclin B/Cdc2 complex functions during the G2 to M phase transition. Thus specific cyclin/Cdk complexes are activated, and their phosphorylation of particular proteins permits the cell cycle processes to continue. The transcription of genes necessary for S phase, for example, is regulated by cyclinD/Cdk4-dependent phosphorylation of the cell cycle regulator pRb. For more extensive reviews of cyclins, Cdks, and cell cycle progression, see References 8a,b,c.

Whereas cyclin binding is required for Cdk kinase activity, other proteins have been identified whose association leads to the inhibition of Cdk activity. Cyclin/Cdk complexes can be bound by Cdk inhibitor (CKI) proteins, which inhibit kinase activity and prevent cell cycle progression. Two separate families of CKI proteins have been identified (8b,d,e). The p21 family, composed of p21, p27, and p57, predominantly inhibits the Cdks of the G1 to S phase transition. The INK4 (inhibitors of Cdk4) family includes p15, p16, p18, and p19, several of which are mutated or deleted in certain types of human cancers.

Numerous genes, including c-*myc*, are known to inhibit or activate cell proliferation by affecting the formation and activity of Cdk complexes. The proto-oncogene c-*myc* is an immediate early gene encoding a protein that functions as a transcription factor. Its activity is dependent on its association with another factor, Max, and this association is required for mitogenesis (9, 10). Expression of c-*myc*, which is exquisitely sensitive to growth factors, is required for quiescent cells to enter the cell cycle (11). The c-Myc protein has been shown to activate transcription of Cdc25, a phosphatase that activates Cdks, and expression of Cdc25 appears necessary for c-*myc*-induced cell cycle activation (12). The G1- to S-phase transition also requires c-Myc, and inhibition of c-*myc* expression leads to growth arrest (13). Conversely, if c-*myc* is expressed in G1-arrested cells in the absence of growth factors, the cells exit G1 and divide, a process that eventually leads to death (14–17). Deregulated expression of this proto-oncogene has been implicated in a number of human malignancies (18, 19). A more detailed discussion of the roles of c-*myc* in apoptosis may be found in the chapter by EB Thompson (this volume).

GLUCOCORTICOIDS, THE CELL CYCLE, AND APOPTOSIS

Glucocorticoids induce death through at least two separate pathways. When proliferating thymocytes are treated with glucocorticoids, the signal to activate apoptosis involves changes in cell cycle components (Figure 1). Glucocorticoids also induce apoptosis in nonproliferating thymocytes, and while not identical, this signaling pathway shares some features in common with that in proliferating cells. In both systems, glucocorticoid binds to its receptor and induces changes in gene expression. However, in nonproliferating cells, the signaling pathway leading to apoptosis does not appear to involve changes in cell cycle proteins. Thus upstream signals induced by glucocorticoids in the circumstances differ depending on whether the cell is progressing through the

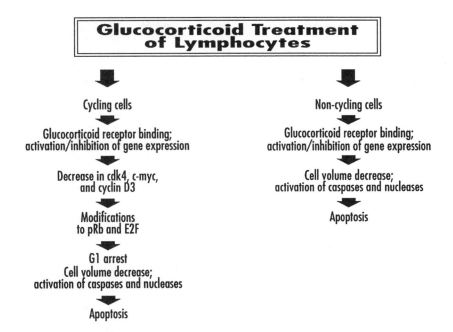

Figure 1 Possible pathways for glucocorticoid-induced apoptosis of lymphoid cells (21–33). Although G1 arrest and cell death appear linked, the mechanism by which these two processes are coordinated remains unknown.

cell cycle. The downstream components of both signaling pathways ultimately appear to activate apoptotic effector molecules that include the caspases and nucleases.

Many apoptotic stimuli induce cell cycle arrest before cell death, thereby affecting both cell cycle and apoptotic machinery. Growth suppressive and lytic effects of glucocorticoids on thymocytes and transformed lymphoid cells have been studied (20, 21). Glucocorticoid treatment of many lymphoid cell lines expressing markers of immature thymocytes induces G1 arrest and, in most cases, this growth suppression is followed by cell death. The precise mechanism by which glucocorticoids induce G1 arrest and apoptosis is currently being investigated but is largely unknown.

Glucocorticoids Regulate Cell Cycle Genes

Glucocorticoids elicit their effects by binding to their cognate receptors, which function as ligand-dependent transcription factors. Glucocorticoids can inhibit gene expression and alter mRNA stability of genes that are critical for the

G1- to S-phase transition. One of the cell cycle genes regulated by this steroid is c-*myc* (22–26). Although an inappropriate increase in c-*myc* expression usually leads to cell death, downregulation of c-*myc* by glucocorticoids causes apoptosis in a lymphoma cell line and in a leukemic cell line (22, 27, 28). Thus at least two pathways involving c-*myc* result in apoptosis. Although the precise molecular mechanism by which glucocorticoids decrease c-*myc* mRNA has not yet been elucidated, this decrease appears to be critical for induction of death. For example, sustained expression of c-*myc* blocks glucocorticoid-induced death in the human leukemic cell line CEM-C7, and antisense c-*myc* oligomers trigger apoptosis in these cells (27). Furthermore, the glucocorticoid antagonist RU 486 blocks steroid-induced cell death, and this inhibition is correlated with an increase in c-*myc* mRNA levels (28). Thus changes in this cell cycle regulator play a prominent role in glucocorticoid-induced apoptosis.

Other cell cycle regulators are also sensitive to glucocorticoid treatment including cyclin D3, the primary isoform of cyclin D in thymocytes, and one of its catalytic subunits Cdk4 (23, 29, 30). In the murine lymphoma cell line P1798, glucocorticoids inhibit the transcription of Cdk4, a cyclin-dependent kinase thought to be involved in progression through G1. Additionally, cyclin D3 mRNA is rapidly downregulated in P1798 cells treated with the synthetic glucocorticoid dexamethasone (23, 29). Destabilization of this mRNA appears to be the main mechanism by which glucocorticoids decrease cyclin D3. In the absence of steroid, the half life of cyclin D3 mRNA is 8 h, whereas in the presence of glucocorticoid, half life is reduced to 1 h (29). The increase in turnover of mRNA is independent of cell cycle progression and dependent on protein synthesis. Thus glucocorticoids induce expression of proteins that accelerate the degradation of cyclin D3 mRNA.

When P1798 lymphoma cells with normal cyclin D3 and c-*myc* are cultured in the absence of serum and treated with dexamethasone, they rapidly undergo apoptosis (23, 31, 32). In the presence of serum, these cells undergo G1 arrest. Cells that overexpress both cyclin D3 and c-*myc* genes override glucocorticoid-induced G1 arrest (23). Additionally, cells that overexpress both proteins in the absence of serum are resistant to glucocorticoid-induced death. Thus, cyclin D3 and c-Myc convey resistance to both G1 arrest and cell death, and glucocorticoid inhibition of both these genes appears to be critical for steroid-mediated growth suppression and apoptosis in P1798 cells. It is unclear whether G1 arrest and apoptosis are parallel, independent functions or sequential, dependent events induced by decreases in c-Myc and cyclin D.

Glucocorticoid treatment of cultured lymphoid cells affects other G1 regulators including pRb and E2F (23, 33). For example, treatment of P1798 cells induced a 75–90% reduction in pRb phosphorylation by a cyclin D3-associated kinase (23). Hypophosphorylation of pRb, G1 arrest, and apoptosis have been observed in other cell types, including Burkitt lymphoma cells treated with an anti-immunoglobulin antibody (34) and in the myeloid leukemic cell lines HL 60 and U937 treated with the DNA-damaging agent cytosine arabinoside (35). Glucocorticoid treatment of P1798 cells induces G1 arrest and causes changes in the proteins associated with the transcription factor E2F (33). Although the role that these changes play in induction of G1 arrest and apoptosis is unclear, it is apparent that G1 checkpoint regulators play a role in both cell cycle regulation and glucocorticoid-induced apoptosis in those cells that are progressing through the cell cycle.

THE G1 CHECKPOINT AND APOPTOSIS

p53

Insight into the roles of cell cycle checkpoints in apoptosis and proliferation has come from in vitro studies of cells and in vivo studies of mice lacking various cell cycle components. The G1 checkpoint regulators p53, pRb, and E2F have been extensively analyzed by both methods (36, 37). The well-characterized tumor suppressor p53 is either inactivated by mutation or sequestered by viral proteins in numerous tumors (37–40). In response to cell damage, p53 has been implicated in controlling the G1- to S-phase transition, blocking cell cycle progression at G1 in response to DNA damage (41). Protein p53 mediates these effects through its transcriptional activation functions. A number of genes controlling cell cycle progression, including the cyclin-dependent kinase inhibitor p21, are transcribed in a p53-dependent manner (42, 43). It has been postulated that p53 induces the expression of p21 in response to ionizing radiation, resulting in G1 arrest. p53 also plays an important role in the induction of apoptosis. When wild-type p53 is transfected into some cell lines lacking p53, apoptosis is induced (44, 45). Within 15 min of exposure to the apoptotic signal delivered to oligodendrocytes by IL-2, p53 translocates from the cytoplasm, and a mutant p53 protects these cells from death (46). Consequently, in cell culture systems, p53 not only regulates progression through the cell cycle but under some circumstances can also induce apoptosis in damaged cells.

p53 KNOCKOUT MICE   To further study the role of p53 in mammalian physiology, p53 knockout mice have been generated (47). These mice are viable but show a high incidence of cancer and typically die from T-cell lymphomas. Furthermore, thymocytes derived from animals lacking p53 are resistant to apoptosis induced by DNA damaging agents such as ionizing radiation and topoisomerase II inhibitors, but not to cell death induced by glucocorticoids or calcium ionophore/phorbol ester treatment (48, 49). Therefore, p53 participates in the induction of some, but not all, forms of apoptosis. Obviously p53 is not an essential component of the machinery that carries out apoptosis but rather is an activator of its function. Both p53-dependent and -independent pathways may be necessary to transduce the large diversity of death signals, or these multiple signaling pathways may provide a fail-safe mechanism if one pathway becomes inactivated.

The mechanism by which p53 induces apoptosis remains unclear. Because p53-dependent cell death may occur in the presence of transcriptional and translational inhibitors, p53 transcriptional activation apparently is not essential (50–53). Additionally, p53 mutants that are unable to transactivate have been shown to induce apoptosis (51). However, others have found that p53 double-point mutants that cannot activate or repress transcription are compromised in their ability to induce apoptosis (52). Using loss- and gain-of-function p53 mutants, Attardi et al (53) have shown that transcriptional activation is necessary for both G1 arrest and apoptosis. However, p53 targets different genes for each process. Rowan et al (54) isolated a mutant that retains transcriptional activation abilities and can induce G1 arrest but does not induce apoptosis, suggesting that these two functions are separable. Discrepancies among results may be due to the existence of multiple transactivation-dependent and transactivation-independent pathways that lead to apoptosis. Additionally, interpretation of mutant studies may be complicated by the possibility that some mutants have lost the ability to activate genes required for cell death but retain the ability to induce genes required for other p53 functions. Thereby, mutants that are transactivation positive would be unable to induce apoptosis even though gene transcription would still be necessary for apoptotic induction. Finally, differences in model systems make comparisons of results difficult. For example, some cell lines employed contain endogenous wild-type p53 in addition to mutant p53 protein, and others have viral proteins that target p53. Further studies will be needed to resolve inconsistencies in results before the role of p53-mediated transcriptional activation and repression in apoptosis is understood.

p53 REGULATES APOPTOSIS GENES   p53 regulates the expression of several proteins known to influence the apoptotic process. In the murine leukemia cell line M1, a temperature-sensitive p53 mutant decreases *bcl*-2 expression and increases *bax* expression (55). Bcl-2 and Bax have opposing effects on cell death: Bcl-2 inhibits or delays cell death, and Bax accelerates apoptosis (56). Furthermore, the ratio of Bcl-2 to Bax has been proposed to influence the propensity of a cell to undergo apoptosis. Additionally, Fas, a cell surface protein that triggers apoptosis upon ligand binding, is encoded by a target gene for transcriptional activation by p53 (57). Both wild-type p53 and a temperature-sensitive p53 mutant (at a permissive temperature) induced a three- to sixfold increase in *fas* expression in several human cell lines. Accordingly, if p53 transcriptional activation and repression functions are required to induce apoptosis, these effects may be mediated through changes in the expression of known apoptotic regulators.

p53, APOPTOSIS, AND CANCER THERAPY   Because p53 is altered in a large number of human cancers, defects in the p53-dependent apoptotic pathway may be a significant obstacle to overcome for successful cancer therapy. Indeed, p53 status in cancer cells does affect the efficacy of cancer treatment (58). Both ionizing radiation and the chemotherapeutic agent adriamycin were more effective in inducing apoptosis in tumor cells that were homozygous for wild-type p53. This information is currently being used to develop new cancer therapy strategies. Reintroduction of normal p53 into tumor cells lacking p53 function has been employed for human cancer treatment. Roth et al (59) injected a retroviral vector containing the wild-type p53 driven by the B actin promoter into lung tumors of human cancer victims. They found p53 DNA in tumor cells, and posttreatment biopsies showed that apoptosis occurred more frequently. Tumor regression or growth stabilization were observed in approximately 60% of the patients treated. This suggests that introducing components necessary for a functional apoptotic pathway into tumor cells can aid in cancer treatment.

pRb

The retinoblastoma protein (pRb), similar to p53, functions as a negative regulator of cell growth and is a tumor suppressor (60). pRb inactivation or deletion is found in many cancers, including retinoblastomas and carcinomas of the lung, breast, bladder, and prostate. Similar to the case with p53, viral-transforming proteins have been shown to inactivate pRb, thus leading to inappropriate cell proliferation and tumor formation (61–63). By binding to and inhibiting transcription factors such as E2F, which are necessary for S-phase entry, pRb is believed to inhibit cell cycle progression. In mid-to-late G1, cyclin-dependent kinases along with their respective cyclins, phosphorylate pRb and the pRb-like proteins p107 and p130. Once phosphorylated, pRb and p130 release the bound transcription factors, including the E2F family. These transcription factors activate expression of genes necessary for the cell to traverse from G1 to S phase. In addition to playing a role in growth arrest, pRb has been shown to suppress apoptosis. In a pRb-defective bladder carcinoma cell line, IFN γ induces apoptosis, but in pRb-positive cells, IFN γ does not induce cell death (64). In the human osteosarcoma cell line SOAS, cells transiently or stably transfected with pRb are protected from radiation-induced apoptosis (65). These cells undergo G1 arrest after irradiation, and this block in cell cycle progression may be responsible for the decrease in susceptibility to apoptosis. Also, pRb inhibits TGF-β1 induced apoptosis in hepatoma cells (66). TGF-β1 treatment of hepatoma cells is associated with inhibition of both pRb expression and phosphorylation and with induction of cell death. Overexpression of pRb in these cells overrides the TGF-β1 death-stimulating pathway and blocks apoptosis.

Recently, pRb was shown to be proteolytically cleaved during apoptosis (67, 68). A member of the caspase family of apoptotic proteases specifically cleaves pRb in tumor necrosis factor, staurosporine, and cytosine arabinoside-induced apoptosis (67, 68). This proteolysis is blocked by tetrapeptide inhibitors of ICE-like enzymes. The destruction of pRb, which acts as an apoptosis suppressor, may be required to induce death.

pRB KNOCKOUT MICE   Deletion of pRb in transgenic mice is an embryonic-lethal mutation that causes death in utero at 14 to 15 days (69–71). The pRb null embryos are defective in erythropoiesis and also show massive cell death in the central and peripheral nervous systems, and in liver, lens, and skeletal muscle precursors. This cell death is associated with inappropriate S-phase entry and increased expression of cyclin E (72). Transgenic mice that express low levels of pRb have also been generated (73). These mice die at birth due to skeletal muscle defects. There is a large increase in myoblast apoptosis, and surviving myoblasts do not differentiate properly. These results suggest a role for pRb in both cell survival and terminal differentiation (74).

p53 and pRB Interaction

There may be complementary roles for p53 and pRb as tumor suppressors, and each may be able to compensate for the loss of the other's tumor suppressor activity. The basis for pRb and p53 cooperativity is being analyzed in several model systems. For example, the interaction between p53 and pRb has been examined in HeLa cells that lack both p53 and pRb (51). When p53 is transiently overexpressed in these cells, apoptosis is induced. However, cell death can be inhibited when pRb is coexpressed with p53. In this case, cell cycle arrest occurs instead of apoptosis. Thus pRb protects the cells from apoptosis, possibly by inducing cell cycle arrest. This lack of aberrant cell proliferation may prevent the induction of p53-dependent apoptosis. In addition to inducing G1 arrest, p53 can induce cell death in response to DNA damage and inappropriate proliferation signals. There appears to be a direct link between p53 and pRb in cell proliferation and apoptosis.

Interactions between p53 and pRb have also been examined in transgenic animals. Mice that are pRb$^{+/-}$ are viable but develop thyroid and pituitary tumors (69–71). Because pRb null mice are nonviable, pRb heterozygotes have been used to analyze pRb and p53 regulation of apoptosis. pRb$^{+/-}$/p53$^{-/-}$ mice show tumors common to each knockout alone, plus additional tumors such as pinealoblastomas and islet tumors (74). Loss of the wild-type Rb allele was associated with tumorigenesis in some tissues. For example, Rb inactivation was frequently seen in pineal blastomas but not in lymphomas. Thus it appears that in some tissues each tumor suppressor can compensate for the loss of the other. Apoptosis is dependent on p53 because embryos that are null for p53 and heterozygous for pRb do not show apoptotic effects seen in mice deficient in pRb alone. Thus pRb deficiency leads to induction of apoptosis in a p53-dependent manner. In lens tissue, p53 and pRb functions have been extremely well characterized. In pRb null mice, lens fiber cells fail to differentiate and undergo apoptosis (75). In a p53 null background, lens fiber cells still do not differentiate properly, but they are not removed by apoptosis; consequently, tumors form in the lens. These results have been confirmed using DNA tumor viruses expressing proteins that inactivate p53 or pRb. When the human papilloma virus oncoprotein E7 is expressed in the developing lens, pRb is inactivated and ectopic mitosis and apoptosis is evident (76). Conversely, if E7 and E6, oncoproteins that inactivate p53, are coexpressed, apoptosis is inhibited and tumor formation occurs. E7 has also been expressed in lens cells in a p53 null background with similar results (77). Similar interactions between p53 and pRb function are also seen in the choroid plexus. A simian virus 40 (SV40) T antigen fragment that inactivates pRb was targeted to epithelial cells in the choroid plexus (78). Inactivation of pRb led to slow growing tumors and an increase in p53-dependent apoptosis. In contrast, when pRb was inactivated in a p53 null background, rapidly growing tumors formed, and there was a decrease in apoptosis. Symonds et al concluded that p53-dependent apoptosis occurring in response to tumorigenic events is a key regulator of tumor formation (78). Therefore, deregulation of the cell cycle by pRb mutation or inactivation and inhibition of apoptosis by p53 disruption result in malignant transformation in numerous tissues. These properties have been exploited by DNA tumor viruses that can simultaneously inactivate both tumor suppressors and cause deregulation of cell cycle progression and apoptosis.

E2F

The pRb protein is a transcriptional repressor that regulates gene expression by physically associating with transcription factors such as those of the E2F family (79). The function of E2Fs in cell proliferation and apoptosis has been characterized in cell culture systems and in knockout mice. The E2F family consists of five closely related transcription factors (36). Some differences in biochemical properties of the E2F members have been noted. E2F-1, -2, and -3 prefer to bind to pRB, whereas E2F-4 and -5 predominantly associate with pRB-related proteins p107 and p130. It is likely that the different isoforms of E2F have different functions or are used to differing extents in specific tissues. E2F-1, the most well characterized member of this family, activates genes whose products are important in the G1- to S-phase transition (60, 79, 80). E2F binds to the DP family of transcription factors, and heterodimers of E2F and DP regulate gene expression necessary for G1/S-phase transition. E2F-1 plays a prominent role in G1/S-phase transition: The ectopic expression of E2F-1 can drive serum-starved, growth-arrested cells through the G1 to S phase, and expression of dominant-negative mutants of E2F-1 inhibits cell cycle progression during this phase of the cell cycle (81–84). Moreover, viral oncoproteins such as SV40 large T antigen and human papilloma virus E7 can transform cells when they bind to pRb and release activated E2F-1 (79). Furthermore, E2F expression alone, and in conjunction with the oncogene *ras*, can transform cells that are then tumorigenic in nude mice (81, 85, 86). E2F-1 has also been shown to play a role in apoptosis in cell culture. Deregulated E2F-1 expression in rat 2 fibroblasts causes early S-phase entry and subsequent apoptosis (82–84), which is dependent on p53 (82, 87). When E2F-1 and p53 are coexpressed in a mouse fibroblast cell line, apoptotic cell death is induced and p53-mediated G1 arrest is overridden. Overexpression of E2F-1 may induce apoptosis by altering transcription of genes necessary for cell survival or by inducing inappropriate progression through the cell cycle.

E2F-1 KNOCKOUT MICE   Mice that are null for E2F-1 have been generated (88, 89). Because E2F is required for S-phase progression, it is perhaps surprising that E2F knockout mice do not show hypoproliferation. Instead, they show enlarged thymus glands and lymph nodes owing to the excess of single positive (CD4+/CD8– or CD4–/CD8+) thymocytes. Additionally, lymphomas, lung tumors, and reproductive tract tumors are detected. Thus, in addition to its role during S phase, E2F-1 appears to suppress inappropriate cell proliferation, perhaps because E2F null mice are defective in normal apoptotic pathways. Depending on the cellular context, E2F-1 may function as an oncogene to promote cell growth or may function as a tumor suppressor to induce apoptosis. For example, when E2F-1 is bound to pRb, cell cycle progression is repressed. However, when pRb is absent, E2F-1 stimulates proliferation. The cellular concentration of E2F or the presence or absence of other cell cycle regulators may influence whether E2F-1 functions to promote cell growth or death.

CONCLUSIONS

Apoptotic stimuli often arrest growth before inducing cell death. Glucocorticoid treatment of transformed lymphoid cells, for example, causes cells to arrest in G1 before entering apoptosis. Glucocorticoids have been shown to inhibit the expression of G1-phase components such as *cdk4, cycD3*, and c-*myc*. Downregulation of c-*myc* is necessary for G1 arrest and the induction of

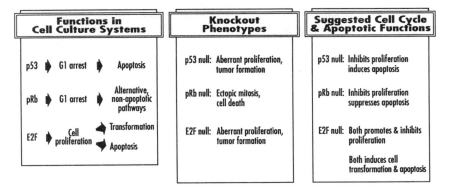

Functions in Cell Culture Systems	Knockout Phenotypes	Suggested Cell Cycle & Apoptotic Functions
p53 ▶ G1 arrest ▶ Apoptosis	p53 null: Aberrant proliferation, tumor formation	p53 null: Inhibits proliferation induces apoptosis
pRb ▶ G1 arrest ▶ Alternative, non-apoptotic pathways	pRb null: Ectopic mitosis, cell death	pRb null: Inhibits proliferation suppresses apoptosis
E2F ▶ Cell proliferation ◀ Transformation ◀ Apoptosis	E2F null: Aberrant proliferation, tumor formation	E2F null: Both promotes & inhibits proliferation

Both induces cell transformation & apoptosis |

Figure 2 Effects of p53, pRb, and E2F mutations in cell culture systems and transgenic mice. All these G1 regulators are capable of altering cell cycle progression and affecting the propensity of a cell to undergo apoptosis (45, 47–49, 51, 64–66, 69–77, 81–85, 88, 89).

apoptosis in CEM cells, and P1798 cells require decreased expression of both cyclin D3 and c-*myc*, which suggests that these cell cycle regulators influence cell death as well as proliferation. Glucocorticoids appear to act through two separate pathways to induce apoptosis—one in proliferating cells and another in nonproliferating cells. These pathways share common upstream and downstream components that include glucocorticoid binding to its receptor, changes in gene expression, and activation of apoptotic effector molecules.

During mouse development, p53, pRb, and E2F function as cell cycle regulators. This is readily apparent in the phenotypes of knockout mice (Figure 2). In all three mouse models, abnormal cell proliferation is visible in some tissues; however, the response to this uncontrolled cell division differs among the three different knockout mice. In p53 and E2F knockout models, proliferation is allowed to continue unchecked, resulting in the formation of tumors. In contrast, pRb knockout mice are nonviable and display massive cell death in response to inappropriate mitosis. Thus it appears that p53 and E2F provide positive signals for apoptosis in response to inappropriate cell proliferation, and removal of these regulators results in lack of cell death and tumor formation. It appears that pRb inhibits inappropriate apoptosis from occurring during embryogenesis by inducing alternative, non-apoptotic pathways to prevent undue growth. When this protein is deleted from cells, growth arrest cannot occur and apoptosis is induced. Animals that are heterozygous for pRb display a different phenotype. These mice show unregulated proliferation and tumor formation, suggesting that pRb has other effects that may be masked by the early death of pRb null embryos. Thus although these three proteins serve as both cell cycle and apoptotic regulators, their functions differ greatly. Whereas pRb induces growth arrest to suppress apoptosis, p53 and E2F are necessary for induction of apoptosis in response to unregulated cell growth. The mechanisms by which these cell cycle regulators influence the apoptotic process remain unknown. In summary, the cell has integrated control of two antagonistic processes—cell proliferation and cell death—at cell cycle checkpoints. This coordinated regulation provides an effective means to control inappropriate cell cycle progression.

Visit the *Annual Reviews home page* at
http://www.AnnualReviews.org.

Literature Cited

1. Schwartzman RA, Cidlowski JA. 1993. Apoptosis: the biochemistry and molecular biology of programmed cell death. *Endocr. Rev.* 14:133–50
2. Golstein P. 1997. Controlling cell death. *Science* 275:1081–82
3. Compton MM, Cidlowski JA. 1986. Rapid in vivo effects of glucocorticoids on the integrity of rat lymphocyte genomic deoxyribonucleic acid. *Endocrinology* 118:38–45
4. McDonnell TJ, Deane N, Platt M, Nunez G, Jaeger U, et al. 1989. bcl-2 immunoglobulin transgenic mice demonstrate extended B cell survival and follicular lympho-proliferation. *Cell* 57:79–88
4a. McDonnell TJ, Korsmeyer SJ. 1991. Progression from lymphoid hyperplasia to high grade malignant lymphoma in mice transgenic for the t(14;18). *Nature* 349:254–56
4b. Stasser A, Harris AW, Cory S. 1991. bcl-2 transgene inhibits T cell death and perturbs thymic self-censorship. *Cell* 67:889–99
5. Meikrantz W, Schlegel R. 1995. Apoptosis and the cell cycle. *J. Cell. Biochem.* 58:160–74
6. King KL, Schwartzman RA, Cidlowski JA. 1996. Apoptosis in life, death, and the cell cycle. *Endocrinol. Metab. 3 Suppl.* A:93–97
7. Murray A, Hunt T. 1993. *The Cell Cycle*. New York: Oxford Univ. Press. 251 pp.
8. Murray A. 1994. Cell cycle checkpoints. *Curr. Opin. Cell Biol.* 6:872–76
8a. Morgan DO. 1995. Principles of Cdk regulation. *Nature* 374:131–34
8b. Hunter T, Pines J. 1994. Cyclins and cancer II: cyclin D and Cdk inhibitors come

of age. *Cell* 79:573–82
8c. Fisher RP. 1997. Cdks and cyclins in transition. *Curr. Opin. Gene Dev.* 7:32–38
8d. Harper JW, Elledge SJ. 1994. Cdk inhibitors in development and cancer. *Curr. Opin. Gene Dev.* 6:56–64
8e. Xiong Y. 1996. Why are there so many Cdk inhibitors? *Biochim. Biophys. Acta* 1288:1–5
9. Amati B, Brooks MW, Levy N, Littlewood TD, Evan GI, et al. 1993. Oncogenic activity of the c-Myc protein requires dimerization with Max. *Cell* 72:233–45
10. Amati B, Littlewood TD, Evan GI, Land H. 1993. The c-Myc protein induces cell cycle progression and apoptosis through dimerization with Max. *EMBO J.* 12:5083–87
11. Eilers M, Schirm S, Bishop JM. 1991. The myc protein activates transcription of the α-prothymosin gene. *EMBO J.* 10:133–41
12. Galaktionov K, Chen X, Beach D. 1996. Cdc25 cell-cycle phosphatase as a target of c-*myc*. *Nature* 382:511–17
13. Heikkila R, Schwab G, Wickstrom E, Loke SL, Pluznik DH, et al. 1987. A c-myc antisense oligodeoxynucleotide inhibits entry into S phase but not progression from G0 to G1. *Nature* 328:445–49
14. Askew D, Ashmun R, Simmons B, Cleveland J. 1991. Constitutive c-*myc* expression in IL-3 dependent myeloid cell line suppresses cycle cell arrest and accelerates apoptosis. *Oncogene* 6:1915–22
15. Evan G, Wyllie A, Gilbert C, Littlewood T, Land H, et al. 1992. Induction of apoptosis in fibroblasts by c-myc protein. *Cell* 63:119–25
16. Wyllie AH, Rose KA, Morris RG, Steel

CM, Foster E, et al. 1987. Rodent fibroblast tumours expressing human *myc* and *ras* genes: growth, metastasis, and endogenous oncogene expression. *Br. J. Cancer* 56:251–59

17. Vogt M, Lesley J, Bogenberger JM, Haggblom C, Swift S, et al. 1987. The induction of growth factor independence in murine myelocytes by oncogenes results in monoclonal cell lines and is correlated with cell crisis and karyotypic instability. *Oncogene Res.* 2:49–63

18. Ryan KM, Birnie GD. 1996. *myc* oncogenes: the enigmatic family. *Biochem. J.* 314:713–21

19. Evan GI, Littlewood TD. 1993. The role of c-*myc* in cell growth. *Curr. Opin. Genet. Dev.* 3:44–49

20. Munck A, Crabtree GR. 1981. Glucocorticoid-induced lymphocyte death. In *Cell Death in Biology and Pathology*, ed. ID Bowen, RA Lockshin, pp. 329–59. New York: Chapman & Hall

21. Cidlowski JA, King KL, Evans-Storms RB, Montague JW, Bortner CD, et al. 1996. The biochemistry and molecular biology of glucocorticoid-induced apoptosis in the immune system. *Rec. Prog. Horm. Res.* 51:457–91

22. Eastman-Reks SB, Vedeckis WV. 1986. Glucocorticoid inhibition of c-*myc*, c-*myb*, and c-*Ki-ras* expression in a mouse lymphoma cell line. *Cancer Res.* 46:2457–62

23. Rhee K, Bresnahan W, Hirai A, Hirai M, Thompson EA. 1995. c-*myc* and *cyclin D* (CcnD3) genes are independent targets for glucocorticoid inhibition of lymphoid cell proliferation. *Cancer Res.* 55:4188–95

24. Ma T, Mahajan PB, Thompson EA. 1992. Glucocorticoid regulation of c-*myc* promoter utilization in P1798 T-lymphoma cells. *Mol. Endocrinol.* 6:960–68

25. Forsthoefel AM, Thompson EA. 1987. Glucocorticoid regulation of transcription of the c-*myc* cellular protooncogene in P1798 cells. *Mol. Endocrinol.* 1:899–907

26. Yuh Y-S, Thompson EB. 1987. Glucocorticoid effect on oncogene/growth related gene expression in human lymphoblastic leukemic cell line CCRF-CEM. *J. Biol. Chem.* 264:10904–10

27. Thulasi R, Harbour DV, Thompson EB. 1993. Supression of c-*myc* is a critical step in glucocorticoid-induced human leukemic cell lysis. *J. Biol. Chem.* 268:18306–12

28. Thompson EB, Thulasi R, Saeed MF, Johnson BH. 1995. Glucocorticoid antagonist RU 486 reverses agonist-induced apoptosis and c-*myc* repression in human leukemic CEM-C7 cells. *Ann. NY Acad. Sci.* 761:261–75

29. Reisman D, Thompson EA. 1995. Glucocorticoid regulation of *cyclin D3* gene transcription and mRNA stability in lymphoid cells. *Mol. Endocrinol.* 9:1500–9

30. Rhee K, Reisman D, Bresnahan W, Thompson EA. 1995. Glucocorticoid regulation of G1 cyclin-dependent kinase genes in lymphoid cells. *Cell Growth Diff.* 6:691–98

31. Thompson EA. 1991. Insensitivity to the cytolytic effects of glucocorticoids in vivo is associated with a novel "slow death" phenotype. *Cancer Res.* 51:5544–50

32. Thompson EA. 1991. Glucocorticoid insensitivity of P1798 lymphoma cells is associated with a factor that attenuates the lytic response. *Cancer Res.* 51:5551–56

33. Rhee K, Ma T, Thompson EA. 1994. The macromolecular state of the transcription factor E2F and glucocorticoid regulation of c-*myc* transcription. *J. Biol. Chem.* 269:17035–42

34. Wang H, Grand RJ, Milner AE, Armitage RJ, Gordon J, et al. 1996. Repression of apoptosis in human B-lymphoma cells by CD40-ligand and Bcl-2: relationship to the cell cycle and role of the retinoblastoma protein. *Oncogene* 13:373–79

35. Dou QP, Lui VW. 1995. Failure to dephosphorylate retinoblastoma protein in drug resistant cells. *Cancer Res.* 55:5222–25

36. Weinberg RA. 1996. E2F and cell proliferation: a world turned upside down. *Cell* 85:457–59

37. Picksley SW, Lane DP. 1994. p53 and Rb: their cellular roles. *Curr. Opin. Cell Biol.* 6:853–58

38. Oren M. 1992. p53: the ultimate tumor suppressor gene? *FASEB J.* 6:3169–76

39. Friend S. 1994. p53: a glimpse at the puppet behind the shadow play. *Science* 265:334–35

40. Berns A. 1994. Is p53 the only real tumor suppressor gene? *Curr. Biol.* 4:137–139

41. Kuerbitz SJ, Plunkett BS, Walsh WV, Kastan MB. 1992. Wild-type p53 is a cell cycle checkpoint determinant following irradiation. *Proc. Natl. Acad. Sci. USA* 89:7491–95

42. Dulic V, Kaufmann WK, Wilson SJ, Tlsty TD, Lees E, et al. 1994. p53-dependent inhibition of cyclin-dependent kinase activities in human fibroblasts during radiation-induced G1 arrest. *Cell* 76:1013–23

43. El-Deiry WS, Tokino T, Velculescu VE, Levy DB, Parsons R, et al. 1993. WAF1, a potential mediator of p53 tumor suppression. *Cell* 75:817–25

44. Yonish-Rouach E, Grunwald D, Wilder S, Kimchi A, May E, et al. 1993. p53-mediated cell death: relationship to cell cycle control. *Mol. Cell. Biol.* 13:1415–23

45. Yonish-Rouach E, Resnitzky D, Lotem J, Sachs L, Kimchi A, et al. 1993. Wild-type p53 induces apoptosis of myeloid leukaemic cells that is inhibited by interleukin-6. *Nature* 352:345–47

46. Eizenberg O, Faber-Elman A, Gottlieb E, Oren M, Rotter V, et al. 1995. Direct involvement of p53 in programmed cell death of oligodendrocytes. *EMBO J.* 14:1136–44

47. Donehower LA, Harvey M, Slagle BL, McArthur MJ, Montgomery CAJ, et al. 1992. Mice deficient for p53 are developmentally normal but susceptible to spontaneous tumors. *Nature* 356:215–21

48. Clarke AR, Purdie CA, Harrison DJ, Morris RG, Bird CC, et al. 1993. Thymocyte apoptosis induced by p53-dependent and independent pathways. *Nature* 362:849–52

49. Lowe SW, Schmitt EM, Smith SW, Osborne BA, Jacks T. 1993. p53 is required for radiation-induced apoptosis in mouse thymocytes. *Nature* 362:847–49

50. Wagner AJ, Kokontis JM, Hays N. 1994. Myc-mediated apoptosis requries wild-type p53 in a manner independent of cell cycle arrest and the ability of p53 to induce p21 WAF1/CIP1. *Genes Dev.* 8:2817–30

51. Haupt Y, Rowan S, Oren M. 1995. p53-mediated apoptosis in HeLa cells can be overcome by excess pRb. *Oncogene* 10:1563–71

52. Sabbatini P, Lin J, Levine AJ, White E. 1995. Essential role for p53-mediated transcription in E1A-induced apoptosis. *Genes Dev.* 9:2184–92

53. Attardi LD, Lowe SW, Brugarolas J, Jacks T. 1996. Transcriptional activation by p53, but not induction of the p21 gene, is essential for oncogene-mediated apoptosis. *EMBO J.* 15:3693–701

54. Rowan S, Ludwig RL, Haupt Y, Bates S, Lu X, et al. 1996. Specific loss of apoptotic but not cell-cycle arrest function in a human tumor derived p53 mutant. *EMBO J.* 15:827–38

55. Miyashita T, Krajewski S, Krajewski M, Wang HG, Lin HK, et al. 1994. Tumor suppressor p53 is a regulator of *bcl-2* and *bax* gene expression in vitro and in vivo. *Oncogene* 9:1799–805

56. Reed JC. 1994. Bcl-2 and the regulation of programmed cell death. *J. Cell Biol.* 124:1–6

57. Owen-Schaub LB, Zhang W, Cusack JC, Angelo LS, Santee SM, et al. 1995. Wild-type human p53 and a temperature sensitive mutant induce Fas/APO-1 expression. *Mol. Cell. Biol.* 15:3032–40

58. Lowe SW, Bodis S, McClatchey A, Remington L, Ruley HE, et al. 1994. p53 status and the efficacy of cancer therapy in vivo. *Science* 266:807–10

59. Roth JA, Nguyen D, Lawrence DD, Kemp BL, Carrasco CH, et al. 1996. Retrovirus-mediated wild-type p53 gene transfer to tumors of patients with lung cancer. *Nat. Med.* 2:985–91

60. Weinberg R. 1995. The retinoblastoma protein and cell cycle control. *Cell* 81:323–30

61. DeCaprio JA, Ludlow JW, Figge J, Shew JY, Huang CM, et al. 1988. SV40 large tumor antigen forms a specific complex with the product of the retinoblastoma susceptibility gene. *Cell* 54:275–83

62. Dyson N, Howley PM, Munger K, Harlow E. 1989. The human papilloma virus-16 E7 oncoprotein is able to bind to the retinoblastoma protein. *J. Virol.* 64:1353–56

63. Whyte P, Buchkovich KJ, Horowitz JM, Friend SH, Raybuck M, et al. 1988. Association between an oncogene and an anti-oncogene: The adenovirus E1A proteins bind to the retinoblastoma gene product. *Nature* 334:124–29

64. Berry DE, Lu Y, Schmidt B, Fallon PG, O'Connell C, et al. 1996. Retinoblastoma protein inhibits IFN-γ induced apoptosis. *Oncogene* 12:1809–19

65. Haas-Kogan DA, Kogan SC, Levi D, Dazin p, T'Ang A, et al. 1995. Inhibition of apoptosis by the retinoblastoma gene product. *EMBO J.* 14:461–72

66. Fan G, Ma X, Kren BT, Steer CJ. 1996. The retinoblastoma gene product inhibits TGF-β1 induced apoptosis in primary rat hepatocytes and human HuH-7 hepatoma cells. *Oncogene* 12:1909–19

67. An B, Dou QP. 1996. Cleavage of retinoblastoma protein during apoptosis: an interleukin 1β-converting enzyme-like protease as candidate. *Cancer Res.* 56:438–42

68. Janicke RU, Walker PA, Lin XY, Porter AG. 1996. Specific cleavage of the retinoblastoma protein by an ICE-like protease in apoptosis. *EMBO J.* 15:6969–78

69. Clarke AR, Maandag ER, van Roon M, van der Lugt NMT, van der Valk M, et al. 1992. Requirement for a functional *Rb-1* gene in murine development. *Nature* 359:328–30

70. Jacks T, Fazeli A, Schmitt EM, Bronson RT, Goodell MA, et al. 1992. Effects of an *Rb* mutation in the mouse. *Nature* 359:295–300

71. Lee EY-HP, Chang C-Y, Hu N, Wang Y-CJ, Lai C-C, et al. 1992. Mice deficient for *Rb* are nonviable and show defects in neurogenesis and haematopoiesis. *Nature* 359:288–94

72. Macleod KF, Hu Y, Jacks T. 1996. Loss of Rb activates both p53-dependent and independent cell death pathways in the developing mouse nervous system. *EMBO J.* 15:6178–88

73. Zacksenhaus E, Jiang Z, Chung D, Marth JD, Phillips RA, et al. 1996. pRb controls proliferation, differentiation, and death of skeletal muscle cells and other lineages during embryogenesis. *Genes Dev.* 10:3051–64

74. Williams BO, Remington L, Alberts DM, Mukai S, Bronson RT, et al. 1994. Cooperative tumorigenic effects of germline mutations in RB and p53. *Nat. Genet.* 7:480–84

75. Morgenbesser SD, Williams BO, Jacks T, Depino RA. 1994. p35-dependent apoptosis produced by *Rb* deficiency in the eye. *Nature* 371:72–74

76. Pan H, Griep AE. 1994. Altered cell cycle regulation in the lens of HPV-16 E6 or E7 transgenic mice: implications for tumor suppressor function in development. *Genes Dev.* 8:1285–99

77. Howes KA, Ransom N, Papermaster DS, Lasudry JGH, Alberts DM, et al. 1994. Apoptosis or retinoblastoma: alternative fates of photoreceptors expressing the HPV-16 E7 gene in the presence or absence of p53. *Genes Dev.* 8:1300–10

78. Symonds H, Krall L, Remington L, Saenz-Robles M, Lowe S, et al. 1994. p53-dependent apoptosis suppresses tumor growth and progression in vivo. *Cell* 78:703–11

79. Lam EW-F, Thangue NBL. 1994. DP and E2F proteins: coordinating transcription with cell cycle progression. *Curr. Opin. Cell Biol.* 6:859–66

80. Sherr CJ. 1993. Mammalian G1 cyclins. *Cell* 73:1059–65

81. Johnson DG, Schwarz JK, Cress WD, Nevins JR. 1993. Expression of transcription factor E2F-1 induces quiescent cells to enter S phase. *Nature* 365:349–52

82. Qin X-Q, Livingston DM, WG, Kaelin J, Adams PD. 1994. Deregulated transcription factor E2F-1 expression leads to S-phase entry and p53-mediated apoptosis. *Proc. Natl. Acad. Sci. USA* 91:10918–22

83. Shan B, Lee W-H. 1994. Deregulated expression of E2F-1 induces S phase entry and leads to apoptosis. *Mol. Cell. Biol.* 14:8166–73

84. Shan B, Durfee T, Lee W-H. 1996. Disruption of RB/E2F-1 interaction by single point mutations in E2F-1 enhances S-phase entry and apoptosis. *Proc. Natl. Acad. Sci. USA* 93:679–84

85. Singh P, Wong SH, Hong W. 1994. Overexpression of E2F-1 in rat embryo fibroblasts leads to neoplastic transformation. *EMBO J.* 13:3329–38

86. Xu G, Livingston DM, Krek W. 1995. Multiple members of the E2F transcription factor family are the products of oncogenes. *Proc. Natl. Acad. Sci. USA* 92:1357–61

87. Wu X, Levine AJ. 1994. p53 and E2F-1 cooperate to mediate apoptosis. *Proc. Natl. Acad. Sci. USA* 91:3602–6

88. Field SJ, Tsai F-Y, Kuo F, Zubiaga AM, W.G. Kaelin J, et al. 1996. E2F-1 functions in mice to promote apoptosis and suppress proliferation. *Cell* 85:549–61

89. Yamasaki L, Jacks T, Bronson R, Goillot E, Harlow E, et al. 1996. Tumor induction and tissue atrophy in mice lacking E2F-1. *Cell* 85:537–48

Annu. Rev. Physiol. 1998. 60:619–42

THE MITOCHONDRIAL DEATH/LIFE REGULATOR IN APOPTOSIS AND NECROSIS

Guido Kroemer[1], Bruno Dallaporta[1], and Michèle Resche-Rigon[2]

[1]Centre National de la Recherche Scientifique, Unité Propre de Recherche 420, 19 rue Guy Moquet, F-94801 Villejuif, France; [2]Roussel-Uclaf-Hoechst, 102 rue de Noisy, F-93230 Romainville, France; e-mail: kroemer@infobiogen.fr

KEY WORDS: cell death, mitochondrial transmembrane potential, permeability, transition, programmed cell death

---

ABSTRACT

Both physiological cell death (apoptosis) and, in some cases, accidental cell death (necrosis) involve a two-step process. At a first level, numerous physiological and some pathological stimuli trigger an increase in mitochondrial membrane permeability. The mitochondria release apoptogenic factors through the outer membrane and dissipate the electrochemical gradient of the inner membrane. Mitochondrial permeability transition (PT) involves a dynamic multiprotein complex formed in the contact site between the inner and outer mitochondrial membranes. The PT complex can function as a sensor for stress and damage, as well as for certain signals connected to receptors. Inhibition of PT by pharmacological intervention on mitochondrial structures or mitochondrial expression of the apoptosis-inhibitory oncoprotein Bcl-2 prevents cell death, suggesting that PT is a rate-limiting event of the death process. At a second level, the consequences of mitochondrial dysfunction (collapse of the mitochondrial inner transmembrane potential, uncoupling of the respiratory chain, hyperproduction of superoxide anions, disruption of mitochondrial biogenesis, outflow of matrix calcium and glutathione, and release of soluble intermembrane proteins) entails a bioenergetic catastrophe culminating in the disruption of plasma membrane integrity (necrosis) and/or the activation of specific apoptogenic proteases (caspases) by mitochondrial proteins that leak into the cytosol (cytochrome c, apoptosis-inducing factor) with secondary endonuclease activation (apoptosis). The relative rate of these two processes (bioenergetic catastrophe versus protease and endonuclease activation) determines whether a cell will undergo primary necrosis or apoptosis. The

619

0066-4278/98/0315-0619$08.00

acquisition of the biochemical and ultrastructural features of apoptosis critically relies on the liberation of apoptogenic proteases or protease activators from mitochondria. The fact that mitochondrial events control cell death has major implications for the development of cytoprotective and cytotoxic drugs.

APOPTOSIS AND NECROSIS—DIFFERENCES BETWEEN TWO MODES OF CELL DEATH

Cell death constitutes one of the key events in biology. At least two modes of cell death can be distinguished: apoptosis and necrosis. Apoptosis is a strictly regulated (programmed) device responsible for the ordered removal of superfluous, aged, or damaged cells (1, 2). Every second, several millions of cells of the human body undergo apoptosis; i.e. in conditions of homeostasis, each mitosis is compensated by one event of apoptosis. It is likely that all cells of the human body possess the intrinsic capacity of undergoing apoptosis, even in the absence of de novo protein synthesis (3), which suggests that all structures and processes required for at least one pathway to apoptosis are ubiquitously present (and probably necessary for cell survival). Of course, macromolecular synthesis may be required for certain agents to cause apoptosis—either because they have differing pathways or because of linkages to the preexisting proteins particular to these agents. Disturbances in apoptosis regulation illustrate the importance of apoptosis for normal homeostasis. An abnormal resistance to apoptosis induction correlates with malformations, autoimmune diseases, or cancer due to the persistence of superfluous, self-specific immunocytes, or mutated cells, respectively. In contrast, enhanced apoptotic decay of cells participates in acute pathologies (infection by toxin-producing microorganisms, ischemia-reperfusion damage, or infarction) as well as in chronic diseases (neurodegenerative and neuromuscular diseases, AIDS). Although apoptosis is necessary for both health and disease, necrosis is always the outcome of severe and acute injury: i.e. abrupt anoxia, sudden shortage of nutrients such as glucose, or extreme physicochemical injury (heat, detergents, strong bases etc).

In contrast to necrosis, apoptosis involves the regulated action of catabolic enzymes (proteases and nucleases) within the limits of a near-to-intact plasma membrane (1, 2). Apoptosis is commonly accompanied by a characteristic change of nuclear morphology (chromatin condensation, pyknosis, karyorrhexis) and of chromatin biochemistry (step-wise DNA fragmentation culminating in the formation of mono- and/or oligomers of 200 base pairs). It also involves the activation of specific cysteine proteases (caspases) that cleave after aspartic acid residues. Caspases catalyze a highly selective pattern of protein degradation (4, 5). Subtle changes in the plasma membrane occur before it ruptures. Thus the surface exposure of phosphatidylserine residues (normally on the inner membrane leaflet) allows for the recognition and elimination of apoptotic cells by their healthy neighbors, before the membrane breaks up and cytosol or organelles spill into the intercellular space and elicit inflammatory reactions (6). Moreover, cells undergoing apoptosis tend to shrink while reducing the intracellular potassium level (7). During the process of apoptosis, mitochondria do not manifest any major ultrastructural abnormalities (8, 9).

In contrast to apoptosis, necrosis does not involve any regular DNA and protein degradation pattern and is accompanied by swelling of the entire cytoplasm (oncosis) and of the mitochondrial matrix, which occur shortly before the cell membrane ruptures (10). The fundamental differences between apoptosis and necrosis are summarized in Table 1.

The morphological features of both modes of cell death—normal or condensed mitochondria in apoptosis and swollen mitochondria in necrosis—have given rise to the erroneous speculation that mitochondria are major players in necrosis but irrelevant to apoptosis. Indeed, the volume of deenergized mitochondria is determined by the cytosolic colloidosmotic pressure (which is

Table 1   Apoptosis versus necrosis: a comparison

Apoptosis	Primary necrosis
Physiological or pathological	Accidental
(subnecrotic damage)	Always pathological
Susceptibility tightly regulated	Unregulated or poorly regulated
Plasma membranes near-to-intact until late	Plasma membrane destroyed early
Heterophagic elimination	Leakage of cell contact
No leakage of cell content; little or	inflammation
no Inflammation	Biochemical and morphological
Cellular enzymes participate, causing	features include
characteristic biochemical or	swelling of the entire cytoplasma
morphological features including	(oncosis),
chromatin condensation (pyknosis),	mitochondrial swelling
nuclear fragmentation (karyorrhexis),	Secondary necrosis
regular DNA fragmentation	Cytolysis secondary to apoptosis
pattern (endonucleolysis),	when dying cells fail to be removed
selective protein degradation by	by heterophagy
specific proteases (caspases),	
subtle changes in plasma membranes	
(loss of membrane asymmetry before	
loss of membrane integrity),	
cell shrinkage,	
no mitochondrial swelling	

maintained in apoptosis and reduced in necrosis) rather than by mitochondrion-intrinsic parameters. Functional analyses conducted during the past few years have revealed that changes in mitochondrial membrane are as critical for the apoptotic process as they are for necrosis. The present review focuses on the role of mitochondria in death/life decision making.

APOPTOSIS AND NECROSIS—SIMILARITIES AND EARLY INVOLVEMENT OF MITOCHONDRIA

Although apoptosis and necrosis have long been viewed as opposed by antinomy, it is now generally assumed that both forms of cell death constitute two extremes of a continuum (Table 2). Moreover, several observations shed doubt on the functional opposition between these two types of cell death. Thus the same toxin can induce apoptosis or necrosis at a low (subnecrotic) or high dose, respectively (11). The equilibrium between apoptosis and necrosis can be influenced by manipulation of the ATP levels and caspase activation. Thus maintenance of high ATP favors apoptosis over necrosis (12, 13), whereas inhibition of caspase activation transforms apoptosis into necrosis (14–16). As shown in Figure 1, thymocytes normally respond to stimulation

Table 2   A few arguments against the antithesis between apoptosis and necrosis

Argument	Reference
After apoptosis, cells undergo secondary necrosis	(1, 11, 80)
The same toxin can induce apoptosis at a low (subnecrotic) dose and primary necrosis at a high dose	(2, 11)
Many pathologies labeled necrotic involve apoptosis (apoplexy, myocardial infraction, anoxia, ischemia-reperfusion damage, etc)	(17, 18, 81, 82)
Mitochondrial permeability transition is involved in both apoptosis and necrosis	(2, 23)
The oncoprotein Bcl-2 can inhibit both apoptosis and, in some models, primary necrosis	(17, 20–22)
Modulation of cellular ATP levels can shift apoptotic responses to necrosis (low ATP) and vice versa (high ATP)	(12, 13)
Overexpression of Bax and Bak causes apoptosis and, in the presence of caspase inhibitors, non-apoptotic (necrotic?) cytolysis	(14, 15)
Classical apoptosis inducers (serum withdrawl, c-Myc overexpression, etoposide, glucocorticoids) induce non-apoptotic cells death in the presence of caspase inhibitors such as Z-VAD.fmk	(15, 16)

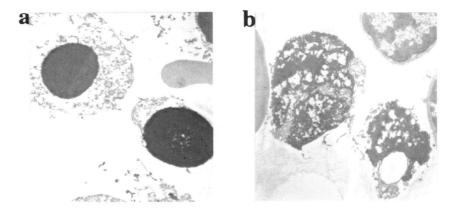

Figure 1 Primary and secondary necrosis. Mouse thymocytes were treated for 12 h with 1 μM dexamethasone, either in the absence (*a*) or in the presence (*b*) of Z-VAD.fmk. Note the typical apoptotic nuclear morphology (condensed, homogeneously electron-dense nuclei) in lysed cells visible in *a*, that is not observed in *b*. The cells have either undergone necrosis after apoptosis (secondary necrosis; *a*) or undergone necrosis in the absence of apoptosis (primary necrosis; *b*).

with glucocorticoids by undergoing apoptosis, followed by secondary necrosis. However, in the presence of the caspase inhibitor *N*-benzyloxycarbonyl-Val-Ala-Asp-fluoromethylketone (Z-VAD.fmk), cells fail to undergo nuclear apoptosis and die from cytolysis without apoptosis (primary necrosis). A number of pathologies previously thought to involve primary necrosis now appear to involve apoptosis: apoplexy (17), myocardial infarction (18), and ischemia/reperfusion damage (19). More importantly, hyperexpression of the apoptosis-inhibitory oncoprotein Bcl-2 inhibits several examples of necrotic cell death: kainate-induced neuronal necrosis (20), occlusion of the midbrain artery (17), anoxia (21), and chemical hypoxia (22). At least in some instances, mitochondrial permeability transition (PT), which is regulated by Bcl-2, constitutes a molecular event involved in both apoptosis and necrosis (2, 23; Table 3). Thus the early phase of both modes of cell death may involve a similar change in mitochondrial membrane permeability. In the following sections, we discuss the role of mitochondrial changes in necrosis and apoptosis.

MITOCHONDRIAL CHANGES IN NECROSIS: THE PUTATIVE ROLE OF PERMEABILITY TRANSITION

The mitochondrial transmembrane potential ($\Delta\Psi_m$) can be monitored in living cells using a number of different potential-sensitive dyes: rhodamine 123, 3,3' dihexyloxacarbocyanine iodide [DiOC$_6$(3)], 5,5',6,6'-tetrachloro-1,1',3,3'-tetraethylbenzimidazolcarbocyanine iodide (JC-1), and chloromethyl-X-

Table 3   Mitochondrial permeability transition in different models of necrosis[a]

Cell type + lethal stimulus	Intervention preventing early $\Delta\Psi_m$ disruption and cell death[b]
Myocardiocytes + oxidative stress	Cyclosporin A (83)
Myocardiocytes + ischemia/reperfusion	Cyclosporin A (84)
Hepatocytes + anoxia/reperfusion	Cyclosporin A or L-carnitine (85)
	Cyclosporin A + BAPTA-AM (intracellular Ca^{2+} chelator) (28)
Hepatocytes + 1-methyl-4-phenylpyridinium	Cyclosporin A (86)
Hepatocytes + protoporphyrin IX	Cyclosporin A (34)
Hepatocytes + ter-butylhydroperoxide	Cyclosporin A (27, 87)
	Cyclosporin A plus trifluoperazin (26, 88)
L929 fibrosarcoid cells + tumor necrosis factor α	Cyclosporin A (35)
Hippocampal neurons + glutamate	Cyclosporin A (89)
Cerebellar granule cells + glutamate	Cyclosporin A (90)
Cortical neurons + glutamate	Cyclosporin A (91)
Cortical neurons + N-methyl-D-aspartate	Cyclosporin A (92)
PC12 pheochromocytoma cells + cyanide	Bcl-2 or Bcl-X_L overexpression (93)

[a]Note that in several instances the indicated treatment may also induce apoptosis.
[b]References are in parentheses.

rosamine (CMXRos) (24). All these dyes share a cationic lipophilic structure allowing them to distribute freely through membranes into the mitochondrial matrix, as a function of the Nernst equation, correlated to the $\Delta\Psi_m$. With use of these dyes, it has been shown in numerous in vitro models of necrosis that following toxin exposure the $\Delta\Psi_m$ dissipates before the plasma membrane disrupts and before cells manifest signs of damage such as vacuolization or cytoplasmic swelling (Table 3). The $\Delta\Psi_m$ results from the unequal distribution of ions (mainly protons) on the inner mitochondrial membrane. The $\Delta\Psi_m$ disruption suggests that the proton-moving force and/or the inner membrane permeability has been affected during cell damage. In a series of elegant confocal microscopy studies, Lemaster and colleagues (25, 26) showed that when calcein, a polyanionic membrane impermeant fluorescein derivative, is incorporated into cells, all cellular compartments are stained except mitochondria. During hepatocyte necrosis this dye can access the mitochondrion as soon as the $\Delta\Psi_m$ breaks down, indicating that the mitochondrial membranes have indeed become permeant.

Pharmacological experiments have shown that cyclosporin A can prevent or retard the $\Delta\Psi_m$ disruption as well as subsequent cell death (Table 3). In addition, the cyclosporin A derivative N-methyl-Val-cyclosporin A, which loses its calcineurin-dependent immunosuppressive effects but conserves its effects on mitochondrial cyclophilin D, remains capable of stabilizing the $\Delta\Psi_m$ and of exerting cytoprotective effects (Table 3). Based on these observations and additional experiments demonstrating the role of mitochondrial Ca^{2+} fluxes (10, 27, 28), it has been postulated that a cyclosporin A-inhibitable mitochondrial megachannel might be involved in necrosis. This megachannel, also called the permeability transition (PT) pore (29, 30), has been subject to extensive pharmacological and functional characterization (see below).

Depending on different physiological effectors, the PT pore complex can adopt an open or closed conformation. In normal circumstances, most if not all PT pores are closed (29, 30). Opening of the pore has dramatic consequences on mitochondrial physiology, including $\Delta\Psi_m$ collapse, uncoupling of the respiratory chain, and efflux of small molecules and some proteins from the mitochondrion (29, 30). In addition to cyclophilin D, the target of cyclosporin A and N-methyl-Val-cyclosporin A, other proteins such as the peripheral benzodiazepin receptor (PBR) and the adenine nucleotide translocator (ANT) have been implicated in the formation and/or regulation of the PT pore (29–33). Substances that specifically act on mitochondrial structures to induce PT can modulate necrosis. Thus protoporphyrin IX (PPIX), a PBR ligand, induces PT and subsequent necrosis in hepatocytes (34). Other ligands of the PBR such as PK11195 and chlorodiazepam can facilitate tumor necrosis factor-α-induced necrosis of L929 cells (35). Moreover, a number of toxic metabolites such as reactive oxygen species, nitric oxide, and supraphysiological Ca^{2+} concentrations have been shown to induce PT in several models of cell death (29, 30).

Based on this evidence, PT has been postulated to underlie mitochondrial changes occurring during the early phase of necrosis.

EVIDENCE FOR THE INVOLVEMENT
OF MITOCHONDRIA IN APOPTOSIS

The absence of changes in mitochondrial ultrastructure, as well as the fact that cells lacking mitochondrial DNA (i.e. cells possessing respiration-deficient mitochondria) can undergo apoptosis (36), initially supported the idea that mitochondria do not intervene in the process of apoptosis. This interpretation is incorrect, as discussed below.

Chronological Evidence Implying Mitochondria in Apoptosis

We and others have observed that cells undergoing apoptosis exhibit a reduction of the cellular uptake of $\Delta\Psi_m$-sensitive fluorochromes [JC-1, $DiOC_6(3)$, rhodamine 123, CMXRos] (23, 24). Dissipation of the $\Delta\Psi_m$ is a general feature of apoptosis, irrespective of the cell type (neurons, fibroblasts, thymocytes, monocytes, hepatocytes, lymphocytes, tumor cells, etc) and of the apoptosis inducer: toxins, suboptimal culture conditions, interventions on second messenger systems, ligation of cell surface receptors (Fas/Apo-1/CD95, TNF-R, etc), glucocorticoid receptor occupancy, or absence of obligatory growth factors (e.g. serum withdrawal) (2, 16, 23, 24, 37–51). The $\Delta\Psi_m$ disruption is also observed in cells lacking mitochondrial DNA (42). Whenever a pharmacological or genetic manipulation succeeds in preventing apoptosis, it also abolishes the $\Delta\Psi_m$ disruption that usually precedes cytolysis (Table 4). The $\Delta\Psi_m$ collapse constitutes an early event vis-à-vis the other manifestations of apoptosis detectable at the levels of the nucleus (chromatin condensation and DNA fragmentation, PARP cleavage), of the cytoplasma (activation of CPP32, shrinkage, calcium influx, and potassium efflux), or of the plasma membrane (phosphatidylserine exposure and later increase in permeability) (Figure 2). Nonetheless, the $\Delta\Psi_m$ collapse marks an already irreversible stage of the apoptotic process. Thus purified cells with a low $\Delta\Psi_m$ proceed to full-blown apoptosis, even after withdrawal of the apoptosis-inducing stimulus (38). Based on these findings, we conclude that the disruption of the $\Delta\Psi_m$ defines an early, irreversible stage of apoptosis. In addition to changes in the $\Delta\Psi_m$, further alterations affecting mitochondrial membrane permeability have become apparent. Thus cytochrome c, which is normally confined in the mitochondrial intermembrane space, is found in the cytosol of cells undergoing apoptosis. Again, this process precedes nuclear apoptosis (52–54). At present, it is a matter of debate whether cytochrome c release is a cause and/or a consequence of PT pore opening (53–55).

Functional Evidence Implying Mitochondria in Apoptosis

The inhibition of the first stage of pre-apoptosis (collapse of the $\Delta\Psi_m$) by cyclosporin A and N-methyl-Val-cyclosporin A (39, 43) established the link with PT, a mitochondrial process that is specifically inhibited by cyclophilin D ligands. We observed that the disruption of the mitochondrial transmembrane potential induced by protonophores or protoporphyrin IX entrains apoptosis (44, 46, 56). In contrast, two agents that act on mitochondria to inhibit PT, bongkrekic acid (a ligand of the adenine nucleotide translocator, another putative constituent of the megachannel) and CMXRos (which acts on mitochondrial matrix thiols), inhibit the disruption of the $\Delta\Psi_m$ as well as the later fragmentation of nuclear DNA (Table 3) (43, 44, 46, 49, 56). The inhibition of PT prevents cytolysis and all apoptotic alterations at the level of the plasma membrane, the nucleus, and the cytoplasma (43, 44, 46, 49–51, 56). These results indicate that the mitochondrial PT constitutes a critical coordinating element of the apoptotic process. This is also suggested by the fact that the oncoprotein Bcl-2 can function as an endogenous inhibitor of PT (see below).

Table 4   Glucocorticoid-induced thymocyte death: mitochondrial and nuclear parameters

Glucocorticoid receptor ligand	Inhibitor (active principle)	$\Delta\Psi_m$ disruption	Nuclear apoptosis	Cytolysis
RU38486 1-10 μM (antagonist)	None	−	−	−
Corticosterone 1 μM (natural agonist)	None	+	+	+
Dexamethasone 1 μM (synthetic agonist)	None	+	+	+
	RU38486 10 μM (GC receptor antagonist)	−	−	−
	Actinomycin D 50 μM (inhibitor of transcription)	−	−	−
	Cycloheximide 35 μM (inhibitor of translation)	−	−	−
	TLCK 100 μM (serine protease inhibitor)	−	−	−
	MG123 50 μM (proteasome inhibitor)	−	−	−
	N-acetylcysteine 30 mM (anti-oxidant)	−	−	−
	Catalase 1000 U/ml (anti-oxidant)	−	−	−
	Monochlorobiman 10 μM (thiol reactive)	−	−	−
	CMXRos 1 μM (thiol-reactive, matrix-targeted)	−	−	−
	Bongkrekic acid 50 μM (PT inhibitor)	−	−	−
	bcl-2 transgene (PT inhibitor)	−	−	−
	Z-VAD.fmk 50 μM (caspase inhibitor)	+	−	+
Partial receptor agonists with reduced trans-activation potential:				
RU 247821 1-10 μM	None	+	+	+
RU 24858 1-10 μM	None	+	+	+
RU 40066 1-10 μM	None	+	+	+

CMXRos, chloromethyl-X-rosamine; TLCK, N-tosyl-L-lysil chloromethylketone; Z-VAD.fmk, N-benzyl-oxycarbonyl-Val-Ala-Asp-fluoromethylketone. Results are from References 38, 39, 43, 49, 50, 56, or G Kroemer, unpublished data. Synthetic glucocorticoids with reduced transactivation potential are described in Reference 94.

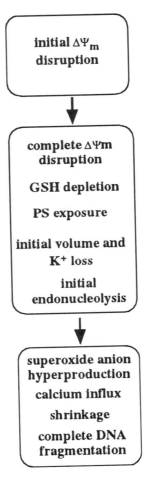

Figure 2 Chronology of some events in thymocyte apoptosis induced by glucorticoids. The first manifestation of apoptosis is a partial reduction of the mitochondrial transmembrane potential ($\Delta\Psi_m$). At the stage at which the $\Delta\Psi_m$ is completely disrupted, glutathione levels are reduced. At a later stage, cells expose phosphatidylserine residues on the surface and start to become Tunel+. It is only later that cells overproduce superoxide anion, manifest a massive Ca^{2+} influx, shrink, and demonstrate DNA loss. A similar sequence of events has been observed in response to genotoxic stimuli (e.g. etoposide, irradiation), as well as in other cell types.

Evidence from Cell-Free Systems

Taken together, the above results demonstrate that mitochondria are implicated in apoptosis. However, they do not elucidate the cause-effect relationship between mitochondrial perturbations and nuclear alterations. To show such a relationship, we have developed an experimental cell-free system in which isolated nuclei are cultured in the presence of isolated mitochondria. In analogy to a system involving *Xenopus laevis* mitochondria and nuclei (57), we found that the presence of mitochondrial products was necessary for the induction of apoptosis in nuclei from mammalian cells (42, 45, 51, 56). We have shown that mouse and human mitochondria are usually inert in such a system. Only when their megachannels are opened, can mitochondria provoke correlates of apoptotic changes (chromatin condensation, DNA fragmentation) in purified nuclei. This apoptogenic activity is due to soluble proteins liberated from the mitochondrion (42, 45, 51, 56). We have purified and analyzed one such apoptosis-inducing factor (AIF) and performed its biochemical analysis (45). AIF has no direct DNAse activity; it acts by the rapid (<5 min) activation of nuclear endonucleases. Moreover, AIF can stimulate the proteolytic activation of caspase 3 (CPP32/Yama/Apopain) (45, 51). In addition to AIF, the intermembrane protein cytochrome c is liberated from mitochondria undergoing PT (55). Cytochrome c by itself is not apoptogenic. However, it can cooperate with other factors to activate caspases and nuclear endonucleases (52).

In conclusion, it appears that apoptogenic proteases and/or protease activators are released from mitochondria upon PT and that these products are necessary for nuclear apoptosis to occur.

THE BCL-2 COMPLEX: A MITOCHONDRIAL REGULATOR

The family of Bcl-2-related proteins constitutes one of the biologically most important classes of apoptosis-regulatory gene products. Bcl-2 belongs to a growing family of apoptosis-regulatory gene products that may be either death antagonists (e.g. Bcl-2, Bcl-X_L, Bcl-w) or death agonists (e.g. Bax, Bak, Bcl-X_S, Bad) (58). The relative amount of death agonists and antagonists from the Bcl-2 family constitutes a regulatory switch whose function is determined, at least in part, by selective protein-protein interactions (59). Homologous recombination reveals that Bcl-2-like apoptosis-inhibitory proteins exert essential cytoprotective functions; their deficiency entails the ablation of determined cell types, for instance that of lymphoid cells in Bcl-2$^{-/-}$ and that of postmitotic neurons in Bcl-X$^{-/-}$ mice (58). The functional importance of these proteins is also underlined by the fact that many tumors hyperexpress apoptosis-inhibitory

Table 5   Apoptosis-inducing regimes in which Bcl-2 preserves mitochondrial function

Cell type	Inducers of apoptosis	Effect of Bcl-2 on mitochondria	Reference
Thymocytes or T cells	Glucocorticoids, ceramide, *ter*-butylhydroperoxide, protoporphyrine IX, mClCCP (protonophore), etoposide (VP16), γ-irradiation, doxorubicin, cytosine arabinoside	Stabilizes $\Delta\Psi_m$	(39) (45) (46) (45) (48) (48) (48)
T cytoplasts	Ceramide	Stabilizes $\Delta\Psi_m$	(43)
B cells	Surface IgM cross-linking, cyclosporin A, etoposide (VP16), γ-irradiation, doxorubicin, cytosine arabinoside, *ter*-butylhydroperoxide, ceramide, serum withdrawal	Stabilizes $\Delta\Psi_m$	(48) (48) (48) (48) Unpubl. Unpubl.
PC12 cells	Cyanide, rotenone, antimycin A, etoposide (VP16), calcium ionophore	Stabilizes $\Delta\Psi_m$	(22) (22) (22)
Fibroblasts	p53	Stabilizes $\Delta\Psi_m$	(95)
HL60 cells	Etoposide, staurosporine	Prevents cytochrome *c* release and $\Delta\Psi_m\downarrow$	(53)

or hypoexpress death-inducing members of the Bcl-2 family. Transgene- or transfection-induced overexpression of Bcl-2 tends to protect cells against most apoptosis-inducing protocols, as well as against some necrosis-provoking regimens (58). Transfection with *bcl-2* or *bcl-X*$_L$ inhibits or retards the early mitochondrial changes associated with apoptosis (2, 22, 39, 43, 48, 51, 60) (Table 5). This finding has been obtained in cells and in cytoplasts (anucleate cells) (43, 48). In contrast, hyperexpression of the Bcl-2 antagonist Bax causes a $\Delta\Psi$ dissipation (14). These findings suggest that Bcl-2 related proteins regulate mitochondrial functions.

Many proteins encoded by the *bcl-2* gene family are predominantly localized in the outer mitochondrial membrane, within the contact site with the inner membrane. In lymphoid cells, Bcl-2 expression correlates stoichiometrically with that of the PBR, suggesting that Bcl-2 might interact with PBR or with a PBR-associated protein (61), perhaps carnitine palmitoyltransferase I, with which Bcl-2 interacts directly (62). Several prominent members of the Bcl-2 family possess C-terminal transmembrane (TM) domains, allowing for their incorporation into intracellular membranes. Deletion mutants or replacement of the TM domain by targeting sequences from other proteins have shown that, at least in some experimental systems, Bcl-2, Bcl-X_L, and Bax act on mitochondrial membranes, rather than on membranes of other intracellular compartments, to prevent (Bcl-2, Bcl-X_L) or induce (Bax) cell death (63, 64). In cell-free systems of apoptosis, Bcl-2 must also be present in mitochondria rather than in the nuclear envelope to inhibit apoptosis (45, 53, 54, 57). Mitochondria purified from cells hyperexpressing Bcl-2 are protected against the PT-inducing effect of several apoptosis inducers such as pro-oxidants, low doses of Ca^{2+}, protoporphyrin IX, and the cytosol of ceramide-treated cells. Concomitantly, Bcl-2 protects against the release of AIF and cytochrome c (45, 51, 53, 54, 56). However, Bcl-2 does not counteract the PT-inducing effect of other agents such as high concentrations of Ca^{2+} (500 μM), the thiol-cross-linking agent diamide, and high doses of recombinant caspase 1 (ICE) (45, 51, 56). Thus Bcl-2 does exert direct PT-inhibitory effects on mitochondria, although with a limited inhibitory spectrum. In contrast, Bcl-2 does not affect the formation of AIF and has only marginal, if any, effects on the action of cytochrome c or AIF on isolated nuclei in vitro (45, 56, 57, 65).

The three-dimensional structure of the Bcl-X_L monomer in the absence of its C-terminal hydrophobic domain (Bcl-$X_L \Delta TM$) consists of two central hydrophobic helices surrounded by five amphipathic helices, as well as a 60 residue flexible loop (66). An elongated hydrophobic pocket is created by the close spatial proximity of domains BH1, BH2, and BH3. This structure bears strong similarity to the pore-forming domains of several bacterial toxins, in particular colicins A and E1, and diphtheria toxin (66). Like these bacterial toxins, Bcl-$X_L \Delta TM$ can insert into synthetic lipid vesicles or planar lipid bilayers and form an ion-conduction channel. This channel is pH sensitive (low pH opens) and becomes cation selective at physiological pH ($K^+ = Na^+ Ca^{2+} > Cl^-$), at which it displays a multiple conductance state with identical ion selectivity (67). The channel-forming domains (α helices 5 and 6 between BH1 and BH2) vary between different members of the Bcl-2 family. Accordingly, Bax possesses a different ion selectivity ($Cl^- > K^+$). At present it is not clear whether Bcl-2 and Bax regulate PT directly or indirectly, for instance, by regulating other mitochondrial functions such as cytochrome c release (53, 54) or the activity of mitochondrial enzymes.

HOW MITOCHONDRIA SENSE DAMAGE AND INTEGRATE SPECIFIC DEATH SIGNALS

The exact composition of the PT pore complex is not known; it is currently believed to involve cytosolic proteins (hexokinase); outer membrane proteins: PBR; porin, also called voltage-dependent anion channel (VDAC);

Table 6   Functions of the permeability transition pore

Function	Principles of modulation	Example
Voltage sensor	Low $\Delta\Psi_m$ induces PT	Anoxia, respiratory inhibitors induce PT
	High $\Delta\Psi_m$ inhibits PT	Hyperpolarization (nigericin) inhibits PT
Thiol sensor	Oxidation of a critical matrix dithiol (in equilibrium with GSH) induces PT	Pro-oxidants and thiol cross-linking induce PT
		Prevention of thiol cross-linking prevents PT
Sensor of pyridine oxidation	Oxidation of $NAD(P)H_2$ favors PT (in equilibrium with GSH oxidation)	$NAD(P)H_2$ prevents PT
		Anti-oxidants prevent PT
Matrix pH sensor	Reversible histidine protonation prevents PT	Akalinization (pH = 7.3) favors PT
		Neutral or acidic pH inhibits PT
Cation sensor	Ca^{2+} induces PT	Increase in matrix Ca^{2+} induces PT
	Other divalent cations inhibit PT	Mg^{2+} and Zn^{2+} prevent PT
ADP/ATP sensor	ADP (and ATP) inhibit PT	Extra ATP (glycolytic substrates) prevents PT
		Oligomycin (F_1 ATPase inhibitor) induces PT
Protease sensor?	Direct action of proteases on outer membrane proteins	Caspase 1 induces PT
		Calpain-like enzyme may induce PT
Lipid acid sensor?	Long chain lipid acids induce PT	Palmitate and stearate induce PT
		Carnitine prevents PT
Peptide sensor?	Amphipathic peptides induce PT	Mastoparan induces PT

intermembrane proteins (creatine kinase); at least one inner membrane protein (the adenine nucleotide translocator (ANT); and at least one matrix protein (cyclophilin D) (29–33). It may also interact with proteins of additional multiprotein complexes, namely the Tim (transporter of the inner membrane) complex, the Tom (transporter of the outer membrane) complex (68), and the Bcl-2 complex (58).

Irrespective of its exact composition, the PT pore complex contains multiple targets for pharmacological interventions and is regulated by numerous endogenous physiological effectors (Table 6, Figure 3).   Such effectors include ions (divalent cations, mainly Ca^{2+} and Mg^{2+}); protons; the $\Delta\Psi_m$; the concentration of adenine nucleotides (ADP, ATP) (29, 30); the pyrimidine redox state (NAD versus $NADH_2$; NADP versus $NADPH_2$); the thiol redox state (controlled by glutathione) (69); reactive oxygen species and nitric oxide (70, 71);

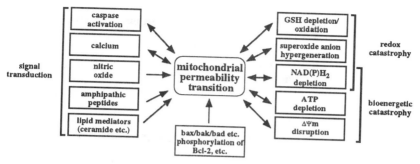

Figure 3 Inducers of permeability transition. Different signal transduction pathways can promote the activation of caspases (e.g. cross-linking of Fas/Apo-1/CD95), increases in cytosolic Ca^{2+} levels (e.g. excitotoxins such as glutamate), nitric oxide, amphipathic peptides (e.g. after withdrawal of NGF), or lipid mediators (e.g. ceramide and sphingosine) can provoke PT. In addition, changes in the composition of the Bcl-2 complex such as hyperexpression of the Bcl-2 antagonist Bax (e.g. in response to p53 overexpression after genotoxic insults) or phosphorylation-mediated inactivation of Bcl-2 (e.g. after treatment with the microtubule disrupting agent taxol) can induce PT. Major changes in the cellular redox balance or in bioenergetic parameters can also trigger PT. Note that, in several cases, PT is a self-amplifying process (*two-way arrows*).

the concentrations of lipoids (lipid acids, acyl-CoA, ceramide and derivatives) (29, 30); the concentrations of determined peptides (amphipathic peptides and perhaps signal sequences of peptides targeting proteins to the mitochondrial import machinery) (72, 73); and changes in the composition or function of the Bcl-2 complex (39, 56, 58). As a rule, it appears that any major change in energy balance (absence of oxygen, depletion of ATP and ADP, depletion of $NAD(P)H^2$, disruption of the $\Delta\Psi_m$) or changes in the redox balance (oxidation/depletion of non-oxidized glutathione or $NAD(P)H_2$, hyperproduction of reactive oxygen species) can provoke PT. This implies that PT integrates stress responses and that major damage of cells will invariably cause PT. Moreover, because PT itself causes such changes in energy and redox balance (see below), massive PT locks the cell into an irreversible stage.

In addition, determined signal transduction pathways triggered via intracellular or cell surface receptors can result in PT. Thus PT is facilitated by a number of second messengers: increases in cytosolic Ca^{2+} concentration, ceramide, and caspase 1-like enzymes such as ICE (interleukin 1β converting enzyme). Because PT is regulated by the Bcl-2 complex, changes in the molecular stoichiometry of this complex, e.g. enhanced synthesis of the Bcl-2 antagonist Bax, or signal transduction pathways, culminating in post-translational modifications of the Bcl-2 complex, can also facilitate PT. The phosphorylation of Bcl-2 or Bcl-2 homologues, e.g. Bad, as well as the subcellular distribution

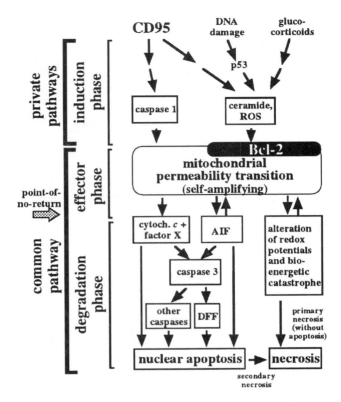

Figure 4   Consequences of permeability transition. Different death-triggering pathways employ distinct (private) signal transduction pathways that will culminate in the induction of permeability transition (PT). Thus PT induced by DNA damage requires p53 activation, whereas induction of PT by ligation of Fas/Apo-1/CD95 requires the activation of ICE-like caspases. PT constitutes the first rate-limiting event of the common pathway of apoptosis and can be induced either in a Bcl-2-regulated or in a Bcl-2-independent fashion. Thus ceramide-induced PT is inhibited by overexpression of Bcl-2. In contrast, PT induced by caspase 1-like proteases is not inhibited by Bcl-2. Upon PT, apoptogenic factors are released from the mitochondrial intermembrane space and leak into the cytosol. At least two such factors have been characterized: cytochrome c (which requires unknown cytosolic factors to activate caspase-3 and to induce nuclear apoptosis) and AIF, which suffices to induce nuclear apoptosis in vitro. Different proteases from the caspase family can participate in the apoptotic degradation phase downstream of PT. In addition, PT causes major changes in cellular redox potentials (depletion of non-oxidized glutathione, depletion of NAD(P)H$_2$, hyperproduction of superoxide anion), energy metabolism (depletion of NAD(P)H$_2$ and ATP), and ion compartmentalization (outflow of Ca^{2+} from the matrix and later Ca^{2+} efflux from the endoplasmic reticulum and influx via the plasma membrane). The scheme provides an explanation for the choice between apoptosis and necrosis. Massive induction of PT with subsequent rapid depletion of energy-rich phosphates causes primary necrosis, i.e. the disruption of plasma membrane integrity before apoptogenic proteases come into action. In contrast, a more subtle, regulated induction of PT allows for the activation and action of proteases, thus giving rise to the apoptotic phenotype.

of Bcl-2-related proteins, e.g. Bad, or Bcl-2-associated proteins, e.g. Bag-1, Raf-1, is regulated by growth factor receptors (58, 74, 75), thus suggesting how growth factor withdrawal can trigger PT indirectly, via changes in the composition of the PT-regulatory Bcl-2 complex (58).

Together these findings indicate, that in addition to integrating various damage responses, PT can be triggered via receptor-connected pathways. PT may constitute the crossroad of both nonspecific damage responses and responses mediated via specific receptors (Figure 4).

HOW MITOCHONDRIA AND THEIR PRODUCTS EXECUTE CELL DEATH

Under normal circumstances, the inner mitochondrial membrane is nearly impermeant. This feature is required for maintaining the inner transmembrane potential ($\Delta\Psi_m$). Opening of the PT pore allows the diffusion of solutes with a M_W of > 1500 kDa, according to gross estimations based on the use of polyethylene glycol polymers (29, 30). The result evinces an immediate dissipation of the $\Delta\Psi_m$, with consequent loss of mitochondrial RNA and protein synthesis, cessation of the import of most proteins synthesized in the cytosol (which depends on the $\Delta\Psi_m$), release of Ca^{2+} and glutathione from the mitochondrial matrix, uncoupling of oxidative phosphorylation with cessation of ATP synthesis, oxidation of $NAD(P)H_2$ and glutathione, and hyperproduction of superoxide anion on the uncoupled repiratory chain. Accordingly, multiparameter fluorescence analyses reveal that the $\Delta\Psi_m$ collapse is closely linked to major changes in cellular redox potentials, namely $NAD(P)H_2$ depletion (40), GSH depletion/oxidation (50), and later increases in superoxide anion generation (39) and massive cytosolic Ca^{2+} elevations (50). Intriguingly, these consequences of PT themselves can provoke PT (29, 30), suggesting the existence of one or several self-amplifying feedback loops that may explain why PT (and cell death) is occurring as an all-or-nothing phenomenon.

The bioenergetic and redox changes of PTs themselves are sufficient to cause necrosis. But how does PT trigger apoptosis? PT allows for the release of proteins usually confined to the mitochondrial compartment. Thus PT causes the release of cytochrome c from the intermembrane space into the cytosol (55). The protein precursor of cytochrome c (apocytochrome c) is synthesized in the cytosol and transported into the intermembrane space, where the heme lyase attaches a heme group to generate holocytochrome c. Neither cytochrome c nor its precursor apocytochrome c itself is apoptogenic, but holocytochrome c, which lacks a heme group, can interact with other yet unknown cytosolic factors to activate the caspases 3 (CPP32/Yama/Apopain) and 6 (Mch-2) and to induce nuclear apoptosis in vitro (52). CPP32 can then activate DNA fragmentation factor

(DFF), which in turn acts to activate nucleases (76). In addition to cytochrome c, mitochondria undergoing PT release AIF, an unstable protein of approximately 50 kDa, that suffices to cause nuclear apoptosis and activation of CPP32 in cell-free systems (45, 51). As is true for cytochrome c, this activity is pre-formed. Exhaustive studies have identified an inhibitor of AIF: N-benzyloxycarbonyl-Val-Ala-Asp.fluoromethylketone (Z-VAD.fmk) (45). This protease inhibitor abolishes all activities of AIF on the nucleus. Z-VAD.fmk is also a universal inhibitor of nuclear apoptosis, occurring in intact cells, irrespective of the cell type (3, 77), thus emphasizing the possible in vivo relevance of AIF. In summary, mitochondria contain several proteins endowed with the capacity of stimulating at least some facets of the apoptotic program in cell-free systems. At present, it appears that at least two biochemical pathways may link mitochondria to nuclear apoptosis: AIF and cyctochrome c plus factor X $\rightarrow$ caspase 3 $\rightarrow$ DFF.

If PT can stimulate both primary necrosis and apoptosis, what does make the difference? As a possibility, the bioenergetic and redox catastrophe ensuing PT (which would induce necrosis) and the activation of catabolic enzymes (caspases and nucleases) might compete with each other in a sort of race. Cells would only die from primary necrosis when apoptogenic proteases fail to come into action, either because they are inhibited (e.g. by addition of Z-VAD.fmk) or because the time frame of the process is too rapid to allow for protease activation. This view of cell death would be compatible with the fact that many substances induce apoptosis at low doses (when PT is induced smoothly and cells can activate proteases) but induce necrosis at higher doses (when PT is caused abruptly and cells lyse before proteases come into action). Finally, it would explain how maintenance of high ATP levels can favor apoptosis over necrosis (12, 13), whereas inhibition of proteases or manipulations that reduce cellular ATP levels favor necrosis over apoptosis (12–16).

CONCLUSIONS AND PERSPECTIVES

The data discussed in this review indicate that mitochondria play a major role in the regulation of both physiological and pathological cell death. The available data are compatible with our current working hypothesis that mitochondrial PT (or an event closely linked to PT) is a central coordinating event of apoptosis and necrosis. This hypothesis predicts that various damage pathways and pro-apoptotic signal transduction cascades converge at the level of PT, in line with the fact that PT can be induced by numerous physiological effectors. Once PT has been triggered, a series of common pathways of cell death are initiated, each of which may be lethal. Thus PT has at least two major consequences: (*a*) a bioenergetic and redox catastrophe disrupting cellular metabolism and (*b*) liberation of protease and endonuclease activators from mitochondria. Depending on which of these processes wins the race, either primary necrosis (lysis before activation of catabolic enzymes) or apoptosis (activation of proteases and endonucleases before lysis) ensues.

The central role of PT in the death process might allow for an operative reinterpretation of a number of hitherto controversial and apparently contradictory observations. Cell death control must function in an on/off fashion rather than in a gradual one. To explain the all-or-nothing nature of apoptosis switching, it is tempting to conceive one or several positive feedback loops in which the consequences of the apoptotic process themselves stimulate the action of the central executioner. Thus once beyond a threshold value, self-amplification would drive the cell into an irreversible death program. Several of the metabolic consequences of mitochondrial PT are well-known by-products of apoptosis: uncoupling of the respiratory chain with hyperproduction of reactive oxygen species (ROS) (39), disruption of mitochondrial (and later extra-mitochondrial) calcium homeostasis (29), and liberation of protease activators with loss of cytochrome *c* (which blocks the repiratory chain) (45, 52, 55). All these consequences of PT themselves favor PT (Figures 3 and 4). This suggests a dual role for certain molecules (Ca^{2+}, ROS, caspases) in apoptosis: as facultative constituents of signal transduction pathways initiating the vicious cycle of PT and as constant by-products of the death process.

Future studies will have to explore numerous incognita: the exact nature of the PT-inducing trigger in different pathways of apoptosis induction; the molecular composition of the PT pore complex; the interactions between the PT pore and the Bcl-2 complex; and the mechanism of how the PT pore is fine-tuned in a cell type-, differentiation-, and activation-dependent fashion. Further investigation of PT and its regulation should furnish invaluable information on the normal physiology of cell death, and by consequence pave the way for the rational design of novel cytoprotective and cytotoxic drugs. Moreover, it will be most important to understand the relationship between apoptosis, PT, and mitochondrial damage as it accumulates during aging (78) or chronic degenerative diseases (79).

ACKNOWLEDGMENTS

We are indebted to Drs. Kathérine Brenner, Tamara Hirsch, Isabel Marzo, Patrice X Petit, Santos A Susin, and Naoufal Zamzami (UPR420, CNRS) for helpful discussions. We thank Dr. Maurice Geuskens (Université Libre de Bruxelles, Belgium) for electron microscopy. Supported by Agence Nationale pour la Recherche contre le SIDA, Association pour la Recherche contre le Cancer, Centre Nationale de la Recherche Scientifique, Fondation pour la Recherche Médicale/Sidaction, Ligue Française contre le Cancer, Institut National de la

Santé et de la Recherche Médicale, NATO, the French Ministry of Science, and Hoechst Marion Roussel (to GK).

Visit the *Annual Reviews home page* at
http://www.AnnualReviews.org.

Literature Cited

1. Thompson CB. 1995. Apoptosis in the pathogenesis and treatment of disease. *Science* 267:1456–62
2. Kroemer G, Petit PX, Zamzami N, Vayssière J-L, Mignotte B. 1995. The biochemistry of apoptosis. *FASEB J.* 9:1277–87
3. Weil M, Jacobson MD, Coles HSR, Davies TJ, Gardner RL, et al. 1996. Constitutive expression of the machinery for programmed cell death. *J. Cell Biol.* 133:1053–59
4. Kumar S, Lavin MF. 1996. The ICE family of cysteine proteases as effectors of cell death. *Cell Death Diff.* 3:255–67
5. Zhivotovsky B, Burgess DH, Vanags DM, Orrenius S. 1997. Involvement of cellular proteolytic machinery in apoptosis. *Biochem. Biophys. Res. Commun.* 230:481–88
6. Savill J. 1996. Phagocyte recognition of apoptotic cells. *Biochem. Soc. Trans.* 24:1065–69
7. Bortner CD, Cidlowski JA. 1996. Absence of volume regulatory mechanisms contributes to the rapid activation of apoptosis in thymocytes. *Am. J. Physiol.* 40:C950–61
8. Kerr JFR, Wyllie AH, Currie AR. 1972. Apoptosis: a basic biological phenomenon with wide-ranging implications in tissue kinetics. *Br. J. Cancer* 26:239–57
9. Willie AH. 1980. Glucocorticoid-induced thymocyte apoptosis is associated with endogenous endonuclease activation. *Nature* 284:555–56
10. Mehendale HM, Roth RA, Gandolfi AJ, Klaunig JE, Lemasters JJ, et al. 1994. Novel mechanisms in chemically induced hepatotoxicity. *FASEB J.* 8:1285–95
11. Kroemer G. 1995. The pharmacology of T cell apoptosis. *Adv. Immunol.* 58:211–96
12. Leist M, Single B, Castoldi AF, Kühnle S, Nicotera P. 1997. Intracellular adenosine triphosphate (ATP) concentration: a switch in the decision between apoptosis and necrosis. *J. Exp. Med.* 185:1481–86
13. Eguchi Y, Shimizu S, Tsujimoto Y. 1997. Intracellular ATP levels determine cell fated by apoptosis or necrosis. *Cancer Res.* 57:1835–40
14. Xiang J, Chao DT, Korsmeyer SJ. 1996. Bax-induced cell death may not require interleukin 1 beta-converting enzyme-like proteases. *Proc. Natl. Acad. Sci. USA* 93:14559–63
15. McCarthy NJ, Whyte MKB, Gilbert CS, Evan GI. 1997. Inhibition of Ced-3/ICE-related proteases does not prevent cell death induced by oncogenes, DNA damage, or the Bcl-2 homologue Bak. *J. Cell Biol.* 136:215–27
16. Hirsch T, Marchetti P, Susin SA, Dallaporta B, Zamzami N, et al. 1997. The apoptosis-necrosis paradox. Apoptogenic proteases activated after mitochondrial permeability transition determine the mode of cell death. *Oncogene* 15:1573–82
17. Martinou JC, Dubois-Dauphin-M, Staple JK, Rodriguez I, Frankowski H, et al. 1994. Overexpression of Bcl-2 in transgenic mice protects neurons from naturally occurring cell death and experimental ischemia. *Neuron* 13:1017–30
18. Itoh G, Tamura J, Suzuki M, Suzuki Y, Ikeda H, et al. 1995. DNA fragmentation of human infarcted myocardial cells demonstrated by the nick end labeling method and DNA agarose gel electrophoresis. *Am. J. Pathol.* 146:1325–31
19. Sasaki H, Matsuno T, Tanaka N, Orita K. 1996. Activation of apoptosis during the reperfusion phase after rat liver ischemia. *Transpl. Proc.* 28:1908–9
20. Kane DJ, Sarafian TA, Anton R, Hahn H, Gralla EB, et al. 1993. Bcl-2 inhibition of neural death: decreased generation of reactive oxygen species. *Science* 262:1274–77
21. Shimizu S, Eguchi Y, Kosaka H, Kamiike W, Matsuda H, et al. 1995. Prevention of hypoxia-induced cell death by Bcl-2 and Bcl-xL. *Nature* 374:811–13
22. Shimizu S, Eguchi Y, Kamiike W, Waguri S, Uchiyama Y, et al. 1996. Bcl-2 blocks loss of mitochondrial membrane potential while ICE inhibitors act at a different step during inhibition of death induced

by respiratory chain inhibitors. *Oncogene* 13:21–29

23. Kroemer G, Zamzami N, Susin SA. 1997. Mitochondrial control of apoptosis. *Immunol. Today* 18:44–51

24. Kroemer G, Lisardo B, Zamzami P, Hortelano S, Martinez-AC 1997. Detection of apoptosis and apoptosis associated alterations. *The Immunology Methods Manual*, ed. R Lefkovitz, 14.2:1111–25. New York: Academic

25. Zahrebelski G, Nieminen AL, Alghoul K, Quian T, Herman B, et al. 1995. Progression of subcellular changes during chemical hypoxia to cultured rat hepatocytes: a laser scanning confocal microscopic study. *Hepatology* 21:1361–72

26. Nieminen AL, Saylor AK, Tesfai SA, Herman B, Lemasters JJ. 1995. Contribution of the mitochondrial permeability transition to lethal injury after exposure of hepatocytes to *t*-butyldydroperoxide. *Biochem. J.* 307:99–106

27. Broekemeier KM, Carpenter DL, Reed DJ, Pfeiffer DR. 1992. Cyclosporin A protects hepatocytes subjected to high Ca^{2+} and oxidative stress. *FEBS Lett.* 304:192–94

28. Pastorino JG, Snyder JW, Hoek JB, Farber JL. 1995. Ca^{2+} depletion prevents anoxic death of hepatocytes by inhibiting mitochondrial permeability transition. *Am. J. Physiol.* 268:C676–85

29. Zoratti M, Szabò I. 1995. The mitochondrial permeability transition. *Biochem. Biophys. Acta* 1241:139–76

30. Bernardi P, Petronilli V. 1996. The permeability transition pore as a mitochondrial calcium release channel: a critical appraisal. *J. Bioenerg. Biomembr.* 28:129–36

31. McEnery MW, Snowman AM, Trifiletti RR, Snyder SH. 1992. Isolation of the mitochondrial benzodiazepine receptor: association with the voltage-dependent anion channel and the adenine nucleotide carrier. *Proc. Natl. Acad. Sci. USA* 89:3170–74

32. Brustovetsky N, Klingenberg M. 1996. Mitochondrial ADP/ATP carrier can be reversibly converted into a large channel by Ca^{2+}. *Biochemistry* 35:8483–88

33. Beutner G, Rück A, Riede B, Welte W, Brdiczka D. 1996. Complexes between kinases, mitochondrial porin, and adenylate translocator in rat brain resemble the permeability transition pore. *FEBS Lett.* 396:189–95

34. Pastorino JG, Simbula G, Gilfor E, Hoek JB, Farber JL. 1994. Protoporphyrin IX, an endogenous ligand of the peripheral benzodiazepin receptor, potentiates induction of the mitochondrial permeability transition and the killing of culture hepatocytes by rotenone. *J. Biol. Chem.* 269:31041–46

35. Pastorino JG, Simbula G, Yamamoto K, Glascott PAJ, Rothman RJ, et al. 1996. The cytotoxicity of tumor necrosis factor depends on induction of the mitochondrial permeability transition. *J. Biol. Chem.* 271:29792–99

36. Jacobson MD, Burne JF, King MP, Miyashita T, Reed JC, et al. 1993. Bcl-2 blocks apoptosis in cells lacking mitochondrial DNA. *Nature* 361:365–69

37. Vayssière J-L, Petit PX, Risler Y, Mignotte B. 1994. Commitment to apoptosis is associated with changes in mitochondrial biogenesis and activity in cell lines conditionally immortalized with simian virus 40. *Proc. Natl. Acad. Sci. USA* 91:11752–56

38. Zamzami N, Marchetti P, Castedo M, Zanin C, Vayssière J-L, et al. 1995. Reduction in mitochondrial potential constitutes an early irreversible step of programmed lymphocyte death in vivo. *J. Exp. Med.* 181:1661–72

39. Zamzami N, Marchetti P, Castedo M, Decaudin D, Macho A, et al. 1995. Sequential reduction of mitochondrial transmembrane potential and generation of reactive oxygen species in early programmed cell death. *J. Exp. Med.* 182:367–77

40. Petit PX, LeCoeur H, Zorn E, Dauguet C, Mignotte B, et al. 1995. Alterations of mitochondrial structure and function are early events of dexamethasone-induced thymocyte apoptosis. *J. Cell. Biol.* 130:157–67

41. Cossarizza A, Franceschi C, Monti D, Salvioli S, Bellesia E, et al. 1995. Protective effect of *N*-acetylcysteine in tumor necrosis factor-alpha-induced apoptosis in U937 cells: the role of mitochondria. *Exp. Cell Res.* 220:232–40

42. Marchetti P, Susin SA, Decaudin D, Gamen S, Castedo M, et al. 1996. Apoptosis-associated derangement of mitochondrial function in cells lacking mitochondrial DNA. *Cancer Res.* 56:2033–38

43. Castedo M, Hirsch T, Susin SA, Zamzami N, Marchetti P, et al. 1996. Sequential acquisition of mitochondrial and plasma membrane alterations during early lymphocyte apoptosis. *J. Immunol.* 157:512–21

44. Marchetti P, Castedo M, Susin SA, Zamzami N, Hirsch T, et al. 1996. Mitochondrial permeability transition is a central

coordinating event of apoptosis. *J. Exp. Med.* 184:1155–60

45. Susin SA, Zamzami N, Castedo M, Hirsch T, Marchetti P, et al. 1996. Bcl-2 inhibits the mitochondrial release of an apoptogenic protease. *J. Exp. Med.* 184:1331–42

46. Marchetti P, Hirsch T, Zamzami N, Castedo M, Decaudin D, et al. 1996. Mitochondrial permeability transition triggers lymphocyte apoptosis. *J. Immunol.* 157:4830–36

47. Macho A, Decaudin D, Castedo M, Hirsch T, Susin SA, et al. 1996. Chloromethyl-X-rosamine is an aldehyde-fixable potential-sensitive fluorochrome for the detection of early apoptosis. *Cytometry* 25:333–40

48. Decaudin D, Geley S, Hirsch T, Castedo M, Marchetti P, et al. 1997. Bcl-2 and Bcl-XL antagonize the mitochondrial dysfunction preceding nuclear apoptosis induced by chemotherapeutic agents. *Cancer Res.* 57:62–67

49. Marchetti P, Decaudin D, Macho A, Zamzami N, Hirsch T, et al. 1997. Redox regulation of apoptosis: impact of thiol redoxidation on mitochondrial function. *Eur. J. Immunol.* 27:289–96

50. Macho A, Hirsch T, Marzo I, Marchetti P, Dallaporta B, et al. 1997. Glutathione depletion is an early and calcium elevation a late event of thymocyte apoptosis. *J. Immunol.* 158:4612–19

51. Susin A, Zamzami N, Castedo M, Daugas E, Wang H-G, et al. 1997. The central executioner of apoptosis. Multiple links between protease activation and mitochondria in Fas/Apo-1/CD95- and ceramide-induced apoptosis. *J. Exp. Med.* 186:25–37

52. Liu X, Kim CN, Yang J, Jemmerson R, Wang X. 1996. Induction of apoptic program in cell-free extracts: requirement for ATP and cytochrome *c. Cell* 86:147–57

53. Yang J, Liu X, Bhalla K, Kim CN, Ibrado AM, et al. 1997. Prevention of apoptosis by Bcl-2: release of cytochrome *c* from mitochondria blocked. *Science* 275:1129–32

54. Kluck RM, Bossy-Wetzel E, Green DR, Newmeyer DD. 1997. The release of cytochrome *c* from mitochondria: a primary site for Bcl-2 regulation of apoptosis. *Science* 275:1132–36

55. Kantrow SP, Piantadosi CA. 1997. Release of cytochrome *c* from liver mitochondria during permeability transition. *Biochem. Biophys. Res. Commun.* 232:669–71

56. Zamzami N, Susin SA, Marchetti P, Hirsch T, Gómez-Monterrey I, et al. 1996. Mitochondrial control of nuclear apoptosis. *J. Exp. Med.* 183:1533–44

57. Newmeyer DD, Farschon DM, Reed JC. 1994. Cell-free apoptosis in Xenopus egg extracts: inhibition by Bcl-2 and requirement for an organelle fraction enriched in mitochondria. *Cell* 79:353–64

58. Kroemer G. 1997. Mode of action of the apoptosis-inhibitory proto-oncogene Bcl-2. *Nat. Med.* 3:614–20

59. Sedlak TW, Oltvai ZN, Yang E, Wang K, Boise LH, et al. 1995. Multiple Bcl-2 family members demonstrate selective dimerizations with Bax. *Proc. Natl. Acad. Sci. USA* 92:7834–38

60. Boise LH, Thompson CB. 1997. Bcl-XL can inhibit apoptosis in cells that have undergone Fas-induced protease activation. *Proc. Natl. Acad. Sci. USA* 94:3759–64

61. Carayon P, Portier M, Dussossoy D, Bord A, Petitpretre G, et al. 1996. Involvement of peripheral benzodiazepine receptors in the protection of hematopoietic cells against oxygen radical species. *Blood* 87:3170–78

62. Paumen MB, Ishida Y, Hen H, Muramatsu M, Eguchi Y, et al. 1997. Direct interaction of the mitochondrial membrane protein carnitine palmitoyltransferase I with Bcl-2. *Biochem. Biophys. Res. Commun.* 231:523–25

63. Zhu W, Cowie A, Wasfy GW, Penn LZ, Leber B, et al. 1996. Bcl-2 mutants with restricted subcellular localization reveal spatially distinct pathways for apoptosis in different cell types. *EMBO J.* 15:4130–41

64. Zha H, Fisk HA, Yaffe MP, Mahajan N, Herman B, et al. 1996. Structure-function comparisons of the pro-apoptotic protein Bax in yeast and mammalian cells. *Mol. Cell. Biol.* 16:6494–508

65. Martin SJ, Newmeyer DD, Mathisa S, Farschon DM, Wang HG, et al. 1995. Cell-free reconstitution of Fas-, UV radiation- and ceramide-induced apoptosis. *EMBO J.* 14:5191–200

66. Muchmore SW, Sattler M, Liang H, Meadows RP, Harlan JE, et al. 1996. X-ray and NMR structure of human Bcl-xL, and inhibitor of programmed cell death. *Nature* 381:335–41

67. Minn AJ, Vélez P, Schendel SL, Liang H, Muchmore SW, et al. 1997. Bcl-XL forms an ion channel in synthetic lipid membranes. *Nature* 385:353–57

68. Kinnally KW, Lohret TA, Campo ML, Mannella CA. 1996. Perspectives on

the mitochondrial multiple conductance channel. *J. Bioenerg. Biomembr.* 28:115–23

69. Costantini P, Chernyak BV, Petronilli V, Bernardi P. 1996. Modulation of the mitochondrial permeability transition pore by pyridine nucleotides and dithiol oxidation at two separate sites. *J. Biol. Chem.* 271:6746–51

70. Packer MA, Murphy MP. 1994. Peroxynitrite causes calcium efflux from mitochondria which is prevented by cyclosporin A. *FEBS Lett.* 345:237–40

71. Costantini P, Petronilli V, Colonna R, Bernardi P. 1995. On the effects of paraquat on isolated mitochondria. Evidence that paraquat causes opening of the cyclosporin A-sensitive permeability transition pore synergistically with nitric oxide. *Toxicology* 99:77–88

72. Pfeiffer DR, Gudz TI, Novgorodov SA, Erdahl WL. 1995. The peptide mastoparan is a potent facilitator of the mitochondrial permeability transition. *J. Biol. Chem.* 270:4923–32

73. Sokolove PM, Kinnally KW. 1996. A mitochondrial signal peptide from *Neurospora crassa* increases the permeability of isolated rat liver mitochondria. *Arch. Biochem. Biophys.* 336:69–76

74. Wang H-G, Rapp UR, Reed JC. 1996. Bcl-2 targets the protein kinase raf-1 to mitochondria. *Cell* 87:629–38

75. Zha JP, Harada H, Yang E, Jockel J, Korsmeyer SJ. 1996. Serine phosphorylation of death agonist BAD in response to survival factor results in binding to 14-3-3 not BGL-X(L). *Cell* 87:619–28

76. Liu X, Zou H, Slaughter C, Wang X. 1997. DFF, a heterodimeric protein that functions downstream of caspase 3 to trigger DNA fragmentation during apoptosis. *Cell* 89:175–84

77. Jacobson MD, Weil M, Raff MC. 1996. Role of Ced-3/ICE-family proteases in staurosporine-induced programmed cell death. *J. Cell. Biol.* 133:1041–51

78. Shigenaga MK, Hagen TM, Ames BN. 1994. Oxidative damage and mitochondrial decay in aging. *Proc. Natl. Acad. Sci. USA* 91:10771–78

79. Hartley A, Stone JM, Heron C, Cooper JM, Schapira AHV. 1994. Complex I inhibitors induce dose-dependent apoptosis in PC12 cells: relevance to Parkinson disease. *J. Neurochem.* 63:1987–90

80. Wertz IE, Hanley MR. 1996. Diverse molecular provocation of programmed cell death. *Trends Biochem. Sci.* 21:359–64

81. Simonian NA, Getz RL, Leveque JC,

Konradi C, Coyle JT. 1996. Kainate induces apoptosis in neurons. *Neuroscience* 74:675–83

82. Fliss H, Gattinger D. 1996. Apoptosis in ischemic and reperfused rat myocardium. *Circ. Res.* 79:949–56

83. Nazareth W, Yaferi N, Crompton M. 1991. Inhibition of anoxia induced injury in heart myocytes by cyclosporin A. *J. Mol. Cell. Cardiol.* 23:1351–58

84. Griffiths EJ, Halestrup AP. 1993. Protection by cyclosporin A of ischemia/reperfusion-induced damage in isolated rat hearts. *J. Mol. Cell. Cardiol.* 25:1461–69

85. Pastorino JG, Snyder JW, Serroni A, Hoek JB, Farber JL. 1993. Cyclosporin and carnitine prevent the anoxic death of cultured hepatocytes by inhibiting the mitochondrial permeability transition. *J. Biol. Chem.* 268:13791–98

86. Snyder JW, Pastorino JG, Attie AM, Farber JL. 1992. Protection by cyclosporin A of cultured hepatocytes from the toxic consequences of the loss of mitochondrial energization produced by 1-methyl-4phenylpyridinium. *Biochem. Pharmacol.* 44:833–35

87. Kass GEN, Juedes MJ, Orrenius S. 1992. Cyclosporin A protects hepatocytes against prooxidant-induced cell killing. *Biochem. Pharmacol.* 44:1995–2003

88. Imberti R, Nieminen AL, Herman B, Lemasters JJ. 1993. Mitochondrial and glycolytic dysfunction in lethal injury to hepatocytes by *t*-butylhydroperoxide: protection by fructose, cyclosporin A and trifluoperazine. *J. Pharmacol. Exp. Ther.* 265:392–400

89. Schinder AF, Olson EC, Spitzer NC, Montal M. 1996. Mitochondrial dysfunction is a primary event in glutamate neurotoxicity. *J. Neurosci.* 16:6125–33

90. Ankarcrona M, Dypbukt JM, Bonfoco E, Zhivotovsky B, Orrenius S, et al. 1995. Glutamate-induced neuronal death: a succession of necrosis or apoptosis depending on mitochondrial function. *Neuron* 15:961–73

91. White RJ, Reynolds IJ. 1996. Mitochondrial depolarization in glutamate-stimulated neurons: an early signal specific to excitotoxin exposure. *J. Neurosci.* 16:5688–97

92. Nieminen AL, Petrie TG, Lemasters JJ, Selman WR. 1996. Cyclosporin A delays mitochondrial depolarization induced by *N*-methyl-D-aspartate in cortical neurons: evidence of the mitochondrial permeability transition. *Neuroscience* 75:993–97

93. Shimizu S, Eguchi Y, Kamiike W, Waguri S, Uchiyama Y, et al. 1996. Retardation of chemical hypoxia-induced necrotic cell death by Bcl-2 and ICE inhibitors: possible involvement of common mediators in apoptotic and necrotic signal transductions. *Oncogene* 12:2045–50

94. Vayssière BM, Dupont S, Choquart A, Petit F, Garcia T, et al. 1997. Synthetic glucocorticoids that dissociate transactivation and AP-1 transrepression exhibit anti-inflammatory activity in vivo. *Mol. Endocrinol.* 11:1245–55

95. Guenal I, Sidoti-Defraisse C, Gaumer S, Mignotte B. 1997. Bcl-2 and hsp27 act at different levels to suppress programmed cell death. *Oncogene* 15:347–60

Annu. Rev. Physiol. 1998. 60:643–65

REGULATION OF CERAMIDE PRODUCTION AND APOPTOSIS

Richard N. Kolesnick

Laboratory of Signal Transduction, Memorial Sloan-Kettering Cancer Center, New York, NY, 10021

Martin Krönke

Institute of Immunology, Medical Center, University of Kiel, 24105 Kiel, Germany

KEY WORDS: sphingomyelinase, caspases, sphingosine, mitochondria, Bcl-2

ABSTRACT

Ceramide is a sphingosine-based lipid signaling molecule that regulates cellular differentiation, proliferation, and apoptosis. The emerging picture suggests that coupling of ceramide to specific signaling cascades is both stimulus and cell-type specific. Ceramide action is determined within the context of other stimuli and by the subcellular topology of its production. Here, we discuss the pathways of ceramide generation and the interaction of ceramide with caspases and other apoptotic signaling cascades.

INTRODUCTION

Ceramide belongs to the group of sphingosine-based lipid second messenger molecules that are involved in regulation of diverse cellular responses to exogenous stimuli (for review, see 1, 2). The mode of ceramide action and the regulation of its production have recently attracted great attention in part due to the emerging role of ceramide as an intracellular effector molecule in apoptosis. Apoptosis is a physiologic form of cell death required to control cell populations during processes such as embryogenesis, the immune response, wound healing, and other examples of normal tissue homeostasis (3–6).

Necrotic cells release their cytoplasmic content of toxic enzymes into the surrounding tissue, which usually causes a local inflammatory reaction. In contrast, apoptosis is a controlled form of cell death, where the integrity of the

643

plasma membrane is preserved until late in the process, thus enabling packaging of disintegrating organelles into membrane-bound vesicles without leakage of toxic intracellular components. Apoptotic cells or cellular fragments are eventually phagocytized by neighboring cells or macrophages without inducing an inflammatory reaction. Thus apoptosis is considered a means of removal of individual cells without producing tissue damage.

The signaling cascades that mediate apoptosis constitute preformed programs present in most if not all cells, albeit in inactive forms. These apoptotic programs can be initiated by a variety of physiologic and stress stimuli that trigger one of several distinct signaling pathways. The specific signaling pathway activated depends on the cell type and on the subcellular element targeted by each type of stress. The various upstream signaling cascades may converge on common final effector mechanisms for dismantling the dying cell.

One way of considering the programmed cell death response has been to divide it into stages (7): (a) a stimulus-dependent death-triggering induction phase; (b) an effector phase during which the initiating signal is converted to a lethal program designated the execution phase (this phase is distinguished by the activation of a family of cysteine proteases, e.g. caspases that disassemble subcellular structures in an orderly fashion); and (c) a degradation phase characterized by biochemical and morphological phenomenona of end-stage apoptosis.

A number of observations support the view that ceramide plays an important role in one or more of these stages of apoptosis: (a) Several cytokines and environmental stresses that initiate apoptosis, including TNF (8, 9), CD95/Fas/APO-1 (10), ionizing radiation, ultraviolet-C, heat shock, and oxidative stress (11, 12), appear to induce rapid ceramide generation, and the ED_{50} for ceramide generation correlates closely with the LD_{50} for induction of apoptosis. (b) Cell-permeable ceramide analogues, but not analogues of other lipid second messengers, mimic the effect of stress to induce apoptosis. The effect of ceramide is stereospecific because analogues of the naturally occurring dihydroceramide failed to initiate the apoptotic program. (c) Furthermore, lymphoblasts from patients with Niemann-Pick disease, an inherited deficiency of acid sphingomyelinase (A-SMase), and A-SMase-deficient mice show defects, but not total loss, of the apoptotic response (13). In vivo, A-SMase knockout mice failed to generate ceramide and to develop typical apoptotic lesions in the lung after exposure to total body radiation.

Although ceramide appears to impact several stages of apoptosis, its involvement in specific apoptotic signaling pathways has not been clearly defined. A large body of evidence indicates that a cascade of cysteine proteases with specificity for aspartic acid residues (caspases) mediate apoptosis (14, 15). It will be critical to elucidate whether ceramide acts up- or downstream of a particular caspase, or whether ceramides induce apoptotic pathways independently of the caspase cascade. Improved understanding of the molecular basis of ceramide action during apoptosis may provide further insights into the pathogenesis of human disease, which might reveal novel strategies for therapeutic modalities in cancer and other proliferative diseases. This review puts in perspective the regulation, kinetics, and topology of ceramide production with regard to possible interactions with specific pro- and anti-apoptotic signaling pathways.

MOLECULAR MECHANISMS OF APOPTOSIS

Caspase Proteases

The pioneering work of Horvitz and coworkers defined three proteins, CED-3, CED-4, and CED-9 (5, 16), that are necessary to control cell death during the development of the nematode *Caenorhabditis elegans*. CED-3 and CED-4 were shown to be required for cell death to occur, whereas CED-9 counteracts CED-4 thereby preventing cell death induced by CED-3. The mammalian homologues of CED-3 are members of interleukin 1β-converting enzyme (ICE)-related family of caspase proteases. At least 12 members of the caspase family have been identified, all of which are expressed as inactive proenzymes that are proteolytically activated to form a heterodimeric catalytic complex (14, 17). The caspase family members can be divided into three subfamilies: ICE-like proteases (caspase-1), ICH-1-like proteases (caspase-2), and CPP32-like proteases (caspase-3). During apoptosis, a hierarchy of *trans*-cleavage and activation of caspases is hypothesized as responsible for the orderly progression of the apoptotic disassembly of cellular organelles. However, it has been difficult to demonstrate ordered caspase activation (7, 8, 14). Nevertheless, ectopic expression of caspases in mammalian cells uniformly results in induction of apoptosis. Several target sequences for the apoptotic action of caspases have been identified (17). Caspase-1 recognizes the sequence Tyr-Val-Ala-Asp (YVAD) present in the proform of Interleukin-1β. However, no direct target has been defined for caspase-1 during the induction of apoptosis. In contrast, caspase-3 recognizes the motif Asp-Glu-Val-Asp (DEVD) and hydrolyzes poly(ADP-ribose) polymerase (PARP) a DNA-dependent protein kinase, the U1-ribonucleoprotein, the nuclear protein lamin, the cytoplasmic protein kinase Cδ, and the membrane protein fodrin, for example. These specific substrate recognition sequences have been used to generate peptide inhibitors selective for the different caspase classes. In vitro, however, caspases display limited substrate specificity. For instance, PARP is cleaved into an 85-kDa polypeptide not only by CPP32 but also by caspases -2, -7, -9, and -10, suggesting that members of the caspase family may be functionally redundant.

Recent investigations have addressed the molecular mechanisms by which extracellular signals activate caspases to effect apoptosis. The apoptotic function of cytokine receptors, such as those for TNF or Fas-ligand, were reported to be linked to the ICE/CED-3 effector mechanism via a receptor-associated death domain adaptor protein system (17–19). These receptors are transmembrane proteins found in cells in the plasma memberanes. Ligand binding to these cytokine receptors initiated formation of a multiprotein complex by binding cytoplasmic proteins through interactions of complementary death domain motifs present on the intracellular portion of the receptors and in the adaptor proteins. For example, via their respective death domains, the 55-kDa TNF receptor and the 34-kDa TRADD (TNF receptor 1-associated death domain) protein (18) associate (19), and this complex binds, in turn, the Fas-associated death domain protein (FADD; also known as MORT-1) (20, 21). As another example of how these interactions vary, CD95 does not complex with TRADD, but rather binds FADD/MORT-1 directly (21). In addition to its death domain, FADD/MORT-1 contains a protein-protein interaction motif, termed the death effector domain (DED). FADD/MORT-1 DED was shown to bind the DED of an ICE/CED-3-like caspase termed FLICE/MACH-1 (caspase-8) (22, 23). Thus ligand binding to the TNF receptor or CD95 appears to activate caspase-8 without an apparent involvement of lipid second messengers. The functional relevance of the adaptor protein system was demonstrated by experiments showing that overexpression of each of these proteins initiates apoptosis, whereas dominant-interfering mutations block ligand-induced apoptosis. From such data, one may ask how effectors such as ceramide are involved.

Although a hierachy of caspase *trans*-cleavage is widely considered responsible for the orderly progression of the apoptotic disassembly of cellular organelles, this view may overestimate the available data. In no instance has a cause-effect relationship been established between a given caspase target and the progression of the apoptotic response. For example, although PARP is a well-known caspase target, PARP knock-out mice develop normally and do not demonstrate perturbations in induction of apoptosis (24). Further, caspase-1 knock-out mice show only limited alterations of the apoptotic response. Li et al reported that the overall phenotype of ICE-deficient mice is overtly normal and that their thymocytes and macrophages undergo apoptosis when stimulated with dexamethasone, ionizing radiation, or ATP, respectively (25). In contrast, Kuida et al found that thymocytes from ICE-deficient mice are resistant to Fas antibody at concentrations >1 ng/ml (26). However, unlike the *lpr/lpr* mutation at the murine Fas locus, ICE-deficient mice do not show autoimmune pathologies. The deficiency of ICE, therefore, does not appear to play a major role in clonal deletion of maturing T cells. Capase-3 has been suggested as more relevant to many apoptotic systems. However, mice deficient in caspase-3 display selective hyperplasia and aberrant cell development in the brain, but no deficit in apoptosis of T cells in response to diverse stimuli (27). Whether some members of the caspase family are functionally redundant and compensate for loss of the primary caspase, or whether utilization of caspases may be restricted to select tissues, is at present uncertain.

Stress-Activated Protein Kinases

Apoptotic stimuli such as TNF and Fas trigger the activation of stress-activated kinases or SAPKs. Isoforms of SAPK1, also called c-JUN N-terminal kinases (JNKs), phosphorylate c-Jun thereby increasing its transcriptional activity. The JNK pathway is activated by many stress stimuli such as oxidative damage, irradiation, and cytokines, any of which may lead to apoptosis (11, 28). The upstream activation pathway of SAPK/JNK is poorly understood. One simple model of the SAPK/JNK signaling system involves sequential activation of kinases MEKK1, SEK1, and SAPK/JNK, which eventually leads to phosphorylation of c-Jun (28). In NIH 3T3 fibroblasts, overexpression of c-Jun was shown to suffice for the induction of apoptosis (29). The amino-terminal transactivation, as well as the carboxy-terminal leucine zipper domain, were found to be necessary, suggesting that c-Jun may activate cell death through its transcriptional activity. c-Jun-mediated apoptosis could be blocked by peptide inhibitors of ICE/CED-3-like caspases (29), confirming that c-Jun induces apoptosis indirectly through protease intermediates.

Baltimore and colleagues have recently identified a novel Fas-associated protein, Daxx, that binds to the death domain of Fas and signals for activation of JNK and apoptosis (30). Involvement of SAPK/JNK in apoptosis was also reported by Xia and coworkers (31). Withdrawal of nerve growth factor (NGF) in PC-12 cells resulted in activation of the SAPK/JNK and p38 signaling systems, and in concomitant inactivation of ERK. These coordinated effects were essential for apoptosis to proceed, and suggested that a balance between SAPK/JNK and ERK may be critical in effecting the apoptotic outcome.

It is worth emphasizing that the SAPK/JNK cascade and apoptosis are not universally coupled. This is not surprising given that c-Jun activity is induced by a large variety of external signals, many that stimulate not only apoptosis but also cell proliferation, differentiation, and transformation. Multiple upstream kinases, including TAK1, ASK, PAK, and multilineage kinases, are now known to couple to the SAPK/JNK signaling system. It seems plausible that the result of JNK signaling initiated through these distinct kinases is different. For instance, TRAF-2-mediated JNK activation was recently shown not to be involved in TNF-induced apoptosis in MCF7 and HeLa cells (32). These apparently contradictory findings may be explained by the heterogeneity of JNK isoforms. Three distinct mammalian genes that encode different JNK enzymes have been identified. In addition, molecular analysis has yielded as many as 12 distinct forms of JNK mRNA species that are generated by alternate splicing. Very recently, Butterfield et al investigated the regulation of individual forms of JNK in the apoptotic response of cultured small cell lung cancer cells (SCLC) to UV radiation (33). These authors produced nonphosphorylatable, dominant-negative mutants of JNK1 and JNK2. Overexpression of dominant-negative mutants of either JNK1 or JNK2 markedly reduced UV-triggered JNK activity. However, only dominant-negative JNK1 increased the resistance of SCLC to UV-induced apoptosis, suggesting that JNK1, but not JNK2, mediates UV-induced apoptosis. Thus different isoforms of JNK may fulfill distinct functions in a cell type–specific manner. JNK may thus serve as one prominent example for tissue-specific control of apoptotic signaling.

Mitochondrial Pro- and Anti-Apoptotic Factors

Accumulating evidence indicates that mitochondria play a fundamental role in apoptosis. In particular, two mitochondria-derived components, apoptosis-inducing factor (AIF) and cytochrome c (Cyt c), have been implicated as important cofactors of apoptosis. AIF is a 50-kDa intermembrane Z-VAD-inhibitable (but not DEVD-inhibitable) ICE-like protease (34) that induces nuclear apoptosis in the absence of other cytoplasmic components. Definitive insights into AIF function await the molecular cloning of this protein. AIF seems to be released following disruption of the mitochondrial transmembrane potential (MTP), which occurs early during apoptosis and prior to DNA fragmentation or phosphatidylserine exposure at the outer leaflet of the plasma membrane (35). Disruption of the MTP appears secondary to permeability transition (PT) of the mitochondrial membrane (for review, see 36; G Kroemer, B Dallaporta & M Resche-Rigon, this volume). PT has been defined as a sudden permeability increase of the inner mitochondrial membrane for substances of less than M_r 1500 Daltons. PT pore opening causes uncoupling of the respiratory chain with collapse of MTP, attenuation of ATP synthesis, and release of calcium, glutathione, and apoptotic substances such as AIF. Kroemer and colleagues reported that inhibitors of ICE such as Ac-YVAD.cmk or crmA prevent MTP collapse and subsequent apoptosis in anti-Fas-treated cultured human leukemia cells (37). Furthermore, recombinant ICE induced PT and MTP disruption of isolated mitochondria. Collectively, these data provide evidence that the apoptotic function of mitochondria is located both up- and downstream of caspases.

Although functional and genetic manipulations suggest that MTP disruption and subsequent nuclear DNA fragmentation cannot be dissociated, recent studies argued that this may not be the case. Two reports provided evidence that Cyt c release from mitochondria is not accompanied by changes in the mitochondrial membrane potential (38, 39). HL-60 cells treated with staurosporine for 2 to 4 h showed no loss of mitochondrial membrane potential, despite release of most of the mitochondrial Cyt c. Similar results were obtained using a cell-free system. Further, Cyt c released from mitochondria activated a DEVD-specific, CPP32-like caspase, leading to fodrin cleavage and nuclear apoptosis. Mitochondrial supernatants alone did not suffice for CPP32 activation, indicating that the activation of CPP32 by Cyt c required other cytosolic factors including dATP (40). Additionally, CPP32 activation was prevented by a monoclonal anti Cyt c antibody, confirming that Cyt c represents a crucial factor in the process of apoptosis.

The anti-apoptotic control of mitochondria function resides in a family of proteins that may serve as the mammalian homologues of CED-9. In *C. elegans,* CED-9 acts as an inhibitor of CED-4 to prevent the death-inducing activity of CED-3 (5, 16). In mammalian systems, Bcl-2 and Bcl-x_L are the main members of this family of CED-9 homologues that inhibit apoptosis. The mechanism by which Bcl-2 and Bcl-x_L effect cell survival is not fully understood. These proteins are located predominantly at the outer mitochondrial membrane, endoplasmic reticulum, and nuclear membrane anchored to these membranes by a hydrophobic C-terminal region (41, 42).

Although Bcl-2-related proteins were first reported to confer anti-apoptotic protection, it was subsequently shown that some members of this family, such as Bax, Bak, and Bad, serve as pro-apoptotic factors (for review, see 43). A common feature of Bcl-2-related proteins is their ability to produce homo- and heterodimers. The composition of these dimers determines the apoptotic outcome in stimulated cells. Heterodimers between a pro-apoptotic factor (Bax or Bad) and an anti-apoptotic protein (Bcl-2 or Bcl-x_L) signal apoptosis, whereas dissociation of these complexes results in anti-apoptotic protection. Zha et al reported that IL-3 stimulated phosphorylation of Bad and that this modification of Bad interfered with its ability to dimerize Bcl-x_L and to initiate apoptosis (44). Similarly, Wang et al reported that Raf-1 can be translocated to the mitochondria, initiating signaling that phosphorylates and inactivates Bad and dissociates it from Bcl-2 (45). Hence, phosphorylation of Bad presumably promotes an anti-apoptotic effect by disassembling heterodimers with Bcl-x_L or Bcl-2.

The release of Cyt c from mitochondria is under the control of Bcl-2 (38, 39). It was recently shown that overexpression of Bcl-2 prevented the efflux of Cyt c from the mitochondria thereby preventing caspase activation and progression of apoptosis. Based on the homolgy of Bcl-x_L to bacterial pore-forming proteins, it has been argued that Bcl-2 may be part of a pore structure that controls the release of Cyt c directly. This model would also account for the observation that Bcl-2 also prevents the release of other molecules, such as calcium and AIF. However, as outlined above, Cyt c release also occurs independently of PT and MTP disruption (38, 39). The mechanisms by which Cyt c is released from mitochondria and how this process is regulated by Bcl-2 is not known. It is thus possible that pro-apoptotic molecules such as Cyt c and AIF, and possibly other factors, are released by various mechanisms under the control of distinct anti-apoptotic constraints.

In sum, a large body of evidence is defining a network of death domain–containing signaling proteins, caspases, and organelles, such as the plasmamembrane and mitochondria, that appear in control of distinct phases of apoptosis. However, other factors have also been implicated. It is particularly intriguing that ceramide can induce apoptosis of many different cell types in an efficient and almost uniform manner. The question arises whether ceramide acts independently of or coordinately with the molecular mechanisms outlined above. Before this issue is addressed, it is instructive to consider some salient biochemical features of ceramide metabolism and the topology of its production.

REGULATION OF CERAMIDE PRODUCTION

Ceramide is one of the most hydrophobic molecules in mammalian cells. Hence, ceramide tends to remain within the membrane bilayer and may exert its function exclusively at the subcellular site of production. The topology of ceramide generation, therefore, may be the determining factor for the selective activation of interacting signaling complexes that colocalize in the same subcellular compartment. A number of different enzymatic mechanisms exist for the production of ceramide. Understanding the signaling functions of ceramide requires an in-depth understanding of these enzymes and their cellular localization.

Ceramide can be synthesized de novo by condensation of serine and palmitoyl-CoA to form ketosphinganine, which is subsequently reduced to dihydrosphingosine (46). The acylation of dihydrosphingosine to dihydroceramide is catalyzed by ceramide synthase (sphinganine N-acyl transferase). Ceramide is formed by the action of dihydroceramide reductase, which catalyzes the oxidation of dihydroceramide to introduce the *trans*-4,5 double bond. Dihydroceramide is generated in the endoplasmic reticulum and in the mitochondria. The subcellular localization of the dihydroceramide reductase has not been determined. The latter enzyme appears to be crucial because ceramide, but not dihydroceramide, is biologically active. Notably, ceramide synthase seems to be a stimulus-responsive enzyme. Bose et al reported that prolonged activation of ceramide synthase can be induced by daunorubicin treatment of P388 and U937 cells (47). The V_{max} of ceramide synthase was increased by 70%, which resulted in sustained elevations of ceramide (and sphingomyelin) levels for several hours. Similarly, Boland et al showed that daunorubicin induced ceramide generation via ceramide synthase activation in HL-60 cells (48).

The catabolic pathway for ceramide involves the action of sphingomyelinases, sphingomyelin-specific forms of phospholipase C, which hydrolyze the phosphodiester bond of sphingomyelin (N-acylsphingosin-1-phosphorylcholine; SM), a phospholipid preferentially found in the plasma membrane of mammalian cells yielding ceramide and phosphorylcholine. There are several isoforms of sphingomyelinase, distinguished by different pH optima. Human and murine A-SMase (pH optimum 4.5–5.0) have been cloned and determined to be the products of a conserved gene, whereas the Mg^{2+}-dependent or -independent neutral sphingomyelinases (N-SMase) have yet to be characterized at the molecular level. However, acid sphingomyelinase knock-out mice retain neutral sphingomyelinase activity, indicating that the neutral forms are products of a distinct gene or genes (49). N-SMase appears to operate at the plasma membrane. In contrast, A-SMase activities seem to be localized in acidic compartments such as the lysosome or endosome. It is important to note that A-SMase activity has also been observed in caveolae of IL-1-treated cells (50). Both neutral and acid SMases are rapidly and transiently activated by diverse exogenous stimuli (51–53). N- and A-SMase appear to be responsible for stimulus-induced increases of ceramide levels within a time frame of seconds or minutes, whereas activation of ceramide synthase occurs within hours. Therefore, SMases are considered as principal pathways for production of ceramide in early signal transduction.

Ceramide can also be generated by breakdown of complex glycosphingolipids through acid hydrolases. Regulation of these acid hydrolysases by exogenous stimuli has not been demonstrated. Thus a role for glycosphingolipid breakdown in transmembrane signaling cannot presently be ascribed.

Ceramide is also subject to extensive modifications. Ceramide can be converted to ceramide-1-phosphate by ceramide kinase and to SM by transfer of phosphorylcholine from phosphatidylcholine to ceramide by the enzyme sphingomyelin synthase. Furthermore, ceramide can be glycosylated by glucosylceramide synthase in the Golgi apparatus, the first step in complex glycosphingolipid synthesis. The kinetics and topology of these reactions are only partially understood. Although these reactions may affect the overall steady state levels of ceramide, they do not seem to be under the control of external stimuli. Perhaps the most important modification of ceramide is its deacylation to sphingosine by ceramidases, because sphingosine has been recognized as a lipid messenger molecule with distinctive signaling functions (see below).

Ceramide Serves as Second Messenger in the Sphingomyelin Pathway

Signaling through the sphingomyelin pathway and the generation of the second messenger ceramide is ubiquitous and evolutionarily conserved. Most if not all mammalian cells appear capable of signaling through the sphingomyelin pathway. Receptors as distinct as those for CD28, CD95, and the TNFα, IL-1β, progesterone, γ-interferon, and glucocorticoid receptors signal via the sphingomyelin pathway following ligand binding (1, 2). For some of these receptors, ceramide signals immediately after cellular activation and hence appears to fulfill the criterion for a classic second messenger, whereas in other instances, ceramide generation is a later response (>6 h after receptor triggering) downstream of a complex set of interacting signals. Ceramide can signal diverse cellular functions, including proliferation of fibroblasts, differentiation of promyelocytes, inhibition of the respiratory burst in human neutrophils, survival of T9 glioma cells, and apoptosis (1, 2, 54), to list a few. The pleiotropic nature of ceramide-mediated signaling suggests that the sphingomyelin pathway may link downstream to a variety of effector systems. This may be brought about, at least in part, by triggering the sphingomyelin pathway at distinct subcellular sites. Studies using mutants of the cytoplasmic domain of the 55-kDa TNF receptor suggest a model that might clarify how ceramide acts to signal both pro-inflammatory and apoptotic effects of TNF (52, 55, 56). Investigations with these mutants showed that specific receptor domains link to different sphingomyelinases. Adam et al recently identified a small motif of 11 amino acid residues at position 309 to 319 in the cytoplasmic portion of the p55 TNF receptor that is both necessary and sufficient for activation of neutral SMase (55). This motif, termed NSD, was shown to specifically bind a novel WD-repeat protein, FAN, that functionally couples this domain of TNF-R55 to neutral SMase (56). Downstream of N-SMase may be the extracellular regulated kinase (ERK) cascade and pro-inflammatory responses. In contrast, the activation of A-SMase is signaled by a region of the C terminus corresponding with the death domain (52). This region binds an adaptor protein, TRADD, that in turn recruits at least three other proteins, TRAF2, FADD, and RIP (for review, see 57). Recent studies revealed that neither TRAF2 nor RIP affected A-SMase activation. In contrast, overexpression of TRADD and FADD enhanced TNF-induced A-SMase activation (R Schwandner & M Krönke, unpublished data). A model depicting how TNF engages the sphingomyelin pathway for signaling is shown in Figure 1. Together these observations suggest that N- and A-SMase are activated through distinct molecular mechanisms, consistent with the notion that signaling through compartmentalized sphingomyelinases may lead to initiation of distinct biological processes. With regard to programmed cell death, the activation of A-SMase through the death domain adaptor protein system suggests that A-SMase, rather than N-SMase, is involved in TNF-mediated apoptotic programs.

Definitive evidence for the critical role of acid sphingomyelinase and ceramide in initiating apoptotic signaling was provided by studies using genetic

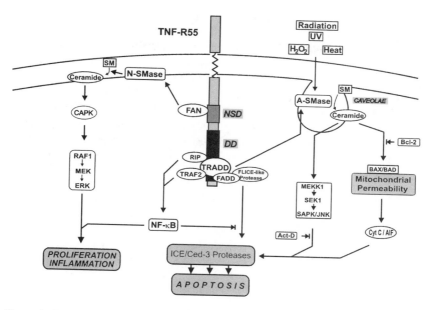

Figure 1 Proposed mechanism for stress- and TNF-induced apoptosis via the sphingomyelin pathway. Environmental stresses act directly on membranes and activate acid sphingomyelinase, generating ceramide and initiating signaling through the SAPK/JNK cascade. It is presumed that SAPK/JNK phosphorylates targets upstream of the ICE/Ced-3 proteases that effect apoptosis. The 55-kDa TNF receptor initiates apoptosis via formation of a death domain-adaptor protein complex that links downstream to acid sphingomyelinase and to the SAPK/JNK and the ICE/Ced-3 systems to signal apoptosis. Proliferative/pro-inflammatory effects of TNF are signaled through a different region of the 55-kDa TNF receptor. A membrane proximal region of the cytoplasmic domain links the adaptor protein FAN to neutral sphingomyelinase, ceramide generation, stimulation of ceramide-activated protein kinase (CAPK), Raf-1, and the ERK cascade. In addition, TRADD may link the TNF receptor to NF-κB activation via RIP and/or TRAF-2.

models of acid sphingomyelinase deficiency. Santana et al reported that lymphoblasts from patients with Niemann-Pick disease (NPD), an inherited deficiency of acid sphingomyelinase, and acid sphingomyelinase knock-out mice, showed defects in the apoptotic response (13). In contrast to normal lymphoblasts, NPD-derived B-cell lines failed to respond to ionizing radiation with ceramide generation and apoptosis. These abnormalities were reversible upon restoration of acid sphingomyelinase activity by retroviral transfer of human acid sphingomyelinase cDNA. Further, acid sphingomyelinase knock-out mice failed to generate ceramide and to develop typical apoptotic lesions in the lung after exposure to total body irradiation. These mice were also defective in the apoptotic response to radiation in the endocardium, the pleura, and pericardium, but not in the thymus. The pattern of tissue apoptosis found in p53 knock-out mice was markedly different. Whereas the thymus of the p53 knock-out mouse was protected against radiation-induced apoptosis, the lung was not. These studies suggest a tissue-restricted involvement of A-SMase in radiation-induced apoptosis.

Additional evidence indicates that stimulated ceramide synthesis via ceramide synthase may play a role in induction of apoptosis. Bose et al showed that daunorubicin-induced activation of ceramide synthase, ceramide generation, and apoptosis were inhibited by fumonisin B1, a fungal toxin specific for ceramide synthase (47). However, TNF-induced ceramide generation and apoptosis, which occurred via sphingomyelinase activation, were unaffected. Recently, Witty et al corroborated this finding showing that daunorubicin-induced, but not UV-induced, apoptosis was abolished by fumonisin B1 in Hen granulosa cells (58). In contrast, UV- but not daunorubicin-induced apoptosis was inhibited by elevation of cAMP levels. Whether ceramide generated via the synthase interacts with the same targets as ceramide generated through SMases is presently uncertain.

Ceramidases Modulate the Ceramide Signal

Ceramide can be deacylated by ceramidases to generate sphingosine, which can be phosphorylated by sphingosine kinase to form sphingosine-1-phosphate (SPP). These reactions may be of great biological significance because both sphingosine and SPP show signaling effects distinct from ceramide (for review, see 59). Sphingosine functions as both a positive and negative modulator of cell proliferation. For example, sphingosine inhibited CHO cell proliferation (60) and arrested lymphoblastic leukemic cells in the G0/G1 phase (61). In contrast, sphingosine induces the proliferation of Swiss 3T3 cells (62). Thus sphingosine can exert opposite effects on cell growth depending on the cell type and context of the signal. The growth factor PDGF has been shown to stimulate the activity of both SMases and a membrane-associated alkaline ceramidase (63). It has been proposed that growth factor–induced coupling of A-SMase and ceramidase reactions would yield a proliferative cell response through generation of sphingosine. According to this model, coregulation of ceramidase activity may modulate the functional consequences of stimulus-dependent ceramide production by SMases. Consistent with this model, endosomal-lysosomal A-SMase copurifies with acid ceramidase, suggesting that these two enzymes may form a complex (64). Whether the PDGF-responsive alkaline ceramidase, which localizes to the plasma membrane also complexes with neutral SMase remains unknown.

It is also noteworthy that the mitogenic effects of sphingosine may be mediated by sphingosine-1-phosphate (SPP). Spiegel and coworkers reported that

SPP is rapidly produced in cells treated with exogenous sphingosine and that SPP is far more efficient than sphingosine in stimulating Swiss 3T3 cell proliferation (65). In addition, a competitive inhibitor of sphingosine kinase, DL-threo-sphinganine, reduced the proliferative response to sphingosine. Furthermore, SPP has been shown to antagonize ceramide-mediated apoptosis. These observations suggest that sphingosine kinase, as well as ceramidase, plays an important role as a modulator of ceramide action through the sphingomyelin pathway.

CERAMIDE-ACTIVATED SIGNALING PATHWAYS

In order to better understand the role of ceramide during apoptosis, it is important to identify direct targets of ceramide action. Ceramide has been reported to regulate directly or indirectly the activity of a number of enzymes and signaling components, including proline-directed kinases such as MAP kinases (66) or the ceramide-activated kinase (CAPK) (67), ceramide-activated phosphatase (CAPP) (68), PKCζ (69, 70), phospholipases such as cPLA2 (53) or PLD (71), transcription factors such as NF-κB (51, 70, 72), and CPP32-like caspases (73, 74). The interpretation of the published data is hampered, however, by the fact that most observations come from studies using synthetic short-chain ceramide analogues to treat cells over prolonged periods of time and may not reflect the transient physiologic generation of small amounts of ceramide in response to exogenous stimuli. Furthermore, synthetic ceramide analogues, when added to intact cells, may serve as the source of other bioactive sphingolipids as described above. So far, only a few proteins have been identified as direct interaction partners for ceramide.

One primary target of ceramide is CAP kinase (CAPK), a membrane-associated proline-directed serine/threonine kinase (67). CAPK is activated in ceramide-treated cells, and partially purified CAPK can be stimulated by ceramide in vitro. CAPK has been reported to phosphorylate and activate Raf-1 kinase. Activation of Raf-1 can trigger the extracellular signal-regulated (ERK) cascade, which may lead to arachidonic acid production by PLA2. Thus CAPK may represent an important mediator of pro-inflammatory TNF action. Recently, CAPK was identified as the mammalian homologue of kinase suppressor of Ras (KSR), which had been characterized genetically in *C. elegans* and *Drosophila* (75). Mouse KSR shares biochemical features with CAPK. In intact cells, TNF or ceramide analogues induced autophosphorylation of KSR and enhanced its ability to phosphorylate and activate Raf-1. Like CAPK, KSR selectively phosphorylated Thr269 of Raf-1. Furthermore, activation of KSR proved to be specific for ceramide. It is hoped that structure-function analysis of CAPK will delineate a ceramide-binding motif.

Ceramide-activated protein phosphatase (CAPP), a heterotrimeric protein phosphatase 2A (PP2A), may represent another target of ceramide. Hannun and coworkers showed that ceramide caused growth arrest in wild-type *Saccharomyces cerevisiae* and that the extracts of yeast contained a ceramide-activated Ser/Thr phosphatase activity (76). Because this activity was sensitive to okadaic acid, this yeast CAPP was concluded to be a member of the 2A class of protein phosphatases. Detailed insights into a possible role for ceramide and PP2A in yeast were provided by an elegant study by Nickels & Broach (77). These authors identified three yeast genes, *TPD3, CDC55,* and *SIT4,* encoding two regulatory subunits and the catalytic subunit of a ceramide-activated protein phosphatase, respectively. They showed that mutation of any one of these genes rendered strains resistant to the antiproliferative effects of ceramide. These results not only provide pertinent genetic evidence that PP2A mediates ceramide-induced G1 arrest of *S. cervisiae* but also highlight the conservation of ceramide-signaling systems in yeast and mammalian cells.

Protein kinase PKCζ was identified as a ceramide-binding target protein, using radioactive C16-ceramide (69, 70). These investigations showed that ceramide not only binds to PKCζ but also regulates kinase activity. Arachidonic acid competed for ceramide binding to and activation of PKCζ. Whether stereoisomeric forms of ceramide, dihydroceramide, or other long-chain sphingoid bases bind to and activate PKCζ remains to be shown. The ceramide-binding motif of PKCζ has not been characterized. It will be interesting to determine whether a cysteine-rich (C1) zinc butterfly motif, which in conventional PKCs constitutes the lipid-binding site for DAG, serves as a ceramide-binding motif.

Recently, Huwiler et al reported that Raf-1 kinase may be a ceramide-activated protein kinase (78). Raf-1 contains a zinc-finger CR1 domain similar to the C1 lipid-binding domain of PKC. The activation of RAF-1 kinase may include several steps. After translocation to the plasma membrane and association with Ras-GTP, Raf-1 kinase becomes phosphorylated at tyrosine and/or serine/threonine residues. It was speculated that the CR1 domain serves as a binding motif for ceramide. Using a radioiodinated photoaffinity labeling analogue of ceramide, Huwiler and colleagues provided evidence that ceramide binds to and activates Raf-1 kinase (78). Competition experiments have not been performed with stereoisomers of ceramide, sphingoid bases, or other neutral lipids. Thus the specificity of ceramide binding to Raf-1 kinase has yet to be established. Furthermore, Zhang et al failed to demonstrate direct activation of Raf-1 by ceramide analogues under conditions where KSR/CAPK was activated (75). Additional structure-function studies appear necessary to delineate the role of the CR1 domain in signal transduction.

Clearly, definitive characterization of direct ceramide targets remains a major goal in lipid messenger research. The identification of downstream targets of ceramide will provide important clues about the involvement of ceramide in specific signaling pathways and about its biological significance in general. Furthermore, structure-function analysis of target proteins should allow the identification and characterization of putative ceramide-binding sites.

INVOLVEMENT OF CERAMIDE IN APOPTOTIC PATHWAYS

Interactions of Ceramide with Apoptotic Proteases

As outlined above, the investigations of death domain–containing membrane receptors have revealed apoptotic signaling cascades involving the family of caspase proteases. Although formation of the death domain adaptor protein complexes appears independent of ceramide, emerging data suggest that its ability to confer apoptosis in some instances may depend on coordinated signaling via ceramide. Deletions of the death domain region of the 55-kDa TNF receptor (52) and CD95 (53), as well as overexpression of dominant-negative FADD/MORT1 (79), blocked ligand-induced ceramide generation and apoptosis. Furthermore, Dixit and coworkers reported that treatment with ceramide analogues can bypass the anti-apoptotic effect of dominant-negative FADD/MORT1 mutants and restore apoptosis, indicating that apoptotic elements downstream of ceramide generation are intact in these cells (79). Similarly, ceramide analogues signal apoptosis in cells containing CD95 death domain deletion mutants. Further support for the notion that ceramide may be downstream of caspases is derived from experiments showing that REAPER-induced ceramide generation was blocked by the caspase inhibitor Z-VAD-fmk (25). Unfortunately, the source of ceramide generation has not been addressed in these studies. Recent observations indicate that overexpression of TRADD and FADD enhances TNF-induced activation of A-SMase, whereas TRAF2 or RIP neither alter the amplitude nor the kinetics of A-SMase activation. TRADD and FADD increased the V_{max} of A-SMase, whereas the K_m remained unchanged (R Schwandner & M Krönke, unpublished data). Together, these findings favor A-SMase over N-SMase as the primary source of ceramide during death domain–induced apoptotic signaling. Consistent with this paradigm, preliminary studies show that CD95-induced apoptosis is abrogated in A-SMase-deficient Niemann-Pick cells and that this defect is reversed upon retroviral transfer of the acid sphingomyelinase gene (L Peña & R Kolesnick, unpublished observation).

These data suggest that ceramide generation may be downstream of caspase proteases stimulated through cytokine receptor activation. There is, however, evidence that ceramide also can signal activation of the ICE/Ced-3 effector system to execute apoptosis. Hannun and coworkers reported that ceramide signaled apoptosis in vincristine-treated ALL-697 leukemia cells via a CPP32-like protease and that this effect was inhibitable by Bcl-2 (73, 74). Cells over-expressing Bcl-2, like wild-type cells, still responded to vincristine treatment with ceramide generation but failed to show PARP cleavage and apoptosis in response to the C6-ceramide analogue. These studies link ceramide signaling to classic effector elements of the apoptotic response. Collectively, these data indicate that ceramide might be both upstream and downstream of caspase proteases. It should be emphasized that in the above studies A-SMase activity was not measured; only ceramide levels were determined. Thus the mechanism of ceramide generation was not revealed. Clearly, more work is required to resolve possible cause-effect relationships between caspase proteases and sphingomyelinases.

Ionizing radiation may signal sphingomyelinase activation by a different mechanism. The fact that ionizing radiation is capable of generating ceramide in isolated membranes implies that ceramide generation might be independent of a death domain adaptor protein system. Thus direct effects of ionizing and UV radiation on the cell membrane structure and function might alter the activity of membrane proteins, such as enzymes and transmembrane receptors (80). In this regard, UV radiation was recently shown to multimerize and activate a variety of cell membrane cytokine receptors, some of which activate caspases (81). However, preliminary studies do not support a role for caspases in mediating radiation-induced sphingomyelinase activation (R Kolesnick & Z Fuks, unpublished observation). Rather, radiation appears to utilize ICE/Ced-3-like caspases downstream of ceramide generation to execute apoptosis. In this regard, Emoto et al showed that in U937 cells, radiation induced PKCδ cleavage and apoptosis and that these effects were blocked by the ICE-like caspase inhibitor Y-VAD (82).

Interactions of Ceramide with Mitochondrial Apoptotic Pathways

Numerous investigations define mitochondrial perturbation as a committed step in ceramide signaling of apoptosis. Evidence indicates that ceramide may signal mitochondrial permeability transition (PT) in intact cells and in cytoplasts (83–85). Kroemer and coworkers showed that Bcl-2 is a highly efficient inhibitor of ceramide-induced PT and release of AIF (37). Notably, Bcl-2 failed to interfere with Fas- and ICE-triggered mitochondrial alterations but prevented ceramide- and prooxidant-induced large amplitude swelling, PT, release of AIF, and apoptosis. Thus mitochondria appear to function as a cellular sensor of ceramide production in response to stress stimuli, under the control of Bcl-2 (see Figure 1).

Regulation of mitchondrial carnitine palmitoyltransferase I (CPTI) activity has also been implicated in ceramide-mediated apoptosis (86). In a subtractive hybridization screen for genes expressed during apoptosis, CPTI was found to be induced. CPTI is another mitochondrial membrane enzyme that catalyzes the transfer of fatty acids including palmitate, into the mitochondria for beta-oxidation. Palmitate is also the precursor for the formation of free sphingoid base, a regulatory step in sphingolipid synthesis. In LyD9 mouse hematopoietic precursor cells, pharmacologic inhibition of CPTI leads to accumulation of palmitate in the cytosol and sphingoid base synthesis, followed by ceramide synthesis and apoptosis. Fumonisin B1, which blocks ceramide synthesis, rescued cells from apoptosis. These observations strongly suggest that inhibition of CPTI enhances de novo synthesis of ceramide, which eventually leads to programmed cell death. Furthermore, CPTI binds to Bcl-2 directly, as evidenced by the yeast two-hybrid system and by co-immunoprecipitation in intact cells. Whether apoptotic signals that affect Bcl-2 function result in the inactivation of CPTI and ceramide generation is the topic of ongoing investigation.

These studies point to a role for mitochondria in ceramide-induced apoptosis. Thus ceramide may signal apoptosis by two independent and perhaps coordinately regulated mechanisms: one involving transcription through SAPK/JNK and the other mediated by direct effects on mitochondrial homeostasis. Further work will be required to unravel the interactions of ceramide or ceramide-stimulated PT-inducers with members of the Bcl-2 superfamily.

ANTI-APOPTOTIC SIGNALING THAT REGULATES CERAMIDE-MEDIATED APOPTOSIS

In addition to the tightly regulated pro-apoptotic systems described above, mammalian cells also operate anti-apoptotic mechanisms. These mechanisms include the Bcl-2 system (42, 87, 88), loss of p53 activity (13, 89), activation of NF-κB (90–92), growth factor stimulation (12, 93, 94), and activation of the 1, 2-diacylglycerol (DAG) -protein kinase C (PKC) signaling system (12, 93, 94). Intriguingly, anti- and pro-apoptotic signaling can also be co-regulated by the same stress, as demonstrated for NF-κB activation. In some cells, TNF, ionizing radiation, or daunorubicin activate NF-κB, which signals anti-apoptosis, attenuating the pro-apoptotic response to these stresses (51, 58, 95).

Verheij et al reported that within minutes of exposure, TNF and environmental stresses (UV and ionizing irradiation, heat shock, and oxidative stress) induced ceramide generation and activation of the SAPK/JNK signaling system in primary cultures of bovine endothelial cells and in U937 monoblastic leukemia cells (11). Direct elevation of intracellular ceramide levels by treatment of cells with ceramide analogues or exogenous sphingomyelinase, like stress, markedly activated the SAPK/JNK cascade but not the ERK kinase cascade. Furthermore, disruption of signaling via the SAPK/JNK pathway by overexpression of dominant-negative mutants of SEK1 and c-Jun abrogated TNF-, stress-, and ceramide-induced apoptosis. Based on these data, it was argued that ceramide initiates SAPK/JNK signaling in response to some environmental stresses. This model was confirmed in studies carried out by Spiegel and coworkers (65). Treatment of U937 monoblastic leukemia cells with TNF or ceramide analogues induced SAPK/JNK activation and apoptosis, whereas the lipid second messenger sphingosine-1-phosphate (SPP) activated the ERK cascade and stimulated proliferation. Addition of SPP concomitant with TNF or ceramide analogues resulted in a rapid blockade of signaling through the SAPK/JNK cascade, ERK activation, and inhibition of apoptosis. SPP did not, however, affect TNF-induced ceramide generation, suggesting that transmodulatory inactivation of SAPK/JNK signaling by SPP may block apoptosis.

Investigations of the mechanisms that control ceramide-mediated apoptosis have defined the DAG/PKC signaling system as an anti-apoptotic regulator of multiple elements of the ceramide/SAPK signaling cascade (12, 93, 94). PKC activated by phorbol ester was shown to inhibit radiation-induced sphingomyelin hydrolysis to ceramide in primary cultures of bovine endothelium, thereby defining sphingomyelinase as an upstream checkpoint of the ceramide-mediated pathway of apoptosis. Jarvis et al reported that PKC activation also abrogated apoptosis in response to ceramide analogues, indicating that PKC is also capable of inhibiting apoptosis at sites distal to ceramide generation (94).

Spiegel et al described a mechanism by which PKC may suppress ceramide-mediated apoptosis via SPP and ERK (65). Whereas TNF increased ceramide levels, activation of PKC attenuated this increase, apparently through ceramide de-acylation by ceramidase. Concomitantly, PKC activated sphingosine kinase to phosphorylate the generated sphingosine, yielding sphingosine-1-phosphate (SPP). SPP then served as a second messenger, as described above, activating the anti-apoptotic ERK p42^{MAPK} pathway and a suppressing SAPK/JNK-mediated apoptosis.

Studies on the mechanisms of anti-apoptotic signaling that regulate ceramide-mediated apoptosis collectively indicate that whereas ceramide initiates the apoptotic pathway, it does not commit the cell to the death process. ERK and PKC signaling or Bcl-2 can attenuate the process at multiple checkpoints along the apoptotic signaling pathway. These anti-apoptotic signaling components are likely to be expressed in a cell type–specific manner. This would provide an additional level of control over apoptosis and may determine whether generation of ceramide leads to apoptosis in select tissues.

CONCLUSIONS

The models of apoptotic signaling via ceramide outlined in this review represent an effort to provide a paradigm that unifies the current state of the literature in this rapidly advancing field (Figure 1). The sphingomyelin system represents an ubiquitous mechanism for transmembrane apoptotic signaling. Much of this system remains unknown, and new information is needed to fill in the gaps. It will be especially interesting to unravel the functional interactions between sphingomyelinases and ceramide with caspases in the initiation and execution phases of apoptosis. Resistance to apoptosis plays an important role in tumorigenesis and viral disease. Interference with apoptotic mechanisms, therefore, holds great promise in the management of disease. However, it has become increasingly clear that the apoptotic signaling function of ceramide, like that of caspases and stress-activated protein kinases, is restricted to select tissues and stimuli; therefore, it is important to focus on the issue of tissue- and stimulus-specific action of ceramide. Improved understanding of ceramide action may yield opportunities to target pro- and anti-apoptotic signaling to specific tissues, which might become a valuable therapeutic modality in cancer and other human diseases.

ACKNOWLEDGMENTS

This work was supported in part by grants CA42385 and CA57400 (RK) from the National Institutes of Health, and Kr 810/8-4 and Kr 810/12-1 (MK) from the Deutsche Forschungsgemeinschaft.

Visit the *Annual Reviews* home page at
http://www.AnnualReviews.org.

Literature Cited

1. Pushkareva M, Obeid LM, Hannun YA. 1995. Ceramide: an endogenous regulator of apoptosis and growth suppression. *Immunol. Today* 16:294–97
2. Spiegel S, Foster D, Kolesnick R. 1996. Signal transduction through lipid second messengers. *Curr. Opin. Cell Biol.* 8:159–67
3. Wyllie AH. 1997. Glucocorticoid-induced thymocyte apoptosis is associated with endonuclease activation. *Nature* 284:554–56
4. Raff MC, Barres BA, Burne JF, Coles HS, Ishizaki Y, et al. 1993. Programmed cell death and the control of cell survival: lessons from the nervous system. *Science* 262:695–700
5. Ellis HM, Horvitz HR. 1986. Genetic control of programmed cell death in the nematode *C. elegans*. *Cell* 44:817–29
6. Yuan J, Shaham S, Ledoux S, Ellis HM, Horvitz HR. 1993. The *C. elegans*. cell death gene *ced-3* encodes a protein sim-

ilar to mammalian interleukin-1 beta-converting enzyme. *Cell* 75:641–52
7. Martin SJ, Green DR. 1995. Protease activation during apoptosis: death by a thousand cuts? *Cell* 82:349–52
8. Jarvis WD, Kolesnick RN, Fornari FA, Traylor RS, Gewirtz DA, et al. 1994. Induction of apoptotic DNA damage and cell death by activation of the sphingomyelin pathway. *Proc. Natl. Acad. Sci. USA* 91:73–77
9. Obeid LM, Linardic CM, Karolak LA, Hannun YA. 1993. Programmed cell death induced by ceramide. *Science* 259:1769–71
10. Gulbins E, Bissonnette R, Mahboubi A, Martin S, Nishioka W, et al. 1995. FAS-induced apoptosis is mediated via a ceramide-initiated RAS signaling pathway. *Immunity* 2:341–51
11. Verheij M, Bose R, Lin XH, Yao B, Jarvis WD, et al. 1996. Requirement

for ceramide-initiated SAPK/JNK signalling in stress-induced apoptosis. *Nature* 380:75–79

12. Haimovitz-Friedman A, Kan CC, Ehleiter D, Persaud RS, McLoughlin M, et al. 1994. Ionizing radiation acts on cellular membranes to generate ceramide and initiate apoptosis. *J. Exp. Med.* 180:525–35

13. Santana P, Pena LA, Haimovitz-Friedman A, Martin S, Green D, et al. 1996. Acid sphingomyelinase-deficient human lymphoblasts and mice are defective in radiation-induced apoptosis. *Cell* 86:189–99

14. Fraser A, Evan G. 1996. A license to kill. *Cell* 85:781–84

15. Alnemri ES, Livingston DJ, Nicholson DW, Salvesen G, Thornberry NA, et al. 1996. Human ICE/CED-3 protease nomenclature. *Cell* 87:171

16. Hengartner MO, Horvitz HR. 1994. C. elegans cell survival gene *ced-9* encodes a functional homolog of the mammalian proto-oncogene bcl-2. *Cell* 76:665–76

17. Nagata S. 1997. Apoptosis by death factor. *Cell* 88:355–65

18. Hsu H, Xiong J, Goeddel DV. 1995. The TNF receptor 1-associated protein TRADD signals cell death and NF-κB activation. *Cell* 81:495–504

19. Tartaglia LA, Ayres TM, Wong GH, Goeddel DV. 1993. A novel domain within the 55 kd TNF receptor signals cell death. *Cell* 74:845–53

20. Chinnaiyan AM, Orth K, O'Rourke K, Duan H, Poirier GG, et al. 1996. Molecular ordering of the cell death pathway. Bcl-2 and Bcl-X_L function upstream of the CED-3-like apoptotic proteases. *J. Biol. Chem.* 271:4573–76

21. Boldin MP, Mett IL, Varfolomeev EE, Chumakov I, Shemer Avni Y, et al. 1995. Self-association of the "death domains" of the p55 tumor necrosis factor (TNF) receptor and Fas/APO1 prompts signaling for TNF and Fas/APO1 effects. *J. Biol. Chem.* 270:387–91

22. Boldin MP, Goncharov TM, Goltsev YV, Wallach D. 1996. Involvement of MACH, a novel MORT1/FADD-interacting protease, in Fas/APO-1- and TNF receptor-induced cell death. *Cell* 85:803–15

23. Muzio M, Chinnaiyan AM, Kischkel FC, O'Rourke K, Shevchenko A, et al. 1996. FLICE, a novel FADD-homologous ICE/CED-3-like protease, is recruited to the CD95 (Fas/APO-1) death-inducing signaling complex. *Cell* 85:817–27

24. Wang ZQ, Auer B, Stingl L, Berghammer H, Haidacher D, et al. 1995. Mice lacking ADPRT and poly(ADP-ribosyl)ation de-

velop normally but are susceptible to skin disease. *Genes Dev.* 9:509–20

25. Pronk GJ, Ramer K, Amiri P, Williams LT. 1996. Requirement of an ICE-like protease for induction of apoptosis and ceramide generation by REAPER. *Science* 271:808–10

26. Kuida K, Lippke JA, Ku G, Harding MW, Livingston DJ, et al. 1995. Altered cytokine export and apoptosis in mice deficient in interleukin-1b converting enzyme. *Science* 267:2000–3

27. Kuida K, Zheng TS, Na S, Kuan C, Yang D, et al. 1996. Decreased apoptosis in the brain and premature lethality in CPP32-deficient mice. *Nature* 384:368–72

28. Kyriakis JM, Banerjee P, Nikolakaki E, Dai T, Rubie EA, et al. 1994. The stress-activated protein kinase subfamily of c-Jun kinases. *Nature* 369:156–60

29. Bossy-Wetzel E, Bakiri L, Yaniv M. 1997. Induction of apoptosis by the transcription factor c-Jun. *EMBO J.* 16:1695–709

30. Yang X, Khosravi-Far R, Chang HY, Baltimore D. 1997. Daxx, a novel Fas-binding protein that activates JNK and apoptosis. *Cell* 89:1067–76

31. Xia Z, Dickens M, Raingeaud J, Davis RJ, Greenberg ME. 1995. Opposing effects of ERK and JNK-p38 MAP kinases on apoptosis. *Science* 270:1326–31

32. Liu ZG, Hsu H, Goeddel DV, Karin M. 1996. Dissection of TNF receptor 1 effector functions: JNK activation is not linked to apoptosis while NF-κB activation prevents cell death. *Cell* 87:565–76

33. Butterfeld I, Storey B, Maas L, Heasley LE. 1997. c-Jun NH_2-terminal kinase regulation of the apoptotic response of small cell lung cancer cells to ultrviolet radiation. *J. Biol. Chem.* 272:10110–16

34. Susin SA, Zamzami N, Castedo M, Hirsch T, Marchetti P, et al. 1996. Bcl-2 inhibits the mitochondrial release of an apoptogenic protease. *J. Exp. Med.* 184:1331–41

35. Zamzami N, Susin SA, Marchetti P, Hirsch T, Gomez Monterrey I, et al. 1996. Mitochondrial control of nuclear apoptosis. *J. Exp. Med.* 183:1533–44

36. Kroemer G, Zamzami N, Susin SA. 1997. Mitochondrial control of apoptosis. *Immunol. Today* 18:44–51

37. Susin SA, Zamzami N, Castedo M, Daugas E, Wang HG, et al. 1997. The central executioner of apoptosis: multiple connections between protease activation and mitochondria in Fas/APO-1/CD95 and ceramide-induced apoptosis. *J. Exp. Med.* 186:25–37

38. Yang J, Liu X, Bhalla K, Kim CN, Ibrado AM, et al. 1997. Prevention of apoptosis by

Bcl-2: release of cytochrome *c* from mitochondria blocked. *Science* 275:1129–32

39. Kluck RM, Bossy-Wetzel E, Green DR, Newmeyer DD. 1997. The release of cytochrome *c* from mitochondria: a primary site for Bcl-2 regulation of apoptosis. *Science* 275:1132–36

40. Liu X, Kim CN, Yang J, Jemmerson R, Wang X. 1996. Induction of apoptotic program in cell-free extracts: requirement for dATP and cytochrome *c*. *Cell* 86:147–57

41. Reed JC. 1994. Bcl-2 and the regulation of programmed cell death. *J. Cell Biol.* 124:1–6

42. Yang E, Korsmeyer SJ. 1996. Molecular thanatopsis: a discourse on the BCL2 family and cell death. *Blood* 88:386–401

43. Kroemer G. 1997. The proto-oncogene Bcl-2 and its role in regulating apoptosis. *Nat. Med.* 3:614–20

44. Zha J, Harada H, Yang E, Jockel J, Korsmeyer SJ. 1996. Serine phosphorylation of death agonist BAD in response to survival factor results in binding to 14-3-3 not BCL-X(L). *Cell* 87:619–28

45. Wang HG, Rapp UR, Reed JC. 1996. Bcl-2 targets the protein kinase Raf-1 to mitochondria. *Cell* 87:629–38

46. Merrill AH Jr, Jones DD. 1990. An update of the enzymology and regulation of sphingomyelin metabolism. *Biochim. Biophys. Acta* 1044:1–12

47. Bose R, Verheij M, Haimovitz-Friedman A, Scotto K, Fuks Z, et al. 1995. Ceramide synthase mediates daunorubicin-induced apoptosis: an alternative mechanism for generating death signals. *Cell* 82:405–14

48. Boland MP, Foster D, O'Neill LAJ. 1997. Daunorubicin activates NF-κLB and induces κB-dependent gene expression in HL-60 promyelocytic and Jurkat T lymphoma cells. *J. Biol. Chem.* 272:12952–60

49. Horinouchi K, Erlich S, Perl DP, Ferlinz K, Bisgaier CL, et al. 1995. Acid sphingomyelinase deficient mice: a model of types A and B Niemann-Pick disease. *Nat. Genet.* 10:288–93

50. Liu P, Anderson RG. 1995. Compartmentalized production of ceramide at the cell surface. *J. Biol. Chem.* 270:27179–85

51. Schütze S, Potthoff K, Machleidt T, Berkovic D, Wiegmann K, et al. 1992. TNF activates NF-κB by phosphatidylcholine-specific phospholipase C-induced "acidic" sphingomyelin breakdown. *Cell* 71:765–76

52. Wiegmann K, Schütze S, Machleidt T, Witte D, Kronke M. 1994. Functional dichotomy of neutral and acidic sphingomyelinases in tumor necrosis factor signaling. *Cell* 78:1005–15

53. Cifone MG, Roncaioli P, De Maria R, Camarda G, Santoni A, et al. 1995. Multiple pathways originate at the Fas/APO-1 (CD95) receptor: sequential involvement of phosphatidylcholine-specific phospholipase C and acidic sphingomyelinase in the propagation of the apoptotic signal. *EMBO J.* 14:5859–68

54. Ballou LR, Lauderkind SJ, Rosloniec EF, Raghow R. 1996. Ceramide signalling and the immune response. *Biochim. Biophys. Acta* 1301:273–87

55. Adam D, Wiegmann K, Adam-Klages S, Ruff A, Kronke M. 1996. A novel cytoplasmic domain of the p55 tumor necrosis factor receptor initiates the neutral sphingomyelinase pathway. *J. Biol. Chem.* 271:14617–22

56. Adam-Klages S, Adam D, Wiegmann K, Struve S, Kolanus W, et al. 1996. FAN, a novel WD-repeat protein, couples the p55 TNF-receptor to neutral sphingomyelinase. *Cell* 86:937–47

57. Wallach D. 1997. Cell death induction by TNF: a matter of self control. *Trends Biol. Sci.* 22:107–9

58. Witty JP, Bridgham JT, Johnson AL. 1996. Induction of apoptotic cell death in hen granulosa cells by ceramide. *Endocrinology* 137:5269–77

59. Spiegel S, Merrill AH Jr. 1996. Sphingolipid metabolism and cell growth regulation. *FASEB J.* 10:1388–97

60. Stevens VL, Nimkar S, Jamison WC, Liotta DC, Merrill AH Jr. 1990. Characteristics of the growth inhibition and cytotoxicity of long-chain (sphingoid) bases for Chinese hamster ovary cells: evidence for an involvement of protein kinase C. *Biochim. Biophys. Acta* 1051:37–45

61. Pushkareva M, Chao R, Bielawska A, Merrill AH Jr, Crane HM, et al. 1995. Stereoselectivity of induction of the retinoblastoma gene product (pRb) dephosphorylation by D-erythro-sphingosine supports a role for pRb in growth suppression by sphingosine. *Biochemistry* 34:1885–92

62. Zhang H, Buckley NE, Gibson K, Spiegel S. 1990. Sphingosine stimulates cellular proliferation via a protein kinase C-independent pathway. *J. Biol. Chem.* 265:76–81

63. Coroneos E, Martinez M, McKenna S, Kester M. 1995. Differential regulation of sphingomyelinase and ceramidase activities by growth factors and cytokines. Implications for cellular proliferation and differentiation. *J. Biol. Chem.* 270:23305–9

64. Bernardo K, Hurwitz R, Zenk T, Desnick RJ, Ferlinz K, et al. 1995. Purification,

characterization, and biosynthesis of human acid ceramidase. *J. Biol. Chem.* 270: 11098–102

65. Cuvillier O, Pirianov G, Kleuser B, Vanek PG, Coso OA, et al. 1996. Suppression of ceramide-mediated programmed cell death by sphingosine-1-phosphate. *Nature* 381:800–3

66. Vietor I, Schwenger P, Li W, Schlessinger J, Vilcek J. 1993. Tumor necrosis factor-induced activation and increased tyrosine phosphorylation of mitogen-activated protein (MAP) kinase in human fibroblasts. *J. Biol. Chem.* 268:18994–99

67. Mathias S, Dressler KA, Kolesnick RN. 1991. Characterization of a ceramide-activated protein kinase: stimulation by tumor necrosis factor α. *Proc. Natl. Acad. Sci. USA* 88:10009–13

68. Dobrowsky RT, Kamibayashi C, Mumby MC, Hannun YA. 1993. Ceramide activates heterotrimeric protein phosphatase 2A. *J. Biol. Chem.* 268:15523–30

69. Müller G, Ayoub M, Storz P, Rennecke J, Fabbro D, et al. 1995. PKC ζ is a molecular switch in signal transduction of TNF-α, bifunctionally regulated by ceramide and arachidonic acid. *EMBO J.* 14:1961–69

70. Lozano J, Berra E, Municio MM, Diaz Meco MT, Dominguez I, et al. 1994. Protein kinase C ζ isoform is critical for κB-dependent promoter activation by sphingomyelinase. *J. Biol. Chem.* 269:19200–2

71. Venable ME, Blobe GC, Obeid LM. 1994. Identification of a defect in the phospholipase D/diacylglycerol pathway in cellular senescence. *J. Biol. Chem.* 269:26040–44

72. Yang Z, Costanzo M, Golde DW, Kolesnick RN. 1993. Tumor necrosis factor activation of the sphingomyelin pathway signals nuclear factor kappa B translocation in intact HL-60 cells. *J. Biol. Chem.* 268:20520–23

73. Zhang J, Alter N, Reed JC, Borner C, Obeid LM, et al. 1996. Bcl-2 interrupts the ceramide-mediated pathway of cell death. *Proc. Natl. Acad. Sci. USA* 93:5325–28

74. Smyth MJ, Perry DK, Zhang J, Poirier GG, Hannun YA, et al. 1996. prICE: a downstream target for ceramide-induced apoptosis and for the inhibitory action of Bcl-2. *Biochem. J.* 316:25–28

75. Zhang Y, Yao B, Delikat S, Bayoumy S, Lin XH, et al. 1997. Kinase suppressor of Ras is ceramide-activated protein kinase. *Cell* 89:63–72

76. Fishbein JD, Dobrowsky RT, Bielawska A, Garrett S, Hannun YA. 1993. Ceramide-mediated growth inhibition and CAPP are conserved in *Saccharomyces cerevisiae*. *J. Biol. Chem.* 268:9255–61

77. Nickels JT, Broach JR. 1996. A ceramide-activated protein phosphatase mediates ceramide-induced G1 arrest of *Saccharomyces cerevisiae*. *Genes Dev.* 10:382–94

78. Huwiler A, Brunner J, Hummel R, Vervoordeldonk M, Stabel S, et al. 1996. Ceramide-binding and activation defines protein kinase c-Raf as a ceramide-activated protein kinase. *Proc. Natl. Acad. Sci. USA* 93:6959–63

79. Chinnaiyan AM, Tepper CG, Seldin MF, O'Rourke K, Kischkel FC, et al. 1996. FADD/MORT1 is a common mediator of CD95 (Fas/APO-1) and tumor necrosis factor receptor-induced apoptosis. *J. Biol. Chem.* 271:4961–65

80. Devary Y, Gottlieb RA, Smeal T, Karin M. 1992. The mammalian ultraviolet response is triggered by activation of Src tyrosine kinases. *Cell* 71:1081–91

81. Rosette C, Karin M. 1996. Ultraviolet light and osmotic stress: activation of the JNK cascade through multiple growth factor and cytokine receptors. *Science* 274:1194–97

82. Emoto Y, Manome Y, Meinhardt G, Kisaki H, Kharbanda S, et al. 1995. Proteolytic activation of protein kinase C delta by an ICE-like protease in apoptotic cells. *EMBO J.* 14:6148–56

83. Pastorino JG, Simbula G, Yamamoto K, Glascott PA Jr, Rothman RJ, et al. 1996. The cytotoxicity of tumor necrosis factor depends on induction of the mitochondrial permeability transition. *J. Biol. Chem.* 271:29792–98

84. Martin SJ, Takayama SJ, McGahon AJ, Miyashita T, Corbeil J, et al. 1995. Inhibition of ceramide-induced apoptosis by Bcl-2. *Cell Death Diff.* 2:253–57

85. Arora AS, Jones BJ, Patel TC, Bronk SF, Gores GJ. 1997. Ceramide induces hepatocyte cell death through disruption of mitochondrial function in the rat. *Hepatology* 25:958–63

86. Paumen MB, Ishida Y, Muramatsu M, Yamamoto M, Honjo T. 1997. Inhibition of carnitine palmitoyltransferase I augments sphingolipid synthesis and palmitate-induced apoptosis. *J. Biol. Chem.* 272: 3324–29

87. Korsmeyer SJ, Yin XM, Oltvai ZN, Veis Novack DJ, Linette GP. 1995. Reactive oxygen species and the regulation of cell death by the Bcl-2 gene family. *Biochim. Biophys. Acta* 1271:63–66

88. Gajewski TF, Thompson CB. 1996. Apoptosis meets signal transduction: elimination of a BAD influence. *Cell* 87:589–92

89. Chen M, Quintans J, Fuks Z, Thompson C, Kufe DW, et al. 1995. Suppression of Bcl-2 messenger RNA production may mediate

apoptosis after ionizing radiation, tumor necrosis factor alpha, and ceramide. *Cancer Res.* 55:991–94

90. Beg AA, Baltimore D. 1996. An essential role for NF-κB in preventing TNF-α-induced cell death. *Science* 274:782–84

91. Wang CY, Mayo MW, Baldwin AS Jr. 1996. TNF- and cancer therapy-induced apoptosis: potentiation by inhibition of NF-κB. *Science* 274:784–87

92. Van Antwerp DJ, Martin SJ, Kafri T, Green DR, Verma IM. 1996. Suppression of TNF-α-induced apoptosis by NF-κB. *Science* 274:787–89

93. Haimovitz-Friedman A, Balaban N, McLoughlin M, Ehleiter D, Michaeli J, et al. 1994. Protein kinase C mediates basic fibroblast growth factor protection of endothelial cells against radiation-induced apoptosis. *Cancer Res.* 54:2591–97

94. Jarvis WD, Fornari FA Jr, Browning JL, Gewirtz DA, Kolesnick RN, et al. 1994. Attenuation of ceramide-induced apoptosis by diglyceride in human myeloid leukemia cells. *J. Biol. Chem.* 269:31685–92

95. Li P, Allen H, Banerjee S, Franklin S, Herzog L, et al. 1995. Mice deficient in IL-1b-converting enzyme are defective in production of mature IL-1b and resistant to endotoxic shock. *Cell* 80:401–11

Annu. Rev. Physiol. 1998. 60:667–87

A VIEW OF SUR/$K_{IR}6.X$, K_{ATP} CHANNELS

A. P. Babenko, L. Aguilar-Bryan,[#] and J. Bryan**

Departments of *Cell Biology and [#]Medicine, Baylor College of Medicine, Houston, Texas 77030; e-mail: jbryan@bcm.tmc.edu

KEY WORDS: potassium channel, inward rectifier, sulfonylureas, KCO, ATP, ADP, ATPase, hyperinsulinism, cardioprotection

ABSTRACT

ATP-sensitive potassium channels, termed K_{ATP} channels, link the electrical activity of cell membranes to cellular metabolism. These channels are heteromultimers of sulfonylurea receptor (SUR) and $K_{IR}6.x$ subunits associated with a 1:1 stoichiometry as a tetramer $(SUR/K_{IR}6.x)_4$. $K_{IR}6.x$ forms the pores, whereas SUR regulates their activity. Changes in $[ATP]_i$ and $[ADP]_i$ gate the channel. The diversity of K_{ATP} channels results from the assembly of SUR and $K_{IR}6.x$ subtypes. $K_{IR}6.1$-based channels differ from $K_{IR}6.2$ channels mainly by their smaller unitary conductance. SUR1- and SUR2-based channels are distinguished by their differential sensitivity to sulfonylureas, whereas SUR2A-based channels are distinguished from SUR2B channels by their differential sensitivity to diazoxide. Mutations that result in the loss of K_{ATP} channels in pancreatic β-cells have been identified in SUR1 and $K_{IR}6.2$. These mutations lead to familial hyperinsulinism. Understanding the mutations in SUR and $K_{IR}6.x$ is allowing insight into how these channels respond to nucleotides, sulfonylureas, and potassium channel openers, KCOs.

HOW ARE K_{ATP} CHANNELS DEFINED?

At one time, application of ATP to the intracellular face of an excised patch was sufficient to define an ATP-sensitive potassium channel or K_{ATP} channel (1–3). However, this phenomenological definition has been enriched, and this family of channels is now defined by their single-channel current properties, pattern of regulation by nucleotides, and a rich and distinctive pharmacology. K_{ATP} channels are weakly inwardly rectifying K^+-selective channels. A prominent

667

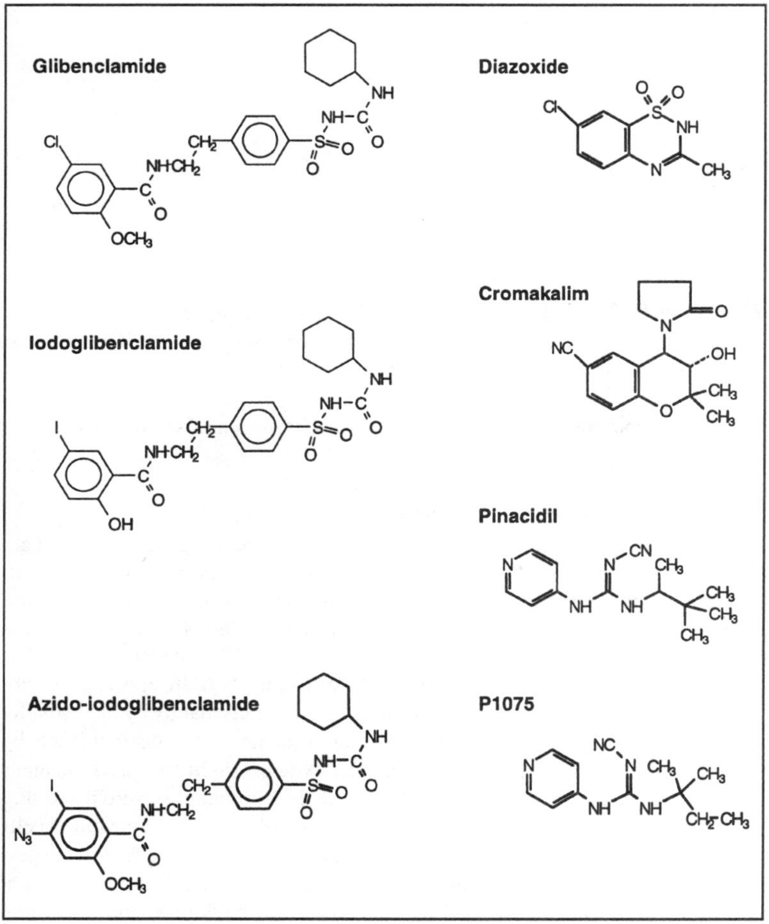

Figure 1 Chemical structures for the K_{ATP} channel inhibitors and openers referred to in the text.

feature of their activity is a bursting behavior, and in excised patches, the application of ATP, independent of Mg^{2+}, results in a reduction in the mean open time by prolonging the interburst intervals and shortening the burst duration (4). ADP, in the presence of Mg^{2+}, stimulates ATP-inhibited channels (5, 6). Two pharmacological criteria have been used to define K_{ATP} channels: inhibition by sulfonylureas such as tolbutamide and glibenclamide, and activation by a diverse group of compounds collectively referred to as potassium channel openers (KCOs) (see Figure 1). Channel subtypes can be classified on the basis of their qualitative and quantitative response to these inhibitors and openers.

With the structural definition of K$_{ATP}$ channels now available, understanding of the diversity of K$_{ATP}$ channel subtypes is possible. This review covers selected information on the structure and regulation of K$_{ATP}$ channels reported since their reconstitution from cloned subunits, sulfonylurea receptors (SUR) and K$_{IR}$6.x, members of the weak inward rectifier family.

HOW DO K$_{ATP}$ CHANNELS WORK?

The activity of K$_{ATP}$ channels is affected by nucleotide levels, thus these channels couple membrane conductance to metabolism. Opening of K$_{ATP}$ channels shifts the membrane potential toward the equilibrium potential for potassium ions, near -80 mV for physiological asymmetric $[K^+]_o/[K^+]_i$. K$_{ATP}$ channels likely regulate the electrical activity of different cells by either controlling the resting membrane potential or modulating the action potential. In pancreatic β-cells, where their physiological role is best understood, their opening sets the resting potential, and their closure depolarizes the plasma membrane. Because pancreatic β-cells are relatively small cells with a high input impedance, opening of a small number of K$_{ATP}$ channels will set their resting membrane potential. Mutations in the channel subunits result in familial hyperinsulinism or persistent hyperinsulinemic hypoglycemia of infancy (PHHI, OMIM 256450). The phenotype of this disorder of newborns and infants, an inappropriately high rate of insulin secretion despite profound hypoglycemia, results from a loss of K$_{ATP}$ channel activity that resets the resting membrane potential to a more depolarized value within the voltage-window for steady state L-type Ca^{2+} channel currents. The ensuing persistent Ca^{2+} influx maintains an increased $[Ca^{2+}]_i$, which drives insulin secretion.

In cardiac and skeletal myocytes and in vascular smooth muscle and neurons, the question of whether K$_{ATP}$ channels are active under normal physiological conditions remains controversial. However, it is accepted that K$_{ATP}$ channels can be opened, even in isolated quiescent myocytes, by hypoxic or ischemic conditions, and their outward current is sufficient to shorten the action potential (7–9). This reduces the influx of Ca^{2+}, which decreases contractile force thus reducing the consumption of ATP and protecting the cell during periods of metabolic impairment. In smooth muscle cells, which have a high input resistance similar to β-cells, a small number of K$_{ATP}$ channels can influence vascular tone. In neurons, opening of K$_{ATP}$ channels reduces the frequency of action potentials, again serving a protective function.

K_{ATP} CHANNELS ARE HETEROMULTIMERS

Work in the past few years has demonstrated that K_{ATP} channels are large heteromultimers composed of two quite dissimilar types of subunits. One type, $K_{IR}6.x$, is a traditional channel protein belonging to the inwardly rectifying potassium channel superfamily (10, 11). The proteins in the K_{IR} family have been predicted by hydropathy analysis to have two transmembrane spanning helices flanking a segment with a -Gly-Phe-Gly- (or -Gly-Tyr-Gly-) sequence like that identified in other K^+ selective channels (see 12 for a review). The second subunit type is referred to as a sulfonylurea receptor (SUR) because the purification and cloning of the founding member of the family was based on its affinity for glibenclamide (13). SURs are members of the ATP-binding cassette (ABC) or transport ATPase superfamily with multiple transmembrane domains and two nucleotide-binding folds. The SURs are part of the multidrug resistance-associated (MRP) branch of the ABC superfamily because they have a highly hydrophobic N-terminal extension, which is predicted from hydropathy analysis to have additional transmembrane domains. The topology of SURs has not been determined experimentally. The most recent topology proposed for the MRP subfamily, based on multisequence alignments and hydropathy analysis, predicts 11 transmembrane helices before the first nucleotide-binding fold, NBF1, then a second region with six predicted transmembrane helices followed by a second nucleotide-binding fold, NBF2 (14). We have reviewed this area previously (15).

Cloning and expression of the β-cell SUR demonstrated that SUR1 was sufficient to reconstitute high-affinity sulfonylurea binding, but not channel activity (13). The co-expression of SUR1 with $K_{IR}6.2$ generated K^+-selective channels that could be activated by metabolic poisoning or by the potassium channel opener diazoxide, whereas expression of $K_{IR}6.2$ alone generated no channel activity (11). Whole-cell channel activity for the hamster SUR1 plus mouse $K_{IR}6.2$ channel was inhibited half maximally by sulfonylureas such as glibenclamide (1.8 nM) and tolbutamide (32 μM) at concentrations expected for the pancreatic β-cell channel. ATP inhibited channel activity in inside-out patches with an apparent IC_{50} of ≈ 10 μM (11); channels partially inhibited by ATP are stimulated by ADP in the presence of Mg^{2+} (16). These results have been confirmed (17, 18) and show that the reconstituted channels are equivalent to native β-cell K_{ATP} channels in their nucleotide regulation, biophysical properties, and pharmacology.

Several lines of evidence indicate that the $K_{IR}6.x$ subunits form the conduction pathway of K_{ATP} channels, as might be expected from the family lineage. It must be stressed however, that $K_{IR}6.x$ subunits expressed alone are silent. The reasons for this are not apparent, but to date the formation or reconstitution of conductances with all the properties that characterize K$_{ATP}$ channels has required co-expression of both subunit types.

SUR AND K$_{IR}$6.X GENES COME IN PAIRS

The mapping of SUR and K$_{IR}$6.x genes to human chromosomes has shown that they are paired. SUR1 (OMIM 600509) and K$_{IR}$6.2 (OMIM 600937) are on the short arm of chromosome 11 at 11p15.1. Long-range PCR put the distance between the 3'-end of the SUR1 gene and the 5'-end of the K$_{IR}$6.2 gene at $\approx$4500 basepairs (11, 19). Sequencing of an 86-kb genomic DNA fragment from chromosome region 11p14.3, which begins in the large intron immediately before exon 17 of SUR1, refines this distance to 4900 basepairs (Evans et al, Genbank Accession No.U90583). The SUR2 (OMIM 601439) gene, at 12p11.12 (20), is paired with K$_{IR}$6.1 (the KCNJ8 gene, OMIM 600935) at 12p11.23 (10). The distance between these two genes is too large for successful PCR, as was done for SUR1 and K$_{IR}$6.2, so the exact distance is not certain. Why these genes are clustered into pairs is unknown; we speculate they may have arisen from a fused ancestral gene that has been split and duplicated. It will be intriguing to discover if the paired subunits are coordinately regulated, although this seems unlikely because, as described below, the K$_{IR}$6.2 subunits appear to pair with both SUR1 and SUR2 subunits expressed in different tissues.

Mapping of the intron-exon boundaries indicates the human SUR1 and SUR2 genes are quite similar (15). The SUR1 gene has 39 exons spanning approximately 100 kb of genomic DNA. It specifies a protein of either 1581 or 1582 amino acids depending on usage of an alternative splice site at the 5' boundary of exon 17, which results in the inclusion of an additional serine residue. It is not clear if there are functional differences between channels formed with the 1581 versus the 1582 amino acid receptors. The SUR2 gene has 38 exons, the lower number the result of a nearly perfect deletion of the corresponding 18th exon of SUR1. The SUR2 gene has been shown to specify two major isoforms, designated SUR2A and SUR2B, which result from differential usage of two 135-bp exons specifying the C-terminal 45 amino acids of the two proteins. Naming of SURs has been chronological in terms of their co-expression with K$_{IR}$6.2 and demonstration that they form K$_{ATP}$ channels. Fortuitously, the designation also corresponds to the order of the two alternative exons in the human genome with 2A being 5' of 2B. RT-PCR from different tissues has indicated that the SUR2 gene may specify additional splice variants. Chutkow et al (20) have cloned a variant of SUR2A from skeletal muscle, designated SUR2AΔ14, which misses exon 14. We have identified two other deletion variants, SUR2Δ17 and SUR2Δ17,18, but have not determined whether they have the 2A or 2B last exon. Their relative abundance appears to be small as determined by RT-PCR, and their functionality has not been determined.

K_{ATP} CHANNELS ASSEMBLE AS TETRAMERS $(SUR/K_{IR}6.x)_4$

The overall structure of the $SUR1/K_{IR}6.2$ channel has been studied in some detail (21). Two lines of evidence indicate that $K_{IR}6.x$ subunits form the conducting pore. In other K_{IR}-type channels, mutations in a specific residue of M2, the second predicted transmembrane helix, have been shown to alter the degree of inward rectification. For example, substitution of an aspartate for an asparagine at position 171 in $K_{IR}1.1$ (ROMK1) greatly reduces the conductance at positive potentials, thus changing the normally weakly rectifying $K_{IR}1.1$ channel into a strong inward rectifier (22, 23). This property is dependent on the presence of Mg^{2+} or polyamines such as spermine at the intracellular face of the channel, and asparagine or aspartic acid are thought to form part of a binding site for these molecules within the channel. The equivalent asparagine → aspartic acid substitution at position 160, N160D, in $K_{IR}6.2$ also converts $SUR1/K_{IR}6.2$ channels to strong rectifiers, implying this residue in M2 is part of the conduction pathway (21). A second line of evidence has come from the observation that truncations ($\Delta C18$, $\Delta C26$, and $\Delta C36$) from the C terminus of $K_{IR}6.2$ result in formation of a potassium conductance in the absence of a SUR (24). In other words, truncation of the C terminus of $K_{IR}6.2$ eliminates the need for a SUR to activate $K_{IR}6.2$. The result indicates that $K_{IR}6.2$ is sufficient to form an inwardly rectifying pore with the same conductance as wild-type channels. A corollary of the conclusion that $K_{IR}6.2$ forms the channel pore is that, as with other members of the K_{IR} subfamily, four subunits are probably used.

The requirement for co-expression of SUR and $K_{IR}6.x$ to form a K_{ATP} channel strongly implies that the two subunits are physically associated. Other ABC proteins, particularly the cystic fibrosis transmembrane conductance regulator (CFTR), have been suggested to regulate outwardly rectifying chloride channels (ORCC) by releasing ATP, which then acts through a purinergic receptor. Al-Awqati (25) suggested a similar mechanism for SUR regulation of K_{IR} channels when reviewing this area. However, regulation through a second messenger does not appear to be necessary because the direct association of SUR1 and $K_{IR}6.2$ has been established several ways (21). Co-expression of the two subunits was shown to affect the glycosylation of the receptor and to result in co-photolabeling of both SUR1 and $K_{IR}6.2$ by ^{125}I-azido-iodoglibenclamide, although $K_{IR}6.2$ did not interact directly with this drug. Chromatography of the photolabeled multimers on wheat germ agarose showed that SUR1 and $K_{IR}6.2$ were associated and demonstrated a preferential association of the inward rectifier subunit with a complex glycosylated form of the receptor versus a core glycosylated form. Expression of SUR1 alone produced predominantly the core glycosylated species, implying that efficient trafficking of the receptor requires K_{IR}6.2. The mass of the multimer formed by K_{IR}6.2 and complex glycosylated SUR1 was estimated by sucrose gradient sedimentation to be 950 kDa, consistent with an overall stoichiometry of (SUR1/K_{IR}6.2)$_4$.

The (SUR1/K_{IR}6.2)$_4$ stoichiometry was supported and related to functional channels by engineering fusion constructs that encoded proteins with fixed 1:1, SUR1 $\sim K_{IR}$6.2; and 1:2, SUR1 $\sim (K_{IR}$6.2)$_2$ ratios (21). Expression of the 1:1 fusion proteins produced K_{ATP} channels with properties similar to native channels indicating a 1:1 stoichiometry was sufficient. Expression of the 1:2 fusion proteins did not produce active channels, but co-expression with SUR1 monomers rescued channel activity, implying a 1:1 stoichiometry was also necessary. Additional experiments, employing 1:2 fusion proteins, where the fused K_{IR} subunits carried the N160D mutation, were done to determine if the pore was a K_{IR}6.2 tetramer. Co-expression of a mixture of 1:2 fusion constructs encoding strong SUR1 $\sim (K_{IR}$6.2N160D)$_2$ and weak SUR1 $\sim (K_{IR}$6.2)$_2$ rectifiers with SUR1 produced three species of channels; the expected parental strong and weak rectifiers plus a heterologous channel with intermediate rectification properties. Assembly of the heterologous channel demonstrated that two 1:2 fusion proteins (four K_{IR}6.2 subunits) were required to form the pore. Figure 2 illustrates the predicted topology of the subunits and shows the proposed channel model derived from the stoichiometry experiments (21).

SUBUNIT COMBINATIONS DETERMINE CHANNEL TYPE

The specific properties of a K_{ATP} channel subtype are determined by its subunit composition. Study in this area is in its infancy and promises to be fertile for research and development of specific compounds targeted to specific channel subtypes. Tables 1 and 2 summarize published properties of the K_{ATP} channel subtypes, and we briefly describe some of them below. A point-for-point quantitative comparison between native and recombinant K_{ATP} channel subtypes is impossible at this time because the characterizations of some of them are preliminary.

SUR1/K_{IR}6.1

Co-expression of this pair of subunits produces potassium channels that can be activated by metabolic inhibition and by diazoxide. Single-channel recordings have proven difficult to obtain because channel rundown is extremely rapid. Current noise analysis, which could yield the magnitude of the unitary

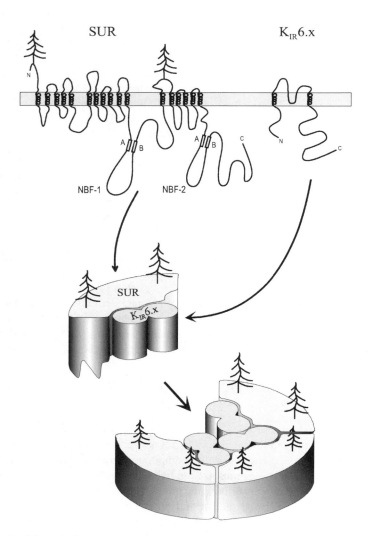

Figure 2 Schematic illustration of the predicted topologies of SUR and $K_{IR}6.x$ subunits and the assembly of these subunits into a K_{ATP} channel. The 17 transmembrane domain model proposed by Tusnady et al (14) is given. NBF-1 and 2 represent the two nucleotide-binding folds with Walker A and B consensus motifs. *N* and *C* indicate the N and C termini of the proteins. The *trees* indicate the positions of the two known glycosylation sites in SUR1. The drawing is not intended to imply any specific shape or conformation for the receptor or the channel pore.

Table 1   Native and recombinant K$_{ATP}$ channels

Type	Subunits	Conductance (pS)[a]		ATP (μM)		Reference
		Native[b]	Recomb	Native[b]	Recomb	
β-cell/neuronal	SUR1/K$_{IR}$6.2	50–65	69–73	10–20	8–10	11
Cardiac	SUR2A/K$_{IR}$6.2	80	79	17–100	100	50
Skeletal	SUR2A/K$_{IR}$6.2	74	79	135	100	50
Smooth Muscle						
K$_{ATP}$	SUR2B/K$_{IR}$6.2	80	80	53	—	60
K$_{NDP}$[c]	SUR2B/K$_{IR}$6.1	15–24[d]	33	activates	activates	53

[a]Quasi-symmetrical high K$^+$ (135–145 mM) at negative potential except where noted.
[b]Values for native channels taken from (94).
[c]See reference (56).
[d][K$^+$]$_o$ = 60 mM; [K$^+$]$_i$ = 130 mM. We calculated the channel conductance (γ) at fixed high [K$^+$]$_i$ assuming that it is a function of [K$^+$]$_o$, as shown for the cardiac K$_{ATP}$ channel (95). For standard quasi-symmetrical conditions, [K$^+$]$_o$ = [K$^+$]$_i$ = 145 mM, γ would be 18–30 pS, slightly lower than single-channel conductance reported for the SUR2B/K$_{IR}$6.1 channel (53).

current, has not been carried out. It is not clear whether this pair is physiologically relevant.

SUR1/K$_{IR}$6.2

This combination of subunits forms the classical β-cell type K$_{ATP}$ channel originally described by Cook & Hales (2). This combination is activated by metabolic inhibition and diazoxide and is sensitive to sulfonylureas at low concentrations (IC$_{50}$ near 1 nM for glibenclamide). This channel subtype has been identified in brain and various neuroendocrine cells using pharmacological (26–31), biochemical (32), electrophysiological (for example, see 33–38), in situ hybridization (39), and drug localization (40–45) methods. The proof that both SUR1 and K$_{IR}$6.2 form this channel subtype is based on reconstitution studies (11), but more critically on the demonstration that mutations in either subunit cause loss of β-cell K$_{ATP}$ channel activity in individuals with familial

Table 2   Native and recombinant K$_{ATP}$ channels—pharmacology

Subunits	Glibenclamide		Potassium channel openers[a]		Reference
	Native[b]	Recomb	Native[b] (Diaz/Pin/Crom[c])	Recomb (Diaz/Pin/Crom[c])	
SUR1/K$_{IR}$6.2	IC$_{50}$ <10 nM	IC$_{50}$ <10 nM	20–100/high/high	65 μM EC$_{50/high/high}$	11
SUR2A/K$_{IR}$6.2	IC$_{50}$ low μM	IC$_{50}$ ~1.2 μM	No/high/high	No/30 μM/30 μM	50
SUR2B/K$_{IR}$6.2	20 μM inhibits	1 μM inhibits	20–100 μM/low/low	200 μM/100 μM/NA	60
SUR2B/K$_{IR}$6.1	25 nM[d]	3 μM inhibits	NA/100 μM/NA	NA/100 mM/NA	53

[a]No indicates inhibition, low indicates activation at low (μM), high indicates activation at high (μM).
[b]Values for native channels taken from (94).
[c]Diaz, diazoxide; Pin, pinacidil; Crom, cromakalim (See Figure 1).
[d]Taken from (56).

hyperinsulinism (46–48). Studies on the reconstituted channels indicate they have all of the essential properties of native channels.

SUR2A/K_{IR}6.1

Interestingly, co-expression of this pair of subunits has failed to induce K^+ conductance that can be activated by metabolic inhibition. Novel channel activity could not be detected by $^{86}Rb^+$ efflux methods (49) or by using patch-clamp recordings from inside-out patches, which raised the possibility that this combination is a creation of molecular biology.

SUR2A/K_{IR}6.2

The SUR2A/K_{IR}6.2 pair was the second K_{ATP} channel subtype to be reconstituted (50). The single-channel conductance was the same as the β-cell channel conductance, but the bursting pattern was similar to that seen for cardiac K_{ATP} channels (4, 15). The IC_{50} for ATP inhibition was approximately 10-fold higher than for the β-cell channel, and the IC_{50} for glibenclamide inhibition was nearly 100-fold higher than for SUR2A/K_{IR}6.2. The SUR2A/K_{IR}6.2 pair was insensitive to diazoxide, but was activated by cromakalim and pinacidil, as observed for native K_{ATP} channels (50). Northern analysis indicates SUR2A mRNA is present in cardiac tissue (50) as is the K_{IR}6.2 message (11). Absent the kind of genetic evidence available for the SUR1/K_{IR}6.2 pair, the tentative conclusion is that SUR2A/K_{IR}6.2 forms the cardiac type K_{ATP} channel, and perhaps the skeletal muscle type K_{ATP} channel, as well. The SUR2A/K_{IR}6.2 channel is presumably the cardiac K_{ATP} channel originally described by Trube & Hescheler (1) and by Noma (3) and possibly the skeletal muscle channel characterized by Standen & Stanfield (51, 52).

SUR2B/K_{IR}6.1

Co-expression of this pair of subunits (53) generates a small conductance K^+ channel similar to that described by Kajioka et al (54, 55), Beech et al (56), and Kamouchi & Kitamura (57) in isolated smooth muscle cells from rat and rabbit portal vein. The unitary conductance of the reconstituted SUR2B/K_{IR}6.1 channel, 33 pS, is lower than that of the K_{IR}6.2 channels. The inward rectification of the SUR2B/K_{IR}6.1 channels, derived from single-channel data in the presence of Mg^{2+}, appears to be markedly weaker than for the K_{IR}6.2-based channels. ATP in the presence of Mg^{2+} appears to be required to maintain these channels in an operational state, but ATP, at physiological concentrations, does not inhibit their activity significantly. Thus it is questionable whether this channel should be classified as a K_{ATP} channel. We have included it here because it appears to contain SUR2B. The SUR2B/K_{IR}6.1 channels are activated by nucleotide diphosphates (GDP and ADP); Beech et al (56) have referred to the native channels as nucleotide diphosphate-dependent K channels (KNDP).

The native channel was inhibited by glibenclamide (56), and application of the KCOs (pinacidil, lemakalim, and nicorandil) induced burst-like openings in cell-attached patches (57). The reported IC_{50} for inhibition of the small conductance channel by glibenclamide is surprisingly low (56, 58), $K_i \approx$ 20–25 nM, in the range usually associated with SUR1. Kovacs & Nelson (59) have reported a binding constant of $\approx$10 nM in canine aortic smooth muscle membranes. These values need to be confirmed to determine whether this feature of the SUR2B receptor represents a novel isoform or splice variant, or is due to the presence of SUR1. In addition, further analysis is needed to determine if the nucleoside diphosphate requirement for activation is a function of the SUR or of K_{IR}6.1.

SUR2B/K_{IR}6.2

Co-expression of SUR2B with K_{IR}6.2 produces an ATP-sensitive potassium channel that is activated by diazoxide and pinacidil (60), similarly to another type of K_{ATP} channel identified in vascular smooth muscle (see 61 for a review). RT-PCR indicates that SUR2B is widely distributed, consistent with this conclusion. The SUR2B/K_{IR}6.2 channel is inhibited by ATP and glibenclamide in isolated patches. Detailed pharmacological studies are needed on the SUR2B/K_{IR}6.x channels to sort out their qualitative and quantitative differences in response to K_{ATP} channel blockers and openers and to determine if these can be exploited for therapeutic purposes.

ATP, ADP, SULFONYLUREAS, AND KCOs

The general conclusion from reconstitution studies on SUR/K_{IR}6.x channels is that their potassium selectivity, inward rectification, and unitary conductance are determined by the K_{IR}6.x subunit, whereas the nucleotide sensitivity and pharmacology depend on the SUR. A hallmark of K_{ATP} channels is the inhibition of their activity by ATP; yet, how this inhibition occurs and the role of ATP in regulation of channel activity is not understood and is the subject of current controversy (see section on truncated channels below). Answers to the questions of the number of binding sites, their location, and which sites are physiologically relevant have become more accessible with the discovery that the SUR is an ATP-binding protein with nucleotide-binding folds that could act and likely function as ATP/ADP sensors. This issue has become somewhat more complex with the observation that expression of truncated K_{IR}6.2 molecules, for example, K_{IR}6.2ΔC26, will form ATP-inhibited potassium channels in the absence of a SUR (see below).

ATP and ADP have multiple effects on K_{ATP} channels. These effects can be divided into at least three categories: inhibition, refreshment, and stimulation.

The application of ATP, with or without Mg^{2+}, to the intracellular face of excised patches inhibits K_{ATP} channels. One puzzling aspect of this inhibition was the finding that the estimated IC_{50} or K_i values were quite low (between 10 and 100 μM for the SUR1/$K_{IR}6.2$ and SUR2A/$K_{IR}6.2$ channels, respectively); values that predicted full inhibition at the cytosolic $[ATP]_i$ level. In some reports, the effect of MgATP is weaker than ATP^{4-}, and Ashcroft & Kakei (62), for example, advanced the argument that only unliganded ATP^{4-} could interact with K_{ATP} channels. Because a significant fraction of ATP is liganded at the intracellular free Mg^{2+} concentration (0.5–1 mM) (see 63 and 64 for reviews), this argument conveniently reduces the effective concentration of inhibitory nucleotide to a value closer to its IC_{50}, which would allow variation in ATP to serve as a regulator. However, Findlay, for example, notes that ATP^{4-} inhibits channel activity, but that application of the same total concentration of ATP with magnesium enhances inhibition (65).

When K_{ATP} channels are put into ATP-free solution they open, but then rundown or lose their activity, which can be restored or refreshed by a brief application of mM concentrations of MgATP. This process can be likened to switching the channel from a nonoperational to an operational state. Nonhydrolyzable analogues, or hydrolyzable nucleotides without Mg^{2+} or Mn^{2+}, do not support this transition to an operational state. Possible explanations for the biochemical basis for the transition include phosphorylation-dephosphorylation (see 66, 67, but also 68–71 for another view), uncoupling of the channel from the actin cytoskeleton (71), and hydrolysis of anionic phospholipids proposed to stabilize the channel in the operational state (72, 73). No consensus exists on whether one or all of these mechanisms is critical, or even if the Mg^{2+}-requiring ATP-effect is directly on channel subunits or on actin filament stability. Understanding this aspect of regulation will be crucial for detailed single-channel analysis of K_{ATP} channels and might provide insight into how channel activity is regulated by coupling to various hormone receptors (74–81).

The application of ADP and many other nucleoside diphosphates (NDPs) to K_{ATP} channels, in the absence of Mg^{2+}, also inhibited their activity, whereas MgADP stimulated activity and could activate channels pre-inhibited by ATP. These observations led to the view that the ATP/ADP ratio is critical for regulation of K_{ATP} channel activity (5, 6). In pancreatic β-cells, where K_{ATP} channels set the resting membrane potential, increased glucose metabolism was proposed to reduce $[ADP]_i$ and increase $[ATP]_i$. Both changes are expected to reduce K_{ATP} channel activity and lead to membrane depolarization, which would activate voltage-gated Ca^{2+} channels and initiate exocytosis of insulin granules. Direct measurements of changes in the ATP/ADP ratio at different glucose concentrations are difficult to make, but several reports in β-cells (82–84) and cardiomyocytes (85) support this general model. The discovery that mutations in SUR1 and K_{IR}6.2 cause familial hyperinsulinism has also provided strong support for the critical role of K_{ATP} channels in regulation of insulin secretion. Pancreatic β-cells from newborns with this disorder lack K_{ATP} channel activity, have a resting membrane potential near -35 mV, show steady state voltage-gated Ca^{2+} channel activity, and have an elevated $[Ca^{2+}]_i$, which results in persistent insulin release (19, 86).

The view that the ATP/ADP ratio is important for controlling K_{ATP} channels implies that fluctuations in ATP and ADP are involved or likely required for regulation of K_{ATP} channel activity. Whether this is correct is uncertain. Mutations in the conserved Walker A motif, -Gly-x-x-Gly-x-Gly-Lys-(Ser/Thr)-, which forms part of the phosphate-binding pocket, have been shown to produce K_{ATP} channels that are inhibited by ATP, but are no longer stimulated by MgADP (87). This uncoupling of ATP inhibition from activation by MgADP is physiologically relevant because other mutations in the second nucleotide-binding fold of SUR1, e.g. the Gly $\rightarrow$ Arg change at position 1479 (16), have the same effect, which results in familial hyperinsulinism. Co-expression of $SUR1_{G1479R}$ with wild-type K_{IR}6.2 in produced channels that were inhibited by ATP with nearly the same IC_{50} as native or wild-type reconstituted channels, but they were not activated by MgADP (16). Interestingly, the $SUR1_{G1479R}/K_{IR}$6.2 channels could not be activated by metabolic inhibition; conditions where $[ATP]_i$ is expected to decrease and $[ADP]_i$ to increase. Exposure to 2-deoxyglucose and oligomycin apparently does not lower the $[ATP]_i$ sufficiently to activate K_{ATP} channels. This behavior explains why the G1479R mutation results in familial hyperinsulinism; ATP, even partially depleted by metabolic inhibition, closes the mutant K_{ATP} channels, but they fail to respond to fluctuations in ADP. The result implies that fluctuations of $[ATP]_i$ in pancreatic β-cells are not sufficient to trigger insulin secretion in these patients. We conclude that in the simplest model, the function(s) of ATP, vis-à-vis SUR1/K_{IR}6.2 K_{ATP} channels, is to inhibit channel activity and maintain an operational state, whereas fluctuations in ADP are critical for physiological regulation.

The response of K_{ATP} channel subtypes to sulfonylureas is well correlated with the affinity of binding and labeling of the receptors. For example, channels reconstituted with SUR1 showed IC_{50} values for channel inhibition by glibenclamide in the nM range, whereas the SUR2A channels typically required 100-fold higher concentrations for the same effect. Biochemical data show that SUR1 binds glibenclamide with a K_d near 1 nM, whereas SUR2A, for example, has a K_d near 1.2 μM (11, 50). Preliminary data indicate that SUR2B is also a low-affinity SUR; thus a differential response to sulfonylureas can be used in classification of channel subtypes.

The target site for potassium channel openers is assumed to be the SUR, based on observations that the response of reconstituted K_{ATP} channels to either diazoxide or pinacidil is correlated with the SUR subtype. The C-terminal end of the SUR appears to be a critical determinant for KCO pharmacology. The SUR1 and SUR2B C termini, for example, are similar, and channels formed from these receptors appear to share responsiveness to diazoxide, whereas the SUR2A/K_{IR}6.2 channel shows essentially no response. Recent biochemical studies (M Schwanstecher, C Sieverding, A Fischer, H Dörschner, D Bassen, C Schwanstecher, G Gonzalez, JP Clement IV, L Aguilar-Bryan & J Bryan, unpublished data) strongly imply that SURs are the target for KCOs and underscore the importance of the C terminus. These studies demonstrate that SUR2B has a K_d of approximately 25 nM for the potassium channel opener P1075, whereas binding to SUR2A is undetectably low. The binding of P1075 requires MgATP and is impaired by mutations in the nucleotide-binding folds. Therefore, it is likely that nucleotide hydrolysis by SURs is important for binding of KCOs. In excised patches, ATP is required for KCOs to stimulate K_{ATP} channels (88–92), but the reason for this requirement was not clear. Direct binding experiments with different KCOs and structure-function studies with the SUR subtypes are needed to establish the number and location of KCO-binding sites on K_{ATP} channels and to correlate binding with channel subtype response.

WHAT HAVE WE LEARNED FROM MODIFIED CHANNELS?

Studies aimed at modifying the function of K_{ATP} channels by introducing mutations into SUR and K_{IR}6.x subunits are beginning, but this area is not yet well developed. At the time of this review, only modifications of SUR1 and K_{IR}6.2 have been reported.

Mutations

The missense mutations discovered in individuals with familial hyperinsulinism have been engineered into either SUR1 or K_{IR}6.2. We have described these studies elsewhere (15). The general conclusion is that reconstitution of the mutant subunits with a wild-type partner does not generate functional channels when activity is measured in intact cells. For example, the Leu147 → Pro mutation in the M2 segment of K_{IR}6.2 (47) does not produce active channels when expressed with wild-type SUR1. The informative G1479R mutation in SUR1, where ADP activation is selectively lost, was described above. Mutations in the conserved lysine residues in the Walker A motifs in both nucleotide-binding folds of SUR1 have been made (Lys719 → Ala and Lys1384 → Met) and appear to result in loss of activation by ADP (87). The results indicate that the mutation of NBF1, but not NBF2, affected activation by diazoxide, whereas both mutations resulted in loss of activation by MgADP. The mutant currents were somewhat more sensitive to ATP; metabolic inhibition was reported to activate the Lys1384 → Met currents, but not the Lys719 → Ala or double-mutant currents. The latter result led Gribble et al (87) to speculate "that there may be a factor in addition to ATP and ADP which regulates K_{ATP} channel activity." The rationale for focusing on the Walker A conserved lysine residues is that equivalent mutations in other ABC proteins inhibit ATP hydrolysis.

Truncations

Truncations have been used effectively with a number of proteins to map important domains. The first two mutations identified in SUR1, which were associated with familial hyperinsulinism, led to splicing problems that resulted in premature termination (93). Engineered constructs that generate truncated receptors similar to those found in PHHI β-cells do not produce functional channels when co-expressed with wild-type K_{IR}6.2 (46). Interestingly, these truncated receptors are made and do retain high-affinity binding for glibenclamide. It is not clear whether these truncated receptors can assemble into a tetramer, (SUR1/K_{IR}6.2)$_4$.

We have engineered a series of smaller truncations from the C-terminal end of SUR1. Like the more extensive truncations identified in familial hyperinsulinism, high-affinity sulfonylurea binding and co-photolabeling of K_{IR}6.2 are retained. Interestingly, removal of as few as 7 residues reduces ^{86}Rb$^+$ efflux by more than 50%, and removal of 15 residues nearly eliminates channel activity, as determined by ^{86}Rb$^+$ efflux. The function of the SUR C-terminal domain is not clear, but together with the importance of this segment in specifying the pharmacology of potassium channel openers, the results indicate it has a key role in regulation of K_{ATP} channel activity.

A truncation of K_{IR}6.2 has also been identified with familial hyperinsulinism. Nestorowicz et al (48) have identified a severe truncation, Tyr12 → Stop, expected to make only a short peptide. As would be anticipated, co-expression of this short fragment with SUR1 did not produce functional channels.

Directed truncations of K_{IR}6.2 are proving informative. Tucker et al (24) have removed 18, 26, 36, and 41 amino acids from the C terminus of K_{IR}6.2. The 18, 26, and 36 amino acid deletions produced potassium channels in the absence of a SUR, whereas the 41 amino acid deletion did not. The channels missing 26 and 36 amino acids appeared to be the more active but were not activated by MgADP or potassium channel openers such as diazoxide and were not inhibited by sulfonylureas; thus these regulatory functions are presumed to require the SUR. Co-expression of SUR1 with K_{IR}6.2ΔC26 qualitatively restores these properties. The truncated K_{IR}6.2 channels are inhibited by ATP, although with 10-fold lower sensitivity. Addition of Mg^{2+} appeared not to affect the

IC_{50} for ATP inhibition as reported for the native channel (62). Co-expression of SUR1 with $K_{IR}6.2\Delta C26$ appeared to enhance the blocking action of ATP. Finally, the activity of the truncated channels shows rundown and refreshment as described above.

The results with the truncated $K_{IR}6.2$ channels confirm there is a segregation of functions between subunits and raise additional possibilities. $K_{IR}6.2$ appears to be sufficient to form the conducting pore of the β-cell channel, as implied by the shift in rectification observed in the $K_{IR}6.2N160D$ channels (21). SUR1 confers sensitivity to openers and blockers and, if the model discussed above is correct, is required for response to ADP, the proposed physiological regulator. The truncation experiments suggest further that the rundown/refreshment phenomena might be from modification of the pore-forming subunit. Finally, Tucker et al (24) have argued that the primary site for the inhibitory action of ATP on K_{ATP} channels may not be on SUR, but rather is located on $K_{IR}6.2$. Furthermore, occupation of a single binding site is sufficient to inhibit channel activity. In terms of understanding how K_{ATP} channels are regulated, this is an important conclusion that, if correct, moves some of the focus of nucleotide regulation away from the SUR. Although this is an attractive hypothesis, the data presented do not rule out the possibility that removal of the C terminus of $K_{IR}6.2$ exposes a cryptic blocking site. Additional evidence is needed to validate the hypothesis.

SUMMARY

ATP-sensitive potassium channels regulate the electrical activity of cells either by controlling their resting membrane potential, or by modulating the action potential. These channels are heteromultimers of SUR and $K_{IR}6.x$ subunits. These associate in a 1:1 stoichiometry, and a tetrameric model, $(SUR/K_{IR}6.x)_4$, has been proposed for the channel. $K_{IR}6.x$ forms the pore that, under physiological conditions, requires SUR for its opening. ATP inhibits and maintains K_{ATP} channels in an operational state; their activation, under physiological conditions, is proposed to occur through changes in $[ADP]_i$, which acts through a SUR. K_{ATP} channel diversity results from the assembly of at least three known SUR subtypes and two known $K_{IR}6.x$ subtypes. $K_{IR}6.1$-based channels are distinguished from $K_{IR}6.2$ channels by their smaller unitary conductance. SUR1-based channels are distinguished by their greater sensitivity to sulfonylureas, whereas SUR2A channels can be distinguished from SUR2B channels because only the latter are sensitive to diazoxide. Mutations in SUR1 and $K_{IR}6.2$ result in loss of K_{ATP} channels in pancreatic β-cells and cause familial hyperinsulinism. Directed mutations promise to be useful in unraveling how these channels respond to nucleotides, sulfonylureas, and KCOs.

ACKNOWLEDGMENTS

The authors thank the members of their laboratories for help and encouragement. We thank the American Diabetes Association, the Juvenile Diabetes Foundation International, the Houston Endowment, and the National Institutes of Health for support for our research in this area.

Literature Cited

1. Trube G, Hescheler J. 1984. Inward-rectifying channels in isolated patches of the heart cell membrane: ATP-dependence and comparison with cell-attached patches. *Pflügers Arch.* 401:178–84

2. Cook DL, Hales CN. 1984. Intracellular ATP directly blocks K$^+$ channels in pancreatic B-cells. *Nature* 311:271–73

3. Noma A. 1983. ATP-regulated K$^+$ channels in cardiac muscle. *Nature* 305:147–48

4. Kakei M, Noma A. 1984. Adenosine-5'-triphosphate-sensitive single potassium channel in the atrioventricular node cell of the rabbit heart. *J. Physiol.* 352:265–84

5. Dunne MJ, Petersen OH. 1986. Intracellular ADP activates K$^+$ channels that are inhibited by ATP in an insulin-secreting cell line. *FEBS Lett.* 208:59–62

6. Misler S, Falke LC, Gillis K, McDaniel ML. 1986. A metabolite-regulated potassium channel in rat pancreatic B cells. *Proc. Natl. Acad. Sci. USA* 83:7119–23

7. Carmeliet E, Storms L, Vereecke Y. 1990. The ATP-dependent K-channel and metabolic inhibition. In *Cardiac Electrophysiology. From Cell to Bedside,* ed. DP Zipes, Yalife, pp. 103–8. Philadelphia: Saunders

8. Babenko AP, Samoilov VO, Kazantseva ST. 1992. Potassium channels in the cardiomyocyte sarcolemma: initial opening under influence of hypoxia. *Basic Appl. Myology* 2:316–23

9. Faivre JF, Findlay I. 1990. Action potential duration and activation of ATP-sensitive potassium current in isolated guinea-pig ventricular myocytes. *Biochim. Biophys. Acta* 1029:167–72

10. Inagaki N, Inazawa J, Seino S. 1995. cDNA sequence, gene structure, and chromosomal localization of the human ATP-sensitive potassium channel, uKATP-1, gene (KCNJ8). *Genomics* 30:102–4

11. Inagaki N, Gonoi T, Clement JP IV, Namba N, Inazawa J, et al. 1995. Reconstitution of IK$_{ATP}$: an inward rectifier subunit plus the sulfonylurea receptor. *Science* 270:1166–70

12. Doupnik CA, Lim NF, Kofuji P, Davidson N, Lester HA. 1995. Intrinsic gating properties of a cloned G protein-activated inward rectifier K$^+$ channel. *J. Gen. Physiol.* 106:1–23

13. Aguilar-Bryan L, Nichols CG, Wechsler SW, Clement JP IV, Boyd AE III, et al. 1995. Cloning of the beta cell high-affinity sulfonylurea receptor: a regulator of insulin secretion. *Science* 268:423–26

14. Tusnády GE, Bakos E, Varadi A, Sarkadi B. 1997. Membrane topology distinguishes a subfamily of the ATP-binding cassette (ABC) transporters. *FEBS Lett.* 402:1–3

15. Aguilar-Bryan L, Clement JP IV, Gonzalez G, Kunjilwar K, Babenko A, et al. 1998. Toward understanding the assembly and structure of K$_{ATP}$ channels. *Physiol. Rev.* In press

16. Nichols CG, Shyng SL, Nestorowicz A, Glaser B, Clement JP IV, et al. 1996. Adenosine diphosphate as an intracellular regulator of insulin secretion. *Science* 272:1785–87

17. Sakura H, Ammala C, Smith PA, Gribble FM, Ashcroft FM. 1995. Cloning and functional expression of the cDNA encoding a novel ATP-sensitive potassium channel subunit expressed in pancreatic beta-cells, brain, heart and skeletal muscle. *FEBS Lett.* 377:338–44

18. Gribble FM, Ashfield R, Ammala C, Ashcroft FM. 1997. Properties of cloned ATP-sensitive K$^+$ currents expressed in

Xenopus oocytes. *J. Physiol.* 498:87–98

19. Aguilar-Bryan L, Bryan J. 1996. ATP-sensitive potassium channels, sulfonylurea receptors and persistent hyperinsulinemic hypoglycemia of infancy. *Diabetes Rev.* 4:336–46

20. Chutkow WA, Simon MC, Le Beau MM, Burant CF. 1996. Cloning, tissue expression, and chromosomal localization of SUR2, the putative drug-binding subunit of cardiac, skeletal muscle, and vascular K_{ATP} channels. *Diabetes* 45:1439–45

21. Clement JP IV, Kunjilwar K, Gonzalez G, Schwanstecher M, Panten U, et al. 1997. Association and stoichiometry of K_{ATP} channel subunits. *Neuron* 18:827–38

22. Lu Z, MacKinnon R. 1994. Electrostatic tuning of Mg^{2+} affinity in an inward-rectifier K^+ channel. *Nature* 371:243–46

23. Taglialatela M, Ficker E, Wible BA, Brown AM. 1995. C-terminus determinants for Mg^{2+} and polyamine block of the inward rectifier K^+ channel IRK1. *EMBO J.* 14:5532–41

24. Tucker SJ, Gribble FM, Zhao C, Trapp S, Ashcroft FM. 1997. Truncation of Kir6.2 produces ATP-sensitive K^+ channels in the absence of the sulphonylurea receptor. *Nature* 387:179–83

25. Al-Awqati Q. 1995. Regulation of ion channels by ABC transporters that secrete ATP. *Science* 269:805–6

26. Kaubisch N, Hammer R, Wollheim C, Renold AE, Offord RE. 1982. Specific receptors for sulfonylureas in brain and in a beta-cell tumor of the rat. *Biochem. Pharmacol.* 31:1171–74

27. Gopalakrishnan M, Johnson DE, Janis RA, Triggle DJ. 1991. Characterization of binding of the ATP-sensitive potassium channel ligand, [³H]glyburide, to neuronal and muscle preparations. *J. Pharmacol. Exp. Therapeut.* 257:1162–71

28. Gopalakrishnan M, Triggle DJ. 1992. Regulation of ATP-sensitive K^+ channels by chronic glyburide and pinacidil administration. *Biochem. Pharmacol.* 44:1843–47

29. Niki I, Ashcroft SJ. 1993. Characterization and solubilization of the sulphonylurea receptor in rat brain. *Neuropharmacology* 32:951–57

30. Schwanstecher M, Schaupp U, Loser S, Panten U. 1992. The binding properties of the particulate and solubilized sulfonylurea receptor from cerebral cortex are modulated by the Mg^{2+} complex of ATP.

31. Zini S, Tremblay E, Roisin MP, Ben-Ari Y. 1991. Two binding sites for [³H]glibenclamide in the rat brain. *Brain Res.* 542:151–54

32. Bernardi H, Fosset M, Lazdunski M. 1988. Characterization, purification, and affinity labeling of the brain [³H]glibenclamide-binding protein, a putative neuronal ATP-regulated K^+ channel. *Proc. Natl. Acad. Sci. USA* 85:9816–20

33. Ashford ML, Boden PR, Treherne JM. 1990. Tolbutamide excites rat glucoreceptive ventromedial hypothalamic neurones by indirect inhibition of ATP-K^+ channels. *Br. J. Pharmacol.* 101:531–40

34. Murphy KP, Greenfield SA. 1991. ATP-sensitive potassium channels counteract anoxia in neurones of the substantia nigra. *Exp. Brain Res.* 84:355–58

35. Treherne JM, Ashford ML. 1992. Extracellular cations modulate the ATP sensitivity of ATP-K^+ channels in rat ventromedial hypothalamic neurons. *Proc. R. Soc. London Ser. B* 247:121–24

36. Ohno-Shosaku T, Yamamoto C. 1992. Identification of an ATP-sensitive K^+ channel in rat cultured cortical neurons. *Pflügers Arch.* 422:260–66

37. Schwanstecher C, Panten U. 1993. Tolbutamide- and diazoxide-sensitive K^+ channel in neurons of substantia nigra pars reticulata. *Naunyn-Schmiedebergs Arch. Pharmacol.* 348:113–17

38. Schwanstecher C, Panten U. 1994. Identification of an ATP-sensitive K^+ channel in spiny neurons of rat caudate nucleus. *Pflügers Arch.* 427:187–89

39. Karschin C, Ecke C, Ashcroft FM, Karschin A. 1997. Overlapping distribution of K(ATP) channel-forming Kir6.2 subunit and the sulfonylurea receptor SUR1 in rodent brain. *FEBS Lett.* 401:59–64

40. Mourre C, Widmann C, Lazdunski M. 1990. Sulfonylurea binding sites associated with ATP-regulated K^+ channels in the central nervous system: autoradiographic analysis of their distribution and ontogenesis, and of their localization in mutant mice cerebellum. *Brain Res.* 519:29–43

41. Treherne JM, Ashford ML. 1991. The regional distribution of sulphonylurea binding sites in rat brain. *Neuroscience* 40:523–31

42. Gehlert DR, Gackenheimer SL, Mais DE, Robertson DW. 1991. Quantitative autoradiography of the binding sites for

[^{125}I]iodoglyburide, a novel high-affinity ligand for ATP-sensitive potassium channels in rat brain. *J. Pharmacol. Exp. Therapeut.* 257:901–7

43. Jiang C, Xia Y, Haddad GG. 1992. Role of ATP-sensitive K$^+$ channels during anoxia: major differences between rat (newborn and adult) and turtle neurons. *J. Physiol.* 448:599–612

44. Zini S, Tremblay E, Pollard H, Moreau J, Ben-Ari Y. 1993. Regional distribution of sulfonylurea receptors in the brain of rodent and primate. *Neuroscience* 55:1085–91

45. Hernandez-Sanchez C, Wood TL, LeRoith D. 1997. Developmental and tissue-specific sulfonylurea receptor gene expression. *Endocrinology* 138:705–11

46. Dunne MJ, Kane C, Shepherd RM, Sanchez JA, James RFL, et al. 1997. Familial persistent hyperinsulinemic hypoglycemia of infancy and mutations in the sulfonylurea receptor. *N. Engl. J. Med.* 336:703–6

47. Thomas P, Ye Y, Lightner E. 1996. Mutations of the pancreatic islet inward rectifier also lead to familial persistent hyperinsulinemic hypoglycemia of infancy. *Hum. Mol. Gen.* 5:1809–12

48. Nestorowicz A, Inagaki N, Gonoi T, Schoor KP, Wilson BA, et al. 1997. A nonsense mutation in the inward rectifier potassium channel gene, K$_{IR}$6.2, is associated with familial hyperinsulinism. *Diabetes* 46:1743–48

49. Aguilar-Bryan L, Clement JP IV, Nelson DA. 1997. Sulfonylurea receptors and ATP-sensitive potassium channels. *Meth. Enzymol.* In press

50. Inagaki N, Gonoi T, Clement JP IV, Wang CZ, Aguilar-Bryan L, et al. 1996. A family of sulfonylurea receptors determines the pharmacological properties of ATP-sensitive K$^+$ channels. *Neuron* 16:1011–17

51. Spruce AE, Standen NB, Stanfield PR. 1985. Voltage-dependent ATP-sensitive potassium channels of skeletal muscle membrane. *Nature* 316:736–38

52. Davis NW, Standen NB, Stanfield PR. 1991. ATP-dependent potassium channels of muscle cells: their properties, regulation, and possible functions. *J. Bioenerg. Biomembr.* 23:509–35

53. Yamada M, Isomoto S, Matsumoto S, Kondo C, Shindo T, et al. 1997. Sulfonylurea receptor 2B, KIR 6.1 form a sulfonylurea-sensitive but ATP-insensitive K$^+$ channel. *J. Physiol.* 499:715–20

54. Kajioka S, Oike M, Kitamura K. 1990. Nicorandil opens a calcium-dependent potassium channel in smooth muscle cells of the rat portal vein. *J. Pharmacol. Exp. Therapeut.* 254:905–13

55. Kajioka S, Kitamura K, Kuriyama H. 1991. Guanosine diphosphate activates an adenosine 5′-triphosphate-sensitive K$^+$ channel in rabbit portal vein. *J. Physiol.* 444:397–418

56. Beech DJ, Zhang H, Nakao K, Bolton TB. 1993. K channel activation by nucleotide diphosphates and its inhibition by glibenclamide in vascular smooth muscle cells. *Br. J. Pharmacol.* 110:573–82

57. Kamouchi M, Kitamura K. 1994. Regulation of ATP-sensitive K$^+$ channels by ATP and nucleotide diphosphate in rabbit portal vein. *Am. J. Physiol.* 266:H1687–98

58. Xu X, Lee KS. 1994. Characterization of the ATP-inhibited K$^+$ current in canine coronary smooth muscle cells. *Pflügers Arch.* 427:110–20

59. Kovacs RJ, Nelson MT. 1991. ATP-sensitive K$^+$ channels from aortic smooth muscle incorporated into planar lipid bilayers. *Am. J. Physiol.* 261:H604–9

60. Isomoto S, Kondo C, Yamada M, Matsumoto S, Higashiguchi O, et al. 1996. A novel sulfonylurea receptor forms with BIR (Kir6.2) a smooth muscle type ATP-sensitive K$^+$ channel. *J. Biol. Chem.* 271:24321–24

61. Nelson MT, Quayle JM. 1995. Physiological roles and properties of potassium channels in arterial smooth muscle. *Am. J. Physiol.* 268:C799–822

62. Ashcroft FM, Kakei M. 1989. ATP-sensitive K$^+$ channels in rat pancreatic beta-cells: modulation by ATP, Mg^{2+} ions. *J. Physiol.* 416:349–67

63. Alvarez-Leefmans FJ, Giraldez F, Gamino SM. 1987. Intracellular free magnesium in excitable cells: its measurement and its biologic significance. *Can. J. Physiol. Pharmacol.* 65:915–25

64. Murphy E. 1993. Measurement of intracellular ionized magnesium. *Miner. Electrolyte Metab.* 19:250–58

65. Findlay I. 1988. ATP4- and ATP.Mg inhibit the ATP-sensitive K$^+$ channel of rat ventricular myocytes. *Pflügers Arch.* 412:37–41

66. Olesen SP, Bundgaard M. 1993. ATP-dependent closure and reactivation of inward rectifier K$^+$ channels in endothelial cells. *Circ. Res.* 73:492–95

67. Light P. 1996. Regulation of ATP-sensitive potassium channels by phospho-

rylation. *Biochim. Biophys. Acta* 1286: 65–73

68. de Weille JR, Muller M, Lazdunski M. 1992. Activation and inhibition of ATP-sensitive K^+ channels by fluorescein derivatives. *J. Biol. Chem.* 267:4557–63

69. Hussain M, Wareham AC. 1994. Rundown and reactivation of ATP-sensitive potassium channels (K_{ATP}) in mouse skeletal muscle. *J. Membr. Biol.* 141:257–65

70. Furukawa T, Virag L, Furukawa N, Sawanobori T, Hiraoka M. 1994. Mechanism for reactivation of the ATP-sensitive K^+ channel by MgATP complexes in guinea-pig ventricular myocytes. *J. Physiol.* 479:95–107

71. Furukawa T, Yamane T, Terai T, Katayama Y, Hiraoka M. 1996. Functional linkage of the cardiac ATP-sensitive K^+ channel to the actin cytoskeleton. *Pflügers Arch.* 431:504–12

72. Hilgemann DW, Ball R. 1996. Regulation of cardiac Na^+, Ca^{2+} exchange and K_{ATP} potassium channels by PIP_2. *Science* 273:956–59

73. Fan Z, Makielski JC. 1997. Anionic phospholipids activate ATP-sensitive potassium channels. *J. Biol. Chem.* 272:5388–95

74. de Weille J, Schmid-Antomarchi H, Fosset M, Lazdunski M. 1988. ATP-sensitive K^+ channels that are blocked by hypoglycemia-inducing sulfonylureas in insulin-secreting cells are activated by galanin, a hyperglycemia-inducing hormone. *Proc. Natl. Acad. Sci. USA* 85:1312–16

75. Rorsman P, Bokvist K, Ammala C, Arkhammar P, Berggren PO, et al. 1991. Activation by adrenaline of a low-conductance G protein-dependent K^+ channel in mouse pancreatic B cells. *Nature* 349:77–79

76. de Weille JR, Schmid AH, Fosset M, Lazdunski M. 1989. Regulation of ATP-sensitive K^+ channels in insulinoma cells: activation by somatostatin and protein kinase C and the role of cAMP. *Proc. Natl. Acad. Sci. USA* 86:2971–75

77. Leech CA, Holz GG, Habener JF. 1996. Signal transduction of PACAP, GLP-1 in pancreatic beta cells. *Ann. NY Acad. Sci.* 805:81–92

78. Nelson MT, Huang Y, Brayden JE, Hescheler J, Standen NB. 1990. Arterial dilations in response to calcitonin gene-related peptide involve activation of K^+ channels. *Nature* 344:770–73

79. Kieffer TJ, Heller RS, Leech CA, Holz GG, Habener JF. 1997. Leptin suppression of insulin secretion by activation of ATP-sensitive K^+ channels in pancreatic β-cells. *Diabetes* 46:1087–93

80. Kirsch GE, Codina J, Birnbaumer L, Brown AM. 1990. Coupling of ATP-sensitive K^+ channels to A1 receptors by G proteins in rat ventricular myocytes. *Am. J. Physiol.* 259:H820–26

81. Barrett-Jolley R, Comtois A, Davies NW, Stanfield PR, Standen NB. 1996. Effect of adenosine and intracellular GTP on K_{ATP} channels of mammalian skeletal muscle. *J. Membr. Biol.* 152:111–16

82. Ghosh A, Ronner P, Cheong E, Khalid P, Matschinsky FM. 1991. The role of ATP and free ADP in metabolic coupling during fuel-stimulated insulin release from islet beta-cells in the isolated perfused rat pancreas. *J. Biol. Chem.* 266:22887–92

83. Detimary P, Jonas JC, Henquin JC. 1996. Stable and diffusible pools of nucleotides in pancreatic islet cells. *Endocrinology* 137:4671–76

84. Olson LK, Schroeder W, Robertson RP, Goldberg ND, Walseth TF. 1996. Suppression of adenylate kinase catalyzed phosphotransfer precedes and is associated with glucose-induced insulin secretion in intact HIT-T15 cells. *J. Biol. Chem.* 271:16544–52

85. Weiss JN, Lamp ST. 1987. Glycolysis preferentially inhibits ATP-sensitive K^+ channels in isolated guinea pig cardiac myocytes. *Science* 238:67–69

86. Permutt MA, Nestorowicz A, Glaser B. 1996. Familial hyperinsulinism: an inherited disorder of spontaneous hypoglycemia in neonates and infants. *Diabetes Rev.* 4:347–55

87. Gribble FM, Tucker SJ, Ashcroft FM. 1997. The essential role of the Walker A motifs of SUR1 in K-ATP channel activation by Mg-ADP and diazoxide. *EMBO J.* 16:1145–52

88. Weik R, Neumcke B. 1990. Effects of potassium channel openers on single potassium channels in mouse skeletal muscle. *Naunyn-Schmiedebergs Arch. Pharmacol.* 342:258–63

89. Arena JP, Kass RS. 1989. Activation of ATP-sensitive K channels in heart cells by pinacidil: dependence on ATP. *Am. J. Physiol.* 257:H2092–96

90. Panten U, Heipel C, Rosenberger F, Scheffer K, Zunkler BJ, et al. 1990. Tolbutamide-sensitivity of the adenosine 5′-triphosphate-dependent K^+ chan-

nel in mouse pancreatic B-cells. *Naunyn-Schmiedebergs Arch. Pharmacol.* 342: 566–74

91. Fan Z, Nakayama K, Hiraoka M. 1990. Pinacidil activates the ATP-sensitive K$^+$ channel in inside-out and cell-attached patch membranes of guinea-pig ventricular myocytes. *Pflügers Arch.* 415:387–94

92. Thuringer D, Escande D. 1989. Apparent competition between ATP and the potassium channel opener RP. 49356 on ATP-sensitive K$^+$ channels of cardiac myocytes. *Mol. Pharmacol.* 36:897–902

93. Thomas PM, Cote GJ, Wohlik N, Haddad B, Mathew PM, et al. 1995. Mutations in the sulfonylurea receptor gene in familial hyperinsulinemic hypoglycemia of infancy. *Science* 268:426–29

Annu. Rev. Physiol. 1998. 60:689–717

ClC AND CFTR CHLORIDE CHANNEL GATING

J. Kevin Foskett

Department of Physiology, University of Pennsylvania, Philadelphia, Pennsylvania
19104-6100; e-mail: foskett@mail.med.upenn.edu

KEY WORDS: cystic fibrosis, ion channels, myotonia, epithelial transport, ABC transporter

---

ABSTRACT

Chloride channels are widely expressed and play important roles in cell volume
regulation, transepithelial transport, intracellular pH regulation, and membrane
excitability. Most chloride channels have yet to be identified at a molecular
level. The ClC gene family and the cystic fibrosis transmembrane conductance
regulator (CFTR) are distinct chloride channels expressed in many cell types, and
mutations in their genes are the cause of several diseases including myotonias,
cystic fibrosis, and kidney stones. Because of their molecular definition and roles
in disease, these channels have been studied intensively over the past several years.
The focus of this review is on recent studies that have provided new insights into
the mechanisms governing the opening and closing, i.e. gating, of the ClC and
CFTR chloride channels.

INTRODUCTION

Chloride plays an important role in cellular homeostasis under normal and
pathological conditions. Although chloride generally represents less than half
of the anionic content of cells—the balance is associated with impermeant
organic molecules—it is of particular physiological relevance because it represents the dominant diffusible anion in most cells. As such, and because
electrical neutrality is preserved in the cytoplasm, changes in cell chloride content under isosmotic conditions, as a result of altered transport across the plasma
membrane, are often reflected in changes in total cell solute content. Because
of the high water permeability of cell membranes, changes in cell solute content have parallel effects on the volume of the cell (1). Cells can exploit the
relationships between cell chloride and solute content and osmotic equilibria

0066-4278/98/0315-0689$08.00

to induce bulk flow of water. Thus cellular transport of chloride is involved not only in setting the volume of a cell under isosmotic conditions, but also in regulating volume following osmotic swelling of cells. Chloride transport is critically involved in bulk flows associated with transepithelial absorption and secretion. Furthermore, chloride plays an important role in maintenance of intracellular pH and is likely involved in regulating the activities of enzymes, including transport proteins.

Chloride transport involves numerous pathways including anion exchangers, cotransporters, and channels. Exchangers and cotransporters enable intracellular chloride concentration ($[Cl^-]_i$) to be maintained away from thermodynamic equilibrium by coupling transport of Cl^- to the gradients of other ions, e.g. Na^+, K^+, or HCO_3^-. Chloride channels allow dissipative flows and therefore play important roles in influencing the membrane potential and in coupling Cl^- movements to electrical gradients, which enable bulk solute transport. Numerous Cl^- channels in a wide variety of cell types throughout the animal and plant kingdoms have been recognized based on pharmacological sensitivities and electrophysiological recordings, and a rich literature exists that describes this diversity, as well as channel modulation and involvement in physiological processes. The reader is directed to several excellent reviews (2–11). The diversity of Cl^- channels known from functional studies greatly exceeds that based on molecular criteria. Nevertheless, many cloned molecules have been associated with Cl^- channel activity, although for some, e.g. phospholemman, pCln, p-glycoprotein, and VDAC, either the physiological relevance or reality of Cl^- channel activity is still debated (4, 7, 12–14). In contrast, ligand-gated Cl^- channels (GABA and glycine receptors), the cystic fibrosis transmembrane conductance regulator (CFTR), and the ClC family of Cl^- channels are recognized as three important Cl^- channel gene families, as underscored by diseases associated with mutations in their genes (15), and recent studies have yielded new insights into the structure, regulation, and roles of these proteins. Because of the rapid growth of information regarding ClC and CFTR Cl^- channels, herein we focus on them, with specific emphasis on recent studies related to the mechanisms that underlie their gating. For a more general review of CFTR and cystic fibrosis (CF), including aspects related to ion permeation, the reader is referred to References 16–19. For reviews on the ClC family of Cl^- channels, see 10, 11, 15, 20–22; for more details regarding the genetics, permeation, and roles of these channels, see 9, 12, 23.

ClC CHANNELS

By expression cloning in *Xenopus* oocytes, Jentsch and colleagues discovered the first member of the ClC family of chloride channels (24), which they called

ClC-0 (25). The predicted protein contains 805 amino acids and several hydrophobic regions, consistent with membrane-spanning helices. The topology is not completely known for any member of the gene family, but the original model has been modified to include 8–10 transmembrane domains, with a large C- and a small N-terminal cytoplasmic domain (22). Subsequent homology-based cloning strategies revealed that ClC-0 is a member of a large gene family, with nine mammalian genes recognized, and homologues present in yeast and bacteria (22). In mammals, the different genes are expressed in different cell types. Some isoforms are expressed predominantly in one cell type (e.g. ClC-1 in skeletal muscle) or in one organ (e.g. ClC-Ka, ClC-Kb in kidney), whereas others appear to be more widely expressed (e.g. ClC-2, ClC-6, and ClC-7) (26, 27). The function of most isoforms is not well understood, and for many the ultrastructural localization is unknown. Diseases associated with mutations in some isoforms have provided important insights into their roles in specific cell types. ClC-1 mutations are associated with myotonias (13, 28), and mutations in ClC-5 cause three diseases associated with formation of kidney stones (29). While the mechanisms by which mutations in ClC-1 can affect membrane electrical properties and cause myotonia are obvious, it is not immediately obvious how loss of function of ClC-5 leads to kidney stones. The problem of determining the roles of the various isoforms has been exacerbated by the inability to functionally express some of them (27, 30). Therefore, the present review is limited to a discussion of three ClC isoforms for which the most detailed information is available.

ClC-1

ClC-1 is comprised of $\approx$990 amino acids, with a predicted molecular mass of 110 kDa (25, 31). ClC-1 is predominantly expressed in skeletal muscle and is responsible for its very high resting membrane Cl^- conductance (25, 32). Support for the notion that ClC-1 is the main component of skeletal muscle Cl^- conductance is provided by its dominant expression in this tissue and by parallel changes in developmental patterns of expression of ClC-1 mRNA and skeletal muscle Cl^- conductance in neonatal mice (25). More important has been the identification of mutations in human and murine ClC-1 genes as the causative factors in recessive and dominant myotonias (13, 15, 28, 32–36). Myotonia refers to diseases of skeletal muscle characterized by abnormal muscle stiffness and relaxation caused by membrane hyperexcitability. Muscle hyperexcitability due to a decrease in Cl^- conductance results in the generation of repetitive action potentials after voluntary contractions. Myotonias associated with decreased Cl^- conductance have been described in human, mouse, and goat (13). In the ADR mouse model of recessive autosomal myotonia, disruption of the ClC-1 gene is the basis of the disease (32). In humans, both autosomal recessive generalized myotonia and autosomal dominant myotonia congenita are due to over 20 different identified mutations in ClC-1 (13, 15, 28, 35). A mutation in the myotonic goat ClC-1 has recently been identified (37).

ClC-1 Gating

The gating of the ClC-1 Cl^- channel is voltage dependent, yet the amino acid sequence contains no regions analogous to the S4 segments that serve as voltage sensors in cation channels (24, 25). Most mutations in ClC-1 affect gating by shifting the voltage dependence of the open probability (P_o). A detailed analysis by Fahlke et al (38) of the voltage dependence of ClC-1 gating was recently undertaken in HEK293 cells, a human embryonic kidney cell line engineered to stably express the channel. Because the single-channel conductance is only ≈ 1 pS (39), analysis of whole-cell currents was undertaken.

During depolarizing steps from -30 mV, Cl^- currents through hClC-1 are time independent, whereas during hyperpolarizing steps, the currents increase instantaneously and then rapidly deactivate to a nonzero steady state level. The time course of the current transients was best fitted by the sum of two exponentials plus a time-independent term. The currents could therefore be resolved into three components: fast-deactivating, slow-deactivating, and non-deactivating. Interestingly, neither of the deactiviation time constants was voltage dependent. The time course of current activation, examined by depolarizing to various voltages, following a prepulse at -85 mV, was also well fitted by the same voltage-independent time constants as deactivation.

In contrast to the voltage-independent time constants, distribution of the channels among three states representing fast, slow, and nondeactivating channels was voltage dependent. The population of channels in each of the three states displays a characteristic voltage dependence: As the test voltage is depolarized, the fast-deactivating component decreases, the nondeactivating component increases, and the slow-deactivating component increases and then decreases in a bell-shaped manner.

Because fractional amplitudes are voltage dependent, whereas deactivation time constants are not, gating of hClC-1 can not be represented by a sequential state model, where populations distributions are determined by the voltage dependencies of the rate constants connecting the different states. Therefore, it was proposed that two distinct processes are involved in gating. The first is an "instantaneous" voltage-sensing mechanism that determines the distribution of channels among the three kinetic states. The second is a voltage-independent mechanism for opening and closing of the channel.

The proposed voltage-dependent mechanism consists of two identical voltage sensors, each of which may assume two positions. Of the resulting four possible configurations, two are equivalent, leaving three different states. The voltage dependencies of the probabilities of the two sensors being in particular positions could be described by a simple binomial distribution of Boltzmann functions. Therefore, the three kinetic states refer to three different channel conformations, and positions of the voltage sensors determine whether channel deactivation is fast, slow, or not at all. The voltage-sensor movement is very fast, enabling the distribution of channels among the three kinetic states to achieve equilibrium before the channels actually gate. External acidification abolishes the voltage dependencies of the fast- and nondeactivating components, and the bell-shape of the slow component is transformed to a monotonic decrease with depolarization. Thus the voltage-sensing structures within the channel can be titrated from the extracellular side. The relative P_o under steady state conditions was determined and fitted with the sum of a Boltzmann distribution and a constant term. The slope factor derived from the fits, which provides an estimate of the equivalent gating charge, was unaffected by pH_e, whereas the constant term was increased by lowering pH_e. This result is consistent with the voltage sensor having one titratable residue existing in a charged state at neutral and alkaline pH_e, possibly a residue containing a carboxylate side group with negative charge at neutral pH. The data also indicate that this voltage-sensor charge moves across the entire membrane electric field and that two voltage sensors are associated with each channel. The latter result is therefore consistent with a homodimeric structure of hClC-1, in agreement with results from other studies (40).

The deactivation rate constants associated with the voltage-independent mechanism responsible for opening and closing of the channel were unaffected by pH_e, indicating that opening and closing does not involve extracellular titratable residues. In contast, acidic intracellular pH (pH_i) increased the activation/deactivation time constants by titrating many sites without altering the voltage independence. The permeant ion, Cl^-, also affected the fast and slow deactivation time constants: more positive E_{Cl} (higher Cl_i^-, lower Cl_o^-) increased the time constants and caused the fraction of nondeactivating current at negative potentials to increase. Reduction of external $[Cl^-]$ shifted the activation curve to more hyperpolarized potentials. This is extremely interesting in light of the opposite effect observed in ClC-0 because it suggests that the gating mechanisms of ClC-1 differ fundamentally from those of ClC-0. This is discussed in more detail below.

Taken together, these results are consistent with the presence of a cytoplasmic gate, which behaves as a blocking particle composed of titratable residues. The ability of $[Cl^-]$ on either side to affect the time constants suggests that the blocking particle directly interacts with the pore, behaving as an open channel blocker, analogous to the ball-and-chain inactivation mechanism in some voltage-dependent cation channels, which can be modeled as a simple first order process with one closed and one open state. Positive E_{Cl} affected only the blocking rate constant, consistent with competition between Cl^- and the gating particle for a binding site within the pore.

A model of voltage-dependent gating of ClC-1 that emerges from this work is one in which two structurally distinct parts of the channel are involved in gating. A pair of identical voltage sensors undergo ultra-fast movements across the entire electric field in response to voltage. These movements cause rapid changes in the rate constants for the interaction between a separate cytoplasmic gate and the channel, by altering the on rate. Thus the final opening and closing transitions are mediated by the cytoplasmic gate and not by the voltage sensor itself.

What is the nature of the voltage sensors? A study by Fahlke et al (41) suggests that they reside intrinsically, at least in part, within the ClC-1 sequence. Substitution of glycine for an aspartate residue at position 136 (D136G) within the predicted first transmembrane domain [resulting in a mutation that causes severe myotonia (36)], was without significant effect on the properties of the conduction pathway, whereas gating was radically altered compared with the wild-type channel. Instead of normal deactivation at hyperpolarizing potentials, the D136G mutant slowly activates, with time constants that are voltage dependent, in contrast to the voltage independence of the activation/deactivation time constants in the wild-type channel. Furthermore, the relative amplitudes of the current components are voltage independent, unlike those of the wild-type channel. The mutant channel lacks the ultra-fast voltage-dependent gating process exhibited by wild-type channels. Interestingly, in light of the strong dependence of ClC-0 gating on [Cl^-] (discussed below), activation of the D136G ClC-1 mutant is strongly coupled to the Cl^- gradient, unlike the wild-type channel. The data are consistent with channel opening through binding of Cl^- to a site within the conduction pathway, with access to that site from the cytoplasmic side of the membrane. Taken together, the results of this analysis suggest that an intrinsic voltage-sensing mechanism in ClC-1 resides in or near D136 in the amino acid sequence, and furthermore that this site does not contribute to the function of the pore.

ClC-0 Gating

Unlike other members of the ClC family of Cl^- channels, gating kinetics of ClC-0 have been examined at both macroscopic and single-channel levels. At the single-channel level, the gating is characterized by bursts of activity separated by longer interburst intervals (42–44). During the bursts, the channels gate between two equally spaced conductance levels (≈ 10 pS in symmetric 150 mM NaCl) in addition to the zero-conductance level. The "double-barreled" properties of the conductance reflect the presence of two separate pores within a homodimeric unit (45–47). The two proto-channels gate independently in a voltage-dependent manner, with depolarizing potentials increasing opening and slowing closing, in a manner described by a single-exponential time course for activation and deactivation (43, 48). In addition to the fast gates associated with opening and closing of each proto-channel, a slow gate operates on both channels simultaneously, accounting for the bursting behavior. It is also voltage dependent, but the dependence is opposite to that of the fast gates. At the single-channel level, gating among the three levels within bursts (fast gating) is described by single-exponential distributions for each level, enabling opening and closing rate constants for each level to be determined (43). The steady state voltage dependence of P_o can be described by a Boltzmann distribution with an effective gating charge of ≈ 1 (43, 49), with P_o approaching 1.0 at stongly depolarizing voltages.

In both macroscopic and single-channel measurements, elevating extracellular [Cl$^-$] shifts the voltage activation curve to hyperpolarized potentials without effecting the gating charge (43, 49). The data are consistent with a model in which extracellular Cl$^-$ has access to a binding site involved in channel gating. Based on analysis of macroscopic currents, Pusch et al (49) postulated that this binding site was located in the Cl$^-$ conduction pathway. Thus in addition to the external Cl$^-$ dependence of gating, they observed that only permeant anions affect gating; a specific mutation affects both permeation and gating; anion selectivity for permeation is similar to that for their effects on gating; and anomalous mole fraction behavior of conduction, which implies the existence of multiple ion binding sites in the pore, is paralleled by similar anomalous behavior of gating (49). Subsequent single-channel analysis by Chen & Miller (43) demonstrated that the channel opening rate is strongly enhanced by both depolarization and external Cl$^-$, whereas the closing rate is significantly less sensitive. A four-state model, in which the channel exists in either open or closed states, either occupied or not by Cl$^-$ at a specific site in the conduction pathway, could account for the effects of external Cl$^-$ on the channel opening rate. Importantly, the model demonstrated that the voltage dependence of gating resides solely in the opening rates and not at all in the binding of Cl$^-$, which is independent of voltage. These results conflict with the earlier interpretation, based on macroscopic measurements, that the voltage dependence of gating is due to the voltage dependence of Cl$^-$ binding to the activation site deep in the pore, with no intrinsic voltage dependence of channel opening (49). To account for the spectrum of channel behaviors over the full range of potentials, a similar model was developed that included an additional Cl$^-$-occupied closed state (43). In this model, transition from a closed, Cl$^-$-occupied state to a new Cl$^-$-liganded closed state represents the voltage-dependent step. From this state, opening occurs very quickly. During the voltage-dependent step, Cl$^-$ is transferred into the electric field, with Cl$^-$ itself being the source of the charge. The Cl^- activation site is probably located initially at the external end of the conduction pathway, outside the electric field. The bound Cl^- favors a conformational change that effectively translocates the Cl^- ion most of the way across the membrane field, thereby providing Cl^- as well as voltage dependencies. These studies therefore demonstrate that in ClC-0 the permeant ion is an integral component of the gating mechanism by providing the gating charge.

Comparison of Gating Behaviors of ClC-1 and ClC-0

As discussed by Fahlke et al (38, 41), the models developed for gating of ClC-1 and ClC-0 are seemingly incompatible. A fundamental difference concerns the nature of the gating charge. For ClC-0, the permeant ion is the gating charge, whereas in ClC-1 the gating charge appears to be intrinsic to the channel, and permeation and gating can be clearly separated. Given that ClC-1 and ClC-0 have only 54% homology (25), it is not surprising that the gating mechanisms are dissimilar. Nevertheless, it is possible that the different voltage-sensitive gating mechanisms in ClC-1 and ClC-0 result from relatively minor differences in amino acid sequence or from methodological inconsistencies. The D136G mutation abolishes the normal voltage-sensing mechanism in ClC-1, but the activation time constants become voltage dependent, with hyperpolarizing voltages activating channel opening, corresponding to the movement of 0.32 e_o over the entire membrane field (41). This is similar to the value (≈ 0.3) obtained for the charge movement associated with activation of ClC-0 at strongly hyperpolarized potentials (anti-gating charge) (43). In ClC-0, this gating charge is associated with transitions of the unliganded and Cl^--liganded closed state directly to the open state, by-passing the voltage-dependent transition to the second Cl^--liganded closed state. In the case of D136G mutations of ClC-1, it is speculated that the gating charge is associated with displacement of the cytoplasmic ball gate from the pore by enhanced competition for this site by cytoplasmic Cl^- (41). By analogy, therefore, it is possible that the voltage-independent gating mechanism in ClC-0 involves opening of a similar cytoplasmic gate by internal Cl^-. In support of this hypothesis, intracellular Cl^- slows the closing rate of ClC-0, and at high $[Cl^-]_i$, the channels deactivate incompletely (43, 48), an effect particularly evident in a ClC-0 K519R mutant (48). In ClC-1, the role of the voltage sensor is to couple a change in potential to a change in affinity of the pore for the cytoplasmic gate. It seems quite possible, therefore, that the voltage sensor in ClC-0, although mechanistically different from that of ClC-1, similarily functions by changing the strength of the gate-pore interaction. Thus both ClC isoforms may have similar pore-localized Cl^--sensitive binding sites for a cytoplasmic gate, suggesting that at least one basic gating mechanism has been conserved in ClC-1 and ClC-0, while each has evolved distinct mechanisms for sensing the voltage.

Methodological inconsistencies may argue for additional similarities between the gating mechanisms of the two ClC isoforms. A recent study by Rychkov et al (50) of rat and human ClC-1 expressed in insect cells and oocytes suggests an extracellular Cl^- dependence of ClC-1 gating very similar to that of ClC-0, e.g. activation depends on external [Cl^-] but not on internal [Cl^-] or the transmembrane Cl^-l gradient. To reconcile these observations with those of Fahlke et al (38), the authors cited their unpublished observations that the anion used to replace Cl^- must be carefully chosen. They suggest that methanesulfonate, the Cl^- substitute employed by Fahlke et al, reacts with the channel in ways that gluconate or glucose do not, and that the effects they observed reflect those conferred by methanesulfonate rather than the change of [Cl^-]. Future studies are obviously necessary to resolve these discrepancies.

The Slow Gate in ClC-0

Gating of ClC-0 may be fundamentally different from that observed for ClC-1 by virtue of an additional slow gate. The slow gate opens over seconds in response to hyperpolarizing voltages and closes even more slowly at depolarizing voltages (42, 48, 49, 51). Because fast gating is intrinsic to each proto-channel in the dimers (45, 46), whereas the slow mechanism gates both channels simultaneously, the slow gate might be a consequence of specific subunit interactions (52). Whereas fast gating of ClC-0 exhibits a Q_{10} of ≈ 2, consistent with a structurally simple conformational change, the temperature dependence of slow gating exhibits a Q_{10} of ≈ 40, indicating a rather complex structural alteration (52). The fraction of ClC-0 channels expressed in oocytes that are not closed by the slow gate is decreased at higher temperatures and, interestingly, higher temperatures also decrease the fraction of channels that are not opened by the slow gate. A model was developed including two open and two closed states, where voltage-dependent steps represent transitions between the two closed states and between the two open states; the temperature-sensitive transitions are those that link the open and closed states (52), and are speculated to be the rate-limiting transitions.

Two important questions need to be addressed. First, what is the nature of the slow gate? Pusch et al (52) demonstrated that the fraction of non-deactivating channels at depolarizing potentials is a function of the level of expression of ClC-0, implying that the slow gate may require channel protomer interactions. This hypothesis is consistent with the dimeric structure of ClC-0 (45, 46). Furthermore, co-expression of a mutant and a wild-type ClC-0 channel indicated that slow gating was determined by both subunits (45).

Second, is the slow gate present in other ClC isoforms? As discussed below, slow gating is observed in ClC-2 (26, 53). Hyperpolarization activation of P_o has been observed in a putative kidney-specific ClC isoform (9). Slow gating kinetics are also observed in the D136G ClC-1 mutant (41) (discussed above) and in wild-type ClC-1 exposed to low extracellular pH (50). Rychkov et al (50) speculated that a slow gate is present and constitutively open in ClC-1. ClC-1, similar to ClC-0, is a functional dimer (40). Because it is likely that dimerization is a general property of all functional ClC channels, if the slow gate requires protomer interactions, then the potential for such interactions is probably also a general feature of these channels, and it is possible that similar slow gates will be a feature of all ClC channels.

ClC-2 Gating

ClC-2 was cloned by screening cDNA libraries using the rat ClC-1 cDNA (26). ClC-2 has 907 amino acids, a molecular mass of 99 kDa, and shares ≈50% homology with ClC-0 and ClC-1. The human homologue has 94% identity with the rat isoform (54). Of considerable interest is its widespead tissue expression, unlike the more limited distribution of ClC-1 (26). ClC-2 expression in epithelial tissues involved in salt transport raises the question of its localization. In fetal lung, ClC-2 may be expressed in the apical membranes of airway cells (55), but further studies are required to determine whether this localization is similar in adult cells and in other tissues. A ClC-2 splice variant expressed in gastric mucosa has properties consistent with the Cl^- conductance believed to be involved in acid secretion (56), suggesting an apical membrane localization. Interestingly, ClC-2 contains a proline-rich domain that is similar to one in the epithelial Na^+ channel, ENaC, which binds to the SH3-domain of spectrin and appears to localize ENaC to the apical membrane (57). However, the role of this domain in ClC-2 (or in other ClCs) has not been explored. The expression of a ClC-2-like Cl^- conductance in salivary gland duct cells, which is activated by high $[Cl^-]_i$ (58, 59; discussed below), suggests that the localization is basolateral, because this tissue absorbs NaCl. The issue of whether ClC-2 is expressed in epithelial cell plasma membranes in a polarized manner assumes potential clinical relevance because it may be expressed in cells that also express CFTR, an apical membrane Cl^- channel. A similar apical membrane localization of ClC-2 might provide an alternate Cl^- pathway in cells affected in cystic fibrosis.

Single channel measurements of ClC-2 have not been reported, although unpublished data suggest a single-channel conductance of ≈2–5 pS (21). Gating of ClC-2 expressed in oocytes has been examined by macroscopic measurements. The Cl^- currents activate slowly (tens of seconds) in response to strong hyperpolarizations (beyond −90 mV) (26, 53, 60). The gating kinetics are reminiscent of the slow gate of ClC-0, and the activation by strongly hyperpolarized voltages is reminiscent of hyperpolarization-activation of the fast gate in ClC-0 (43) and the D136G-ClC-1 mutant (41) and in wild-type

ClC-1 exposed to low extracellular pH (50). With regard to ClC-0, the slow gate is predicted to involve interacting domains in the protomers of the dimeric channel, as discussed above. The similar structure of ClC-2 suggests that its functional unit is a homodimer. Indeed, co-expression of ClC-2 and ClC-1 in oocytes produces currents with novel properties, consistent with the formation of hetero-oligomers (61). Deletion of an N-terminal domain in ClC-2 abolished the time dependence of activation, and the currents were constitutively active (53). Restoration of the wild-type kinetics by introduction of the N-terminal domain into the C-terminal region suggests that the domain effects are largely position independent, indicating that it likely functions as a cytoplasmic ball that interacts via a chain with the pore. If the slow gate of ClC-0 is mediated by subunit interactions, is it possible that the N-terminal domain is involved in oligomer interactions in ClC-2? This has not been directly addressed. However, co-expression of ClC-2 with ClC-1, which may possess a constitutively open slow gate, abolishes the slow gate in the hetero-oligomers (61), and in ClC-2 chimeras in which the amino terminus is replaced with those of either ClC-1 or ClC-0, the slow hyperpolarization-activation is similarly abolished (53). Without single-channel measurements to determine whether ClC-2 behaves like ClC-0 as a double-barreled channel with two independently gating protomers, these results can not be unambiguously interpreted. At least they are consistent with a requirement for subunit interactions involving the amino termini of ClC-2, and a specific interaction with a structure within the pore in ClC-2 homodimers, to generate a ball-and-chain mechanism responsible for the slow hyperpolarization-activation of ClC-2. It is noteworthy that a slow gate in ClC-1 can be revealed by the D136G mutation (41), which is located near the amino terminus.

As mentioned above, the activation by strong hyperpolarization is reminiscent of hyperpolarization-activation of the fast gate in ClC-0 (43) and in the D136G ClC-1 mutant (41) and wild-type ClC-1 exposed to low extracellular pH (50). Because we speculate that the hyperpolarization-activated gating mechanism in these channels is the opening of a cytoplasmic gate by internal Cl^- (discussed above), the question arises whether the hyperpolarization-activation of ClC-2 exhibits any $[Cl^-]$ dependence. This has not been examined directly, but indirect evidence suggests that gating of ClC-2 depends on internal $[Cl^-]$. Mouse salivary gland duct cells demonstrate a hyperpolarization-activated whole-cell Cl^- conductance with features very reminiscent of those of ClC-2, including its voltage dependence, I/V relationship, anion selectivity, and pharmacological sensitivities (although some inhibitor sensitivities differ) (59). Of particular interest is the observation that the magnitude of the conductance is a strong function of $[Cl^-]_i$ for $[Cl^-]_i > 80$ mM (58). Indirect evidence suggests that hyperpolarization-activated gating of other ClC channels is also sensitive to $[Cl^-]_i$. A Cl^- channel from rabbit outer medullary vesicles and cultured kidney cells has been studied in lipid bilayers and shown to possess many of the properties expected for ClC, including ion selectivity, pharmacological sensitivities, and activation by hyperpolarization with a voltage dependence of P_o having an effective gating charge of 1 (9, 62). The incidence of channel incorporation into bilayers was reduced by treatment of cultured kidney cells with antisense oligonucleotides to ClC-K2 (63), one of two closely related ClC isoforms expressed exclusively in the kidney [ClC-K1 and ClC-K2 (Ka and Kb in human) (30, 64, 65)]. Furthermore, ClC-K1 antibodies block the channel activity in bilayers (63). These data strongly suggest that the channel studied in bilayers is the rabbit isoform of ClC-K2, although the lack of single-channel data from expressed clones makes this conclusion tentative. There is considerable controversy regarding the ability to express functional ClC-K channels (21, 23, 66). Of particular relevance for the present discussion is the strong dependence of the rabbit kidney Cl^- channel, not only on $[Cl^-]_o$, as expected for a ClC channel, but on $[Cl^-]_i$ as well (9, 67, 68). Increasing $[Cl^-]_i$ from 2 to 50 mM doubles P_o, with an apparent K_m of 15 mM. Changes in $[Cl^-]_i$ affected P_o by altering the voltage-independent gating mechanisms, without effect on the gating charge (≈ 1). Further evidence suggesting a $[Cl^-]_i$ sensitivity of ClC-2 has been obtained in T-84 cells, an intestinal cell line that expresses ClC-2 (26, 54) and exhibits a hyperpolarization-activated Cl^- conductance, which has an anion selectivity and pharmacological profile expected for ClC-2 (69). Activation of the current was markedly sensitive to $[Cl^-]_i$ between 20 and 30 mM.

It appears that a hyperpolarization-activation mechanism exists in all ClC isoforms in which it has been examined that is sensitive to $[Cl^-]_i$. It will be interesting to determine whether all members of the ClC family are similarly sensitive to $[Cl^-]_i$, and whether the gate that is affected by $[Cl^-]_i$ is the same in all these studies and among isoforms. Also, it would be informative to examine the $[Cl^-]_i$ dependence of the slow gate of ClC-0 and whether distinct $[Cl^-]_i$ sensitivities of various isoforms reflect those of their cytoplasmic balls' affinities for the pore.

Is There a Physiological Role for Internal [Cl⁻] Dependence of ClC Gating?

The $[Cl^-]_i$ dependence of gating of ClC isoforms, which are widely expressed, raises the possibility that $[Cl^-]_i$ may play an important role in regulating Cl^- conductance in cells. Three issues are relevant: First, is $[Cl^-]_i$ sufficiently high? Second, does $[Cl^-]_i$ change sufficiently during physiological stimulation to significantly affect ClC gating? Finally, what is the physiological significance of $[Cl^-]_i$ sensitivity of Cl^- conductances?

Although $[Cl]_i$ is at or near thermodynamic equilibrium in some cells, e.g. skeletal muscle, and therefore maintained at low levels (<5–10 mM), in most cells $[Cl^-]_i$ is maintained at levels considerably above equilibrium values. This is not surprising given the widespread expression of the Na^+-K^+-$2Cl^-$ cotransporter (70) and Cl^--HCO_3^- exchanger (71). In the absence of dissipative flows, the equilibrium levels of $[Cl^-]_i$, which can be attained by operation of these transporters (assuming maintenance of normal $[Na^+]_i$ and $[K^+]_i$ by the Na^+/K^+-ATPase), exceed 80–90 mM (72). In secretory epithelial cells, $[Cl^-]_i$ has been measured at 50–90 mM (1, 73). Even cells such as fibroblasts and endocrine cells that do not participate in bulk salt movements maintain $[Cl^-]_i$ at ≈60 mM (74, 75). Thus $[Cl^-]_i$ is sufficiently high in many or most cell types to influence ClC gating. During activation of fluid-secreting epithelial cells, $[Cl^-]_i$ may fall by as much as 30 mM (73). Changes in NaCl transport by absorptive epithelial cells may be associated with increases of $[Cl^-]_i$ of 10 mM (9). In response to mediators that increase $[Ca^{2+}]_i$ and activate Ca^{2+}-dependent Cl^- conductances, nonepithelial cells lose considerable amounts of Cl^- (76–78) substantially lowering $[Cl^-]_i$ (73, 79). Thus changes of sufficient magnitude occur in cells to both stimulate and inhibit ClC gating. The physiological significance of these effects may be important. In transporting epithelial cells, the $[Cl^-]_i$ sensitivity of ClC gating may facilitate coordination between the transport rates at the apical and basolateral membranes, with $[Cl^-]_i$ serving as a messenger for cross talk (80). The $[Cl^-]_i$ sensitivity may also be important in setting $[Cl^-]_i$, which in turn is a dominant factor in controlling the volume of cells under normal isosmotic conditions (81, 82).

CFTR

CFTR contains structural domains similar to those in other proteins of the ATP-binding cassette family, including 12 predicted transmembrane helices in two groups of six and two cytoplasmic nucleotide-binding domains (NBDs), as well as a cytoplasmic region containing numerous consensus sequences for phosphorylation (83, 84). Whereas several members of this family, which includes p-glycoprotein, have known transport functions (83, 84), and although not all the functions of CFTR have been established, various evidence demonstrates that CFTR is a cAMP-regulated Cl^- channel. First, expression of CFTR in nonepithelial cells confers a cAMP-regulated Cl^- conductance (74, 85, 86). Second, site-directed mutagenesis of CFTR alters channel properties associated with its expression (19). Finally, reconstitution of purified CFTR into planar lipid bilayers reveals cAMP-activated Cl^- channels with properties similar to those in CFTR-expressing cells (87).

It is generally believed that an underlying defect of cystic fibrosis (CF) is abnormal epithelial ion and fluid transport (88) due to mutations in CFTR. In CF, the Cl^- channel function of CFTR is defective (19, 88). Over 700 different mutations in the gene have been reported (88; L-C Tsui, personal communication). Electrophysiological and biochemical analyses indicate that mutations can affect CFTR Cl⁻-channel function in different ways, which have been catalogued (19) into discrete, not necessarily exclusive, classes: Class 1 mutations are associated with improper protein production due to premature termination signals in the gene. Class 2 mutations impede exit of the fully translated protein from the endoplasmic reticulum (ER), where it is synthesized and subsequently degraded (89, 90). Class 3 mutations cause the protein to be defectively regulated by phosphorylation or ATP binding and hydrolysis. Class 4 mutations affect the Cl⁻ conduction pathway.

Immunolocalization of CFTR to the apical membranes of epithelial cells involved in CF (17) has provided evidence consistent with a model in which fluid and salt transport by these epithelia involves Cl⁻ transport across the apical membrane through CFTR. Some recent observations suggest that CFTR may also function to regulate other epithelial conductances, by mechanisms seemingly independent of its Cl⁻ channel function. Regulation by cAMP of another airway Cl⁻ channel, the outwardly rectifying Cl⁻ channel (ORCC), may also be defective in CF (91). Although ORCC was originally believed to be the defective Cl⁻ channel basis of epithelial impermeability to Cl⁻ in CF (91) (the molecular identity of the ORCC is not known), ORCC and CFTR are clearly separate gene products (92). Expression of CFTR in airway epithelial cells corrects defective ORCC regulation (92–94) by a mechanism that may be associated with the ability of intracellular ATP to activate the ORCC from the extracellular side of the membrane (95). Some groups have reported that CFTR either can conduct ATP or is closely associated with an ATP channel (95–97). However, these results are currently controversial because they have not been observed by all investigators (98–101). In addition to Cl⁻ impermeability, airway cells from CF patients may be more permeable to Na⁺ (102–105). Apical membrane-localized amiloride-sensitive Na⁺ channels in cells from CF patients have a higher P_o (106, 107), whereas the number of channels appears normal (108). Co-expression of CFTR and ENaC Na⁺ channel subunits (109–111) in vitro can reconstitute CFTR-mediated Na⁺ channel regulation (107, 112), although the mechanisms are still unknown.

CFTR Gating

CFTR is acutely regulated by kinases (in particular protein kinase A; PKA) and phosphatases (113–130) and by adenine nucleotides, Mg^{2+}, and inorganic phosphate (P_i) (127, 131–155).

When CFTR is strongly activated in cell-attached patches by exposing the cell to reagents designed to raise intracellular cAMP, or in excised patches by exposing their cytosolic faces to high concentrations of the PKA catalytic subunit, channel gating kinetics are characteristically slow with long openings and closings and little voltage dependence. In most analyses, gating can be described by one open-time constant and two closed-time constants. Open-time constants have been reported between 60 and 200 ms (131, 133, 145, 146, 151, 156, 157) or in the 1–2 s range (123, 158–163). The long closed-time constant is 100 to 400 ms (133, 145, 146, 150, 151, 156, 157) or in the range of 1–4 s (123, 156–163). In addition, a short closed-time constant of $\approx$2–10 ms is often reported (145, 146, 151, 156). The fast closures are more prominent at negative (physiological) membrane potentials (124, 156), and add a flickery component to the voltage-independent slower kinetics. The presence of two kinetically distinct closed times has led to the idea that CFTR is a bursting channel (131, 145). However, recent studies suggest that the fast closures reflect flicker block of the channel by impermeant intracellular anions, or anions in the bath in excised patch recordings. Thus impermeant gluconate and glutamate cause voltage-dependent block of CFTR from the cytoplasmic, but not the extracellular, side of the channel (164), and the anionic form of the pH buffer MOPS (3-(N-morpholino) propane-sulfonate) causes a similar voltage-dependent flickery block (165). These data suggest that the rapid closures do not reflect the activity of a gate intrinsic to CFTR itself, but rather the interactions of other molecules with CFTR pore. The notion that CFTR exhibits bursting behavior may therefore be incorrect. Rather, intrinsic CFTR gating may simply involve single open and closed states, with the open state punctuated by rapid blocking events. Calculated burst durations should be reinterpreted as the open channel time. In burst analyses applied to CFTR, a variety of burst delimiter time constants have been employed, ranging from 5 to 60 ms. This range may explain the widely different open-time constants reported for CFTR, because inclusion of the rapid closures in the kinetic analyses will have the effect of shortening the apparent open- and closed-time constants. For example, in one study (166), a burst discriminator of 5 ms was used that yielded calculated values for open- and closed-time constants of 161 and 117 ms, respectively. The sulfonourea glibenclamide caused an open channel block but also reduced the calculated burst duration to 33 ms. This result demonstrates that an analysis based on bursting was likely inappropriate, because burst duration would not be expected to change as a result of rapid open channel block.

Gating of CFTR Cl⁻ Conductance Requires Phosphorylation of the CFTR Molecule

CFTR gating can be acutely modified by phosphorylation. Phosphorylation by cAMP-dependent kinase activates the channel activity by reducing the closed-time constant (123, 167). The phosphorylation requirement appears to be within the CFTR molecule itself because (a) purified CFTR can be activated by PKA (87); (b) CFTR is phosphorylated by the same kinases that activate gating

(114, 115, 122, 168–173); (c) mutagenesis of identified phosphorylation sites in CFTR affects channel gating (117, 122, 128, 129); and (d) replacement of phosphorylation sites in CFTR with negatively charged residues renders channel gating constitutively active and insensitive to phosphorylation (128). The mechanisms by which the phosphorylation state of CFTR affects its gating are unknown but presumably involve changes in its structure, which destabilize a closed state. Most of the residues in CFTR that become phosphorylated are located in the large cytoplasmic R-domain (117, 122, 129, 168, 171). Deletion of the R-domain renders CFTR constitutively active in the absence of phosphorylation (174). It has been proposed that the R-domain functions as a cytoplasmic pore-blocking particle, by analogy with ball-and-chain models for cation channels (128). Addition of purified R-domain peptide indeed causes a phosphorylation-dependent block of CFTR (170). However, binding sites for the R-domain in other parts of the molecule, which might participate in the block, have not been identified. Mutagenesis of some of the intracellular loops that link transmembrane helices and could provide interaction sites affects gating (159, 160, 175, 176), but a relationship between those sites and the R-domain has not been examined. The R-domain-deleted CFTR requires ATP to open, as does the phosphorylated wild-type channel (discussed below; 134), indicating that the normal closed state does not reflect pore occlusion by the R-domain. Phosphorylation of purified R-domain changes its structure (168, 169), suggesting that conformational changes in this domain may cause CFTR to enter a new closed state, rather than simply an unoccluded state, from which gating becomes possible. It is likely, therefore, that the R-domain plays a role in regulating other parts of CFTR involved in gating and that this regulation depends on its phosphorylation state. Graded phosphorylation of the R-domain may enable graded changes in channel open probability (117, 122, 129) by regulating access to phosphorylation-independent gating processes.

Gating of CFTR Cl⁻ Conductance Requires Nucleoside Triphosphate Hydrolysis

The most unusual feature of CFTR gating is its dependence on nucleoside triphosphate hydrolysis (134, 177). Once phosphorylated by PKA, the channel requires hydrolyzable nucleoside triphosphates (127, 134, 177), as well as Mg^{2+} (150, 151), on the cytoplasmic side of the channel to open (but see 132, 152, 155). The channel open probability is a function of [ATP] (131–133, 135, 148) owing to an ATP-induced destabilization of the long closed state (131, 133, 148, 151). Inorganic phosphate analogues VO_4 and BeF_3, which inhibit phosphotransferases and ATPases by binding to ADP in the nucleotide-binding pocket and forming a structural analogue of the bipyrimidal pentacovalent transition state intermediate that precedes hydrolysis of the β-γ phosphate bond of ATP, stabilize the open state of CFTR in the presence of ATP (147, 148). In the presence of ATP, nonhydrolyzable analogues sometimes prolong the channel open duration (127, 148).

Biochemical studies indicate that the effects of ATP on channel gating are direct. Membrane-associated CFTR binds 8-N_3ATP at concentrations that regulate its activity (145). Purified full-length CFTR possesses intrinsic ATPase activity (151). Interestingly, the ATPase activity was stimulated three- to four-fold by PKA phosphorylation of the channel (151). In contrast, 8-N_3ATP binding was unaffected by phosphorylation (145). Thus the R-domain may play a role in regulating transitions of ATP-bound CFTR to states from which ATP hydrolysis can occur. Activation of ATPase activity by phosphorylation changes the ATPase kinetics from hyperbolic, for the partially phosphorylated molecule, to sigmoidal (Hill coefficient 1.7), for the fully phosphorylated state. This suggests that phosphorylation of the R-domain induces cooperativity between the two ATPase sites, possibly through exposure of a second catalytic site (151).

The molecular basis for ATPase activity in CFTR was originally predicted from sequence analysis to reside in two putative NBDs in CFTR (84). Subsequent biochemical analyses of purified NBDs have demonstrated that they can bind (140, 141, 149, 178–183) and that NBD1 can hydrolyze (178) ATP. The two NBDs in CFTR share sequence homology with each other, as well as with domains in other ABC proteins and nucleotide-hydrolyzing proteins (84, 144, 184–186). Three regions characterize each domain in CFTR. The Walker A consensus motif forms a phosphate-binding loop in the hydrolytic core of ATPases and GTPases and contains a lysine involved in binding and hydrolysis by its associations with the β and γ phosphates. In CFTR, these correspond to residues K464 and K1250 in NBD1 and NBD2, respectively. The Walker B consensus motif also contributes to the phosphate-binding part of the pocket and contains an aspartic acid residue that participates in binding coordination of Mg^{2+} and in hydrolysis. In CFTR, these correspond to residues D572 and D1370. Finally, a LSGGQ motif, which is homologous to a similar region in GTP-binding proteins (138, 144), contains an invariant glycine at G551 and G1349 in the two NBDs. In GTP-binding proteins, this region is critical for hydrolysis. In CFTR, mutation of G551 or G1349 to aspartic acid (G551D, G1349D; both are CF mutations), decreases ATP binding (149) and the G551D mutation inhibits ATP hydrolysis (151).

In addition to observations that mutations in both NBDs are associated with CF, various evidence also suggests that both NBDs participate in channel gating. First, as mentioned above, analyses of the ATP dependence of ATP binding and hydrolysis and channel open probability suggest that two sites are involved, with possible cooperativity (135, 148, 151). Second, electrophysiological studies of wild-type and mutant CFTRs suggest that both NBDs participate in gating, by regulating channel closing as well as opening (153). A key finding was that whereas nonhydrolyzable nucleoside triphosphate analogues, transition state phosphate analogues, and polyphosphates were unable to open phosphorylated channels, they nevertheless interfered with the ability of ATP-activated channels to close again (127, 147, 148). These results suggest that opening as well as closing of the channel requires ATP hydrolysis and that the two processes are mediated by sites with different properties a hypothesis consistent with the biochemical evidence for two sites (above). An elegant model was proposed in which ATP hydrolysis at one site (NBDA) was required for channel opening and to enable nucleotide binding to a second site (NBDB) (147). Only this latter site can interact with nonhydrolyzable analogues, which inhibit its role in channel closing. Furthermore, this site is not made accessible unless the channel is in a highly, not partially, phosphorylated state (127), implying that the R-domain plays an important role in coordinating the opening and closing activities of the two NBDs. In this scheme, closings of partially phosphorylated channels are due to release of the hydrolysis products (ADP, P_i) from NBDA. The observation that the transition state phosphate analogues VO_4 and BeF_3 stabilize the open state in partially phosphorylated channels may indicate that P_i is released before ADP. Baukrowitz et al (147) suggest that channel opening coincides with exit of P_i from NBDA, whereas subsequent ADP release is associated with closing. In highly phosphorylated channels, ATP binding at NBDB delays ADP release from NBDA, thereby prolonging channel opening. Thus the channel remains in the open state until ATP hydrolysis at NBDB, enabling NBDB to effectively act as a timer regulating channel open duration through its rate of hydrolysis.

The relationship between ATP hydrolysis cycles and channel gating was further clarified by the observation that the open channel conductance could achieve two values (O1, O2), which differ by $\approx 10\%$ (150). The transition $C \rightarrow O1 \rightarrow O2 \rightarrow C$ was much more frequent than the reverse $C \rightarrow O2 \rightarrow O1 \rightarrow C$ pathway, indicating that the channel conformations were not in thermodynamic equilibrium, which therefore implied that an external energy input was required for gating. Polyphosphates and nonhydrolyzable analogues inhibit channel closing by locking the channel in the O1 conformation, suggesting that the predominant irreversible step in the gating cycle is the O1 to O2 transition, and channel closing results from relative instability of the O2 state (150).

The molecular correspondence between the two NBDs in CFTR and the two indicated by biochemical and electrophysiological analyses has been studied by examining the effects of NBD mutations. Biochemical measurements of the effects of NBD mutations on ATP hydrolysis have not kept pace with examination of electrophysiological consequences, so their effects usually need to be inferred from the known roles of comparable residues in other ATP- and

GTPases. In one study, ATP hydrolysis by a recombinant NBD1-maltose-binding protein fusion protein was inhibited by replacement of the Walker A lysine with alanine (K464A) (179), confirming predictions. K464A CFTR channels have reduced P_o (135, 145). Kinetic analysis indicates that the mutation stabilizes the long closed state by two- to fourfold (145, 150, 153, 154; M Sugita & K Foskett, unpublished observation) suggesting that ATP hydrolysis at NBD1 is involved in channel opening. Thus NBDA is likely NBD1. The mutation may also destabilize the channel open state (145, 154; M Sugita & K Foskett, unpublished observation). Interestingly, however, this mutant exhibits the wild-type gating transition cycle (150). Other mutations also support a role of ATP hydrolysis at NBD1 in channel opening. Activation of D572 and G551 mutants is inhibited (153, 154), and channel gating of Q552 mutants is altered (138) similarly to those for the K464A mutant. Thus mutations in the ATP-binding pocket in NBD1 stabilize the closed state, supporting a role for this domain in channel opening.

In contrast, mutations of the equivalent residues in NBD2 have more pronounced and different effects. Thus K1250A CFTR is characterized by markedly prolonged openings (145, 150, 154; M Sugita & K Foskett, unpublished observation), loss of sensitivity to channel inhibition by ADP (135), and lack of transitions from the O1 to the O2 state (150). These data suggest that ATP hydrolysis at NBD2 is responsible for channel closing and that the O1 to O2 transition reflects a conformational change in the permeation pathway induced by this hydrolysis reaction. They also indicate that ADP, polyphosphates, and nonhydrolyzable analogues exert their effects on gating by binding to NBD2. Therefore, NBDB (above) is likely NBD2. The prolonged openings observed in the K1250A mutant are distinguished from those induced by nonhydrolyzable ATP analogues because they are independent of the degree of channel phosphorylation (145), whereas nonhydrolyzable analogues may only affect fully phosphorylated channels (127). The LSGGQ motif in NBD2, which is homologous to a similar region in GTP-binding proteins, where glutamine plays a critical role in GTPase activity, contains a histidine rather than glutamine. Mutation of this residue to glutamine (H1350Q; predicted to increase ATP hydrolysis rate) but not to alanine (H1350A; predicted to have no effect on hydrolysis) destabilized the open state (138), again supporting a role for hydrolysis at NBD2 in controlling the duration of the open state. An interesting contrast to the effects of the K1250A mutation in the Walker A motif was revealed in a D1370N mutant in the Walker B motif. In the latter, openings as well as closings were prolonged, but the prolonged openings (≈ 1.5 s) were considerably shorter than those seen in the K1250A mutant (tens of seconds) (150). Similar kinetics were observed in the wild-type channel upon chelation of Mg^{2+}, consistent with the proposed role of the D1370 residue in coordinating

Mg^{2+}. In both cases, the O1 to O2 transition was eliminated. These data suggest that the major irreversible step in the gating cycle is ATP hydrolysis at NBD2 (150). Furthermore, they suggest that the prolonged openings induced by polyphosphates and the K1250A mutation require Mg^{2+} and nucleotide binding at NBD2. Thus the two classes of mutants define two kinetic states of the O1 conductance level—Mg^{2+}-independent reversible and Mg^{2+}-dependent irreversible states. Mutations predicted to abolish nucleotide binding at NBD2, a G1247D/G1249E double mutant, exhibit low P_o because of extended closed times and only brief openings (to O1 only), which are independent of ATP (150). These results led Gunderson & Kopito to propose a model (150) of CFTR gating in which ATP binding to NBD2 opens the channel to the O1 state. Subsequent binding of Mg^{2+} induces formation of a tightly bound, slowly reversible prehydrolysis complex. Rare dissociation from this complex accounts for O1 to C transitions, whereas predominant ATP hydrolysis accounts for the O1 to O2 transitions. Subsequent release of P_i and ADP result in the O1 to C transition.

The role of NBD1 is not well-defined in this model, although it is possible (150) that because gating is apparently so closely associated with a ATP hydrolysis cycle at NBD2, and because mutations that slow ATP hydrolysis at NBD1 have relatively modest effects on gating, ATP hydrolysis at NBD1 serves a priming or permissive role for the more dominant role of NBD2. Further studies are obviously required to more clearly define the role of ATP hydrolysis at NBD1. Furthermore, examination of the available mutagenesis data suggests that the NBDs must interact, and future studies focusing on the mechanism of such cross talk and on the role of the R-domain in mediating or regulating it should provide insights into the complex roles of these domains and nucleotide hydrolysis in regulating channel gating.

Is There a Physiological Role for ATP Sensitivity of CFTR Gating?

The picture emerging from analysis of the nucleotide dependencies of CFTR gating is one in which openings and closings of a single channel provide a real-time view of ATP hydrolysis cycles. Within each hydrolysis cycle, the channel normally spends about 50% of the time conducting Cl^-. During each opening, millions of Cl^- ions transverse the membrane, driven not by CFTR-mediated ATP hydrolysis, but by electrochemical gradients established ultimately by the energy of ATP hydrolysis by the Na^+/K^+-ATPase. Nevertheless, it appears that the cell invests a considerable amount of energy in CFTR hydrolysis cycles to regulate this translocation. It is possible that the ATP hydrolysis cycle serves an additional function, for example substrate transport, with Cl^- conduction representing a secondary phenomenon. Alternatively, the metabolic expense of regulating Cl^- channel function may be reasonable if offset by benefits. It has been speculated that the nucleotide sensitivity of CFTR may enable it to sense the metabolic state of the cell and regulate its activity accordingly (134, 136, 137). In Cl^- secreting cells, Cl^- enters the cell across the basolateral membrane coupled to Na^+ influx, driven by the Na^+ gradient established by the Na^+/K^+-ATPase. When NaCl influx is active, the pump and CFTR consume ATP, causing $[ATP]_i$ to fall (187, 188). A fall of ATP will inhibit the Na^+ pump, thus having the undesirable consequence of causing $[Na^+]_i$ to rise, because Na^+ influx across the basolateral membrane continues. By also coupling CFTR channel activity to $[ATP]_i$, Cl^- efflux across the apical membrane will be simultaneously inhibited, with the result that $[Cl^-]_i$ will also rise because its influx is coupled to that of Na^+. Although it is undesirable for a cell to accumulate NaCl because it causes cell swelling, elevated $[Cl^-]_i$ has been demonstrated, in turn, to feed back to inhibit the Na^+ influx pathways in the basolateral membrane (80). By inhibiting Na^+ influx, the elevated $[Cl^-]_i$ therefore enables the pump to catch up with the cytoplasmic Na^+ load, become less active, and thereby enable $[ATP]_i$ to recover. Thus by constantly sensing $[ATP]_i$, CFTR activity in the apical membrane may be regulated to efficiently titrate $[Cl^-]_i$ to a level that sets the rate of NaCl influx at the basolateral membrane at optimal levels for the pump to operate without compromising $[ATP]_i$. I propose that nucleotide sensitivity of CFTR is a mechanism of cross talk between apical and basolateral membranes in epithelial cells that coordinates the transport activities in the two membranes, where preservation of $[ATP]_i$ is the goal.

Visit the *Annual Reviews home page* at
http://www.AnnualReviews.org.

Literature Cited

1. Foskett JK. 1990. Optical studies of ion and water transport in single cells. In *Noninvasive Techniques in Cell Biology,* ed. JK Foskett, S Grinstein, pp. 237–72. New York: Wiley-Liss
2. Strange K, Emma F, Jackson PS. 1996. Cellular and molecular physiology of volume-sensitive anion channels. *Am. J. Physiol.* 270:C711–30
3. Franciolini F, Petris A. 1990. Chloride channels of biological membranes. *Biochim. Biophys. Acta* 1031:247–59
4. Valverde MA, Hardy SP, Sepúlveda FV. 1995. Chloride channels: a state of flux. *FASEB J.* 9:509–15
5. Gögelein H. 1988. Chloride channels in epithelia. *Biochim. Biophys. Acta* 947: 521–47
6. Vaughan PC, French AS. 1989. Non-ligand-activated chloride channels of skeletal muscle and epithelia. *Prog. Biophys. Mol. Biol.* 54:59–79
7. Nilius B, Eggermont J, Voets T, Droogmans G. 1996. Volume-activated Cl^- channels. *Gen. Pharmacol.* 27:1131–40
8. Large WA, Wang Q. 1996. Characteristics and physiological role of the Ca^{2+}-activated Cl^- conductance in smooth muscle. *Am. J. Physiol.* 271:C435–54
9. Reeves WB, Winters CJ, Zimniak L, Andreoli TE. 1994. Epithelial chloride channels, from kidney to airway cells. *Adv. Neurol.* 23:177–90
10. Jentsch TJ. 1993. Chloride channels. *Curr. Opin. Neurobiol.* 3:316–21

11. Fong P, Jentsch TJ. 1995. Molecular basis of epithelial Cl channels. *J. Membr. Biol.* 144:189–97

12. Paulmichl M, Geschwentner M, Wöll E, Schmarda A, Ritter M, et al. 1993. Insight into the structure-function relation of chloride channels. *Cell. Physiol. Biochem.* 3:374–87

13. Pusch M, Jentsch TJ. 1994. Molecular physiology of voltage-gated chloride channels. *Physiol. Rev.* 74:813–28

14. Wine JJ, Luckie DB. 1996. Cell-volume regulation: P-glycoprotein—a cautionary tale. *Curr. Biol.* 6:1410–12

15. Jentsch TJ, Günther W. 1997. Chloride channels: an emerging molecular picture. *BioEssays* 19:117–26

16. Fuller CM, Benos DJ. 1992. CFTR. *Am. J. Physiol.* 263:C267–86

17. Frizzell RA. 1995. Functions of the cystic fibrosis transmembrane conductance regulator protein. *Am. J. Respir. Crit. Care Med.* 151:S54–58 (Suppl.)

18. Welsh MJ, Smith AE. 1995. Cystic fibrosis. *Sci. Am.* 273:52–59

19. Welsh MJ, Smith AE. 1993. Molecular mechanisms of CFTR chloride channel dysfunction in cystic fibrosis. *Cell* 73:1251–54

20. Jentsch TJ, Pusch M, Rehfeldt A, Steinmeyer K. 1993. The ClC family of voltage-gated chloride channels: structure and function. *Ann. NY Acad. Sci.* 707:285–93

21. Jentsch TJ, Günther W, Pusch M, Schwappach B. 1995. Properties of voltage-gated chloride channels of the ClC gene family. *J. Physiol.* 482P:19–25S (Suppl.)

22. Jentsch TJ. 1996. Chloride channels: a molecular perspective. *Curr. Opin. Neurobiol.* 6:303–10

23. Uchida S, Marumo F. 1996. Molecular characterization of chloride channels in the kidney. *Exp. Nephrol.* 4:135–38

24. Jentsch TJ, Steinmeyer K, Schwarz G. 1990. Primary structure of *Torpedo marmorata* chloride channel isolated by expression cloning in *Xenopus* oocytes. *Nature* 348:510–14

25. Steinmeyer K, Ortland C, Jentsch TJ. 1991. Primary structure and functional expression of a developmentally regulated skeletal muscle chloride channel. *Nature* 354:301–4

26. Thiemann A, Gründer S, Pusch M, Jentsch TJ. 1992. A chloride channel widely expressed in epithelial and non-epithelial cells. *Nature* 356:57–60

27. Brandt S, Jentsch TJ. 1995. ClC-6 and ClC-7 are two novel broadly expressed members of the CLC chloride channel family. *FEBS Lett.* 377:15–20

28. Hoffman EP, Lehmann-Horn F, Rüdel R. 1995. Overexcited or inactive: ion channels in muscle disease. *Cell* 80:681–86

29. Lloyd SE, Pearce SHS, Fisher SE, Steinmeyer K, Schwappach B, et al. 1996. A common molecular basis for three inherited kidney stone diseases. *Nature* 379:445–49

30. Kieferle S, Fong P, Bens M, Vandewalle A, Jentsch TJ. 1994. Two highly homologous members of the ClC chloride channel family in both rat and human kidney. *Proc. Natl. Acad. Sci. USA* 91:6943–47

31. Steinmeyer K, Lorenz C, Pusch M, Koch MC, Jentsch TJ. 1994. Multimeric structure of ClC-1 chloride channel revealed by mutations in dominant myotonia congenita (Thomsen). *EMBO J.* 13:737–43

32. Steinmeyer K, Klocke R, Ortland C, Gronemeier M, Jockusch H, et al. 1991. Inactivation of muscle chloride channel by transposon insertion in myotonic mice. *Nature* 354:304–8

33. Koch MC, Steinmeyer K, Lorenz C, Ricker K, Wolf F, et al. 1992. The skeletal muscle chloride channel in dominant and recessive human myotonia. *Science* 257:797–800

34. Lehmann-Horn F, Mailander V, Heine R, George A. 1995. Myotonia levior is a chloride channel disorder. *Hum. Mol. Genet.* 4:1397–402

35. George AL, Çrackower MA, Abdalla JA, Hudson AJ, Ebers GC. 1993. Molecular basis of Thomsen's disease (autosomal dominant myotonia congenita). *Nat. Genet.* 3:305–9

36. Heine R, George AL Jr, Pika U, Deymeer F, Rudel R, et al. 1994. Proof of a non-functional muscle chloride channel in recessive myotonia congenita (Becker) by detection of a four base-pair deletion. *Hum. Mol. Genet.* 3:1123–28

37. Beck CL, Fahlke C, George AL Jr. 1996. Molecular basis for decreased muscle chloride conductance in the myotonic goat. *Proc. Natl. Acad. Sci. USA* 93:11248–52

38. Fahlke C, Rosenbohm A, Mitrovic N, George AL Jr, Rudel R. 1996. Mechanism of voltage-dependent gating in skeletal muscle chloride channels. *Biophys. J.* 71:695–706

39. Pusch M, Steinmeyer K, Jentsch TJ. 1994. Low single channel conductance of the major skeletal muscle chloride channel, ClC-1. *Biophys. J.* 66:149–52

40. Fahlke C, Knittle T, Gurnett CA, Campbell KP, George AL Jr. 1997. Subunit

stoichiometry of human muscle chloride channels. *J. Gen. Physiol.* 109:93–104

41. Fahlke C, Rüdel R, Mitrovic N, Zhou M, George AL Jr. 1995. An aspartic acid residue important for voltage-dependent gating of human muscle chloride channels. *Neuron* 15:463–72

42. Miller C. 1982. Open-state substructure of single chloride channels from Torpedo electroplax. *Philos. Trans. R. Soc. London Ser. B* 299:401–11

43. Chen TY, Miller C. 1996. Nonequilibrium gating and voltage dependence of the ClC-0 Cl⁻ channel. *J. Gen. Physiol.* 108:237–50

44. Bauer CK, Steinmeyer K, Schwarz JR, Jentsch TJ. 1991. Completely functional double-barreled chloride channel expressed from a single *Torpedo* cDNA. *Proc. Natl. Acad. Sci. USA* 88:11052–56

45. Ludewig U, Pusch M, Jentsch TJ. 1996. Two physically distinct pores in the dimeric ClC-0 chloride channel. *Nature* 383:340–43

46. Middleton RE, Pheasant DJ, Miller C. 1996. Homodimeric architecture of a ClC-type chloride ion channel. *Nature* 383:337–40

47. Middleton RE, Pheasant DJ, Miller C. 1994. Purification, reconstitution, and subunit composition of a voltage-gated chloride channel from *Torpedo* electroplax. *Biochemistry* 33:13189–98

48. Ludewig U, Jentsch TJ, Pusch M. 1997. Analysis of a protein region involved in permeation and gating of the voltage-gated *Torpedo* chloride channel ClC-0. *J. Physiol.* 498:691–702

49. Pusch M, Ludewig U, Rehfeldt A, Jentsch TJ. 1995. Gating of the voltage-dependent chloride channel ClC-O by the permeant anion. *Nature* 373:527–31

50. Rychkov GY, Pusch M, Astill DS, Roberts ML, Jentsch TJ, et al. 1996. Concentration and pH dependence of skeletal muscle chloride channel ClC-1. *J. Physiol.* 497:423–35

51. Miller C, Richard EA. 1990. The voltage-dependent chloride channel of *Torpedo* electroplax. Intimations of molecular structure from quirks of single-channel function. In *Chloride Channels and Carriers in Nerve, Muscle, and Glial Cells,* ed. FJ Alvarez-Leefmans, JM Russell, pp. 383–405. New York: Plenum

52. Pusch M, Ludewig U, Jentsch TJ. 1997. Temperature dependence of fast and slow gating relaxations of ClC-O chloride channels. *J. Gen. Physiol.* 109:105–16

53. Gründer S, Thiemann A, Pusch M,

Jentsch TJ. 1992. Regions involved in the opening of ClC-2 chloride channel by voltage and cell volume. *Nature* 360:759–62

54. Cid LP, Montrose-Rafizadeh C, Smith DI, Guggino WB, Cutting GR. 1995. Cloning of a putative human voltage-gated chloride channel (ClC-2) cDNA widely expressed in human tissues. *Hum. Mol. Genet.* 4:407–13

55. Murray CB, Morales MM, Flotte TR, McGrath-Morrow SA, Guggino WB, et al. 1995. ClC-2: a developmentally dependent chloride channel expressed in the fetal lung and downregulated after birth. *Am. J. Respir. Cell Mol. Biol.* 12:597–604

56. Malinowska DH, Kupert EY, Bahinski A, Sherry AM, Cuppoletti J. 1995. Cloning, functional expression, and characterization of a PKA-activated gastric Cl⁻ channel. *Am. J. Physiol.* 268:C191–200

57. Rotin D, Bar-Sagi D, O'Brodovich H, Merilainen J, Lehto VP, et al. 1994. An SH3 binding region in the epithelial Na⁺ channel (αrENaC) mediates its localization at the apical membrane. *EMBO J.* 13:4440–50

58. Dinudom A, Young JA, Cook DI. 1993. Na⁺ and Cl⁻ conductances are controlled by cytosolic Cl⁻ concentration in the intralobular duct cells of mouse mandibular glands. *J. Membr. Biol.* 135:289–95

59. Komwatana P, Dinudom A, Young JA, Cook DI. 1994. Characterization of the Cl⁻ conductance in the granular duct cells of mouse mandibular glands. *Pflügers Arch.* 428:641–47

60. Jordt SE, Jentsch TJ. 1997. Molecular dissection of gating in the ClC-2 chloride channel. *EMBO J.* 16:1582–92

61. Lorenz L, Pusch M, Jentsch TJ. 1996. Heteromultimeric CLC chloride channels with novel properties. *Proc. Natl. Acad. Sci. USA* 93:13362–66

62. Reeves WB, Andreoli TE. 1990. Cl⁻ transport in basolateral renal medullary vesicles: II. Cl⁻ channels in planar lipid bilayers. *J. Membr. Biol.* 113:57–65

63. Zimniak L, Winters CJ, Reeves WB, Andreoli TE. 1996. Cl⁻ channels in basolateral renal medullary vesicles. VI. *rbClC-Ka* cDNA encodes basolateral MTAL Cl⁻ channels. *Am. J. Physiol.* 270:F1066–72

64. Uchida S, Sasaki S, Furukawa T, Hiraoka M, Imai T, et al. 1993. Molecular cloning of a chloride channel that is regulated by dehydration and expressed predominantly in kidney medulla. *J. Biol. Chem.* 268:3821–24

65. Adachi S, Uchida S, Ito H, Hata M, Hiroe

M, et al. 1994. Two isoforms of a chloride channel predominantly expressed in thick ascending limb of Henle's loop and collecting ducts of rat kidney. *J. Biol. Chem.* 269:17677–83

66. Reeves WB, Andreoli TE. 1996. Chloride channels in renal epithelial cells. *Curr. Opin. Nephrol. Hyperten.* 5:408–10

67. Winters CJ, Reeves WB, Andreoli TE. 1990. Cl^- channels in basolateral renal medullary membranes: III. Determinants of single-channel activity. *J. Membr. Biol.* 118:269–78

68. Winters CJ, Reeves WB, Andreoli TE. 1991. Cl^- channels in the basolateral renal medullary vesicles. IV. Analogous channel activation by Cl^- or cAMP-dependent protein kinase. *J. Membr. Biol.* 122:89–95

69. Fritsch J, Edelman A. 1996. Modulation of the hyperpolarization-activated Cl^- current in human intestinal T84 epithelial cells by phosphorylation. *J. Physiol.* 490:115–28

70. Haas M. 1994. The Na-K-Cl cotransporters. *Am. J. Physiol.* 267:C869–85

71. Alper SL. 1991. The band 3-related anion-exchanger (AE) gene family. *Annu. Rev. Physiol.* 53:549–64

72. Grinstein S. 1987. Intracellular chloride concentration: determinants and consequences. In *Genetics and Epithelial Cell Dysfunction in Cystic Fibrosis,* ed. JR Riordan, M Buchwald, pp. 31–44. New York: Liss

73. Foskett JK. 1990. $[Ca^{2+}]_i$ modulation of Cl^- content controls cell volume in single salivary acinar cells during fluid secretion. *Am. J. Physiol.* 259:C998–1004

74. Rommens JM, Dho S, Bear CE, Kartner N, Kennedy D, et al. 1991. Cyclic-AMP-inducible chloride conductance in mouse fibroblast lines stably expressing human cystic fibrosis transmembrane conductance regulator (CFTR). *Proc. Natl. Acad. Sci. USA* 88:7500–4

75. Garcia L, Fahmi M, Prevarskaya N, Dufy B, Sartor P. 1997. Modulation of voltage-dependent Ca^{2+} conductance by changing Cl^- concentration in rat lactotrophs. *Am. J. Physiol.* 272:C1178–85

76. Shimizu Y, Daniels RH, Elmore MA, Finnen MJ, Hill ME, et al. 1993. Agonist-stimulated Cl^- efflux from human neutrophils. A common phenomenon during neutrophil activation. *Biochem. Pharmacol.* 45:1743–51

77. Ritter M, Wöll E, Häussinger D, Lang F. 1992. Effects of bradykinin on cell volume and intracellular pH in NIH 3T3 fibroblasts expressing the ras oncogene. *FEBS Lett.* 307:367–70

78. Lambert IH. 1989. Leukotriene-D4 induced cell shrinkage in Ehrlich ascites tumor cells. *J. Membr. Biol.* 108:165–76

79. Foskett JK. 1993. Optical imaging of ion transport in single living cells. *Comments Mol. Cell. Biophys.* 8:115–35

80. Robertson MA, Foskett JK. 1994. Na^+ transport pathways in secretory acinar cells: membrane cross talk mediated by $[Cl^-]_i$. *Am. J. Physiol.* 267:C146–56

81. Foskett JK. 1994. The role of calcium in the control of volume-regulatory transport pathways. In *Cellular and Molecular Physiology of Cell Volume Regulation,* ed. K Strange, pp. 259–77. Boca Raton: CRC Press

82. Foskett JK, Wong MMM, Sue-A-Quan G, Robertson MA. 1994. Isosmotic modulation of cell volume and intracellular ion activities during stimulation of single exocrine cells. *J. Exp. Zool.* 268:104–10

83. Rommens JM, Iannuzzi MC, Bat-sheva K, Drumm ML, Melmer G, et al. 1989. Identification of the cystic fibrosis gene: chromosome walking and jumping. *Science* 245:1059–65

84. Riordan JR, Rommens JM, Kerem B-S, Alon N, Rozmahel R, et al. 1989. Identification of the cystic fibrosis gene: cloning and characterization of complementary DNA. *Science* 245:1066–72

85. Kartner N, Hanrahan JW, Jensen TJ, Naismith AL, Sun S, et al. 1991. Expression of the cystic fibrosis gene in non-epithelial invertebrate cells produces a regulated anion conductance. *Cell* 64:681–91

86. Anderson MP, Rich DP, Gregory RJ, Smith AE, Welsh MJ. 1991. Generation of cAMP-activated chloride currents by expression of CFTR. *Science* 251:679–82

87. Bear CE, Li C, Kartner N, Bridges RJ, Jensen TJ, et al. 1992. Purification and functional reconstitution of the cystic fibrosis transmembrane conductance regulator (CFTR). *Cell* 68:809–18

88. Tsui L-C, Buchwald M. 1991. Biochemical and molecular genetics of cystic fibrosis. In *Advances in Human Genetics,* ed. H Harris, K Hirschhorn, 20:153–266. New York: Plenum

89. Lukacs GL, Mohamed A, Kartner N, Chang X-B, Riordan JR, et al. 1994. Conformational maturation of CFTR but not its mutant counterpart (DeltaF508) occurs in the endoplasmic reticulum and requires ATP. *EMBO J.* 13:6076–86

90. Ward CL, Kopito RR. 1994. Intracellular turnover of cystic fibrosis transmem-

brane conductance regulator. Inefficient processing and rapid degradation of wild-type and mutant proteins. *J. Biol. Chem.* 269:25710–18

91. Guggino WB. 1993. Outwardly rectifying chloride channels and CF: a divorce and remarriage. *J. Bioenerg. Biomembr.* 25:27–35

92. Gabriel SE, Clarke LL, Boucher RC, Stutts MJ. 1993. CFTR and outwardly rectifying chloride channels are distinct proteins with a regulatory relationship. *Nature* 363:263–66

93. Egan M, Flotte T, Afione S, Solow R, Zeitlin PL, et al. 1992. Defective regulation of outwardly rectifying Cl⁻ channels by protein kinase A corrected by insertion of CFTR. *Nature* 358:581–84

94. Jovov B, Ismailov II, Benos DJ. 1995. Cystic fibrosis transmembrane conductance regulator is required for protein kinase A activation of an outwardly rectified anion channel purified from bovine tracheal epithelia. *J. Biol. Chem.* 270:1521–28

95. Schwiebert EM, Egan ME, Hwang T-H, Fulmer SB, Allen SS, et al. 1995. CFTR regulates outwardly rectifying chloride channels through an autocrine mechanism involving ATP. *Cell* 81:1063–73

96. Reisin IL, Prat AG, Abraham EH, Amara JF, Gregory RJ, et al. 1994. The cystic fibrosis transmembrane conductance regulator is a dual ATP and chloride channel. *J. Biol. Chem.* 269:20584–91

97. Pasyk EA, Foskett JK. 1997. Cystic fibrosis transmembrane conductance regulator-associated ATP and adenosine 3′-phosphate 5′-phosphosulfate channels in endoplasmic reticulum and plasma membranes. *J. Biol. Chem.* 272:7746–51

98. Li CH, Ramjeesingh M, Bear CE. 1996. Purified cystic fibrosis transmembrane conductance regulator (CFTR) does not function as an ATP channel. *J. Biol. Chem.* 271:11623–26

99. Grygorczyk R, Tabcharani JA, Hanrahan JW. 1996. CFTR channels expressed in CHO cells do not have detectable ATP conductance. *J. Membr. Biol.* 151:139–48

100. Grygorczyk R, Hanrahan JW. 1997. CFTR-independent ATP release from epithelial cells triggered by mechanical stimuli. *Am. J. Physiol.* 272:C1058–66

101. Reddy MM, Quinton PM, Haws C, Wine JJ, Grygorczyk R, et al. 1996. Failure of the cystic fibrosis transmembrane conductance regulator to conduct ATP. *Science* 271:1876–79

102. Boucher RC, Stutts MJ, Knowles MR,

Cantley L, Gatzy JT. 1986. Na⁺ transport in cystic fibrosis respiratory epithelia. Abnormal basal rate and response to adenylate cyclase activation. *J. Clin. Invest.* 78:1245–52

103. Boucher RC. 1994. Human airway ion transport—Part one. *Am. J. Respir. Crit. Care Med.* 150:271–81

104. Boucher RC. 1994. Human airway ion transport—Part Two. *Am. J. Respir. Crit. Care Med.* 150:581–93

105. Cotton CU, Stutts MJ, Knowles MR, Gatzy JT, Boucher RC. 1987. Abnormal apical cell membrane in cystic fibrosis respiratory epithelium. An in vivo electrophysiologic analysis. *J. Clin. Invest.* 79:80–85

106. Chinet TC, Fullton JM, Yankaskas JR, Boucher RC, Stutts MJ. 1994. Mechanism of sodium hyperabsorption in cultured cystic fibrosis nasal epithelium: a patch-clamp study. *Am. J. Physiol.* 266:C1061–68

107. Stutts MJ, Rossier BC, Boucher RC. 1997. Cystic fibrosis transmembrane conductance regulator inverts protein kinase A-mediated regulation of epithelial sodium channel single channel kinetics. *J. Biol. Chem.* 272:14037–40

108. Burch LH, Talbot CR, Knowles MR, Canessa CM, Rossier BC, et al. 1995. Relative expression of the human epithelial Na⁺ channel subunits in normal and cystic fibrosis airways. *Am. J. Physiol.* 269:C511–18

109. Canessa CM, Horisberger J-D, Rossier BC. 1993. Epithelial sodium channel related to proteins involved in neurodegeneration. *Nature* 361:467–70

110. Canessa CM, Schild L, Buell G, Thorens B, Gautschi I, et al. 1994. Amiloride-sensitive epithelial Na⁺ channel is made of three homologous subunits. *Nature* 367:463–67

111. Voilley N, Lingueglia E, Champigny G, Mattei M-G, Waldman R, et al. 1994. The lung amiloride-sensitive Na⁺ channel: biophysical properties, pharmacology, ontogenesis, and molecular cloning. *Proc. Natl. Acad. Sci. USA* 91:247–51

112. Stutts MJ, Canessa CM, Olsen JC, Hamrick M, Cohn JA, et al. 1995. CFTR as a cAMP-dependent regulator of sodium channels. *Science* 269:847–50

113. Becq F, Fanjul M, Merten M, Figarella C, Hollande E, et al. 1993. Possible regulation of CFTR-chloride channels by membrane-bound phosphatases in pancreatic duct cells. *FEBS Lett.* 327:337–42

114. Becq F, Jensen TJ, Chang X-B, Savoia A, Rommens JM, et al. 1994. Phosphatase inhibitors activate normal and defective CFTR chloride channels. *Proc. Natl. Acad. Sci. USA* 91:9160–64

115. Berger HA, Travis SM, Welsh MJ. 1993. Regulation of the cystic fibrosis transmembrane conductance regulator Cl⁻ channel by specific protein kinases and protein phosphatases. *J. Biol. Chem.* 268:2037–47

116. Illek B, Fischer H, Santos GF, Widdicombe JH, Machen TE, et al. 1995. cAMP-independent activation of CFTR Cl channels by the tyrosine kinase inhibitor genistein. *Am. J. Physiol.* 268: C886–93

117. Seibert FS, Tabcharani JA, Chang X-B, Dulhanty AM, Mathews C, et al. 1995. cAMP-dependent protein kinase-mediated phosphorylation of cystic fibrosis transmembrane conductance regulator residue Ser-753 and its role in channel activation. *J. Biol. Chem.* 270:2158–62

118. Gadsby DC, Hwang T-C, Horie M, Nagel G, Nairn AC. 1993. Cardiac chloride channels: incremental regulation by phosphorylation/dephosphorylation. *Ann. NY Acad. Sci.* 707:259–74

119. Tabcharani JA, Chang X-B, Riordan JR, Hanrahan JW. 1991. Phosphorylation-regulated Cl⁻ channel in CHO cells stably expressing the cystic fibrosis gene. *Nature* 352:628–31

120. Becq F, Verrier B, Chang XB, Riordan JR, Hanrahan JW. 1996. cAMP- and Ca²⁺-independent activation of cystic fibrosis transmembrane conductance regulator channels by phenylimidazothiazole drugs. *J. Biol. Chem.* 271:16171–79

121. Reenstra WW, Yurko-Mauro K, Dam A, Raman S, Shorten S. 1996. CFTR chloride channel activation by genistein: the role of serine/threonine protein phosphatases. *Am. J. Physiol.* 271:C650–57

122. Townsend RR, Lipniunas PH, Tulk BM, Verkman AS. 1996. Identification of protein kinase A phosphorylation sites on NBD1 and R domains of CFTR using electrospray mass spectrometry with selective phosphate ion monitoring. *Protein Sci.* 5:1865–73

123. Jia YL, Mathews CJ, Hanrahan JW. 1997. Phosphorylation by protein kinase C is required for acute activation of cystic fibrosis transmembrane conductance regulator by protein kinase A. *J. Biol. Chem.* 272:4978–84

124. Fischer H, Machen TE. 1996. The tyrosine kinase p60ᶜ⁻ˢʳᶜ regulates the fast gate

of the cystic fibrosis transmembrane conductance regulator chloride channel. *Biophys. J.* 71:3073–82

125. Winpenny JP, McAlroy HL, Gray MA, Argent BE. 1995. Protein kinase C regulates the magnitude and stability of CFTR currents in pancreatic duct cells. *Am. J. Physiol.* 268:C823–28

126. Yang ICH, Cheng TH, Wang F, Price EM, Hwang TC. 1997. Modulation of CFTR chloride channels by calyculin A and genistein. *Am. J. Physiol.* 272:C142–55

127. Hwang T-C, Nagel G, Nairn AC, Gadsby DC. 1994. Regulation of the gating of the cystic fibrosis transmembrane conductance regulator Cl channels by phosphorylation and ATP hydrolysis. *Proc. Natl. Acad. Sci. USA* 91:4698–702

128. Rich DP, Berger HA, Cheng SH, Travis SM, Saxena M, et al. 1993. Regulation of the cystic fibrosis transmembrane conductance regulator Cl⁻ channel by negative charge in the R domain. *J. Biol. Chem.* 268:20259–67

129. Chang X-B, Tabcharani JA, Hou Y-X, Jensen TJ, Kartner N, et al. 1993. Protein kinase A (PKA) still activates CFTR chloride channel after mutagenesis of all 10 PKA consensus phosphorylation sites. *J. Biol. Chem.* 268:11304–11

130. Cheng SH, Rich DP, Marshall J, Gregory RJ, Welsh, MJ et al. 1991. Phosphorylation of the R domain by cAMP-dependent protein kinase regulates the CFTR chloride channel. *Cell* 66:1027–36

131. Winter MC, Sheppard DN, Carson MR, Welsh MJ. 1994. Effect of ATP concentration on CFTR Cl⁻ channels: a kinetic analysis of channel regulation. *Biophys. J.* 66:1398–403

132. Schultz BD, Venglarik CJ, Bridges RJ, Frizzell RA. 1995. Regulation of CFTR Cl⁻ channel gating by ADP and ATP analogues. *J. Gen. Physiol.* 105:329–61

133. Venglarik CJ, Schultz BD, Frizzell RA, Bridges RJ. 1994. ATP alters current fluctuations of cystic fibrosis transmembrane conductance regulator: evidence for a three-state activation mechanism. *J. Gen. Physiol.* 104:123–46

134. Anderson MP, Berger HA, Rich DP, Gregory RJ, Smith AE, et al. 1991. Nucleoside triphosphates are required to open the CFTR chloride channel. *Cell* 67:775–84

135. Anderson MP, Welsh MJ. 1992. Regulation by ATP and ADP of CFTR chloride channels that contain mutant nucleotide-binding domains. *Science* 257:1701–4

136. Quinton PM, Reddy MM. 1992. Con-

trol of CFTR chloride conductance by ATP levels through non-hydrolytic binding. *Nature* 360:79–81

137. Bell CL, Quinton PM. 1993. Regulation of CFTR Cl⁻ conductance in secretion by cellular energy levels. *Am. J. Physiol.* 264:C925–31

138. Carson MR, Welsh MJ. 1995. Structural and functional similarities between the nucleotide-binding domains of CFTR and GTP-binding proteins. *Biophys. J.* 69:2443–48

139. Carson MR, Welsh MJ. 1993. 5′-Adenylylimidodiphosphate does not activate CFTR chloride channels in cell-free patches of membrane. *Am. J. Physiol.* 265:L27–32

140. Ko YH, Delannoy M, Pedersen PL. 1997. Cystic fibrosis transmembrane conductance regulator: the first nucleotide binding fold targets the membrane with retention of its ATP binding function. *Biochemistry* 36:5053–64

141. Travis SM, Carson MR, Ries DR, Welsh MJ. 1993. Interaction of nucleotides with membrane-associated cystic fibrosis transmembrane conductance regulator. *J. Biol. Chem.* 268:15336–39

142. Ko YH, Thomas PJ, Pedersen PL. 1994. The cystic fibrosis transmembrane conductance regulator. Nucleotide binding to a synthetic peptide segment from the second predicted nucleotide binding fold. *J. Biol. Chem.* 269:14584–88

143. Randak C, Roscher AA, Hadorn H-B, Assfalg-Machleidt I, Auerswald EA, et al. 1995. Expression and functional properties of the second predicted nucleotide binding fold of the cystic fibrosis transmembrane conductance regulator fused to glutathione-*S*-transferase. *FEBS Lett.* 363:189–94

144. Manavalan P, Dearborn DG, McPherson JM, Smith AE. 1995. Sequence homologies between nucleotide binding regions of CFTR and G-proteins suggest structural and functional similarities. *FEBS Lett.* 366:87–91

145. Carson MR, Travis SM, Welsh MJ. 1995. The two nucleotide-binding domains of cystic fibrosis transmembrane conductance regulator (CFTR) have distinct functions in controlling channel activity. *J. Biol. Chem.* 270:1711–17

146. Carson MR, Travis SM, Winter MC, Sheppard DN, Welsh MJ. 1994. Phosphate stimulates CFTR Cl⁻ channels. *Biophys. J.* 67:1867–75

147. Baukrowitz T, Hwang T-C, Nairn AC, Gadsby DC. 1994. Coupling of CFTR Cl⁻ channel gating to an ATP hydrolysis cycle. *Neuron* 12:473–82

148. Gunderson KL, Kopito RR. 1994. Effects of pyrophosphate and nucleotide analogs suggest a role for ATP hydrolysis in cystic fibrosis transmembrane regulator channel gating. *J. Biol. Chem.* 269:19349–53

149. Logan J, Hiestand D, Daram P, Huang Z, Muccio DD, et al. 1994. Cystic fibrosis transmembrane conductance regulator mutations that disrupt nucleotide binding. *J. Clin. Invest.* 94:228–36

150. Gunderson KL, Kopito RR. 1995. Conformational states of CFTR associated with channel gating: the role of ATP binding and hydrolysis. *Cell* 82:231–39

151. Li CH, Ramjeesingh M, Wang W, Garami E, Hewryk M, et al. 1996. ATPase activity of the cystic fibrosis transmembrane conductance regulator. *J. Biol. Chem.* 271:28463–68

152. Reddy MM, Quinton PM. 1996. Hydrolytic and nonhydrolytic interactions in the ATP regulation of CFTR Cl⁻ conductance. *Am. J. Physiol.* 271:C35–42

153. Smit LS, Wilkinson DJ, Mansoura MK, Collins FS, Dawson DC. 1993. Functional roles of the nucleotide-binding folds in the activation of the cystic fibrosis transmembrane conductance regulator. *Proc. Natl. Acad. Sci. USA* 90:9963–67

154. Wilkinson DJ, Mansoura MK, Watson PY, Smit LS, Collins FS, et al. 1996. CFTR: The nucleotide binding folds regulate the accessibility and stability of the activated state. *J. Gen. Physiol.* 107:103–19

155. Schultz BD, Bridges RJ, Frizzell RA. 1996. Lack of conventional ATPase properties in CFTR chloride channel gating. *J. Membr. Biol.* 151:63–75

156. Fischer H, Machen TE. 1994. CFTR displays voltage dependence and two gating modes during stimulation. *J. Gen. Physiol.* 104:541–66

157. Gray MA, Greenwell JR, Argent BE. 1988. Secretin-regulated chloride channel on the apical plasma membrane of pancreatic duct cells. *J. Membr. Biol.* 105:131–42

158. Champigny G, Imler J-L, Puchelle E, Dalemans W, Gribkoff V, et al. 1995. A change in gating mode leading to increased intrinsic Cl⁻ channel activity compensates for defective processing in a cystic fibrosis mutant corresponding to a mild form of the disease. *EMBO J.* 14:2417–23

159. Seibert FS, Linsdell P, Loo TW, Hanrahan JW, Clarke DM, et al. 1996. Disease-

associated mutations in the fourth cytoplasmic loop of cystic fibrosis transmembrane conductance regulator compromise biosynthetic processing and chloride channel activity. *J. Biol. Chem.* 271:15139–45

160. Seibert FS, Linsdell P, Loo TW, Hanrahan JW, Riordan JR, et al. 1996. Cytoplasmic loop three of cystic fibrosis transmembrane conductance regulator contributes to regulation of chloride channel activity. *J. Biol. Chem.* 271:27493–99

161. Haws C, Finkbeiner WE, Widdicombe JH, Wine JJ. 1994. CFTR in Calu-3 human airway cells: channel properties and role in cAMP-activated Cl⁻ conductance. *Am. J. Physiol.* 266:L502–12

162. Haws CM, Nepomuceno IB, Krouse ME, Wakelee H, Law T, et al. 1996. DeltaF508-CFTR channels: kinetics, activation by forskolin, and potentiation by xanthines. *Am. J. Physiol.* 270:C1544–55

163. Dalemans W, Barbry P, Champigny G, Jallet S, Dott K, et al. 1991. Altered chloride ion channel kinetics associated with the ΔF508 cystic fibrosis mutation. *Nature* 354:526–28

164. Linsdell P, Hanrahan JW. 1996. Flickery block of single CFTR chloride channels by intracellular anions and osmolytes. *Am. J. Physiol.* 271:C628–34

165. Ishihara H, Welsh MJ. 1997. Block by MOPS reveals a conformational change in the CFTR pore produced by ATP hydrolysis. *Am. J. Physiol.* 273:C1278–89

166. Schultz BD, DeRoos ADG, Venglarik CJ, Singh AK, Frizzell RA, et al. 1996. Glibenclamide blockade of CFTR chloride channels. *Am. J. Physiol.* 271:L192–200

167. Gray MA, Harris A, Coleman L, Greenwell JR, Argent BE. 1989. Two types of chloride channel on duct cells cultured from human fetal pancreas. *Am. J. Physiol.* 257:C240–51

168. Dulhanty AM, Chang X-B, Riordan JR. 1995. Mutation of potential phosphorylation sites in the recombinant R domain of the cystic fibrosis transmembrane conductance regulator has significant effects on domain conformation. *Biochem. Biophys. Res. Commun.* 206:207–14

169. Dulhanty AM, Riordan JR. 1994. Phosphorylation by cAMP-dependent protein kinase causes a conformational change in the R domain of the cystic fibrosis transmembrane conductance regulator. *Biochemistry* 33:4072–79

170. Ma J, Tasch JE, Tao T, Zhao J, Xie J, et al. 1996. Phosphorylation-dependent block of cystic fibrosis transmembrane conductance regulator chloride channel by exogenous R domain protein. *J. Biol. Chem.* 271:7351–56

171. Picciotto MR, Cohn JA, Bertuzzi G, Greengard P, Nairn AC. 1992. Phosphorylation of the cystic fibrosis transmembrane conductance regulator. *J. Biol. Chem.* 267:12742–52

172. Dilda P, Lelievre LG. 1994. Functional characterization of cystic fibrosis transmembrane conductance regulator (CFTR) in apical membranes purified from bovine tracheal epithelium. *J. Biol. Chem.* 269:7801–6

173. Gregory RJ, Cheng SH, Rich DP, Marshall J, Paul S, et al. 1990. Expression and characterization of the cystic fibrosis transmembrane conductance regulator. *Nature* 347:382–86

174. Rich DP, Gregory RJ, Anderson MP, Manavalan P, Smith AE, et al. 1991. Effect of deleting the R domain on CFTR-generated chloride channels. *Science* 253:205–7

175. Cotten JF, Ostedgaard LS, Carson MR, Welsh MJ. 1996. Effect of cystic fibrosis-associated mutations in the fourth intracellular loop of cystic fibrosis transmembrane conductance regulator. *J. Biol. Chem.* 271:21279–84

176. Xie JX, Drumm ML, Ma JJ, Davis PB. 1995. Intracellular loop between transmembrane segments IV and V of cystic fibrosis transmembrane conductance regulator is involved in regulation of chloride channel conductance state. *J. Biol. Chem.* 270:28084–91

177. Nagel G, Hwang T-C, Nastiuk KL, Nairn AC, Gadsby DC. 1992. The protein kinase A-regulated cardiac Cl⁻ channel resembles the cystic fibrosis transmembrane conductance regulator. *Nature* 360:81–84

178. Ko YH, Pedersen PL. 1995. The first nucleotide binding fold of the cystic fibrosis transmembrane conductance regulator can function as an active ATPase. *J. Biol. Chem.* 270:22093–96

179. Randak C, Roscher AA, Hadorn H-B, Assfalg-Machleidt I, Auerswald EA, et al. 1995. Expression and functional properties of the second predicted nucleotide binding fold of the cystic fibrosis transmembrane conductance regulator fused to glutathione-S-transferase. *FEBS Lett.* 363:189–94

180. Yike I, Ye J, Zhang Y, Manavalan P, Gerken TA, et al. 1996. A recombinant peptide model of the first nucleotide-binding fold of the cystic fibrosis trans-

membrane conductance regulator: comparison of wild-type and DeltaF508 mutant forms. *Protein Sci.* 5:89–97

181. Randak C, Neth P, Auerswald EA, Assfalg-Machleidt I, Roscher AA, et al. 1996. A recombinant polypeptide model of the second predicted nucleotide binding fold of the cystic fibrosis transmembrane conductance regulator is a GTP-binding protein. *FEBS Lett.* 398:97–100

182. Hartman J, Huang Z, Rado TA, Peng S, Jilling T, et al. 1992. Recombinant synthesis, purification, and nucleotide binding characteristics of the first nucleotide binding domain of the cystic fibrosis gene product. *J. Biol. Chem.* 267:6455–58

183. Ko YH, Thomas PJ, Delannoy MR, Pedersen PL. 1993. The cystic fibrosis transmembrane conductance regulator. Overexpression, purification and characterization of wild type and ΔF508 mutant forms of the first nucleotide binding fold in fusion with the maltose-binding protein. *J. Biol. Chem.* 268:24330–38

184. Higgins CF. 1992. ABC transporters: from microorganisms to man. *Annu. Rev. Cell Biol.* 8:67–113

185. Hyde SC, Emsley P, Hartshorn MJ, Mimmack MM, Gileadi U, et al. 1990. Structural model of ATP-binding proteins associated with cystic fibrosis, multidrug resistance and bacterial transport. *Nature* 346:362–65

186. Annereau JP, Wulbrand U, Vankeerberghen A, Cuppens H, Bontems F, et al. 1997. A novel model for the first nucleotide binding domain of the cystic fibrosis transmembrane conductance regulator. *FEBS Lett.* 407:303–8

187. Lynch RM, Mejia R, Balaban RS. 1988. Energy transduction at the plasmalemma: coupling through membrane associated adenosine triphosphate? *Comments Mol. Cell. Biophys.* 5:151–70

188. Brown GC. 1992. Control of respiration and ATP synthesis in mammalian mitochondria and cells. *Biochem. J.* 284:1–13

Annu. Rev. Physiol. 1998. 60:719–39

FUNCTIONAL PROPERTIES AND PHYSIOLOGICAL ROLES OF ORGANIC SOLUTE CHANNELS

Kiaran Kirk

Division of Biochemistry and Molecular Biology, The Australian National University, Canberra, Australia; e-mail: kiaran.kirk@anu.edu.au

Kevin Strange

Laboratory of Cellular and Molecular Physiology, Departments of Anesthesiology and Pharmacology, Vanderbilt University Medical Center, Nashville, Tennessee 37232; e-mail: kevin.strange@mcmail.vanderbilt.edu

KEY WORDS: organic osmolytes, anion channels, porins, cell volume regulation, metabolites

---

ABSTRACT

Membrane channels provide routes for the rapid, passive movement of solutes across plasma and intracellular membranes. It is generally assumed that the major physiological role of membrane channels is to transport inorganic ions for processes such as transepithelial salt absorption and secretion, cell volume regulation, signal transduction, and control of membrane electrical properties. Increasing evidence indicates, however, that channels play an important role in organic solute transport in a wide variety of cell types and organisms. Some of the major physiological roles of organic solute channels include uptake of nutrients, excretion of metabolic waste products, volume-regulatory organic osmolyte transport, and control of mitochondrial metabolism. This article reviews the functions and characteristics of channels that participate in the transport and regulation of both charged and electroneutral organic solutes.

INTRODUCTION

Membrane channels are traditionally viewed as water-filled pores that provide routes for passive diffusion of specific inorganic ions across the lipid bilayer. It is commonly assumed that the primary physiological role of membrane channels is to control cellular electrical properties (e.g. stabilization of membrane potential, propagation of action potentials), to provide a pathway for bulk transport of inorganic ions (e.g. transepithelial salt absorption and secretion, volume-regulatory ion fluxes), and to mediate ion (e.g. Ca^{2+}) fluxes that are involved in signal transduction. Although numerous studies have demonstrated permeation of charged organic solutes through membrane channels, these observations are usually viewed as only providing insight into the geometry of the channel pore. There is little appreciation of the physiological roles and importance of membrane channels in organic solute transport and regulation. This review describes the functions, characteristics, and regulation of channels that provide a physiologically relevant route for the transmembrane movement of both electroneutral and charged organic solutes.

PORIN: THE ARCHETYPAL ORGANIC SOLUTE CHANNEL

Gram-negative bacteria are surrounded by a double membrane. The inner membrane functions as a selective permeability barrier and contains a large number of highly specific transport pathways. In contrast, the outer membrane functions as a molecular sieve that is typically freely permeable to hydrophilic solutes of <1 kDa. The sieving properties of the outer membrane protect the bacterium from environmental insults such as bile acids, digestive enzymes, antibiotics, host defense factors, etc. Exchange of metabolic waste products and organic nutrients between the cytosol and extracellular medium occurs through a class of membrane channels termed porins (1–3).

Mitochondria are also surrounded by a double membrane system with functional properties similar to those of bacterial membranes. Solutes with a molecular mass no larger than ≈ 1–2 kDa pass unimpeded through the outer membrane (4). The high permeability of the outer membrane is due to the presence of a mitochondrial porin, the voltage-dependent anion channel (VDAC) (4, 5). In addition to the bacterial and mitochondrial porins, porin-like channels have been described in plant chloroplasts, leucoplasts, and peroxisomes (1, 6).

Functional Properties

Porins can be divided into two groups: (a) general diffusion porins, which select between hydrophilic solutes primarily on the basis of molecular size; and (b) specific porins, which contain saturable binding sites for certain solutes. Porins that are selective for mono- and disaccharides (LamB, ScrY), nucleosides (TsX), and anions (protein P) have been described in bacteria. The general diffusion porins of bacteria discriminate poorly between anions and cations, have unitary conductances of ≈ 1–3 nS in 1 M KCl, and typically exhibit voltage-dependent closing. General diffusion porins have estimated pore diameters of $\approx$1–3 nm. Specific porins have smaller single channel conductances than general diffusion porins and exhibit transport rates that saturate with increasing substrate concentration (1–3).

VDAC is a general diffusion porin with an estimated pore diameter of 2.5–3 nm. It is the major pathway for the transport of metabolites, particularly adenine nucleotides and anionic substrates such as citrate and succinate, across outer mitochondrial membranes. Various metabolic enzymes such as hexokinase, glucokinase, creatine kinase, and glycerol kinase bind to VDAC. This binding is thought to provide the enzymes with preferential access to mitochondrial substrates and ATP (4, 5).

VDAC is weakly anion selective with a unitary conductance of $\approx$4 nS in 1 M KCl. At voltages between $+10$ to -10 mV, the channel has an open probability (P_o) near unity. With hyperpolarizing or depolarizing voltages of $\approx$20–30 mV, VDAC enters partially closed substates (5). A VDAC modulator protein (7) and micromolar concentrations of cytosolic NADH increase channel voltage sensitivity (8). Closed channels are poorly permeable to ATP and anionic metabolites (9, 10). Voltage-dependent gating of VDAC may therefore play a central role in regulating mitochondrial metabolism and in controlling the flux of adenine nucleotides between the cytoplasm and mitochondrial spaces (5, 9, 10).

Porin Structure

Porins have molecular masses of 30–50 kDa. The native functional state of most bacterial porins is a trimer, where each subunit forms a distinct channel (Figure 1A) (1, 3). Disruption of the trimer structure requires harsh heat and detergent treatments and usually irreversibly denatures the protein. VDAC (4) and certain bacterial porins such as OmpA and OprF (1) are the exceptions to the trimer generalization. The functional state of these porins is believed to be a monomer.

There is little sequence homology between different types of porins, but all contain large numbers of charged amino acids and lack stretches of hydrophobic residues long enough to span the membrane (1, 3). The biochemical characteristics of porins have stimulated much research into how the porin protein forms a transmembrane channel. Porins isolated from bacteria have the most thoroughly defined structures. Indeed, along with gramicidin, they are the only membrane channel whose structure is known with atomic resolution. Bacterial porins are composed predominantly of antiparallel β sheets tilted at an $\approx$45° angle to the membrane plane. These β sheets form a β cylinder or barrel with an hourglass-shaped, water-filled pore. Pore substructure is defined by three regions: an external mouth and vestibule, an intrapore constriction region, and an internal vestibule and mouth (Figure 1B). Clusters of charged residues located

A

B

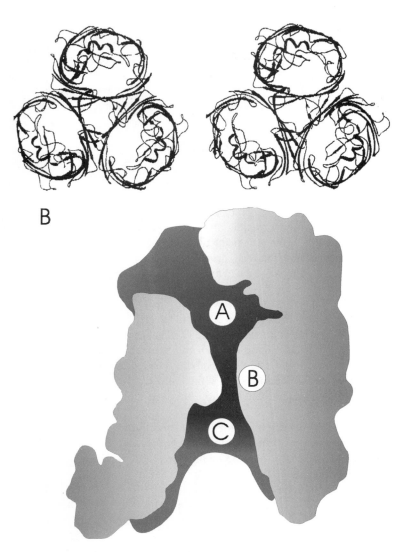

Figure 1   (*A*) Stereo pair ribbon diagram of the trimer structure of bacterial porin OmpF (63, 64). View is from the external medium. The helix projecting into each channel forms the constriction region and determines pore diameter. (Figure kindly provided by M Garavito.) (*B*) Diagram showing a side view of a PhoE porin monomer. *A*, external vestibule; *B*, constriction region; *C*, internal vestibule. Note hourglass shape of pore. [Drawing modified from (1, 63)].

in the external mouth are likely important for determining ionic selectivity. The size cutoff for permeable solutes is determined by the constriction region. Charged residues in the constriction region also appear to play a role in ionic selectivity. The structural properties of the internal vestibule suggest that it provides a region of minimal resistance for the egress of solutes from the channel (1, 3). VDAC is structurally less well defined than bacterial porins, but it is generally believed that the pore region is also defined by a β barrel (5).

The pore region of various bacterial porins studied to date is composed of 16 strands. LamB or maltoporin is the exception, however, and is composed of 18 strands (1). These two additional strands may be important for conferring maltose and maltodextrin selectivity on LamB. The constriction region of LamB is much narrower than that of general diffusion porins. Furthermore, a series of aromatic amino acid residues, termed the greasy slide, extends from the outer vestibule through the constriction region and into the periplasmic opening (11). Schirmer et al (11) postulate that these residues may bind and align sugar substrates with the pore axis, allowing guided diffusion across the membrane.

VOLUME-SENSITIVE ORGANIC SOLUTE CHANNELS

Volume-Regulatory Solute Loss

Regulation of cell volume in response to swelling, a process termed regulatory volume decrease, is mediated by the loss of Na^+, K^+, Cl^-, unidentified organic anions (e.g. 12), and a group of largely electroneutral organic solutes known as organic osmolytes. In mammalian cells, organic osmolytes fall into three broad classes: polyols (e.g. sorbitol, *myo*-inositol), amino acids and their derivatives (e.g. taurine, proline, alanine), and methylamines (e.g. betaine, glycerophosphorylcholine) (Figure 2). Organic osmolytes are present at high intracellular concentrations (i.e. tens to hundreds of millimolar) in all organisms from bacteria to humans. These solutes play a central role in cell osmoregulation and may function as general cytoprotectants (13, 14).

Characteristics of Organic Osmolyte Efflux Pathways

In most major groups of organisms, including bacteria, algae, protozoa, plants, invertebrates, lower vertebrates, and mammals, cell swelling leads to a rapid (i.e. seconds to minutes) increase in organic osmolyte permeability and efflux. The efflux of organic osmolytes is passive and occurs under physiological conditions down chemical gradients of $\approx 10^3$ to 10^7 (15–17).

Volume-sensitive organic osmolyte efflux mechanisms have been characterized in several cell types. The transport pathways responsible for organic osmolyte loss are Na^+ independent, show a linear dependence on substrate concentrations of up to hundreds of millimolar, and do not exhibit *trans* stimulation

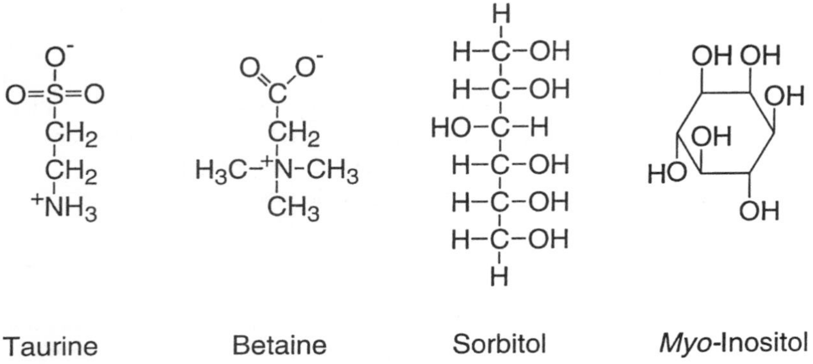

Taurine   Betaine   Sorbitol   *Myo*-Inositol

Figure 2   Structures of solutes that serve as organic osmolytes in a wide range of cell types and that exit the cells via a swelling-activated anion-selective channel.

or substrate competition (15–17). These observations have led to the widely accepted conclusion that organic osmolyte efflux occurs by diffusion through membrane channels rather than by carrier-mediated transport.

Selectivity Properties of Organic Osmolyte Efflux Pathways: Role of Anion Channels

A substantial body of data suggests that a single, broadly selective channel provides a common pathway for the efflux of most if not all the major organic osmolytes present in vertebrate cells (15–17). This channel also appears to be permeable to a variety of other organic solutes such as sucrose and pyrimidine nucleosides (17). The determinants of the selectivity properties of the channel are poorly understood. Size is certainly an important factor. Based on solute permeability measurements, a pore diameter for the channel of 8–9 Å has been estimated. It has also been suggested that the channel shows some preference for hydrophobic over hydrophilic solutes (17).

Numerous observations, which have been summarized in detail elsewhere (15–17), support the hypothesis that organic osmolyte efflux is mediated largely in many cell types by a swelling-activated anion channel. This channel has been termed VSOAC for Volume-Sensitive organic Osmolyte/Anion Channel. VSOAC is observed ubiquitously in mammalian cells and is also present in cells of lower vertebrates such as *Xenopus* (18) and the saltwater skate *Raja erinacea* (19). The channel is outwardly rectifying with a unitary conductance of 40–50 pS at +120 mV. In many cell types, VSOAC is voltage sensitive and inactivates with strong depolarization (Figure 3). VSOAC is selective for anions. Relative cation permeabilities (P_{cation}/P_{Cl}) of <0.03–0.05 are typically reported

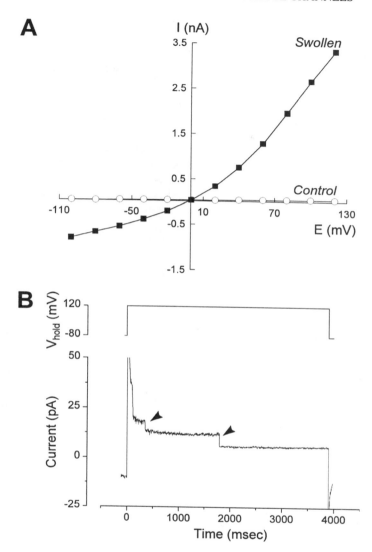

Figure 3 Electrophysiological characteristics of VSOAC. (*A*) Current-to-voltage relationship of whole cell, swelling-activated VSOAC current recorded from a C6 glioma cell. (*B*) Patch-clamp recording of single VSOAC channels. Membrane patch was pulled in the outside-out configuration from a swollen C6 glioma cell. Channel activity is not readily observable at negative holding potentials (21). Step-wise reductions in membrane current represent the closing of single VSOAC channels when the membrane is strongly depolarized. Step size is 5.4 pA, which corresponds to a single channel conductance at +120 mV of 45 pS (21). In both *A* and *B*, cells were patch clamped and bathed with solutions containing 140 mM CsCl.

for many vertebrate cell types (15). The channel observed in skate hepatocytes, however, is somewhat less anion selective: Cs^+ and Na^+ permeabilities relative to Cl^- are ≈ 0.2 and $P_{choline}/P_{Cl}$ is ≈ 0.55. Relative cation permeability increases with decreasing concentrations of CsCl in the patch pipette solution, consistent with the hypothesis that the channel pore contains saturable anion and cation binding sites with different anion and cation affinities (19). The anion permeability sequence of the channel is typically reported as $SCN^- > I > NO_3^- > Br^- > Cl^- > F^- >$ isethionate $>$ gluconate, corresponding to Eisenman's sequence I. Multivalent anion permeability is extremely low (15, 20).

As noted above, organic osmolytes are electroneutral, which precludes direct electrophysiological measurements of their permeation through VSOAC. Taurine, however, is a titratable zwitterion. At physiological pH, a small fraction of the total taurine in solution is present as an anion. Alkalinization increases the proportion of anionic to total taurine. The relative taurine permeability (i.e. $P_{taurine}/P_{Cl}$) of the channel measured at both physiological and alkaline pH is 0.15–0.2 (15). VSOAC is also highly permeable to structurally unrelated organic solutes such as pyruvate, short chain fatty acids, ketone bodies, amino acids, isethionate, and gluconate ($Px/P_{Cl} = 0.1$–0.4) (19, 20).

Regulation of VSOAC Activity

Unlike many ligand- and voltage-gated channels, swelling-induced changes in VSOAC activity do not occur by graded increases in the open probability (P_o) of a fixed number of functional channels. Instead, swelling switches channels from an OFF state, where $P_o = 0$, to an ON state, where P_o is close to unity and spontaneous channel closures are very brief (Figure 4). Cell shrinkage switches channels back to the OFF state (21, 22). A consequence of this mode of channel activation is that graded changes in whole-cell currents and solute fluxes are due to changes in the number of active channels in the cell membrane rather than graded changes in channel P_o. The mechanisms responsible for activating VSOAC in response to cell swelling are poorly understood (see 15 for a detailed review of this topic).

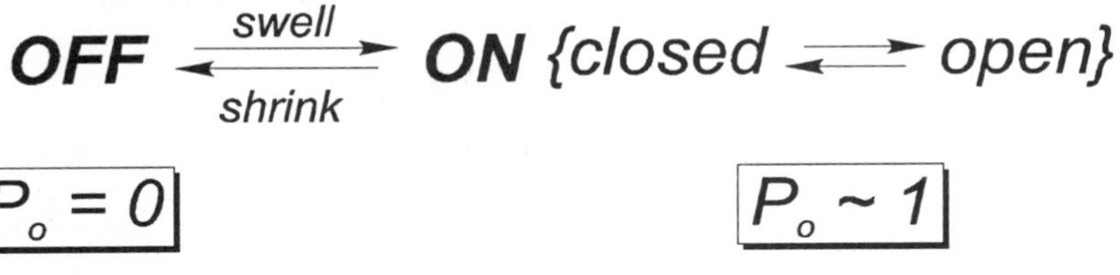

$$OFF \underset{shrink}{\overset{swell}{\rightleftharpoons}} ON \{closed \rightleftharpoons open\}$$

$$\boxed{P_o = 0} \qquad\qquad \boxed{P_o \sim 1}$$

Figure 4   Scheme illustrating control of VSOAC channel activity by cell swelling or shrinkage. VSOAC gates between closed and open states once the channel is switched ON by swelling. In the ON state, the channel is mostly open ($P_o \approx 1$) and mean channel closed time is very brief (21, 22).

VSOAC activation is sensitive to intracellular ATP levels (15, 20). Early studies demonstrated that swelling-induced channel activation is prevented by dialysis of metabolically poisoned cells with ATP-free solutions. More recently, however, it has been observed that the requirement for ATP is a function of the rate of cell swelling. Channel activation occurs at normal or near-normal rates in the absence of ATP when cells are swollen at higher rates with larger osmotic gradients (23, 24). This suggests that the metabolic state of the cell may modify the volume sensitivity or set-point of VSOAC. The mechanisms by which ATP modulates channel activation are poorly understood and may involve both ATP binding (15, 20) and phosphorylation reactions (22).

The volume sensitivity of VSOAC is also modulated by intracellular salt concentration. Increasing salt levels increase channel volume set-point by unknown mechanisms. The effect of intracellular electrolytes has been observed in both patch-clamped and intact cells (25). Regulation of VSOAC volume sensitivity by electrolytes allows cells to selectively utilize electrolytes or a combination of electrolytes and organic osmolytes for regulatory volume decrease. This in turn provides a mechanism for controlling intracellular ionic composition and preventing increases in cytoplasmic ionic strength during volume-regulatory solute loss (15, 25).

Other Organic Osmolyte Channels

In addition to VSOAC, it is likely that other volume-sensitive organic osmolyte channels exist. For example, studies in renal inner medullary collecting duct (IMCD) cells by Kinne and coworkers have suggested that swelling-induced taurine and *myo*-inositol efflux are mediated primarily by VSOAC or a related channel (26, 27). The characteristics of swelling-induced sorbitol and betaine efflux, however, are distinct from one another and from the *myo*-inositol/taurine channel (28). This suggests that there are separate channels for betaine and sorbitol loss. The yeast *FPS1* gene encodes a protein belonging to the major intrinsic protein (MIP) family found in the mammalian lens (29). MIPs are related to the aquaporin family of water channels (30). Studies of yeast deletion mutants suggest that Fps1 may function as a volume-sensitive glycerol efflux channel (31).

ORGANIC SOLUTE CHANNELS IN MALARIA-INFECTED ERYTHROCYTES

The malaria parasite, *Plasmodium* sp., is a unicellular, eukaryotic organism that, during the course of its life cycle, invades the red blood cells of its vertebrate hosts. This strategy helps the parasite evade detection by the host's immune system, but presents it with significant challenges in regard to the transfer of solutes (nutrients, metabolic wastes) between the parasite and the plasma. The mechanisms by which solute exchange occurs are not well understood. There is, however, increasing evidence for the involvement of membrane channels.

A Parasite-Induced Channel in the Host Red Cell Membrane

Following infection of human red cells by *Plasmodium falciparum,* there is a dramatic increase in the permeability of the red cell membrane to a wide range of low molecular weight organic and inorganic solutes (32, 33). These include monovalent cations and anions, amino acids, monosaccharides and other polyols, and pyrimidine and purine nucleosides (Figure 5). Available data are consistent with the view that much of the increased flux of solutes is mediated by a single pathway of low specificity and that this pathway plays an important role in both the uptake of essential nutrients and the efflux of metabolic wastes. The pathway is nonsaturable up to millimolar substrate concentrations, does not exhibit substrate competition, and does not discriminate between stereoisomers. These properties are those expected of a pore or channel.

The parasite-induced channel is anion selective; its permeability is more than two orders of magnitude greater to monovalent anions than it is to monovalent cations (33) (cf the two panels of Figure 5). Monovalent cation flux varies with the nature of the anion present and is increased markedly by replacement of Cl^-

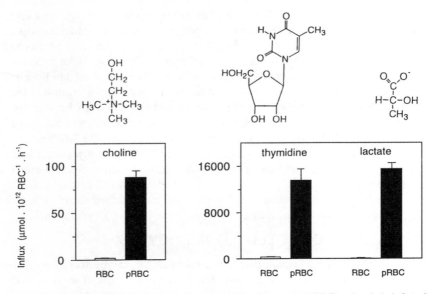

Figure 5   Transport of three structurally unrelated solutes into normal (RBC) and malaria-infected (PRBC) human red blood cells under conditions where the endogenous transporters for each of the solutes were inhibited by pharmacological agents (adapted from 33, 65).

with either NO_3^- or SCN^- in the suspending medium (34). The channel is inhibited, in some cases at submicromolar concentrations, by compounds known to block anion channels elsewhere. These compounds include NPPB, furosemide, niflumate, MK-196, glibenclamide, quinine, and phloridzin (33, 35, 36). The pharmacological and selectivity characteristics of the pathway are very similar to those of anion-selective channels described in many other cell types. However, its electrophysiological characteristics remain to be established.

In addition to playing a likely role in nutrient uptake and waste excretion, the parasite-induced channel may also regulate the volume of the parasitized red cell. Digestion of hemoglobin to its constituent amino acids by the parasite increases the amount of osmotically active solute within the infected cell. By mediating the net efflux of amino acids from the red cell, the parasite-induced channel dissipates the osmotic challenge they pose, thereby protecting the cell from premature osmotic lysis (37).

An Organic Solute Channel on the Parasitophorous Vacuole Membrane

Within the malaria-infected red cell, the intracellular parasite is enclosed inside a parasitophorous vacuole membrane (PVM). Desai et al (38) have obtained single-channel recordings of a high-conductance channel present at high density in the PVM of *P. falciparum*. The channel has a P_o near unity and does not discriminate between cations or anions. Reconstitution of membranes from parasitized cells into planar lipid bilayers has indicated that the PVM channel is permeable to solutes with molecular mass up to 1.4 kDa. The estimated effective pore diameter of the channel is 23 Å (36).

A similar channel is thought to be present on the PVM of another intracellular parasite, *Toxoplasma gondii* (39), which invades nucleated cells. Observations of the movement of fluorescent compounds microinjected into *T. gondii*-infected human fibroblasts indicate that solutes with a molecular mass up to 1.9 kDa cross the PVM.

It has been proposed that the PVM channel mediates the transfer of nutrients and ions between the cytoplasm of the host cell and the parasitophorous vacuolar space (38, 39). There are obvious parallels between the characteristics and putative roles of these channels and those of porins described above. Whether these parallels reflect similarities at the molecular level is, as yet, unknown.

CHANNELS THAT MEDIATE THE EFFLUX OF METABOLIC WASTES

The end products of anaerobic metabolism are mono- and dicarboxylate anions. Such compounds are, to varying extents, secreted from the cells in which they are produced, thereby preventing their accumulation in the cytoplasm.

Electrophysiological studies carried out by Martin and coworkers on muscle cells from *Ascaris suum* (a parasitic worm that inhabits the gut of pigs) have demonstrated the presence in the plasma membrane of a Ca^{2+}-activated, anion-selective channel with high organic anion permeability (40, 41). The relative permeability of the channel to monocarboxylate anions (Px/P_{Cl}) ranges from 0.74 in the case of formate to 0.07 for the much larger heptanoate ion (41). There is a strong inverse correlation between the size (Stokes diameter) and relative permeability of monocarboxylate anions; a plot of one against the other yields an estimated pore diameter of 6.55 Å. The dicarboxylate anions succinate and oxaloacetate have Px/P_{Cl} values of 0.20 and 0.32, respectively. A third dicarboxylate anion, malate, has a high relative permeability $(Px/P_{Cl} = 0.5)$ but a negligible conductance (41).

It has been postulated that the major function of the Ca^{2+}-activated anion channel in *Ascaris* muscle is the passive excretion of the anionic end products of anaerobic metabolism, driven by the membrane potential (-35 mV) (40, 41). Intracellular Ca^{2+} concentration increases during muscle activity, which tends

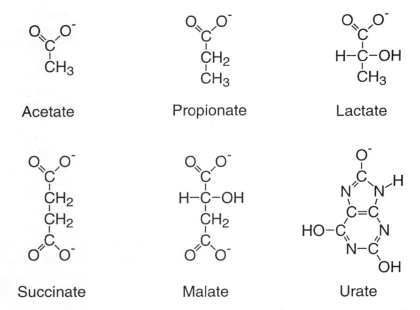

Figure 6 Structures of organic anions postulated to be physiological substrates of the Ca^{2+}-activated anion channel in the plasma membrane of muscle cells from *Ascaris suum* (acetate, propionate, lactate, succinate), anion-selective channels in the vacuolar and plasma membranes of plant cells (malate), and channel activity associated with UAT and the oxidative enzyme uricase (urate).

to increase the frequency of channel opening. Compounds that may leave the cell via this route include acetate, propionate, succinate, lactate, α-methyl-butyrate, and α-methyl-valerate (see Figure 6). The low malate conductance of the channel may provide a mechanism to minimize the loss of this important metabolic intermediate from the cell (40, 41).

Calcium-activated anion channels are present in a wide variety of cell types. In most cases, however, their permeability to organic anions has not been investigated in detail. It is intriguing to speculate that such channels might generally provide a route for the rapid excretion of the end products of anaerobic metabolism.

MALATE CHANNELS IN PLANTS

Malate (see Figure 6) is the most abundant organic anion in plant cells. It is present at concentrations ranging from tens to hundreds of millimolar and serves a variety of important physiological functions. Several of these functions require that malate be transported across either the intracellular vacuolar membrane or the cell plasma membrane. Recent evidence suggests a central role for anion-selective channels in these processes.

Malate Channels in the Vacuolar Membrane

The vacuole of higher plant cells serves as storage compartment for ions and metabolites. In the green, photosynthetically active cells of crassulacean acid metabolism (CAM) plants, large quantities of malic acid produced during night-time CO_2 fixation are stored in the vacuole. Malic acid accumulates in the vacuole throughout the night and is released during the day into the cytosol, where it is decarboxylated to provide CO_2 for the Calvin Cycle (42).

The mechanisms involved in the transfer of malic acid between the vacuole and the cytosol are not fully understood. However, a number of recent studies have implicated an anion-selective channel (termed VMAL for Vacuolar MALate channel) as the major route for the uptake of malate into the vacuole (42). Electrophysiological studies on vacuoles from several plant species have demonstrated whole-vacuole and single-channel currents attributable to the flux of malate across the vacuolar membrane from cytosol to vacuole lumen (42–46). The currents are strongly rectifying such that there is little malate flux into the cytosol. The channels responsible for the malate currents show voltage-dependent behavior and have complex regulatory characteristics. Channel activity is influenced by both cytosolic malate and vacuolar Cl^- concentrations (45, 46). These regulatory features, along with uncertainty over the number of channel types that contribute to the observed currents, have made it difficult to assess channel selectivity. Estimates of P_{malate}/P_{Cl} range from 0.2 to 5.0 (45, 46).

Malate Channels in Plant Cell Plasma Membranes

Hedrich and coworkers have described a voltage-dependent anion channel in the plasma membrane of plant stomatal guard cells (i.e. specialized epidermal cells that form the stomatal opening). This channel, termed GCAC1 for Guard Cell Anion Channel, is modulated by extracellular malate. At normal resting membrane potentials, channel P_o is low in the absence of malate. Application of malate to the cell surface alters channel voltage-sensitivity such that P_o increases at the resting potential (47).

Extracellular malate concentration in leaves increases under conditions where CO_2 levels exceed those that can be used by the plant's photosynthetic machinery (e.g. following the transition from light to dark). The source of this malate is uncertain, but it may be released from the photosynthetic tissue and/or the guard cells themselves via unknown pathways. It is postulated that the buildup of extracellular malate induces activation of GCAC1, with the resulting efflux of cytosolic anions and accompanying cations causing a decrease in cell volume, a loss of turgor and, hence, stomatal closure. The modulation of GCAC1 by malate thus provides a mechanism to ensure that the stomata do not remain open, which would leave the plant prone to water loss through transpiration, under conditions where the photosynthetic tissues are unable to utilize available CO_2 (47, 48).

In addition to being regulated by extracellular malate, the guard cell anion channel has a significant malate permeability ($P_{malate}/P_{Cl} = 0.1$) (47). Because malate is an abundant cytosolic anion, its efflux from the cell following channel activation by extracellular malate is a major component of the osmotically active solute loss that causes stomatal closure (47).

In the apical root cells of aluminum-tolerant wheat seedlings, malate efflux is stimulated by extracellular Al^{3+}. The released malate chelates and thereby detoxifies aluminum in the immediate vicinity of the roots (49, 50). Malate efflux is inhibited by a range of broad-specificity anion transport inhibitors such as niflumic acid, NPPB, IAA-94, and 9AC. Recent electrophysiological studies have identified an anion channel on the plasma membrane of protoplasts isolated from wheat roots (51). This channel is activated by Al^{3+} and is inhibited by niflumic acid, consistent with its role as a Al^{3+}-stimulated malate release pathway. However, the permeability of the channel to malate has not been measured directly.

URATE CHANNELS

Uric acid (see Figure 6) is an end product of purine metabolism. Because it is relatively water insoluble, the concentration of uric acid in cells must be kept low, and it must be excreted efficiently from the body. Clearance of uric acid from the extracellular compartment occurs via the kidneys and intestine.

Renal excretion of uric acid occurs by glomerular filtration and nephron transport. Studies in rabbit renal brush border membranes have identified channel-like as well as saturable urate transport pathways (52). Recently, a urate transporter, UAT, was cloned from rat kidney and shown to be expressed in a variety of tissues (53). The UAT cDNA encodes a 322 amino acid protein. Reconstitution of recombinant UAT protein into planar lipid bilayers gave rise to channel activity. The channels have a linear current-voltage relationship, with an estimated slope conductance of 9.5 pS in symmetrical 2.5 mM urate 220 mM KCl solutions, and are highly selective for urate compared with K^+, Cs^+, Ca^{2+}, Cl^-, and SO_4^-. The channel structure is unknown; the amino acid sequence of UAT predicts only a single α helix and no β sheet.

Leal-Pinto et al (53) suggest that UAT functions in both renal and intestinal urate excretion, as well as in a general housekeeping role by mediating the efflux of urate from many different cell types. At this time it is unclear if UAT functions in vivo as a saturable urate carrier or as a channel that allows passive urate diffusion. If UAT is indeed a carrier, the channel activity seen in bilayers may reflect an alternate functional mode of the transporter similar to what has been observed for various neurotransmitter and excitatory amino acid transporters (54, 55).

In addition to renal and intestinal excretion, uric acid is also cleared from the body by conversion to water-soluble allantoin. This occurs in liver peroxisomes and is mediated by the oxidative enzyme uricase. Pordy et al (56) have shown that when uricase is incorporated into liposomes, it mediates the transport of urate across the bilayer. When reconstituted into planar lipid bilayers, the enzyme functions as a highly selective urate channel (57). In the presence of symmetrical 2.5 mM urate/220 mM KCl solutions, the channel is strongly rectifying with a slope conductance of 8 pS at positive voltages. The selectivity of the channel for urate over K^+ or Cl^- is at least 80-fold. Oxonate and pyrazinoate also readily permeate the channel. Channel P_o is voltage sensitive; at voltages above +25 mV, P_o is >0.8. At present, it is unclear how uricase forms a functional channel. No transmembrane (α helices or β sheets) are predicted from the primary amino acid sequence of the enzyme.

The physiological relevance of the uricase channel activity observed in vitro is unknown. It is interesting to note, however, that UAT was cloned by screening a renal cDNA library with a polyclonal antibody to pig liver uricase despite the fact that UAT and uricase have no amino acid sequence homology (53). Leal-Pinto et al (53) speculate that there are regions of structural homology between uricase and UAT when the proteins are folded into their tertiary structures. If this is true, it may explain how uricase gives rise to urate channel activity in planar lipid bilayers.

GAP JUNCTION CHANNELS

Gap junction channels are specialized intercellular channels that connect the cytosols of adjoining cells. They are formed from structures known as connexons, each of which is composed of a ring of six identical protein subunits termed connexins. The connexons in the plasma membrane of one cell align with those from an adjacent cell to form an aqueous channel that extends across the two lipid bilayers. More than a dozen different connexin proteins have been identified, and many cells express more than one type (58).

Gap junction channels are permeable to ions and neutral molecules up to ≈ 1 kDa or 15 Å diameter. Channels comprised of different connexin proteins differ somewhat in their permeability properties. The channels are gated, oscillating between open and closed states, and they are closed, rapidly and reversibly, in response to elevated cytosolic Ca^{2+} or decreased cytosolic pH (58, 59).

Gap junction channels have been postulated to serve a range of physiological roles, a number of which involve the transport of organic solutes (58, 59). Their permeability to metabolites allows them to facilitate the nourishment of sick or metabolically deprived cells by healthier, neighboring cells and, more generally, to allow cells of low metabolic capacity to benefit from the higher metabolic activity of cells nearby. Similarly, the channels facilitate the elimination of potentially harmful metabolic by-products from more metabolically active cells. The channels are permeable to second messengers (e.g. cAMP, cGMP, Ca^{2+}, and IP_3), and the passage of these solutes between cells in hormone-sensitive tissues is postulated to play a role in ensuring a coordinated response to hormone action. Another postulated role for these channels is to buffer the harmful effects of xenobiotic chemicals, by dispersing these agents from the site of exposure to other cells in the tissue. Finally, there is evidence that the passage of unidentified regulatory molecules via gap junction channels plays a critical role in maintaining meiotic arrest in oocytes and in controlling tissue development and differentiation.

PHOSPHOLEMMAN

Phospholemman (PLM) is an 8-kDa transmembrane protein found in heart and certain other tissues. It is a major plasma membrane substrate for phosphorylation by protein kinase A and C (60). Mat-8 is a PLM-like protein expressed in human breast tumors (61). Expression of either PLM or Mat-8 in *Xenopus* oocytes induces a Cl⁻ conductance (60, 61). When reconstituted into planar lipid bilayers, recombinant PLM forms anion-selective channels (62). These channels display a linear current-voltage relationship, have a unitary conductance of $\approx$700 pS in symmetrical 150 mM NaCl solutions, and are open most of the time at voltages between -75 and $+75$ mV. The PLM channel is highly permeable to a number of organic anions; its permeability to lactate, glutamate, isethionate, and gluconate relative to Cl^- is in the range of 0.65–0.79, whereas its permeability to the anionic form of taurine is nearly 70-fold higher than that of Cl^-. Given the high concentrations (30–60 mM) of taurine found normally in the heart, Moorman et al (62) postulated that PLM functions as a volume-regulatory taurine channel. Direct physiological evidence for this hypothesis is lacking, however.

SUMMARY AND FUTURE PERSPECTIVES

Membrane channels provide routes for the rapid, passive movement of solutes across plasma and intracellular membranes. It is generally assumed that the major physiological role of membrane channels is to transport inorganic ions for processes such as transepithelial salt absorption and secretion, cell volume regulation, signal transduction, and control of membrane electrical properties. As described above, however, there is increasing evidence that channels play an important role in organic solute transport in a wide variety of cell types and organisms. Major physiological functions of organic solute channels include uptake of nutrients, excretion of metabolic waste products, and volume-regulatory organic osmolyte transport. Organic solute channels may also play a role in transepithelial organic solute absorption and secretion. VDAC channels in the outer membrane of mitochondria appear to function critically in regulating mitochondrial metabolism. In plants, organic solute channels play a number of roles in carbon metabolism and in the detoxification of cytotoxic metal ions. The channels described in this review fall loosely into the following two classes:

1. Anion-selective channels. These channels have a relatively low cation permeability and, in each of the cases considered here, are present in membranes across which it is important to maintain cation gradients (e.g. the plasma membrane or membranes enclosing intracellular organelles). Anion-selective organic solute channels may transport both anionic and electroneutral organic solutes. It is possible that the transport of electroneutral solutes could be served equally well by nonselective or even cation-selective channels. However, the activation of nonselective or cation-selective channels, with pore diameters sufficient to accommodate various organic solutes (see Figures 2 and 6), would likely disrupt transmembrane cation (Na^+, K^+, Ca^{2+}, H^+) gradients critical to cell function. Although anion-selective organic solute channels have the potential to dissipate transmembrane Cl^- gradients,

the consequences of this for most cells or organelles is likely to be relatively minor, at least in the short term because Cl⁻ distribution is frequently at or close to electrochemical equilibrium.

2. Nonselective channels. Channels showing a much lower degree of ionic selectivity than the anion-selective organic solute channels are typically found in membranes that are not required to support cation electrochemical gradients (e.g. the outer membrane of gram-negative bacteria and the vacuolar membrane enclosing intracellular parasites).

Channels within each of these two broad classes share a number of apparent similarities with one another. The degree of significance that can be attached to such similarities is unclear at present. It is possible that at least some of the channels are related at a molecular level, perhaps even comprising one or more distinct gene families. Much work remains to be done, however, before any rigorous conclusions can be drawn. The full extent to which organic solute channels participate in cellular functions is poorly understood and needs to be defined. Similarly, the mechanisms by which organic solute channels are regulated need to be established. Finally, with the exception of the porins and gap junctions, there is no clear molecular picture of an organic solute channel that can be related to its physiological function. Given the important physiological roles played by organic solute channels, detailed biophysical, cellular, and molecular characterization is clearly warranted. Such studies will undoubtedly provide new insights into membrane function and the structure of membrane proteins.

ACKNOWLEDGMENTS

Work in K Kirk's laboratory at the University of Oxford was supported by the Lister Institute of Preventive Medicine, and the Wellcome Trust, and at the Australian National University by the Australian National Health and Medical Research Council. K Strange was supported by National Institutes of Health grants NS30591, DK45628, and DK51610. The authors are grateful to Drs. Peter Ryan and JAC Smith for providing preprints of papers prior to publication.

> Visit the *Annual Reviews home page* at
> http://www.AnnualReviews.org.

Literature Cited

1. Jap BK, Walian PJ. 1996. Structure and functional mechanism of porins. *Physiol. Rev.* 76:1073–88
2. Benz R. 1988. Structure and function of porins from gram-negative bacteria. *Annu. Rev. Microbiol.* 42:359–93
3. Welte W, Nestel U, Wacker T, Diederichs K. 1995. Structure and function of the porin channel. *Kidney Intl.* 48:930–40
4. Mannella CA. 1992. The 'ins' and 'outs' of mitochondrial membrane channels. *Trends Biochem. Sci.* 17:315–20

5. Colombini M, Blachly-Dyson E, Forte M. 1996. VDAC, a channel in the outer mitochondrial membrane. *Ion Channels* 4:169–202

6. Reumann S, Maier E, Benz R, Heldt HW. 1995. The membrane of leaf peroxisomes contains a porin-like channel. *J. Biol. Chem.* 270:17559–65

7. Holden MJ, Colombini M. 1993. The outer mitochondrial membrane channel, VDAC, is modulated by a protein localized in the intermembrane space. *Biochim. Biophys. Acta* 1144:396–402

8. Zizi M, Forte M, Blachly-Dyson E, Colombini M. 1994. NADH regulates the gating of VDAC, the mitochondrial outer membrane channel. *J. Biol. Chem.* 269:1614–16

9. Hodge T, Colombini M. 1997. Regulation of metabolite flux through voltage-gating of VDAC channels. *J. Membr. Biol.* 157:271–79

10. Rostovtseva T, Colombini M. 1997. VDAC channels mediate and gate the flow of ATP: implication on regulation of mitochondrial function. *Biophys. J.* 72:1954–62

11. Schirmer T, Keller TA, Wang YF, Rosenbusch JP. 1995. Structural basis for sugar translocation through maltoporin channels at 3.1 Å resolution. *Science* 267:512–14

12. Hallows KR, Knauf PA. 1994. Regulatory volume decrease in HL-60 cells: importance of rapid changes in permeability of Cl⁻ and organic solutes. *Am. J. Physiol.* 267:C1045–56

13. Garcia-Perez A, Burg MB. 1991. Renal medullary organic osmolytes. *Physiol. Rev.* 71:1081–115

14. Yancey PH. 1994. Compatible and counteracting solutes. In *Cellular and Molecular Physiology of Cell Volume Regulation,* ed. K Strange, pp. 81–109. Boca Raton: CRC Press

15. Strange K, Emma F, Jackson PS. 1996. Cellular and molecular physiology of volume-sensitive anion channels. *Am. J. Physiol.* 270:C711–30

16. Strange K, Jackson PS. 1995. Swelling-activated organic osmolyte efflux: a new role for anion channels. *Kidney Intl.* 48:994–1003

17. Kirk K. 1997. Physiological roles and functional properties of swelling-activated organic osmolyte channels. *J. Membr. Biol.* 158:1–16

18. Hand M, Morrison R, Strange K. 1997. Characterization of volume-sensitive organic osmolyte efflux and anion current in *Xenopus* oocytes. *J. Membr. Biol.* 157:9–16

19. Jackson PS, Churchwell K, Ballatori N,

20. Boyer JL, Strange K. 1996. Swelling-activated anion conductance in skate hepatocytes: regulation by cell Cl⁻ and ATP. *Am. J. Physiol.* 270:C57–66

20. Jackson PS, Morrison R, Strange K. 1994. The volume-sensitive organic osmolyte-anion channel VSOAC is regulated by nonhydrolytic ATP binding. *Am. J. Physiol.* 267:C1203–9

21. Jackson PS, Strange K. 1995. Single channel properties of a swelling-activated anion conductance. Current activation occurs by abrupt switching of closed channels to an open state. *J. Gen. Physiol.* 105:643–60

22. Meyer K, Korbmacher C. 1996. Cell swelling activates ATP-dependent voltage-gated Cl⁻ channels in M-1 mouse cortical collecting duct cells. *J. Gen. Physiol.* 108:177–93

23. Volk KA, Zhang C, Husted RF, Stokes JB. 1996. Cl⁻ current in IMCD cells activated by hypotonicity: time course, ATP dependence, and inhibitors. *Am. J. Physiol.* 271:F552–59

24. Basavappa S, Strange K. 1997. Regulation of VSOAC volume sensitivity by intracellular ATP. *J. Gen. Physiol.* (Abstr.) 110:39A–40

25. Emma F, McManus M, Strange K. 1997. Intracellular electrolytes regulate the volume set point of the organic osmolyte/anion channel VSOAC. *Am. J. Physiol.* 272:C1766–75

26. Ruhfus B, Kinne RKH. 1996. Hypotonicity-activated efflux of taurine and myoinositol in rat inner medullary collecting duct cells: evidence for a major common pathway. *Renal Physiol. Biochem.* 19:317–24

27. Boese SH, Wehner F, Kinne RHK. 1996. Taurine permeation through the swelling-activated anion conductance in rat IMCD cells in primary culture. *Am. J. Physiol.* 271:F498–507

28. Ruhfus B, Tinel H, Kinne RK. 1996. Role of G-proteins in the regulation of organic osmolyte efflux from isolated rat renal inner medullary collecting duct cells. *Pflügers Arch.* 433:35–41

29. Pao GM, Wu LF, Johnson KD, Hofte H, Chrispeels MJ, et al. 1991. Evolution of the MIP family of integral membrane transport proteins. *Mol. Microbiol.* 5:33–37

30. Nielsen S, Agre P. 1995. The aquaporin family of water channels in kidney. *Kidney Intl.* 48:1057–68

31. Luyten K, Albertyn J, Skibbe WF, Prior BA, Ramos J, et al. 1995. Fps1, a yeast member of the MIP family of channel proteins, is a facilitator for glycerol uptake and

efflux and is inactive under osmotic stress. *EMBO J.* 14:1360–71

32. Ginsburg H, Kutner S, Krugliak M, Cabantchik ZI. 1985. Characterization of permeation pathways appearing in the host membrane of *Plasmodium falciparum* infected red blood cells. *Mol. Biochem. Parasitol.* 14:313–22

33. Kirk K, Horner HA, Elford BC, Ellory JC, Newbold CI. 1994. Transport of diverse substrates into malaria-infected erythrocytes via a pathway showing functional characteristics of a chloride channel. *J. Biol. Chem.* 269:3339–47

34. Kirk K, Homer HA. 1995. Novel anion dependence of induced cation transport in malaria-infected erythrocytes. *J. Biol. Chem.* 270:24270–75

35. Kutner S, Breuer WV, Ginsburg H, Cabantchik ZI. 1987. On the mode of action of phlorizin as an antimalarial agent in vitro cultures of *Plasmodium falciparum*. *Biochem. Pharmacol.* 36:123–29

36. Desai SA, Rosenberg RL. 1997. Pore size of the malaria parasite's nutrient channel. *Proc. Natl. Acad. Sci. USA* 94:2045–49

37. Zarchin S, Krugliak M, Ginsburg H. 1986. Digestion of the host erythrocyte by malaria parasites is the primary target for quinoline-containing antimalarials. *Biochem. Pharmacol.* 35:2435–42

38. Desai SA, Krogstad DJ, McCleskey EW. 1993. A nutrient-permeable channel on the intraerythrocytic malaria parasite. *Nature* 362:643–46

39. Schwab JC, Beckers CJ, Joiner KA. 1994. The parasitophorous vacuole membrane surrounding intracellular *Toxoplasma gondii* functions as a molecular seive. *Proc. Natl. Acad. Sci. USA* 91:509–13

40. Valkanov MA, Martin RJ. 1995. A Cl channel in *Ascaris suum* selectivity conducts dicarboxylic anion product of glucose fermentation and suggests a role in removal of waste organic anions. *J. Membr. Biol.* 148:41–49

41. Valkanov M, Martin RJ, Dixon DM. 1994. The Ca-activated chloride channel of *Ascaris suum* conducts volatile fatty acids produced by anaerobic respiration: a patch-clamp study. *J. Membr. Biol.* 138:133–41

42. Cheffings CM, Smith JAC. 1997. Malate transport and vacuolar ion channels in CAM plants. *J. Exp. Bot.* 48:623–31

43. Iwasaki I, Arata H, Kijima H, Nishimura M. 1992. Two types of channels involved in the malate ion transport across the tonoplast of a Crassulacean acid metabolism plant. *Plant Physiol.* 98:1494–97

44. Pantoja O, Gelli A, Blumwald E. 1992. Characterization of vacuolar malate and K^+ channels under physiological conditions. *Plant Physiol.* 100:1137–41

45. Cerana R, Giromini L, Colombo R. 1995. Malate-regulated channels permeable to anions in vacuoles of *Arabidopsis thaliana*. *Aust. J. Plant Physiol.* 22:115–21

46. Plant PJ, Gelli A, Blumwald E. 1994. Vacuolar chloride regulation of an anionselective tonoplast channel. *J. Membr. Biol.* 140:1–12

47. Hedrich R, Marten I. 1993. Malate-induced feedback regulation of plasma membrane anion channels could provide a CO_2 sensor to guard cells. *EMBO J.* 12:897–901

48. Hedrich R, Marten I, Lohse G, Dietrich P, Winter H, et al. 1994. Malate-sensitive anion channels enable guard cells to sense changes in the ambient CO_2 concentration. *Plant J.* 6:741–48

49. Ryan PR, Delhaize E, Randall PJ. 1995. Characterisation of Al-stimulated efflux of malate from the apices of Al-tolerant wheat roots. *Planta* 196:103–10

50. Delhaize E, Ryan PR, Randall PJ. 1993. Aluminum tolerance in wheat (*Triticum aestivum* L.). *Plant Physiol.* 103:695–702

51. Ryan PR, Skerrett M, Findlay GP, Delhaize E, Tyerman SD. 1997. Aluminum activates an anion channel in the apical cells of wheat roots. *Proc. Natl. Acad. Sci. USA* 94:6547–52

52. Knorr BA, Beck JC, Abramson RG. 1994. Classical and channel-like urate transporters in rabbit renal brush border membranes. *Kidney Intl.* 45:727–36

53. Leal-Pinto E, Tao WJ, Rappaport J, Richardson M, Knorr BA, Abramson RG. 1997. Molecular cloning and functional reconstitution of a urate transporter/channel. *J. Biol. Chem.* 272:617–25

54. Galli A. Blakely RD, DeFelice LJ. 1996. Norepinephrine transporters have channel modes of conduction. *Proc. Natl. Acad. Sci. USA* 93:8671–76

55. Sonders MS, Amara SG. 1996. Channels in transporters. *Curr. Opin. Neurobiol.* 6:294–302

56. Pordy WT, Lipkowitz MS, Abramson RG. 1987. Evidence for the transport function of uricase, an oxidative enzyme. *Am. J. Physiol.* 253:F702–11

57. Leal-Pinto E, London RD, Knorr BA, Abramson RG. 1995. Reconstitution of hepatic uricase in planar lipid bilayer reveals a functional organic anion channel. *J. Membr. Biol.* 146:123–32

58. Holder JW, Elmore E, Barrett JC. 1993. Gap junction function and cancer. *Cancer Res.* 53:3475–85

59. Elfgang C, Eckert R, Lichtenberg-Frate H, Butterweck A, Rraub O, et al. 1995. Specific permeability and selective formation of gap junction channels in connexin-transfected HeLa cells. *J. Cell Biol.* 129:805–17

60. Moorman JR, Palmer CJ, John JE III, Durieux ME, Jones LR. 1992. Phospholemman expression induces a hyperpolarization-activated chloride current in *Xenopus* oocytes. *J. Biol. Chem.* 267:14551–54

61. Morrison BW, Moorman JR, Kowdley GC, Kobayashi YM, Jones LR, Leder P. 1995. Mat-8, a novel phospholemman-like protein expressed in human breast tumors, induces a chloride conductance in *Xenopus* oocytes. *J. Biol. Chem.* 270:2176–82

62. Moorman JR, Ackerman SJ, Kowdley GC, Griffin MP, Mounsey JP, et al. 1995. Unitary anion currents through phospholemman channel molecules. *Nature* 377:737–40

63. Cowan SW, Schirmer T, Rummel G, Steiert M, Ghosh R, et al. 1992. Crystal structures explain functional properties of two *E. coli* porins. *Nature* 358:727–33

64. Cowan SW, Garavito RM, Jansonius JN, Jenkins JA, Karlsson R, et al. 1995. The structure of OmpF porin in a tetragonal crystal form. *Structure* 3:1041–50

65. Kirk K, Horner HA. 1995. In search of a selective inhibitor of the induced transport of small solutes in *Plasmodium falciparum*-infected erythrocytes: effects of arylaminobenzoates. *Biochem. J.* 311:761–68

SUBJECT INDEX

A

CUMULATIVE INDEXES

CONTRIBUTING AUTHORS, VOLUMES 56–60